Instructor's Solutions Manual

Cindy Trimble & Associates

Intermediate Algebra

A GRAPHING APPROACH

FOURTH EDITION

Elayn Martin-Gay

Margaret Greene

PEARSON

Prentice
Hall

Upper Saddle River, NJ 07458

Editorial Director, Mathematics: Christine Hoag
Editor-in-Chief: Paul Murphy
Sponsoring Editor: Mary Beckwith
Assistant Editor: Georgina Brown
Associate Managing Editor: Bayani Mendoza de Leon
Senior Managing Editor: Linda Mihatov Behrens
Project Manager: Raegan Keida Heerema
Art Director: Heather Scott
Supplement Cover Manager: Paul Gourhan
Supplement Cover Designer: Victoria Colotta
Operations Specialist: Ilene Kahn
Senior Operations Supervisor: Diane Peirano

© 2009 Pearson Education, Inc.

Pearson Prentice Hall

Pearson Education, Inc.

Upper Saddle River, NJ 07458

Printed in the United States of America

10 9 8 7 6 5 4 3 2

ISBN-13:   978-0-13-603128-4

ISBN-10:   0-13-603128-5

Pearson Education Ltd., *London*
Pearson Education Singapore, Pte. Ltd.
Pearson Education Canada, Inc.
Pearson Education—*Japan*
Pearson Education Australia PTY, Limited
Pearson Education North Asia, Ltd., *Hong Kong*
Pearson Educación de Mexico, S.A. de C.V.
Pearson Education Malaysia, Pte. Ltd.
Pearson Education Upper Saddle River, New Jersey

Contents

Chapter 1

Practice Exercises

1. Let $b = 3.5$ and $h = 8$.

$$A = \frac{1}{2}bh$$

$$A = \frac{1}{2}(3.5)(8) = 14$$

The area is 14 square centimeters.

2. Let $p = 17$ and $q = 3$.
$$2p - q = 2(17) - 3 = 34 - 3 = 31$$

3. **a.** $\{6, 7, 8, 9\}$

   b. $\{41, 42, 43, \ldots\}$

4. **a.** True, since 7 is a natural number and therefore an element of the set.

   b. True, since 6 is not an element of the set $\{1, 3, 5, 7\}$.

5. **a.** True; every integer is a real number.

   b. False; $\sqrt{8}$ is an irrational number.

   c. True; every whole number is a rational number.

   d. False; since the element 2 in the first set is not an element of the second set.

6. **a.** $|4| = 4$ since 4 is located 4 units from 0 on the number line.

   b. $\left|-\frac{1}{2}\right| = \frac{1}{2}$ since $-\frac{1}{2}$ is $\frac{1}{2}$ unit from 0 on the number line.

   c. $|1| = 1$ since 1 is 1 unit from 0 on the number line.

   d. $-|6.8| = -6.8$
   The negative sign outside the absolute value bars means to take the opposite of the absolute value of 6.8.

   e. $-|-4| = -4$
   Since $|-4| = 4$, $-|-4| = -4$.

7. **a.** The opposite of 5.4 is -5.4.

   b. The opposite of $-\frac{3}{5}$ is $\frac{3}{5}$.

   c. The opposite of 18 is -18.

8. **a.** $3 \cdot x$ or $3x$

   b. $2x - 5$

   c. $3\frac{5}{8} + x$

   d. $\frac{x}{2}$

   e. $x - 14$

   f. $5(x + 10)$

Vocabulary and Readiness Check

1. Letters that represent numbers are called <u>variables</u>.

2. Finding the <u>value</u> of an expression means evaluating the expression.

3. The <u>absolute value</u> of a number is that number's distance from 0 on the number line.

4. An <u>expression</u> is formed by numbers and variables connected by operations such as addition, subtraction, multiplication, division, raising to powers, and/or taking roots.

5. The <u>natural numbers</u> are $\{1, 2, 3, \ldots\}$.

6. The <u>whole numbers</u> are $\{0, 1, 2, 3, \ldots\}$.

7. The <u>integers</u> are $\{\ldots, -3, -2, -1, 0, 1, 2, 3, \ldots\}$.

8. The number $\sqrt{5}$ is an <u>irrational number</u>.

9. The number $\frac{5}{7}$ is a <u>rational number</u>.

10. The opposite of a is <u>$-a$</u>.

Exercise Set 1.2

2. $3y = 3(45) = 135$

4. $7.1a = 7.1(1.5) = 10.65$

6. $yz = \dfrac{2}{3} \cdot \dfrac{1}{5} = \dfrac{2}{15}$

8. $2a - b = 2(12) - 7 = 24 - 7 = 17$

10. $1.5x = 1.5(30) = 45$
30 encyclopedias need 45 inches of shelf space.

12. $\dfrac{x}{5} = \dfrac{2}{5}$

You are $\dfrac{2}{5}$ of a mile away from the lightning.

14. $2193.16t = 2193.16 \cdot 1.7 = 3728.372$ mi

16. $\{7, 8, 9, ...\}$

18. $\{1, 3, 5, ...\}$

20. $\varnothing$

22. $\{1, 3, 5, 7\}$

24.
number line with points at $-5, -4, -3, -2, -1, 0$; marks at -3 and -1

26.
$0\ 1\ 2\ 3\ 4\ 5\ 6\ 7\ 8\ 9\ 10\ 11$

28.
$\dfrac{1}{4}\ \dfrac{1}{3}$ marked between 0 and 1

30. Answers may vary

32. $\left\{3, 0, \sqrt{36}, -134\right\}$

34. $\left\{3, 0, \sqrt{36}, \dfrac{2}{5}, -134\right\}$

36. $\left\{3, 0, \sqrt{7}, \sqrt{36}, \dfrac{2}{5}, -134\right\}$

38. $0 \notin \{x | x$ is a positive integer$\}$

40. $12 \in \{1, 2, 3, ...\}$

42. $0 \notin \{1, 2, 3, ...\}$

44. $0 \notin \{x | x$ is a natural number$\}$

46. False; the number $\sqrt{2}$, for example, is not a natural number.

48. True; $\dfrac{1}{2}$ is a ratio of the two integers 1 and 2.

50. True; every integer is a rational number.

52. False; π is a real number.

54. False; the number $\sqrt{2}$, for example, is an irrational number, but it is not a natural number.

56. True; every natural number is a rational number.

58. Answers may vary

60. $|8| = 8$ since 8 is located 8 units from 0 on the number line.

62. $|-6| = 6$ since -6 is located 6 units from 0 on the number line.

64. $|-1| = 1$ since -1 is located 1 unit from 0 on the number line.

66. Since $|-11|$ is 11, $-|-11| = -11$.

68. Answers may vary

70. The opposite of -7.8 is $-(-7.8) = 7.8$.

72. The opposite of $\dfrac{9}{5}$ is $-\dfrac{9}{5}$.

74. The opposite of $-\dfrac{14}{3}$ is $-\left(-\dfrac{14}{3}\right) = \dfrac{14}{3}$.

76. The opposite of 10.3 is -10.3.

78. $6x$

80. $6x + 1$

82. $x - 7$

84. $25 - x$

86. $\dfrac{x}{13}$

88. $3x - 4$

90. $15.7 + x$ or $15\dfrac{7}{10} + x$

92. $x - 2\dfrac{3}{4}$

94. $\dfrac{4}{x+1}$

96. $8(x - 9)$

98. The height of the bar representing France is about 91. Therefore, 91 million tourists are predicted for France.

100. The height of the bar representing Hong Kong is about 56. Therefore, 56 million tourists are predicted for Hong Kong.

102. Answers may vary

Section 1.3

Practice Exercises

1. a. $-6 + (-2) = -(6 + 2) = -8$

  b. $5 + (-8) = -3$

  c. $-4 + 9 = 5$

  d. $(-3.2) + (-4.9) = -8.1$

  e. $-\dfrac{3}{5} + \dfrac{2}{3} = -\dfrac{9}{15} + \dfrac{10}{15} = \dfrac{1}{15}$

2. a. $3 - 11 = 3 + (-11) = -8$

  b. $-6 - (-3) = -6 + (3) = -3$

  c. $-7 - 5 = -7 + (-5) = -12$

  d. $4.2 - (-3.5) = 4.2 + 3.5 = 7.7$

  e. $\dfrac{5}{7} - \dfrac{1}{3} = \dfrac{5 \cdot 3}{7 \cdot 3} - \dfrac{1 \cdot 7}{3 \cdot 7} = \dfrac{15}{21} + \left(-\dfrac{7}{21}\right) = \dfrac{8}{21}$

  f. $3 - 1.2 = 3 + (-1.2) = 1.8$

  g. $2 - 9 = 2 + (-9) = -7$

3. a. $13 + 5 - 6 = 18 - 6 = 12$

b. $-6 - 2 + 4 = -8 + 4 = -4$

4. a. Since the signs of the two numbers are different or unlike, the product is negative.
$(-5)(3) = -15$

  b. Since the signs of the two numbers are the same, the product is positive.
$(-7)\left(-\dfrac{1}{14}\right) = \dfrac{7}{14} = \dfrac{1}{2}$

  c. $5.1(-2) = -10.2$

  d. $14(0) = 0$

  e. $\left(-\dfrac{1}{4}\right)\left(\dfrac{8}{13}\right) = -\dfrac{8}{52} = -\dfrac{2}{13}$

  f. $6(-1)(-2)(3) = -6(-2)(3) = 12(3) = 36$

  g. $5(-2.3) = -11.5$

5. a. Since the signs are different or unlike, the quotient is negative.
$\dfrac{-16}{8} = -2$

  b. Since the signs are the same, the quotient is positive.
$\dfrac{-15}{-3} = 5$

  c. $-\dfrac{2}{3} \div 4 = -\dfrac{2}{3} \cdot \dfrac{1}{4} = -\dfrac{1}{6}$

  d. $\dfrac{54}{-9} = -6$

  e. $-\dfrac{1}{12} \div \left(-\dfrac{3}{4}\right) = -\dfrac{1}{12} \cdot -\dfrac{4}{3} = \dfrac{1}{9}$

  f. $\dfrac{0}{-7} = 0$

6. a. $2^3 = 2 \cdot 2 \cdot 2 = 8$

  b. $\left(\dfrac{1}{3}\right)^2 = \left(\dfrac{1}{3}\right)\left(\dfrac{1}{3}\right) = \dfrac{1}{9}$

  c. $-6^2 = -(6 \cdot 6) = -36$

d. $(-6)^2 = (-6)(-6) = 36$

e. $-4^3 = -(4 \cdot 4 \cdot 4) = -64$

f. $(-4)^3 = (-4)(-4)(-4) = -64$

7. a. $\sqrt{49} = 7$ since 7 is positive and $7^2 = 49$.

b. $\sqrt{\dfrac{1}{16}} = \dfrac{1}{4}$ since $\left(\dfrac{1}{4}\right)^2 = \dfrac{1}{16}$.

c. $-\sqrt{64} = -8$

d. $\sqrt{-64}$ is not a real number.

e. $\sqrt{100} = 10$ since $10^2 = 100$.

8. a. $\sqrt[3]{64} = 4$ since $4^3 = 64$.

b. $\sqrt[5]{-1} = -1$ since $(-1)^5 = -1$.

c. $\sqrt[4]{10,000} = 10$ since $10^4 = 10,000$.

9. a. $14 - 3 \cdot 4 = 14 - 12 = 2$

b. $3(5-8)^2 = 3(-3)^2 = 3(9) = 27$

c. $\dfrac{|-5|^2 + 4}{\sqrt{4} - 3} = \dfrac{5^2 + 4}{2 - 3} = \dfrac{25 + 4}{-1} = \dfrac{29}{-1} = -29$

10. $\begin{aligned}
5 - [(3-5) + 6(2-4)] &= 5 - [-2 + 6(-2)] \\
&= 5 - [-2 + (-12)] \\
&= 5 - [-14] \\
&= 5 + 14 \\
&= 19
\end{aligned}$

11. $\begin{aligned}
\dfrac{-2\sqrt{12+4} - (-3)^2}{6^2 + |1-9|} &= \dfrac{-2\sqrt{16} - (-3)^2}{6^2 + |-8|} \\
&= \dfrac{-2(4) - 9}{36 + 8} \\
&= \dfrac{-8 - 9}{44} \\
&= -\dfrac{17}{44}
\end{aligned}$

12. For each expression, replace x with 16 and y with -5.

a. $2x - 7y = 2(16) - 7(-5) = 32 + 35 = 67$

```
16→X: -5→Y
                   -5
2X-7Y
                   67
■
```

b. $-4y^2 = -4(-5)^2 = -4(25) = -100$

```
16→X: -5→Y
                   -5
-4Y²
                 -100
```

c. $\begin{aligned}
\dfrac{\sqrt{x}}{y} - \dfrac{y}{x} &= \dfrac{\sqrt{16}}{-5} - \dfrac{-5}{16} \\
&= -\dfrac{4}{5} + \dfrac{5}{16} \\
&= -\dfrac{4}{5} \cdot \dfrac{16}{16} + \dfrac{5}{16} \cdot \dfrac{5}{5} \\
&= -\dfrac{64}{80} + \dfrac{25}{80} \\
&= -\dfrac{39}{80}
\end{aligned}$

```
16→X: -5→Y
                   -5
√(X)/Y-Y/X
              -.4875
■
```

13. a. $5x^2 + 1;\ x = 3$
$$3^2 = 9$$
$$5 \cdot 9 = 45$$
$$45 + 1 = 46$$

b. $5x^2 + 1;\ x = 11$
$$11^2 = 121$$
$$5 \cdot 121 = 605$$
$$605 + 1 = 606$$

c. $5x^2 + 1;\ x = 4.86$

```
4.86→X
                 4.86
5X²+1
             119.098
■
```

The value of $5x^2 + 1$ when $x = 4.86$ is 119.098.

14. When $x = -5$,
$$\frac{9}{5}x + 32 = \frac{9}{5}(-5) + 32 = -9 + 32 = 23.$$
When $x = 10$,
$$\frac{9}{5}x + 32 = \frac{9}{5}(10) + 32 = 18 + 32 = 50.$$
When $x = 25$,
$$\frac{9}{5}x + 32 = \frac{9}{5}(25) + 32 = 45 + 32 = 77.$$
The completed table is

Degrees Celsius	x	-5	10	25
Degrees Fahrenheit	$\frac{9}{5}x + 32$	23	50	77

Vocabulary and Readiness Check

1. $-\dfrac{1}{7} = \dfrac{-1}{7} = \dfrac{1}{-7}$; b, c

2. $\dfrac{-x}{y} = \dfrac{x}{-y} = -\dfrac{x}{y}$; a, b

3. $\dfrac{5}{-(x+y)} = \dfrac{-5}{(x+y)} = -\dfrac{5}{(x+y)}$; b, d

4. $-\dfrac{(y+z)}{3y} = \dfrac{-(y+z)}{3y} = \dfrac{(y+z)}{-3y}$; a, d

5. $\dfrac{-9x}{-2y} = \dfrac{9x}{2y}$; b

6. $\dfrac{-a}{-b} = \dfrac{a}{b}$; a

7. $0 \cdot a = \underline{0}$

8. $\dfrac{0}{4}$ simplifies to $\underline{0}$ while $\dfrac{4}{0}$ is <u>undefined</u>.

9. The <u>reciprocal</u> of the nonzero number b is $\dfrac{1}{b}$.

10. The fraction $-\dfrac{a}{b} = \dfrac{-a}{\underline{b}} = \dfrac{a}{\underline{-b}}$.

11. An <u>exponent</u> is a shorthand notation for repeated multiplication of the same number.

12. In $(-5)^2$, the 2 is the <u>exponent</u> and the -5 is the <u>base</u>.

13. The opposite of squaring a number is taking the <u>square root</u> of a number.

14. Using order of operations, $9 \div 3 \cdot 3 = \underline{9}$.

Exercise Set 1.3

2. $12 + (-7) = 5$

4. $-5 + (-9) = -14$

6. $-8.2 - (-6.6) = -8.2 + 6.6 = -1.6$

8. $15 - (-1) = 15 + 1 = 16$

10. $\dfrac{7}{10} - \dfrac{4}{5} = \dfrac{7}{10} + \left(-\dfrac{8}{10}\right) = -\dfrac{1}{10}$

12. $-13 - 4 + 9 = -17 + 9 = -8$

14. $-\dfrac{5}{2} - \left(-\dfrac{2}{3}\right) = -\dfrac{5}{2} + \dfrac{2}{3} = -\dfrac{15}{6} + \dfrac{4}{16} = -\dfrac{11}{6}$

16. $-3 - 9 = -12$

18. $-3 \cdot 8 = -24$

20. $-5 \cdot 0 = 0$

22. $\dfrac{-2}{0}$ is undefined.

24. $\dfrac{-20}{5} = -4$

26. $\dfrac{-36}{-6} = 6$

28. $5\left(-\dfrac{1}{50}\right) = -\dfrac{5}{50} = -\dfrac{1}{10}$

30. $(-0.9)(-0.5) = 0.45$

32. $22.5 \div (-2.5) = \dfrac{22.5}{1} \cdot \dfrac{1}{-2.5} = -9$

34. Multiplying from left to right gives
$-5(-3)(-2) = 15(-2) = -30.$

36. $(-7)^2 = (-7) \cdot (-7) = 49$

38. $-6^2 = -(6 \cdot 6) = -36$

40. $-2^3 = -(2 \cdot 2 \cdot 2) = -8$

42. $\left(-\dfrac{1}{2}\right)^4 = \left(-\dfrac{1}{2}\right)\left(-\dfrac{1}{2}\right)\left(-\dfrac{1}{2}\right)\left(-\dfrac{1}{2}\right) = \dfrac{1}{16}$

44. $\sqrt{81} = 9$ since 9 is positive and $9^2 = 81$.

46. $-\sqrt{\dfrac{4}{25}} = -\dfrac{2}{5}$ since $\left(\dfrac{2}{5}\right)^2 = \dfrac{4}{25}$.

48. $\sqrt[5]{32} = 2$ since $2^5 = 32$.

50. $\sqrt[3]{1} = 1$ since $1^3 = 1$.

52. not a real number

54. $7(3-8)^2 = 7(-5)^2 = 7(25) = 175$

56. $-5^2 - 2^4 = -25 - 16 = -25 + (-16) = -41$

58. $\dfrac{4.2 - (-8.2)}{-0.4} = \dfrac{4.2 + 8.2}{-0.4} = \dfrac{12.4}{-0.4} = -31$

60. $(-15)^2 - 2^4 = 225 - 16 = 209$

62. $-20 \div 5 \cdot 4 = -4 \cdot 4 = -16$

64. $-10\left(-\dfrac{2}{5}\right) - 10 = 4 - 10 = -6$

66. $8 - [(4-7) + (8-1)] = 8 - [-3 + 7] = 8 - (4) = 4$

68. $\dfrac{(-1-2)(-3^2)}{-6-3} = \dfrac{(-3)(-9)}{-9} = -3$

70. $\left(\sqrt[3]{27}\right)(-5) - \left(\sqrt{25}\right)(-3) = 3(-5) - (5)(-3)$
$= -15 - (-15)$
$= -15 + 15$
$= 0$

72. $10 - [(4-5)^2 + (12-14)]^4 = 10 - [(-1)^2 + (-2)]^4$
$= 10 - [1-2]^4$
$= 10 - [-1]^4$
$= 10 - 1$
$= 9$

74. $\dfrac{-\sqrt{16} - (6-2.4)}{-2} = \dfrac{-4 - (6-2.4)}{-2}$
$= \dfrac{-4 - 3.6}{-2}$
$= \dfrac{-7.6}{-2}$
$= 3.8$

76. $\dfrac{|-14| - |2-7|}{-15} = \dfrac{14 - |2-7|}{-15} = \dfrac{14-5}{-15} = \dfrac{9}{-15} = -\dfrac{3}{5}$

78. $\dfrac{-1-2}{2(-3)+10} - \dfrac{2(-5)}{-1(8)+1} = \dfrac{-1-2}{-6+10} - \dfrac{2(-5)}{-8+1}$
$= \dfrac{-3}{4} - \dfrac{-10}{-7}$
$= -\dfrac{3}{4} - \dfrac{10}{7}$
$= -\dfrac{21}{28} - \dfrac{40}{28}$
$= -\dfrac{61}{28}$

80. $\dfrac{\frac{1}{5} \cdot 20 - 6}{10 + \frac{1}{4} \cdot 12} = \dfrac{4-6}{10+3} = \dfrac{-2}{13} = -\dfrac{2}{13}$

82. $2\{-1 + 3[7 - 4(-10+12)]\} = 2\{-1 + 3[7 - 4(2)]\}$
$= 2\{-1 + 3[7-8]\}$
$= 2\{-1 + 3[-1]\}$
$= 2\{-1 + [-3]\}$
$= 2\{-4\}$
$= -8$

84. $\dfrac{(-2)^4 + 3\sqrt{120-20}}{4^3 + |5(-1)|} = \dfrac{(-2)^4 + 3\sqrt{100}}{4^3 + |-5|}$
$= \dfrac{16 + 3(10)}{64 + 5}$
$= \dfrac{16+30}{64+5}$
$= \dfrac{46}{69}$
$= \dfrac{2}{3}$

86. Let $x = 9$, $y = -2$.
$$4x - 10y = 4(9) - 10(-2) = 36 + 20 = 56$$

88. Let $y = -2$.
$$-7y^2 = -7(-2)^2 = -7(4) = -28$$

90. Let $x = 9$, $y = -2$.
$$\begin{aligned}
\frac{y}{2x} - \frac{\sqrt{x}}{3y} &= \frac{-2}{2(9)} - \frac{\sqrt{9}}{3(-2)} \\
&= \frac{-2}{18} - \frac{3}{-6} \\
&= -\frac{1}{9} + \frac{1}{2} \\
&= -\frac{2}{18} + \frac{9}{18} \\
&= \frac{7}{18}
\end{aligned}$$

92. Let $x = 9$, $y = -2$.
$$\begin{aligned}
\frac{5 + 2|y - x|}{x + 6y} &= \frac{5 + 2|-2 - 9|}{9 + 6(-2)} \\
&= \frac{5 + 2|-11|}{9 + (-12)} \\
&= \frac{5 + 2(11)}{-3} \\
&= \frac{5 + 22}{-3} \\
&= \frac{27}{-3} \\
&= -9
\end{aligned}$$

94. Let $x = 9$, $y = -2$.
$$\begin{aligned}
\frac{y^2 + \sqrt{x + 7}}{|3x - y|} &= \frac{(-2)^2 + \sqrt{9 + 7}}{|3(9) - (-2)|} \\
&= \frac{4 + \sqrt{16}}{|27 + 2|} \\
&= \frac{4 + 4}{|29|} \\
&= \frac{8}{29}
\end{aligned}$$

96.

```
1.4→X: -6.2→Y
                -6.2
5Y²+X
            193.6
```

When $x = 1.4$ and $y = -6.2$, $5y^2 + x = 193.6$.

98.

```
1.4→X: -6.2→Y
                -6.2
√(X-Y)/(2X)
    .9845749109
```

When $x = 1.4$ and $y = -6.2$, $\dfrac{\sqrt{x - y}}{2x} \approx 0.98$.

100.

```
1.4→X: -6.2→Y
                -6.2
1.6(3X²+1.8)
            12.288
```

When $x = 1.4$ and $y = -6.2$,
$$1.6(3x^2 + 1.8) = 12.29.$$

102. When $2x - y^2$ is evaluated for $x = 5.1$ and $y = -3$, the result is 1.2.

104. When $\dfrac{1}{2}BH$ or $(1/2)BH$ is evaluated for $B = 8$ and $H = 4.5$, the result is 18.

106. a.

```
4→X
                4
12/(X-2)
                6
12/X-2
                1
```

b. They are different; answers may vary

108. a. $r = 2$: $\pi r^2 = \pi(2^2) = \pi(4) \approx 12.56$
$r = 3$: $\pi r^2 = \pi(3^2) = \pi(9) \approx 28.26$
$r = 7$: $\pi r^2 = \pi(7^2) = \pi(49) \approx 153.86$
$r = 10$: $\pi r^2 = \pi(10^2) = \pi(100) \approx 314$
The completed table is:

Radius	r	2	3	7	10
Area	πr^2	12.56	28.26	153.86	314

b. Area increases as radius increases; answers may vary.

110. a. $c = -10$:
$1.8c + 32 = 1.8(-10) + 32 = -18 + 32 = 14$
$c = 0$: $1.8c + 32 = 1.8(0) + 32 = 0 + 32 = 32$
$c = 50$:
$1.8c + 32 = 1.8(50) + 32 = 90 + 32 = 122$
The completed table is:

Degrees Celsius	c	-10	0	50
Degrees Fahrenheit	$1.8c + 32$	14	32	122

   b. Degrees Fahrenheit increase as degrees Celsius increase; answers may vary.

112. Let $x_1 = 2$, $x_2 = 4$, $y_1 = -3$, $y_2 = 2$.

$$\sqrt{(x_2 - x_1)^2 + (y_2 - y_1)^2} = \sqrt{(4-2)^2 + (2-(-3))^2}$$
$$= \sqrt{2^2 + (2+3)^2}$$
$$= \sqrt{2^2 + 5^2}$$
$$= \sqrt{4 + 25}$$
$$= \sqrt{29}$$

114. $1 - \left(\dfrac{2}{9} + \dfrac{1}{6} + \dfrac{1}{4}\right) = 1 - \left(\dfrac{8}{36} + \dfrac{6}{36} + \dfrac{9}{36}\right)$

$$= 1 - \left(\dfrac{14}{36} + \dfrac{9}{36}\right)$$
$$= 1 - \dfrac{23}{36}$$
$$= \dfrac{13}{36}$$

116. The difference in heights is $29{,}028 - (-1319) = 30{,}347$ feet. (We must use -1319 because the Dead Sea is 1319 feet below sea level.)

118. $6 - (5 \cdot 2 + 2) = 6 - (10 + 2) = 6 - 12 = -6$

120. Answers may vary

122. $\sqrt{273} \approx 16.5227$

124. $\sqrt{19.6} \approx 4.4272$

126. $\dfrac{(-5.161)(3.222)}{7.955 - 19.676} = \dfrac{-16.628742}{-11.721} \approx 1.4187$

Section 1.4

Practice Exercises

  1. The product of -4 and x is 20.

$$-4x \qquad = 20$$

  2. Three times the difference of z and 3 equals 9.

$$3 \qquad (z-3) \qquad = \quad 9$$

3. $\underbrace{\text{The sum of } x \text{ and } 5}$ $\underbrace{\text{is the same as}}$ $\underbrace{\text{3 less than twice } x.}$

$\qquad\qquad x+5 \qquad\qquad = \qquad\qquad 2x-3$

4. $\underbrace{\text{The sum of } y \text{ and } 2}$ $\underset{\downarrow}{\text{is}}$ $\underbrace{\text{4 more than the quotient of } z \text{ and } 8.}$

$\qquad\qquad y+2 \qquad\quad = \qquad\qquad 4+\dfrac{z}{8}$

5. a. $-6 < -5$ since -6 lies to the left of -5 on the number line.

$\qquad$ $-10\,{-}9\,{-}8\,{-}7\,{-}6\,{-}5\,{-}4\,{-}3\,{-}2\,{-}1\ 0\ 1$

b. $\dfrac{24}{3} = 8$

c. $0 > -7$ since 0 lies to the right of -7 on the number line.

$\qquad$ $-9\,{-}8\,{-}7\,{-}6\,{-}5\,{-}4\,{-}3\,{-}2\,{-}1\ 0\ 1\ 2$

d. $2.76 > 2.67$ since 2.76 lies to the right of 2.67 on the number line.

$\qquad\qquad\quad$ 2.67   2.76

$\qquad\qquad 1 \qquad\quad 2 \qquad\quad 3$

6. a. $x - 3 \le 5$

b. $y \ne -4$

c. $2 < 4 + \dfrac{1}{2}z$

7. a. The opposite of -7 is $-(-7) = 7$.

b. The opposite of 4.7 is -4.7.

c. The opposite of $-\dfrac{3}{8}$ is $-\left(-\dfrac{3}{8}\right) = \dfrac{3}{8}$.

8. a. The reciprocal of $-\dfrac{5}{3}$ is $-\dfrac{3}{5}$ because $-\dfrac{5}{3}\left(-\dfrac{3}{5}\right) = 1$.

b. The reciprocal of 14 is $\dfrac{1}{14}$.

c. The reciprocal of -2 is $-\dfrac{1}{2}$.

9. $8 + 13x = 13x + 8$

10. $3 \cdot (11b) = (3 \cdot 11)b = 33b$

11. a. $4(x + 5y) = 4 \cdot x + 4 \cdot 5y = 4x + 20y$

b. $-(3-2z) = -1(3-2z)$
$$= -1 \cdot 3 + (-1)(-2z)$$
$$= -3 + 2z$$

c. $0.3x(y-3) = 0.3x \cdot y - 0.3x \cdot 3$
$$= 0.3xy - 0.9x$$

12. a. $-(-11.7) = 11.7$ illustrates the double negative property.

b. $7(y+5) = 7 \cdot y + 7 \cdot 5$ illustrates the distributive property.

c. $2 + (a+b) = (2+a) + b$ illustrates the associative property of addition.

13. a.   In words: Value of a dime   ·   number of dimes

  ↓   ↓

  Translate: 0.10 x , or $0.10x$

b.   In words: number of grams of   ·   number of
  carbohydrates in one   cookies
  cookie

  ↓   ↓

  Translate: 26 y , or $26y$

c.   In words: cost of one   ·   number of cards
  birthday card

  ↓   ↓

  Translate: 1.75 z , or $1.75z$

d.   In words: Discount   ·   purchase price

  ↓   ↓

  Translate: 0.15 t , or $0.15t$

14. a.   If two numbers have a sum of 16 and one number is x, the other number is the rest of 16.

  In words: Sixteen   minus x

  ↓   ↓   ↓

  Translate: 16   – x

b.   In words: One hundred   minus   one angle, x
  eighty

  ↓   ↓   ↓

  Translate: 180   – x

c.   The next consecutive even integer is always two more than the previous even integer.

In words:	first integer	plus	two
	$\downarrow$	$\downarrow$	$\downarrow$
Translate:	x	$+$	2

d.

In words:	younger brother's age	plus	nine
	$\downarrow$	$\downarrow$	$\downarrow$
Translate:	x	$+$	9

15. a. $6ab - ab = 6ab - 1ab = (6-1)ab = 5ab$

b. $4x - 5 + 6x = 4x + 6x - 5$
$$= (4+6)x - 5$$
$$= 10x - 5$$

c. $17p - 9$ cannot be simplified further since $17p$ and -9 are not like terms.

16. a. $5pq - 2pq - 11 - 4pq + 18 = 5pq - 2pq - 4pq - 11 + 18$
$$= (5 - 2 - 4)pq + (-11 + 18)$$
$$= -1pq + (7)$$
$$= -pq + 7$$

b. $3x^2 + 7 - 2(x^2 - 6) = 3x^2 + 7 - 2x^2 + 12$
$$= 3x^2 - 2x^2 + 7 + 12$$
$$= x^2 + 19$$

c. $(3.7x + 2.5) - (-2.1x - 1.3) = 3.7x + 2.5 + 2.1x + 1.3$
$$= 3.7x + 2.1x + 2.5 + 1.3$$
$$= 5.8x + 3.8$$

d. $\dfrac{1}{5}(15c - 25d) - \dfrac{1}{2}(8c + 6d + 1) + \dfrac{3}{4} = 3c - 5d - 4c - 3d - \dfrac{1}{2} + \dfrac{3}{4}$
$$= -c - 8d + \dfrac{1}{4}$$

Vocabulary and Readiness Check

	Symbol	Meaning
1.	$<$	is less than
2.	$>$	is greater than
3.	$\neq$	is not equal to
4.	$=$	is equal to
5.	$\geq$	is greater than or equal to
6.	$\leq$	is less than or equal to

7. The opposite or <u>additive inverse</u> of nonzero number a is $-a$.

8. The reciprocal or <u>multiplicative inverse</u> of nonzero number a is $\dfrac{1}{a}$.

9. The <u>commutative</u> property has to do with "order."

10. The <u>associative</u> property has to do with "grouping."

11. $a(b + c) = ab + ac$ illustrates the <u>distributive</u> property.

12. Terms with the same variable(s) raised to the same powers are called <u>like</u> terms.

13. The <u>terms</u> of an expression are the addends of the expression.

14. The process of adding or subtracting like terms is called <u>combining</u> like terms.

15. The $\underline{x^{-1}}$ key on a calculator is used to find the multiplicative inverse of a number.

Exercise Set 1.4

2. $\underbrace{\text{The difference of } y \text{ and } 3}\ \underbrace{\text{amounts to}}\ \overset{\downarrow}{12.}$

$$y - 3 \qquad = \qquad 12$$

or $y - 3 = 12$

4. $\underbrace{\text{Three more than the product of 4 and } c}\ \overset{\downarrow}{\text{is}}\ \overset{\downarrow}{7.}$

$$4c + 3 \qquad = 7$$

or $4c + 3 = 7$

6. $\underbrace{\text{The quotient of 8 and } y}\ \overset{\downarrow}{\text{is}}\ \underbrace{3 \text{ more than } y.}$

$$\frac{8}{y} \qquad = \qquad y + 3$$

or $\dfrac{8}{y} = y + 3$

8. $\underbrace{\text{Five added to one-fourth } q}\ \underbrace{\text{is the same as}}\ \underbrace{4 \text{ more than } q.}$

$$5 + \frac{1}{4}q \qquad = \qquad q + 4$$

or $5 + \dfrac{1}{4}q = q + 4$

10. $\underbrace{\text{10 subtracted from the reciprocal of } x}\ \underbrace{\text{is greater than}}\ \overset{\downarrow}{0.}$

$$\frac{1}{x} - 10 \qquad\qquad > \qquad 0$$

or $\dfrac{1}{x} - 10 > 0$

12. $\underbrace{\text{Four times the sum of 5 and } x}$ $\underbrace{\text{is not equal to}}$ $\underbrace{\text{the opposite of 15.}}$

$\qquad\qquad 4(5+x) \qquad\qquad\qquad \neq \qquad\qquad\qquad -15$

or $4(5+x) \neq -15$

14. $\underbrace{\text{5 times the sum of 6 and } y}$ is $-35.$
$\qquad\qquad\qquad\qquad\qquad\qquad\quad \downarrow \quad\; \downarrow$

$\qquad\qquad 5(6+y) \qquad\qquad = -35$

or $5(6+y) = -35$

16. $-14 > -24$ since -14 is to the right of -24 on the number line.

18. $\dfrac{7}{2} = \dfrac{35}{10}$ since $\dfrac{7 \cdot 5}{2 \cdot 5} = \dfrac{35}{10}.$

20. $\dfrac{9}{20} > \dfrac{3}{20}$ since $9 > 3.$

22. $\dfrac{3}{4} < \dfrac{7}{8}$ since $\dfrac{3}{4}$ is to the left of $\dfrac{7}{8}$ on the number line.

24. $-13.07 > -13.7$ since -13.07 is to the right of -13.7 on the number line.

	Number	Opposite	Reciprocal
26.	7	-7	$\frac{1}{7}$
28.	-4	4	$-\frac{1}{4}$
30.	$\frac{1}{11}$	$-\frac{1}{11}$	11
32.	1	-1	1
34.	$-\frac{23}{5}$	$\frac{23}{5}$	$-\frac{5}{23}$

36. Zero is the only real number that is its own opposite. If x is a real number and x is its own inverse, then $x + x = 0$ or $2x = 0$. Dividing both sides of this equation by 2 gives $x = 0$.

38. $3a + 2b = 2b + 3a$

40. $r \cdot s = s \cdot r$

42. $\dfrac{x}{2} \cdot \dfrac{9}{10} = \dfrac{9}{10} \cdot \dfrac{x}{2}$

44. No, division is not commutative. For example, notice that $4 \div 2 \neq 2 \div 4.$

46. $3 \cdot (10z) = (3 \cdot 10)z$

48. $5q + (2r + s) = (5q + 2r) + s$

50. $(9.2x) \cdot y = 9.2(x \cdot y)$

52. $24 \div (6 \div 3) = 24 \div 2 = 12$, while

$(24 \div 6) \div 3 = 4 \div 3 = \dfrac{4}{3}$. Because $12 \neq \dfrac{4}{3}$, we

know that division is not associative.

54. $7(y + 2) = 7 \cdot y + 7 \cdot 2 = 7y + 14$

56. $-(c + 7d) = -1(c + 7d) = -c - 7d$

58. $5(3a + b + 9c) = 5 \cdot 3a + 5 \cdot b + 5 \cdot 9c$
$= 15a + 5b + 45c$

60. $-10(2a - 3b - 4) = -10 \cdot 2a - 10(-3b) - 10(-4)$
$= -20a + 30b + 40$

62. $1.2m(9n - 4) = 1.2m \cdot 9n - 1.2m \cdot 4$
$= 10.8mn - 4.8m$

64. $8 + 0 = 8$

66. $4(x + 3) = 4x + 12$

68. $0 \cdot (-5.4) = 0$

70. $9y + (x + 3z) = (9y + x) + 3z$

72. The screen illustrates the distributive property.

74. The screen illustrates the associative property of multiplication.

76. In words: $\boxed{\text{Value of a nickel}} \cdot \boxed{\text{Number of nickels}}$
Translate: $0.05 \cdot n$ or $0.05n$

78. If two numbers have a sum of 25 and one number is x, then the other number is the "rest of 25." So, in other words, we have
$\boxed{\text{Twenty-five}} - \boxed{x}$
Translate: $25 - x$

80. In words: $\boxed{\text{One hundred eighty}} - \boxed{x}$
Translate: $180 - x$

82. In words:
$\boxed{\text{Cost of compact disc}} \cdot \boxed{\text{Number of discs}}$
Translate: $\$6.49 \cdot x$ or $\$6.49x$

84. The next odd integer would be 2 more than the given odd integer.
In words: $\boxed{\text{Odd integer}} + \boxed{\text{Two}}$
Translate: $x + 2$

86. $-9 + 4x + 18 - 10x = 4x - 10x + 18 - 9$
$= (4 - 10)x + (18 - 9)$
$= -6x + 9$

88. $5k - (3k - 10) = 5k - 3k + 10$
$= (5 - 3)k + 10$
$= 2k + 10$

90. $(3x + 4) - (6x - 1) = 3x + 4 - 6x + 1$
$= 3x - 6x + 4 + 1$
$= (3 - 6)x + 5$
$= -3x + 5$

92. $3(xy - 2) + xy + 15 - x^2 = 3xy - 6 + xy + 15 - x^2$
$= 4xy + 9 - x^2$
$= -x^2 + 4xy + 9$

94. $-(n + 5) + (5n - 3) = -1(n + 5) + (5n - 3)$
$= -n - 5 + 5n - 3$
$= 4n - 8$

96. $4(6n^2 - 3) - 3(8n^2 + 4) = 24n^2 - 12 - 24n^2 - 12$
$= 24n^2 - 24n^2 - 12 - 12$
$= (24 - 24)n^2 - 24$
$= 0n^2 - 24$
$= -24$

98. $3x - 2(x - 5) + x = 3x - 2x + 10 + x$
$= 3x - 2x + x + 10$
$= (3 - 2 + 1)x + 10$
$= 2x + 10$

100. $1.5x + 2.3 - 0.7x - 5.9 = (1.5 - 0.7)x + (2.3 - 5.9)$
$= 0.8x - 3.6$

102. $\dfrac{3}{4}b - \dfrac{1}{2} + \dfrac{1}{6}b - \dfrac{2}{3} = \left(\dfrac{3}{4} + \dfrac{1}{6}\right)b + \left(-\dfrac{1}{2} - \dfrac{2}{3}\right)$
$= \dfrac{11}{12}b - \dfrac{7}{6}$

104. $2(3x + 7) = 6x + 14$

106. $\dfrac{1}{4}(8x - 4) - \dfrac{1}{5}(20x - 6y) = 2x - 1 - 4x + \dfrac{6}{5}y$
$= 2x - 4x - 1 + \dfrac{6}{5}y$
$= (2 - 4)x - 1 + \dfrac{6}{5}y$
$= -2x - 1 + \dfrac{6}{5}y$
$= -2x + \dfrac{6}{5}y - 1$

108. $\dfrac{1}{6}(24a-18b)-\dfrac{1}{7}(7a-21b-2)-\dfrac{1}{5}$

$= 4a-3b-a+3b+\dfrac{2}{7}-\dfrac{1}{5}$

$= 3a+\dfrac{3}{35}$

110. $3(x+4)=3x+12$

112. $8.1z+7.3(z+5.2)-6.85$

$= 8.1z+7.3z+37.96-6.85$

$= 15.4z+31.11$

114. No; Cylinder 1 volume = 63.2 cu in.
Cylinder 2 volume = 81.8 cu in.

116. Locate 1970 on the 'Year' axis. Travel up vertically until you hit the line. Travel left horizontally until you hit the 'Population' axis. Read the value. The population over 65 in 1970 was 20 million.

118. Locate 2030 on the 'Year' axis. Travel up vertically until you hit the line. Travel left horizontally until you hit the 'Population' axis. Read the value. The predicted population over 65 in 2030 is 70 million.

120. The population over 65 is increasing as time passes.

Integrated Review

1. Let $z=-4$.

$z^2 = (-4)^2 = (-4)(-4)=16$

2. Let $z=-4$.

$-z^2 = -(-4)^2 = -(-4)(-4)=-16$

3. Let $x=-1$, $y=3$, $z=-4$.

$\dfrac{4x-z}{2y} = \dfrac{4(-1)-(-4)}{2(3)} = \dfrac{-4+4}{6} = \dfrac{0}{6} = 0$

4. Let $x=-1$, $y=3$, $z=-4$.

$x(y-2z) = -1[3-2(-4)]$

$= -1[3+8]$

$= -1[11]$

$= -11$

5. $-7-(-2)=-7+2=-5$

6. $\dfrac{9}{10}-\dfrac{11}{12}=\dfrac{9}{10}\cdot\dfrac{6}{6}-\dfrac{11}{12}\cdot\dfrac{5}{5}=\dfrac{54}{60}-\dfrac{55}{60}=-\dfrac{1}{60}$

7. $\dfrac{-13}{2-2}=\dfrac{-13}{0}$ is undefined.

8. $(1.2)^2-(2.1)^2=1.44-4.41=-2.97$

9. $\sqrt{64}-\sqrt[3]{64}=8-4=4$

10. $-5^2-(-5)^2=-25-25=-50$

11. $9+2[(8-10)^2+(-3)^2]=9+2[(-2)^2+(-3)^2]$

$= 9+2(4+9)$

$= 9+2(13)$

$= 9+26$

$= 35$

12. $8-6\left[\sqrt[3]{8}(-2)+\sqrt{4}(-5)\right]=8-6[2(-2)+2(-5)]$

$= 8-6[(-4)+(-10)]$

$= 8-6(-14)$

$= 8+84$

$= 92$

13. $-15-2x$

14. $3x+5$

15. 0 is a whole number that is not a natural number.

16. True

17. $-5(9x)=(-5\cdot9)x=-45x$

18. $(3x-7)-(4x+1)=3x-7-4x-1$

$= 3x-4x-7-1$

$= (3-4)x-7-1$

$= -x-8$

19. $8.6a+2.3b-a+4.9b=8.6a-a+2.3b+4.9b$

$= (8.6-1)a+(2.3+4.9)b$

$= 7.6a+7.2b$

20. $\dfrac{2}{3}y - \dfrac{2}{3} + y - \dfrac{1}{9}y + \dfrac{9}{10}$

$= \dfrac{2}{3}y + y - \dfrac{1}{9}y - \dfrac{2}{3} + \dfrac{9}{10}$

$= \left(\dfrac{2}{3} + 1 - \dfrac{1}{9}\right)y + \left(-\dfrac{2}{3} + \dfrac{9}{10}\right)$

$= \left(\dfrac{6}{9} + \dfrac{9}{9} - \dfrac{1}{9}\right)y + \left(-\dfrac{20}{30} + \dfrac{27}{30}\right)$

$= \dfrac{6+9-1}{9}y + \dfrac{-20+27}{30}$

$= \dfrac{14}{9}y + \dfrac{7}{30}$

Section 1.5

Practice Exercises

1. $3x + 7 = 22$
$3x + 7 - 7 = 22 - 7$
$3x = 15$
$\dfrac{3x}{3} = \dfrac{15}{3}$
$x = 5$

2. $2.5 = 3 - 2.5t$
$2.5 - 3 = 3 - 2.5t - 3$
$-0.5 = -2.5t$
$\dfrac{-0.5}{-2.5} = \dfrac{-2.5t}{-2.5}$
$0.2 = t$

3. $-8x - 4 + 6x = 5x + 11 - 4x$
$-2x - 4 = x + 11$
$-2x - 4 - x = x + 11 - x$
$-3x - 4 = 11$
$-3x - 4 + 4 = 11 + 4$
$-3x = 15$
$\dfrac{-3x}{-3} = \dfrac{15}{-3}$
$x = -5$

4. $3(x - 5) = 6x - 3$
$3x - 15 = 6x - 3$
$3x - 15 - 6x = 6x - 3 - 6x$
$-3x - 15 = -3$
$-3x - 15 + 15 = -3 + 15$
$-3x = 12$
$\dfrac{-3x}{-3} = \dfrac{12}{-3}$
$x = -4$

5. $\dfrac{y}{2} - \dfrac{y}{5} = \dfrac{1}{4}$
$20\left(\dfrac{y}{2} - \dfrac{y}{5}\right) = 20\left(\dfrac{1}{4}\right)$
$20\left(\dfrac{y}{2}\right) - 20\left(\dfrac{y}{5}\right) = 5$
$10y - 4y = 5$
$6y = 5$
$\dfrac{6y}{6} = \dfrac{5}{6}$
$y = \dfrac{5}{6}$

6. $x - \dfrac{x-2}{12} = \dfrac{x+3}{4} + \dfrac{1}{4}$
$12\left(x - \dfrac{x-2}{12}\right) = 12\left(\dfrac{x+3}{4} + \dfrac{1}{4}\right)$
$12 \cdot x - 12\left(\dfrac{x-2}{12}\right) = 12\left(\dfrac{x+3}{4}\right) + 12 \cdot \dfrac{1}{4}$
$12x - (x - 2) = 3(x + 3) + 3$
$12x - x + 2 = 3x + 9 + 3$
$11x + 2 = 3x + 12$
$11x + 2 - 3x = 3x + 12 - 3x$
$8x + 2 = 12$
$8x + 2 - 2 = 12 - 2$
$8x = 10$
$\dfrac{8x}{8} = \dfrac{10}{8}$
$x = \dfrac{5}{4}$

7. $0.15x - 0.03 = 0.2x + 0.12$
$100(0.15x - 0.03) = 100(0.2x + 0.12)$
$100(0.15x) - 100(0.03) = 100(0.2x) + 100(0.12)$
$15x - 3 = 20x + 12$
$15x - 20x = 12 + 3$
$-5x = 15$
$\dfrac{-5x}{-5} = \dfrac{15}{-5}$
$x = -3$

8. $4x - 3 = 4(x + 5)$
$4x - 3 = 4x + 20$
$4x - 3 - 4x = 4x + 20 - 4x$
$-3 = 20$
This equation is false no matter what value the variable x might have. Thus, there is no solution. The solution set is $\{\ \}$ or $\varnothing$.

9.
$$5x - 2 = 3 + 5(x - 1)$$
$$5x - 2 = 3 + 5x - 5$$
$$5x - 2 = -2 + 5x$$
$$5x - 2 + 2 = -2 + 5x + 2$$
$$5x = 5x$$
$$5x - 5x = 5x - 5x$$
$$0 = 0$$

Since $0 = 0$ is a true statement for every value of x, all real numbers are solutions. The solution set is $\{x | x$ is a real number$\}$.

Vocabulary and Readiness Check

1. Equations with the same solution set are called <u>equivalent</u> equations.

2. A value for the variable in an equation that makes the equation a true statement is called a <u>solution</u> of the equation.

3. By the <u>addition</u> property of equality, $y = -3$ and $y - 7 = -3 - 7$ are equivalent equations.

4. By the <u>multiplication</u> property of equality,
$2y = -3$ and $\dfrac{2y}{2} = \dfrac{-3}{2}$ are equivalent equations.

5. $\dfrac{1}{3}x - 5$ <u>expression</u>

6. $2(x - 3) = 7$ <u>equation</u>

7. $\dfrac{5}{9}x + \dfrac{1}{3} = \dfrac{2}{9} - x$ <u>equation</u>

8. $\dfrac{5}{9}x + \dfrac{1}{3} - \dfrac{2}{9} - x$ <u>expression</u>

9. $2x + 3 = 2x + 3$
Since the two sides of the equation are identical, the equation is true for any value of x. All real numbers are solutions.

10. $2x + 1 = 2x + 3$
Adding 1 to a number and adding 3 to the same number will not result in equal numbers for any value of x. There is no solution.

11. $5x - 2 = 5x - 7$
Subtracting 2 from a number and subtracting 7 from the same number will not result in equal numbers for any value of x. There is no solution.

12. $5x - 3 = 5x - 3$
Since the two sides of the equation are identical,

the equation is true for any value of x. All real numbers are solutions.

Exercise Set 1.5

2.
$$-2x = 18$$
$$\frac{-2x}{-2} = \frac{18}{-2}$$
$$x = -9$$

The solution is -9.

4.
$$-25 = y + 30$$
$$-25 - 30 = y + 30 - 30$$
$$-55 = y$$

The solution is -55.

6.
$$y - 8.6 = -6.3$$
$$y - 8.6 + 8.6 = -6.3 + 8.6$$
$$y = 2.3$$

The solution is 2.3.

8.
$$5y - 3 = 11 + 3y$$
$$5y - 3y = 11 + 3$$
$$2y = 14$$
$$\frac{2y}{2} = \frac{14}{2}$$
$$y = 7$$

The solution is 7.

10.
$$10.3 - 6x = -2.3$$
$$10.3 - 6x - 10.3 = -2.3 - 10.3$$
$$-6x = -12.6$$
$$\frac{-6x}{-6} = \frac{-12.6}{-6}$$
$$x = 2.1$$

```
2.1→X           2.1
10.3-6X
               -2.3
```

The solution is 2.1.

12.
$$4x + 14 = 6x + 8$$
$$4x - 6x = 8 - 14$$
$$-2x = -6$$
$$\frac{-2x}{-2} = \frac{-6}{-2}$$
$$x = 3$$

```
3→X              3
4X+14
                26
6X+8
                26
```

The solution is 3.

14.
$$13x - 15x + 8 = 4x + 2 - 24$$
$$-2x + 8 = 4x - 22$$
$$-2x - 4x = -22 - 8$$
$$-6x = -30$$
$$x = 5$$

```
5→X              5
13X-15X+8
                -2
4X+2-24
                -2
```

The solution is 5.

16.
$$6 + 3x + x = -x + 8 - 26 + 24$$
$$6 + 4x = -x + 6$$
$$5x = 0$$
$$x = 0$$

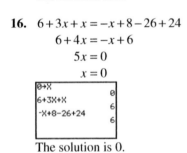

```
0→X              0
6+3X+X
                 6
-X+8-26+24
                 6
```

The solution is 0.

18.
$$2(4x + 3) = 7x + 5$$
$$8x + 6 = 7x + 5$$
$$x + 6 = 5$$
$$x = -1$$

```
-1→X            -1
2(4X+3)
                -2
7X+5
                -2
■
```

The solution is −1.

20.
$$6x = 4(x - 5)$$
$$6x = 4x - 20$$
$$2x = -20$$
$$x = -10$$

```
-10→X          -10
6X
               -60
4(X-5)
               -60
```

The solution is −10.

22.
$$-4(3n - 2) - n = -11(n - 1)$$
$$-12n + 8 - n = -11n + 11$$
$$-13n + 8 = -11n + 11$$
$$-13n + 11n = 11 - 8$$
$$-2n = 3$$
$$n = -\frac{3}{2}$$

```
-3/2→N         -1.5
-4(3N-2)-N
              27.5
-11(N-1)
              27.5
■
```

The solution is $-\dfrac{3}{2}$.

24.
$$\frac{x}{2} + \frac{x}{5} = \frac{5}{4}$$
$$20\left(\frac{x}{2} + \frac{x}{5}\right) = 20\left(\frac{5}{4}\right)$$
$$10x + 4x = 25$$
$$14x = 25$$
$$x = \frac{25}{14}$$

```
25/14→X
           1.785714286
X/2+X/5
                  1.25
5/4
                  1.25
```

The solution is $\dfrac{25}{14}$.

26.
$$\frac{4r}{5} - \frac{r}{10} = 7$$
$$10\left(\frac{4r}{5} - \frac{r}{10}\right) = 10(7)$$
$$2(4r) - r = 70$$
$$8r - r = 70$$
$$7r = 70$$
$$r = 10$$

```
10→R
           10
4R/5-R/10
            7
```

The solution is 10.

28.
$$\frac{2+h}{9} + \frac{h-1}{3} = \frac{1}{3}$$
$$9\left(\frac{2+h}{9} + \frac{h-1}{3}\right) = 9\left(\frac{1}{3}\right)$$
$$2 + h + 3(h-1) = 3$$
$$2 + h + 3h - 3 = 3$$
$$4h - 1 = 3$$
$$4h = 4$$
$$h = 1$$

```
1→H
                 1
(2+H)/9+(H-1)/3
          .3333333333
1/3
          .3333333333
■
```

The solution is 1.

30.
$$0.3x + 2.4 = 0.1x + 4$$
$$10(0.3x + 2.4) = 10(0.1x + 4)$$
$$3x + 24 = 1x + 40$$
$$2x = 16$$
$$x = 8$$

```
8→X
              8
.3X+2.4
            4.8
.1X+4
            4.8
```

The solution is 8.

32.
$$\frac{2z+7}{8} - 2 = z + \frac{z-1}{2}$$
$$8\left(\frac{2z+7}{8} - 2\right) = 8\left(z + \frac{z-1}{2}\right)$$
$$2z + 7 - 16 = 8z + 4(z-1)$$
$$2z + 7 - 16 = 8z + 4z - 4$$
$$2z - 9 = 12z - 4$$
$$-10z = 5$$
$$z = -\frac{1}{2}$$

```
-1/2→Z
             -.5
(2Z+7)/8-2
          -1.25
Z+(Z-1)/2
          -1.25
```

The solution is $-\frac{1}{2}$.

34.
$$2.4(2x + 3) = -0.1(2x + 3)$$
$$10[2.4(2x + 3)] = 10[-0.1(2x + 3)]$$
$$48x + 72 = -2x - 3$$
$$50x = -75$$
$$x = -1.5$$

```
-1.5→X
            -1.5
2.4(2X+3)
              0
-.1(2X+3)
              0
```

The solution is -1.5.

36.
$$6(4n + 4) = 8(3 + 3n)$$
$$24n + 24 = 24 + 24n$$
$$24n + 24 - 24n = 24 + 24n - 24n$$
$$24 = 24$$
$$0 = 0$$
Therefore, all real numbers are solutions.

38.
$$4(x + 2) + 4 = 4x - 8$$
$$4x + 8 + 4 = 4x - 8$$
$$4x + 12 = 4x - 8$$
$$12 = -8$$
This is false for any x. Therefore, no solution exists, $\varnothing$.

40.
$$5(x - 4) + x = 6(x - 2) - 8$$
$$5x - 20 + x = 6x - 12 - 8$$
$$6x - 20 = 6x - 20$$
$$-20 = -20$$
This is true for all x. Therefore, all real numbers are solutions.

42.
$$9(x - 2) = 8(x - 3) + x$$
$$9x - 18 = 8x - 24 + x$$
$$9x - 18 = 9x - 24$$
$$-18 = -24$$
This is false for any x. Therefore, no solution exists, $\varnothing$.

44. The screen shows that the solution of $7x - 2 = 5x$ is $x = 1$.

46. The screen shows that the solution of $7(C + 2) = 5C + 4$ is $C = -5$.

48.
$$\frac{a}{2}+\frac{7}{4}=5$$
$$4\left(\frac{a}{2}+\frac{7}{4}\right)=4\cdot 5$$
$$2a+7=20$$
$$2a=13$$
$$a=\frac{13}{2}$$

50.
$$4x-7=2x-7$$
$$4x-2x=-7+7$$
$$2x=0$$
$$x=0$$

52.
$$3x+2(x+4)=5(x+1)+3$$
$$3x+2x+8=5x+5+3$$
$$5x+8=5x+8$$
$$0=0$$
Therefore, all real numbers are solutions.

54.
$$-(w+0.2)=0.3(4-w)$$
$$-w-0.2=1.2-0.3w$$
$$-w+0.3w=1.2+0.2$$
$$-0.7w=1.4$$
$$w=-2$$

56.
$$\frac{1}{3}(8+2c)=\frac{1}{5}(3c-5)$$
$$\frac{8}{3}+\frac{2}{3}c=\frac{3}{5}c-1$$
$$\frac{8}{3}+1=\frac{3}{5}c-\frac{2}{3}c$$
$$\frac{8}{3}+\frac{3}{3}=\frac{9}{15}c-\frac{10}{15}c$$
$$\frac{11}{3}=-\frac{1}{15}c$$
$$-\frac{15}{1}\cdot\frac{11}{3}=c$$
$$-55=c$$

58.
$$9c-3(6-5c)=c-2(3c+9)$$
$$9c-18+15c=c-6c-18$$
$$24c-18=-5c-18$$
$$24c+5c=-18+18$$
$$29c=0$$
$$c=0$$

60.
$$10x-2(x+4)=8(x-2)+6$$
$$10x-2x-8=8x-16+6$$
$$8x-8=8x-10$$
$$8x-8x=-10+8$$
$$0=-2$$
This is false for any x. Therefore, the solution set is $\varnothing$.

62.

$$\frac{n+1}{8} - \frac{2-n}{3} = \frac{5}{6}$$

$$24\left(\frac{n+1}{8} - \frac{2-n}{3}\right) = 24\left(\frac{5}{6}\right)$$

$$3(n+1) - 8(2-n) = 4(5)$$

$$3n+3-16+8n = 20$$

$$11n - 13 = 20$$

$$11n = 33$$

$$n = 3$$

64.

$$10y - 18 - 4y = 12y - 13$$

$$6y - 18 = 12y - 13$$

$$6y - 12y = -13 + 18$$

$$-6y = 5$$

$$y = -\frac{5}{6}$$

66.

$$-4(2x-3) - (10x+7) - 2 = -(12x-5) - (4x+9) - 1$$

$$-8x + 12 - 10x - 7 - 2 = -12x + 5 - 4x - 9 - 1$$

$$-18x + 3 = -16x - 5$$

$$-2x = -8$$

$$x = 4$$

68.

$$\frac{1}{5}(2y-1) - 2 = \frac{1}{2}(3y-5) + 3$$

$$10 \cdot \left(\frac{1}{5}(2y-1) - 2\right) = 10 \cdot \left(\frac{1}{2}(3y-5) + 3\right)$$

$$2(2y-1) - 20 = 5(3y-5) + 30$$

$$4y - 22 = 15y + 5$$

$$-11y = 27$$

$$y = -\frac{27}{11}$$

70.

$$3[8 - 4(n-2)] + 5n = -20 + 2[5(1-n) - 6n]$$

$$3[8 - 4n + 8] + 5n = -20 + 2[5 - 5n - 6n]$$

$$3(16 - 4n) + 5n = -20 + 2(5 - 11n)$$

$$48 - 12n + 5n = -20 + 10 - 22n$$

$$48 - 7n = -10 - 22n$$

$$15n = -58$$

$$n = -\frac{58}{15}$$

72. $-3(-4) = 12$ not -12;

$$-3(x-4) = 10$$

$$-3x + 12 = 10$$

$$-3x = -2$$

$$\frac{-3x}{-3} = \frac{-2}{-3}$$

$$x = \frac{2}{3}$$

74. $3\left(\dfrac{x}{3}+7\right)=x+21;$

$$\dfrac{x}{3}+7=\dfrac{5x}{3}$$

$$3\left(\dfrac{x}{3}+7\right)=3\left(\dfrac{5x}{3}\right)$$

$$x+21=5x$$

$$21=4x$$

$$\dfrac{21}{4}=\dfrac{4x}{4}$$

$$\dfrac{21}{4}=x$$

76. Answers may vary

78. Answers may vary

80. $-7.6y-10=-1.1y+12$

$\qquad -7.6y=-1.1y+22$

From this we see that $K=22$.

82. $\qquad \dfrac{x}{6}+4=\dfrac{x}{3}$

$$6\left(\dfrac{x}{6}+4\right)=6\left(\dfrac{x}{3}\right)$$

$$x+24=2x$$

From this we see that $K=24$.

84. Answers may vary

86. $7x^2+2x-3=6x(x+4)+x^2$

$\quad 7x^2+2x-3=6x^2+24x+x^2$

$\quad 7x^2+2x-3=7x^2+24x$

$\qquad\qquad 2x-3=24x$

$\qquad\qquad\; -3=22x$

$\qquad\qquad\quad x=-\dfrac{3}{22}$

88. $x(x+1)+16=x(x+5)$

$\quad x^2+x+16=x^2+5x$

$\qquad\; x+16=5x$

$\qquad\quad 16=4x$

$\qquad\quad\; x=4$

90. $-9.112y=-47.537304$

$\qquad\quad y=5.217$

```
5.217→Y
           5.217
-9.112Y
        -47.537304
```

92. $1.25x-20.175=-8.15$

$\qquad 1.25x=-8.15+20.175$

$\qquad 1.25x=12.025$

$\qquad\quad x=9.62$

```
9.62→X
            9.62
1.25X-20.175
           -8.15
■
```

The Bigger Picture

1. $\qquad 3x-4=3(2x-1)+7$

$\qquad 3x-4=6x-3+7$

$\qquad 3x-4=6x+4$

$3x-4-6x=6x+4-6x$

$\qquad -3x-4=4$

$\quad -3x-4+4=4+4$

$\qquad\quad -3x=8$

$\qquad\quad \dfrac{-3x}{-3}=\dfrac{8}{-3}$

$\qquad\qquad x=-\dfrac{8}{3}$

2. $\qquad 5+2x=5(x+1)$

$\qquad 5+2x=5x+5$

$5+2x-5x=5x+5-5x$

$\qquad 5-3x=5$

$\quad 5-3x-5=5-5$

$\qquad\; -3x=0$

$\qquad\; \dfrac{-3x}{-3}=\dfrac{0}{-3}$

$\qquad\quad x=0$

3. $\qquad \dfrac{x+3}{2}=1$

$$2\left(\dfrac{x+3}{2}\right)=2(1)$$

$\qquad x+3=2$

$x+3-3=2-3$

$\qquad\; x=-1$

4. $\qquad \dfrac{x-2}{2}-\dfrac{x-4}{3}=\dfrac{5}{6}$

$$6\left(\dfrac{x-2}{2}-\dfrac{x-4}{3}\right)=6\left(\dfrac{5}{6}\right)$$

$3(x-2)-2(x-4)=5$

$\quad 3x-6-2x+8=5$

$\qquad\qquad x+2=5$

$\qquad x+2-2=5-2$

$\qquad\qquad x=3$

5.　　$\dfrac{7}{5} + \dfrac{y}{10} = 2$

$$10\left(\dfrac{7}{5} + \dfrac{y}{10}\right) = 10(2)$$
$$2(7) + y = 20$$
$$14 + y = 20$$
$$14 + y - 14 = 20 - 14$$
$$y = 6$$

6.　　$5 + 2x = 2(x+1)$
$$5 + 2x = 2x + 2$$
$$5 + 2x - 2x = 2x + 2 - 2x$$
$$5 = 2 \quad \text{False}$$

This false statement indicates that there is no solution. The solution set is $\varnothing$.

7.　$4(x-2) + 3x = 9(x-1) - 2$
$$4x - 8 + 3x = 9x - 9 - 2$$
$$7x - 8 = 9x - 11$$
$$7x - 8 - 9x = 9x - 11 - 9x$$
$$-2x - 8 = -11$$
$$-2x - 8 + 8 = -11 + 8$$
$$-2x = -3$$
$$\dfrac{-2x}{-2} = \dfrac{-3}{-2}$$
$$x = \dfrac{3}{2}$$

8.　$6(x+1) - 2 = 6x + 4$
$$6x + 6 - 2 = 6x + 4$$
$$6x + 4 = 6x + 4$$
$$6x + 4 - 6x = 6x + 4 - 6x$$
$$4 = 4 \quad \text{True}$$

This true statement indicates that all real numbers are solutions of the equation. The solution set is $(-\infty, \infty)$.

Section 1.6

Practice Exercises

1. a.

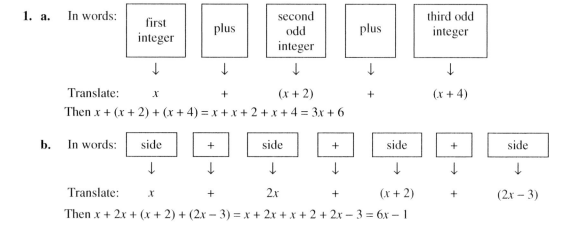

In words:

first integer	plus	second odd integer	plus	third odd integer
↓	↓	↓	↓	↓

Translate:　　x　　　　$+$　　　$(x+2)$　　　$+$　　　$(x+4)$

Then $x + (x+2) + (x+4) = x + x + 2 + x + 4 = 3x + 6$

b.　In words:

side	+	side	+	side	+	side
↓	↓	↓	↓	↓	↓	↓

Translate:　　x　　$+$　　$2x$　　$+$　　$(x+2)$　　$+$　　$(2x-3)$

Then $x + 2x + (x+2) + (2x-3) = x + 2x + x + 2 + 2x - 3 = 6x - 1$

2. If x = number of arrivals and departures at Frankfurt airport,
   then $x + 15.7$ = number at London, and $x + 1.6$ = number at Paris.

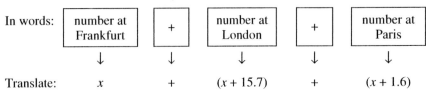

   In words:

   | number at Frankfurt | + | number at London | + | number at Paris |

   Translate: x $+$ $(x + 15.7)$ $+$ $(x + 1.6)$

   Then $x + (x + 15.7) + (x + 1.6) = x + x + 15.7 + x + 1.6 = 3x + 17.3$

3. Let x = the first number, then $3x - 8$ = the second number, and $5x$ = the third number.
   The sum of the three numbers is 118.
   $$x + (3x - 8) + 5x = 118$$
   $$x + 3x + 5x - 8 = 118$$
   $$9x - 8 = 118$$
   $$9x = 126$$
   $$x = 14$$
   The numbers are 14, $3x - 8 = 3(14) - 8 = 34$, and $5x = 5(14) = 70$.

4. Let x = the original price. Then $0.4x$ = the discount. The original price, minus the discount, is equal to $270.
   $$x - 0.4x = 270$$
   $$0.6x = 270$$
   $$x = \frac{270}{0.6} = 450$$
   The original price was $450.

5. Let x = width, then $2x - 16$ = length.
   The perimeter is 160 inches.
   $$2(x) + 2(2x - 16) = 160$$
   $$2x + 4x - 32 = 160$$
   $$6x - 32 = 160$$
   $$6x = 192$$
   $$x = 32$$
   $2x - 16 = 2(32) - 16 = 48$
   The width is 32 inches and the length is
   48 inches.

6. Let x = first odd integer, then $x + 2$ = second odd integer, and $x + 4$ = third odd integer.
   The sum of the integers is 81.
   $$x + (x + 2) + (x + 4) = 81$$
   $$3x + 6 = 81$$
   $$3x = 75$$
   $$x = 25$$
   $x + 2 = 27$
   $x + 4 = 29$
   The integers are 25, 27, and 29.

Vocabulary and Readiness Check

1. 130% of a number __>__ the number.

2. 70% of a number __<__ the number.

3. 100% of a number __=__ the number.

4. 200% of a number $\underline{\ >\ }$ the number.

	First Integer	All Described Integers
5. Four consecutive integers	31	31, 32, 33, 34
6. Three consecutive odd integers	31	31, 33, 35
7. Three consecutive even integers	18	18, 20, 22
8. Four consecutive even integers	92	92, 94, 96, 98
9. Three consecutive integers	y	$y, y+1, y+2$
10. Three consecutive even integers	z (z is even)	$z, z+2, z+4$
11. Four consecutive integers	p	$p, p+1, p+2, p+3$
12. Three consecutive odd integers	s (s is odd)	$s, s+2, s+4$

Exercise Set 1.6

2. The perimeter is the sum of the lengths of the four sides.
$$x+(x-5)+x+(x-5)=x+x+x+x-5-5$$
$$=4x-10$$

4. Let x = first odd integer, then
$x + 2$ = second odd integer, and
$x + 4$ = third odd integer.
$$x+(x+2)+(x+4)=x+x+x+2+4=3x+6$$

6. Find the sum of y quarters worth 25¢ each, $7y$ dimes worth 10¢ each, and $(2y-1)$ nickels worth 5¢ each.
$$25y+10(7y)+5(2y-1)=25y+70y+10y-5$$
$$=105y-5$$
The total amount is $(105y-5)$ cents.

8. $4x+5(3x-15)=4x+15x-75=19x-75$

10. The length of the side denoted by ? is $18 - 10 = 8$. Similarly, the length of the unmarked side is
$(x+14)-(x+8)=x+14-x-8=6$.
The perimeter of the floor plan is
$18+(x+8)+10+6+8+(x+14)=2x+64$

12. Let x = the number.
$$2(x+3)=5x-1-4x$$
$$2x+6=x-1$$
$$x=-7$$
The number is –7.

14. Let x = the first number, then
$x - 6$ = the second number, and
$2x$ = the third number.
$$x+(x-6)+2x=306$$
$$4x-6=306$$
$$4x=312$$
$$x=78$$
$x-6=72$
$2x=156$
The numbers are 78, 72, and 156.

16. $90\% \cdot 70 = 0.90 \cdot 70 = 63$
$70 - 63 = 7$
7 million acres are not federally owned.

18. 25.5% of $958 = 0.255 \cdot 958 \approx 244$
Approximately 244 tornadoes occurred during April 2006.

20. 9.1% of $17,029,300 = 0.091 \cdot 17,029,300$
$$\approx 1,549,666$$
Approximately 1,549,666 worked in the restaurant and food service industry in California.

22. Look for the largest sector, which is 55%.
15–60 minutes is the most common time spent on e-mail per day.

24. 9% of $278 = 0.09 \cdot 278 = 25.02$
About 25 employees spend between 2 and 3 hours per day using e-mail.

26. Let x = average cost in 2005.
$$x+0.068x=96.73$$
$$1.068x=96.73$$
$$x\approx 90.57$$
The average hotel room cost in 2005 was $90.57.

28. $3x + x + (x + 10) = 180$
$$5x + 10 = 180$$
$$5x = 170$$
$$x = 34$$
$3x = 3(34) = 102$
$x + 10 = 34 + 10 = 44$
The angles measure $34°$, $44°$, and $102°$.

30. $(2x) + (3.5x) + (3x + 7) = 75$
$$8.5x + 7 = 75$$
$$8.5x = 68$$
$$x = 8$$
$2x = 2(8) = 16$
$3.5x = 3.5(8) = 28$
$3x + 7 = 3(8) + 7 = 31$
The sides measure 16 centimeters, 28 centimeters, and 31 centimeters.

32. $7.3x + (9.2x - 3) + 7.3x + (9.2x - 3) = 324$
$$33x - 6 = 324$$
$$33x = 330$$
$$x = 10$$
$7.3x = 7.3(10) = 73$
$9.2x - 3 = 9.2(10) - 3 = 89$
The sides measure 73 feet, 73 feet, 89 feet, and 89 feet.

34. Let x = the first odd integer, then $x + 2$ = the second odd integer and $x + 4$ = the third odd integer.
$x + x + 2 + x + 4 = 327$
$$3x + 6 = 327$$
$$3x = 321$$
$$x = 107$$
The numbers are 107, 109, 111.

36. Let x = first integer, then $x + 1$ = second integer, and $x + 2$ = third integer.
$x + (x + 1) + 3(x + 2) = 2637$
$$x + x + 1 + 3x + 6 = 2637$$
$$5x + 7 = 2637$$
$$5x = 2630$$
$$x = 526$$
$x + 1 = 527$
$x + 2 = 528$
The score for Alabama was 526, for Louisiana was 527, and for Michigan was 528.

38. $\left(\dfrac{3}{2}x + 1\right) + x + (x - 1) = 105$
$$\frac{7}{2}x = 105$$
$$x = 105 \cdot \frac{2}{7}$$
$$x = 30$$
$\dfrac{3}{2}x + 1 = \dfrac{3}{2}(30) + 1 = 46$
$x - 1 = 30 - 1 = 29$

Occupation	Percent Increase in Number of Jobs from 2000 to 2012
Computer software engineers	46%
Management analysts	30%
Receptionist and information clerks	29%
Total	105%

40. Let x = thousands of fishers, then $2x + 8$ = thousands of telephone operators, and
$10x - 1$ = thousands of sewing machine operators
$$x + (2x + 8) + (10x - 1) = 137$$
$$13x + 7 = 137$$
$$13x = 130$$
$$x = 10$$
$2x + 8 = 2(10) + 8 = 28$
$10x - 1 = 10(10) - 1 = 99$
The declines are as follows: telephone operators: 28 thousand; sewing machine operators: 99 thousand; fishers: 10 thousand.

42. Let x = NY governor's salary, then $x + 27,500$ = CA governor's salary, and
$x + 27,500 - 120,724$ = AK governor's salary.
$$x + (x + 27,500) + (x + 27,500 - 120,724) = 471,276$$
$$3x - 65,724 = 471,276$$
$$3x = 537,000$$
$$x = 179,000$$
$x + 27,500 = 206,500$
$x + 27,500 - 120,724 = 85,776$
The governor salaries are as follows: CA: \$206,500; NY: \$179,000; AK: \$85,776

44. Let x = price before taxes.
$$x + 0.09x = 158.60$$
$$1.09x = 158.60$$
$$x = 145.50$$
The price of the book was \$145.50.

46. Let x = population in 2005.
$$33.2 = x + 0.015x$$
$$33.2 = 1.015x$$
$$32.7 = x$$
The population in 2005 was 32.7 million.

48. Let x = measure of complement; then $2x + 30$ = measure of angle.
$$x + 2x + 30 = 90$$
$$3x = 60$$
$$x = 20$$
$2x + 30 = 2(20) + 30 = 70$
The angles measure $20°$ and $70°$.

50. Let x = base angle; then $3x - 10$ = third angle.
$$2x + 3x - 10 = 180$$
$$5x - 10 = 180$$
$$5x = 190$$
$$x = 38$$
$$3x - 10 = 3 \cdot 38 - 10 = 104$$
The angles measure 38°, 38°, and 104°.

52. Let x = length of side of pentagon, then $x + 7$ = length of side of square.
$$5x = 4(x + 7)$$
$$5x = 4x + 28$$
$$x = 28$$
$$x + 7 = 28 + 7 = 35$$
The pentagon has a side length of 28 inches and the square has a side length of 35 inches.

54. Let x = first integer, then
$x + 1$ = second integer, and
$x + 2$ = third integer, and
$x + 3$ = fourth integer.
$$(x + 1) + (x + 3) = 110$$
$$2x + 4 = 110$$
$$2x = 106$$
$$x = 53$$
$$x + 1 = 54$$
$$x + 2 = 55$$
$$x + 3 = 56$$
The integers are 53, 54, 55, and 56.

56. $(x + 2) + 2x + x + (2x - 3) = 110$
$$6x - 1 = 110$$
$$6x = 111$$
$$x = 18.5$$
$$x + 2 = 18.5 + 2 = 20.5$$
$$2x = 2(18.5) = 37$$
$$2x - 3 = 2(18.5) - 3 = 34$$
The bases measure 18.5 meters and 37 meters, and the sides measure 20.5 meters and 34 meters.

58. $x + (x + 15.7) + (x + 1.6) = 173.9$
$$3x + 17.3 = 173.9$$
$$3x = 156.6$$
$$x = 52.2$$
$$x + 15.7 = 52.2 + 15.7 = 67.9$$
$$x + 1.6 = 52.2 + 1.6 = 53.8$$
The arrivals and departures are as follows:
London: 67.9 million, Paris: 53.8 million, Frankfurt: 52.2 million

60. Let x = height of Galter Pavilion; then
$x + 67$ = height of Guy's Tower and
$x + 47$ = height of Queen Mary
$$x + (x + 67) + (x + 47) = 1320$$
$$3x + 114 = 1320$$
$$3x = 1206$$
$$x = 402$$
$$x + 67 = 402 + 67 = 469$$
$$x + 47 = 402 + 47 = 449$$
Galter Pavilion: 402 ft
Guy's Tower: 469 ft
Queen Mary: 449 ft

62. Let x = number of seats in Heinz Field; then
$x + 11,675$ = number of seats in Mile High.
$$x + (x + 11,675) = 140,575$$
$$2x + 11,675 = 140,575$$
$$2x = 128,900$$
$$x = 64,450$$
$$x + 11,675 = 64,450 + 11,675 = 76,125$$
Mile High stadium has 76,125 seats and Heinz Field has 64,450 seats.

64. a. Let x = deaths in 1950s.
$$x - 0.592x = 579$$
$$0.408x = 579$$
$$x \approx 1419$$
There were 1419 deaths caused by tornadoes in the 1950s.

   b. Answers may vary

66. Let x = number of returns filed electronically in 2005.
$$x + 1.088x = \text{number in 2006}$$
$$x + 1.088x = 74.2$$
$$2.088x = 74.2$$
$$x \approx 35.5$$
Approximately 35.5 million tax returns were filed electronically in 2005.

68. Let x = first integer (Dye), then
$x + 1$ = second integer (Berkman), and
$x + 2$ = third integer (Soriano).
$$x + (x + 1) + (x + 2) = 135$$
$$3x + 3 = 135$$
$$3x = 132$$
$$x = 44$$
$$x + 1 = 45$$
$$x + 2 = 46$$
The home runs are as follows: Soriano: 46; Berkman: 45; Dye: 44

70. Yes; answers may vary

72. Answers may vary

74. Let x = the total number of trees used for newsprint each year. Since 27% of newsprint is recycled, $100 - 27 = 73\%$ is not recycled. 73% of the total number of trees is 30 million trees.
$$0.73x = 30$$
$$x \approx 41.1$$
The total number of trees is about 41.1 million. 27% of these are recycled.
$$0.27(41.1) \approx 11$$
About 11 million trees' worth of newsprint is recycled each year.

76. $R = C$
$$24x = 100 + 20x$$
$$4x = 100$$
$$x = 25$$
It will take 25 skateboards to break even.

78. The company loses money.

80. To get the answers shown here, use your calculator values for each year rather than the rounded values to compute the number for the following year.
2008: $76.8 + 0.042(76.8) \approx 80.0$ million
2009: $80.0 + 0.042(80.0) \approx 83.4$ million
2010: $83.4 + 0.042(83.4) \approx 86.9$ million
2011: $86.9 + 0.042(86.9) \approx 90.5$ million

Section 1.7

Practice Exercises

1. In words: $2000 plus 6% of sales
Translate: $2000 \quad + \quad 0.06x$

The completed table is:

Sales, x	1000	3000	5000	7000
Gross pay	2060	2180	2300	2420

Find the 2540 entry in the y_1 (gross pay) column. The corresponding x-value (sales) figure is 9000. She must average $9000 in sales per month to earn a gross pay of $2540 per month.

2. Let x be the number of hours. The charge for the first plumber is $35 + 25x$, while the charge for the second plumber is $35x$.

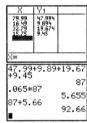

The first plumber charges $160 for 5 hours and the second plumber charges $175, so the first plumber charges $15 less for 5 hours.

3. First, find the discounted price, which is 40% off the original price.

In words:	Discounted price	is	60%	of	original price
Translate:	Discounted price	=	0.60	·	x

Thus $y_1 = 0.60x$ is the discounted price.
The sales tax rate is 6.5%.

In words:	Sales tax	is	6.5%	of	discounted price
Translate:	Sales tax	=	0.065	·	$(0.60x)$

The total price for the discounted items was $87.00. Including tax, she paid $92.66 for the items.

4. Let x be the number of items produced and sold. The cost is $5600 + 4x$ and the revenue is $11x$.

No. of items	600	700	800	900	1000
Cost (x items)	8000	8400	8800	9200	9600
Revenue (x items)	6600	7700	8800	9900	11,000

Since the table entries for 800 items are the same for cost and revenue, the sale and production of 800 items produces the break-even point.

5. $y = -16x^2 + 112x$

X	Y1	
1	96	
2	160	
3	192	
4	192	
5	160	
6	96	
7	0	

$Y_1 \blacksquare -16X^2 + 112X$

    a. Since the window height is 160 feet, the rocket first passes the window 2 seconds after it is shot off.

    b. The rocket passes the window again at 5 seconds.

    c. At 7 seconds, the height is 0, indicating that the rocket has hit the ground.

    d. The rocket appears to reach its maximum height between 3 and 4 seconds.

X	Y1	
3	192	
3.1	193.44	
3.2	194.56	
3.3	195.36	
3.4	195.84	
3.5	196	
3.6	195.84	

$X=3$

    The maximum height, 196 feet, occurs 3.5 seconds after the rocket is launched.

Vocabulary and Readiness Check

1. Each y_1-value is -2 times the x-value, so $y = -2x$; f.

2. Each y_1-value is 5 times the x-value, so $y = 5x$; a.

3. Each y_1-value is 1 more than 3 times the x-value, so $y = 3x + 1$; b.

4. Each y_1-value is 5 more than -1 times the x-value, so $y = -x + 5$; e.

5. Each y_1-value is 1 more than the square of the x-value, so $y = x^2 + 1$; d.

6. Each y_1-value is the square of the x-value, so $y = x^2$; c.

Exercise Set 1.7

2.

X	Y1	
2	37.699	
3	84.823	
4	150.8	
5	235.62	
6	339.29	
7	461.81	
8	603.19	

$Y_1 \blacksquare 3\pi X^2$

Radius of Cylinder	x	2	3	4	5	6
Volume (If height is 3 Units)	$3\pi x^2$	37.70	84.82	150.80	235.62	339.29

    a.   The volume of a cylinder with height 3 inches and radius 5 inches is about 235.62 cubic inches.

    b.   The volume of a cylinder with height 3 meters and radius 4 meters is about 150.80 cubic meters.

    c.   A cylinder with height 3 kilometers and volume 150.8 cubic kilometers has a radius of about 4 kilometers.

4.

Minutes on Phone	x	7	7.5	8	8.5
Total Charge (Dollars)	$1.30 + 0.15x$	2.35	2.43	2.5	2.58

   a.

     A person with \$3.25 can talk for 13 minutes on a pay phone.

   b.

     To spend no more than \$4 on a single phone call, the call must be less than 18 minutes long.

6. a. $y_1 = 69.75x$

  b. $y_2 = 263.25x$

  c.

Credit Hours	2	3	4	5	6
In-State Cost (Dollars)	139.50	209.25	279.00	348.75	418.50
Out-of-State Cost (Dollars)	526.50	789.75	1053.00	1316.25	1579.50

  d.   Her total tuition will be \$1061.25.

8.

Radius of Sphere	x	3	7.1	43	50
Volume	$\frac{4}{3}\pi x^3$	113.1	1499.2	333,038.14	523,598.78
Surface Area	$4\pi x^2$	113.1	633.47	23,235.22	31,415.93

   a.　A sphere with radius 1.7 centimeters has volume 20.58 cubic centimeters and surface area 36.32 square centimeters.

   b.　A sphere with radius 25 feet has volume 64,449.85 cubic feet and surface area 7853.98 square feet.

10. a.　Use $y_1 = 23,500 + 1000(x-1)$ for Company A and $y_2 = 25,000 + 475(x-1)$ for Company B.

Years	1	2	3	4	5
Gross Pay A	23,500	24,500	25,500	26,500	27,500
Gross Pay B	25,000	25,475	25,950	26,425	26,900

   b.　She makes more money in 5 years with Company B ($129,750) than with Company A ($127,500).

12. a.　$y_1 = 6.00 + 1.72x$

   b.

Gallons of Water Used (Thousands)	0	1	2	3	4	5	6
Monthly Cost (Dollars)	6	7.72	9.44	11.16	12.88	14.6	16.32

14. a.　$y_1 = 850 - 25x$

   b.

Days Elapsed	0	10	15	20	25	30
Cars Remaining	850	600	475	350	225	100

   c.

His lot will be empty of cars after 34 days.

16. a. Use $y_1 = 35,000 + 650(x-1)$ for Plan A and $y_2 = 32,000 + 1000(x-1)$ for Plan B.

Year	1	2	3	4	5	6
Plan A	35,000	35,650	36,300	36,950	37,600	38,250
Plan B	32,000	33,000	34,000	35,000	36,000	37,000

    b. Answers may vary

18. a. $y_1 = 10 + 0.09850x$

    b.

X	Y1
0	10
500	59.25
1000	108.5
1500	157.75
2000	207
2500	256.25
3000	305.5

$Y_1 = 10 + .09850X$

Kilowatt-Hours	0	500	1000	1500	2000
Monthly Cost (Dollars)	10	59.25	108.5	157.75	207

20. a. $y_1 = 1000 - 1.5x$

    b.

X	Y1
0	1000
60	910
120	820
180	730
240	640
300	550
360	460

$Y_1 = 1000 - 1.5X$

Minutes	0	60	120	180	240	300	360
ml Solution Remaining	1000	910	820	730	640	550	460

    c.

X	Y1
360	460
420	370
480	280
540	190
600	100
660	10
720	-80

$Y_1 = 1000 - 1.5X$

She should return in 660 minutes, which is 11 hours. She should return at 12 midnight.

22. a. A rate of 24 miles per gallon corresponds to $\dfrac{1}{24}$ gallon per mile.

$$y_1 = 14 - \frac{x}{24}$$

    b. A rate of 30 miles per gallon corresponds to $\dfrac{1}{30}$ gallon per mile.

$$y_2 = 14 - \frac{x}{30}$$

    c.

X	Y1	Y2
0	14	14
50	11.917	12.333
100	9.8333	10.667
150	7.75	9
200	5.6667	7.3333
250	3.5833	5.6667
300	1.5	4

$Y_1 = 14 - X/24$

X	Y1	Y2
100	9.8333	10.667
150	7.75	9
200	5.6667	7.3333
250	3.5833	5.6667
300	1.5	4
350	-.5833	2.3333
400	-2.667	.66667

$Y_2 = 14 - X/30$

Miles	0	50	100	150	200	250	300	350	400
City	14	11.9	9.8	7.8	5.7	3.6	1.5	−0.6	−2.7
Highway	14	12.3	10.7	9	7.3	5.7	4	2.3	0.7

d. After 300 miles of city driving, there are 1.5 gallons left in the tank.

e. After 300 miles of highway driving, there are 4 gallons left in the tank.

f.

He can drive 420 miles on the highway before his tank is empty.

g.

He can drive 336 miles in the city before his tank is empty.

h. Answers may vary

24. a. If the regular price is x dollars, the sale price is $x - 0.30x = 0.70x$ dollars.
$y_1 = 0.70x$

b.

Item	Hammer	Drill	Sander	Glue Gun	Screwdriver Set	Socket Wrench Set
Price Tag	$9.95	$29.95	$49.75	$19.95	$27.95	$79.95
Sale Price	$6.97	$20.97	$34.83	$13.97	$19.57	$55.97

c.

His total bill before taxes is $152.28 if he purchases all the items on sale.

d.

His total after taxes is $162.94.

e.

He saves $65.22 by waiting for the sale.

26. Let $y_1 = 1750 + 21x$ for the cost equation and $y_2 = 35x$ for the revenue equation.

X	Y1	Y2
25	2275	875
50	2800	1750
75	3325	2625
100	3850	3500
125	4375	4375
150	4900	5250
175	5425	6125

Y1∎1750+21X

x Books	25	50	75	100	125
Cost	2275	2800	3325	3850	4375
Revenue	875	1750	2625	3500	4375

The break-even point is when 125 books are produced and sold.

28. When 100 books are produced and sold, there is a loss of $3850 - $3500 = $350.

30. Let x be the diameter of the pizza. Use $y_1 = \pi\left(\dfrac{x}{2}\right)^2$ for the area, $y_2 = \pi x$ for the circumference, $y_3 = 0.05y_1$ for the cost based on area, and $y_4 = 0.25y_2$ for the cost based on circumference.

X	Y1	Y2
6	28.274	18.85
12	113.1	37.699
18	254.47	56.549
24	452.39	75.398
30	706.86	94.248
36	1017.9	113.1
42	1385.4	131.95

Y1∎π(X/2)²

X	Y3	Y4
6	1.4137	4.7124
12	5.6549	9.4248
18	12.723	14.137
24	22.619	18.85
30	35.343	23.562
36	50.894	28.274
42	69.272	32.987

Y4∎.25Y2

Diameter (Inches)	Area	Circumference	Cost (Area)	Cost (Circumference)
6	28.274	18.85	$1.41	$4.71
12	113.1	37.699	$5.65	$9.42
18	254.17	56.549	$12.72	$14.14
24	452.39	75.398	$22.62	$18.85
30	706.86	94.248	$35.34	$23.56
36	1017.9	113.1	$50.89	$28.27

Answers may vary

32. a.

X	Y1
1	84
2	136
3	156
4	144
5	100
6	24
7	-84

Y1∎-16X²+100X

Seconds	1	2	3	4	5
Height (Feet)	84	136	156	144	100

b. The rocket rises, peaks, then falls.

c.

X	Y1
6	24
6.05	19.36
6.1	14.64
6.15	9.84
6.2	4.96
6.25	0
6.3	-5.04

X=6

If the rocket doesn't explode in the air, it hits the ground after 6.3 seconds.

34. a. $C = 35 + 25x$

b.

Hours on Job	1.5	2	2.5	3
Cost (Dollars)	72.5	85	97.5	110

36. a.   Since the object is dropped, the maximum height is where it starts, at 1050 feet.

b.

The object hits the ground after approximately 8.1 seconds.

38.   Let x be the length of the sides perpendicular to the patio. Then $52 - 2x$ is the length of the side parallel to the patio and the area is $x(52 - 2x)$.

The largest area, 338 square feet, occurs when $x = 13$. Then
$52 - 2x = 52 - 2(13) = 52 - 26 = 26$ and the dimensions are 13 feet by 26 feet.

40.

a.   The lowest high temperature occurs when $x = 4$, which corresponds to Wednesday.

b.   The lowest high temperature is 72.7°F.

c.   No; answers may vary

Section 1.8

Practice Exercises

1. $I = Prt$

$$\frac{I}{Pr} = \frac{Prt}{Pr}$$

$$\frac{I}{Pr} = t \text{ or } t = \frac{I}{Pr}$$

2. $7x - 2y = 5$
$$7x - 2y - 7x = 5 - 7x$$
$$-2y = 5 - 7x$$
$$\frac{-2y}{-2} = \frac{5 - 7x}{-2}$$
$$y = \frac{7}{2}x - \frac{5}{2}$$

3. $A = P + Prt$
$$A - P = P + Prt - P$$
$$A - P = Prt$$
$$\frac{A - P}{Pt} = \frac{Prt}{Pt}$$
$$\frac{A - P}{Pt} = r \text{ or } r = \frac{A - P}{Pt}$$

4.   Let $P = 8000$, $r = 6\% = 0.06$, $t = 4$, $n = 2$.
$$A = P\left(1 + \frac{r}{n}\right)^{nt}$$
$$A = 8000\left(1 + \frac{0.06}{2}\right)^{2 \cdot 4}$$
$$A = 8000(1.03)^8$$
$$A \approx 8000(1.266770081)$$
$$A \approx 10{,}134.16$$
Russ will have \$10,134.16 in his account.

5.   Let $d = 192$ and $r = 7.5$.
$$d = rt$$
$$192 = 7.5t$$
$$\frac{192}{7.5} = \frac{7.5t}{7.5}$$
$$25.6t = t$$
They spent 25.6 hours cycling, or 25 hours 36 minutes.

6. $C = \dfrac{5}{9}(F - 32)$
$$\frac{9}{5}C = F - 32$$
$$\frac{9}{5}C + 32 = F$$
Use $y_1 = \dfrac{9}{5}x + 32$.

Celsius	−40	−30	10	30
Fahrenheit	−40	−22	50	86

7. Let x be the width of the pen. Then the length of the pen along the shed is $(88 - 2x)$ feet, and the area is $x(88 - 2x)$.

X	Y1
19	950
20	960
21	966
22	968
23	966
24	960
25	950

$Y_1 \blacksquare X(88-2X)$

The largest area is 968 square feet when the width is 22 feet and the length is $88 - 2 \cdot 22 = 44$ feet.

Exercise Set 1.8

2.
$$W = gh$$
$$\frac{W}{h} = \frac{gh}{h}$$
$$\frac{W}{h} = g$$
$$g = \frac{W}{h}$$

4.
$$V = lwh$$
$$\frac{V}{wh} = \frac{lwh}{wh}$$
$$\frac{V}{wh} = l$$
$$l = \frac{V}{wh}$$

6.
$$2x + 3y = 17$$
$$2x + 3y - 2x = 17 - 2x$$
$$3y = 17 - 2x$$
$$\frac{3y}{3} = \frac{17 - 2x}{3}$$
$$y = \frac{17 - 2x}{3}$$

8.
$$A = 3M - 2N$$
$$A + 2N = 3M$$
$$2N = 3M - A$$
$$\frac{2N}{2} = \frac{3M - A}{2}$$
$$N = \frac{3M - A}{2}$$

10.
$$y = mx + b$$
$$y - b = mx$$
$$\frac{y - b}{m} = \frac{mx}{m}$$
$$x = \frac{y - b}{m}$$

12.
$$A = Prt + P$$
$$A = P(rt + 1)$$
$$\frac{A}{rt + 1} = \frac{P(rt + 1)}{rt + 1}$$
$$P = \frac{A}{rt + 1}$$

14.
$$A = 5H(b + B)$$
$$A = 5Hb + 5HB$$
$$A - 5HB = 5Hb$$
$$\frac{A - 5HB}{5H} = \frac{5Hb}{5H}$$
$$\frac{A - 5HB}{5H} = b$$
$$b = \frac{A - 5HB}{5H}$$

16.
$$S = 2\pi r^2 + 2\pi rh$$
$$S - 2\pi r^2 = 2\pi rh$$
$$\frac{S - 2\pi r^2}{2\pi r} = \frac{2\pi rh}{2\pi r}$$
$$\frac{S - 2\pi r^2}{2\pi r} = h$$
$$h = \frac{S - 2\pi r^2}{2\pi r}$$

18.
$$A = P(1 + rt)$$
$$A = P + Prt$$
$$A - P = Prt$$
$$\frac{A - P}{Pr} = \frac{Prt}{Pr}$$
$$\frac{A - P}{Pr} = t$$
$$t = \frac{A - P}{Pr}$$

20.
$$C = \frac{5}{9}(F - 32)$$
$$9C = 5(F - 32)$$
$$9C = 5F - 160$$
$$9C + 160 = 5F$$
$$\frac{9C + 160}{5} = \frac{5F}{5}$$
$$\frac{9C + 160}{5} = F$$
$$F = \frac{9}{5}C + 32$$

22.
$$L = a + (n - 1)d$$
$$L - a = (n - 1)d$$
$$\frac{L - a}{n - 1} = \frac{(n - 1)d}{n - 1}$$
$$\frac{L - a}{n - 1} = d$$
$$d = \frac{L - a}{n - 1}$$

24.
$$T = 3vs - 4ws + 5vw$$
$$T + 4ws = 3vs + 5vw$$
$$T + 4ws = v(3s + 5w)$$
$$\frac{T + 4ws}{3s + 5w} = \frac{v(3s + 5w)}{3s + 5w}$$
$$\frac{T + 4ws}{3s + 5w} = v$$
$$v = \frac{T + 4ws}{3s + 5w}$$

26. $A = P\left(1 + \frac{r}{n}\right)^{nt} = 5000\left(1 + \frac{0.06}{n}\right)^{15n}$

n	1	2	4	12	365
A	\$11,982.79	\$12,136.31	\$12,216.10	\$12,270.47	\$12,297.11

28. a. Using the formula $A = P\left(1 + \frac{r}{n}\right)^{nt}$, we have

$$A = 25{,}000\left(1 + \frac{0.05}{2}\right)^{2 \cdot 2}$$
$$= 25{,}000(1.025)^4$$
$$\approx 25{,}000(1.103812891)$$
$$\approx 27{,}595.32$$

The amount in the account is \$27,595.32.

b. $A = 25,000\left(1 + \dfrac{0.05}{4}\right)^{4 \cdot 2}$

$= 25,000(1.0125)^8$

$\approx 25,000(1.104486101)$

$\approx 27,612.15$

The amount in the account is \$27,612.15.

c. $A = 25,000\left(1 + \dfrac{0.05}{12}\right)^{12 \cdot 2}$

$\approx 25,000(1.00416666)^{24}$

$\approx 25,000(1.104941335)$

$\approx 27,623.53$

The amount in the account is \$27,623.53.

30. Using the formula $F = \dfrac{9}{5}C + 32$, we have

$F = \dfrac{9}{5}C + 32 = \dfrac{9}{5}(-15) + 32 = -27 + 32 = 5$

The temperature was 5°F.

32. We use $d = rt$ and want to find r, the average rate or speed. Notice that the total distance traveled is $2 \cdot 154 = 308$.

$d = rt$

$308 = r\left(5\dfrac{1}{2}\right)$

$308 = 5.5r$

$r = \dfrac{308}{5.5}$

$r = 56$

Their average speed was 56 mph.

34. The total area of the ceiling is $18(12) = 216$ square feet. Each package can cover up to 50 square feet. Thus, the number of packages needed is $\dfrac{216}{50} = 4.32$. Therefore, 5 packages must be purchased.

36. Using the formula $A = P\left(1 + \dfrac{r}{n}\right)^{nt}$, we have

$A = 4000\left(1 + \dfrac{0.055}{2}\right)^{2 \cdot 3}$

$A = 4000(1.0275)^6$

$A \approx 4000(1.176768361)$

$A \approx 4707.07$

Yes, the amount is enough.

38. Note that the wall covers $21 \cdot 8 = 168$ square feet. Because we wish to paint three coats, we actually must cover a total of $168 \cdot 3 = 504$ square feet. Since each gallon covers 300 square feet, we need $\dfrac{504}{300} = 1.68$ gallons of paint. 2 gallons should be purchased.

40. Note that the radius of the circle is equal to $22,248 + 4000 = 26,248$.

$C = 2\pi r$

$C = 2\pi(26,248)$

$C = 52,496\pi$

$C \approx 164,921.0479$

The "length" of the Clarke belt is approximately 164,921 miles.

42. $V = \pi r^2 h$

$V = \pi(2.3)^2(18.3)$

$V = 96.807\pi \text{ m}^3$

$V \approx 304.12816 \text{ m}^3$

The volume of the cargo bay is approximately 304.12816 cubic meters.

44. $8 \text{ miles} \times \dfrac{5280 \text{ ft}}{1 \text{ mile}} = 42,240 \text{ ft}$

$7.5 \text{ hours} \times \dfrac{60 \text{ min}}{1 \text{ hour}} \times \dfrac{60 \text{ sec}}{1 \text{ min}} = 27,000 \text{ sec}$

Using $d = rt$ we have:

$42,240 = r(27,000)$

$r = \dfrac{42,240}{27,000} \approx 1.6$

The drill can be removed at a rate of 1.6 ft/sec.

46. Using the formula $V = \dfrac{4}{3}\pi r^3$, we have

$V = \dfrac{4}{3}\pi(20.6)^3$

$V \approx 36,618$

The volume of Eartha is about 36,618 cu ft.

48. $d = rt$

$135 = 60t$

$t = 2.25$

It will take Mark 2.25 hours or 2 hours 15 minutes.

50. $C = 4h + 9f + 4p$

$4h = C - 9f - 4p$

$h = \dfrac{C - 9f - 4p}{4}$

52. $C = 4h + 9f + 4p$

$C = 4(30) + 9(9) + 4(2)$

$C = 209$

There are 209 calories in this serving.

54. $f = \dfrac{C - 4h - 4p}{9}$

$f = \dfrac{120 - 4(21) - 4(5)}{9}$

$f \approx 1.8$

There are 1.8 grams of fat per serving.

56. Answers may vary

58. 12 times a year; answers may vary

60. $N = R^* \times f_p \times n_e \times f_l \times f_i \times f_c \times L$

$n_e = \dfrac{N}{R^* \times f_p \times f_l \times f_i \times f_c \times L}$

62. $P(\text{green}) = \dfrac{1}{8}$

64. $P(\text{black}) = \dfrac{1}{8}$

66. $P(\text{green or blue}) = P(\text{green}) + P(\text{blue})$

$= \dfrac{1}{8} + \dfrac{3}{8}$

$= \dfrac{4}{8}$

$= \dfrac{1}{2}$

68. $P(\text{red, green, or black})$

$= P(\text{red}) + P(\text{green}) + P(\text{black})$

$= \dfrac{1}{8} + \dfrac{1}{8} + \dfrac{1}{8}$

$= \dfrac{3}{8}$

70. $P(\text{white}) = 0$

72. 0

Chapter 1 Vocabulary Check

1. An <u>algebraic expression</u> is formed by numbers and variables connected by the operations of addition, subtraction, multiplication, division, raising to powers, and/or taking roots.

2. The <u>opposite</u> of a number a is $-a$.

3. $3(x - 6) = 3x - 18$ by the <u>distributive</u> property.

4. The <u>absolute value</u> of a number is the distance between the number and 0 on the number line.

5. An <u>exponent</u> is a shorthand notation for repeated multiplication of the same factor.

6. A letter that represents a number is called a <u>variable</u>.

7. The symbols $<$ and $>$ are called <u>inequality</u> symbols.

8. If a is not 0, then a and $\dfrac{1}{a}$ are called <u>reciprocals</u>.

9. $A + B = B + A$ by the <u>commutative</u> property.

10. $(A + B) + C = A + (B + C)$ by the <u>associative</u> property.

11. The numbers 0, 1, 2, 3, ... are called <u>whole</u> numbers.

12. If a number corresponds to a point on the number line, we know that number is a <u>real</u> number.

13. An equation in one variable that has no solution is called a <u>contradiction</u>.

14. An equation in one variable that has every number (for which the equation is defined) as a solution is called an <u>identity</u>.

15. The equation $d = rt$ is also called a <u>formula</u>.

16. When a variable in an equation is replaced by a number and the resulting equation is true, then that number is called a <u>solution</u> of the equation.

17. The integers 17, 18, 19 are examples of <u>consecutive integers</u>.

18. The statement $5x - 0.2 = 7$ is an example of a <u>linear equation in one variable</u>.

Chapter 1 Review

1. $7x = 7(3) = 21$

2. $st = (1.6)(5) = 8$

3. One hour is $60(60) = 3600$ seconds.
   $90t = 90(3600) = 324,000$
   $324,000$ wing beats per hour.

4. $\{x|x$ is an odd integer between -2 and $4\}$
   $= \{-1, 1, 3\}$

5. $\{x|x$ is an even integer between -3 and $7\}$
   $= \{-2, 0, 2, 4, 6\}$

6. There are no whole numbers that are negative.
   $\varnothing$

7. All natural numbers are rational numbers.
   $\varnothing$

8. $\{x|x$ is a whole number greater than $5\}$
   $= \{6, 7, 8, ...\}$

9. $\{x|x$ is an integer less than $3\} = \{..., -1, 0, 1, 2\}$

10. Since $D = \{2, 4, 6, 8, 10, ..., 16\}$, $10 \in D$ is true.

11. Since $B = \{5, 9, 11\}$, $B \in 9$ is false.

12. $\sqrt{169} = 13$, which is a rational number. So
    $\sqrt{169} \notin G$ is true.

13. Since $F = \{\ \ \}$ and 0 is not an element of the empty set, then $0 \notin F$ is true.

14. Since $E = \{x|x$ is a rational number$\}$ and π is irrational, then $\pi \in E$ is false.

15. Since $H = \{x|x$ is a real number$\}$ and π is a real number, then $\pi \in H$ is true.

16. Since $\sqrt{4} = 2$ and $G = \{x|x$ is an irrational number$\}$, and 2 is a rational number, then $\sqrt{4} \in G$ is false.

17. Since $E = \{x|x$ is a rational number$\}$ and -9 is a rational number, then $-9 \in E$ is true.

18. Since $A = \{6, 10, 12\}$ and
    $D = \{2, 4, 6, 8, 10, 12, 14, 16\}$, then $A \subseteq D$ is true.

19. Since $C = \{..., -3, -2, -1, 0, 1, 2, 3, ...\}$ and
    $B = \{5, 9, 11\}$, then $C \nsubseteq B$ is true.

20. Since $C = \{..., -3, -2, -1, 0, 1, 2, 3, ...\}$ and
    $E = \{x|x$ is a rational number$\}$, and all integers are rational numbers, then $C \nsubseteq E$ is false.

21. Since $F = \{\ \ \}$ and $H = \{x|x$ is a real number$\}$, and the empty set is a subset of all sets, then $F \subseteq H$ is true.

22. A set is always a subset of itself, so $B \subseteq B$ is true.

23. $D = \{2, 4, 6, ..., 16\}$ and
    $C = \{..., -3, -2, -1, 0, 1, 2, 3, ...\}$
    Every element of D is also an element of C, so
    $D \subseteq C$ is true.

24. $C = \{..., -3, -2, -1, 0, 1, 2, 3, ...\}$ and
    $H = \{x|x$ is a real number$\}$.
    Every integer is a real number, so $C \subseteq H$ is true.

25. $G = \{x|x$ is an irrational number$\}$ and
    $H = \{x|x$ is a real number$\}$
    Every irrational number is also a real number, so
    $G \subseteq H$ is true.

26. Since $B = \{5, 9, 11\}$, and B does not contain the set $\{5\}$, then $\{5\} \in B$ is false.

27. Since $B = \{5, 9, 11\}$, and $\{5\}$ is a subset of B, then $\{5\} \subseteq B$ is true.

28. Whole numbers: $\left\{5, \dfrac{8}{2}, \sqrt{9}\right\}$

29. Natural numbers: $\left\{5, \dfrac{8}{2}, \sqrt{9}\right\}$

30. Rational numbers: $\left\{5, -\dfrac{2}{3}, \dfrac{8}{2}, \sqrt{9}, 0.3, 1\dfrac{5}{8}, -1\right\}$

31. Irrational numbers: $\left\{\sqrt{7}, \pi\right\}$

32. Real numbers:
    $\left\{5, -\dfrac{2}{3}, \dfrac{8}{2}, \sqrt{9}, 0.3, \sqrt{7}, 1\dfrac{5}{8}, -1, \pi\right\}$

33. Integers: $\left\{5, \dfrac{8}{2}, \sqrt{9}, -1\right\}$

34. The opposite of $-\dfrac{3}{4}$ is $-\left(-\dfrac{3}{4}\right) = \dfrac{3}{4}$.

35. The opposite of 0.6 is –0.6.

36. The opposite of 0 is –0 = 0.

37. The opposite of 1 is –1.

38. The reciprocal of $-\dfrac{3}{4}$ is $\dfrac{1}{\left(-\frac{3}{4}\right)} = -\dfrac{4}{3}$.

39. The reciprocal of 0.6 is $\dfrac{1}{0.6}$.

40. The reciprocal of 0 is $\dfrac{1}{0}$ which is undefined.

41. The reciprocal of 1 is $\dfrac{1}{1} = 1$.

42. $-7 + 3 = -4$

43. $-10 + (-25) = -35$

44. $5(-0.4) = -2$

45. $(-3.1)(-0.1) = 0.31$

46. $-7 - (-15) = -7 + 15 = 8$

47. $9 - (-4.3) = 9 + 4.3 = 13.3$

48. $(-6)(-4)(0)(-3) = 0$

49. $(-12)(0)(-1)(-5) = 0$

50. $(-24) \div 0$ is undefined.

51. $0 \div (-45) = 0$

52. $(-36) \div (-9) = 4$

53. $60 \div (-12) = -5$

54. $\left(-\dfrac{4}{5}\right) - \left(-\dfrac{2}{3}\right) = -\dfrac{4}{5} + \dfrac{2}{3} = -\dfrac{12}{15} + \dfrac{10}{15} = -\dfrac{2}{15}$

55. $\left(\dfrac{5}{4}\right) - \left(-2\dfrac{3}{4}\right) = \dfrac{5}{4} + \dfrac{11}{4} = \dfrac{16}{4} = 4$

56. $1 - \dfrac{1}{4} - \dfrac{1}{3} = \dfrac{12}{12} - \dfrac{3}{12} - \dfrac{4}{12} = \dfrac{5}{12}$

57. $-5 + 7 - 3 - (-10) = 2 - 3 + 10 = -1 + 10 = 9$

58. $8 - (-3) + (-4) + 6 = 8 + 3 - 4 + 6$
$$= 11 - 4 + 6$$
$$= 7 + 6$$
$$= 13$$

59. $3(4-5)^4 = 3(-1)^4 = 3(1) = 3$

60. $6(7-10)^2 = 6(-3)^2 = 6(9) = 54$

61. $\left(-\dfrac{8}{15}\right) \cdot \left(-\dfrac{2}{3}\right)^2 = -\dfrac{8}{15} \cdot \dfrac{4}{9} = -\dfrac{32}{135}$

62. $\left(-\dfrac{3}{4}\right)^2 \cdot \left(-\dfrac{10}{21}\right) = \left(\dfrac{9}{16}\right)\left(-\dfrac{10}{21}\right) = -\dfrac{15}{56}$

63. $\dfrac{-\frac{6}{15}}{\frac{8}{25}} = -\dfrac{6}{15} \div \dfrac{8}{25} = -\dfrac{6}{15} \cdot \dfrac{25}{8} = -\dfrac{150}{120} = -\dfrac{5}{4}$

64. $\dfrac{\frac{4}{9}}{-\frac{8}{45}} = \dfrac{4}{9} \div \left(-\dfrac{8}{45}\right) = \dfrac{4}{9} \cdot \left(-\dfrac{45}{8}\right) = -\dfrac{180}{72} = -\dfrac{5}{2}$

65. $-\dfrac{3}{8} + 3(2) \div 6 = -\dfrac{3}{8} + 6 \div 6 = -\dfrac{3}{8} + 1 = -\dfrac{3}{8} + \dfrac{8}{8} = \dfrac{5}{8}$

66. $5(-2) - (-3) - \dfrac{1}{6} + \dfrac{2}{3} = -10 + 3 - \dfrac{1}{6} + \dfrac{2}{3}$
$$= -7 - \dfrac{1}{6} + \dfrac{2}{3}$$
$$= -\dfrac{42}{6} - \dfrac{1}{6} + \dfrac{4}{6}$$
$$= -\dfrac{39}{6}$$
$$= -6\dfrac{1}{2}$$

67. $\left|2^3 - 3^2\right| - |5 - 7| = |8 - 9| - |-2|$
$$= |-1| - 2$$
$$= 1 - 2$$
$$= -1$$

68. $\left|5^2 - 2^2\right| + \left|9 \div (-3)\right| = \left|25 - 4\right| + \left|-3\right|$
$$= \left|21\right| + 3$$
$$= 21 + 3$$
$$= 24$$

69. $(2^3 - 3^2) - (5 - 7) = (8 - 9) - (-2) = -1 + 2 = 1$

70. $(5^2 - 2^4) + [9 \div (-3)] = (25 - 16) + (-3)$
$$= 9 + (-3)$$
$$= 6$$

71. $\dfrac{(8-10)^3 - (-4)^2}{2 + 8(2) \div 4} = \dfrac{(-2)^3 - 16}{2 + 16 \div 4}$
$$= \dfrac{-8 - 16}{2 + 4}$$
$$= \dfrac{-24}{6}$$
$$= -4$$

72. $\dfrac{(2+4)^2 + (-1)^5}{12 \div 2 \cdot 3 - 3} = \dfrac{(6)^2 + (-1)}{6 \cdot 3 - 3}$
$$= \dfrac{36 - 1}{18 - 3}$$
$$= \dfrac{35}{15}$$
$$= \dfrac{7}{3}$$

73. $\dfrac{(4-9) + 4 - 9}{10 - 12 \div 4 \cdot 8} = \dfrac{(-5) + 4 - 9}{10 - 3 \cdot 8}$
$$= \dfrac{-1 - 9}{10 - 24}$$
$$= \dfrac{-10}{-14}$$
$$= \dfrac{5}{7}$$

74. $\dfrac{3 - 7 - (7 - 3)}{15 + 30 \div 6 \cdot 2} = \dfrac{-4 - (4)}{15 + 5 \cdot 2} = \dfrac{-8}{15 + 10} = \dfrac{-8}{25} = -\dfrac{8}{25}$

75. $\dfrac{\sqrt{25}}{4 + 3 \cdot 7} = \dfrac{5}{4 + 21} = \dfrac{5}{25} = \dfrac{1}{5}$

76. $\dfrac{\sqrt{64}}{24 - 8 \cdot 2} = \dfrac{8}{24 - 16} = \dfrac{8}{8} = 1$

77. Let $x = 0, y = 3, z = -2$.
$$x^2 - y^2 + z^2 = (0)^2 - (3)^2 + (-2)^2$$
$$= 0 - 9 + 4$$
$$= -5$$

78. Let $x = 0, y = 3, z = -2$.
$$\dfrac{5x + z}{2y} = \dfrac{5(0) + (-2)}{2(3)} = \dfrac{0 - 2}{6} = \dfrac{-2}{6} = -\dfrac{1}{3}$$

79. Let $y = 3, z = -2$.
$$\dfrac{-7y - 3z}{-3} = \dfrac{-7(3) - 3(-2)}{-3} = \dfrac{-21 + 6}{-3} = \dfrac{-15}{-3} = 5$$

80. Let $x = 0, y = 3, z = -2$.
$$(x - y + z)^2 = (0 - 3 + (-2))^2$$
$$= (-3 - 2)^2$$
$$= (-5)^2$$
$$= 25$$

81. a. When $r = 1$, $2\pi r = 2\pi(1) = 2(3.14) = 6.28$.
When $r = 10$,
$2\pi r = 2\pi(10) = 20(3.14) = 62.8$.
When $r = 100$,
$2\pi r = 2\pi(100) = 200(3.14) = 628$.

r	1	10	100
$2\pi r$	6.28	62.8	628

  b. As the radius increases, the circumference increases.

82. $5xy - 7xy + 3 - 2 + xy = 5xy - 7xy + xy + 3 - 2$
$$= (5 - 7 + 1)xy + (3 - 2)$$
$$= (-1)xy + 1$$
$$= -xy + 1$$

83. $4x + 10x - 19x + 10 - 19$
$$= (4 + 10 - 19)x + (10 - 19)$$
$$= -5x + (-9)$$
$$= -5x - 9$$

84. $6x^2 + 2 - 4(x^2 + 1) = 6x^2 + 2 - 4x^2 - 4$
$$= 6x^2 - 4x^2 + 2 - 4$$
$$= (6 - 4)x^2 + (2 - 4)$$
$$= 2x^2 + (-2)$$
$$= 2x^2 - 2$$

85. $-7(2x^2-1)-x^2-1 = -14x^2+7-x^2-1$
$$= -14x^2-x^2+7-1$$
$$= (-14-1)x^2+(7-1)$$
$$= -15x^2+6$$

86. $(3.2x-1.5)-(4.3x-1.2) = 3.2x-1.5-4.3x+1.2$
$$= 3.2x-4.3x-1.5+1.2$$
$$= (3.2-4.3)x-0.3$$
$$= -1.1x-0.3$$

87. $(7.6x+4.7)-(1.9x+3.6) = 7.6x+4.7-1.9x-3.6$
$$= 7.6x-1.9x+4.7-3.6$$
$$= (7.6-1.9)x+4.7-3.6$$
$$= 5.7x+1.1$$

88. Twelve is the product of x and negative 4.

$\quad\quad 12 \quad = \quad\quad\quad -4x$

or $12 = -4x$

89. The sum of n and twice n is negative fifteen.

$\quad\quad\quad n+2n \quad\quad = \quad -15$

90. Four times the sum of y and three is -1.

$\quad\quad 4 \quad\cdot\quad\quad (y+3) \quad\quad = -1$

or $4(y+3) = -1$

91. The difference of t and 5, multiplied by six is four.

$\quad\quad\quad (t-5) \quad\quad\quad\quad\cdot\quad 6 = 4$

or $6(t-5) = 4$

92. Seven subtracted from z is six.

$\quad\quad\quad z-7 \quad\quad = 6$

or $z-7 = 6$

93. Ten less than the product of x and nine is five.

$\quad\quad\quad\quad 9x-10 \quad\quad\quad = 5$

or $9x-10 = 5$

94. The difference of x and 5 is at least 12.

$\quad\quad\quad x-5 \quad\quad\quad \geq \quad 12$

or $x-5 \geq 12$

95. The opposite of four is less than the product of y and seven.

$$\quad\quad -4 \quad\quad\quad\quad < \quad\quad\quad\quad 7y$$

or $-4 < 7y$

96. Two-thirds is not equal to twice the sum of n and one-fourth.

$$\quad \frac{2}{3} \quad\quad\quad \neq \quad\quad 2\cdot \quad\quad\quad \left(n+\frac{1}{4}\right)$$

or $\dfrac{2}{3} \neq 2\left(n+\dfrac{1}{4}\right)$

97. The sum of t and six is not more than negative twelve.

$$\quad\quad t+6 \quad\quad\quad\quad \leq \quad\quad\quad -12$$

or $t + 6 \leq -12$

98. $(M + 5) + P = M + (5 + P)$: Associative Property of Addition

99. $5(3x - 4) = 15x - 20$: Distributive Property

100. $(-4) + 4 = 0$: Additive Inverse Property

101. $(3 + x) + 7 = 7 + (3 + x)$: Commutative Property of Addition

102. Associative and Commutative Properties of Multiplication
To see this: $(XY)Z = X(YZ) = (YZ)X$

103. $\left(-\dfrac{3}{5}\right)\cdot\left(-\dfrac{5}{3}\right) = 1$: Multiplicative Inverse Property

104. $T \cdot 0 = 0$: Multiplication Property of Zero

105. $(ab)c = a(bc)$: Associative Property of Multiplication

106. $A + 0 = A$: Additive Identity Property

107. $8 \cdot 1 = 8$: Multiplicative Identity Property

108. $5x - 15z = 5(x - 3z)$

109. $(7 + y) + (3 + x) = (3 + x) + (7 + y)$

110. $0 = 2 + (-2)$, for example

111. $1 = 2\cdot\dfrac{1}{2}$, for example

112. $[(3.4)(0.7)]5 = (3.4)[(0.7)(5)]$

113. $7 = 7 + 0$

114. $-9 > -12$, since -9 is to the right of -12 on the number line.

115. $-3 < -1$, since -3 is to the left of -1 on the number line.

116. $7 = |-7|$

117. $-5 < -(-5)$, since $-(-5) = 5$.

118. $-(-2) > -2$, since $-(-2) = 2$.

119. $4(x-5) = 2x - 14$
$$4x - 20 = 2x - 14$$
$$2x = 6$$
$$x = 3$$

120. $x + 7 = -2(x + 8)$
$$x + 7 = -2x - 16$$
$$3x = -23$$
$$x = -\frac{23}{3}$$

121. $3(2y - 1) = -8(6 + y)$
$$6y - 3 = -48 - 8y$$
$$14y = -45$$
$$y = -\frac{45}{14}$$

122. $-(z + 12) = 5(2z - 1)$
$$-z - 12 = 10z - 5$$
$$-11z = 7$$
$$z = -\frac{7}{11}$$

123. $n - (8 + 4n) = 2(3n - 4)$
$$n - 8 - 4n = 6n - 8$$
$$-3n = 6n$$
$$-9n = 0$$
$$n = 0$$

124. $4(9v + 2) = 6(1 + 6v) - 10$
$$36v + 8 = 6 + 36v - 10$$
$$36v + 8 = 36v - 4$$
$$8 = -4$$
No solution, or $\varnothing$

125. $0.3(x - 2) = 1.2$
$$10[0.3(x - 2) = 10(1.2)$$
$$3(x - 2) = 12$$
$$3x - 6 = 12$$
$$3x = 18$$
$$x = 6$$

126. $1.5 = 0.2(c - 0.3)$
$$1.5 = 0.2c - 0.06$$
$$100(1.5) = 100(0.2c - 0.06)$$
$$150 = 20c - 6$$
$$156 = 20c$$
$$7.8 = c$$

127. $-4(2 - 3x) = 2(3x - 4) + 6x$
$$-8 + 12x = 6x - 8 + 6x$$
$$-8 + 12x = 12x - 8$$
$$-8 = -8$$
All real numbers

128. $6(m - 1) + 3(2 - m) = 0$
$$6m - 6 + 6 - 3m = 0$$
$$3m = 0$$
$$m = 0$$

129. $6 - 3(2g + 4) - 4g = 5(1 - 2g)$
$$6 - 6g - 12 - 4g = 5 - 10g$$
$$-6 - 10g = 5 - 10g$$
$$-6 = 5$$
No solution, $\varnothing$

130. $20 - 5(p + 1) + 3p = -(2p - 15)$
$$20 - 5p - 5 + 3p = -2p + 15$$
$$15 - 2p = -2p + 15$$
$$15 = 15$$
All real numbers

131. $\frac{x}{3} - 4 = x - 2$
$$3\left(\frac{x}{3} - 4\right) = 3(x - 2)$$
$$x - 12 = 3x - 6$$
$$-2x = 6$$
$$x = -3$$

132. $\frac{9}{4}y = \frac{2}{3}y$
$$12\left(\frac{9}{4}y\right) = 12\left(\frac{2}{3}y\right)$$
$$27y = 8y$$
$$19y = 0$$
$$y = 0$$

133.
$$\frac{3n}{8} - 1 = 3 + \frac{n}{6}$$
$$24\left(\frac{3n}{8} - 1\right) = 24\left(3 + \frac{n}{6}\right)$$
$$9n - 24 = 72 + 4n$$
$$5n = 96$$
$$n = \frac{96}{5}$$

134.
$$\frac{z}{6} + 1 = \frac{z}{2} + 2$$
$$6\left(\frac{z}{6} + 1\right) = 6\left(\frac{z}{2} + 2\right)$$
$$z + 6 = 3z + 12$$
$$-2z = 6$$
$$z = -3$$

135.
$$\frac{y}{4} - \frac{y}{2} = -8$$
$$4\left(\frac{y}{4} - \frac{y}{2}\right) = 4(-8)$$
$$y - 2y = -32$$
$$-y = -32$$
$$y = 32$$

136.
$$\frac{2x}{3} - \frac{8}{3} = x$$
$$2x - 8 = 3x$$
$$-8 = x$$

137.
$$\frac{b-2}{3} = \frac{b+2}{5}$$
$$5(b-2) = 3(b+2)$$
$$5b - 10 = 3b + 6$$
$$2b = 16$$
$$b = 8$$

138.
$$\frac{2t-1}{3} = \frac{3t+2}{15}$$
$$15\left(\frac{2t-1}{3}\right) = 15\left(\frac{3t+2}{15}\right)$$
$$5(2t-1) = 3t + 2$$
$$10t - 5 = 3t + 2$$
$$7t = 7$$
$$t = 1$$

139.
$$\frac{2(t+1)}{3} = \frac{2(t-1)}{3}$$
$$3\left[\frac{2(t+1)}{3}\right] = 3\left[\frac{2(t-1)}{3}\right]$$
$$2(t+1) = 2(t-1)$$
$$2t + 2 = 2t - 2$$
$$2 = -2$$
No solution, $\varnothing$

140.
$$\frac{3a-3}{6} = \frac{4a+1}{15} + 2$$
$$30\left(\frac{3a-3}{6}\right) = 30\left(\frac{4a+1}{15} + 2\right)$$
$$5(3a-3) = 2(4a+1) + 30(2)$$
$$15a - 15 = 8a + 2 + 60$$
$$15a - 15 = 8a + 62$$
$$7a = 77$$
$$a = 11$$

141. Let $x =$ the number.
$$2(x-3) = 3x + 1$$
$$2x - 6 = 3x + 1$$
$$-7 = x$$
The number is -7.

142. Let $x =$ smaller number, then
$x + 5 =$ larger number.
$$x + x + 5 = 285$$
$$2x = 280$$
$$x = 140$$
$$x + 5 = 145$$
The numbers are 140 and 145.

143. Let $x =$ number of CDs sold in 2000.
$$x - 0.25x = 705.4$$
$$0.75x = 705.4$$
$$x \approx 940.5$$
There were 940.5 million music CDs sold by U.S. manufacturers in 2000.

144. Let $n =$ the first integer, then
$n + 1 =$ the second integer,
$n + 2 =$ the third integer, and
$n + 3 =$ the fourth integer.
$$(n+1) + (n+2) + (n+3) - 2n = 16$$
$$n + 6 = 16$$
$$n = 10$$
Therefore, the integers are 10, 11, 12, and 13.

145. Let x = smaller odd integer, then
$x + 2$ = larger odd integer.
$$5x = 3(x+2) + 54$$
$$5x = 3x + 6 + 54$$
$$2x = 60$$
$$x = 30$$
Since this is not odd, no such consecutive odd integers exist.

146. Let x = width of the playing field, then
$2x - 5$ = length of the playing field.
$$2x + 2(2x - 5) = 230$$
$$2x + 4x - 10 = 230$$
$$6x = 240$$
$$x = 40$$
Then $2x - 5 = 2(40) - 5 = 75$. The field is 75 meters long and 40 meters wide.

147. Let m = number of miles of driven.
$$2(19.95) + 0.12(m - 200) = 46.86$$
$$39.90 + 0.12m - 24 = 46.86$$
$$0.12m + 15.90 = 46.86$$
$$0.12m = 30.96$$
$$m = 258$$

148.

X	Y1
1	10.472
1.5	23.562
2	41.888
2.5	65.45
3	94.248
3.5	128.28
4	167.55

Y1■10/3πX²

Radius of Cone	x	1	1.5	2	2.5	3
Volume (If Height is 10 Inches)	$\frac{10}{3}\pi x^2$	10.47	23.56	41.89	65.45	94.25

149.

X	Y1
2	34
4.68	39.36
9.5	49
12.68	55.36

Y1■30+2X

Width of Rectangle	x	2	4.68	9.5	12.68
Perimeter (If Length is 15 Units)	$30 + 2x$	34	39.36	49	55.36

150.

X	Y1
5	28.75
10	57.5
15	86.25
20	115
25	143.75
30	172.5
35	201.25

Y1■5.75X

Hours	5	10	15	20	25	30
Gross Pay (Dollars)	28.75	57.5	86.25	115	143.75	172.5

151. Use $y_1 = 8 + 1.10(x-4)$ for Coast Waterworks and $y_2 = 12 + 1.50(x-5)$ for Cross Gates Water Company.

X	Y1	Y2
5	9.1	12
6	10.2	13.5
7	11.3	15
8	12.4	16.5
9	13.5	18
10	14.6	19.5
11	15.7	21

Y1□8+1.10(X-4)

Gallons (In Thousands Used)	5	6	7	8
Coast Charge (Dollars)	9.1	10.2	11.3	12.4
Cross Gates Charge (Dollars)	12	13.5	15	16.5

152. a.

X	Y1
0	500
1	524
2	516
3	476
4	404
5	300
6	164

Y1□-16X²+40X+500

Seconds	0	1	2	3	4	5
Height in Feet	500	524	516	476	404	300

b.

X	Y1
1.1	524.64
1.2	524.96
1.3	524.96
1.4	524.64
1.5	524
1.6	523.04
1.7	521.76

X=1.1

The maximum height of the rock is 525 feet.

c.

X	Y1
6.5	84
6.6	67.04
6.7	49.76
6.8	32.16
6.9	14.24
7	-4
7.1	-22.56

X=6.5

The rock strikes the ground after
7.0 seconds.

153. $V = lwh$

$$w = \frac{V}{lh}$$

154. $C = 2\pi r$

$$\frac{C}{2\pi} = r$$

155. $5x - 4y = -12$

$5x + 12 = 4y$

$$y = \frac{5x+12}{4}$$

156. $5x - 4y = -12$

$5x = 4y - 12$

$$x = \frac{4y-12}{5}$$

157. $y - y_1 = m(x - x_1)$

$$m = \frac{y - y_1}{x - x_1}$$

158. $y - y_1 = m(x - x_1)$

$y - y_1 = mx - mx_1$

$y - y_1 + mx_1 = mx$

$$\frac{y - y_1 + mx_1}{m} = x$$

159. $E = I(R + r)$

$E = IR + Ir$

$I - IR = Ir$

$$\frac{E - IR}{I} = r$$

160. $S = vt + gt^2$

$S - vt = gt^2$

$$\frac{S - vt}{t^2} = g$$

161. $T = gr + gvt$

$T = g(r + vt)$

$$g = \frac{T}{r + vt}$$

162. $I = Prt + P$

$I = P(rt + 1)$

$$\frac{I}{rt + 1} = P$$

163. $A = \frac{h}{2}(B + b)$

$2A = hB + hb$

$2A - hb = hB$

$$\frac{2A - hb}{h} = B$$

164. $V = \frac{1}{3}\pi r^2 h$

$3V = \pi r^2 h$

$$\frac{3V}{\pi r^2} = h$$

165. $R = \frac{r_1 + r_2}{2}$

$2R = r_1 + r_2$

$2R - r_2 = r_1$

166. $\dfrac{V_1}{T_1} = \dfrac{V_2}{T_2}$

$V_1 T_2 = V_2 T_1$

$$T_2 = \frac{V_2 T_1}{V_1}$$

167. $A = P\left(1 + \dfrac{r}{n}\right)^{nt} = 3000\left(1 + \dfrac{0.03}{n}\right)^{7n}$

   a. $A = 3000\left(1 + \dfrac{0.03}{2}\right)^{14} \approx \$3695.27$

   b. $A = 3000\left(1 + \dfrac{0.03}{52}\right)^{364} \approx \$3700.81$

168. Let x = original width, then
$x + 2$ = original length.

$(x + 4)(x + 2 + 4) = x(x + 2) + 88$

$(x + 4)(x + 6) = x^2 + 2x + 88$

$x^2 + 10x + 24 = x^2 + 2x + 88$

$8x = 64$

$x = 8$

$x + 2 = 10$

The original width is 8 in. and the original length is 10 in.

169.

```
 X   |Y1|
-40  |-40
-15  |5
10   |50
60   |140
0    |32
100  |212
Y1B(9X+160)/5
```

   a.

Celsius	−40	−15	10	60
Fahrenheit	−40	5	50	140

   b. 100 degrees Celsius is 212 degrees Fahrenheit.

   c. 0 degrees Celsius is 32 degrees Fahrenheit.

170. a.

```
 X   |Y1|
0    |0
.25  |13.75
.5   |27.5
.75  |41.25
1    |55
1.25 |68.75
1.5  |82.5
Y1B55X
```

Hours	0	0.25	0.50	0.75	1	1.25	1.5
Miles	0	13.75	27.5	41.25	55	68.75	82.5

b.

X	Y1
3	165
3.25	178.75
3.5	192.5
3.75	206.25
4	220
4.25	233.75
4.5	247.5

Y1■55X

It takes 3.5 hours to travel 192.5 miles at 55 mph.

171. $8 \cdot 21 = 378$

The area of the floor is 378 square feet.

$$\frac{378}{24} = 15.75$$

It takes 16 packages to tile the floor.

172. $V_{\text{box}} = lwh = 8 \cdot 5 \cdot 3 = 120 \text{ in}^3$, while $V_{\text{cyl}} = \pi r^2 h = \pi \cdot 3^2 \cdot 6 = 54\pi \approx 170 \text{ in}^3$

Therefore, the cylinder holds more ice cream.

173. The opposite of $-\dfrac{3}{4}$ is $\dfrac{3}{4}$.

The reciprocal of $-\dfrac{3}{4}$ is $-\dfrac{4}{3}$.

174. If the opposite of the number is -5, then the number is $-(-5) = 5$. The reciprocal of 5 is $\dfrac{1}{5}$.

175.
$$-2\left(5x + \frac{1}{2}\right) + 7.1 = -2 \cdot 5x + (-2) \cdot \frac{1}{2} + 7.1$$
$$= -10x - 1 + 7.1$$
$$= -10x + 6.1$$

176. $\sqrt{36} \div 2 \cdot 3 = 6 \div 2 \cdot 3 = 3 \cdot 3 = 9$

177. $-\dfrac{7}{11} - \left(-\dfrac{1}{11}\right) = -\dfrac{7}{11} + \dfrac{1}{11} = -\dfrac{6}{11}$

178.
$$10 - (-1) + (-2) + 6 = 10 + 1 + (-2) + 6$$
$$= 11 + (-2) + 6$$
$$= 9 + 6$$
$$= 15$$

179.
$$\left(-\frac{2}{3}\right)^3 \div \frac{10}{9} = -\frac{8}{27} \div \frac{10}{9}$$
$$= -\frac{8}{27} \cdot \frac{9}{10}$$
$$= -\frac{2 \cdot 4 \cdot 9}{3 \cdot 9 \cdot 2 \cdot 5}$$
$$= -\frac{4}{15}$$

180.
$$\frac{(3-5)^2+(-1)^3}{1+2(3-(-1))^2}=\frac{(-2)^2+(-1)^3}{1+2(3+1)^2}$$
$$=\frac{4+(-1)}{1+2(4)^2}$$
$$=\frac{3}{1+2(16)}$$
$$=\frac{3}{1+32}$$
$$=\frac{3}{33}$$
$$=\frac{1}{11}$$

181.
$$\frac{x-2}{5}+\frac{x+2}{2}=\frac{x+4}{3}$$
$$30\left(\frac{x-2}{5}+\frac{x+2}{2}\right)=30\left(\frac{x+4}{3}\right)$$
$$6(x-2)+15(x+2)=10(x+4)$$
$$6x-12+15x+30=10x+40$$
$$21x+18=10x+40$$
$$11x=22$$
$$x=2$$

182.
$$\frac{2z-3}{4}-\frac{4-z}{2}=\frac{z+1}{3}$$
$$12\left(\frac{2z-3}{4}-\frac{4-z}{2}\right)=12\left(\frac{z+1}{3}\right)$$
$$3(2z-3)-6(4-z)=4(z+1)$$
$$6z-9-24+6z=4z+4$$
$$12z-33=4z+4$$
$$8z=37$$
$$z=\frac{37}{8}$$

183. Let x = number of tourists for France, then
$x+9$ = number of tourists for United States, and
$x+44$ = number of tourists for China.
$$x+(x+9)+(x+44)=332$$
$$3x+53=332$$
$$3x=279$$
$$x=93$$

$x+9=102$
$x+44=137$
China is predicted to have 137 million tourists, whereas the United States is predicted to have 102 million and France, 93 million.

184.
$$A = \frac{h}{2}(B + b)$$
$$2A = hB + hb$$
$$2A - hb = hB$$
$$\frac{2A - hb}{h} = B$$

185.
$$V = \frac{1}{3}\pi r^2 h$$
$$3V = \pi r^2 h$$
$$\frac{3V}{\pi r^2} = h$$

186. Since $h = 6$, use $y_1 = \frac{1}{3}\pi x^2 \cdot 6 = 2\pi x^2$.

Height h	6	6	6	6	6
Radius x	1	1.5	2	2.25	3
Volume	6.28	14.14	25.13	31.81	56.55

187. Since $h = 10$, use $y_1 = \frac{1}{3}\pi x^2 \cdot 10 = \frac{10}{3}\pi x^2$.

Height h	10	10	10	10	10
Radius x	1.5	2.1	2.75	3	3.5
Volume	23.56	46.18	79.19	94.25	128.28

Chapter 1 Test

1. True; -2.3 lies to the right of -2.33 on the number line.

2. False; $-6^2 = -36$, while $(-6)^2 = 36$.

3. False; $-5 - 8 = -13$, while $-(5 - 8) = -(-3) = 3$.

4. False; $(-2)(-3)(0) = 0$, while $\frac{(-4)}{0}$ is undefined.

5. True

6. False; for example, $\dfrac{1}{2}$ is a rational number that is not an integer.

7. $5 - 12 \div 3(2) = 5 - 4(2) = 5 - 8 = -3$

8. $5^2 - 3^4 = 25 - 81 = -56$

9.
$$(4-9)^3 - \left|-4-6\right|^2 = (-5)^3 - \left|-10\right|^2$$
$$= -125 - 10^2$$
$$= -125 - 100$$
$$= -225$$

10.
$$12 + \{6 - [5 - 2(-5)]\} = 12 + \{6 - [5 + 10]\}$$
$$= 12 + (6 - 15)$$
$$= 12 + (-9)$$
$$= 12 - 9$$
$$= 3$$

11.
$$\frac{6(7-9)^3 + (-2)}{(-2)(-5)(-5)} = \frac{6(-2)^3 - 2}{10(-5)}$$
$$= \frac{6(-8) - 2}{-50}$$
$$= \frac{-48 - 2}{-50}$$
$$= \frac{-50}{-50}$$
$$= 1$$

12.
$$\frac{\left(4 - \sqrt{16}\right) - (-7 - 20)}{-2(1-4)^2} = \frac{(4-4) - (-27)}{-2(-3)^2}$$
$$= \frac{0 + 27}{-2(9)}$$
$$= \frac{27}{-18}$$
$$= -\frac{3}{2}$$

13. Let $q = 4$ and $r = -2$.
$$q^2 - r^2 = (4)^2 - (-2)^2 = 16 - 4 = 12$$

14. Let $q = 4$, $r = -2$, and $t = 1$.
$$\frac{5t - 3q}{3r - 1} = \frac{5(1) - 3(4)}{3(-2) - 1} = \frac{5 - 12}{-6 - 1} = \frac{-7}{-7} = 1$$

15. a. When $x = 1$, $5.75x = 5.75(1) = 5.75$.
When $x = 3$, $5.75x = 5.75(3) = 17.25$.
When $x = 10$, $5.75x = 5.75(10) = 57.50$.
When $x = 20$, $5.75x = 5.75(20) = 115.00$.

x	1	3	10	20
$5.75x$	5.75	17.25	57.50	115.00

b.   As the number of adults increases the total cost increases.

16. $\underbrace{\text{Twice}}$ $\underbrace{\text{the sum of } x \text{ and five}}$ $\underset{\downarrow}{\text{is}}$ $\underset{\downarrow}{30.}$

$\quad\quad 2\cdot \quad\quad\quad (x+5) \quad\quad\quad = 30$

or $2(x+5) = 30$

17. $\underbrace{\text{The square of the difference of six and } y}$ $\underbrace{\text{divided by}}$ $\underbrace{\text{seven}}$ $\underbrace{\text{is not equal to}}$ $\underbrace{10}.$

$\quad\quad\quad\quad (6-y)^2 \quad\quad\quad\quad\quad \div \quad\quad 7 \quad\quad \neq \quad\quad 10$

or $\dfrac{(6-y)^2}{7} \neq 10$

18. $\underbrace{\text{The product of nine and } z}$, $\underbrace{\text{divided by}}$ $\underbrace{\text{the absolute value of } -12}$ $\underbrace{\text{is not equal to}}$ $\underset{\downarrow}{10.}$

$\quad\quad\quad 9z \quad\quad\quad\quad \div \quad\quad\quad |{-12}| \quad\quad\quad \neq \quad\quad 10$

or $\dfrac{9z}{|{-12}|} \neq 10$

19. $\underbrace{\text{Three}}$ $\underbrace{\text{times}}$ $\underbrace{\text{the quotient of } n \text{ and five}}$ $\underbrace{\text{is}}$ $\underbrace{\text{the opposite of } n}.$

$\quad\quad 3 \quad\quad\quad \cdot \quad\quad\quad \dfrac{n}{5} \quad\quad\quad\quad = \quad\quad -n$

or $3\left(\dfrac{n}{5}\right) = -n$

20. $\underbrace{\text{Twenty}}$ $\underbrace{\text{is equal to}}$ $\underbrace{6 \text{ subtracted from twice } x}.$

$\quad\quad 20 \quad\quad\quad = \quad\quad\quad\quad 2x-6$

or $20 = 2x - 6$

21. $\underbrace{\text{Negative two}}$ $\underbrace{\text{is equal to}}$ $\underbrace{x}$ $\underbrace{\text{divided by}}$ $\underbrace{\text{the sum of } x \text{ and five}}.$

$\quad\quad\quad -2 \quad\quad\quad = \quad x \quad \div \quad\quad\quad (x+5)$

or $-2 = \dfrac{x}{x+5}$

22. $6(x-4) = 6x - 24$: Distributive Property

23. $(4+x)+z = 4+(x+z)$: Associative Property of Addition

24. $(-7)+7 = 0$: Additive Inverse Property

25. $(-18)(0) = 0$: Multiplication Property of Zero

26.   Let 0.05 be the value of each nickel and 0.1 be the value of each dime. If there are n nickels, and d dimes, then the total amount of money is $0.05n + 0.1d$.

27. $-2(3x + 7) = -6x - 14$

28.
$$\frac{1}{3}a - \frac{3}{8} + \frac{1}{6}a - \frac{3}{4} = \frac{1}{3}a + \frac{1}{6}a - \frac{3}{8} - \frac{3}{4}$$
$$= \left(\frac{1}{3} + \frac{1}{6}\right)a - \frac{3}{8} - \frac{3}{4}$$
$$= \left(\frac{2}{6} + \frac{1}{6}\right)a - \frac{3}{8} - \frac{6}{8}$$
$$= \left(\frac{3}{6}\right)a - \frac{9}{8}$$
$$= \frac{1}{2}a - \frac{9}{8}$$

29.
$$4y + 10 - 2(y + 10) = 4y + 10 - 2y - 20$$
$$= 4y - 2y + 10 - 20$$
$$= (4 - 2)y - 10$$
$$= 2y - 10$$

30.
$$(8.3x - 2.9) - (9.6x - 4.8) = 8.3x - 2.9 - 9.6x + 4.8$$
$$= 8.3x - 9.6x - 2.9 + 4.8$$
$$= (8.3 - 9.6)x + 1.9$$
$$= -1.3x + 1.9$$

31.

```
-3.1→X
              -3.1
.2X^3+5X²-6.2X+3
         64.3118
■
```

The value is 64.3118.

32. Let x be the diameter. Use $y_1 = \dfrac{1}{2}x$ for the radius, $y_2 = \pi x$ for the circumference, and $y_3 = \pi(y_1)^2$ for the area.

```
 X   Y₁   Y2           X    Y2    Y3
 2   1    6.2832       2    6.2832 3.1416
 3.8 1.9  11.938       3.8  11.938 11.341
 10  5    31.416       10   31.416 78.54
 14.9 7.45 46.81       14.9 46.81  174.37

Y2=πX                  Y3=πY1²
```

Diameter	d	2	3.8	10	14.9
Radius	r	1	1.9	5	7.45
Circumference	πd	6.28	11.94	31.42	46.81
Area	πr^2	3.14	11.34	78.54	174.37

33.
$$8x + 14 = 5x + 44$$
$$3x = 30$$
$$x = 10$$

34.
$$3(x + 2) = 11 - 2(2 - x)$$
$$3x + 6 = 11 - 4 + 2x$$
$$3x + 6 = 7 + 2x$$
$$x + 6 = 7$$
$$x = 1$$

35. $3(y-4)+y=2(6+2y)$
$3y-12+y=12+4y$
$4y-12=12+4y$
$-12=12$
No solution, $\varnothing$

36. $7n-6+n=2(4n-3)$
$8n-6=8n-6$
$-6=-6$
All real numbers

37. $\dfrac{7w}{4}+5=\dfrac{3w}{10}+1$
$20\left(\dfrac{7w}{4}+5\right)=20\left(\dfrac{3w}{10}+1\right)$
$35w+100=6w+20$
$29w=-80$
$w=-\dfrac{80}{29}$

38. $3x-4y=8$
$3x-8=4y$
$y=\dfrac{3x-8}{4}$

39. $S=gt^2+gvt$
$S=g(t^2+vt)$
$g=\dfrac{S}{t^2+vt}$

40. $F=\dfrac{9}{5}C+32$
$F-32=\dfrac{9}{5}C$
$C=\dfrac{5}{9}(F-32)$

41. Let $x=$ the number in 2004.
$x+0.55x=357,000$
$1.55x=357,000$
$x\approx 230,323$
Approximately 230,323 people were employed as network systems and data communications analysts in 2004.

42. $C=2\pi r$
$78.5=2(3.14)r$
$\dfrac{78.5}{6.28}=r$
$12.5=r$
$A=\pi r^2=3.14(12.5)^2=490.625$
$\dfrac{490.625}{60}\approx 8.2$
Approximately 8 dogs can be kept in the pen.

43. $A=P\left(1+\dfrac{r}{n}\right)^{nt}$
$=2500\left(1+\dfrac{0.035}{4}\right)^{4(10)}$
$=2500(1.00875)^{40}$
≈ 3542.27
There will be \$3542.27 in the account.

44. Let $x=$ the population of New York.
Then Seoul's population is $x+1.3$ and Tokyo's population is $2x-10.2$.
$x+x+1.3+2x-10.2=78.3$
$4x-8.9=78.3$
$4x=-87.2$
$x=21.8$
$x+1.3=21.8+1.3=23.1$
$2x-10.2=2(21.8)-10.2=43.6-10.2=33.4$
New York's population is 21.8 million, Seoul's is 23.1 million, and Tokyo's is 33.4 million.

45. a.   Use $y_1=1500+0.05x_0$

Sales (Dollars)	8000	9000	10,000	11,000	12,000
Gross Monthly Pay (Dollars)	1900	1950	2000	2050	2100

b. $12(2050)=24,600$
If her sales are \$11,000 per month, her gross annual income is \$24,600.

c.   To achieve a monthly pay of \$2200, her sales must be \$14,000.

46.

a.   The height of the rocket is 116 feet at 2 seconds and 3 seconds.

b.   The rocket's maximum height is 120 feet.

c.   The rocket reaches it maximum height after 2.5 seconds.

d.   The rocket explodes $2.5+0.5=3.0$ seconds after being launched.

Chapter 2

Practice Exercises

1. The six points are graphed as shown.

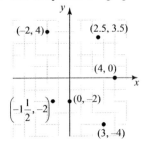

  a. $(3, -4)$ lies in quadrant IV.

  b. $(0, -2)$ is on the y-axis.

  c. $(-2, 4)$ lies in quadrant II.

  d. $(4, 0)$ is on the x-axis.

  e. $\left(-1\frac{1}{2}, -2\right)$ is in quadrant III.

  f. $(2.5, 3.5)$ is in quadrant I.

2.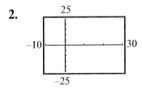

3. Let $x = 1$ and $y = 4$.
$$4x + y = 8$$
$$\overset{?}{4(1) + 4 = 8}$$
$$\overset{?}{4 + 4 = 8}$$
$$8 = 8 \quad \text{True}$$
Let $x = 0$ and $y = 6$.
$$4x + y = 8$$
$$\overset{?}{4(0) + 6 = 8}$$
$$\overset{?}{0 + 6 = 8}$$
$$6 = 8 \quad \text{False}$$

Let $x = 3$ and $y = -4$.
$$4x + y = 8$$
$$\overset{?}{4(3) + (-4) = 8}$$
$$\overset{?}{12 - 4 = 8}$$
$$8 = 8 \quad \text{True}$$
Thus, $(0, 6)$ is not a solution, but both $(1, 4)$ and $(3, -4)$ are solutions.

4. **a.** Since x is products sold, find 6000 along the x-axis and move vertically up until you reach a point on the line. From this point on the line, move horizontally to the left until you reach the y-axis. Its value on the y-axis is 4200, which means if \$6000 worth of products is sold, the salary for the month is \$4200.

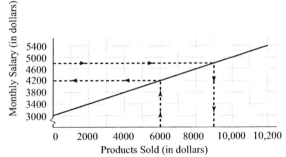

  b. Since y is monthly salary, find 4800 along the y-axis and move horizontally to the right until you reach a point on the line. Move vertically downward until you reach the x-axis. The corresponding x-value is 9000. This means that \$9000 worth of products sold gives a salary of \$4800 for the month. For the salary to be greater than \$4800, products sold must be greater than \$9000.

5. $y = -3x - 2$
This is a linear equation. (In standard form, it is $3x + y = -2$.) Since the equation is solved for y, we choose three x-values.
Let $x = 0$.
$$y = -3x - 2$$
$$y = -3 \cdot 0 - 2$$
$$y = -2$$
Let $x = -1$.
$$y = -3x - 2$$
$$y = -3(-1) - 2$$
$$y = 1$$

Let $x = -2$.
$$y = -3x - 2$$
$$y = -3(-2) - 2$$
$$y = 4$$
The three ordered pairs $(0, -2)$, $(-1, 1)$, and $(-2, 4)$ are listed in the table.

x	y
0	-2
-1	1
-2	4

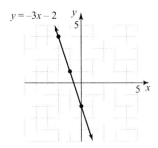

6. $y = -\dfrac{1}{2}x$

To avoid fractions, we choose x-values that are multiples of 2. To find the y-intercept, we let $x = 0$.

If $x = 0$, then $y = -\dfrac{1}{2}(0)$, or 0.

If $x = 2$, then $y = -\dfrac{1}{2}(2)$, or -1.

If $x = -2$, then $y = -\dfrac{1}{2}(-2)$, or 1.

x	y
0	0
2	-1
-2	1

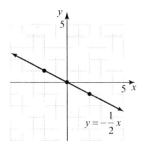

7. First solve the equation for y.
$$7x - 2y = 21$$
$$7x - 7x - 2y = -7x + 21$$
$$-2y = -7x + 21$$
$$y = \frac{-7x + 21}{-2}$$

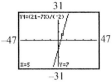

8. $y = 2x^2$

This equation is not linear because of the x^2 term. Its graph is not a line.

If $x = -3$, then $y = 2(-3)^2$, or 18.

If $x = -2$, then $y = 2(-2)^2$, or 8.

If $x = -1$, then $y = 2(-1)^2$, or 2.

If $x = 0$, then $y = 2(0)^2$, or 0.

If $x = 1$, then $y = 2(1)^2$, or 2.

If $x = 2$, then $y = 2(2)^2$, or 8.

If $x = 3$, then $y = 2(3)^2$, or 18.

x	y
-3	18
-2	8
-1	2
0	0
1	2
2	8
3	18

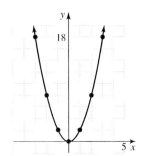

9.

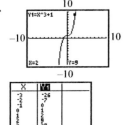

For each integer *x*-value from −3 to 3, the *y*-values in the Practice 9 table are 1 unit greater than those in the Example 9 table.

10. $y = -|x|$

This equation is not linear because it cannot be written in the form $Ax + By = C$. Its graph is not a line.

If $x = -3$, then $y = -|-3|$, or −3.

If $x = -2$, then $y = -|-2|$, or −2.

If $x = -1$, then $y = -|-1|$, or −1.

If $x = 0$, then $y = -|0|$, or 0.

If $x = 1$, then $y = -|1|$, or −1.

If $x = 2$, then $y = -|2|$, or −2.

If $x = 3$, then $y = -|3|$, or −3.

x	y
−3	−3
−2	−2
−1	−1
0	0
1	−1
2	−2
3	−3

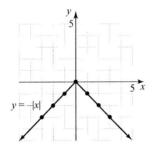

11.

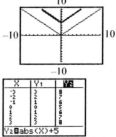

The graph of $y = |x| + 5$ is the same as the graph of $y = |x|$, except raised 5 units.

Vocabulary and Readiness Check

1. Point A is (5, 2).

2. Point B is (2, 5).

3. Point C is (3, 0).

4. Point D is (−1, 3).

5. Point E is (−5, −2).

6. Point F is (−3, 5).

7. Point G is (−1, 0).

8. Point H is (0, −3).

9. (2, 3); QI

10. (0, 5); *y*-axis

11. (−2, 7); QII

12. (−3, 0); *x*-axis

13. (−1, −4); QIII

14. (4, −2); QIV

15. (0, −100); *y*-axis

16. (10, 30); QI

17. (−10, −30); QIII

18. (0, 0); *x*- and *y*-axis

19. (−87, 0); *x*-axis

20. (−42, 17); QII

Exercise Set 2.1

2. $(2, -1)$ is in quadrant IV.

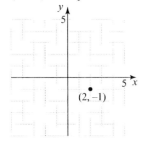

4. $(-3, -1)$ is in quadrant III.

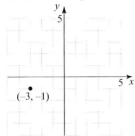

6. $\left(-2, 6\frac{1}{3}\right)$ is in quadrant II.

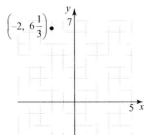

8. $(-5.2, 0)$ is on the *x*-axis.

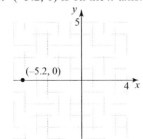

10. $(-4.2, 0)$ is on the *x*-axis.

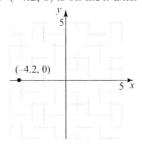

12. $(-x, y)$ lies in quadrant II.

14. $(0, -y)$ lies on the *y*-axis.

16. $(0, 0)$ is the origin.

18. Each tick mark on the *x*-axis represents 1 unit, while each tick mark on the *y*-axis represents 2 units. Thus, the point shown is $(-3, 2)$ in quadrant II.

20. Each tick mark on both the *x*-axis and *y*-axis represents 1 unit. Thus, the point shown is $(-2, -3)$ in quadrant III.

22. Possible answer: $[-15, 15, 1]$ by $[-15, 15, 1]$

24. Possible answer: $[-150, 150, 10]$ by $[-150, 150, 10]$

26. The screen shows window setting B.

28. The screen shows window setting A.

30.

X	Y1
-3	13
-2	11
-1	9
0	7
1	5
2	3
3	1

Y1⊟-2X+7

$(1, 5)$ is a solution; $(-2, 3)$ is not a solution.

32.

X	Y1
0	-3
2.4	1

Y1⊟(9-5X)/-3

Neither $(0, 3)$ nor $\left(\frac{12}{5}, -1\right)$ are solutions.

34.

X	Y1
-3	6
-2	4
-1	2
0	0
1	2
2	4
3	6

Y1⊟2abs(X)

$(-1, 2)$ is a solution; $(0, 2)$ is not a solution.

36.

Equation	Linear or Nonlinear	Shape (Line, Parabola, Cubic, V-shaped)
$x + y = 3$	linear	line
$y = 4 - x$	linear	line
$y = 2x^2 - 5$	nonlinear	parabola
$y = -8x + 6$	linear	line
$y = |x - 3|$	nonlinear	V-shaped
$y = 7x^2$	nonlinear	parabola
$2x - y = 5$	linear	line
$y = -|x - 1|$	nonlinear	V-shaped
$y = x^3 - 2$	nonlinear	cubic

38. $-6x + y = 2$
$$6x - 6x + y = 6x + 2$$
$$y = 6x + 2$$

40. $5x - 11y = -1.2$
$$-5x + 5x - 11y = -5x - 1.2$$
$$-11y = -5x - 1.2$$
$$\frac{-11y}{-11} = \frac{-5x - 1.2}{-11}$$
$$y = \frac{-5x - 1.5}{-11}$$

42.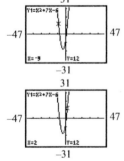

The points are (−9, 12) and (2, 12).

44. An integer window only displays coordinates with integer x-values, thus (1.7, 4) would not be displayed; a.

46. $y = x + 5$ is a line; D.

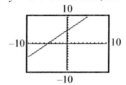

48. The graph of $y = |x| + 3$ is V-shaped; B.

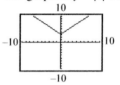

50. The graph of $y = -x^2 + 4$ is a parabola; B.

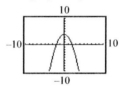

52. The graph of $y = |x + 3|$ is V-shaped; A.

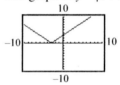

54. The graph shows a parabola that is the same as $y = x^2$ but raised by 3 units; B.

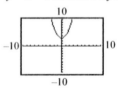

56. The graph is V-shaped and is the same as $y = |x|$ but lowered by 3 units; D.

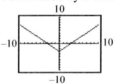

58.

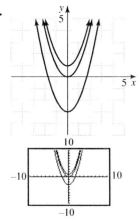

60.

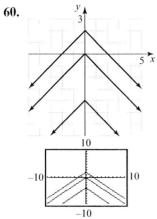

62. $y - x = 8$

x	0	-8	-4
y	8	0	4

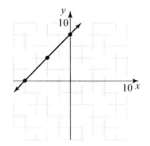

64. $y = 6x$

x	-1	0	1
y	-6	0	6

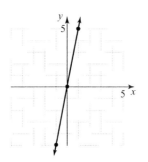

66. $y = 6x - 5$

x	0	$\frac{1}{2}$	1
y	-5	-2	1

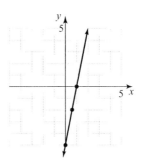

68. $y = |x| + 2$

x	-3	-2	-1	0	1	2	3
y	5	4	3	2	3	4	5

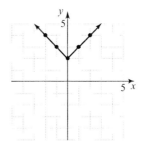

70. $4x - y = 7$

x	0	1	2
y	-7	-3	1

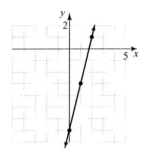

72. $y = 3x^2$

x	−3	−2	−1	0	1	2	3
	27	12	3	0	3	12	27

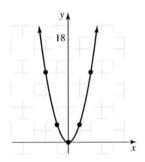

74. $y = x^2 + 3$

x	−3	−2	−1	0	1	2	3
y	12	7	4	3	4	7	12

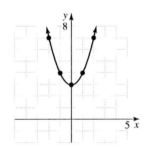

76. $y = -3x$

x	−1	0	1
y	3	0	−3

78. $y = -3x + 2$

x	−1	0	1
y	5	2	−1

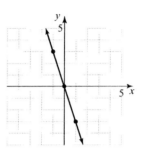

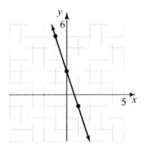

80. $y = |x - 1|$

x	−1	0	1	2	3	4
y	2	1	0	1	2	3

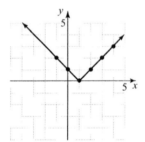

82. $y = x^3 - 2$

x	−3	−2	−1	0	1	2
y	−29	−10	−3	−2	−1	6

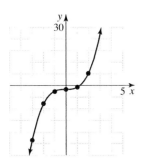

84. $y = -x^2$

x	-3	-2	-1	0	1	2	3
y	-9	-4	-1	0	-1	-4	-9

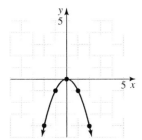

86.

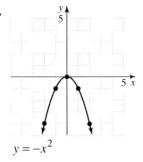

$y = -x^2$

88. a. The shape of the graph from 20°C to 60°C resembles a <u>parabola</u>.

   b. The shape of the graph from 0°C to 20°C resembles a <u>line</u>.

90. a. The shape of the graph from 600 nm to 700 nm resembles a <u>parabola</u>.

   b. The shape of the graph from 550 nm to 625 nm resembles a <u>line</u>.

92. $y = 50x$

   a.

x	0	3	6
y	0	150	300

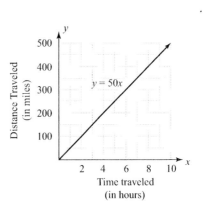

   b. When x is 6, y is 300. Thus, the distance traveled after 6 hours is 300 miles.

94. $\begin{aligned} 5 + 7(x+1) &= 12 + 10x \\ 5 + 7x + 7 &= 12 + 10x \\ 7x + 12 &= 12 + 10x \\ -3x &= 0 \\ x &= 0 \end{aligned}$

The solution is 0.

96. $\begin{aligned} \frac{1}{6} + 2x &= \frac{2}{3} \\ 1 + 12x &= 4 \\ 12x &= 3 \\ x &= \frac{1}{4} \end{aligned}$

The solution is $\frac{1}{4}$.

98. The first coordinate, 0, indicates that the point is on the y-axis. The second coordinate, $-\frac{3}{4}$, indicates that the point is $\frac{3}{4}$ unit below the x-axis. The answer is d.

100. Look for the graph where the decrease in y-values from 40 to 0 and increase from 0 to 60 is gradual. The answer is d.

102. Look for the graph that ends in February. The answer is a.

104. The first segment in the graph with y-coordinate greater than 0.30 begins in January 1995. Thus, 1995 is the first year that the price of a first-class stamp rose above \$0.30.

106. The price increased to \$0.41 in 2007. The difference is \$0.41 − \$0.02 or \$0.39.

108. When x is 7, y is 3.5. Thus, the value in 7 years is \$3500.

110. $6500 - 6000 = \$500$

112. Answers may vary

114. "The y-value is -3 decreased by twice the x-value" is written as $y = -3 - 2x$.

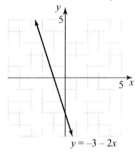

116. "The y-value is 5 decreased by the square of the x-value" is written as $y = 5 - x^2$.

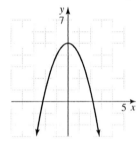

Section 2.2

Practice Exercises

1. a. The domain is the set of all first coordinates, $\{4, 5\}$. The range is the set of all second coordinates, $\{1, -3, -2, 6\}$.

    b. Ordered pairs are not listed here but are given in graph form. The relation is $\{(3, -4), (3, -3), (3, -2), (3, -1), (3, 0),$ $(3, 1), (3, 2), (3, 3), (3, 4)\}$. The domain is $\{3\}$. The range is $\{-4, -3, -2, -1, 0, 1, 2, 3, 4\}$.

    c. The domain is the set of inputs, $\{$Administrative Secretary, Game Developer, Engineer, Restaurant Manager, Marketing$\}$. The range is comprised of the numbers in the set of outputs that correspond to elements in the set of inputs, $\{27, 73, 50, 35\}$.

2. a. Although the ordered pairs $(3, 1)$ and $(9, 1)$ have the same y-value, each x-value is assigned to only one y-value, so this set of ordered pairs is a function.

    b. The x-value -2 is assigned to two y-values, -3 and 4, in this graph, so this relation does not define a function.

    c. This relation is a function because although two different people may have the same birth date, each person has only one birth date. This means that each element in the first set is assigned to only one element in the second set.

3. The relation $y = -3x + 5$ is a function if each x-value corresponds to just one y-value. For each x-value substituted into the equation $y = -3x + 5$, the multiplication and addition performed on each gives a single result, so only one y-value will be associated with each x-value. Thus, $y = -3x + 5$ is a function.

4. The relation $y = -x^2$ is a function if each x-value corresponds to just one y-value. For each x-value substituted into the equation $y = -x^2$, squaring each gives a single result, so only one y-value will be associated with each x-value. Thus, $y = -x^2$ is a function.

5. a. Yes, this is the graph of a function since no vertical line will intersect this graph more than once.

    b. Yes, this is the graph of a function since no vertical line will intersect this graph more than once.

    c. No, this is not the graph of a function. Note that vertical lines can be drawn that intersect the graph in two points.

    d. Yes, this is the graph of a function since no vertical line will intersect this graph more than once.

    e. No, this is not the graph of a function. A vertical line can be drawn that intersects this line at every point.

    f. Yes, this is the graph of a function since no vertical line will intersect this graph more than once.

6. a. By the vertical line test, the graph is the graph of a function. The x-values are graphed from -1 to 2, so the domain is $\{x|-1 \le x \le 2\}$. The y-values are graphed from -2 to 9, so the range is $\{y|-2 \le y \le 9\}$.

b. By the vertical line test, the graph is not the graph of a function. The x-values are graphed from -1 to 1, so the domain is $\{x|-1 \le x \le 1\}$. The y-values are graphed from -4 to 4, so the range is $\{y|-4 \le y \le 4\}$.

c. By the vertical line test, the graph is the graph of a function. The arrows indicate that the graph continues forever. All x-values are graphed, so the domain is all real numbers. The y-values for 4 and numbers less than 4 are graphed, so the range is $\{y|y \le 4\}$.

d. By the vertical line test, the graph is the graph of a function. The arrows indicate that the graph continues forever. All x-values and all y-values are graphed, so the domain is all real numbers and the range is all real numbers.

7. a. Substitute 1 for x in $f(x)$.
$$f(x) = 3x - 2$$
$$f(1) = 3(1) - 2 = 3 - 2 = 1$$

b. Substitute 1 for x in $g(x)$.
$$g(x) = 5x^2 + 2x - 1$$
$$g(1) = 5(1)^2 + 2(1) - 1$$
$$= 5 + 2 - 1$$
$$= 6$$

c. Substitute 0 for x in $f(x)$.
$$f(x) = 3x - 2$$
$$f(0) = 3(0) - 2 = 0 - 2 = -2$$

d. Substitute -2 for x in $g(x)$.
$$g(x) = 5x^2 + 2x - 1$$
$$g(-2) = 5(-2)^2 + 2(-2) - 1$$
$$= 5(4) - 4 - 1$$
$$= 20 - 4 - 1 = 15$$

8. a. Define $y_1 = 2.6x^2 - 4$ and graph using a decimal window. Move the cursor to find $x = 2$.

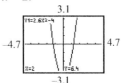

Since 2 is paired with 6.4, $f(2) = 6.4$.

b. Move the cursor to $x = -4$ and see that $y = 37.6$, so $f(-4) = 37.6$.

c. Move the cursor to $x = 0$ and see that $y = -4$, so $f(0) = -4$.

d. Move the cursor to $x = 0.7$ and see that $y = -2.726$, so $f(0.7) = -2.726$.

9. a. To find $f(1)$, find the y-value when $x = 1$. We see from the graph that when $x = 1$, y or $f(x) = -3$.
Thus, $f(1) = -3$.

b. $f(0) = -2$ from the ordered pair $(0, -2)$.

c. $g(-2) = 3$ from the ordered pair $(-2, 3)$.

d. $g(0) = 1$ from the ordered pair $(0, 1)$.

e. To find x-values such that $f(x) = 1$, we are looking for any ordered pairs on the graph of f whose $f(x)$ or y-value is 1. They are $(-1, 1)$ and $(3, 1)$. Thus, $f(-1) = 1$ and $f(3) = 1$. The x-values are -1 and 3.

f. Find ordered pairs on the graph of g whose $g(x)$ or y-value is -2. There is one such ordered pair, $(-3, -2)$. Thus, $g(-3) = -2$. The only x-value is -3.

10. Use $R(w) = w + 0.15w$.

```
15→W:W+.15W        38.50→W:W+.15W
        17.25             44.275
22.75→W:W+.15W     53→W:W+.15W
        26.1625           60.95
■                  ■
```

Wholesale Cost	w	$15.00	$22.75	$38.50	$53.00
Retail Price	$R(w)$	$17.25	$26.16	$44.28	$60.95

11. Find the year 2003 and move upward until you reach the graph. From the point on the graph, move horizontally to the left until the other axis is reached. In 2003, approximately $35 billion was spent.

12. Find $f(2012)$.

$$f(x) = 2.602x - 5178$$
$$f(2012) = 2.602(2012) - 5178$$
$$= 57.224$$

We predict that $57.224 billion will be spent in 2012.

Vocabulary and Readiness Check

1. The intersection of the *x*-axis and *y*-axis is a point, called the origin.

2. To find an *x*-intercept, let $y = 0$ and solve for x.

3. To find a *y*-intercept, let $x = 0$ and solve for y.

4. The graph of $Ax + By = C$, where *A* and *B* are not both 0 is a line.

5. The graph of $y = |x|$ looks V-shaped.

6. The graph of $y = x^2$ is a parabola.

7. A relation is a set of ordered pairs.

8. The range of a relation is the set of all second components of the ordered pairs.

9. The domain of a relation is the set of all first components of the ordered pairs.

10. A function is a relation in which each first component in the ordered pairs corresponds to *exactly* one second component.

11. By the vertical line test, all linear equations are functions except those whose graphs are vertical lines.

12. If $f(-2) = 1.7$, the corresponding ordered pair is (−2, 1.7).

Exercise Set 2.2

2. The domain is the set of all first coordinates and the range is the set of all second coordinates.
Domain = {4, −4, 2, 10}
Range = {9, 3, −5}
Function since each *x*-value corresponds to exactly one *y*-value.

4. The domain is the set of all first coordinates and the range is the set of all second coordinates.
Domain = {6, 5, 7}
Range = {6, –2}
Not a function since 5 is paired with both 6 and –2.

6. The domain is the set of all first coordinates and the range is the set of all second coordinates.
Domain = {1, 2, 3, 4}
Range = {1}
Function since each *x*-value corresponds to exactly one *y*-value.

8. The domain is the set of all first coordinates and the range is the set of all second coordinates.
Domain = {π, 0, –2, 4}
Range = {0, π, 4, –2}
Function since each *x*-value corresponds to exactly one *y*-value.

10. The domain is the set of all first coordinates and the range is the set of all second coordinates.
Domain = $\left\{\dfrac{1}{2}, 0\right\}$

Range = $\left\{\dfrac{1}{4}, \dfrac{7}{8}, \pi\right\}$

Not a function since $\dfrac{1}{2}$ (or 0.5) is paired with

both $\dfrac{1}{4}$ and π.

12. Points on graph: (–1, 1), (0, 0), (1, –1), (2, –2)
Domain = {–1, 0, 1, 2}
Range = {–2, –1, 0, 1}
Function since each *x*-value corresponds to exactly one *y*-value.

14. Domain = {Polar Bear, Cow, Chimpanzee, Giraffe, Gorilla, Kangaroo, Red Fox}
Range = {20, 15, 10, 7}
Function since each input corresponds to exactly one output.

16. Domain = {Cat, Dog, To, Of, Given}
Range = {3, 5, 2}
Function since each input corresponds to exactly one output.

18. Domain = {A, B, C}
Range = {1, 2, 3}
Not a function since the input A corresponds to two different outputs, 1 and 2.

20. This relation is a function because although two different people may have the same birth date, each person has only one birth date. This means that each element in the first set is assigned to only one element in the second set.

22. This relation is not a function because at least one of the numbers 0 to 4 will have to be assigned to more than one of the 50 women. This means that one element in the first set is assigned to more than one element in the second set.

24. No, this is not the graph of a function. Note that a vertical line can be drawn that intersects the graph in more than one point. The line itself is the vertical line.

26. No, this is not the graph of a function. Note that vertical lines can be drawn that intersect the graph in two points. The *y*-axis is such a vertical line.

28. No, this is not the graph of a function. Note that vertical lines can be drawn that intersect the graph in two or more points. The *y*-axis is such a vertical line.

30. No, this is not the graph of a function. Note that vertical lines can be drawn that intersect the graph in two points. The line *x* = 1 is such a vertical line.

32. Yes, this is the graph of a function since no vertical line will intersect this graph more than once.

34. The *x*-values go on forever;
domain = all real numbers
The *y*-values are graphed from 0 to ∞;
range = $\{y | y \geq 0\}$
Function since it passes the vertical line test.

36. The *x*-values are graphed from –3 to 3;
domain = $\{x | -3 \leq x \leq 3\}$
The *y*-values are graphed from –3 to 3;
range = $\{y | -3 \leq y \leq 3\}$
Not a function since it fails the vertical line test (try *x* = 0).

38. The *x*-values do not include –2 < *x* < 2;
domain = $\{x | x \leq -2 \text{ or } x \geq 2\}$
The *y*-values go on forever;
range = all real numbers
Not a function since it fails the vertical line test (try *x* = 3).

40. The *x*-values are graphed from 3 to ∞;
domain = $\{x | x \geq 3\}$
The *y*-values go on forever;
range = all real numbers
Not a function since it fails the vertical line test
(try *x* = 4).

42. The *x*-values go on forever;
domain = all real numbers
The only *y*-value is 3; range = {3}
Function since it passes the vertical line test.

44. The *x*-values go on forever;
domain = all real numbers
The *y*-values go on forever;
range = all real numbers
Function since it passes the vertical line test.

46. The *x*-values go on forever;
domain = all real numbers
The *y*-values are graphed from −5 to ∞;
range = $\{y | y \geq -5\}$
Function since it passes the vertical line test.

48. Answers may vary

50. $y = x - 1$
For each *x*-value substituted into the equation
$y = x - 1$, the subtraction performed gives a
single result, so only one *y*-value will be
associated with each *x*-value. Thus, $y = x - 1$ is a
function.

52. $y = x^2$
For each *x*-value substituted into the equation
$y = x^2$, the squaring *x* gives a single result, so
only one *y*-value will be associated with each
x-value. Thus, $y = x^2$ is a function.

54. $2x - 3y = 9$
For each *x*-value substituted into the equation
$2x - 3y = 9$, the process of solving for *y* gives a
single result, so only one *y*-value will be
associated with each *x*-value. Thus, $2x - 3y = 9$
is a function.

56. $y = \dfrac{1}{x - 3}$
For each *x*-value substituted into the equation
$y = \dfrac{1}{x - 3}$, the subtraction and division

performed gives a single result, so only one
y-value will be associated with each *x*-value.

Thus, $y = \dfrac{1}{x - 3}$ is a function.

58. $y = \dfrac{1}{2}x + 4$

For each *x*-value substituted into the equation

$y = \dfrac{1}{2}x + 4$ the multiplication and addition

performed on each gives a single result, so only
one *y*-value will be associated with each *x*-value.

Thus, $y = \dfrac{1}{2}x + 4$ is a function.

60. $x = |y|$
The *x*-value 2 is associated with two *y*-values, −2
and 2. Thus, $x = |y|$ is not a function.

62. $f(x) = 3x + 3$
$f(-1) = 3(-1) + 3 = 0$

64. $h(x) = 5x^2 - 7$
$h(0) = 5(0)^2 - 7 = -7$

66. $g(x) = 4x^2 - 6x + 3$
$g(1) = 4(1)^2 - 6(1) + 3 = 1$

68. $h(x) = 5x^2 - 7$
$h(-2) = 5(-2)^2 - 7 = 20 - 7 = 13$

70. $g(x) = -\dfrac{1}{3}x$

    a. $g(0) = -\dfrac{1}{3}(0) = 0$

    b. $g(-1) = -\dfrac{1}{3}(-1) = \dfrac{1}{3}$

    c. $g(3) = -\dfrac{1}{3}(3) = -1$

72. $h(x) = -x^2$

    a. $h(-5) = -(-5)^2 = -25$

    b. $h\left(-\dfrac{1}{3}\right) = -\left(-\dfrac{1}{3}\right)^2 = -\dfrac{1}{9}$

    c. $h\left(\dfrac{1}{3}\right) = -\left(\dfrac{1}{3}\right)^2 = -\dfrac{1}{9}$

74. $h(x) = 7$

    a. $h(7) = 7$

    b. $h(542) = 7$

    c. $h\left(-\dfrac{3}{4}\right) = 7$

76. $g(x) = 2.7x^2 + 6.8x - 10.2$

    a. $g(1) = 2.7(1)^2 + 6.8(1) - 10.2 = -0.7$

    b. $\begin{aligned} g(-5) &= 2.7(-5)^2 + 6.8(-5) - 10.2 \\ &= 23.3 \end{aligned}$

    c. $\begin{aligned} g(7.2) &= 2.7(7.2)^2 + 6.8(7.2) - 10.2 \\ &= 178.728 \end{aligned}$

78. a. $f(-4) = 124$

    b. $f(2) = -14$

    c. $f(6) = -426$

80. $f(-2) = -3$

82. If $f(-5) = -10$, then $y = -10$ when $x = -5$. The ordered pair is $(-5, -10)$.

84. If $g(-2) = 8$, then $y = 8$ when $x = -2$. The ordered pair is $(-2, 8)$.

86. The ordered pair $(-2, -1)$ is on the graph of f. Thus, $f(-2) = -1$.

88. The ordered pair $(-4, -5)$ is on the graph of g. Thus, $g(-4) = -5$.

90. There are two ordered pairs on the graph of f with a y-value of -2, $(-3, -2)$ and $(-1, -2)$. The x-values are -3 and -1.

92. Since $g(x) = 0$ for values of x where the graph crosses the x-axis, the x-values are -3, 0, and 2.

94. 1; otherwise, it would fail the vertical line test.

96.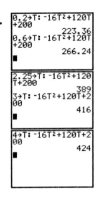

Time in Hours	t	0.5	1	1.5	2.5	3
Total Cost	$C(t)$	12.63	15.25	17.88	23.13	25.75

98.

a. $h(0.2) = 223.36$

b. $h(0.6) = 266.24$

c. $h(2.25) = 389$

d. $h(3) = 416$

e. $h(4) = 424$

100. a. Find the year 1999 and move upward until you reach the graph. From the point on the graph, move horizontally to the left until the other axis is reached. In 1999, approximately $23 billion was spent.

b. Find $f(1999)$.
$$f(x) = 2.602x - 5178$$
$$f(1999) = 2.602(1999) - 5178 = 23.398$$
Approximately $23.398 billion was spent in 1999.

102. Since 2015 is 15 years after 2000, find $f(15)$.
$$f(x) = 0.42x + 10.5$$
$$f(15) = 0.42(15) + 10.5 = 16.8$$
We predict that diamond production will be $16.8 billion in 2015.

104. Answers may vary

106. $A(r) = \pi r^2$
$$A(8) = \pi(8)^2 = 64\pi \text{ square feet}$$

108. $V(x) = x^3$
$$V(1.7) = (1.7)^3 = 4.913 \text{ cubic cm}$$

110. $H(t) = 2.72t + 61.28$
$$H(35) = 2.72(35) + 61.28$$
$$= 156.48 \text{ centimeters}$$

112. $D(x) = \dfrac{136}{25}x$
$$D(50) = \dfrac{136}{25}(50) = 272 \text{ milligrams}$$

114. $y = -0.09x + 8.02$

    a. $x = 1995 - 1970 = 25$
$$y = -0.09(25) + 8.02 = 5.77 \text{ days}$$

    b. $x = 2011 - 1970 = 41$
$$y = -0.09(41) + 8.02 = 4.33 \text{ days}$$

116. $2x + 3y = 10$

x	0	5	2
y	$\frac{10}{3}$	0	2

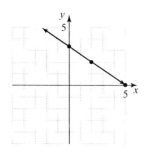

118. $5y - x = -15$

x	0	15	-2
y	-3	0	$-\frac{17}{5}$

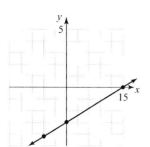

120. $y = -2x$

x	0	0	-2
y	0	0	4

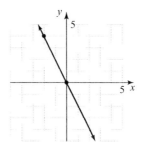

122. $f(7) = 50$ means that $y = 50$ when $x = 7$. Thus, $(7, 50)$ is an ordered pair of the function. The given statement is true.

124. Since $f(7) = 50$ when $f(x) = x^2 + 1$, the statement is true.

126. $f(x) = 2x + 7$

    a. $f(2) = 2(2) + 7 = 11$

    b. $f(a) = 2a + 7$

128. $h(x) = x^2 + 7$

    a. $h(3) = (3)^2 + 7 = 16$

    b. $h(a) = a^2 + 7$

130. Answers may vary

Section 2.3

Practice Exercises

    1. $f(x) = 4x, \ g(x) = 4x - 3$

x	$f(x)$	$g(x)$
0	0	-3
-1	-4	-7
1	4	1

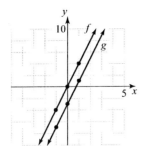

2.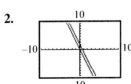

The graph of $g(x) = -3x + 2$ can be obtained from the graph of $f(x) = -3x$ by <u>shifting the graph of $f(x)$ up 2 units</u>.

3.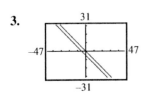

The graph of $y_2 = -x - 5$ can be obtained from the graph of $y_1 = -x$ by <u>shifting the graph of y_1 down 5 units</u>.

4. $4x - 5y = -20$

Let $x = 0$.
$$4x - 5y = -20$$
$$4 \cdot 0 - 5y = -20$$
$$-5y = -20$$
$$y = 4$$

Let $y = 0$.
$$4x - 5y = -20$$
$$4x - 5 \cdot 0 = -20$$
$$4x = -20$$
$$x = -5$$

Let $x = -2$.
$$4x - 5y = -20$$
$$4(-2) - 5y = -20$$
$$-8 - 5y = -20$$
$$-5y = -12$$
$$y = \frac{12}{5} = 2\frac{2}{5}$$

The ordered pairs are in the table.

x	y
0	4
-5	0
-2	$2\frac{2}{5}$

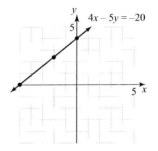

Solve for y to check.
$$4x - 5y = -20$$
$$-5y = -4x - 20$$
$$y = \frac{-4x - 20}{-5}$$

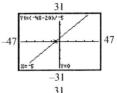

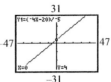

5. a. The y-intercept of $f(x) = \dfrac{3}{4}x - \dfrac{2}{5}$ is

$\left(0, \ -\dfrac{2}{5}\right)$.

b. The y-intercept of $y = 2.6x + 4.1$ is $(0, 4.1)$.

6. $y = -3x$

If $x = 0$, then $y = -3(0) = 0$.
If $x = 1$, then $y = -3(1) = -3$.
If $x = -1$, then $y = -3(-1) = 3$.
The ordered pairs are in the table.

x	y
0	0
1	−3
−1	3

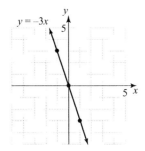

7. $x = -4$

The equation can be written as $x + 0y = -4$. For any y-value chosen, notice that x is −4.

x	y
−4	−3
−4	0
−4	3

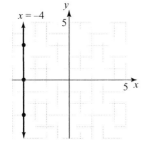

8. $y = 4$

The equation can be written as $0x + y = 4$. For any x-value chosen, notice that y is 4.

x	y
−3	4
0	4
3	4

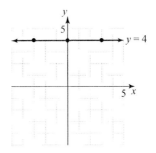

9. Define $y_1 = 79 + 0.10x$ and graph in a $[0, 500, 50]$ by $[0, 150, 25]$ window. The graph shows the cost for 50 miles.

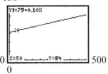

No. of miles (x)	50	175	230	450
Cost $C(x)$	84	96.50	102	124

Vocabulary and Readiness Check

1. A <u>linear</u> function can be written in the form $f(x) = mx + b$.

2. In the form $f(x) = mx + b$, the y-intercept is <u>$(0, b)$</u>.

3. The graph of $x = c$ is a <u>vertical</u> line with x-intercept <u>$(c, 0)$</u>.

4. The graph of $y = c$ is a <u>horizontal</u> line with y-intercept <u>$(0, c)$</u>.

5. To find an x-intercept, let <u>$y = 0$</u> or <u>$f(x) = 0$</u> and solve for <u>x</u>.

6. To find a y-intercept, let <u>$x = 0$</u> and solve for <u>y</u>.

Exercise Set 2.3

2. $f(x) = 2x$

x	0	−1	1
y	0	−2	2

Plot the points to obtain the graph.

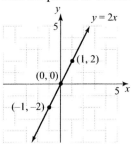

4. $f(x) = 2x + 6$

x	0	−1	−2
y	6	4	2

Plot the points to obtain the graph.

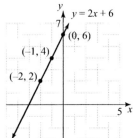

6. $f(x) = \dfrac{1}{3}x$

x	0	3	−3
y	0	1	−1

Plot the points to obtain the graph.

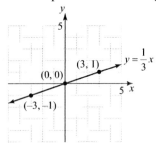

8. $f(x) = \dfrac{1}{3}x - 2$

x	0	3	−3
y	−2	−1	−3

Plot the points to obtain the graph.

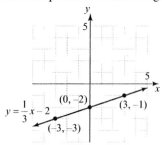

10. The graph of $f(x) = 5x - 2$ is the graph of $f(x) = 5x$ shifted down 2 units. The correct graph is A.

12. The graph of $f(x) = 5x + 3$ is the graph of $f(x) = 5x$ shifted up 3 units. The correct graph is B.

14. $x - y = -4$

x	$x - y = -4$	y
0	$0 - y = -4$	4
−4	$x - 0 = -4$	0
−2	$-2 - y = -4$	2

x-intercept: (−4, 0), y-intercept: (0, 4)
$f(x) = x + 4$

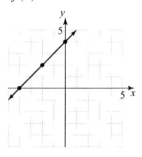

16. $2x = y$

x	$2x = y$	y
0	$2(0) = y$	0
2	$2(2) = y$	4
−2	$2(-2) = y$	−4

x-intercept: (0, 0), y-intercept: (0, 0)
$f(x) = 2x$

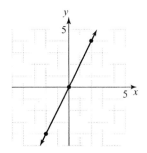

18. $x - 2y = -8$

x	$x - 2y = -8$	y
0	$0 - 2y = -8$	4
-8	$x - 2(0) = -8$	0
-4	$-4 - 2y = -8$	2

x-intercept: $(-8, 0)$, y-intercept: $(0, 4)$

$f(x) = \dfrac{1}{2}x + 4$

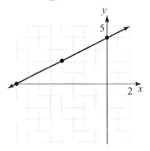

20. $2x + 3y = 6$

x	$2x + 3y = 6$	y
0	$2(0) + 3y = 6$	2
3	$2x + 3(0) = 6$	0
-3	$2(-3) + 3y = 6$	4

x-intercept: $(3, 0)$, y-intercept: $(0, 2)$

$f(x) = -\dfrac{2}{3}x + 2$

22. Answers may vary; it's a good way to check one's work.

24. $y = 5$

Horizontal line with y-intercept at 5

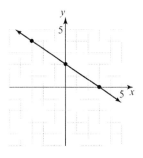

26. $x = 0$

Vertical line with x-intercept at 0; the line is the y-axis.

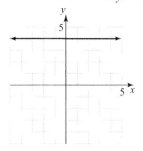

28. $x - 3 = 0$

$x = 3$

Vertical line with x-intercept at 3

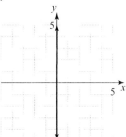

30. The graph of $x = -3$ is a vertical line with x-intercept $(-3, 0)$. The correct graph is D.

32. The graph of $y + 1 = 0$ or $y = -1$ is a horizontal line with *y*-intercept $(0, -1)$. The correct graph is B.

34. The horizontal line $y = 0$ has *x*-intercepts.

36. $x - 3y = 3$

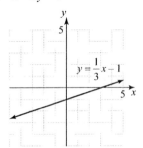

38. $3x - 2y = 5$

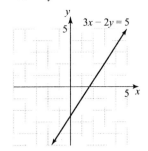

40. $x - 3y = 9$

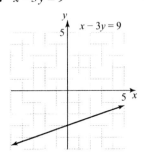

42. $4 = x - 3y$

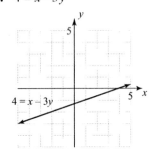

44. $-x + 9 = -y$

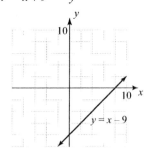

46. $x = \dfrac{3}{2}$

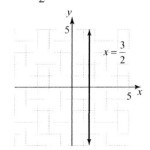

48. $4x + y = 5$

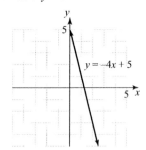

50. $y - 6 = 0$, or $y = 6$

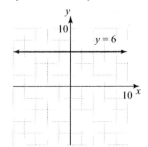

52. $f(x) = \dfrac{4}{3}x + 2$

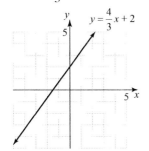

54. $f(x) = -x$

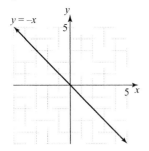

56. $f(x) = -2x$

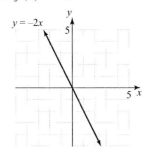

58. $f(x) = -3x + \dfrac{3}{4}$

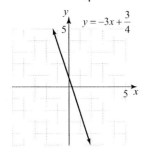

60. $f(x) = 3$

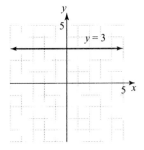

62. The graph shows the x-intercept of $(-2, 0)$, so $g(-2) = 0$. Statements a and c are true.

64.

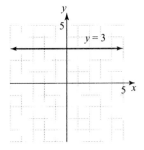

No. of Overtime Hours	2	10	12.5	15.75
Salary in Dollars	358.62	458.70	489.98	530.63

66. $\dfrac{4-5}{-1-0} = \dfrac{-1}{-1} = 1$

68. $\dfrac{12-3}{10-9} = \dfrac{9}{1} = 9$

70. $\dfrac{2-2}{3-5} = \dfrac{0}{-2} = 0$

72. $55x + 75y = 33,000$

   a. $55(0) + 75y = 33,000$
$$75y = 33,000$$
$$y = 440$$
   $(0, 440)$; If no basic models are produced, 440 deluxe models can be produced.

   b. $55x + 75(0) = 33,000$
$$55x = 33,000$$
$$x = 600$$
   $(600, 0)$; If no deluxe models are produced, 600 basic models can be produced.

   c. $55x + 75(350) = 33,000$
$$55x + 26,250 = 33,000$$
$$55x = 6750$$
$$x = 122.7$$
   122 basic models

74. $C(x) = 4x + 10$

    a. $C(8) = 4(8) + 10 = \$42$

    b.

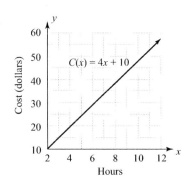

    c.   The line moves upward from left to right.

76. $f(x) = 291.5x + 2944.05$

    a.   Since 2015 is 15 years after 2000, find $f(15)$.
$$f(15) = 291.5(15) + 2944.05$$
$$= 4372.5 + 2944.05$$
$$= 7316.55$$
In 2015, the yearly cost of attending a public four-year college will be approximately $7316.55.

    b.   Let $f(x) = 6000$.
$$6000 = 291.5x + 2944.05$$
$$3055.95 = 291.5x$$
$$10.48 \approx x$$
Round up to 11. The yearly cost of attending a public four-year college will first exceed $6000 in 2011, 11 years after 2000.

    c.   Answers may vary.

78. The graph shows the graph of $y = |x|$ shifted up 3 units. Its equation is $y = |x| + 3$. The correct answer is d.

80. The graph shows the graph of $y = |x|$ shifted down 3 units. Its equation is $y = |x| - 3$. The correct answer is c.

Section 2.4

Practice Exercises

1. Let $(x_1, y_1) = (4, 0)$ and $(x_2, y_2) = (-2, 3)$.
$$m = \frac{y_2 - y_1}{x_2 - x_1}$$
$$= \frac{3 - 0}{-2 - 4}$$
$$= \frac{3}{-6}$$
$$= -\frac{1}{2}$$

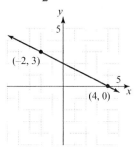

2. Let $(x_1, y_1) = (-5, -4)$ and $(x_2, y_2) = (5, 2)$.
$$m = \frac{y_2 - y_1}{x_2 - x_1}$$
$$= \frac{2 - (-4)}{5 - (-5)}$$
$$= \frac{6}{10}$$
$$= \frac{3}{5}$$

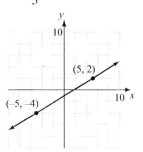

3. $2x - 3y = 9$

Write the equation in slope-intercept form by solving for y.
$$2x - 3y = 9$$
$$-3y = -2x + 9$$
$$\frac{-3y}{-3} = \frac{-2x}{-3} + \frac{9}{-3}$$
$$y = \frac{2}{3}x - 3$$

The coefficient of x, $\dfrac{2}{3}$, is the slope, and the

y-intercept is $(0, -3)$.

4. $f(x) = 2.7x + 38.64$

The year 2012 corresponds to $x = 16$.

$f(16) = 2.7(16) + 38.64$

$ = 43.2 + 38.64$

$ = 81.84$

We predict that in 2012 the price of an adult one-day pass will be about \$81.84.

5. $x = 4$

The graph of $x = 4$ is a vertical line. We choose two points on the line, $(4, 0)$ and $(4, 3)$. Let $(x_1, y_1) = (4, 0)$ and $(x_2, y_2) = (4, 3)$.

$m = \dfrac{y_2 - y_1}{x_2 - x_1}$

$ = \dfrac{3 - 0}{4 - 4}$

$ = \dfrac{3}{0}$

Since $\dfrac{3}{0}$ is undefined, the slope of the vertical line $x = 4$ is undefined.

6. $y = -3$

The graph of $y = -3$ is a horizontal line. We choose two points on the line, $(0, -3)$ and $(4, -3)$. Let $(x_1, y_1) = (0, -3)$ and $(x_2, y_2) = (4, -3)$.

$m = \dfrac{y_2 - y_1}{x_2 - x_1}$

$ = \dfrac{-3 - (-3)}{4 - 0}$

$ = \dfrac{0}{4}$

$ = 0$

The slope of the horizontal line $y = -3$ is 0.

7. **a.** Find the slope of each line.

$x - 2y = 3$

$-2y = -x + 3$

$\dfrac{-2y}{-2} = \dfrac{-x}{-2} + \dfrac{3}{-2}$

$y = \dfrac{1}{2}x - \dfrac{3}{2}$

The slope is $\dfrac{1}{2}$.

$2x + y = 3$

$y = -2x + 3$

The slope is -2. The product of the slopes is -1 $\left[\dfrac{1}{2}(-2) = -1\right]$. The lines are perpendicular.

b. Find the slope of each line.

$4x - 3y = 2$

$-3y = -4x + 2$

$\dfrac{-3y}{-3} = \dfrac{-4x}{-3} + \dfrac{2}{-3}$

$y = \dfrac{4}{3}x - \dfrac{2}{3}$

The slope is $\dfrac{4}{3}$. The y-intercept is $\left(0, -\dfrac{2}{3}\right)$.

$-8x + 6y = -6$

$6y = 8x - 6$

$\dfrac{6y}{6} = \dfrac{8x}{6} - \dfrac{6}{6}$

$y = \dfrac{4}{3}x - 1$

The slope is $\dfrac{4}{3}$. The y-intercept is $(0, -1)$.

The slopes of both lines are $\dfrac{4}{3}$. The y-intercepts are different, so the lines are not the same. Therefore, the lines are parallel.

Vocabulary and Readiness Check

1. The measure of the steepness or tilt of a line is called slope.

2. The slope of a line through two points is measured by the ratio of vertical change to horizontal change.

3. If a linear equation is in the form $y = mx + b$, or $f(x) = mx + b$, the slope of the line is $\underline{m}$ and the y-intercept is $\underline{(0, b)}$.

4. The form $y = mx + b$ or $f(x) = mx + b$ is the slope-intercept form.

5. The slope of a horizontal line is 0.

6. The slope of a vertical line is undefined.

7. Two perpendicular lines have slopes whose product is $\underline{-1}$.

8. Two non-vertical lines are parallel if they have the same slope and different y-intercepts.

9. $m = \dfrac{7}{6}$ slants upward.

10. $m = -3$ slants downward.

11. Since $m = 0$, the line is horizontal.

12. Since the slope is undefined, the line is vertical.

Exercise Set 2.4

2. $m = \dfrac{11-6}{7-1} = \dfrac{5}{6}$

4. $m = \dfrac{11-7}{-2-3} = \dfrac{4}{-5} = -\dfrac{4}{5}$

6. $m = \dfrac{6-(-4)}{-1-(-3)} = \dfrac{10}{2} = 5$

8. $m = \dfrac{0-2}{4-4} = \dfrac{-2}{0}$; undefined slope

10. $m = \dfrac{-5-(-5)}{3-(-2)} = \dfrac{0}{5} = 0$

12. $m = \dfrac{-6-(-2)}{-1-3} = \dfrac{-4}{-4} = 1$

14. $m = \dfrac{11-(-17)}{2-(-5)} = \dfrac{28}{7} = 4$

16. Use $(0, -6)$ and $(5, 4)$.
$m = \dfrac{4-(-6)}{5-0} = \dfrac{10}{5} = 2$

18. Use $(0, 2)$ and $(2, -6)$.
$m = \dfrac{-6-2}{2-0} = \dfrac{-8}{2} = -4$

20. The slope of l_1 is negative, and the slope of l_2 is positive. Since a positive number is greater than any negative number, l_2 has the greater slope.

22. The slope of l_1 is 0, and the slope of l_2 is positive. Since 0 is less than any positive number, l_2 has the greater slope.

24. Both lines have positive slope. Since l_1 is steeper, it has the greater slope.

26. $f(x) = -2x + 6$ or $y = -2x + 6$
$m = -2$, $b = 6$ so y-intercept is $(0, 6)$.

28. $-5x + y = 10$
$\qquad y = 5x + 10$
$m = 5$, $b = 10$ so y-intercept is $(0, 10)$.

30. $-3x - 4y = 6$
$\qquad -4y = 3x + 6$
$\qquad\quad y = -\dfrac{3}{4}x - \dfrac{3}{2}$
$m = -\dfrac{3}{4}$, $b = -\dfrac{3}{2}$ so y-intercept is $\left(0, -\dfrac{3}{2}\right)$.

32. $f(x) = -\dfrac{1}{4}x$ or $y = -\dfrac{1}{4}x + 0$
$m = -\dfrac{1}{4}$, $b = 0$ so y-intercept is $(0, 0)$.

34. $f(x) = 2x - 3$
The slope is 2, and the y-intercept is $(0, -3)$. The correct graph is D.

36. $f(x) = -2x - 3$
The slope is -2, and the y-intercept is $(0, -3)$. The correct graph is C.

38. $y = -2$ is a horizontal line.
$m = 0$

40. $x = 4$ is a vertical line. m is undefined.

42. $y - 7 = 0$
$\quad y = 7$
This is a horizontal line.
$m = 0$

44. Answers may vary

46. $f(x) = x + 2$ or $y = x + 2$
$m = 1$, $b = 2$ so y-intercept is $(0, 2)$.

48. $4x - 7y = 28$
$\qquad y = \dfrac{4}{7}x - 4$
$m = \dfrac{4}{7}$, $b = -4$ so y-intercept is $(0, -4)$.

50. $2y - 7 = x$

$$y = \frac{1}{2}x + \frac{7}{2}$$

$m = \frac{1}{2}, b = \frac{7}{2}$ so y-intercept is $\left(0, \frac{7}{2}\right)$.

52. $x = 7$

m is undefined, no y-intercept

54. $f(x) = \frac{1}{7}x$ or $y = \frac{1}{7}x + 0$

$m = \frac{1}{7}$, $b = 0$ so y-intercept is $(0, 0)$.

56. $x - 7 = 0$

$x = 7$

m is undefined, no y-intercept

58. $2y + 4 = -7$

$$y = -\frac{11}{2}$$

$m = 0, b = -\frac{11}{2}$ so y-intercept is $\left(0, -\frac{11}{2}\right)$.

60. $f(x) = 5x - 6$ $g(x) = 5x + 2$
$m = 5$ $m = 5$
Parallel, since their slopes are equal.

62. $2x - y = -10$ $2x + 4y = 2$
$\quad -y = -2x - 10$ $\quad 4y = -2x + 2$
$\quad y = 2x + 10$ $\quad y = -\frac{1}{2}x + \frac{1}{2}$

$m = 2$ $m = -\frac{1}{2}$

Perpendicular, since slopes are negative reciprocals.

64. $x + 4y = 7$ $2x - 5y = 0$
$\quad 4y = -x + 7$ $\quad -5y = -2x$
$\quad y = -\frac{1}{4}x + \frac{7}{4}$ $\quad y = \frac{2}{5}x$

Neither since their slopes are not equal and their product is not -1.

66. Answers may vary

68. Two points on the line: $(0, 3), (1, 0)$

$$m = \frac{0 - 3}{1 - 0} = \frac{-3}{1} = -3$$

70. Two points on the line: $(-3, -1), (2, 4)$

$$m = \frac{4 - (-1)}{2 - (-3)} = \frac{5}{5} = 1$$

72. $m = \dfrac{3 \text{ miles}}{25 \text{ miles}} = \dfrac{3}{25}$

74. $m = \dfrac{15 \text{ ft}}{100 \text{ ft}} = \dfrac{3}{20}$

76. $y = 1059.6x + 36,827.4$

   a. The year 2009 corresponds to $x = 9$.
$$\begin{aligned}
y &= 1059.6(9) + 36,827.4 \\
&= 9536.4 + 36,827.4 \\
&= 46,363.8
\end{aligned}$$
We predict that in 2009 an American woman with a bachelor's degree will earn $46,363.80.

   b. The slope is 1059.6. The annual average income increases $1059.60 every year.

   c. The y-intercept is $(0, 36,827.4)$. When $x = 0$, or in 2000, the average annual income was $36,827.40.

78. $-266x + 10y = 27,409$

   a. Solve for y.
$$\begin{aligned}
-266x + 10y &= 27,409 \\
10y &= 266x + 27,409 \\
\frac{10y}{10} &= \frac{266x}{10} + \frac{27,409}{10} \\
y &= 26.6x + 2740.9
\end{aligned}$$
The slope is 26.6, and the y-intercept is $(0, 2740.9)$.

   b. The number of people employed as nurses increases 26.6 thousand for every 1 year.

   c. There were 2740.9 thousand nurses employed in 2000.

80. $f(x) = 107.3x + 1245.62$

   a. The slope is 107.3. The yearly cost of tuition increases $107.30 every 1 year.

   b. The y-intercept is $(0, 1245.62)$. The yearly cost of tuition when $x = 0$, or in 2000, was $1245.62.

82. $y - 0 = -3[x - (-10)]$
$\quad\quad y = -3[x + 10]$
$\quad\quad y = -3x - 30$

84. $y - 9 = -8[x - (-4)]$
$\quad\quad y - 9 = -8[x + 4]$
$\quad\quad y - 9 = -8x - 32$
$\quad\quad\quad y = -8x - 23$

86. The denominator in the first fraction should be $-3 - (-1)$.
$$m = \frac{9 - 4}{-3 - (-1)} = \frac{5}{-2} = -\frac{5}{2}$$

88. The numerator and the denominator should be switched.
$$m = \frac{-4 - (-6)}{0 - (-6)} = \frac{2}{6} = \frac{1}{3}$$

90. $f(x) = x$
$\quad m = 1$
The slope of a parallel line is 1.

92. $f(x) = x$
$\quad m = 1$
The slope of a perpendicular line is -1.

94. $-3x + 4y = 10 \implies y = \frac{3}{4}x - \frac{5}{2}$
$$m = \frac{3}{4}$$
The slope of a parallel line is $\frac{3}{4}$.

96. Since $\frac{4}{2} = 2$, the lines are parallel.

98. $\frac{8}{2} = 4$
Since $4(-0.25) = -1$, the lines are perpendicular.

100. a. $m_1 = \dfrac{-2 - 4}{2 - (-1)} = \dfrac{-6}{3} = -2$

$\quad\quad m_2 = \dfrac{2 - 6}{-4 - (-8)} = \dfrac{-4}{4} = -1$

$\quad\quad m_3 = \dfrac{0 - (-4)}{-6 - 0} = \dfrac{4}{-6} = -\dfrac{2}{3}$

$\quad\quad m_1 = -2, \ m_2 = -1, \ m_3 = -\dfrac{2}{3}$

b. lesser

Section 2.5

Practice Exercises

1. We are given the slope, $-\dfrac{3}{4}$, and the y-intercept, $(0, 4)$.

Let $m = -\dfrac{3}{4}$ and $b = 4$.

$y = mx + b$

$y = -\dfrac{3}{4}x + 4$

2. $y = \dfrac{3}{4}x + 2$

The slope is $\dfrac{3}{4}$, and the y-intercept is $(0, 2)$. Plot $(0, 2)$. Then plot a second point by starting at $(0, 2)$, rising 3 units up, and running 4 units to the right. The second point is $(4, 5)$.

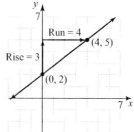

3. $x + 2y = 6$
Solve for y.
$x + 2y = 6$
$\quad 2y = -x + 6$
$\quad\quad y = -\dfrac{1}{2}x + 3$

The slope is $-\dfrac{1}{2}$, and the y-intercept is $(0, 3)$.

Plot $(0, 3)$. Then plot a second point by starting at $(0, 3)$, moving 1 unit down, and moving 2 units to the right. The second point is $(2, 2)$.

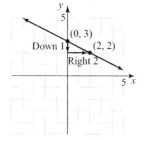

4. Use the point-slope form with $m = -4$ and $(x_1, y_1) = (-2, 5)$.
$$y - y_1 = m(x - x_1)$$
$$y - 5 = -4[x - (-2)]$$
$$y - 5 = -4(x + 2)$$
$$y - 5 = -4x - 8$$
$$y = -4x - 3$$

5. First find the slope.
$$m = \frac{0 - 2}{2 - (-1)} = \frac{-2}{3} = -\frac{2}{3}$$

Use the slope and one of the points in the point-slope form. We use $(2, 0)$.
$$y - y_1 = m(x - x_1)$$
$$y - 0 = -\frac{2}{3}(x - 2)$$
$$y = -\frac{2}{3}x + \frac{4}{3}$$
$$f(x) = -\frac{2}{3}x + \frac{4}{3}$$

6. The points on the graph have coordinates $(-2, 3)$ and $(1, 1)$. Find the slope.
$$m = \frac{1 - 3}{1 - (-2)} = \frac{-2}{3} = -\frac{2}{3}$$

Use the slope and one of the points in the point-slope form. We use $(1, 1)$.

$$y - y_1 = m(x - x_1)$$
$$y - 1 = -\frac{2}{3}(x - 1)$$
$$3(y - 1) = -2(x - 1)$$
$$3y - 3 = -2x + 2$$
$$2x + 3y = 5$$

7. Let x = the number of years after 2000 and y = the number of houses sold in the year corresponding to x. We have two ordered pairs, $(2, 7513)$ and $(6, 9198)$. Find the slope.
$$m = \frac{9198 - 7513}{6 - 2}$$
$$= \frac{1685}{4}$$
$$= 421.25$$

Use the slope and one of the points in the point-slope form. We use $(2, 7513)$.
$$y - y_1 = m(x - x_1)$$
$$y - 7513 = 421.25(x - 2)$$
$$y - 7513 = 421.25x - 842.5$$
$$y = 421.25x + 6670.5$$

The year 2014 corresponds to $x = 14$.

$$y = 421.25(14) + 6670.5$$
$$= 5897.5 + 6670.5$$
$$= 12,568$$

We predict that there will 12,568 house sales in 2014.

8. A horizontal line has an equation of the form $y = b$. Since the line contains the point $(6, -2)$, the equation is $y = -2$.

9. Since the line has undefined slope, the line must be vertical. A vertical line has an equation of the form $x = c$. Since the line contains the point $(6, -2)$, the equation is $x = 6$.

10. Solve the given equation for y.
$$3x + 4y = 1$$
$$4y = -3x + 1$$
$$y = -\frac{3}{4}x + \frac{1}{4}$$

The slope of this line is $-\frac{3}{4}$, so the slope of any line parallel to it is also $-\frac{3}{4}$. Use this slope and the point $(8, -3)$ in the point-slope form.

$$y - y_1 = m(x - x_1)$$
$$y - (-3) = -\frac{3}{4}(x - 8)$$
$$4(y + 3) = -3(x - 8)$$
$$4y + 12 = -3x + 24$$
$$3x + 4y = 12$$

11. Solve the given equation for y.
$$3x + 4y = 1$$
$$4y = -3x + 1$$
$$y = -\frac{3}{4}x + \frac{1}{4}$$

The slope of this line is $-\frac{3}{4}$, so the slope of any line perpendicular to it is the negative reciprocal of $-\frac{3}{4}$, or $\frac{4}{3}$. Use this slope and the point $(8, -3)$ in the point-slope form.

$$y - y_1 = m(x - x_1)$$
$$y - (-3) = \frac{4}{3}(x - 8)$$
$$3(y + 3) = 4(x - 8)$$
$$3y + 9 = 4x - 32$$
$$3y = 4x - 41$$
$$y = \frac{4}{3}x - \frac{41}{3}$$
$$f(x) = \frac{4}{3}x - \frac{41}{3}$$

Vocabulary and Readiness Check

1. $m = -4$, $b = 12$ so y-intercept is $(0, 12)$.

2. $m = \frac{2}{3}$, $b = -\frac{7}{2}$ so y-intercept is $\left(0, -\frac{7}{2}\right)$.

3. $m = 5$, $b = 0$ so y-intercept is $(0, 0)$.

4. $m = -1$, $b = 0$ so y-intercept is $(0, 0)$.

5. $m = \frac{1}{2}$, $b = 6$ so y-intercept is $(0, 6)$.

6. $m = -\frac{2}{3}$, $b = 5$ so y-intercept is $(0, 5)$.

7. The lines both have slope 12 and they have different y-intercepts, $(0, 6)$ and $(0, -2)$, so they are parallel.

8. The lines both have slope -5 and they have different y-intercepts, $(0, 8)$ and $(0, -8)$, so they are parallel.

9. The line have slopes -9 and $\frac{3}{2}$. The slopes are not equal and their product is not -1, so the lines are neither parallel nor perpendicular.

10. The line have slopes 2 and $\frac{1}{2}$. The slopes are not equal and their product is not -1, so the lines are neither parallel nor perpendicular.

Exercise Set 2.5

2. $m = \frac{1}{2}$, $b = -6$
$$y = mx + b$$
$$y = \frac{1}{2}x - 6$$

4. $m = -3$, $b = -\frac{1}{5}$
$$y = mx + b$$
$$y = -3x - \frac{1}{5}$$

6. $m = -\frac{4}{5}$, $b = 0$
$$y = mx + b$$
$$y = -\frac{4}{5}x + 0$$
$$y = -\frac{4}{5}x$$

8. $y = 2x + 1$
possible points: $(0, 1)$, $(1, 3)$

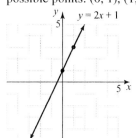

10. $3x + y = 9$
$$y = -3x + 9$$
possible points: $(0, 9)$, $(1, 6)$

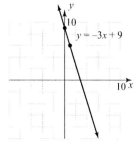

12. $-2x + 5y = -16$

$$5y = 2x - 16$$

$$y = \frac{2}{5}x - \frac{16}{5}$$

possible points: $\left(0, -\frac{16}{5}\right), \left(5, -\frac{6}{5}\right)$

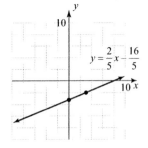

14. $y - y_1 = m(x - x_1)$

$$y - 1 = 4(x - 5)$$

$$y - 1 = 4x - 20$$

$$y = 4x - 19$$

16. $y - y_1 = m(x - x_1)$

$$y - (-4) = -4(x - 2)$$

$$y + 4 = -4x + 8$$

$$y = -4x + 4$$

18. $y - y_1 = m(x - x_1)$

$$y - 4 = \frac{2}{3}[x - (-9)]$$

$$y - 4 = \frac{2}{3}(x + 9)$$

$$y - 4 = \frac{2}{3}x + 6$$

$$y = \frac{2}{3}x + 10$$

20. $y - y_1 = m(x - x_1)$

$$y - (-6) = -\frac{1}{5}(x - 4)$$

$$y + 6 = -\frac{1}{5}x + \frac{4}{5}$$

$$y = -\frac{1}{5}x - \frac{26}{5}$$

22. $m = \dfrac{8 - 0}{7 - 3} = \dfrac{8}{4} = 2$

$$y - 0 = 2(x - 3)$$

$$y = 2x - 6$$

$$f(x) = 2x - 6$$

24. $m = \dfrac{6 - (-4)}{2 - 7} = \dfrac{10}{-5} = -2$

$$y - 6 = -2(x - 2)$$

$$y - 6 = -2x + 4$$

$$y = -2x + 10$$

$$f(x) = -2x + 10$$

26. $m = \dfrac{10 - (-2)}{-3 - (-9)} = \dfrac{12}{6} = 2$

$$y - 10 = 2[x - (-3)]$$

$$y - 10 = 2(x + 3)$$

$$y - 10 = 2x + 6$$

$$y = 2x + 16$$

$$f(x) = 2x + 16$$

28. $m = \dfrac{-8 - (-3)}{4 - 8} = \dfrac{-5}{-4} = \dfrac{5}{4}$

$$y - (-3) = \frac{5}{4}(x - 8)$$

$$y + 3 = \frac{5}{4}x - 10$$

$$y = \frac{5}{4}x - 13$$

$$f(x) = \frac{5}{4}x - 13$$

30. $m = \dfrac{\frac{3}{4} - \left(-\frac{1}{4}\right)}{\frac{3}{2} - \frac{1}{2}} = \dfrac{1}{1} = 1$

$$y - \frac{3}{4} = 1\left(x - \frac{3}{2}\right)$$

$$y - \frac{3}{4} = x - \frac{3}{2}$$

$$y = x - \frac{3}{4}$$

$$f(x) = x - \frac{3}{4}$$

32. $(0, -2), (2, 2)$

$$m = \frac{2 - (-2)}{2 - 0} = \frac{4}{2} = 2 \text{ and } b = -2$$

$$y = 2x - 2$$

$$2x - y = 2$$

34. $(-4, 0), (3, -1)$

$$m = \frac{-1-0}{3-(-4)} = -\frac{1}{7} \text{ and}$$

$$y - 0 = -\frac{1}{7}(x+4)$$
$$7y = -x - 4$$
$$x + 7y = -4$$

36. $f(-1) = -4$

38. $f(1) = 0$

40. $f(x) = 4$
$f(3) = 4$
$x = 3$

42. Every horizontal line is in the form $y = c$. Since the line passes through the point $(-3, 1)$, its equation is $y = 1$.

44. Every vertical line is in the form $x = c$. Since the line passes through $(2, 6)$, its equation is $x = 2$.

46. Lines with undefined slopes are vertical. Vertical lines have the form $x = c$. Since the line passes through $(0, 5)$, its equation is $x = 0$.

48. $y = 3x - 4$ so $m = 3$

$$y - 5 = 3(x - 1)$$
$$y - 5 = 3x - 3$$
$$y = 3x + 2$$
$$f(x) = 3x + 2$$

50. $2x - 3y = 1$ or $y = \frac{2}{3}x - \frac{1}{3}$ so

$$m = \frac{2}{3} \text{ and } m_\perp = -\frac{3}{2}$$

$$y - 8 = -\frac{3}{2}(x + 4)$$
$$y - 8 = -\frac{3}{2}x - 6$$
$$y = -\frac{3}{2}x + 2$$
$$f(x) = -\frac{3}{2}x + 2$$

52. $3x + 2y = 5$

$$2y = -3x + 5$$
$$y = -\frac{3}{2}x + \frac{5}{2} \text{ so } m_\perp = \frac{2}{3}$$
$$y + 3 = \frac{2}{3}(x + 2)$$
$$y + 3 = \frac{2}{3}x + \frac{4}{3}$$
$$y = \frac{2}{3}x - \frac{5}{3}$$
$$f(x) = \frac{2}{3}x - \frac{5}{3}$$

54.
$$y - 2 = 3[x - (-4)]$$
$$y - 2 = 3(x + 4)$$
$$y - 2 = 3x + 12$$
$$3x - y = -14$$

56. $m = \frac{6-9}{8-2} = \frac{-3}{6} = -\frac{1}{2}$

$$y - 9 = -\frac{1}{2}(x - 2)$$
$$2y - 18 = -x + 2$$
$$x + 2y = 20$$

58.
$$y = -4x + \frac{2}{9}$$
$$f(x) = -4x + \frac{2}{9}$$

60. $m = \frac{-3-(-8)}{-4-2} = \frac{5}{-6} = -\frac{5}{6}$

$$y + 8 = -\frac{5}{6}(x - 2)$$
$$6y + 48 = -5x + 10$$
$$5x + 6y = -38$$

62.
$$y + 1 = -\frac{3}{5}(x - 4)$$
$$5y + 5 = -3x + 12$$
$$3x + 5y = 7$$

64. Every horizontal line is in the form $y = c$. Since the line passes through the point $(1, 0)$, its equation is $y = 0$.

66. $6x + 2y = 5$

$$y = -3x + \frac{5}{2} \quad \text{so} \quad m = -3$$
$$y + 3 = -3(x - 8)$$
$$y + 3 = -3x + 24$$
$$3x + y = 21$$

68. Lines with undefined slope are vertical lines. Every vertical line is in the form $x = c$. Since the line passes through the point $(10, -8)$, its equation is $x = 10$.

70. $2x - y = 8$

$$y = 2x - 8 \quad \text{so} \quad m = 2 \text{ and } m_\perp = -\frac{1}{2}$$

$$y - 5 = -\frac{1}{2}(x - 3)$$
$$2y - 10 = -x + 3$$
$$x + 2y = 13$$

72. A line parallel to $y = 9$ will have the form $y = c$. Since the line passes through $(-3, -5)$, its equation is $y = -5$.

74. $m = \dfrac{5 - (-2)}{-6 - (-4)} = \dfrac{7}{-2} = -\dfrac{7}{2}$

$$y + 2 = -\frac{7}{2}(x + 4)$$
$$y + 2 = -\frac{7}{2}x - 14$$
$$y = -\frac{7}{2}x - 16$$
$$f(x) = -\frac{7}{2}x - 16$$

76. a. We have two ordered pairs, $(2, 2000)$ and $(4, 800)$. Find the slope.
$$m = \frac{800 - 2000}{4 - 2} = \frac{-1200}{2} = -600$$
Use the slope and one of the ordered pairs, $(2, 2000)$, to write the equation.
$$y - 2000 = -600(x - 2)$$
$$y - 2000 = -600x + 1200$$
$$y = -600x + 3200$$

   b. The year 2008 corresponds to $x = 5$.
$$y = -600(5) + 3200$$
$$= -3000 + 3200$$
$$= 200$$
We estimate that the computer was worth $200 in 2008.

78. a. $(7, 165,000), (12, 180,000)$
$$m = \frac{180,000 - 165,000}{12 - 7} = 3000$$
$$y - 165,000 = 3000(x - 7)$$
$$y - 165,000 = 3000x - 21,000$$
$$y = 3000x + 144,000$$

   b. $x = 2010 - 1990 = 20$
$$y = 3000(20) + 144,000 = \$204,000$$

80. a. $(4, 4116), (0, 4060)$
$$m = \frac{4060 - 4116}{0 - 4} = 14$$
$$y - 4060 = 14(x - 0)$$
$$y = 14x + 4060$$

   b. $x = 2013 - 2000 = 13$
$$y = 14(13) + 4060$$
$$= 4242 \text{ thousand births}$$

   c. The number of births increases by 14 thousand every year

82. a. $(0, 487), (10, 640)$
$$m = \frac{640 - 487}{10 - 0} = \frac{153}{10} = 15.3$$
$$y - 487 = 15.3(x - 0)$$
$$y = 15.3x + 487$$

   b. $x = 2012 - 2004 = 8$
$$y = 15.3(8) + 487$$
$$= 609.4 \text{ thousand people}$$

84. $-3x + 1 = 0$
$$-3x = -1$$
$$x = \frac{1}{3}$$

86. $-2(x + 1) = -x + 10$
$$-2x - 2 = -x + 10$$
$$-x = 12$$
$$x = -12$$

88. $\dfrac{x}{5} - \dfrac{3}{10} = \dfrac{x}{2} - 1$
$$2x - 3 = 5x - 10$$
$$-3x = -7$$
$$x = \frac{7}{3}$$

90. Since two distinct vertical lines will never intersect, they are parallel. The statement is true.

92. $m = \dfrac{-1-(-3)}{-8-(-6)} = \dfrac{2}{-2} = -1$ so $m_\perp = 1$

$M((-6,-3),(-8,-1)) = \left(\dfrac{-14}{2}, \dfrac{-4}{2}\right)$

$\qquad\qquad\qquad\qquad = (-7,-2)$

$y+2 = 1(x+7)$

$y+2 = x+7$

$x-y = -5$

94. $m = \dfrac{2-8}{7-5} = \dfrac{-6}{2} = -3$ so $m_\perp = \dfrac{1}{3}$

$M((5,8),(7,2)) = \left(\dfrac{12}{2}, \dfrac{10}{2}\right) = (6,5)$

$y-5 = \dfrac{1}{3}(x-6)$

$3y-15 = x-6$

$x-3y = -9$

96. $m = \dfrac{-2-8}{-4-(-6)} = \dfrac{-10}{2} = -5$ so $m_\perp = \dfrac{1}{5}$

$M((-6,8),(-4,-2)) = \left(\dfrac{-10}{2}, \dfrac{6}{2}\right)$

$\qquad\qquad\qquad\qquad = (-5,3)$

$y-3 = \dfrac{1}{5}(x+5)$

$5y-15 = x+5$

$x-5y = -20$

Integrated Review

1. $y = -2x$

x	-1	0	1
y	2	0	-2

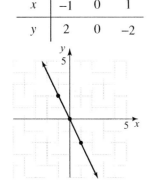

2. $3x - 2y = 6$

x	0	2	4
y	-3	0	3

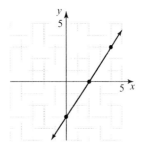

3. $x = -3$

The graph of $x = -3$ is a vertical line.

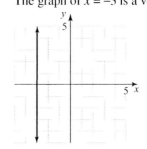

4. $y = 1.5$

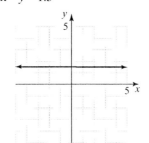

5. $m = \dfrac{-5-(-5)}{3-(-2)} = \dfrac{0}{5} = 0$

6. $m = \dfrac{5-2}{0-5} = \dfrac{3}{-5} = -\dfrac{3}{5}$

7. $y = 3x - 5$

$m = 3;\ (0,-5)$

8. $5x - 2y = 7$

$$-2y = -5x + 7$$

$$y = \frac{5}{2}x - \frac{7}{2}$$

$$m = \frac{5}{2}; \ \left(0, -\frac{7}{2}\right)$$

9. $y = 8x - 6 \quad y = 8x + 6$

$\quad m = 8 \qquad\quad m = 8$

Parallel, since their slopes are equal.

10. $y = \frac{2}{3}x + 1$ $2y + 3x = 1$

$\qquad m = \frac{2}{3}$ $2y = -3x + 1$

$\qquad\qquad\qquad\qquad\quad y = -\frac{3}{2}x + \frac{1}{2}$

$\qquad\qquad\qquad\qquad\quad\quad m = -\frac{3}{2}$

Perpendicular, since the product of their slopes is -1.

11. $m = \dfrac{2-6}{5-1} = \dfrac{-4}{4} = -1$

$$y - 6 = -1(x - 1)$$

$$y - 6 = -x + 1$$

$$y = -x + 7$$

12. Every vertical line is in the form $x = c$. Since the line passes through the point $(-2, -10)$, its equation is $x = -2$.

13. Every horizontal line is in the form $y = c$. Since the line passes through the point $(1, 0)$, its equation is $y = 0$.

14. $m = \dfrac{-5 - (-9)}{-6 - 2} = \dfrac{4}{-8} = -\dfrac{1}{2}$

$$y - (-9) = -\frac{1}{2}(x - 2)$$

$$2(y + 9) = -1(x - 2)$$

$$2y + 18 = -x + 2$$

$$2y = -x - 16$$

$$y = -\frac{1}{2}x - 8$$

$$f(x) = -\frac{1}{2}x - 8$$

15. $y - 4 = -5[x - (-2)]$

$$y - 4 = -5(x + 2)$$

$$y - 4 = -5x - 10$$

$$y = -5x - 6$$

$$f(x) = -5x - 6$$

16. $\qquad y = -4x + \dfrac{1}{3}$

$$f(x) = -4x + \frac{1}{3}$$

17. $\qquad y = \dfrac{1}{2}x - 1$

$$f(x) = \frac{1}{2}x - 1$$

18. $y - 0 = 3\left(x - \dfrac{1}{2}\right)$

$$y = 3x - \frac{3}{2}$$

19. $3x - y = 5$

$$y = 3x - 5$$

$$m = 3$$

$$y - (-5) = 3[x - (-1)]$$

$$y + 5 = 3(x + 1)$$

$$y + 5 = 3x + 3$$

$$y = 3x - 2$$

20. $4x - 5y = 10$

$$-5y = -4x + 10$$

$$y = \frac{4}{5}x - 2; \ m = \frac{4}{5} \ \text{ so } \ m_{\perp} = -\frac{5}{4}$$

Therefore, $y = -\dfrac{5}{4}x + 4$.

21. $4x + y = \dfrac{2}{3}$

$$y = -4x + \frac{2}{3}; \ m = -4 \ \text{ so } \ m_{\perp} = \frac{1}{4}$$

$$y - (-3) = \frac{1}{4}(x - 2)$$

$$4(y + 3) = x - 2$$

$$4y + 12 = x - 2$$

$$4y = x - 14$$

$$y = \frac{1}{4}x - \frac{7}{2}$$

22. $5x + 2y = 2$

$$2y = -5x + 2$$

$$y = -\frac{5}{2}x + 1$$

$$m = -\frac{5}{2}$$

$$y - 0 = -\frac{5}{2}[x - (-1)]$$

$$y = -\frac{5}{2}(x + 1)$$

$$2y = -5(x + 1)$$

$$2y = -5x - 5$$

$$y = -\frac{5}{2}x - \frac{5}{2}$$

23. A line having undefined slope is vertical. Therefore, the equation is $x = -1$.

24. $y - 3 = 0[x - (-1)]$

$$y - 3 = 0$$

$$y = 3$$

Section 2.6

Practice Exercises

1. $2004 - 1995 = 9$
Trace to $x = 9$ or evaluate the function for $x = 9$.

There were approximately 9.28 billion passengers in 2004.

2.

The amount that will be spent in 2016 is predicted to be \$27.29 per customer. The average increase in the amount spent for these services was \$0.54 per year between 2001 and 2006.

3. b.

If a and b are rounded to two decimal places, the regression equation is $y = 0.25x + 2.29$. Since the slope (0.25) is positive, the line is increasing.

  c. The number of sick or injured workers is increasing at a rate of 0.25 per 100 workers per year.

  d.
```
Y1(25)
            8.54
```

$Y1(25)$ is equal to 8.54 or approximately 8.54 workers per 100 in the year 2015.

4. a.
```
LinReg
y=ax+b
a=195.9052559
b=38438.48391
r²=.5639736509
r=.7509817913
```

The regression equation is $y = 195.91x + 38,438.48$.

  b.
```
Y1(1662)
        364033.0192
```

A home with 1662 square feet of living area is expected to sell for \$364,040.02.

5.
```
Y1(30)
            43.939
```

It is expected that 43.94% of workers will be 55 or older in 2020.

Vocabulary and Readiness Check

1. <u>Regression analysis</u> is the process of fitting a line or a curve to a set of data points.

2. Enter the <u>data</u> into the calculator using <u>lists</u>.

3. Use the <u>Stat Plot</u> feature to indicate the <u>scatter plot</u> as the type of graph.

4. When finding an appropriate window, make sure the <u>domain</u> and <u>range</u> are both included in your choice.

5. Use a <u>linear regression equation</u> to find the line of best fit.

Exercise Set 2.6

2.

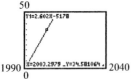

$34.9 billion was spent in 2003.

4.

The price will be $84.54 in 2013.

6. a.

The regression equation is
$y = 33.486x + 874.8$.

b. The expenditures are increasing at the rate of $33.49 per year.

c.

The expenditures are expected to be $1410.57 in 2016.

d. In the year 2000, the average annual expenditure for phone services was $874.80.

8. a.

The regression equation is
$y = -0.409x + 36.806$.

b.

The percent of female smokers is predicted to be 15.2% in 2013.

c. The percent of female smokers is decreasing at the rate of 0.409% per year.

10. a.

The regression equation is
$y = 3.737x + 7.076$.

b.

There are predicted to be 134 thousand or 134,000 female prisoners in 2014.

c. The number of female prisoners is increasing at the rate of 4 thousand or 4000 per year.

12. a.

The regression equation is
$y = 280.335x + 4465.242$.

b.

There are predicted to be 16,239 teams in 2012.

c. The number of teams is increasing at the rate of about 280 per year.

14.

The regression equation is
$y = 82.173x - 51,054.198$.

16.

A home with 2400 square feet is predicted to sell for $146,161.

18.

The regression equation is $y = 0.05x + 300$.

20. a.

The regression equation is
$y = 0.303x + 51.163$.

b. The life expectancy at birth of females is increasing at the rate of 0.303 years annually.

c.

The life expectancy at birth of a female born in 2015 is predicted to be 86.0 years.

22. a.

The regression equation is
$y = 2.348x + 15.668$.

b.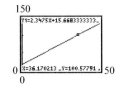

It is predicted that there will be 90.788 million HMO members in 2012.

c.

There will be over 100 million HMO members in 2016.

d. The number of HMO members is increasing at the rate of 2.348 million per year.

24. a.

The regression equation is
$y = 3.008x - 8.012$.

b.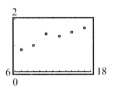

The average top ticket price is predicted to be $121.33 per ticket in 2013.

c. The cost is rising at the rate of about $3.01 per year.

26. a.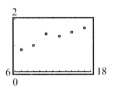

b.

The regression equation is
$y = 0.079x + 0.360$.

c. The cost is increasing at the rate of $0.079 million or $79,000 per year.

d.

The cost is expected to be $2.246 million or $2,246,000 in 2014.

28.
$$5(x-2) = 4(x+7)$$
$$5x - 10 = 4x + 28$$
$$x - 10 = 28$$
$$x = 38$$

30.
$$y + 0.8 = 0.3(y-2)$$
$$y + 0.8 = 0.3y - 0.6$$
$$10y + 8 = 3y - 6$$
$$7y + 8 = -6$$
$$7y = -14$$
$$y = -2$$

32. Answers may vary

Section 2.7

Practice Exercises

1. $f(x) = \begin{cases} -4x - 2 & \text{if } x \le 0 \\ x + 1 & \text{if } x > 0 \end{cases}$

Since $4 > 0$, $f(4) = 4 + 1 = 5$.
Since $-2 \le 0$, $f(-2) = -4(-2) - 2 = 8 - 2 = 6$.
Since $0 \le 0$, $f(0) = -4(0) - 2 = 0 - 2 = -2$.

2. $f(x) = \begin{cases} -4x - 2 & \text{if } x \le 0 \\ x + 1 & \text{if } x > 0 \end{cases}$

For $x \le 0$:

x	$f(x)$
-2	6
-1	2
0	-2

For $x > 0$:

x	$f(x)$
1	2
2	3
3	4

Graph a closed circle at $(0, -2)$. Graph an open circle at $(0, 1)$, which is found by substituting 0 for x in $f(x) = x + 1$.

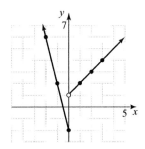

3. $f(x) = x^2$ and $g(x) = x^2 - 3$

The graph of $g(x) = x^2 - 3$ is the graph of $f(x) = x^2$ moved downward 3 units.

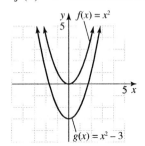

4. $f(x) = \sqrt{x}$ and $g(x) = \sqrt{x} + 1$

The graph of $g(x) = \sqrt{x} + 1$ is the graph of $f(x) = \sqrt{x}$ moved upward 1 unit.

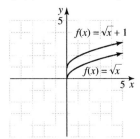

5. $f(x) = |x|$ and $g(x) = |x - 3|$

x	$f(x)$	$g(x)$
-2	2	5
-1	1	4
0	0	3
1	1	2
2	2	1
3	3	0
4	4	1
5	5	2

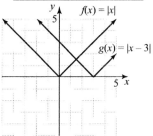

6. $f(x) = |x|$ and $g(x) = |x - 2| + 3$

The graph of $g(x)$ is the same as the graph of $f(x)$ shifted 2 units to the right and 3 units up.

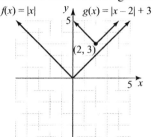

7. $h(x) = -(x + 2)^2 - 1$

The graph of $h(x) = -(x + 2)^2 - 1$ is the same as the graph of $f(x) = x^2$ reflected about the x-axis, then moved 2 units to the left and 1 unit downward.

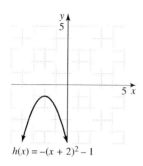

$$h(x) = -(x + 2)^2 - 1$$

Vocabulary and Readiness Check

1. The graph that corresponds to $y = \sqrt{x}$ is C.

2. The graph that corresponds to $y = x^2$ is B.

3. The graph that corresponds to $y = x$ is D.

4. The graph that corresponds to $y = |x|$ is A.

Exercise Set 2.7

2. $f(x) = \begin{cases} 3x & \text{if } x < 0 \\ x+2 & \text{if } x \geq 0 \end{cases}$

For $x < 0$:   For $x \geq 0$:

x	$f(x)$
-2	-6
-1	-3

x	$f(x)$
0	2
1	3
2	4

Graph a closed circle at $(0, 2)$. Graph an open circle at $(0, 0)$, which is found by substituting 0 for x in $f(x) = 3x$.

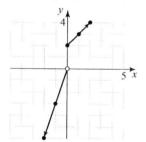

4. $f(x) = \begin{cases} 5x+4 & \text{if } x \leq 0 \\ \frac{1}{3}x-1 & \text{if } x > 0 \end{cases}$

For $x \leq 0$:   For $x > 0$:

x	$f(x)$
-2	-6
-1	-1
0	4

x	$f(x)$
1	$-\frac{2}{3}$
2	$-\frac{1}{3}$
3	0

Graph a closed circle at $(0, 4)$. Graph an open circle at $(0, -1)$, which is found by substituting 0 for x in $f(x) = \frac{1}{3}x-1$.

6. $g(x) = \begin{cases} 3x-1 & \text{if } x \leq 2 \\ -x & \text{if } x > 2 \end{cases}$

For $x \leq 2$:   For $x > 2$:

x	$g(x)$
0	-1
1	2
2	5

x	$g(x)$
3	-3
4	-4
5	-5

Graph a closed circle at $(2, 5)$. Graph an open circle at $(2, -2)$, which is found by substituting 2 for x in $g(x) = -x$.

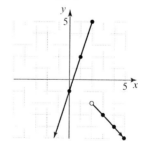

8. $f(x) = \begin{cases} 4 & \text{if } x < -3 \\ -2 & \text{if } x \geq -3 \end{cases}$

For $x < -3$:   For $x \geq -3$:

x	$f(x)$
-6	4
-5	4
-4	4

x	$f(x)$
-3	-2
-2	-2
-1	-2

Graph a closed circle at $(-3, -2)$. Graph an open circle at $(-3, 4)$, which is found by substituting -3 for x in $f(x) = 4$.

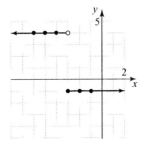

10. $f(x) = \begin{cases} -3x & \text{if } x \leq 0 \\ 3x+2 & \text{if } x > 0 \end{cases}$

For $x \leq 0$:   For $x > 0$:

x	$f(x)$
-1	3
0	0

x	$f(x)$
1	5
2	8

Graph a closed circle at $(0, 0)$. Graph an open circle at $(0, 2)$, which is found by substituting 0 for x in $f(x) = 3x + 2$.

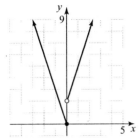

The function is defined for all real numbers, so the domain is all real numbers. The function takes on all y-values greater than or equal to 0, so the range is $\{y|y \geq 0\}$.

12. $f(x) = \begin{cases} 4x-4 & \text{if } x < 2 \\ -x+1 & \text{if } x \geq 2 \end{cases}$

For $x < 2$:   For $x \geq 2$:

x	$f(x)$
0	-4
1	0

x	$f(x)$
2	-1
3	-2

Graph a closed circle at $(2, -1)$. Graph an open circle at $(2, 4)$, which is found by substituting 2 for x in $f(x) = 4x - 4$.

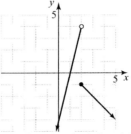

The function is defined for all real numbers, so the domain is all real numbers. The function takes on all y-values less than 4, so the range is $\{y|y < 4\}$.

14. $h(x) = \begin{cases} x+2 & \text{if } x < 1 \\ 2x+1 & \text{if } x \geq 1 \end{cases}$

For $x < 1$:   For $x \geq 1$:

x	$h(x)$
-2	0
-1	1
0	2

x	$h(x)$
1	3
2	5
3	7

Graph a closed circle at $(1, 3)$. The graph of $h(x) = x + 2$ for $x < 1$ also approaches the point $(1, 3)$.

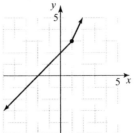

The function is defined for all real numbers, so the domain is all real numbers. The function takes on all y-values, so the range is all real numbers.

16. $f(x) = \begin{cases} -1 & \text{if } x \le 0 \\ -3 & \text{if } x \ge 2 \end{cases}$

For $x \le 0$:　　　　For $x \ge 2$:

x	$f(x)$
-2	-1
-1	-1
0	-1

x	$f(x)$
2	-3
3	-3
4	-3

Graph closed circles at $(0, -1)$ and $(2, -3)$.

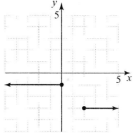

The function is defined for $x \le 0$ or $x \ge 2$, so the domain is $\{x | x \le 0 \text{ or } x \ge 2\}$. The function takes on two y-values, -1 and -3, so the range is $\{-3, -1\}$.

18. $f(x) = |x| - 2$ is graph D.

20. $f(x) = \sqrt{x} + 3$ is graph C.

22. $f(x) = |x + 3|$ is graph D.

24. $f(x) = \sqrt{x - 2}$ is graph B.

26. $y = (x + 4)^2$

The graph of $y = (x + 4)^2$ is the same as the graph of $y = x^2$ shifted left 4 units.

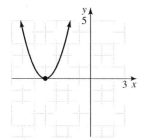

28. $f(x) = x^2 - 4$

The graph of $f(x) = x^2 - 4$ is the same as the graph of $y = x^2$ shifted down 4 units.

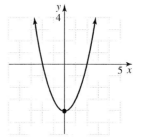

30. $f(x) = \sqrt{x - 1} + 3$

The graph of $f(x) = \sqrt{x - 1} + 3$ is the same as the graph of $y = \sqrt{x}$ shifted right 1 unit and up 3 units.

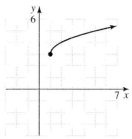

32. $f(x) = |x - 3| + 2$

The graph of $f(x) = |x - 3| + 2$ is the same as the graph of $y = |x|$ shifted right 3 units and up 2 units.

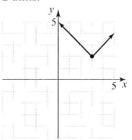

34. $f(x) = \sqrt{x + 3} + 2$

The graph of $f(x) = \sqrt{x + 3} + 2$ is the same as the graph of $y = \sqrt{x}$ shifted left 3 units and up 2 units.

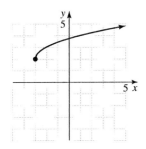

36. $f(x) = |x+1| - 4$

The graph of $f(x) = |x+1| - 4$ is the same as the graph of $y = |x|$ shifted left 1 unit and down 4 units.

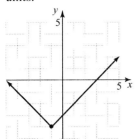

38. $h(x) = (x+2)^2 + 2$

The graph of $h(x) = (x+2)^2 + 2$ is the same as the graph of $y = x^2$ shifted left 2 units and up 2 units.

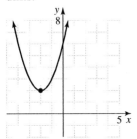

40. $f(x) = (x+2)^2 + 4$

The graph of $f(x) = (x+2)^2 + 4$ is the same as the graph of $y = x^2$ shifted left 2 units and up 4 units.

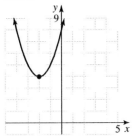

42. $g(x) = -(x+2)^2$

The graph of $g(x) = -(x+2)^2$ is the same as the graph of $y = x^2$ reflected about the x-axis and then shifted left 2 units.

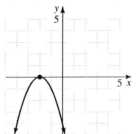

44. $f(x) = -\sqrt{x+3}$

The graph of $f(x) = -\sqrt{x+3}$ is the same as the graph of $y = \sqrt{x}$ reflected about the x-axis and then shifted left 3 units.

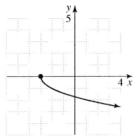

46. $g(x) = -|x+1| + 1$

The graph of $g(x) = -|x+1| + 1$ is the same as the graph of $y = |x|$ reflected about the x-axis and then shifted left 1 unit and up 1 unit.

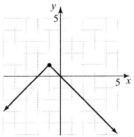

48. $f(x) = (x-1) + 4$

Since the function can be simplified to $f(x) = x + 3$, we see that its graph is a line with slope $m = 1$ and y-intercept $(0, 3)$.

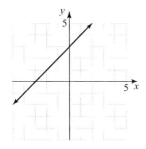

50. The graph of $x = -1$ is a vertical line with x-intercept $(-1, 0)$. The correct graph is C.

52. The graph of $y = 3$ is a horizontal line with y-intercept $(0, 3)$. The correct graph is B.

54. Answers may vary

56. $f(x) = \begin{cases} -\frac{1}{3}x & \text{if } x \leq 0 \\ x+2 & \text{if } 0 < x \leq 4 \\ 3x-4 & \text{if } x > 4 \end{cases}$

Some points for $x \leq 0$: $(-6, 2)$, $(-3, 1)$, $(0, 0)$
Closed dot at $(0, 0)$
Some points for $0 < x \leq 4$: $(1, 3)$, $(2, 4)$, $(4, 6)$
Open dot at $(0, 2)$, closed dot at $(4, 6)$
Some points for $x > 4$: $(5, 11)$, $(6, 14)$
Open dot at $(4, 8)$

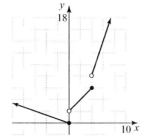

58. $f(x) = \sqrt{x-1} + 3$

The function is defined when $x - 1 \geq 0$, or $x \geq 1$, so the domain is $\{x | x \geq 1\}$. The function takes on all y-values greater than or equal to 3, so the range is $\{y | y \geq 3\}$.

60. $g(x) = -|x+1| + 1$

The function is defined for all real numbers, so the domain is all real numbers. The function takes on all y-values less than or equal to 1, so the range is $\{y | y \leq 1\}$.

62. $g(x) = -3\sqrt{x+5}$

The function is defined when $x + 5 \geq 0$, or $x \geq -5$, so the domain is $\{x | x \geq -5\}$.

64. $f(x) = -3|x+5.7|$

The function is defined for all real numbers, so the domain is all real numbers.

66. $h(x) = \sqrt{x-17} - 3$

The function is defined when $x - 17 \geq 0$, or $x \geq 17$, so the domain is $\{x | x \geq 17\}$.

68. $f(x) = \begin{cases} x^2 & \text{if } x < 0 \\ \sqrt{x} & \text{if } x \geq 0 \end{cases}$

For $x < 0$:   For $x \geq 0$:

x	$f(x)$
-3	9
-2	4
-1	1

x	$f(x)$
0	0
1	1
4	2

Graph a closed circle at $(0, 0)$. The graph of $f(x) = x^2$ for $x < 0$ also approaches the point $(0, 0)$.

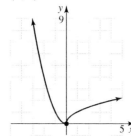

The function is defined for all real numbers, so the domain is all real numbers. The function takes on all y-values greater than or equal to 0, so the range is $\{y | y \geq 0\}$.

70. $g(x) = \begin{cases} -|x+1| - 1 & \text{if } x < -2 \\ \sqrt{x+2} - 4 & \text{if } x \geq -2 \end{cases}$

For $x < -2$:   For $x \geq -2$:

x	$g(x)$
-5	-5
-4	-4
-3	-3

x	$g(x)$
-2	-4
-1	-3
2	-2

Graph an open circle at $(-2, -2)$. Graph a closed circle at $(-2, -4)$.

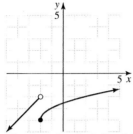

The function is defined for all real numbers, so the domain is all real numbers. The function takes on all y-values, so the range is all real numbers.

Chapter 2 Vocabulary Check

1. A <u>relation</u> is a set of ordered pairs.

2. The graph of every linear equation in two variables is a <u>line</u>.

3. The equation $y - 8 = -5(x + 1)$ is written in <u>point-slope</u> form.

4. <u>Standard</u> form of linear equation in two variables is $Ax + By = C$.

5. The <u>range</u> of a relation is the set of all second components of the ordered pairs of the relation.

6. <u>Parallel</u> lines have the same slope and different y-intercepts.

7. <u>Slope-intercept</u> form of a linear equation in two variables is $y = mx + b$.

8. A <u>function</u> is a relation in which each first component in the ordered pairs corresponds to exactly one second component.

9. In the equation $y = 4x - 2$, the coefficient of x is the <u>slope</u> of its corresponding graph.

10. Two lines are <u>perpendicular</u> if the product of their slopes is -1.

11. To find the x-intercept of a linear equation, let $y = 0$ and solve for the other variable.

12. The <u>domain</u> of a relation is the set of all first components of the ordered pairs of the relation.

13. A <u>linear function</u> is a function that can be written in the form $f(x) = mx + b$.

14. To find the y-intercept of a linear equation, let $x = 0$ and solve for the other variable.

Chapter 2 Review

1. $A(2, -1)$, quadrant IV
   $B(-2, 1)$, quadrant II
   $C(0, 3)$, y-axis
   $D(-3, -5)$, quadrant III

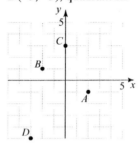

2. $A(-3, 4)$, quadrant II
   $B(4, -3)$, quadrant IV
   $C(-2, 0)$, x-axis
   $D(-4, 1)$, quadrant II

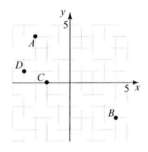

3. $7x - 8y = 56$
   $(0, 56)$; No
   $7(0) - 8(56) \stackrel{?}{=} 56$
   $\quad\quad -448 = 56$, False
   $(8, 0)$; Yes
   $7(8) - 8(0) \stackrel{?}{=} 56$
   $\quad\quad\quad 56 = 56$, True

4. $-2x + 5y = 10$
   $(-5, 0)$; Yes
   $-2(-5) + 5(0) \stackrel{?}{=} 10$
   $\quad\quad\quad\quad 10 = 10$, True
   $(1, 1)$, No
   $-2(1) + 5(1) \stackrel{?}{=} 10$
   $\quad\quad\quad\quad 3 = 10$, False

5. $x = 13$
   $(13, 5)$; Yes
   $13 = 13$, True
   $(13, 13)$; Yes
   $13 = 13$, True

6. $y = 2$

(7, 2); Yes

2 = 2, True

(2, 7); No

7 = 2, False

7. $y = 3x$; Linear

x	−1	0	1
y	−3	0	3

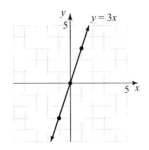

8. $y = 5x$; Linear

x	−1	0	1
y	−5	0	5

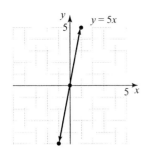

9. $3x - y = 4$; Linear

Find three ordered pair solutions, or find x- and y-intercepts, or find m and b.

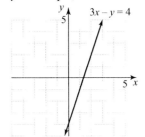

10. $x - 3y = 2$; Linear

Find three ordered pair solutions, or find x- and y-intercepts, or find m and b.

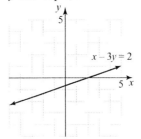

11. $y = |x| + 4$; Nonlinear

x	−3	−2	−1	0	1	2	3
y	7	6	5	4	5	6	7

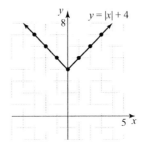

12. $y = x^2 + 4$; Nonlinear

x	−3	−2	−1	0	1	2	3
y	13	8	5	4	5	8	13

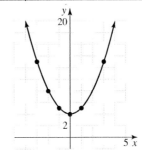

13. $y = -\dfrac{1}{2}x + 2$; Linear

Find three ordered pair solutions, or find x- and y-intercepts, or find m and b.

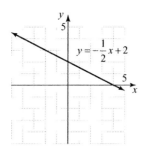

14. $y = -x + 5$; Linear

Find three ordered pair solutions, or find x- and y-intercepts, or find m and b.

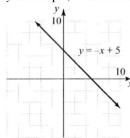

15. The graph shown is the graph of $y = x^2 + 2$; d.

16. The graph shown is the graph of $y = x^2 - 4$; a.

17. The graph shown is the graph of $y = |x| + 2$; c.

18. The graph shown is the graph of $y = -|x| + 2$; b.

19. The domain is the set of all first coordinates (or inputs) and the range is the set of all second coordinates (or outputs).

Domain: $\left\{ -\dfrac{1}{2}, 6, 0, 25 \right\}$

Range: $\left\{ \dfrac{3}{4}, -12, 25 \right\}$

Function since each x-value corresponds to exactly one y-value.

20. The domain is the set of all first coordinates (or inputs) and the range is the set of all second coordinates (or outputs).

Domain: $\left\{ \dfrac{3}{4}, -12, 25 \right\}$

Range: $\left\{ -\dfrac{1}{2}, 6, 0, 25 \right\}$

Not a function since $\dfrac{3}{4}$ (or 0.75) is paired with

both $-\dfrac{1}{2}$ and 6.

21. The domain is the set of all first coordinates (or inputs) and the range is the set of all second coordinates (or outputs).
Domain: {2, 4, 6, 8}
Range: {2, 4, 5, 6}
Not a function since 2 is paired with both 2 and 4.

22. The domain is the set of all first coordinates (or inputs) and the range is the set of all second coordinates (or outputs).
Domain:
{Triangle, Square, Rectangle, Parallelogram}
Range: {3, 4}
Function since each input is paired with exactly one output.

23. Domain: all real numbers
Range: $\{ y | y \leq -1 \text{ or } y \geq 1 \}$
Not a function since it fails the vertical line test.

24. Domain: $\{-3\}$
Range: all real numbers
Not a function since it fails the vertical line test.

25. Domain: all real numbers
Range: {4}
Function since it passes the vertical line test.

26. Domain: $\{ x | -1 \leq x \leq 1 \}$
Range: $\{ y | -1 \leq y \leq 1 \}$
Not a function since it fails the vertical line test.

27. $f(x) = x - 5$
$f(2) = (2) - 5 = -3$

28. $g(x) = -3x$
$g(0) = -3(0) = 0$

29. $g(x) = -3x$
$g(-6) = -3(-6) = 18$

30. $h(x) = 2x^2 - 6x + 1$
$h(-1) = 2(-1)^2 - 6(-1) + 1$
$= 2(1) + 6 + 1$
$= 9$

31. $h(x) = 2x^2 - 6x + 1$
$h(1) = 2(1)^2 - 6(1) + 1 = 2 - 6 + 1 = -3$

32. $f(x) = x - 5$
$f(5) = (5) - 5 = 0$

33. $J(x) = 2.54x$
$J(150) = 2.54(150) = 381$ pounds

34. $J(x) = 2.54x$
$J(2000) = 2.54(2000) = 5080$ pounds

35. The point $(-1, 0)$ is on the graph, so $f(-1) = 0$.

36. The point $(1, -2)$ is on the graph, so $f(1) = -2$.

37. $f(x) = 1$
$f(-2) = f(4) = 1$
$x = -2, 4$

38. $f(x) = -1$
$f(0) = f(2) = -1$
$x = 0, 2$

39. $f(x) = x$ or $y = x$
$m = 1, \ b = 0$

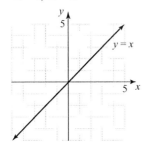

40. $f(x) = -\dfrac{1}{3}x$ or $y = -\dfrac{1}{3}x$
$m = -\dfrac{1}{3}, \ b = 0$

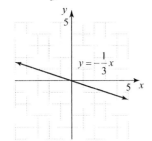

41. $g(x) = 4x - 1$ or $y = 4x - 1$
$m = 4, \ b = -1$

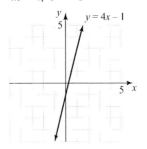

42. $f(x) = 3x + 1$
The y-intercept should be $(0, 1)$. The correct graph is C.

43. $f(x) = 3x - 2$
The y-intercept should be $(0, -2)$. The correct graph is A.

44. $f(x) = 3x + 2$
The y-intercept should be $(0, 2)$. The correct graph is B.

45. $f(x) = 3x - 5$
The y-intercept should be $(0, -5)$. The correct graph is D.

46. $4x + 5y = 20$
Let $x = 0$ Let $y = 0$
$4(0) + 5y = 20$ $4x + 5(0) = 20$
       $y = 4$ $x = 5$
$(0, 4)$ $(5, 0)$

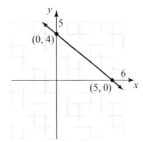

47. $3x - 2y = -9$

Let $x = 0$ Let $y = 0$

$3(0) - 2y = -9$ $3x - 2(0) = -9$

$\qquad y = \dfrac{9}{2}$ $\qquad x = -3$

$\qquad\qquad\qquad\qquad (-3, 0)$

$\left(0, \dfrac{9}{2}\right)$

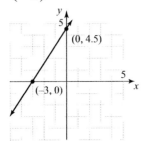

48. $4x - y = 3$

Let $x = 0$ Let $y = 0$

$4(0) - y = 3$ $4x - (0) = 3$

$\qquad y = -3$ $\qquad x = \dfrac{3}{4}$

$(0, -3)$

$\qquad\qquad\qquad\qquad \left(\dfrac{3}{4}, 0\right)$

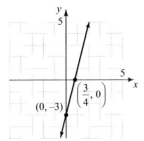

49. $2x + 6y = 9$

Let $x = 0$ Let $y = 0$

$2(0) + 6y = 9$ $2x + 6(0) = 9$

$\qquad y = \dfrac{3}{2}$ $\qquad x = \dfrac{9}{2}$

$\left(0, \dfrac{3}{2}\right)$ $\left(\dfrac{9}{2}, 0\right)$

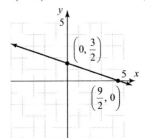

50. $y = 5$

Horizontal line with y-intercept 5.

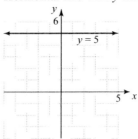

51. $x = -2$

Vertical line with x-intercept -2.

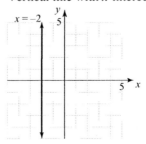

52. $x - 2 = 0$

$\qquad x = 2$

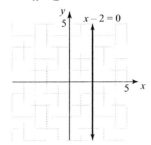

53. $y + 3 = 0$

$\qquad y = -3$

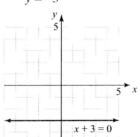

54. $C(x) = 0.3x + 42$

a. $C(150) = 0.3(150) + 42$

$\qquad\qquad = 45 + 42$

$\qquad\qquad = 87$

$\qquad$ $\$87$

b. $m = 0.3, \ b = 42$

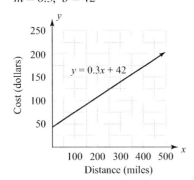

55. $m = \dfrac{-4-8}{6-2} = \dfrac{-12}{4} = -3$

56. $m = \dfrac{13-9}{5-(-3)} = \dfrac{4}{8} = \dfrac{1}{2}$

57. $m = \dfrac{6-(-4)}{-3-(-7)} = \dfrac{10}{4} = \dfrac{5}{2}$

58. $m = \dfrac{7-(-2)}{-5-7} = \dfrac{9}{-12} = -\dfrac{3}{4}$

59. $6x - 15y = 20$
$$-15y = -6x + 20$$
$$y = \dfrac{2}{5}x - \dfrac{4}{3}$$
$m = \dfrac{2}{5}, \ b = -\dfrac{4}{3}, \ y\text{-intercept} \left(0, -\dfrac{4}{3}\right)$

60. $4x + 14y = 21$
$$14y = -4x + 21$$
$$y = -\dfrac{2}{7}x + \dfrac{3}{2}$$
$m = -\dfrac{2}{7}, \ b = \dfrac{3}{2}, \ y\text{-intercept} \left(0, \dfrac{3}{2}\right)$

61. $y - 3 = 0$
$$y = 3; \ \text{Slope} = 0$$

62. $x = -5$; Vertical line
Slope is undefined.

63. The slope of l_1 is negative, and the slope of l_2 is positive. Since a positive number is greater than any negative number, l_2 has the greater slope.

64. The slope of l_1 is 0, and the slope of l_2 is positive. Since a positive number is greater than 0, l_2 has the greater slope.

65. The slope of l_1 and the slope of l_2 are both positive. Since l_2 is steeper, it has the greater slope.

66. The slope of l_1 is 0, and the slope of l_2 is negative. Since a negative number is less than 0, l_1 has the greater slope.

67. $y = 0.3x + 42$

   a. $m = 0.3$; the cost increases by \$0.30 for each additional mile driven.

   b. $b = 42$; the cost for 0 miles driven is \$42.

68. $f(x) = -2x + 6$ $g(x) = 2x - 1$
$m = -2$ $m = 2$
Neither; The slopes are not the same and their product is not -1.

69. $-x + 3y = 2$ $6x - 18y = 3$
$\quad\quad y = \dfrac{1}{3}x + \dfrac{2}{3}$ $y = \dfrac{1}{3}x - \dfrac{1}{6}$
$m = \dfrac{1}{3}$ $m = \dfrac{1}{3}$
Parallel, since their slopes are equal.

70. $y = -x + 1$
$m = -1, \ b = 1$

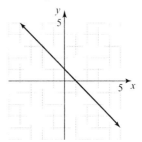

71. $y = 4x - 3$
$m = 4, \ b = -3$

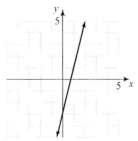

72. $3x - y = 6$

$\quad\quad y = 3x - 6$

$\quad m = 3, \ b = -6$

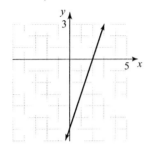

73. $y = -5x$

$\quad m = -5, \ b = 0$

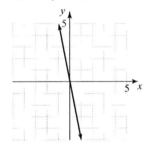

74. Every horizontal line is in the form $y = c$. Since the line passes through the point $(3, -1)$, its equation is $y = -1$.

75. Every vertical line has the form $x = c$. Since the line passes through the point $(-2, -4)$, its equation is $x = -2$.

76. A line parallel to $x = 6$ has the form $x = c$. Since the line passes through $(-4, -3)$, its equation is $x = -4$.

77. Lines with slope 0 are horizontal, and have the form $y = c$. Since it passes through $(2, 5)$, its equation is $y = 5$.

78. $y - y_1 = m(x - x_1)$

$\quad\quad y - 5 = 3[x - (-3)]$

$\quad\quad y - 5 = 3(x + 3)$

$\quad\quad y - 5 = 3x + 9$

$\quad\quad 3x - y = -14$

79. $y - y_1 = m(x - x_1)$

$\quad y - (-2) = 2(x - 5)$

$\quad\quad y + 2 = 2x - 10$

$\quad\quad 2x - y = 12$

80. $m = \dfrac{-2 - (-1)}{-4 - (-6)} = \dfrac{-1}{2} = -\dfrac{1}{2}$

$\quad\quad y - y_1 = m(x - x_1)$

$\quad\quad y - (-1) = -\dfrac{1}{2}[x - (-6)]$

$\quad\quad 2(y + 1) = -(x + 6)$

$\quad\quad 2y + 2 = -x - 6$

$\quad\quad x + 2y = -8$

81. $m = \dfrac{-8 - 3}{-4 - (-5)} = \dfrac{-11}{1} = -11$

$\quad\quad y - y_1 = m(x - x_1)$

$\quad\quad y - 3 = -11[x - (-5)]$

$\quad\quad y - 3 = -11(x + 5)$

$\quad\quad y - 3 = -11x - 55$

$\quad\quad 11x + y = -52$

82. $x = 4$ has undefined slope.

A line perpendicular to $x = 4$ has slope $= 0$ and is therefore horizontal.

$\quad y = 3$

83. $y = 8$ has slope $= 0$

A line parallel to $y = 8$ has slope $= 0$.

$\quad y = -5$

84. $\quad y = mx + b$

$\quad\quad y = -\dfrac{2}{3}x + 4$

$\quad f(x) = -\dfrac{2}{3}x + 4$

85. $\quad y = mx + b$

$\quad\quad y = -x - 2$

$\quad f(x) = -x - 2$

86. $6x + 3y = 5$

$\quad\quad 3y = -6x + 5$

$\quad\quad y = -2x + \dfrac{5}{3} \quad$ so $\ m = -2$

$\quad\quad y - y_1 = m(x - x_1)$

$\quad y - (-6) = -2(x - 2)$

$\quad\quad y + 6 = -2x + 4$

$\quad\quad y = -2x - 2$

$\quad f(x) = -2x - 2$

87. $3x + 2y = 8$

$2y = -3x + 8$

$y = -\dfrac{3}{2}x + 4$ so $m = -\dfrac{3}{2}$

$y - y_1 = m(x - x_1)$

$y - (-2) = -\dfrac{3}{2}[x - (-4)]$

$2(y + 2) = -3(x + 4)$

$2y + 4 = -3x - 12$

$2y = -3x - 16$

$y = -\dfrac{3}{2}x - 8$

$f(x) = -\dfrac{3}{2}x - 8$

88. $4x + 3y = 5$

$3y = -4x + 5$

$y = -\dfrac{4}{3}x + \dfrac{5}{3}$

so $m = -\dfrac{4}{3}$ and $m_\perp = \dfrac{3}{4}$

$y - y_1 = m(x - x_1)$

$y - (-1) = \dfrac{3}{4}[x - (-6)]$

$4(y + 1) = 3(x + 6)$

$4y + 4 = 3x + 18$

$4y = 3x + 14$

$y = \dfrac{3}{4}x + \dfrac{7}{2}$

$f(x) = \dfrac{3}{4}x + \dfrac{7}{2}$

89. $2x - 3y = 6$

$-3y = -2x + 6$

$y = \dfrac{2}{3}x - 2$

so $m = \dfrac{2}{3}$ and $m_\perp = -\dfrac{3}{2}$

$y - y_1 = m(x - x_1)$

$y - 5 = -\dfrac{3}{2}[x - (-4)]$

$2(y - 5) = -3(x + 4)$

$2y - 10 = -3x - 12$

$2y = -3x - 2$

$y = -\dfrac{3}{2}x - 1$

$f(x) = -\dfrac{3}{2}x - 1$

90. a. Use ordered pairs (0, 71) and (5, 82)

$m = \dfrac{82 - 71}{5 - 0} = \dfrac{11}{5} = 2.2$ and $b = 71$

$y = 2.2x + 71$

b. $x = 2009 - 2000 = 9$

$y = 2.2(9) + 71 = 90.8$

About 91% of US drivers will be wearing seat belts.

91. a. Use ordered pairs (0, 43) and (22, 60)

$m = \dfrac{60 - 43}{22 - 0} = \dfrac{17}{22}$ and $b = 43$

$y = \dfrac{17}{22}x + 43$

b. $x = 2010 - 1998 = 12$

$y = \dfrac{17}{22}(12) + 43 \approx 52.3$

There will be about 52 million people reporting arthritis.

92. a.

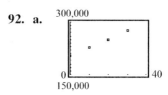

b. The regression equation is $y = 2381.74x + 202,740.4$.

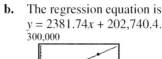

c.

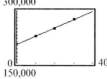

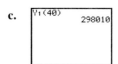

The population of the United States is predicted to be 298.010 thousand.

93. $g(x) = \begin{cases} -\dfrac{1}{5}x & \text{if } x \le -1 \\ -4x+2 & \text{if } x > -1 \end{cases}$

For $x \le -1$:

x	$g(x)$
-5	1
-3	$\dfrac{3}{5}$
-1	$\dfrac{1}{5}$

For $x > -1$:

x	$g(x)$
0	2
1	-2
2	-6

Graph a closed circle at $\left(-1, \dfrac{1}{5}\right)$. Graph an open circle at $(-1, 6)$, which is found by substituting -1 for x in $g(x) = -4x+2$.

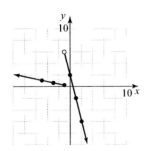

94. $f(x) = \begin{cases} -3x & \text{if } x < 0 \\ x-3 & \text{if } x \ge 0 \end{cases}$

For $x < 0$:

x	$f(x)$
-3	9
-2	6
-1	3

For $x \ge 0$:

x	$f(x)$
0	-3
1	-2
2	-1

Graph a closed circle at $(0, -3)$. Graph an open circle at $(0, 0)$, which is found by substituting 0 for x in $f(x) = -3x$.

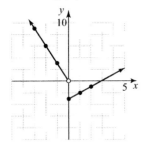

95. $f(x) = \sqrt{x-4}$

The graph of $f(x) = \sqrt{x-4}$ is the same as the graph of $y = \sqrt{x}$ shifted right 4 units.

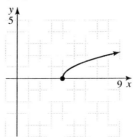

96. $y = \sqrt{x} - 4$

The graph of $f(x) = \sqrt{x} - 4$ is the same as the graph of $y = \sqrt{x}$ shifted down 4 units.

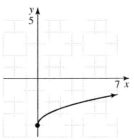

97. $h(x) = -(x+3)^2 - 1$

The graph of $h(x) = -(x+3)^2 - 1$ is the same as the graph of $y = x^2$ reflected about the x-axis and then shifted left 3 units and down 1 unit.

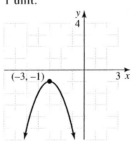

98. $g(x) = |x-2| - 2$

The graph of $g(x) = |x-2| - 2$ is the same as the graph of $y = |x|$ shifted right 2 units and down 2 units.

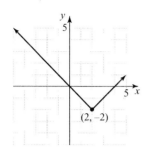

99. $x = -4y$ or $y = -\dfrac{1}{4}x$

The slope is $-\dfrac{1}{4}$, and the y-intercept is $(0, 0)$.

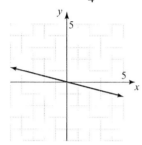

100. $3x - 2y = -9$

Let $x = 0$.   Let $y = 0$.

$3x - 2y = -9$
$3(0) - 2y = -9$
$-2y = -9$
$y = \dfrac{9}{2}$

$3x - 2y = -9$
$3x - 2(0) = -9$
$3x = -9$
$x = -3$

The intercepts are $\left(0, \ \dfrac{9}{2}\right)$ and $(-3, 0)$.

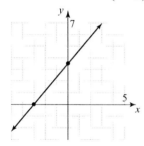

101. Vertical; through $\left(-7, \ -\dfrac{1}{2}\right)$

A vertical line has an equation of the form $x = a$, where a is the x-coordinate of any point on the line. The equation is $x = -7$.

102. Slope 0; through $\left(-4, \ \dfrac{9}{2}\right)$

A line with slope 0 is horizontal, and a horizontal line has an equation of the form $y = b$, where b is the y-coordinate of any point on the line. The equation is $y = \dfrac{9}{2}$.

103. Slope $\dfrac{3}{4}$; through $(-8, -4)$

$y - y_1 = m(x - x_1)$
$y - (-4) = \dfrac{3}{4}(x - (-8))$
$y + 4 = \dfrac{3}{4}(x + 8)$
$4(y + 4) = 3(x + 8)$
$4y + 16 = 3x + 24$
$4y = 3x + 8$
$y = \dfrac{3}{4}x + 2$

104. Through $(-3, 8)$ and $(-2, 3)$
Find the slope.

$m = \dfrac{3 - 8}{-2 - (-3)} = \dfrac{-5}{1} = -5$

Use the slope and one of the points in the point-slope form. We use $(-2, 3)$.

$y - y_1 = m(x - x_1)$
$y - 3 = -5(x - (-2))$
$y - 3 = -5(x + 2)$
$y - 3 = -5x - 10$
$y = -5x - 7$

105. Through $(-6, 1)$; parallel to $y = -\dfrac{3}{2}x + 11$

The slope of a line parallel to $y = -\dfrac{3}{2}x + 11$ will have the same slope, $-\dfrac{3}{2}$.

$y - y_1 = m(x - x_1)$
$y - 1 = -\dfrac{3}{2}(x - (-6))$
$y - 1 = -\dfrac{3}{2}(x + 6)$
$2(y - 1) = -3(x + 6)$
$2y - 2 = -3x - 18$
$2y = -3x - 16$
$y = -\dfrac{3}{2}x - 8$

106. Through $(-5, 7)$; perpendicular to $5x - 4y = 10$

Find the slope of $5x - 4y = 10$.

$$5x - 4y = 10$$
$$-4y = -5x + 10$$
$$y = \frac{5}{4}x - \frac{5}{2}$$

The slope is $\frac{5}{4}$. The slope of any line

perpendicular to this line is the negative

reciprocal of $\frac{5}{4}$, or $-\frac{4}{5}$.

$$y - y_1 = m(x - x_1)$$
$$y - 7 = -\frac{4}{5}(x - (-5))$$
$$y - 7 = -\frac{4}{5}(x + 5)$$
$$5(y - 7) = -4(x + 5)$$
$$5y - 35 = -4x - 20$$
$$5y = -4x + 15$$
$$y = -\frac{4}{5}x + 3$$

107. $f(x) = \begin{cases} x - 2 & \text{if } x \le 0 \\ -\frac{x}{3} & \text{if } x \ge 3 \end{cases}$

For $x \le 0$:   For $x \ge 3$:

x	$f(x)$
-2	-4
-1	-3
0	-2

x	$f(x)$
3	-1
4	$-\frac{4}{3}$
6	-2

Graph closed circles at $(0, -2)$ and $(3, -1)$.

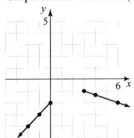

108. $g(x) = \begin{cases} 4x - 3 & \text{if } x \le 1 \\ 2x & \text{if } x > 1 \end{cases}$

For $x \le 1$:   For $x > 1$:

x	$g(x)$
-1	-7
0	-3
1	1

x	$g(x)$
2	4
3	6
4	8

Graph a closed circle at $(1, 1)$. Graph an open circle at $(1, 2)$, which is found by substituting 1 for x in $g(x) = 2x$.

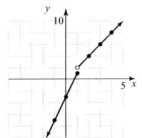

109. $f(x) = \sqrt{x - 2}$

The graph of $f(x) = \sqrt{x - 2}$ is the same as the

graph of $y = \sqrt{x}$ shifted right 2 units.

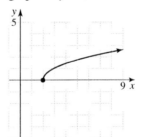

110. $f(x) = |x + 1| - 3$

The graph of $f(x) = |x + 1| - 3$ is the same as the

graph of $y = |x|$ shifted left 1 unit and down

3 units.

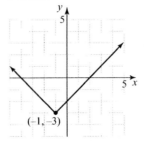

Chapter 2 Test

1.

A is in quadrant IV.
B is on the *x*-axis, no quadrant.
C is in quadrant II.

2. $2x - 3y = -6$
$$-3y = -2x - 6$$
$$y = \frac{2}{3}x + 2$$
$$m = \frac{2}{3}, \ b = 2$$

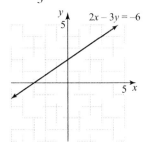

3. $4x + 6y = 7$
$$6y = -4x + 7$$
$$y = -\frac{2}{3}x + \frac{7}{6}$$
$$m = -\frac{2}{3}, \ b = \frac{7}{6}$$

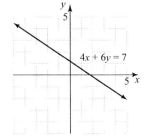

4. $f(x) = \frac{2}{3}x$ or $y = \frac{2}{3}x$

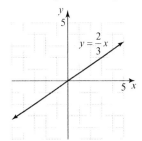

5. $y = -3$
Horizontal line with *y*-intercept at –3.

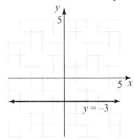

6. $m = \frac{10 - (-8)}{-7 - 5} = \frac{18}{-12} = -\frac{3}{2}$

7. $3x + 12y = 8$
$$12y = -3x + 8$$
$$y = -\frac{1}{4}x + \frac{2}{3}$$
$$m = -\frac{1}{4}, \ b = \frac{2}{3}, \text{ so } y\text{-intercept is } \left(0, \frac{2}{3}\right).$$

8. Horizontal; through (2, –8)
A horizontal line has an equation of the form $y = b$, where *b* is the *y*-coordinate of any point on the line. The equation is $y = -8$.

9. Vertical; through (–4, –3)
A vertical line has an equation of the form $x = a$, where *a* is the *x*-coordinate of any point on the line. The equation is $x = -4$.

10. Perpendicular to $x = 5$; through (3, –2)
The line $x = 5$ is vertical, so any line perpendicular to it is horizontal. A horizontal line has an equation of the form $y = b$, where *b* is the *y*-coordinate of any point on the line. The equation is $y = -2$.

11.
$$y - y_1 = m(x - x_1)$$
$$y - (-1) = -3(x - 4)$$
$$y + 1 = -3x + 12$$
$$3x + y = 11$$

12.
$$y - y_1 = m(x - x_1)$$
$$y - (-2) = 5(x - 0)$$
$$y + 2 = 5x$$
$$5x - y = 2$$

13. $m = \dfrac{-3 - (-2)}{6 - 4} = \dfrac{-1}{2} = -\dfrac{1}{2}$
$$y - y_1 = m(x - x_1)$$
$$y - (-2) = -\frac{1}{2}(x - 4)$$
$$2(y + 2) = -(x - 4)$$
$$2y + 4 = -x + 4$$
$$2y = -x$$
$$y = -\frac{1}{2}x$$
$$f(x) = -\frac{1}{2}x$$

14. $3x - y = 4$
$$y = 3x - 4$$
$$m = 3 \text{ so } m_\perp = -\frac{1}{3}$$
$$y - y_1 = m(x - x_1)$$
$$y - 2 = -\frac{1}{3}[x - (-1)]$$
$$3(y - 2) = -(x + 1)$$
$$3y - 6 = -x - 1$$
$$3y = -x + 5$$
$$y = -\frac{1}{3}x + \frac{5}{3}$$
$$f(x) = -\frac{1}{3}x + \frac{5}{3}$$

15. $2y + x = 3$
$$2y = -x + 3$$
$$y = -\frac{1}{2}x + 3 \text{ so } m = -\frac{1}{2}$$
$$y - y_1 = m(x - x_1)$$
$$y - (-2) = -\frac{1}{2}(x - 3)$$
$$2(y + 2) = -(x - 3)$$
$$2y + 4 = -x + 3$$
$$2y = -x - 1$$
$$y = -\frac{1}{2}x - \frac{1}{2}$$
$$f(x) = -\frac{1}{2}x - \frac{1}{2}$$

16. $2x - 5y = 8$
$$-5y = -2x + 8$$
$$y = \frac{2}{5}x - \frac{8}{5} \text{ so } m_1 = \frac{2}{5}$$
$$m_2 = \frac{-1 - 4}{-1 - 1} = \frac{-5}{-2} = \frac{5}{2}$$
Therefore, lines L_1 and L_2 are neither parallel nor perpendicular since their slopes are not equal and the product of their slopes is not -1.

17. The graph shown is a parabola. It is the graph of $y = x^2 + 2x + 3$; B.

18. The graph shown is V-shaped. It is the graph of $y = 2|x - 1| + 3$; A.

19. The graph shown is linear. It is the graph of $y = 2x + 3$; D.

20. The graph shown is cubic. It is the graph of $y = 2(x - 1)^3 + 3$; C.

21. Domain: all real numbers
Range: {5}
Function since it passes the vertical line test.

22. Domain: {−2}
Range: all real numbers
Not a function since it fails the vertical line test.

23. Domain: all real numbers
Range: $\{y | y \geq 0\}$
Function since it passes the vertical line test.

24. Domain: all real numbers
Range: all real numbers
Function since it passes the vertical line test.

25. $f(x) = 1031x + 25,193$

   a. $x = 0$
     $f(0) = 1031(0) + 25,193 = 25,193$
     The average earnings in 2000 were \$25,193.

   b. $x = 2007 - 2000 = 7$
     $f(7) = 1031(7) + 25,193 = 32,410$
     The average earnings in 2007 were \$32,410.

   c. $40,000 \le 1031x + 25,193$
     $14,807 \le 1031x$
     $14.4 \le x$
     $2000 + 15 = 2015$
     The average earnings will be greater than
     \$40,000 in 2015.

   d. slope = 1031; the yearly earnings for high
     school graduates increases \$1031 per year.

   e. (0, 25,193); the yearly earnings for a high
     school graduate in 2000 were \$25,193.

26. $f(x) = \begin{cases} -\frac{1}{2}x & \text{if } x \le 0 \\ 2x - 3 & \text{if } x > 0 \end{cases}$

   For $x \le 0$:   For $x > 0$:

x	$f(x)$
-4	2
-2	1
0	0

x	$f(x)$
1	-1
2	1
3	3

Graph a closed circle at (0, 0). Graph an open
circle at (0, −3), which is found by substituting 0
for x in $f(x) = 2x - 3$.

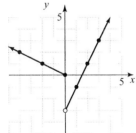

The domain is all real numbers.
The range is $\{y | y > -3\}$.

27. $f(x) = (x - 4)^2$

The graph of $f(x) = (x-4)^2$ is the same as the
graph of $y = x^2$ shifted right 4 units.

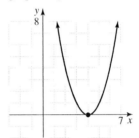

28. $g(x) = |x| + 2$
The graph of $g(x) = |x| + 2$ is the same as the
graph of $y = |x|$ shifted up 2 units.

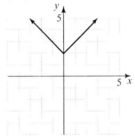

29. $g(x) = -|x + 2| - 1$

The graph of $g(x) = -|x + 2| - 1$ is the same as
the graph of $y = |x|$ reflected about the
x-axis and then shifted left 2 units and down
1 unit.

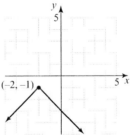

The domain is all real numbers.
The range is $\{y | y \le -1\}$.

30. $h(x) = \sqrt{x} - 1$

The graph of $h(x) = \sqrt{x} - 1$ is the same as the
graph of $y = \sqrt{x}$ shifted down 1 unit.

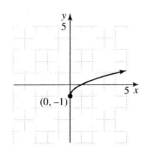

(0, −1)

Chapter 2 Cumulative Review

1. $3x - y = 3(15) - (4) = 45 - 4 = 41$

2. **a.** $-4 + (-3) = -7$

   b. $\dfrac{1}{2} - \left(-\dfrac{1}{3}\right) = \dfrac{3}{6} + \dfrac{2}{6} = \dfrac{5}{6}$

   c. $7 - 20 = -13$

3. **a.** True, 3 is a real number

   b. False, $\dfrac{1}{5}$ is not an irrational number.

   c. False, every rational number is not an integer, for example, $\dfrac{2}{3}$.

   d. False, since 1 is not in the second set.

4. **a.** The opposite of −7 is 7.

   b. The opposite of 0 is 0.

   c. The opposite of $\dfrac{1}{4}$ is $-\dfrac{1}{4}$.

5. **a.** $2 - 8 = -6$

   b. $-8 - (-1) = -8 + 1 = -7$

   c. $-11 - 5 = -16$

   d. $10.7 - (-9.8) = 10.7 + 9.8 = 20.5$

   e. $\dfrac{2}{3} - \dfrac{1}{2} = \dfrac{4}{6} - \dfrac{3}{6} = \dfrac{1}{6}$

   f. $1 - 0.06 = 0.94$

   g. $4 - 7 = -3$

6. **a.** $\dfrac{-42}{-6} = 7$

   b. $\dfrac{0}{14} = 0$

   c. $-1(-5)(-2) = 5(-2) = -10$

7. **a.** $3^2 = 3 \cdot 3 = 9$

   b. $\left(\dfrac{1}{2}\right)^4 = \dfrac{1}{2^4} = \dfrac{1}{16}$

   c. $-5^2 = -(5 \cdot 5) = -25$

   d. $(-5)^2 = (-5)(-5) = 25$

   e. $-5^3 = -(5 \cdot 5 \cdot 5) = -125$

   f. $(-5)^3 = (-5)(-5)(-5) = -125$

8. **a.** Distributive Property

   b. Commutative Property of Addition

9. **a.** $-1 > -2$ since −1 is to the right of −2 on the number line.

   b. $\dfrac{12}{4} = 3$

   c. $-5 < 0$ since −5 is to the left of 0 on the number line.

   d. $-3.5 \le -3.05$ since −3.5 is to the left of −3.05 on the number line.

10. $2x^2$

    a. $2(7)^2 = 2(49) = 98$

    b. $2(-7)^2 = 2(49) = 98$

11. **a.** The reciprocal of 11 is $\dfrac{1}{11}$.

    b. The reciprocal of −9 is $-\dfrac{1}{9}$.

c. The reciprocal of $\dfrac{7}{4}$ is $\dfrac{4}{7}$.

12. $-2 + 3[5 - (7 - 10)] = -2 + 3[5 - (-3)]$
$= -2 + 3(8)$
$= -2 + 24$
$= 22$

13. $0.6 = 2 - 3.5c$
$-1.4 = -3.5c$
$\dfrac{-1.4}{-3.5} = \dfrac{-3.5c}{-3.5}$
$0.4 = c$

14. $2(x - 3) = -40$
$2x - 6 = -40$
$2x = -34$
$x = -17$

15. $3x + 5 = 3(x + 2)$
$3x + 5 = 3x + 6$
$5 = 6$ False
The solution is $\varnothing$.

16. $5(x - 7) = 4x - 35 + x$
$5x - 35 = 5x - 35$
$-35 = -35$ True for any number
The solution is all real numbers.

17. a. If x is the first integer, then the next two consecutive integers are $x + 1$ and $x + 2$. The sum is $x + (x + 1) + (x + 2) = 3x + 3$.

b. The perimeter is found by adding the lengths of the sides.
$x + 5x + (6x - 3) = 12x - 3$

18. 25% of $16 = 0.25(16) = 4$

19. Let x = the lowest of the scores. Then the other two scores are $x + 2$ and $x + 4$.
$x + (x + 2) + (x + 4) = 264$
$3x + 6 = 264$
$3x = 258$
$x = 86$
$x + 2 = 86 + 2 = 88$
$x + 4 = 86 + 4 = 90$
The scores are 86, 88, and 90.

20. Let x = first odd integer, then
$x + 2$ = next odd integer and
$x + 4$ = third odd integer.
$x + (x + 2) + (x + 4) = 213$
$3x + 6 = 213$
$3x = 207$
$x = 69$
$x + 2 = 69 + 2 = 71$
$x + 4 = 69 + 4 = 73$
The integers are 69, 71, and 73.

21. $V = lwh$
$\dfrac{V}{lw} = \dfrac{lwh}{lw}$
$\dfrac{V}{lw} = h$

22. $7x + 3y = 21$
$3y = -7x + 21$
$y = -\dfrac{7}{3}x + 7$

23. a. $(2, -1)$ is in quadrant IV.

b. $(0, 5)$ is not in any quadrant, it is on the y-axis.

c. $(-3, 5)$ is in quadrant II.

d. $(-2, 0)$ is not in any quadrant, it is on the x-axis.

e. $\left(-\dfrac{1}{2}, -4\right)$ is in quadrant III.

f. $(1.5, 1.5)$ is in quadrant I.

24. a. $(0, -2)$ is on the y-axis.

b. $(-1, -2.5)$ is in quadrant III.

c. $\left(\dfrac{1}{2}, 0\right)$ is on the x-axis.

d. $(4, -0.5)$ is in quadrant IV.

25. $3x - y = 12$

$3(0) - (-12) \stackrel{?}{=} 12$

$\qquad 12 = 12$ True

$(0, -12)$ is a solution.

$3(1) - 9 \stackrel{?}{=} 12$

$\qquad -6 = 12$ False

$(1, 9)$ is not a solution.

$3(2) - (-6) \stackrel{?}{=} 12$

$\qquad 6 + 6 \stackrel{?}{=} 12$

$\qquad 12 = 12$ True

$(2, -6)$ is a solution.

26. $7x + 2y = 10$

$\qquad 2y = -7x + 10$

$\qquad y = -\dfrac{7}{2}x + 5$

$m = -\dfrac{7}{2}$, y-intercept $= (0, 5)$

27. Yes, $y = 2x + 1$ is a function (graph the function and use the vertical line test).

28. No, it is not a function (by the vertical line test).

29. a. $f(x) = \dfrac{1}{2}x + \dfrac{3}{7}$

$y = mx + b$

$b = \dfrac{3}{7}$

y-intercept $= \left(0, \dfrac{3}{7}\right)$

b. $y = -2.5x - 3.2$

$y = mx + b$

$b = -3.2$

y-intercept $= (0, -3.2)$

30. $m = \dfrac{y_2 - y_1}{x_2 - x_1} = \dfrac{9 - 6}{0 - (-1)} = \dfrac{3}{1} = 3$

31. $f(x) = \dfrac{2}{3}x + 4$

$y = mx + b$

The slope of the line is m, the coefficient of x, $\dfrac{2}{3}$.

32. Vertical; through $\left(-2, -\dfrac{3}{4}\right)$

A vertical line has an equation of the form $x = a$, where a is the x-coordinate of any point on the line. The equation is $x = -2$.

33. y-intercept $= (0, -3)$ means that $b = -3$. Using the equation $y = mx + b$, we have $y = \dfrac{1}{4}x - 3$.

34. Horizontal; through $\left(-2, -\dfrac{3}{4}\right)$

A horizontal line has an equation of the form $y = b$, where b is the y-coordinate of any point on the line. The equation is $y = -\dfrac{3}{4}$.

Chapter 3

Section 3.1

Practice Exercises

1. $2(x-1) + 6 = 8$
   Algebraic Solution:
   $$2(x-1)+6=8$$
   $$2x-2+6=8$$
   $$2x+4=8$$
   $$2x=4$$
   $$x=2$$
   Check: $2(x-1)+6=8$
   $$2(2-1)+6 \stackrel{?}{=} 8$$
   $$2(1)+6 \stackrel{?}{=} 8$$
   $$8=8 \quad \text{True}$$
   The solution is 2.
   Graphical Solution:
   Graph $y_1 = 2(x-1)+6$ and $y_2 = 8$. Use a
   [−10, 10, 1] by [−10, 10, 1] window.

   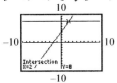

   The *x*-coordinate of the point of intersection is 2.
   Thus, the solution is 2.

2. $3(x-10) + 5(x+2) - 25 = 9 - x$
   Graph $y_1 = 3(x-10)+5(x+2)-25$ and
   $y_2 = 9-x$ in an integer window.

   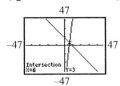

   The point of intersection (6, 3) indicates that the
   solution is 6.
   Check:

   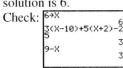

3. Define $y_1 = 3.51x + 5.728$ and $y_2 = x - 3.41$ and
   graph in a standard window.

   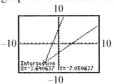

   The solution is approximately −3.641.

4. Two years is $2 \cdot 365 \cdot 24 = 17,520$ hours.
   Use a [0, 20,000, 1000] by [0, 2000, 100]
   window.

   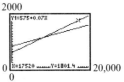

   The $575 refrigerator costs $1801.40 at the end
   of 2 years.

   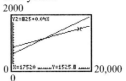

   The $825 refrigerator costs $1525.80 at the end
   of 2 years.
   The $575 refrigerator costs
   $1801.40 − $1525.80 = $275.60 more to run for
   2 years.

5.

   In 2012, the average annual expenditure for cell
   phone usage is predicted to be $876.48.

   In 2012, the average annual expenditure for
   residential phone usage is predicted to be
   $375.12.

6. $5(x - 1) - 3(x + 7) = 2x - 26$

Algebraic Solution:

$5(x-1) - 3(x+7) = 2x - 26$

$5x - 5 - 3x - 21 = 2x - 26$

$2x - 26 = 2x - 26$

Since both sides are the same, all real numbers are solutions.

Graphical Solution:

Graph $y_1 = 5(x-1) - 3(x+7)$ and $y_2 = 2x - 26$.

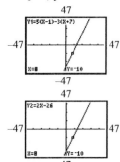

By tracing along y_1 and y_2, we see that the lines are identical. The equation is an identity; all real numbers are solutions and the solution set is $\{x | x \text{ is a real number}\}$.

7. $2x - 7 = 7(x + 1) - 5(x - 2)$

Algebraic Solution:

$2x - 7 = 7(x+1) - 5(x-2)$

$2x - 7 = 7x + 7 - 5x + 10$

$2x - 7 = 2x + 17$

$-7 = 17$

This equation is false no matter what value the variable x has.

Graphical Solution:

Graph $y_1 = 2x - 7$ and $y_2 = 7(x+1) - 5(x-2)$.

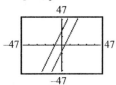

The graphs appear to be parallel lines. Check the slope of each graph.

$y_1 = 2x - 7$

$y_2 = 7(x+1) - 5(x-2) = 2x + 17$

The lines both have slope 2, but are distinct, so they are parallel.

The equation is a contradiction and the solution set is $\{\ \}$ or $\varnothing$.

8. Write the equation so that one side equals 0 by subtracting $2x$ from and adding 1 to both sides.

$2.5(x-1) + 3.4 = 2x - 1$

$2.5(x-1) + 3.4 - 2x + 1 = 0$

Define $y_1 = 2.5(x-1) + 3.4 - 2x + 1$ and graph in a standard window. Then use the root or zero feature.

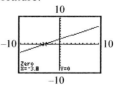

The x-intercept is $(-3.8, 0)$, which means that the solution is -3.8.

Vocabulary and Readiness Check

1. To solve an equation by the <u>intersection-of-graphs</u> method, graph the left-hand side of the equation in y_1, the right-hand side of the equation in y_2, and find the intersection point of the two graphs.

2. To solve an equation by the <u>x-intercept</u> method, first write the equation as an equivalent equation with one side 0.

3. for the intersection-of-graphs method, the <u>x</u>-coordinate of the point of intersection is the solution of the equation.

4. For the intersection-of-graphs method, the <u>y</u>-coordinate of the point of intersection is the value of each side of the equation when the solution is substituted into the equation.

5. Two other terms for the solution of an equation are <u>root</u> and <u>zero</u>.

6. $4x = 24$

$\dfrac{4x}{4} = \dfrac{24}{4}$

$x = 6$

7. $6x = -12$

$\dfrac{6x}{6} = \dfrac{-12}{6}$

$x = -2$

8.
$$2x + 10 = 20$$
$$2x + 10 - 10 = 20 - 10$$
$$2x = 10$$
$$\frac{2x}{2} = \frac{10}{2}$$
$$x = 5$$

9.
$$5x + 25 = 30$$
$$5x + 25 - 25 = 30 - 25$$
$$5x = 5$$
$$\frac{5x}{5} = \frac{5}{5}$$
$$x = 1$$

10.
$$-3x = 0$$
$$\frac{-3x}{-3} = \frac{0}{-3}$$
$$x = 0$$

11.
$$-2x = -14$$
$$\frac{-2x}{-2} = \frac{-14}{-2}$$
$$x = 7$$

12.
$$2x + 3 = 2x - 1$$
$$2x - 2x + 3 = 2x - 2x - 1$$
$$3 = -1$$
This statement is false, so the equation has no solution; $\varnothing$.

13.
$$2(x - 5) = 2x - 10$$
$$2x - 10 = 2x - 10$$
Both sides of the equation are the same, so the equation is an identity; all real numbers are solutions.

Exercise Set 3.1

2. $2x + 9 = 3x + 7$
Algebraic Solution:
$$2x + 9 = 3x + 7$$
$$9 = x + 7$$
$$2 = x$$
The solution is 2.
Graphical Solution:
Graph $y_1 = 2x + 9$ and $y_2 = 3x + 7$ in a
$[-20, 20, 5]$ by $[-20, 20, 5]$ viewing window
and find the intersection point.

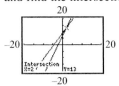

The point of intersection (2, 13) indicates that the solution is 2.

4. $3 - 4x = 2 - 3x$
Algebraic Solution:
$$3 - 4x = 2 - 3x$$
$$3 = 2 + x$$
$$1 = x$$
The solution is 1.
Graphical Solution:
Graph $y_1 = 3 - 4x$ and $y_2 = 2 - 3x$ in a standard
viewing window and find the intersection·point.

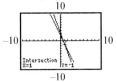

The point of intersection $(1, -1)$ indicates that the solution is 1.

6. $3(2 - x) + 4 = 2x + 3$
Algebraic Solution:
$$3(2 - x) + 4 = 2x + 3$$
$$6 - 3x + 4 = 2x + 3$$
$$-3x + 10 = 2x + 3$$
$$-5x + 10 = 3$$
$$-5x = -7$$
$$x = \frac{-7}{-5} = \frac{7}{5} = 1.4$$

The solution is $\frac{7}{5} = 1.4$.

Graphical Solution:
Graph $y_1 = 3(2 - x) + 4$ and $y_2 = 2x + 3$ in a
$[-20, 20, 5]$ by $[-20, 20, 5]$ viewing window
and find the intersection point.

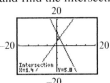

The point of intersection (1.4, 5.8) indicates that the solution is 1.4.

8.
$$y_1 = y_2$$
$$3x - 4 = 4(x - 2)$$
The point of intersection (4, 8) indicates that the solution is 4.

10. $y_1 = y_2$

$5x + 2 = 2(x-1) + 3x$

The two line are parallel, so the equation has no solution. That is, $\varnothing$ or { }.

12. $6x - 9 = 6(x-3)$

Algebraic Solution:

$6x - 9 = 6(x - 3)$

$6x - 9 = 6x - 18$

$\qquad -9 = -18$ False

This equation is a false statement no matter what value the variable x might have. The equation is a contradiction and has no solution. The solution set is $\varnothing$ or { }.

Graphical Solution:

Graph $y_1 = 6x - 9$ and $y_2 = 6(x-3)$ in a $[-20, 20, 5]$ by $[-20, 20, 5]$ viewing window.

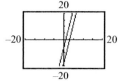

The parallel lines indicate that the equation is a contradiction and has no solution. The solution set is $\varnothing$ or { }.

14. $8x - (2x + 3) = 6(x + 5)$

Algebraic Solution:

$8x - (2x + 3) = 6(x + 5)$

$8x - 2x - 3 = 6x + 30$

$\qquad 6x - 3 = 6x + 30$

$\qquad\qquad -3 = 30$ False

This equation is a false statement no matter what value the variable x might have. The equation is a contradiction and has no solution. The solution set is $\varnothing$ or { }.

Graphical Solution:

Graph $y_1 = 8x - (2x + 3)$ and $y_2 = 6(x + 5)$ in a $[-20, 20, 5]$ by $[-20, 20, 5]$ viewing window.

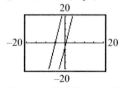

The parallel lines indicate that the equation is a contradiction and has no solution. The solution set is $\varnothing$ or { }.

16. $(5x + 8) - 2(x + 3) = (7x - 4) - (4x + 6)$

Algebraic Solution:

$(5x + 8) - 2(x + 3) = (7x - 4) - (4x + 6)$

$5x + 8 - 2x - 6 = 7x - 4 - 4x - 6$

$\qquad 3x + 2 = 3x - 10$

$\qquad\qquad 2 = -10$ False

This equation is a false statement no matter what value the variable x might have. The equation is a contradiction and has no solution. The solution set is $\varnothing$ or { }.

Graphical Solution:

Graph $y_1 = (5x + 8) - 2(x + 3)$ and

$y_2 = (7x - 4) - (4x + 6)$ in a $[-20, 20, 5]$ by $[-20, 20, 5]$ viewing window.

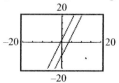

The parallel lines indicate that the equation is a contradiction and has no solution. The solution set is $\varnothing$ or { }.

18. $2(x + 3) - 7 = 4 + 2x$

Algebraic Solution:

$2(x + 3) - 7 = 4 + 2x$

$2x + 6 - 7 = 4 + 2x$

$\qquad 2x - 1 = 4 + 2x$

$\qquad\qquad -1 = 4$ False

This equation is a false statement no matter what value the variable x might have. The equation is a contradiction and has no solution. The solution set is $\varnothing$ or { }.

Graphical Solution:

Graph $y_1 = 2(x + 3) - 7$ and $y_2 = 4 + 2x$ in a $[-20, 20, 5]$ by $[-20, 20, 5]$ viewing window.

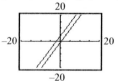

The parallel lines indicate that the equation is a contradiction and has no solution. The solution set is $\varnothing$ or { }.

20. $2(x+1.3)-4(5-x)=15$

Algebraic Solution:
$$2(x+1.3)-4(5-x)=15$$
$$2x+2.6-20+4x=15$$
$$6x-17.4=15$$
$$6x=32.4$$
$$x=5.4$$

The solution is 5.4.

Graphical Solution:

Graph $y_1=2(x+1.3)-4(5-x)$ and $y_2=15$ in an integer viewing window centered at the origin and find the intersection point.

The point of intersection $(5.4, 15)$ indicates that the solution is 5.4.

22. $8(b+2)-4(b-5)=b+12$

Algebraic Solution:
$$8(b+2)-4(b-5)=b+12$$
$$8b+16-4b+20=b+12$$
$$4b+36=b+12$$
$$3b+36=12$$
$$3b=-24$$
$$b=-8$$

The solution is -8.

Graphical Solution:

Graph $y_1=8(x+2)-4(x-5)$ and $y_2=x+12$ in an integer viewing window centered at the origin and find the intersection point.

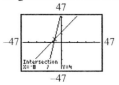

The point of intersection $(-8, 4)$ indicates that the solution is -8.

24. $3(x+2)-5(x-7)=x+3$

Algebraic Solution:
$$3(x+2)-5(x-7)=x+3$$
$$3x+6-5x+35=x+3$$
$$-2x+41=x+3$$
$$-3x+41=3$$
$$-3x=-38$$
$$x=\frac{-38}{-3}=\frac{38}{3}\approx12.67$$

The solution is $\frac{38}{3}\approx12.67$.

Graphical Solution:

Graph $y_1=3(x+2)-5(x-7)$ and $y_2=x+3$ in an integer viewing window centered at the origin and find the intersection point.

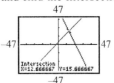

Rounded to the nearest hundredth, the point of intersection $(12.67, 15.67)$ indicates that the solution is approximately 12.67.

26. $3x+2(x+4)=5(x+1)+3$

Algebraic Solution:
$$3x+2(x+4)=5(x+1)+3$$
$$3x+2x+8=5x+5+3$$
$$5x+8=5x+8$$

Since both sides are the same, this equation is a true statement no matter what value the variable x might have. The equation is an identity and the solution set is all real numbers.

Graphical Solution:

Graph $y_1=3x+2(x+4)$ and $y_2=5(x+1)+3$ in a $[-20, 20, 5]$ by $[-20, 20, 5]$ viewing window.

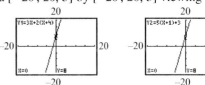

The graphs of y_1 and y_2 are the same. When we trace along y_1, we have the same ordered pairs as when we trace along points of y_2. We know that the lines are identical because two points uniquely determine a line. The equation is an identity and the solution is the set of all real numbers.

28. $-(w+0.2)=0.3(4-w)$

Algebraic Solution:
$$-(w+0.2)=0.3(4-w)$$
$$-w-0.2=1.2-0.3w$$
$$-0.7w-0.2=1.2$$
$$-0.7w=1.4$$
$$w=-2$$

The solution is -2.

Graphical Solution:

Graph $y_1=-(x+0.2)$ and $y_2=0.3(4-x)$ in a

standard viewing window and find the intersection point.

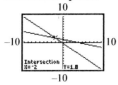

The point of intersection $(-2, 1.8)$ indicates that the solution is -2.

30. $9c - 3(6 - 5c) = c - 2(3c + 9)$

Algebraic Solution:
$$9c - 3(6 - 5c) = c - 2(3c + 9)$$
$$9c - 18 + 15c = c - 6c - 18$$
$$24c - 18 = -5c - 18$$
$$29c - 18 = -18$$
$$29c = 0$$
$$c = 0$$

The solution is 0.

Graphical Solution:

Graph $y_1 = 9x - 3(6 - 5x)$ and

$y_2 = x - 2(3x + 9)$ in a $[-10, 10, 1]$ by

$[-100, 100, 10]$ viewing window.

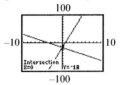

The point of intersection $(0, -18)$ indicates that the solution is 0.

32. $4(x + 5) = 3(x - 4) + x$

Algebraic Solution:
$$4(x + 5) = 3(x - 4) + x$$
$$4x + 20 = 3x - 12 + x$$
$$4x + 20 = 4x - 12$$
$$20 = -12 \quad \text{False}$$

This equation is a false statement no matter what value the variable x might have. The equation is a contradiction and has no solution. The solution set is $\varnothing$ or $\{\ \}$.

Graphical Solution:

Graph $y_1 = 4(x + 5)$ and $y_2 = 3(x - 4) + x$ in a $[-20, 20, 5]$ by $[-20, 20, 5]$ viewing window.

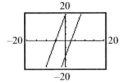

The parallel lines indicate that the equation is a

contradiction and has no solution. The solution set is $\varnothing$ or $\{\ \}$.

34. $\dfrac{2r - 5}{3} - \dfrac{r}{5} = 4 - \dfrac{r + 8}{10}$

Algebraic Solution:
$$\frac{2r - 5}{3} - \frac{r}{5} = 4 - \frac{r + 8}{10}$$
$$30\left(\frac{2r - 5}{3} - \frac{r}{5}\right) = 30\left(4 - \frac{r + 8}{10}\right)$$
$$10(2r - 5) - 6r = 120 - 3(r + 8)$$
$$20r - 50 - 6r = 120 - 3r - 24$$
$$14r - 50 = -3r + 96$$
$$17r - 50 = 96$$
$$17r = 146$$
$$r = \frac{146}{17} \approx 8.59$$

The solution is $\dfrac{146}{17} \approx 8.59$.

Graphical Solution:

Graph $y_1 = (2x - 5)/3 - x/5$ and

$y_2 = 4 - (x + 8)/10$ in a $[-20, 20, 5]$ by

$[-20, 20, 5]$ viewing window and find the intersection point.

Rounded to the nearest hundredth, the point of intersection $(8.59, 2.34)$ indicates that the solution is approximately 8.59.

36. $4(t - 3) - 3(t - 2) = 2t + 8$

Algebraic Solution:
$$4(t - 3) - 3(t - 2) = 2t + 8$$
$$4t - 12 - 3t + 6 = 2t + 8$$
$$t - 6 = 2t + 8$$
$$-t - 6 = 8$$
$$-t = 14$$
$$t = -14$$

The solution is -14.

Graphical Solution:

Graph $y_1 = 4(x - 3) - 3(x - 2)$ and $y_2 = 2x + 8$ in a $[-50, 50, 5]$ by $[-50, 50, 5]$ viewing window and find the intersection point.

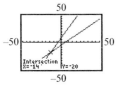

The point of intersection $(-14, -20)$ indicates that the solution is -14.

38. $2.4(2x+3) = -0.1(2x+3)$

Algebraic Solution:

$2.4(2x+3) = -0.1(2x+3)$

$4.8x + 7.2 = -0.2x - 0.3$

$5x + 7.2 = -0.3$

$5x = -7.5$

$x = -1.5$

The solution is -1.5.

Graphical Solution:

Graph $y_1 = 2.4(2x+3)$ and $y_2 = -0.1(2x+3)$ in a standard viewing window and find the intersection point.

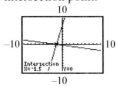

The point of intersection $(-1.5, 0)$ indicates that the solution is -1.5.

40. $\frac{1}{3}(8+2c) = \frac{1}{5}(3c-5)$

Algebraic Solution:

$\frac{1}{3}(8+2c) = \frac{1}{5}(3c-5)$

$15 \cdot \frac{1}{3}(8+2c) = 15 \cdot \frac{1}{5}(3c-5)$

$5(8+2c) = 3(3c-5)$

$40 + 10c = 9c - 15$

$c + 40 = -15$

$c = -55$

The solution is -55.

Graphical Solution:

Graph $y_1 = (1/3)(8+2x)$ and

$y_2 = (1/5)(3x-5)$ in a $[-100, 100, 10]$ by

$[-100, 100, 10]$ viewing window and find the intersection point.

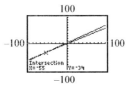

The point of intersection $(-55, -34)$ indicates that the solution is -55.

42. a. $G_1(3) = 50 + 35(3) = \$155$

$G_2(3) = 50(3) = \$150$

If the job takes 3 hours, then the second graphic artist will cost less.

b. $G_1(5) = 50 + 35(5) = \$225$

$G_2(5) = 50(5) = \$250$

If the job takes 5 hours, then the first graphic artist will cost less.

c. Graph $y_1 = 50 + 35x$ and $y_2 = 50x$ and find the point of intersection.

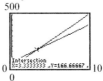

The intersection point $(3.\overline{3}, 166.\overline{6})$ indicates that the cost of hiring each graphing artist will be the same if the job

takes $3\frac{1}{3}$ hours (or 3 hour 20 minutes).

44. a. $C_1(500) = 18 + 0.03(500) = \$33$

$C_2(500) = 0.05(500) = \$25$

For 500 copies, Duplicate, Inc. charges less.

b. $C_1(1000) = 18 + 0.03(1000) = \$48$

$C_2(1000) = 0.05(1000) = \$50$

For 1000 copies, Copycat Printing charges less.

c. Graph $y_1 = 18 + 0.03x$ and $y_2 = 0.05x$ and find the point of intersection.

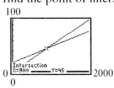

The intersection point $(900, 45)$ indicates that the cost of using each company will be the same for 900 copies.

46. Let x = the number of hours Cheryl works.
Graph $y_1 = 500$ and $y_2 = 150 + 125x$.

The intersection point (2.8, 500) indicates that the charges are the same for 2.8 hours.

48. Let x = the number of CD packets produced and sold. Graph $y_1 = 550 + 2(10)x$ and $y_2 = 45x$.

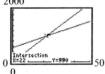

The intersection point (22, 990) indicates that when 22 students buy the packet the cost and revenue will be $990.

50. $x > 1$
{2, 3}

52. $x - 3 \geq -7$
$\quad x \geq -4$
$\{-3, -2, -1, 0, 1, 2, 3\}$

54. Answers may vary

56. When $x < 12$, the graph of y_1 is below the graph of y_2. Thus, if x is less than 12, y_1 is less than y_2.

58. False. If $x = 45$, then $y_1 > y_2$.

60. Graph $y_1 = 3.1x + 5.6$ and $y_2 = 0$ in a standard viewing window and find the intersection point.

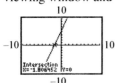

Rounding to the nearest hundredth, the point of intersection (−1.81, 0) indicates that the solution is approximately −1.81.

Check.

Since $-0.011 \approx 0$, the approximate solution −1.81 checks.

62. Graph $y_1 = 4.8x - 2.3$ and $y_2 = 6.8x + 2.7$ in a $[-10, 10, 1]$ by $[-50, 50, 5]$ viewing window and find the intersection point.

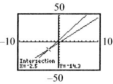

The point of intersection $(-2.5, -14.3)$ indicates that the solution is −2.5.

Check.

Since $-14.3 = -14.3$, the solution −2.5 checks.

64. Graph $y_1 = 0.9x + \sqrt{3}$ and $y_2 = 2.5x - \sqrt{5}$ in a standard viewing window and find the intersection point.

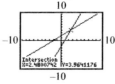

Rounding to the nearest hundredth, the point of intersection (2.48, 3.96) indicates that the solution is approximately 2.48.

Check.

Since $3.964050808 \approx 3.963932023$, the approximate solution 2.48 checks.

66. Graph $y_1 = -\pi x + 1.2$ and $y_2 = 0.3(x - 5)$ in a standard viewing window and find the intersection point.

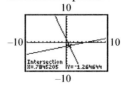

Rounding to the nearest hundredth, the point of intersection $(0.78, -1.26)$ indicates that the solution is approximately 0.78.

Check.

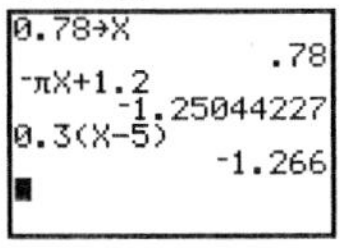

Since $-1.25044227 \approx -1.266$, the approximate solution 0.78 checks.

68. If the intersection-of-graphs method leads to the same line, then the solution of the equation is the set of all real numbers for which the equation is defined.

Section 3.2

Practice Problems

1. a. $\{x \mid x < 3.5\}$ $(-\infty, 3.5)$

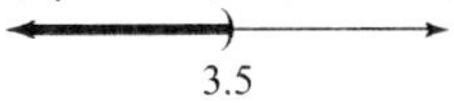

<!-- number line with open circle at 3.5, shaded left -->
         3.5

b. $\{x \mid x \geq -3\}$ $[-3, \infty)$

<!-- number line with closed bracket at -3, shaded right -->
      -3

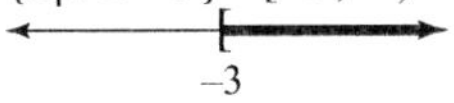

c. $\{x \mid -1 \leq x < 4\}$ $[-1, 4)$

<!-- number line from -1 to 4 -->
    -1   4

2. $x + 5 > 9$

$x + 5 - 5 > 9 - 5$

$\qquad x > 4$

$(4, \infty)$

<!-- number line, open circle at 4, shaded right -->
     4

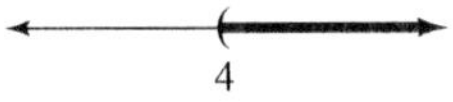

3. $8x + 21 \leq 2x - 3$

$8x + 21 - 2x \leq 2x - 3 - 2x$

$\qquad 6x + 21 \leq -3$

$6x + 21 - 21 \leq -3 - 21$

$\qquad\qquad 6x \leq -24$

$\qquad\qquad \dfrac{6x}{6} \leq \dfrac{-24}{6}$

$\qquad\qquad\quad x \leq -4$

$(-\infty, -4]$

<!-- number line, closed bracket at -4, shaded left -->
    -4

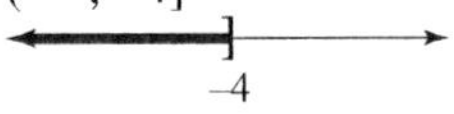

4. a. $\dfrac{2}{5}x \geq \dfrac{4}{15}$

$\dfrac{5}{2} \cdot \dfrac{2}{5}x \geq \dfrac{5}{2} \cdot \dfrac{4}{15}$

$\qquad x \geq \dfrac{2}{3}$

$\left[\dfrac{2}{3}, \infty\right)$

<!-- number line, closed bracket at 2/3, shaded right -->
      $\dfrac{2}{3}$

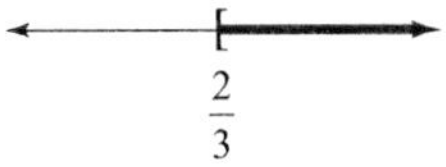

b. $-2.4x < 9.6$

$\dfrac{-2.4x}{-2.4} > \dfrac{9.6}{-2.4}$

$\qquad x > -4$

$(-4, \infty)$

<!-- number line, open circle at -4, shaded right -->
    -4

5. $-(4x + 6) \leq 2(5x + 9) + 2x$

$-4x - 6 \leq 10x + 18 + 2x$

$-4x - 6 \leq 12x + 18$

$-4x - 6 + 4x \leq 12x + 18 + 4x$

$\qquad -6 \leq 16x + 18$

$-6 - 18 \leq 16x + 18 - 18$

$\qquad -24 \leq 16x$

$\qquad \dfrac{-24}{16} \leq \dfrac{16x}{16}$

$\qquad -\dfrac{3}{2} \leq x$

$\left[-\dfrac{3}{2}, \infty\right)$

<!-- number line, closed bracket at -3/2, shaded right -->
      $-\dfrac{3}{2}$

Check:

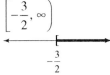

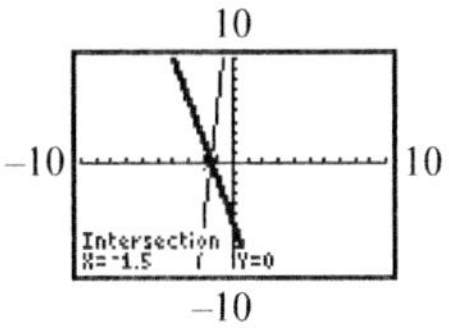

6. $\dfrac{3}{5}(x-3) \ge x-7$

$5\left[\dfrac{3}{5}(x-3)\right] \ge 5(x-7)$

$3(x-3) \ge 5(x-7)$

$3x-9 \ge 5x-35$

$3x-9-5x \ge 5x-35-5x$

$-2x-9 \ge -35$

$-2x-9+9 \ge -35+9$

$-2x \ge -26$

$\dfrac{-2x}{-2} \le \dfrac{-26}{-2}$

$x \le 13$

$(-\infty,\ 13]$

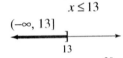

Check:

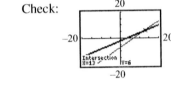

7. a. $4(x-2) < 4x+5$

$4x-8 < 4x+5$

$4x-8-4x < 4x+5-4x$

$-8 < 5$

This is a true statement for all values of x.

$(-\infty,\ \infty)$

b.   Solving $4(x-2) > 4x+5$ in a similar fashion leads to the statement $-8 > 5$. This statement is false for all values of x. Thus, the solution set is $\varnothing$.

8.   In words:

| 900 | + | commission (15% of sales) | ≥ | 2400 |

Translate: 900 $+$ $0.15x$ $\ge$ 2400

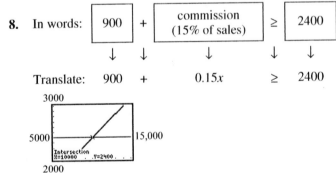

Sales must be greater than or equal to $10,000 per month.

9. $-9.2t + 527.33 < 250$

$-9.2t < -277.33$

$t > 30.14$

The annual consumption of cigarettes will be less than 250 billion more than 30.14 years after 1990, or in approximately $31 + 1990 = 2021$ and after.

Vocabulary and Readiness Check

1. d. $(-\infty, -5)$

2. c. $[-11, \infty)$

3. b. $\left(-2.5, \dfrac{7}{4}\right]$

4. a. $\left[-\dfrac{10}{3}, 0.2\right)$

5. The set $\{x | x \geq -0.4\}$ written in interval notation is $\underline{[-0.4, \infty)}$.

6. The set $\{x | x < -0.4\}$ written in interval notation is $\underline{(-\infty, -0.4)}$.

7. The set $\{x | x \leq -0.4\}$ written in interval notation is $\underline{(-\infty, -0.4]}$.

8. The set $\{x | x > -0.4\}$ written in interval notation is $\underline{(-0.4, \infty)}$.

9. $3x > -14$ no

10. $-3x \leq 14$ yes

11. $-3x < -14$ yes

12. $-x \geq 23$ yes

Exercise Set 3.2

2. $\{x | x > 5\}$
   $(5, \infty)$

4. $\{x | x < -0.2\}$
   $(-\infty, -0.2)$

6. $\{x | -5 \leq x \leq -1\}$
   $[-5, -1]$

8. $\{x | -3 > x \geq -7\}$
   $[-7, -3)$

10. $x + 2 \leq -1$
    $x \leq -3$
    $(-\infty, -3]$

12. $7x - 1 \geq 6x - 1$
    $x \geq 0$
    $[0, \infty)$

14. $\dfrac{5}{6}x \geq 5$
    $\dfrac{6}{5} \cdot \dfrac{5}{6}x \geq \dfrac{6}{5} \cdot 5$
    $x \geq 6$
    $[6, \infty)$

16. $-4x < 11.2$
    $x > -2.8$
    $(-2.8, \infty)$

18. The graph of y_1 is above the x-axis when $x > -8$, so the solution of $y_1 \geq 0$ is $[-8, \infty)$.

20. The graph of y_1 is above the graph of y_2 when $x < 4$, so the solution of $y_1 > y_2$ is $(-\infty, 4)$.

22. The graph of y_1 is below the graph of y_2 for all values of x, so the solution of $y_1 < y_2$ is $(-\infty, \infty)$.

24. $8 - 5x \leq 23$
    $-5x \leq 15$
    $x \geq -3$
    $[-3, \infty)$

26. $20 + x < 6x - 15$
    $20 - 5x < -15$
    $-5x < -35$
    $\dfrac{-5x}{-5} > \dfrac{-35}{-5}$
    $x > 7$
    $(7, \infty)$

28. $6(2-3x) \geq 12$
$12-18x \geq 12$
$-18x \geq 0$
$x \leq 0$
$(-\infty, 0]$

30. $5(x+4) \leq 4(2x+3)$
$5x+20 \leq 8x+12$
$-3x \leq -8$
$x \geq \dfrac{8}{3}$
$\left[\dfrac{8}{3}, \infty\right)$

32. $\dfrac{1-2x}{3} + \dfrac{3x+7}{7} > 1$
$21\left(\dfrac{1-2x}{3} + \dfrac{3x+7}{7}\right) > 21(1)$
$7(1-2x)+3(3x+7) > 21$
$7-14x+9x+21 > 21$
$-5x+28 > 21$
$-5x > -7$
$x < \dfrac{7}{5}$
$\left(-\infty, \dfrac{7}{5}\right)$

34. $-2(4x+2) > -5[1+2(x-1)]$
$-8x-4 > -5(1+2x-2)$
$-8x-4 > -5(2x-1)$
$-8x-4 > -10x+5$
$2x-4 > 5$
$2x > 9$
$x > \dfrac{9}{2}$
$\left(\dfrac{9}{2}, \infty\right)$

36. $x-9 < -12$
$x-9+9 < -12+9$
$x < -3$
$(-\infty, -3)$
Check:
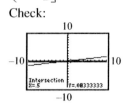

38. $-x > -2$
$\dfrac{-x}{-1} < \dfrac{-2}{-1}$
$x < 2$
$(-\infty, 2)$
Check:
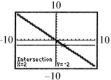

40. $-6x \leq 4.2$
$\dfrac{-6x}{-6} \geq \dfrac{4.2}{-6}$
$x \geq -0.7$
$[-0.7, \infty)$
Check:
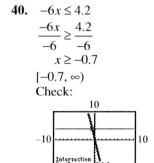

42. $\dfrac{3}{4} - \dfrac{2}{3} \geq \dfrac{x}{6}$
$12\left(\dfrac{3}{4} - \dfrac{2}{3}\right) \geq 12\left(\dfrac{x}{6}\right)$
$9-8 \geq 2x$
$1 \geq 2x$
$\dfrac{1}{2} \geq x$
$\left(-\infty, \dfrac{1}{2}\right]$
Check:
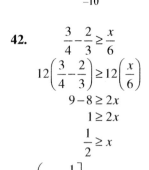

44. $-6x+2 < -3(x+4)$
$-6x+2 < -3x-12$
$2 < 3x-12$
$14 < 3x$
$\dfrac{14}{3} < x$
$\left(\dfrac{14}{3}, \infty\right)$

Check:

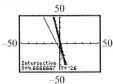

46. $\dfrac{4}{5}(x+1) \le x+1$

$5\left[\dfrac{4}{5}(x+1)\right] \le 5(x+1)$

$4(x+1) \le 5(x+1)$

$4x+4 \le 5x+5$

$-x+4 \le 5$

$-x \le 1$

$x \ge -1$

$[-1, \infty)$

Check:

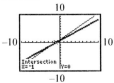

48. $0.7x - x > 0.45$

$-0.3x > 0.45$

$x < -1.5$

$(-\infty, -1.5)$

Check:

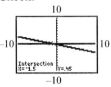

50. $7(2x+3)+4x \le 7+5(3x-4)+x$

$14x+21+4x \le 7+15x-20+x$

$18x+21 \le -13+16x$

$2x+21 \le -13$

$2x \le -34$

$x \le -17$

$(-\infty, -17]$

Check:

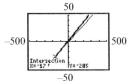

52. $13y-(9y+2) \le 5(y-6)+10$

$13y-9y-2 \le 5y-30+10$

$4y-2 \le 5y-20$

$-2 \le y-20$

$18 \le y$ or $y \ge 18$

$[18, \infty)$

Check:

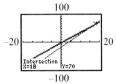

54. $\dfrac{2}{3}(x+3) < \dfrac{1}{6}(2x-8)+2$

$6\left[\dfrac{2}{3}(x+3)\right] < 6\left[\dfrac{1}{6}(2x-8)+2\right]$

$4(x+3) < (2x-8)+12$

$4x+12 < 2x+4$

$2x+12 < 4$

$2x < -8$

$x < -4$

$(-\infty, -4)$

Check:

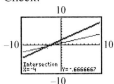

56. $\dfrac{3-4x}{6} - \dfrac{1-2x}{12} \le -2$

$12\left(\dfrac{3-4x}{6} - \dfrac{1-2x}{12}\right) \le 12(-2)$

$2(3-4x)-(1-2x) \le -24$

$6-8x-1+2x \le -24$

$5-6x \le -24$

$-6x \le -29$

$x \ge \dfrac{29}{6}$

$\left[\dfrac{29}{6}, \infty\right)$

Check:

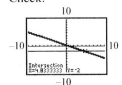

58.
$$\frac{x-4}{2} - \frac{x-2}{3} > \frac{5}{6}$$
$$6\left(\frac{x-4}{2} - \frac{x-2}{3}\right) > 6\left(\frac{5}{6}\right)$$
$$3(x-4) - 2(x-2) > 5$$
$$3x - 12 - 2x + 4 > 5$$
$$x - 8 > 5$$
$$x > 13$$
$(13, \infty)$
Check:

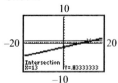

60.
$$\frac{3x+2}{18} - \frac{1+2x}{6} \leq -\frac{1}{2}$$
$$18\left(\frac{3x+2}{18} - \frac{1+2x}{6}\right) \leq 18\left(-\frac{1}{2}\right)$$
$$3x + 2 - 3(1+2x) \leq -9$$
$$3x + 2 - 3 - 6x \leq -9$$
$$-3x - 1 \leq -9$$
$$-3x \leq -8$$
$$x \geq \frac{8}{3}$$
$\left[\frac{8}{3}, \infty\right)$
Check:

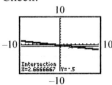

62.
$$0.2(8x - 2) < 1.2(x - 3)$$
$$10[0.2(8x - 2)] < 10[1.2(x - 3)]$$
$$2(8x - 2) < 12(x - 3)$$
$$16x - 4 < 12x - 36$$
$$4x - 4 < -36$$
$$4x < -32$$
$$x < -8$$
$(-\infty, -8)$
Check:

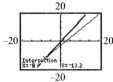

64.
$$\frac{7}{12}x - \frac{1}{3} \leq \frac{3}{8}x - \frac{5}{6}$$
$$24\left[\frac{7}{12}x - \frac{1}{3}\right] \leq 24\left[\frac{3}{8}x - \frac{5}{6}\right]$$
$$2 \cdot 7x - 8 \leq 3 \cdot 3x - 4 \cdot 5$$
$$14x - 8 \leq 9x - 20$$
$$5x - 8 \leq -20$$
$$5x \leq -12$$
$$x \leq -\frac{12}{5}$$
$\left(-\infty, -\frac{12}{5}\right]$
Check:

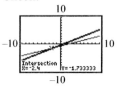

66.
$$3x + 1 < 3(x - 2)$$
$$3x + 1 < 3x - 6$$
$$1 < -6$$
$\varnothing$
Check:

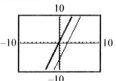

68.
$$8(x + 3) \leq 7(x + 5) + x$$
$$8x + 24 \leq 7x + 35 + x$$
$$8x + 24 \leq 8x + 35$$
$$24 \leq 35$$
$(-\infty, \infty)$
Check:

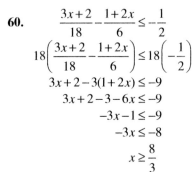

70. a. Let x be the time on the last trial.
$$\frac{1}{4}(6.85 + 7.04 + 6.92 + x) < 7.0$$
$$6.85 + 7.04 + 6.92 + x < 28.0$$
$$20.81 + x < 28.0$$
$$x < 7.19$$
$\{x | x < 7.19\}$

b. A time of 7.19 minutes or less will result in an average time under 7.0 minutes.

72. a. Let x be the number of half-hours parked.
$$1+0.6(x-1) \le 4$$
$$1+0.6x-0.6 \le 4$$
$$0.6x+0.4 \le 4$$
$$0.6x \le 3.6$$
$$x \le 6$$
Since 6 represents half-hours, then 3 represents hours.
$$\{x|x \le 3\}$$

b. You can park for 3 hours or less.

74. a.
$$0.42+0.17(x-1) \le 2.50$$
$$100[0.42+0.17(x-1)] \le 100(2.50)$$
$$42+17(x-1) \le 250$$
$$42+17x-17 \le 250$$
$$17x+25 \le 250$$
$$17x \le 225$$
$$x \le 13.2$$
$$\{x|x \le 13\}$$

b. Thirteen ounces or less can be mailed for $2.50 or less.

76. a. Let x be the number of daily miles driven.
$$36 < 24+0.15x$$
$$12 < 0.15x$$
$$\frac{12}{0.15} < \frac{0.15x}{0.15}$$
$$80 < x$$
$$\{x|x > 80\}$$

b. If you drive more than 80 miles a day, plan A is more economical.

78. Given that $F \ge 977$, we know the following:
$$C \ge \frac{5}{9}(F-32)$$
$$C \ge \frac{5}{9}(977-32)$$
$$C \ge \frac{5}{9}(945)$$
$$C \ge 525$$
$$\{C|C \ge 525°\}$$
So stibnite melts when the temperature is at least 525°C.

80. a.
$$1573x+125,217 > 160,000$$
$$1573x > 34,783$$
$$x > 22.1$$
x is more than 22.1 so $x \ge 23$.
$$1990 + 23 = 2013$$
The civilian labor force will be greater than 160,000 in 2013.

b. Answers may vary

82. The consumption of nonfat milk is decreasing. The graph of the line is going down over time.

84. $t = 2010 - 2000 = 10$
$$y = -0.07t + 3.5$$
$$y = -0.07(10) + 3.5$$
$$y = -0.7 + 3.5$$
$$y = 2.8$$
The consumption of nonfat milk in 2010 will be 2.8 gallons per person per year.

86.
$$-0.07t+3.5 < 3$$
$$-0.07t < -0.5$$
$$t > 7.14$$
$$2000 + 7 = 2007$$
Consumption of nonfat milk will be less than 3 gallons per person per year during 2007.

88. Answers may vary

90. $x \ge 0$ and $x \le 7$
The integers are 0, 1, 2, 3, 4, 5, 6, 7.

92. $x < 6$ and $x < -5$
The integers are −6, −7, −8, ...

94.
$$3x-12 = 3$$
$$3x-12+12 = 3+12$$
$$3x = 15$$
$$\frac{3x}{3} = \frac{15}{3}$$
$$x = 5$$

96.
$$-5x-4 = -x-4$$
$$-5x+x = -4+4$$
$$-4x = 0$$
$$\frac{-4x}{-4} = \frac{0}{-4}$$
$$x = 0$$

98. $\{x|x > -4\}$; $(-4, \infty)$

100.

$(-\infty, 5]$

102. $\{x|-3.7 \le x < 4\}$

104.
$$2x - 3 < 5$$
$$2x - 3 + 3 < 5 + 3$$
$$2x < 8$$
$$\frac{2x}{2} < \frac{8}{2}$$
$$x < 4$$
$$(-\infty, 4)$$

106. Answers may vary

108. Answers may vary

110. Answers may vary

The Bigger Picture

1.
$$7x - 2 = 5(2x + 1) + 3$$
$$7x - 2 = 10x + 5 + 3$$
$$7x - 2 = 10x + 8$$
$$7x - 7x - 2 = 10x - 7x + 8$$
$$-2 = 3x + 8$$
$$-2 - 8 = 3x + 8 - 8$$
$$-10 = 3x$$
$$\frac{-10}{3} = \frac{3x}{3}$$
$$-\frac{10}{3} = x$$

2.
$$5 + 9x = 5(x + 1)$$
$$5 + 9x = 5x + 5$$
$$5 + 9x - 5x = 5x + 5 - 5x$$
$$5 + 4x = 5$$
$$5 + 4x - 5 = 5 - 5$$
$$4x = 0$$
$$\frac{4x}{4} = \frac{0}{4}$$
$$x = 0$$

3.
$$\frac{x + 3}{2} > 1$$
$$2\left(\frac{x + 3}{2}\right) > 2(1)$$
$$x + 3 > 2$$
$$x + 3 - 3 > 2 - 3$$
$$x > -1$$
$$(-1, \infty)$$

4.
$$\frac{x + 2}{2} + \frac{x + 4}{3} = \frac{29}{6}$$
$$6\left(\frac{x + 2}{2} + \frac{x + 4}{3}\right) = 6\left(\frac{29}{6}\right)$$
$$3(x + 2) + 2(x + 4) = 29$$
$$3x + 6 + 2x + 8 = 29$$
$$5x + 14 = 29$$
$$5x + 14 - 14 = 29 - 14$$
$$5x = 15$$
$$\frac{5x}{5} = \frac{15}{5}$$
$$x = 3$$

5.
$$\frac{7}{5} - \frac{y}{10} = 2$$
$$10\left(\frac{7}{5} - \frac{y}{10}\right) = 10(2)$$
$$2(7) - y = 20$$
$$14 - y = 20$$
$$14 - y - 14 = 20 - 14$$
$$-y = 6$$
$$y = -6$$

6.
$$5 + 9x = 9(x + 1)$$
$$5 + 9x = 9x + 2$$
$$5 + 9x - 9x = 9x + 2 - 9x$$
$$5 = 2 \quad \text{False}$$
This false statement indicates that there is no solution. The solution set is $\varnothing$.

7.
$$4(x - 2) + 3x \geq 9(x - 1) - 2$$
$$4x - 8 + 3x \geq 9x - 9 - 2$$
$$7x - 8 \geq 9x - 11$$
$$7x - 8 - 9x \geq 9x - 11 - 9x$$
$$-2x - 8 \geq -11$$
$$-2x - 8 + 8 \geq -11 + 8$$
$$-2x \geq -3$$
$$\frac{-2x}{-2} \leq \frac{-3}{-2}$$
$$x \leq \frac{3}{2}$$
$$\left(-\infty, \frac{3}{2}\right]$$

8. $8(x+1)-2 = 8x+6$

$8x+8-2 = 8x+6$

$8x+6 = 8x+6$

$8x+6-8x = 8x+6-8x$

$6 = 6$ True

This true statement indicates that all real numbers are solutions of the equation. The solution set is $(-\infty, \infty)$.

Integrated Review

1. $-4x = 20$

$\dfrac{-4x}{-4} = \dfrac{20}{-4}$

$x = -5$

2. $-4x < 20$

$\dfrac{-4x}{-4} > \dfrac{20}{-4}$

$x > -5$

$(-5, \infty)$

3. $\dfrac{3x}{4} \geq 2$

$4\left(\dfrac{3x}{4}\right) \geq 4(2)$

$3x \geq 8$

$x \geq \dfrac{8}{3}$

$\left[\dfrac{8}{3}, \infty\right)$

4. $5x+3 \geq 2+4x$

$x+3 \geq 2$

$x \geq -1$

$[-1, \infty)$

5. $6(y-4) = 3(y-8)$

$6y-24 = 3y-24$

$3y = 0$

$y = 0$

6. $-4x \leq \dfrac{2}{5}$

$-20x \leq 2$

$x \geq -\dfrac{1}{10}$

$\left[-\dfrac{1}{10}, \infty\right)$

7. $-3x \geq \dfrac{1}{2}$

$2(-3x) \geq 2\left(\dfrac{1}{2}\right)$

$-6x \geq 1$

$x \leq -\dfrac{1}{6}$

$\left(-\infty, -\dfrac{1}{6}\right]$

8. $5(y+4) = 4(y+5)$

$5y+20 = 4y+20$

$y = 0$

9. $7x < 7(x-2)$

$7x < 7x-14$

$0 < -14$ (False)

No Solution; $\varnothing$

10. $\dfrac{-5x+11}{2} \leq 7$

$2\left(\dfrac{-5x+11}{2}\right) \leq 2(7)$

$-5x+11 \leq 14$

$-5x \leq 3$

$x \geq -\dfrac{3}{5}$

$\left[-\dfrac{3}{5}, \infty\right)$

11. $-5x+1.5 = -19.5$

$-5x+1.5-1.5 = -19.5-1.5$

$-5x = -21$

$\dfrac{-5x}{-5} = \dfrac{-21}{-5}$

$x = 4.2$

12. $-5x+4 = -26$

$-5x = -30$

$x = 6$

13. $5+2x-x = -x+3-14$

$5+x = -x-11$

$5+2x = -11$

$2x = -16$

$x = -8$

14. $12x + 14 < 11x - 2$
$x + 14 < -2$
$x < -16$
$(-\infty, -16)$

15. $\dfrac{x}{5} - \dfrac{x}{4} = \dfrac{x-2}{2}$
$20\left(\dfrac{x}{5} - \dfrac{x}{4}\right) = 20\left(\dfrac{x-2}{2}\right)$
$4x - 5x = 10(x-2)$
$-x = 10x - 20$
$-11x = -20$
$x = \dfrac{20}{11}$

16. $12x - 12 = 8(x-1)$
$12x - 12 = 8x - 8$
$4x - 12 = -8$
$4x = 4$
$x = 1$

17. $2(x-3) > 70$
$2x - 6 > 70$
$2x > 76$
$x > 38$
$(38, \infty)$

18. $-3x - 4.7 = 11.8$
$-3x - 4.7 + 4.7 = 11.8 + 4.7$
$-3x = 16.5$
$\dfrac{-3x}{-3} = \dfrac{16.5}{-3}$
$x = -5.5$

19. $-2(b-4) - (3b-1) = 5b + 3$
$-2b + 8 - 3b + 1 = 5b + 3$
$-5b + 9 = 5b + 3$
$-10b = -6$
$b = \dfrac{-6}{-10} = \dfrac{3}{5}$

20. $8(x+3) < 7(x+5) + x$
$8x + 24 < 7x + 35 + x$
$8x + 24 < 8x + 35$
$24 < 35$ (True for all x)
All real numbers; $(-\infty, \infty)$

21. $\dfrac{3t+1}{8} = \dfrac{5+2t}{7} + 2$
$56\left(\dfrac{3t+1}{8}\right) = 56\left(\dfrac{5+2t}{7}\right) + 56(2)$
$7(3t+1) = 8(5+2t) + 112$
$21t + 7 = 40 + 16t + 112$
$21t + 7 = 16t + 152$
$5t = 145$
$t = 29$

22. $4(x-6) - x = 8(x-3) - 5x$
$4x - 24 - x = 8x - 24 - 5x$
$3x - 24 = 3x - 24$
$-24 = -24$ (True for all x)
The solution is all real numbers.

23. $\dfrac{x}{6} + \dfrac{3x-2}{2} < \dfrac{2}{3}$
$6\left(\dfrac{x}{6} + \dfrac{3x-2}{2}\right) < 6\left(\dfrac{2}{3}\right)$
$x + 3(3x-2) < 4$
$x + 9x - 6 < 4$
$10x - 6 < 4$
$10x < 10$
$x < 1$
$(-\infty, 1)$

24. $\dfrac{y}{3} + \dfrac{y}{5} = \dfrac{y+3}{10}$
$30\left(\dfrac{y}{3}\right) + 30\left(\dfrac{y}{5}\right) = 30\left(\dfrac{y+3}{10}\right)$
$10y + 6y = 3(y+3)$
$16y = 3y + 9$
$13y = 9$
$y = \dfrac{9}{13}$

25. $5(x-6) + 2x > 3(2x-1) - 4$
$5x - 30 + 2x > 6x - 3 - 4$
$7x - 30 > 6x - 7$
$x > 23$
$(23, \infty)$

26. $14(x-1) - 7x \leq 2(3x-6) + 4$
$14x - 14 - 7x \leq 6x - 12 + 4$
$7x - 14 \leq 6x - 8$
$x \leq 6$
$(-\infty, 6]$

27. $\frac{1}{4}(3x+2)-x \ge \frac{3}{8}(x-5)+2$

$8\left[\frac{1}{4}(3x+2)-x\right] \ge 8\left[\frac{3}{8}(x-5)+2\right]$

$2(3x+2)-8x \ge 3(x-5)+16$

$6x+4-8x \ge 3x-15+16$

$-2x+4 \ge 3x+1$

$3 \ge 5x$

$\frac{3}{5} \ge x \quad \text{or} \quad x \le \frac{3}{5}$

$\left(-\infty, \frac{3}{5}\right]$

28. $\frac{1}{3}(x-10)-4x > \frac{5}{6}(2x+1)-1$

$6\left[\frac{1}{3}(x-10)-4x\right] > 6\left[\frac{5}{6}(2x+1)-1\right]$

$2(x-10)-24x > 5(2x+1)-6$

$2x-20-24x > 10x+5-6$

$-22x-20 > 10x-1$

$-19 > 32x$

$-\frac{19}{32} > x \quad \text{or} \quad x < -\frac{19}{32}$

$\left(-\infty, -\frac{19}{32}\right)$

Section 3.3

Practice Exercises

1. $A = \{1, 3, 5, 7, 9\}$ and $B = \{1, 2, 3, 4\}$
The numbers 1 and 3 are in sets A and B.
The intersection is $\{1, 3\}$. $A \cap B = \{1, 3\}$.

2. $x+3 < 8 \quad \text{and} \quad 2x-1 < 3$

$x < 5 \quad \text{and} \quad 2x < 4$

$x < 5 \quad \text{and} \quad x < 2$

$\{x|x < 5\}, (-\infty, 5)$

$\{x|x < 2\}, (-\infty, 2)$

$\{x|x < 5 \text{ and } x < 2\} = \{x|x < 2\}$

The solution set is $(-\infty, 2)$.

3. $4x \le 0 \quad \text{and} \quad 3x+2 > 8$

$x \le 0 \quad \text{and} \quad 3x > 6$

$x \le 0 \quad \text{and} \quad x > 2$

$\{x|x \le 0\}, (-\infty, 0]$

$\{x|x > 2\}, (2, \infty)$

$\{x|4x \le 0 \text{ and } 3x + 2 > 8\} = \{\ \} \text{ or } \varnothing$

4. $3 < 5-x < 9$

$3-5 < 5-x-5 < 9-5$

$-2 < -x < 4$

$\frac{-2}{-1} > \frac{-x}{-1} > \frac{4}{-1}$

$2 > x > -4$

or $-4 < x < 2$

The solution set is $(-4, 2)$.

5. $-4 \le \frac{x}{2}-1 \le 3$

$2(-4) \le 2\left(\frac{x}{2}-1\right) \le 2(3)$

$-8 \le x-2 \le 6$

$-8+2 \le x-2+2 \le 6+2$

$-6 \le x \le 8$

The solution set is $[-6, 8]$.
Check:

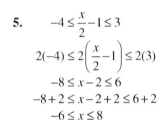

6. $A = \{1, 3, 5, 7, 9\}$ and $B = \{2, 3, 4, 5, 6\}$.
The numbers that are in either set or both sets are $\{1, 2, 3, 4, 5, 6, 7, 9\}$. This set is the union, $A \cup B$.

7. $8x+5 \le 8 \quad \text{or} \quad x-1 \ge 2$

$8x \le 3 \quad \text{or} \quad x \ge 3$

$x \le \frac{3}{8} \quad \text{or} \quad x \ge 3$

$\left\{x\middle|x \le \frac{3}{8}\right\}, \left(-\infty, \frac{3}{8}\right]$

$\{x \mid x \geq 3\}$, $[3, \infty)$

$\left\{x \mid x \leq \dfrac{3}{8} \text{ or } x \geq 3\right\} = \left(-\infty, \dfrac{3}{8}\right] \cup [3, \infty)$

The solution set is $\left(-\infty, \dfrac{3}{8}\right] \cup [3, \infty)$.

8. $\quad -3x - 2 > -8 \quad$ or $\quad 5x > 0$

$\qquad -3x > -6 \quad$ or $\qquad x > 0$

$\qquad\quad x < 2 \quad$ or $\qquad x > 0$

$\{x \mid x < 2\}$, $(-\infty, 2)$

$\{x \mid x > 0\}$, $(0, \infty)$

$\{x \mid x < 2 \text{ or } x > 0\}$, $(-\infty, \infty)$

The solution set is $(-\infty, \infty)$.

Vocabulary and Readiness Check

1. Two inequalities joined by the words "and" or "or" are called <u>compound</u> inequalities.

2. The word <u>and</u> means intersection.

3. The word <u>or</u> means union.

4. The symbol $\cap$ means intersection.

5. The symbol $\cup$ represents union.

6. The symbol $\varnothing$ is the empty set.

7. The inequality $-2 \leq x < 1$ means $-2 \leq x$ <u>and</u> $x < 1$.

8. $\{x \mid x < 0 \text{ and } x > 0\} = \underline{\varnothing}$.

Exercise Set 3.3

2. $C \cap D = \{4, 5\}$

4. $A \cup D = \{x \mid x \text{ is an even integer or } x = 5 \text{ or } x = 7\}$

6. $A \cap B = \varnothing$

8. $B \cup D = \{x \mid x \text{ is an odd integer or } x = 4 \text{ or } x = 6\}$

10. $B \cap C = \{3, 5\}$

12. $A \cup C = \{x \mid x \text{ is an even integer or } x = 3 \text{ or } x = 5\}$

14. $x \leq 0$ and $x \geq -2$

$-2 \leq x \leq 0$

$[-2, 0]$

16. $x < 2$ and $x > 4$

$\varnothing$

18. $x \geq -4$ and $x > 1$

$x > 1$

$(1, \infty)$

20. $\quad x + 2 \geq 3 \quad$ and $\quad 5x - 1 \geq 9$

$\qquad\quad x \geq 1 \quad$ and $\qquad 5x \geq 10$

$\qquad\qquad\qquad\qquad\qquad\quad x \geq 2$

$x \geq 2$

$[2, \infty)$

22. $\quad 2x + 4 > 0 \quad$ and $\quad 4x > 0$

$\qquad\quad 2x > -4 \quad$ and $\qquad x > 0$

$\qquad\qquad x > -2$

$(0, \infty)$

24. $\quad -7x \leq -21 \quad$ and $\quad x - 20 \leq -15$

$\qquad\qquad x \geq 3 \quad$ and $\qquad\qquad x \leq 5$

$3 \leq x \leq 5$

$[3, 5]$

26. $\quad -2 \leq x + 3 \leq 0$

$\quad -5 \leq x \leq -3$

$[-5, -3]$

28. $\qquad 1 < 4 + 2x < 7$

$\quad 1 - 4 < 4 + 2x - 4 < 7 - 4$

$\qquad -3 < 2x < 3$

$\qquad \dfrac{-3}{2} < x < \dfrac{3}{2}$

$\left(-\dfrac{3}{2}, \dfrac{3}{2}\right)$

30. $-2 < \dfrac{1}{2}x - 5 < 1$

$3 < \dfrac{1}{2}x < 6$

$6 < x < 12$

$(6, 12)$

32. $-4 \le \dfrac{-2x+5}{3} \le 1$

$3(-4) \le 3\left(\dfrac{-2x+5}{3}\right) \le 3(1)$

$-12 \le -2x + 5 \le 3$

$-17 \le -2x \le -2$

$\dfrac{17}{2} \ge x \ge 1$

$1 \le x \le \dfrac{17}{2}$

$\left[1, \dfrac{17}{2}\right]$

34. $x \ge -2$ or $x \le 2$

$(-\infty, \infty)$

36. $x < 0$ or $x < 1$

$(-\infty, 1)$

38. $x \ge -3$ or $x \le -4$

$(-\infty, -4] \cup [-3, \infty)$

40. $-5x \le 10$ or $3x - 5 \ge 1$

$\quad x \ge -2$ or $\quad 3x \ge 6$

$\qquad\qquad\qquad\qquad x \ge 2$

$x \ge -2$

$[-2, \infty)$

42. $x + 9 < 0$ or $4x > -12$

$\quad x < -9$ or $\quad x > -3$

$(-\infty, -9) \cup (-3, \infty)$

44. $5(x-1) \ge -5$ or $5 - x \le 11$

$\quad x - 1 \ge -1$ or $\quad -x \le 6$

$\qquad x \ge 0$ or $\qquad x \ge -6$

$x \ge -6$

$[-6, \infty)$

46. $x < \dfrac{5}{7}$ and $x < 1$

$x < \dfrac{5}{7}$

$\left(-\infty, \dfrac{5}{7}\right)$

48. $x < \dfrac{5}{7}$ or $x < 1$

$x < 1$

$(-\infty, 1)$

50. $3 < 5x + 1 < 11$

$2 < 5x < 10$

$\dfrac{2}{5} < x < 2$

$\left(\dfrac{2}{5}, 2\right)$

52. $\dfrac{2}{3} < x + \dfrac{1}{2} < 4$

$6\left(\dfrac{2}{3}\right) < 6\left(x + \dfrac{1}{2}\right) < 6(4)$

$4 < 6x + 3 < 24$

$1 < 6x < 21$

$\dfrac{1}{6} < x < \dfrac{7}{2}$

$\left(\dfrac{1}{6}, \dfrac{7}{2}\right)$

54. $2x - 1 \ge 3$ and $-x > 2$

$\quad 2x \ge 4$ and $\quad x < -2$

$\qquad x \ge 2$ and $\qquad x < -2$

$\varnothing$

56. $\dfrac{3}{8}x + 1 \le 0$ or $-2x < -4$

$\quad \dfrac{3}{8}x \le -1$ or $\quad x > 2$

$\qquad x \le -\dfrac{8}{3}$ or $\qquad x > 2$

$\left(-\infty, -\dfrac{8}{3}\right] \cup (2, \infty)$

58. $-2 < \dfrac{-2x-1}{3} < 2$

$3(-2) < 3\left(\dfrac{-2x-1}{3}\right) < 3(2)$

$-6 < -2x - 1 < 6$

$-5 < -2x < 7$

$\dfrac{-5}{-2} > x > \dfrac{7}{-2}$

$-\dfrac{7}{2} < x < \dfrac{5}{2}$

$\left(-\dfrac{7}{2}, \dfrac{5}{2}\right)$

60. $-5 < 2(x+4) < 8$

$-5 < 2x + 8 < 8$

$-13 < 2x < 0$

$-\dfrac{13}{2} < x < 0$

$\left(-\dfrac{13}{2}, 0\right)$

62. $5x \le 0$ and $-x + 5 < 8$

$x \le 0$ and ${-x} < 3$

$x \le 0$ and ${x} > -3$

$(-3, 0]$

64. $-x < 7$ or $3x + 1 < -20$

$x > -7$ or ${3x} < -21$

$x > -7$ or ${x} < -7$

$(-\infty, -7) \cup (-7, \infty)$

66. $-2x < -6$ or $1 - x > -2$

$x > 3$ or ${-x} > -3$

$x > 3$ or ${x} < 3$

$(-\infty, 3) \cup (3, \infty)$

68. $-\dfrac{1}{2} \le \dfrac{3x-1}{10} < \dfrac{1}{2}$

$10\left(-\dfrac{1}{2}\right) \le 10\left(\dfrac{3x-1}{10}\right) < 10\left(\dfrac{1}{2}\right)$

$-5 \le 3x - 1 < 5$

$-4 \le 3x < 6$

$-\dfrac{4}{3} \le x < 2$

$\left[-\dfrac{4}{3}, 2\right)$

70. $-\dfrac{1}{4} < \dfrac{6-x}{12} < -\dfrac{1}{6}$

$12\left(-\dfrac{1}{4}\right) < 12\left(\dfrac{6-x}{12}\right) < 12\left(-\dfrac{1}{6}\right)$

$-3 < 6 - x < -2$

$-9 < -x < -8$

$9 > x > 8$

$(8, 9)$

72. $-0.7 \le 0.4x + 0.8 < 0.5$

$-1.5 \le 0.4x < -0.3$

$-3.75 \le x < -0.75$

$[-3.75, -0.75)$

74. a. The graph of y_2 is between the graphs of y_1 and y_2 when $-3.5 < x < 2.5$, so the solution of $y_1 < y_2 \le y_3$ is $(-3.5, 2.5)$.

b. The graph of y_2 is below the graph of y_1 when $x > 2.5$. The graph of y_2 is above the graph of y_3 when $x < -3.5$. Thus, the solution of $y_2 < y_1$ or $y_2 > y_3$ is $(-\infty, -3.5) \cup (2.5, \infty)$.

76. a. The graph of y_2 is between the graphs of y_1 and y_2 when $-6.5 < x < 0$, so the solution of $y_1 \le y_2 \le y_3$ is $[-6.5, 0]$.

b. The graph of y_2 is below the graph of y_1 when $x < -6.5$. The graph of y_2 is above the graph of y_3 when $x > 0$. Thus, the solution of $y_2 \le y_1$ or $y_2 \ge y_3$ is $(-\infty, -6.5] \cup [0, \infty)$.

78. $|-7 - 19| = |-26| = 26$

80. $|-4| - (-4) + |-20| = 4 + 4 + 20 = 28$

82. $|x| = 5$

$x = -5, 5$

84. $|x| = -2$

$\varnothing$

86. The years that consumption of bottled water were less than 15 gallons per person were 1998 and 1999. The years that consumption of diet soda were greater than 14 gallons per person were 2003, 2004, and 2005. The union of the years is 1998, 1999, 2003, 2004, and 2005.

88.
$$-10 \leq C \leq 18$$
$$-10 \leq \frac{5}{9}(F - 32) \leq 18$$
$$\frac{9}{5}(-10) \leq \frac{9}{5}\left(\frac{5}{9}(F - 32)\right) \leq \frac{9}{5}(18)$$
$$-18 \leq F - 32 \leq \frac{162}{5}$$
$$14 \leq F \leq 64.4$$
$$14° \leq F \leq 64.4°$$

90. Let x be Wendy's grade on the final exam.
$$80 \leq \frac{1}{6}(2x + 80 + 90 + 82 + 75) \leq 89$$
$$480 \leq 2x + 327 \leq 534$$
$$153 \leq 2x \leq 207$$
$$76.5 \leq x \leq 103.5$$
$$76.5 \leq x \leq 100$$
If Wendy scores between 76.5 and 100 inclusive on her final exam, she will receive a B in the course.

92. $x + 3 < 2x + 1 < 4x + 6$

$x + 3 < 2x + 1$	and	$2x + 1 < 4x + 6$
$2 < x$	and	$-5 < 2x$
$x > 2$	and	$-\frac{5}{2} < x$
$x > 2$	and	$x > -\frac{5}{2}$

$(2, \infty)$

94. $7x - 1 \leq 7 + 5x \leq 3(1 + 2x)$

$7x - 1 \leq 7 + 5x$	and	$7 + 5x \leq 3 + 6x$
$2x \leq 8$	and	$4 \leq x$
$x \leq 4$	and	$x \geq 4$

$\{4\}$

96. $1 + 2x < 3(2 + x) < 1 + 4x$

$1 + 2x < 6 + 3x$	and	$6 + 3x < 1 + 4x$
$-5 < x$	and	$5 < x$
$x > -5$	and	$x > 5$

$(5, \infty)$

The Bigger Picture

1.

$x - 2 \leq 1$	and	$3x - 1 \geq -4$
$x \leq 3$	and	$3x \geq -3$
		$x \geq -1$

$-1 \leq x \leq 3$
$[-1, 3]$

2.
$$-2 < x - 1 < 5$$
$$-2 + 1 < x - 1 + 1 < 5 + 1$$
$$-1 < x < 6$$
$$(-1, 6)$$

3.
$$-2x + 2.5 = -7.7$$
$$-2x = -10.2$$
$$x = 5.1$$

4.
$$-5x > 20$$
$$\frac{-5x}{-5} < \frac{20}{-5}$$
$$x < -4$$
$$(-\infty, -4)$$

5. $x \leq -3$ or $x \leq -5$
$$x \leq -3$$
$$(-\infty, -3]$$

6. $5x < -10$ or $3x - 4 > 2$

$x < -2$	or	$3x > 6$
		$x > 2$

$(-\infty, -2) \cup (2, \infty)$

7.
$$\frac{5t}{2} - \frac{3t}{4} = 7$$
$$4\left(\frac{5t}{2} - \frac{3t}{4}\right) = 4(7)$$
$$2(5t) - 3t = 28$$
$$10t - 3t = 28$$
$$7t = 28$$
$$t = 4$$

8.
$$5(x - 3) + x + 2 \geq 3(x + 2) + 2x$$
$$5x - 15 + x + 2 \geq 3x + 6 + 2x$$
$$6x - 13 \geq 5x + 6$$
$$6x - 5x \geq 13 + 6$$
$$x \geq 19$$
$$[19, \infty)$$

Section 3.4

Practice Exercises

1. $|q| = 7$
$q = 7$ or $q = -7$
The solution set is $\{-7, 7\}$.

2. $|2x - 3| = 5$

$2x - 3 = 5$	or	$2x - 3 = -5$
$2x = 8$	or	$2x = -2$
$x = 4$	or	$x = -1$

The solution set is $\{-1, 4\}$.
Check:

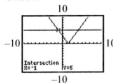 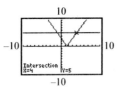

3. $\left|\dfrac{x}{5}+1\right|=15$

$\dfrac{x}{5}+1=15$ or $\dfrac{x}{5}+1=-15$

$\dfrac{x}{5}=14$ or $\dfrac{x}{5}=-16$

$x=70$ or $x=-80$

The solutions are -80 and 70.

4. $|3x|+8=14$

$|3x|=6$

$3x=6$ or $3x=-6$

$x=2$ or $x=-2$

The solutions are -2 and 2.

5. $|z|=0$
The solution is 0.

6. $3|z|+9=7$
Algebraic Solution:

$3|z|+9=7$

$3|z|=-2$

$|z|=-\dfrac{2}{3}$

The absolute value of a number is never negative, so there is no solution. The solution set is $\{\ \}$ or $\varnothing$.
Graphical Solution:

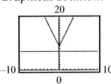

Since the graphs do not intersect, there is no solution. The solution set is $\{\ \}$ or $\varnothing$.

7. $\left|\dfrac{5x+3}{4}\right|=-8$

The absolute value of a number is never negative, so there is no solution. The solution set is $\{\ \}$ or $\varnothing$.

8. $|2x+4|=|3x-1|$

$2x+4=3x-1$ or $2x+4=-(3x-1)$

$-x+4=-1$ \qquad\qquad $2x+4=-3x+1$

$-x=-5$ \qquad\qquad\qquad $5x+4=1$

$x=5$ \qquad\qquad\qquad\quad $5x=-3$

\qquad\qquad\qquad\qquad\qquad $x=-\dfrac{3}{5}$

The solutions are $-\dfrac{3}{5}$ and 5.

Check:

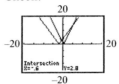 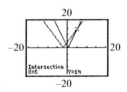

9. $|x-2|=|8-x|$

$x-2=8-x$ or $x-2=-(8-x)$

$2x-2=8$ \qquad\qquad $x-2=-8+x$

$2x=10$ \qquad\qquad $-2=-8$ False

$x=5$

The solution is 5.

Vocabulary and Readiness Check

1. $|x-2|=5$
C. $x-2=5$ or $x-2=-5$

2. $|x-2|=0$
A. $x-2=0$

3. $|x-2|=|x+3|$
B. $x-2=x+3$ or $x-2=-(x+3)$

4. $|x+3|=5$
E. $x+3=5$ or $x+3=-5$

5. $|x+3|=-5$
D. $\varnothing$

Exercise Set 3.4

2. $|y|=15$
$y=-15$ or $y=15$

4. $|6n|=12.6$
$6n=12.6$ or $6n=-12.6$
$n=2.1$ or $n=-2.1$

6. $|6 + 2n| = 4$

   $6 + 2n = -4$ or $6 + 2n = 4$

   $2n = -10$ or $2n = -2$

   $n = -5$ or $n = -1$

8. $\left|\dfrac{n}{3} + 2\right| = 4$

   $\dfrac{n}{3} + 2 = -4$ or $\dfrac{n}{3} + 2 = 4$

   $\dfrac{n}{3} = -6$ or $\dfrac{n}{3} = 2$

   $n = -18$ or $n = 6$

10. $|x| + 1 = 3$

    $|x| = 2$

    $x = -2$ or $x = 2$

12. $|2x| - 6 = 4$

    $|2x| = 10$

    $2x = -10$ or $2x = 10$

    $x = -5$ or $x = 5$

14. $|7z| = 0$

    $7z = 0$

    $z = 0$

16. $|3z - 2| + 8 = 1$

    $|3z - 2| = -7$

    which is impossible.
    The solution set is $\varnothing$.

18. $|3y + 2| = 0$

    $3y + 2 = 0$

    $3y = -2$

    $y = -\dfrac{2}{3}$

20. $|x| = 2$

22. $|9y + 1| = |6y + 4|$

    $9y + 1 = -(6y + 4)$ or $9y + 1 = 6y + 4$

    $9y + 1 = -6y - 4$ or $3y = 3$

    $15y = -5$ or $y = 1$

    $y = -\dfrac{1}{3}$ or $y = 1$

24. $|2x - 5| = |2x + 5|$

    $2x - 5 = -(2x + 5)$ or $2x - 5 = 2x + 5$

    $2x - 5 = -2x - 5$ or $-5 = 5$

    $4x = 0$ or   false

    $x = 0$

    The only solution is 0.

26. Answers may vary

28. The graphs intersect when

    $x = -3.\overline{3} = -3\dfrac{1}{3} = -\dfrac{10}{3}$ and $x = 6$, so the solution

    set is $\left\{-\dfrac{10}{3}, 6\right\}$.

30. The graphs intersect when $x = 0.5 = \dfrac{1}{2}$, so the

    solution set is $\left\{\dfrac{1}{2}\right\}$.

32. $|x| = 1$

    $x = 1$ or $x = -1$

34. The absolute value of any expression is never negative, so no solution exists. The solution set is $\varnothing$.

36. $|4m + 5| = 5$

    $4m + 5 = 5$ or $4m + 5 = -5$

    $4m = 0$ or $4m = -10$

    $m = 0$ or $m = -\dfrac{10}{4}$

    $m = 0$ or $m = -\dfrac{5}{2}$

38. $|7z| + 1 = 22$

    $|7z| = 21$

    $7z = 21$ or $7z = -21$

    $z = 3$ or $z = -3$

40. $|x + 4| - 4 = 1$

    $|x + 4| = 5$

    $x + 4 = 5$ or $x + 4 = -5$

    $x = 1$ or $x = -9$

42. The absolute value of any expression is never negative, so no solution exists. The solution set is $\varnothing$.

44. The absolute value of any expression is never negative, so no solution exists. The solution set is $\varnothing$.

46. $|5x - 2| = 0$
$$5x - 2 = 0$$
$$5x = 2$$
$$x = \frac{2}{5}$$

48. $|2 + 3m| - 9 = -7$
$$|2 + 3m| = 2$$

$2 + 3m = 2$ or $2 + 3m = -2$
$3m = 0$ or $3m = -4$
$m = 0$ or $m = -\frac{4}{3}$

50. $|8 - 6c| = 1$

$8 - 6c = 1$ or $8 - 6c = -1$
$-6c = -7$ or $-6c = -9$
$c = \frac{-7}{-6}$ or $c = \frac{-9}{-6}$
$c = \frac{7}{6}$ or $c = \frac{3}{2}$

52. $|3x + 5| = |-4|$
$$|3x + 5| = 4$$

$3x + 5 = 4$ or $3x + 5 = -4$
$3x = -1$ or $3x = -9$
$x = -\frac{1}{3}$ or $x = -3$

54. $|3 + 6n| = |4n + 11|$

$3 + 6n = 4n + 11$ or $3 + 6n = -(4n + 11)$
$2n = 8$ or $3 + 6n = -4n - 11$
$n = 4$ or $10n = -14$
$n = 4$ or $n = -\frac{7}{5}$

56. $|4 - 5y| = -|-3|$
$$|4 - 5y| = -3$$
The absolute value of any expression is never negative, so no solution exists. The solution set is $\varnothing$.

58. $|4n + 5| = |4n + 3|$

$4n + 5 = -(4n + 3)$ or $4n + 5 = 4n + 3$
$4n + 5 = -4n - 3$ or $5 = 3$
$8n = -8$ or   false
$n = -1$

The only solution is -1.

60. $\left|\dfrac{1 + 3n}{4}\right| = 4$

$\dfrac{1 + 3n}{4} = 4$ or $\dfrac{1 + 3n}{4} = -4$
$1 + 3n = 16$ or $1 + 3n = -16$
$3n = 15$ or $3n = -17$
$n = 5$ or $n = -\dfrac{17}{3}$

62. $8 + |4m| = 24$
$$|4m| = 16$$

$4m = 16$ or $4m = -16$
$m = 4$ or $m = -4$

64. $\left|\dfrac{5x + 2}{2}\right| = |-6|$

$\left|\dfrac{5x + 2}{2}\right| = 6$

$\dfrac{5x + 2}{2} = 6$ or $\dfrac{5x + 2}{2} = -6$
$5x + 2 = 12$ or $5x + 2 = -12$
$5x = 10$ or $5x = -14$
$x = 2$ or $x = -\dfrac{14}{5}$

66. $|5z - 1| = |7 - z|$

$5z - 1 = -(7 - z)$ or $5z - 1 = 7 - z$
$5z - 1 = -7 + z$ or $6z = 8$
$4z = -6$ or $z = \dfrac{4}{3}$
$z = -\dfrac{3}{2}$

68. $\left|\dfrac{2r-6}{5}\right| = |-2|$

$\left|\dfrac{2r-6}{5}\right| = 2$

$\dfrac{2r-6}{5} = 2 \quad$ or $\quad \dfrac{2r-6}{5} = -2$

$2r-6 = 10 \quad$ or $\quad 2r-6 = -10$

$2r = 16 \quad$ or $\quad 2r = -4$

$r = 8 \quad$ or $\quad r = -2$

70. $|8 - y| = |y + 2|$

$8 - y = -(y + 2) \quad$ or $\quad 8 - y = y + 2$

$8 - y = -y - 2 \quad$ or $\quad 6 = 2y$

$8 = -2 \quad\quad$ or $\quad 3 = y$

$\quad$ false $\quad\quad$ or $\quad 3 = y$

The only solution is 3.

72. $\left|\dfrac{5d+1}{6}\right| = -|-9|$

$\left|\dfrac{5d+1}{6}\right| = -9$

The absolute value of any expression is never negative, so no solution exists. The solution set is $\varnothing$.

74. Answers may vary

76. $4\%(360°) = 0.04(360°) = 14.4°$

78. $|x| \le 3$

Answers may vary

3, 2, 1, 0, −1, for example

80. $|y| > -10$

Answers may vary

0, 1, 2, 3, 4, for example

82. $|x - 1| = 5$

84. $|x| = 6$

86. $|x - 2| = |3x - 4|$

88.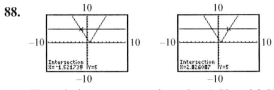

The solutions are approximately −1.52 and 2.83.

90.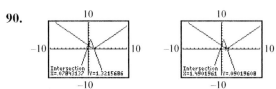

The solutions are approximately 0.08 and 1.49.

Section 3.5

Practice Exercises

1. $|x| < 2$

The solution set of this inequality contains all numbers whose distance from 0 is less than 2. The solution set is $(-2, 2)$.

2. $|b + 1| < 3$

Algebraic Solution:

$|b + 1| < 3$

$-3 < b + 1 < 3$

$-3 - 1 < b + 1 - 1 < 3 - 1$

$-4 < b < 2$

$(-4, 2)$

Graphical Solution:

Graph $y_1 = |x + 1|$ and $y_2 = 3$ in a standard window.

y_1 is below y_2 for x-values between −4 and 2.

Thus the solution set of $|x + 1| < 3$ is $(-4, 2)$.

3. $|3x - 2| + 5 \le 9$

$|3x - 2| \le 9 - 5$

$|3x - 2| \le 4$

$-4 \le 3x - 2 \le 4$

$-4 + 2 \le 3x - 2 + 2 \le 4 + 2$

$-2 \le 3x \le 6$

$-\dfrac{2}{3} \le x \le 2$

$\left[-\dfrac{2}{3}, 2\right]$

4. $\left|3x+\dfrac{5}{8}\right| < -4$

The absolute value of a number is always nonnegative and can never be less than −4. The solution set is { } or ∅.

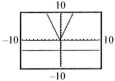

The absolute value graph is always above the horizontal line $y = -4$, so the solution set is { } or ∅.

5. $|y+4| \geq 6$
Algebraic Solution:
$|y+4| \geq 6$

$$
\begin{array}{lll}
y+4 \leq -6 & \text{or} & y+4 \geq 6 \\
y+4-4 \leq -6-4 & \text{or} & y+4-4 \geq 6-4 \\
y \leq -10 & \text{or} & y \geq 2
\end{array}
$$

$(-\infty, -10] \cup [2, \infty)$

Graph $y_1 = |x+4|$ and $y_2 = 6$.

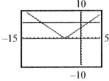

y_1 intersects or is above y_2 for x-values less than or equal to −10 and also x-values greater than or equal to 2, or $(-\infty, -10] \cup [2, \infty)$.

6. $|4x+3|+5 > 3$
$|4x+3|+5-5 > 3-5$
$|4x+3| > -2$

The absolute value of any number is always nonnegative and thus is always greater than −2.
$(-\infty, \infty)$

Graph $y_1 = |4x+3|+5$ and $y_2 = 3$.

$y_1 > y_2$ or $|4x + 3| + 5 > 3$ for all real numbers.

7. $\left|\dfrac{x}{2}-3\right|-3 > 0$

Graph $y_1 = \left|\dfrac{x}{2}-3\right|-3$ and find x-values where

the graph of y_1 is above the x-axis.

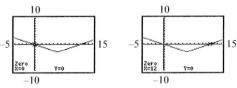

The graph of $y = \left|\dfrac{x}{2}-3\right|-3$ is above the x-axis

for x-values less than 0 or greater than 12.
The solution set is $(-\infty, 0) \cup (12, \infty)$.

8. $\left|\dfrac{3(x-2)}{5}\right| \leq 0$

$\dfrac{3(x-2)}{5} = 0$

$5\left[\dfrac{3(x-2)}{5}\right] = 5(0)$

$3(x-2) = 0$
$3x-6 = 0$
$3x = 6$
$x = 2$

The solution set is {2}.

Vocabulary and Readiness Check

1. D

2. E

3. C

4. B

5. A

Exercise Set 3.5

2. $|x| < 6$
$-6 < x < 6$
The solution set is (−6, 6).

4. $|y-7| \leq 5$
$-5 \leq y-7 \leq 5$
$2 \leq y \leq 12$
The solution set is [2, 12].

6. $|x+4| < 6$

$-6 < x+4 < 6$

$-10 < x < 2$

The solution set is $(-10, 2)$.

8. $|5x-3| \le 18$

$-18 \le 5x-3 \le 18$

$-15 \le 5x \le 21$

$-3 \le x \le \dfrac{21}{5}$

The solution set is $\left[-3, \dfrac{21}{5}\right]$.

10. $|x|+6 \le 7$

$|x| \le 1$

$-1 \le x \le 1$

The solution set is $[-1, 1]$.

12. $|8x-3| < -2$

The absolute value of an expression is never negative, so no solution exists. The solution set is $\varnothing$.

14. $|z+2|-7 < -3$

$|z+2| < 4$

$-4 < z+2 < 4$

$-4-2 < z+2-2 < 4-2$

$-6 < z < 2$

The solution set is $(-6, 2)$.

16. $|y| \ge 4$

$y \le -4$ or $y \ge 4$

The solution set is $(-\infty, -4] \cup [4, \infty)$.

18. $|x-9| \ge 2$

$x-9 \le -2$ or $x-9 \ge 2$

$x \le 7$ or $x \ge 11$

The solution set is $(-\infty, 7] \cup [11, \infty)$.

20. $|x|-1 > 3$

$|x| > 4$

$x < -4$ or $x > 4$

The solution set is $(-\infty, -4) \cup (4, \infty)$.

22. $|4x-11| > -1$

An absolute value is always greater than a negative number. Thus, the answer is $(-\infty, \infty)$.

24. $|10+3x|+1 > 2$

$|10+3x| > 1$

$10+3x < -1$ or $10+3x > 1$

$3x < -11$ or $3x > -9$

$x < -\dfrac{11}{3}$ or $x > -3$

The solution set is $\left(-\infty, -\dfrac{11}{3}\right) \cup (-3, \infty)$.

26. $|x| \ge 0$

An absolute value is always greater than or equal to 0. Thus, the answer is $(-\infty, \infty)$.

28. $|5x-6| < 0$

The absolute value of an expression is never negative, so no solution exists. The solution set is $\varnothing$.

30. $|z| < 8$

$-8 < z < 8$

$(-8, 8)$

32. $|x| \ge 10$

$x \le -10$ or $x \ge 10$

$(-\infty, -10] \cup [10, \infty)$

34. $|-3+x| \le 10$

$-10 \le -3+x \le 10$

$-7 \le x \le 13$

$[-7, 13]$

36. $|1 + 0.3x| \geq 0.1$

$\quad 1 + 0.3x \leq -0.1 \quad$ or $\quad 1 + 0.3x \geq 0.1$

$\quad\quad 0.3x \leq -1.1 \quad$ or $\quad\quad 0.3x \geq -0.9$

$\quad\quad \dfrac{0.3x}{0.3} \leq -\dfrac{1.1}{0.3} \quad$ or $\quad \dfrac{0.3x}{0.3} \geq -\dfrac{0.9}{0.3}$

$\quad\quad\quad x \leq -\dfrac{11}{3} \quad$ or $\quad\quad x \geq -3$

$\left(-\infty, -\dfrac{11}{3}\right] \cup [-3, \infty)$

38. $8 + |x| < 1$

$\quad\quad |x| < -7$

An absolute value is never negative, so no solution exists. The solution set is $\varnothing$.

40. $|x| \leq -7$

An absolute value is never negative, so no solution exists. The solution set is $\varnothing$.

42. $|5x + 2| < 8$

$\quad -8 < 5x + 2 < 8$

$\quad -10 < 5x < 6$

$\quad\quad -2 < x < \dfrac{6}{5}$

The solution set is $\left(-2, \dfrac{6}{5}\right)$.

44. $\quad |-1 + x| - 6 > 2$

$\quad |-1 + x| - 6 + 6 > 2 + 6$

$\quad\quad |-1 + x| > 8$

$\quad -1 + x < -8 \quad$ or $\quad -1 + x > 8$

$\quad\quad x < -7 \quad$ or $\quad\quad x > 9$

$(-\infty, -7) \cup (9, \infty)$

46. $|x| < 0$

An absolute value is never negative, so no solution exists. The solution set is $\varnothing$.

48. $5 + |x| \geq 4$

$\quad\quad |x| \geq -1$

An absolute value is always greater than or equal to 0. Thus, the answer is $(-\infty, \infty)$.

50. $-3 + |5x - 2| \leq 4$

$\quad\quad |5x - 2| \leq 7$

$\quad -7 \leq 5x - 2 \leq 7$

$\quad -5 \leq 5x \leq 9$

$\quad -1 \leq x \leq \dfrac{9}{5}$

The solution set is $\left[-1, \dfrac{9}{5}\right]$.

52. $\left|\dfrac{3}{4}x - 1\right| \geq 2$

$\quad \dfrac{3}{4}x - 1 \leq -2 \quad$ or $\quad \dfrac{3}{4}x - 1 \geq 2$

$\quad\quad \dfrac{3}{4}x \leq -1 \quad$ or $\quad\quad \dfrac{3}{4}x \geq 3$

$\quad\quad x \leq -\dfrac{4}{3} \quad$ or $\quad\quad x \geq 4$

$\left(-\infty, -\dfrac{4}{3}\right] \cup [4, \infty)$

54. $|4 + 9x| \geq -6$

An absolute value is always greater than or equal to 0. Thus, the answer is $(-\infty, \infty)$.

56. $\left|\dfrac{5x + 6}{2}\right| \leq 0$

$\quad \dfrac{5x + 6}{2} = 0$

$\quad 5x + 6 = 0$

$\quad\quad 5x = -6$

$\quad\quad x = -\dfrac{6}{5}$

$\left\{-\dfrac{6}{5}\right\}$

58. $|7x-3|-1 \le 10$

$|7x-3| \le 11$

$-11 \le 7x-3 \le 11$

$-8 \le 7x \le 14$

$-\dfrac{8}{7} \le x \le 2$

$\left[-\dfrac{8}{7}, 2\right]$

60. $\left|\dfrac{7+x}{2}\right| \ge 4$

$\dfrac{7+x}{2} \le -4$ or $\dfrac{7+x}{2} \ge 4$

$7+x \le -8$ or $7+x \ge 8$

$x \le -15$ or $x \ge 1$

The solution set is $(-\infty, -15] \cup (1, \infty]$.

62. $-9+|3+4x| < -4$

$-9+|3+4x|+9 < -4+9$

$|3+4x| < 5$

$-5 < 3+4x < 5$

$-8 < 4x < 2$

$-2 < x < \dfrac{2}{4}$

$-2 < x < \dfrac{1}{2}$

$\left(-2, \dfrac{1}{2}\right)$

64. $\left|\dfrac{3}{5}+4x\right|-6 < -1$

$\left|\dfrac{3}{5}+4x\right| < 5$

$-5 < \dfrac{3}{5}+4x < 5$

$-25 < 3+20x < 25$

$-28 < 20x < 22$

$-\dfrac{28}{20} < \dfrac{20x}{20} < \dfrac{22}{20}$

$-\dfrac{7}{5} < x < \dfrac{11}{10}$

$\left(-\dfrac{7}{5}, \dfrac{11}{10}\right)$

66. $|2x-3| > 7$

$2x-3 < -7$ or $2x-3 > 7$

$2x < -4$ or $2x > 10$

$x < -2$ or $x > 5$

$(-\infty, -2) \cup (5, \infty)$

68. $|5-6x| = 29$

$5-6x = -29$ or $5-6x = 29$

$-6x = -34$ or $-6x = 24$

$x = \dfrac{17}{3}$ or $x = -4$

The solution set is $\left\{-4, \dfrac{17}{3}\right\}$.

70. $|x+4| \ge 20$

$x+4 \le -20$ or $x+4 \ge 20$

$x \le -24$ or $x \ge 16$

The solution set is $(-\infty, -24] \cup [16, \infty)$.

72. $|9+4x| \ge 0$

An absolute value is always greater than or equal to 0. Thus, the answer is $(-\infty, \infty)$.

74. $8+|5x-3| \ge 11$

$|5x-3| \ge 3$

$5x-3 \le -3$ or $5x-3 \ge 3$

$5x \le 0$ or $5x \ge 6$

$x \le 0$ or $x \ge \dfrac{6}{5}$

The solution set is $(-\infty, 0] \cup \left[\dfrac{6}{5}, \infty\right)$.

76. $|5x-3|+2 = 4$

$|5x-3| = 2$

$5x-3 = -2$ or $5x-3 = 2$

$5x = 1$ or $5x = 5$

$x = \dfrac{1}{5}$ or $x = 1$

The solution set is $\left\{\dfrac{1}{5}, 1\right\}$.

78. $|4x - 4| = -3$

An absolute value is never negative, so no solution exists. The solution set is $\varnothing$.

80. $\left|\dfrac{6-x}{4}\right| = 5$

$\dfrac{6-x}{4} = -5$ or $\dfrac{6-x}{4} = 5$

$6 - x = -20$ or $6 - x = 20$

$26 = x$ or $-14 = x$

The solution set is $\{-14, 26\}$.

82. $\left|\dfrac{4x-7}{5}\right| < 2$

$-2 < \dfrac{4x-7}{5} < 2$

$-10 < 4x - 7 < 10$

$-3 < 4x < 17$

$-\dfrac{3}{4} < x < \dfrac{17}{4}$

The solution set is $\left(-\dfrac{3}{4}, \dfrac{17}{4}\right)$.

84. a. The graphs of $y_1 = |x+5| - 4$ and $y_2 = 3$ intersect at the points $(-12, 3)$ and $(2, 3)$. Thus the solution set of $|x + 5| - 4 = 3$ is $\{-12, 2\}$.

    b. The graph of y_1 is below the graph of y_2 for x-values between -12 and 2. Thus the solution set of $|x + 5| - 4 \le 3$ is $[-12, 2]$.

    c. The graph of y_1 is above the graph of y_2 for x-values less than -12 or greater than 2. Thus the solution set of $|x + 5| - 4 > 3$ is $(-\infty, -12) \cup (2, \infty)$.

86. a. The graphs of $y_1 = |x+2| + 1$ and $y_2 = -5$ do not intersect. Thus the solution set of $|x + 2| + 1 = -5$ is $\varnothing$.

    b. There are no x-values for which the graph of y_1 is below the graph of y_2. Thus the solution set of $|x + 2| + 1 < -5$ is $\varnothing$.

    c. The graph of y_1 is above the graph of y_2 for all x-values. Thus the solution set of $|x + 2| + 1 > -5$ is $(-\infty, \infty)$.

88. $P(\text{rolling a } 5) = \dfrac{1}{6}$

90. $P(\text{rolling a } 0) = 0$

92. $P(\text{rolling a } 1, 2, 3, 4, 5, \text{ or } 6) = 1$

94. $3x - 4y = 12$

$3x - 4(-1) = 12$

$3x + 4 = 12$

$3x = 8$

$x = \dfrac{8}{3}$

96. $3x - 4y = 12$

$3(4) - 4y = 12$

$12 - 4y = 12$

$-4y = 0$

$y = 0$

98. $|x| > 4$

100. $|x| > 1$

102. Answers may vary

104. $\left|0.2 - \dfrac{51}{256}\right| = |0.2 - 0.19921875|$

$= |0.00078125|$

$= 0.00078125$

The absolute error is 0.00078125.

The Bigger Picture

1. $9x - 14 = 11x + 2$

$9x - 11x = 14 + 2$

$-2x = 16$

$x = -8$

2. $|x - 4| = 17$

$x - 4 = -17$ or $x - 4 = 17$

$x = -13$ or $x = 21$

3. $x - 1 \le 5$ or $3x - 2 \le 10$

$x \le 6$ or $3x \le 12$

$x \le 6$ or $x \le 4$

$(-\infty, 6]$

4. $-x < 7$ and $4x \le 20$

$x > -7$ and $x \le 5$

$(-7, 5]$

5. $|x-2| = |x+15|$

$$x-2 = x+15 \qquad \text{or} \qquad x-2 = -(x+15)$$
$$-2 = 15 \quad \text{False} \qquad\qquad x-2 = -x-15$$
$$2x-2 = -15$$
$$2x = -13$$
$$x = -\frac{13}{2}$$

The only solution is $-\dfrac{13}{2}$.

6. $9y-6y+1 = 4y+10-y+3$

$$3y+1 = 3y+13$$
$$1 = 13$$

$\varnothing$

7. $\qquad 1.5x-3 = 1.2x-18$

$$1.5x-1.2x = 3-18$$
$$0.3x = -15$$
$$x = -50$$

8. $\qquad \dfrac{7x+1}{8}-3 = x+\dfrac{2x+1}{4}$

$$8\left(\frac{7x+1}{8}-3\right) = 8\left(x+\frac{2x+1}{4}\right)$$
$$7x+1-8\cdot 3 = 8x+2(2x+1)$$
$$7x+1-24 = 8x+4x+2$$
$$7x-23 = 12x+2$$
$$7x-12x = 2+23$$
$$-5x = 25$$
$$x = -5$$

9. $|5x+2|-10 \le -3$

$$|5x+2| \le 7$$
$$-7 \le 5x+2 \le 7$$
$$-9 \le 5x \le 5$$
$$-\frac{9}{5} \le x \le 1$$
$$\left[-\frac{9}{5},1\right]$$

10. $|x+11| > 2$

$$x+11 > 2 \qquad \text{or} \quad x+11 < -2$$
$$x > -9 \quad \text{or} \qquad x < -13$$
$$(-\infty,-13) \cup (-9,\infty)$$

11. $|9x+2|-1=24$

$\qquad |9x+2|=25$

$\quad 9x+2=-25 \quad$ or $\quad 9x+2=25$

$\qquad 9x=-27 \quad$ or $\qquad 9x=23$

$\qquad\quad x=-3 \quad$ or $\qquad\quad x=\dfrac{23}{9}$

12. $\left|\dfrac{3x-1}{2}\right|=|2x+5|$

$\qquad \dfrac{3x-1}{2}=-(2x+5) \qquad$ or $\qquad \dfrac{3x-1}{2}=2x+5$

$\quad 2\left(\dfrac{3x-1}{2}\right)=2[-(2x+5)] \quad$ or $\quad 2\left[\dfrac{3x-1}{2}\right]=2(2x+5)$

$\qquad\quad 3x-1=-4x-10 \qquad$ or $\qquad 3x-1=4x+10$

$\qquad 3x+4x=-10+1 \qquad$ or $\qquad 3x-4x=10+1$

$\qquad\quad\; 7x=-9 \qquad$ or $\qquad\quad -x=11$

$\qquad\qquad x=-\dfrac{9}{7} \qquad$ or $\qquad\qquad x=-11$

Section 3.6

Practice Exercises

1. $3x+y<8$

The boundary line is $3x+y=8$. Graph a dashed boundary line because the inequality symbol is $<$. The point $(0, 0)$ is not on the boundary line, so we use it as a test point. Replace x with 0 and y with 0 in the original inequality.

$\quad 3x+y<8$

$3(0)+0<8$

$\qquad 0<8 \quad$ True

Since $(0, 0)$ satisfies the inequality, shade the half-plane that contains $(0, 0)$. Every point in the shaded half-plane satisfies the original inequality.

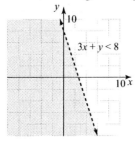

2. $x \geq 3y$

First graph the boundary line $x=3y$. Graph a solid boundary line because the inequality symbol is $\geq$. We choose $(0, 1)$ as a test point.

$x \geq 3y$

$0 \geq 3(1)$

$0 \geq 3 \quad$ False

Since this point does not satisfy the inequality, shade the half-plane on the opposite side of the boundary line from $(0, 1)$. The graph of $x \geq 3y$ is the boundary line together with the shaded region.

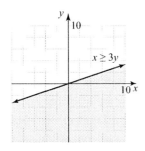

3. The intersection of $x \leq 3$ and $y \leq x - 2$

   Graph each inequality. The intersection of the two graphs is all points common to both regions, as shown by the darker shading in the graph.

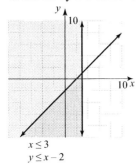

4. The union of $2x - 3y \leq -2$ or $y \geq 1$

   Graph each inequality. The union of the two inequalities is both shaded regions, including the boundary lines, as shown in the graph.

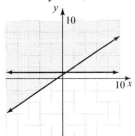

Exercise Set 3.6

2. $x > -3$

   Graph the boundary line $x = -3$ as a dashed line because the inequality symbol is >.
   Test: (0, 0)
   $0 > -3$ True
   Shade the half-plane that contains (0, 0).

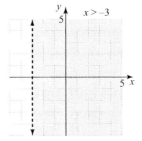

4. $3x + y \leq 1$

   Graph the boundary line $3x + y = 1$ as a solid line because the inequality symbol is ≤.
   Test: (0, 0)
   $3(0) + 0 \leq 1$
   $\quad 0 \leq 1$ True
   Shade the half-plane that contains (0, 0).

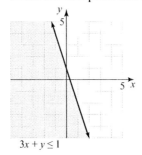

6. $2x + y > 2$

   Graph the boundary line $2x + y = 2$ as a dashed line because the inequality symbol is >.
   Test: (0, 0)
   $2(0) + 0 > 2$
   $\quad 0 > 2$ False
   Shade the half-plane that does not contain (0, 0).

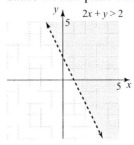

8. $y \leq 3x$

   Graph the boundary line $y = 3x$ as a solid line because the inequality symbol is ≤.
   Test: (1, 1)
   $1 \leq 3(1)$
   $1 \leq 3$ True
   Shade the half-plane that contains (1, 1).

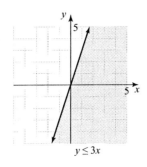

$y \le 3x$

10. $2x + 6y \le 12$

Graph the boundary line $2x + 6y = 12$ as a solid line because the inequality symbol is $\le$.
Test: (0, 0)
$2(0) + 6(0) \le 12$
$\qquad 0 \le 12$ True
Shade the half-plane that contains (0, 0).

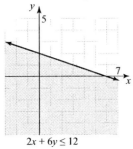

$2x + 6y \le 12$

12. $2x + 5y < -20$

Graph the boundary line $2x + 5y = -20$ as a dashed line because the inequality symbol is $<$.
Test: (0, 0)
$2(0) + 5(0) < -20$
$\qquad 0 < -20$ False
Shade the half-plane that does not contain (0, 0).

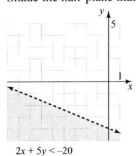

$2x + 5y < -20$

14. Answers may vary. One possibility follows: The boundary line separates the points that are solutions to the inequality from the points that are not solutions. We choose a test point to determine which side contains the solutions and which side does not.

16. $x \ge 3$ or $y \le -2$

Graph each inequality. The union of the two inequalities is both shaded regions, as shown by the shading in the graph below.

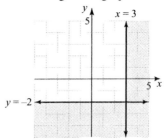

18. $x \le -2$ and $y \ge 4$

Graph each inequality. The intersection of the two inequalities is all points common to both regions, as shown by the shading in the graph below.

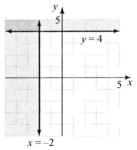

20. $2x > y$ and $y > x + 2$

Graph each inequality. The intersection of the two inequalities is all points common to both regions, as shown by the shading in the graph below.

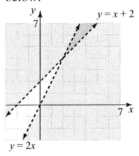

154

22. $x - y \le 3$ or $x + y > -1$

Graph each inequality. The union of the two inequalities is both shaded regions, as shown by the shading in the graph below.

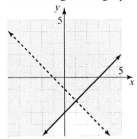

24. $y \le 4$

Graph the boundary line $y = 4$ as a solid line because the inequality symbol is $\le$.
Test: $(0, 0)$
$0 \le 4$ True
Shade the half-plane that contains $(0, 0)$.

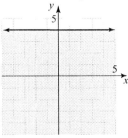

26. $x - 4y < 8$

Graph the boundary line $x - 4y = 8$ as a dashed line because the inequality symbol is $<$.
Test: $(0, 0)$
$0 - 4(0) < 8$
$0 < 8$ True
Shade the half-plane that contains $(0, 0)$.

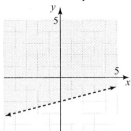

28. $y \ge -2$

Graph the boundary line $y = -2$ as a solid line because the inequality symbol is $\ge$.
Test: $(0, 0)$
$0 \ge -2$ True
Shade the half-plane that contains $(0, 0)$.

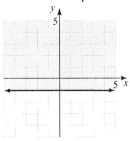

30. $-3x + y \le 9$

Graph the boundary line $-3x + y = 9$ as a solid line because the inequality symbol is $\le$.
Test: $(0, 0)$
$-3(0) + 0 \le 9$
$0 \le 9$ True
Shade the half-plane that contains $(0, 0)$.

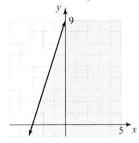

32. $x + 2y > 0$

Graph the boundary line $x + 2y = 0$ as a dashed line because the inequality symbol is $>$.
Test: $(0, 1)$
$0 + 2(1) > 0$
$2 > 0$ True
Shade the half-plane that contains $(0, 1)$.

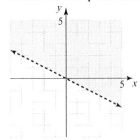

34. $2x - 3y \le 9$

Graph the boundary line $2x - 3y = 9$ as a solid

line because the inequality symbol is $\le$.
Test: (0, 0)
   $2(0) - 3(0) \le 9$
          $0 \le 9$ True
Shade the half-plane that contains (0, 0).

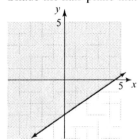

36. $x - y < 3$ or $x > 4$

Graph each inequality. The union of the two
inequalities is both shaded regions, as shown by
the shading in the graph below.

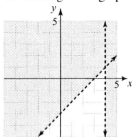

38. $y \ge x$ and $2x - 4y \ge 6$

Graph each inequality. The intersection of the
two inequalities is all points common to both
regions, as shown by the shading in the graph
below.

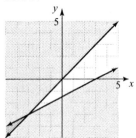

40. $3x + y < 9$ or $y \le 2$

Graph each inequality. The union of the two
inequalities is both shaded regions, as shown by
the shading in the graph below.

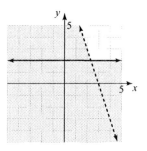

42. $x \ge -4$ and $x \le 3$

Graph each inequality. The intersection of the
two inequalities is all points common to both
regions, as shown by the shading in the graph
below.

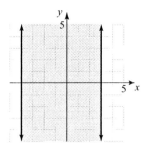

44. $x + y \le 0$ and $3x - 6y \ge 12$

Graph each inequality. The intersection of the
two inequalities is all points common to both
regions, as shown by the shading in the graph
below.

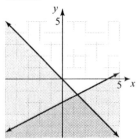

46. $2x - y > 3$ or $x > 0$

Graph each inequality. The union of the two
inequalities is both shaded regions, as shown by
the shading in the graph below.

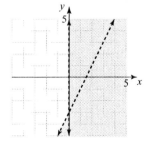

48. $y < 2x + 3$

The boundary line should be dashed, and the half-plane below the boundary line should be shaded. The correct graph is C.

50. $y \geq 2x + 3$

The boundary line should be solid, and the half-plane above the boundary line should be shaded. The correct graph is B.

52. The boundary line is the horizontal line $y = 1$. It is solid, so the inequality symbol must be either $\leq$ or $\geq$. Since the shaded region is to the above boundary, the inequality is $y \geq 1$.

54. The boundary line is the vertical line $x = -3$. It is solid, so the inequality symbol must be either $\leq$ or $\geq$. Since the shaded region is to the left of the boundary, the inequality is $x \leq -3$.

56. The boundary line is the horizontal line $y = -1$. It is dashed, so the inequality symbol must be either $<$ or $>$. Since the shaded region is above the boundary, the inequality is $y > -1$.

58. The boundary line is the vertical line $x = -3$. It is dashed, so the inequality symbol must be either $<$ or $>$. Since the shaded region is to the right of the boundary, the inequality is $x > -3$.

60. $3^2 = 3 \cdot 3 = 9$

62. $(-5)^2 = (-5)(-5) = 25$

64. $-2^4 = -(2 \cdot 2 \cdot 2 \cdot 2) = -16$

66. $\left(\dfrac{2}{7}\right)^2 = \left(\dfrac{2}{7}\right)\left(\dfrac{2}{7}\right) = \dfrac{4}{49}$

68. Domain: $(-\infty, -2] \cup [2, \infty)$

Range: $(-\infty, \infty)$

Not a function since it fails the vertical line test.

70. The statement "spends between 2 and 6 hours watching movies" translates into $2 < x < 6$. The statement "spends fewer than 5 hours watching TV shows" translates into $0 \leq y < 5$. Thus, we have the conjunction $2 < x < 6$ and $0 \leq y < 5$. Graph each inequality. The intersection of the inequalities is all points common to the regions, as shown by the shading in the graph below.

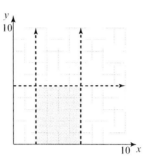

Chapter 3 Vocabulary Check

1. Two inequalities joined by the words "and" or "or" is called a <u>compound inequality</u>.

2. An equation in one variable that has no solution is called a <u>contradiction</u>.

3. The <u>intersection</u> of two sets is the set of all elements common to both sets.

4. The <u>union</u> of two sets is the set of all elements that belong to either of the sets.

5. An equation in one variable that has every number (for which the equation is defined) as a solution is called an <u>identity</u>.

6. A number's distance from 0 is called its <u>absolute value</u>.

7. When a variable in an equation is replaced by a number and the resulting equation is true, then that number is called a <u>solution</u> of the equation.

8. The statement $5x - 0.2 < 7$ is an example of a <u>linear inequality in one variable</u>.

9. The statement $5x - 0.2 = 7$ is an example of a <u>linear equation in one variable</u>.

Chapter 3 Review

1. $4(x - 6) + 3 = 27$

   Algebraic Solution:
   $$4(x - 6) + 3 = 27$$
   $$4x - 24 + 3 = 27$$
   $$4x - 21 = 27$$
   $$4x = 48$$
   $$x = 12$$
   The solution is 12.

Graphical Solution:

Graph $y_1 = 4(x-6)+3$ and $y_2 = 27$ in a $[-50, 50, 5]$ by $[-50, 50, 5]$ viewing window and find the intersection point.

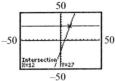

The point of intersection $(12, 27)$ indicates that the solution is 12.

2. $15(x+2)-6 = 18$

    Algebraic Solution:
    $$15(x+2)-6 = 18$$
    $$15x+30-6 = 18$$
    $$15x+24 = 18$$
    $$15x = -6$$
    $$x = \frac{-6}{15} = -\frac{2}{5} = -0.4$$

    The solution is $-\frac{2}{5} = -0.4$.

    Graphical Solution:

    Graph $y_1 = 15(x+2)-6$ and $y_2 = 18$ in a $[-20, 20, 5]$ by $[-20, 20, 5]$ viewing window and find the intersection point.

    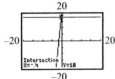

    The point of intersection $(-0.4, 18)$ indicates that the solution is $-0.4 = -\frac{2}{5}$.

3. $5x+15 = 3(x+2)+2(x-3)$

    Algebraic Solution:
    $$5x+15 = 3x+6+2x-6$$
    $$5x+15 = 5x$$
    $$15 = 0 \quad \text{False}$$

    This equation is a false statement no matter what value the variable x might have. The equation is a contradiction and has no solution. The solution set is $\varnothing$ or { }.

    Graphical Solution:

    Graph $y_1 = 5x+15$ and $y_2 = 3(x+2)+2(x-3)$ in a $[-20, 20, 5]$ by $[-20, 20, 5]$ viewing window.

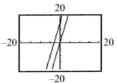

The parallel lines indicate that the equation is a contradiction and has no solution. The solution set is $\varnothing$ or { }.

4. $2x-5+3(x-4) = 5(x+2)-27$

    Algebraic Solution:
    $$2x-5+3(x-4) = 5(x+2)-27$$
    $$2x-3+3x-12 = 5x+10-27$$
    $$5x-15 = 5x-15$$

    Since both sides are the same, this equation is a true statement no matter what value the variable x might have. The equation is an identity and the solution is the set of all real numbers.

    Graphical Solution:

    Graph $y_1 = 2x-5+3(x-4)$ and $y_2 = 5(x+2)-27$ in a $[-20, 20, 5]$ by $[-20, 20, 5]$ viewing window.

    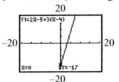 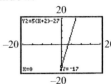

    The graphs of y_1 and y_2 are the same. When we trace along y_1, we have the same ordered pairs as when we trace along points of y_2. We know that the lines are identical because two points uniquely determine a line. The equation is an identity and the solution is the set of all real numbers.

5. $14-2(x+3) = 3(x-9)+18$

    Algebraic Solution:
    $$14-2(x+3) = 3(x-9)+18$$
    $$14-2x-6 = 3x-27+18$$
    $$-2x+8 = 3x-9$$
    $$-5x+8 = -9$$
    $$-5x = -17$$
    $$x = \frac{-17}{-5} = \frac{17}{5} = 3.4$$

    The solution is $\frac{17}{5} = 3.4$.

    Graphical Solution:

    Graph $y_1 = 14-2(x+3)$ and $y_2 = 3(x-9)+18$ in a $[-20, 20, 5]$ by $[-20, 20, 5]$ viewing window and find the intersection point.

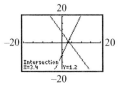

The point of intersection $(3.4,\ 1.2)$ indicates that the solution is $3.4 = \dfrac{17}{5}$.

6.　$16 + 2(5 - x) = 19 - 3(x + 2)$

Algebraic Solution:
$$16 + 2(5 - x) = 19 - 3(x + 2)$$
$$16 + 10 - 2x = 19 - 3x - 6$$
$$-2x + 26 = -3x + 13$$
$$x + 26 = 13$$
$$x = -13$$

The solution is -13.

Graphical Solution:
Graph $y_1 = 16 + 2(5 - x)$ and $y_2 = 19 - 3(x + 2)$ in a $[-100,\ 100,\ 10]$ by $[-100,\ 100,\ 10]$ viewing window and find the intersection point.

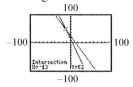

The point of intersection $(-13,\ 52)$ indicates that the solution is -13.

7.　$0.4(x - 6) = \pi x + \sqrt{3}$

Graph $y_1 = 0.4(x - 6)$ and $y_2 = \pi x + \sqrt{3}$ in a standard viewing window and find the intersection point.

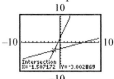

Rounding to the nearest hundredth, the point of intersection $(-1.51, -3.00)$ indicates that the solution is approximately -1.51.

8.　$1.7x + \sqrt{7} = -0.4x - \sqrt{6}$

Graph $y_1 = 1.7x + \sqrt{7}$ and $y_2 = -0.4x - \sqrt{6}$ in a standard viewing window and find the intersection point.

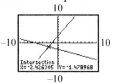

Rounding to the nearest hundredth, the point of intersection $(-2.43, -1.48)$ indicates that the solution is approximately -2.43.

9.　$3(x - 5) > -(x + 3)$
$$3x - 15 > -x - 3$$
$$4x > 12$$
$$x > 3$$
$(3,\ \infty)$

10.　$-2(x + 7) \ge 3(x + 2)$
$$-2x - 14 \ge 3x + 6$$
$$-5x \ge 20$$
$$x \le -4$$
$(-\infty,\ -4]$

11.　$4x - (5 + 2x) < 3x - 1$
$$4x - 5 - 2x < 3x - 1$$
$$2x - 5 < 3x - 1$$
$$-x < 4$$
$$x > -4$$
$(-4,\ \infty)$

12.　$3(x - 8) < 7x + 2(5 - x)$
$$3x - 24 < 7x + 10 - 2x$$
$$3x - 24 < 5x + 10$$
$$-2x < 34$$
$$x > -17$$
$(-17,\ \infty)$

13.　$24 \ge 6x - 2(3x - 5) + 2x$
$$24 \ge 6x - 6x + 10 + 2x$$
$$24 \ge 10 + 2x$$
$$14 \ge 2x$$
$$7 \ge x$$
$(-\infty,\ 7]$

14.

$$\frac{x}{3}+\frac{1}{2}>\frac{2}{3}$$

$$6\left(\frac{x}{3}+\frac{1}{2}\right)>6\left(\frac{2}{3}\right)$$

$$2x+3>4$$

$$2x>1$$

$$x>\frac{1}{2}$$

$$\left(\frac{1}{2},\ \infty\right)$$

15.

$$x+\frac{3}{4}<-\frac{x}{2}+\frac{9}{4}$$

$$4\left(x+\frac{3}{4}\right)<4\left(-\frac{x}{2}+\frac{9}{4}\right)$$

$$4x+3<-2x+9$$

$$6x<6$$

$$x<1$$

$$(-\infty,\ 1)$$

16.

$$\frac{x-5}{2}\le\frac{3}{8}(2x+6)$$

$$8\left(\frac{x-5}{2}\right)\le 8\left[\frac{3}{8}(2x+6)\right]$$

$$4(x-5)\le 3(2x+6)$$

$$4x-20\le 6x+18$$

$$-2x\le 38$$

$$x\ge -19$$

$$[-19,\ \infty)$$

17. Let n = number of pounds of laundry.

$$15<0.5(10)+0.4(n-10)$$

$$15<5+0.4n-4$$

$$15<1+0.4n$$

$$14<0.4n$$

$$35<n$$

It is more economical to use the housekeeper for more than 35 pounds of laundry per week.

18. $500\le F\le 1000$

$$500\le\frac{9}{5}C+32\le 1000$$

$$468\le\frac{9}{5}C\le 968$$

$$260\le C\le 538$$

Rounded to the nearest degree, firing temperatures range from 260°C to 538°C.

19. Let x = the score from the last judge.

$$\frac{9.5+9.7+9.9+9.7+9.7+9.6+9.5+x}{8}\ge 9.65$$

$$67.6+x\ge 77.2$$

$$x\ge 9.6$$

The last judge must give Nana at least a 9.6 for her to win the silver medal.

20. Let x = the amount saved each summer.

$$4000\le 2x+500\le 8000$$

$$3500\le 2x\le 7500$$

$$1750\le x\le 3750$$

She must save between \$1750 and \$3750 each summer.

21. $1\le 4x-7\le 3$

$$8\le 4x\le 10$$

$$2\le x\le\frac{5}{2}$$

$$\left[2,\ \frac{5}{2}\right]$$

22. $-2\le 8+5x<-1$

$$-10\le 5x\le -9$$

$$-2\le x\le -\frac{9}{5}$$

$$\left[-2,\ \frac{9}{5}\right)$$

23. $-3<4(2x-1)<12$

$$-3<8x-4<12$$

$$1<8x<16$$

$$\frac{1}{8}<x<2$$

$$\left(\frac{1}{8},\ 2\right)$$

24. $-6<x-(3-4x)<-3$

$$-6<x-3+4x<-3$$

$$-6<5x-3<-3$$

$$-3<5x<0$$

$$-\frac{3}{5}<x<0$$

$$\left(-\frac{3}{5},\ 0\right)$$

25.
$$\frac{1}{6} < \frac{4x-3}{3} \le \frac{4}{5}$$
$$30\left(\frac{1}{6}\right) < 30\left(\frac{4x-3}{3}\right) \le 30\left(\frac{4}{5}\right)$$
$$5 < 10(4x-3) \le 24$$
$$5 < 40x - 30 \le 24$$
$$35 < 40x < 54$$
$$\frac{7}{8} < x \le \frac{27}{20}$$
$$\left(\frac{7}{8}, \frac{27}{20}\right]$$

26. $x \le 2$ and $x > -5$
$$-5 < x \le 2$$
$$(-5, 2]$$

27. $3x - 5 > 6$ or $-x < -5$
     $3x > 11$ or $x > 5$
       $x > \dfrac{11}{3}$ or $x > 5$
$$x > \frac{11}{3}$$
$$\left(\frac{11}{3}, \infty\right)$$

28. $|x - 7| = 9$
     $x - 7 = 9$ or $x - 7 = -9$
       $x = 16$ or $x = -2$

29. $|8 - x| = 3$
     $8 - x = 3$ or $8 - x = -3$
      $-x = -5$ or $-x = -11$
       $x = 5$ or $x = 11$

30. $|2x + 9| = 9$
     $2x + 9 = 9$ or $2x + 9 = -9$
      $2x = 0$ or $2x = -18$
       $x = 0$ or $x = -9$

31. $|-3x + 4| = 7$
     $-3x + 4 = 7$ or $-3x + 4 = -7$
      $-3x = 3$ or $-3x = -11$
       $x = -1$ or $x = \dfrac{11}{3}$

32. $|3x - 2| + 6 = 10$
$$|3x - 2| = 4$$
     $3x - 2 = 4$ or $3x - 2 = -4$
       $3x = 6$ or $3x = -2$
        $x = 2$ or $x = -\dfrac{2}{3}$

33. $5 + |6x + 1| = 5$
$$|6x + 1| = 0$$
$$6x + 1 = 0$$
$$6x = -1$$
$$x = -\frac{1}{6}$$

34. $-5 = |4x - 3|$
The solution set is $\varnothing$.

35. $|5 - 6x| + 8 = 3$
$$|5 - 6x| = -5$$
The solution set is $\varnothing$.

36. $-8 = |x - 3| - 10$
$$2 = |x - 3|$$
     $x - 3 = 2$ or $x - 3 = -2$
       $x = 5$ or $x = 1$

37. $\left|\dfrac{3x - 7}{4}\right| = 2$
$$\frac{3x-7}{4} = 2 \quad \text{or} \quad \frac{3x-7}{4} = -2$$
   $3x - 7 = 8$ or $3x - 7 = -8$
     $3x = 15$ or $3x = -1$
       $x = 5$ or $x = -\dfrac{1}{3}$

38. $|6x + 1| = |15 + 4x|$
   $6x + 1 = 15 + 4x$ or $6x + 1 = -(15 + 4x)$
     $2x = 14$ or $6x + 1 = -15 - 4x$
      $x = 7$ or $10x = -16$
$$x = -\frac{8}{5}$$

39. $|5x - 1| < 9$
$$-9 < 5x - 1 < 9$$
$$-8 < 5x < 10$$
$$-\frac{8}{5} < x < 2$$

$\left(-\dfrac{8}{5}, 2\right)$

40. $|6 + 4x| \geq 10$

$6 + 4x \leq -10$ or $6 + 4x \geq 10$

$4x \leq -16$ or $4x \geq 4$

$x \leq -4$ or $x \geq 1$

$(-\infty, -4] \cup [1, \infty)$

41. $|3x| - 8 > 1$

$|3x| > 9$

$3x < -9$ or $3x > 9$

$x < -3$ or $x > 3$

$(-\infty, -3) \cup (3, \infty)$

42. $9 + |5x| < 24$

$|5x| < 15$

$-15 < 5x < 15$

$-3 < x < 3$

$(-3, 3)$

43. $|6x - 5| \leq -1$

The solution set is $\varnothing$.

44. $\left|3x + \dfrac{2}{5}\right| \geq 4$

$3x + \dfrac{2}{5} \leq -4$ or $3x + \dfrac{2}{5} \geq 4$

$5\left(3x + \dfrac{2}{5}\right) \leq 5(-4)$ or $5\left(3x + \dfrac{2}{5}\right) \geq 5(4)$

$15x + 2 \leq -20$ or $15x + 2 \geq 20$

$15x \leq -22$ or $15x \geq 18$

$x \leq -\dfrac{22}{15}$ or $x \geq \dfrac{6}{5}$

$\left(-\infty, -\dfrac{22}{15}\right] \cup \left[\dfrac{6}{5}, \infty\right)$

45. $\left|\dfrac{x}{3} + 6\right| - 8 > -5$

$\left|\dfrac{x}{3} + 6\right| > 3$

$\dfrac{x}{3} + 6 < -3$ or $\dfrac{x}{3} + 6 > 3$

$\dfrac{x}{3} < -9$ or $\dfrac{x}{3} > -3$

$x < -27$ or $x > -9$

$(-\infty, -27) \cup (-9, \infty)$

46. $\left|\dfrac{4(x-1)}{7}\right| + 10 < 2$

$\left|\dfrac{4(x-1)}{7}\right| < -8$

The solution set is $\varnothing$.

47. $\dfrac{1}{2}x - y < 2$

$y > \dfrac{1}{2}x - 2$

Graph the boundary line as dashed.
Test: (0, 0)

$\dfrac{1}{2}(0) - 0 < 2$ True

Shade the half-plane that contains (0, 0).

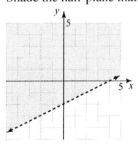

48. $3x + y > 4$

$y > -3x + 4$

Graph the boundary line as dashed.

Test: $(0, 0)$

$3(0) + 0 > 4$ False

Shade the half-plane that does not include $(0, 0)$.

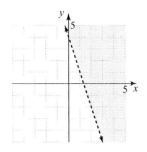

49. $3y \geq x$

$y \geq \dfrac{x}{3}$

Graph the boundary line as solid.

Test: $(0, 1)$

$3(1) \geq 0$ True

Shade the half-plane that contains $(0, 1)$.

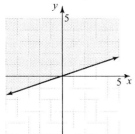

50. $5x - 2y \leq 9$

$-2y \leq -5x + 9$

$y \geq \dfrac{5}{2}x - \dfrac{9}{2}$

Graph the boundary line as solid.

Test: $(0, 0)$

$5(0) - 2(0) \leq 9$ True

Shade the half-plane that contains $(0, 0)$.

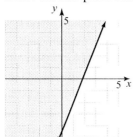

51. $x > -2$

Graph the boundary line as dashed. Shade the half-plane to the right of $x = -2$.

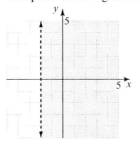

52. $y < 1$

Graph the boundary line as dashed. Shade the half-plane below $y = 1$.

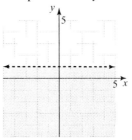

53. $2x < 3y + 8$ and $y \geq -2$

Graph each inequality. The intersection of the two inequalities is all points common to both regions, as shown by the shading in the graph below.

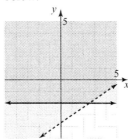

54. $y > 2x + 3$ or $x \leq -3$

Graph each inequality. The union of the two inequalities is both shaded regions, as shown by the graph below.

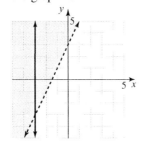

55.
$$\frac{x-2}{5}+\frac{x+2}{2}=\frac{x+4}{3}$$
$$30\left(\frac{x-2}{5}+\frac{x+2}{2}\right)=30\left(\frac{x+4}{3}\right)$$
$$6(x-2)+15(x+2)=10(x+4)$$
$$6x-12+15x+30=10x+40$$
$$21x+18=10x+40$$
$$11x=22$$
$$x=2$$

56.
$$\frac{2z-3}{4}-\frac{4-z}{2}=\frac{z+1}{3}$$
$$12\left(\frac{2z-3}{4}-\frac{4-z}{2}\right)=12\left(\frac{z+1}{3}\right)$$
$$3(2z-3)-6(4-z)=4(z+1)$$
$$6z-9-24+6z=4z+4$$
$$12z-33=4z+4$$
$$8z=37$$
$$z=\frac{37}{8}$$

57.
$$\frac{3(x-2)}{5}>\frac{-5(x-2)}{3}$$
$$15\left[\frac{3(x-2)}{5}\right]>15\left[\frac{-5(x-2)}{3}\right]$$
$$9(x-2)>-25(x-2)$$
$$9x-18>-25x+50$$
$$34x>68$$
$$x>2$$
$$(2,\infty)$$

58.
$$0\le\frac{2(3x+4)}{5}\le3$$
$$5(0)\le5\left[\frac{2(3x+4)}{5}\right]\le5(3)$$
$$0\le2(3x+4)\le15$$
$$0\le6x+8\le15$$
$$-8\le6x\le7$$
$$-\frac{4}{3}\le x\le\frac{7}{6}$$
$$\left[-\frac{4}{3},\frac{7}{6}\right]$$

59. $x\le2$ or $x>-5$
$$(-\infty,\infty)$$

60. $-2x\le6$ and $-2x+3<-7$
$\qquad x\ge-3$ and $\qquad-2x<-10$
$\qquad x\ge-3$ and $\qquad\quad x>5$
$x>5$
$(5,\infty)$

61. $|7x|-26=-5$
$\qquad|7x|=21$
$7x=21$ or $7x=-21$
$x=3$ or $\quad x=-3$

62. $\left|\dfrac{9-2x}{5}\right|=-3$
The solution set is $\varnothing$.

63. $|x-3|=|7+2x|$
$x-3=7+2x$ or $x-3=-(7+2x)$
$-10=x$ or $x-3=-7-2x$
$\qquad\qquad\qquad\quad 3x=-4$
$\qquad\qquad\qquad\quad x=-\frac{4}{3}$

64. $|6x-5|\ge-1$
Since $|6x-5|$ is nonnegative for all numbers x, the solution set is $(-\infty,\infty)$.

65. $\left|\dfrac{4x-3}{5}\right|<1$
$$-1<\frac{4x-3}{5}<1$$
$$-5<4x-3<5$$
$$-2<4x<8$$
$$-\frac{1}{2}<x<2$$
$$\left(-\frac{1}{2},2\right)$$

66. $48+x\ge5(2x+4)-2x$
$48+x\ge10x+20-2x$
$48+x\ge8x+20$
$28\ge7x$
$4\ge x$
$(-\infty,4]$

Chapter 3 Test

1. $15x + 26 = -2(x + 1) - 1$

   Algebraic Solution:
   $15x + 26 = -2(x + 1) - 1$
   $15x + 26 = -2x - 2 - 1$
   $15x + 26 = -2x - 3$
   $17x + 26 = -3$
   $17x = -29$
   $x = -\dfrac{29}{17} \approx -1.71$

   The solution is $-\dfrac{29}{17} \approx -1.71$.

   Graphical Solution:
   Graph $y_1 = 15x + 26$ and $y_2 = -2(x + 1) - 1$ in a $[-10, 10, 1]$ by $[-10, 10, 1]$ viewing window and find the intersection point.

   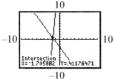

   Rounding to the nearest hundredth, the point of intersection $(-1.71, 0.41)$ indicates that the solution is approximately -1.71.

2. $-3x - \sqrt{5} = \pi(x - 1)$

   Graph $y_1 = -3x - \sqrt{(5)}$ and $y_2 = \pi(x - 1)$ in a standard viewing window and find the intersection point.

   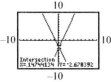

   Rounding to the nearest hundredth, the point of intersection $(0.15, -2.68)$ indicates that the solution is approximately 0.15.

3. $|6x - 5| - 3 = -2$
   $|6x - 5| = 1$
   $6x - 5 = 1 \quad$ or $\quad 6x - 5 = -1$
   $6x = 6 \quad$ or $\quad 6x = 4$
   $x = 1 \quad$ or $\quad x = \dfrac{2}{3}$

4. $|8 - 2t| = -6$
   No solution, $\varnothing$

5. $3(2x - 7) - 4x > -(x + 6)$
   $6x - 21 - 4x > -x - 6$
   $2x - 21 > -x - 6$
   $3x > 15$
   $x > 5$

   $(5, \infty)$

6. $8 - \dfrac{x}{2} \geq 7$
   $2\left(8 - \dfrac{x}{2}\right) \geq 2(7)$
   $16 - x \geq 14$
   $-x \geq -2$
   $x \leq 2$

   The solution set is $(-\infty, 2]$.

7. $-3 < 2(x - 3) \leq 4$
   $-3 < 2x - 6 \leq 4$
   $3 < 2x \leq 10$
   $\dfrac{3}{2} < x \leq 5$

   $\left(\dfrac{3}{2}, 5\right]$

8. $|3x + 1| > 5$
   $3x + 1 < -5 \quad$ or $\quad 3x + 1 > 5$
   $3x < -6 \quad$ or $\quad 3x > 4$
   $x < -2 \quad$ or $\quad x > \dfrac{4}{3}$

   $(-\infty, -2) \cup \left(\dfrac{4}{3}, \infty\right)$

9. $x \leq -2$ and $x \leq -5$
   $x \leq -5$
   The solution set is $(-\infty, -5]$.

10. $x \leq -2$ or $x \leq -5$
    $x \leq -2$
    The solution set is $(-\infty, -2]$.

11. $-x > 1 \quad$ and $\quad 3x + 3 \geq x - 3$
    $x < -1$ and $\qquad 2x \geq -6$
    $\qquad\qquad\qquad\qquad x \geq -3$
    $-3 \leq x < -1$
    The solution set is $[-3, -1)$.

12. $6x + 1 > 5x + 4 \quad$ or $\quad 1 - x > -4$
    $x > 3 \qquad\qquad$ or $\qquad 5 > x$

    $(-\infty, \infty)$

13. $|x-5|-4<-2$

$|x-5|<2$

$-2<x-5<2$

$3<x<7$

$(3,7)$

14. $\left|\dfrac{5x-7}{2}\right|=4$

$\dfrac{5x-7}{2}=4$ or $\dfrac{5x-7}{2}=-4$

$5x-7=8$ or $5x-7=-8$

$5x=15$ or $5x=-1$

$x=3$ or $x=-\dfrac{1}{5}$

The solution set is $\left\{-\dfrac{1}{5},\ 3\right\}$.

15. $\left|17x-\dfrac{1}{5}\right|>-2$ is true for all real values of x.

The solution set is $(-\infty,\infty)$.

16. $|x-5|=|x+2|$

$x-5=x+2$ or $x-5=-(x+2)$

$-5=2$ False or $x-5=-x-2$

                            $2x=3$

                             $x=\dfrac{3}{2}$

Since $-5=2$ is not possible, the only solution is $\dfrac{3}{2}$.

17. $x\le-4$

Graph a solid boundary line and shade the half-plane to the left of $x=-4$.

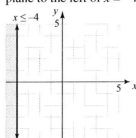

18. $2x-y>5$

$y<2x-5$

Graph the boundary line as a dashed line.
Test: $(0,0)$
$2(0)-0>5$ False
Shade the half-plane that does not contain the

point $(0,0)$.

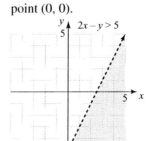

19. $2x+4y<6$ and $y\le-4$

$4y<-2x+6$ and $y\le-4$

$y<-\dfrac{1}{2}x+\dfrac{3}{2}$ and $y\le-4$

Graph each inequality. The intersection of the two inequalities is all points common to both regions, as shown by the shading in the graph below.

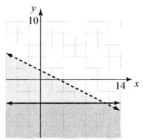

20. The graph of y_1 is below the graph of y_2 when $x<-3$. Thus, the solution of the inequality $y_1<y_2$ is $(-\infty,-3)$.

21. The graph of y_1 is above the graph of y_2 when $x>-3$. Thus, the solution of the inequality $y_1>y_2$ is $(-3,\infty)$.

22. Solve $R>C$.

$7.4x>3910+2.8x$

$4.6x>3910$

$x>850$

Therefore, more than 850 sunglasses must be produced and sold in order for them to yield a profit.

Chapter 3 Cumulative Review

1. a. $\{101, 102, 103, \dots\}$

   b. $\{2, 3, 4, 5\}$

2. a. $\{-2, -1, 0, 1, 2, 3, 4\}$

   b. $\{4\}$

3. a. $|3| = 3$

   b. $|-5| = 5$

   c. $-|2| = -2$

   d. $-|-8| = -8$

   e. $|0| = 0$

4. a. The opposite of $\dfrac{2}{3}$ is $-\dfrac{2}{3}$.

   b. The opposite of -9 is 9.

   c. The opposite of 1.5 is -1.5.

5. a. $-3 + (-11) = -14$

   b. $3 + (-7) = -4$

   c. $-10 + 15 = 5$

   d. $-8.3 + (-1.9) = -10.2$

   e. $-\dfrac{2}{3} + \dfrac{3}{7} = -\dfrac{14}{21} + \dfrac{9}{21} = -\dfrac{5}{21}$

6. a. $-2 - (-10) = -2 + 10 = 8$

   b. $1.7 - 8.9 = -7.2$

   c. $-\dfrac{1}{2} - \dfrac{1}{4} = -\dfrac{2}{4} - \dfrac{1}{4} = -\dfrac{3}{4}$

7. a. $\sqrt{9} = 3$ since $3^2 = 9$.

   b. $\sqrt{25} = 5$ since $5^2 = 25$.

   c. $\sqrt{\dfrac{1}{4}} = \dfrac{1}{2}$ since $\left(\dfrac{1}{2}\right)^2 = \dfrac{1}{4}$.

   d. $-\sqrt{36} = -6$ since $6^2 = 36$.

   e. $\sqrt{-36}$ is not a real number.

8. a. $-3(-2) = 6$

   b. $-\dfrac{3}{4}\left(-\dfrac{4}{7}\right) = \dfrac{3}{7}$

   c. $\dfrac{0}{-2} = 0$

   d. $\dfrac{-20}{-2} = 10$

9. a. $z - y = (-3) - (-1) = -2$

   b. $z^2 = (-3)^2 = 9$

   c. $\dfrac{2x + y}{z} = \dfrac{2(2) + (-1)}{-3} = \dfrac{3}{-3} = -1$

10. a. $\sqrt[4]{1} = 1$ since $1^4 = 1$.

   b. $\sqrt[3]{8} = 2$ since $2^3 = 8$.

   c. $\sqrt[4]{81} = 3$ since $3^4 = 81$.

11. a. $x + 5 = 20$

   b. $2(3 + y) = 4$

   c. $x - 8 = 2x$

   d. $\dfrac{z}{9} = 9 + z$

12. a. $-3 > -5$ since -3 is to the right of -5 on the number line.

   b. $\dfrac{-12}{-4} = 3$

   c. $0 > -2$ since 0 is to the right of -2 on the number line.

13. $7x + 5 = 5 + 7x$

14. $5 \cdot (7x) = (5 \cdot 7)x = 35x$

15. $2x + 5 = 9$
$$2x = 4$$
$$x = 2$$

16. $11.2 = 1.2 - 5x$
$$10 = -5x$$
$$-2 = x$$

17. $6x - 4 = 2 + 6(x - 1)$
$6x - 4 = 2 + 6x - 6$
$6x - 4 = 6x - 4$
$-4 = -4,$ which is always true.
All real numbers

18. $2x + 1.5 = -0.2 + 1.6x$
$0.4x = -1.7$
$x = -4.25$

19. a. Let $x =$ the first integer. Then
$x + 1 =$ the second integer and
$x + 2 =$ the third integer.
$x + (x + 1) + (x + 2) = 3x + 3$

   b. $x + (5x) + (6x - 3) = 12x - 3$

20. a. Let $x =$ the first integer. Then
$x + 1 =$ the second integer and
$x + 2 =$ the third integer.
$x + (x + 1) + (x + 2) = 3x + 3$

   b. $4(3x + 1) = 12x + 4$

21. Let $x =$ first number, then
$2x + 3 =$ second number and
$4x =$ third number.
$x + (2x + 3) + 4x = 164$
$7x + 3 = 164$
$7x = 161$
$x = 23$
$2x + 3 = 2(23) + 3 = 49$
$4x = 4(23) = 92$
The three numbers are 23, 49 and 92.

22. Let $x =$ first number, then
$3x + 2 =$ second number.
$(3x + 2) - x = 24$
$2x + 2 = 24$
$2x = 22$
$x = 11$
$3x + 2 = 3(11) + 2 = 35$
The two numbers are 11 and 35.

23. $3y - 2x = 7$
$3y = 2x + 7$
$y = \dfrac{2x + 7}{3},$ or $y = \dfrac{2x}{3} + \dfrac{7}{3}$

24. $7x - 4y = 10$
$7x = 4y + 10$
$x = \dfrac{4y + 10}{7},$ or $x = \dfrac{4y}{7} + \dfrac{10}{7}$

25. $A = \dfrac{1}{2}(B + b)h$
$2A = (B + b)h$
$2A = Bh + bh$
$2A - Bh = bh$
$\dfrac{2A - Bh}{h} = b$

26. $P = 2l + 2w$
$P - 2w = 2l$
$\dfrac{P - 2w}{2} = l$

27. a. $\{x \mid x \geq 2\}$

    $[2, \infty)$

   b. $\{x \mid x < -1\}$

    $(-\infty, -1)$

   c. $\{x \mid 0.5 < x \leq 3\}$

    $(0.5, 3]$

28. a. $\{x \mid x \leq -3\}$

    $(-\infty, -3]$

   b. $\{x \mid -2 \leq x < 0.1\}$

    $[-2, 0.1)$

29. $-(x - 3) + 2 \leq 3(2x - 5) + x$
$-x + 3 + 2 \leq 6x - 15 + x$
$-x + 5 \leq 7x - 15$
$20 \leq 8x$
$\dfrac{5}{2} \leq x$

$\left[\dfrac{5}{2}, \infty\right)$

30. $2(7x - 1) - 5x > -(-7x) + 4$
$14x - 2 - 5x > 7x + 4$
$9x - 2 > 7x + 4$
$2x > 6$
$x > 3$

$(3, \infty)$

31. a. $2(x+3) > 2x+1$
$$2x+6 > 2x+1$$
$$6 > 1; \text{ True for all real numbers } x.$$
$$(-\infty, \infty)$$

b. $2(x+3) < 2x+1$
$$2x+6 < 2x+1$$
$$6 < 1; \text{ False}$$
$$\varnothing$$

32. $4(x+1)-3 < 4x+1$
$$4x+4-3 < 4x+1$$
$$4x+1 < 4x+1$$
$$1 < 1 \quad \text{Never true}$$
$$\varnothing$$

33. $A = \{2, 4, 6, 8\}$, $B = \{3, 4, 5, 6\}$; the numbers 4 and 6 are in both sets so the intersection of A and B is $\{4, 6\}$.

34. The elements in either set or both sets are $-2, -1, 0, 1, 2, 3, 4,$ and 5, so the union is $\{-2, -1, 0, 1, 2, 3, 4, 5\}$.

35. $x - 7 < 2$ and $2x + 1 < 9$
$$x < 9 \quad \text{and} \quad 2x < 8$$
$$x < 4$$
$$x < 4$$
$$(-\infty, 4)$$

36. $x + 3 \le 1$ or $3x - 1 < 8$
$$x \le -2 \quad \text{or} \quad 3x < 9$$
$$x < 3$$
$$x < 3$$
$$(-\infty, 3)$$

37. $A = \{2, 4, 6, 8\}$ and $B = \{3, 4, 5, 6\}$, so the union of A and B is $\{2, 3, 4, 5, 6, 8\}$.

38. $\varnothing$; there are no elements in common.

39. $-2x - 5 < -3$ or $6x < 0$
$$-2x < 2 \quad \text{or} \quad x < 0$$
$$x > -1$$
All real numbers
$$(-\infty, \infty)$$

40. $-2x - 5 < -3$ and $6x < 0$
$$-2x < 2 \quad \text{and} \quad x < 0$$
$$x > -1$$
$$-1 < x < 0$$
$$(-1, 0)$$

41. $|p| = 2$
$$p = 2 \quad \text{or} \quad p = -2$$

42. $|x| = 5$
$$x = 5 \quad \text{or} \quad x = -5$$

43. $\left|\dfrac{x}{2} - 1\right| = 11$
$$\frac{x}{2} - 1 = 11 \quad \text{or} \quad \frac{x}{2} - 1 = -11$$
$$\frac{x}{2} = 12 \quad \text{or} \quad \frac{x}{2} = -10$$
$$x = 24 \quad \text{or} \quad x = -20$$

44. $\left|\dfrac{y}{3} + 2\right| = 10$
$$\frac{y}{3} + 2 = 10 \quad \text{or} \quad \frac{y}{3} + 2 = -10$$
$$\frac{y}{3} = 8 \quad \text{or} \quad \frac{y}{3} = -12$$
$$y = 24 \quad \text{or} \quad y = -36$$

45. $|x - 3| = |5 - x|$
$$x - 3 = 5 - x \quad \text{or} \quad x - 3 = -(5 - x)$$
$$2x = 8 \quad\quad \text{or} \quad x - 3 = -5 + x$$
$$x = 4 \quad\quad \text{or} \quad -3 = -5$$
Since $-3 = -5$ is not possible, the only solution is 4.

46. $|x + 3| = |7 - x|$
$$x + 3 = 7 - x \quad \text{or} \quad x + 3 = -(7 - x)$$
$$2x = 4 \quad\quad \text{or} \quad x - 3 = -7 + x$$
$$x = 2 \quad\quad \text{or} \quad -3 = -7$$
Since $-3 = -7$ is not possible, the only solution is 2.

47. $|x| \le 3$
$$-3 \le x \le 3$$
$$[-3, 3]$$

48. $|x| > 1$
$$x < -1 \quad \text{or} \quad x > 1$$
$$(-\infty, -1) \cup (1, \infty)$$

49. $|2x + 9| + 5 > 3$
$$|2x + 9| > -2$$
Since $|2x + 9|$ is nonnegative for all numbers x, the solution set is $(-\infty, \infty)$.

50. $|3x + 1| + 9 < 1$
$$|3x + 1| < -8$$
The solution set is $\varnothing$.

Chapter 4

Section 4.1

Practice Exercises

1. a. $\begin{cases} -x - 4y = 1 \\ 2x + y = 5 \end{cases}$

Replace x with 3 and y with -1 in each equation.

$$-x - 4y = 1$$
$$-3 - 4(-1) \stackrel{?}{=} 1$$
$$-3 + 4 \stackrel{?}{=} 1$$
$$1 = 1 \quad \text{True}$$

$$2x + y = 5$$
$$2(3) + (-1) \stackrel{?}{=} 5$$
$$6 - 1 \stackrel{?}{=} 5$$
$$5 = 5 \quad \text{True}$$

Since $(3, -1)$ makes both equations true, it is a solution.

b. $\begin{cases} 4x + y = -4 \\ -x + 3y = 8 \end{cases}$

Replace x with -2 and y with 4 in each equation.

$$4x + y = -4$$
$$4(-2) + 4 \stackrel{?}{=} -4$$
$$-8 + 4 \stackrel{?}{=} -4$$
$$-4 = -4 \quad \text{True}$$

$$-x + 3y = 8$$
$$-(-2) + 3(4) \stackrel{?}{=} 8$$
$$2 + 12 \stackrel{?}{=} 8$$
$$14 = 8 \quad \text{False}$$

Since $(-2, 4)$ does not make both equations true, it is not a solution.

2. a. $\begin{cases} 3x - 2y = 4 \\ -9x + 6y = -12 \end{cases}$

Solve each equation for y.

$$\begin{cases} y = \dfrac{4 - 3x}{-2} \\ y = \dfrac{-12 + 9x}{6} \end{cases}$$

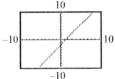

The graphs appear to be the same line. Notice that if both sides of the first equation are multiplied by -3, the result is the second equation. Any solution of one equation satisfies the other equation as well. There are an infinite number of solutions in the form $\{(x, y) | 3x - 2y = 4\}$ or $\{(x, y) | -9x + 6y = -12\}$.

b. $\begin{cases} y = 5x \\ 2x + y = 7 \end{cases}$

Solve the second equation for y.

$$\begin{cases} y = 5x \\ y = 7 - 2x \end{cases}$$

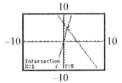

$(1, 5)$ is the solution of the system.

c. $\begin{cases} y = \dfrac{3}{4}x + 1 \\ 3x - 4y = 12 \end{cases}$

Solve the second equation for y.

$$\begin{cases} y = \dfrac{3}{4}x + 1 \\ y = \dfrac{12 - 3x}{4} \end{cases}$$

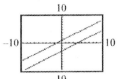

The lines appear to be parallel. The first equation is in point-slope. Write the second equation in point-slope form.

$$3x - 4y = 12$$
$$-4y = -3x + 12$$
$$y = \frac{3}{4}x - 3$$

The graphs have the same slope, $\dfrac{3}{4}$, but different y-intercepts, so the lines are parallel. The system has no solution.

170

3. $\begin{cases} y - 0.25x = 1.6 \\ y + 1.03x = -5.1 \end{cases}$

Solve both equations for y.

$\begin{cases} y = 1.6 + 0.25x \\ y = -5.1 - 1.03x \end{cases}$

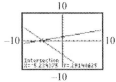

The approximate point of intersection is $(-5.23, 0.29)$.

4. $\begin{cases} y = 4x + 7 \\ 2x + y = 4 \end{cases}$

In the first equation, we are told that y is equal to $4x + 7$, so we substitute $4x + 7$ for y in the second equation and solve for x.

$$2x + y = 4$$
$$2x + (4x + 7) = 4$$
$$6x + 7 = 4$$
$$6x = -3$$
$$x = \frac{-3}{6} = -\frac{1}{2}$$

To find the y-coordinate, we replace x with $-\frac{1}{2}$ in the first equation.

$$y = 4x + 7$$
$$y = 4\left(-\frac{1}{2}\right) + 7$$
$$y = -2 + 7 = 5$$

The solution is $\left(-\frac{1}{2}, 5\right)$.

5. $\begin{cases} -\dfrac{x}{3} + \dfrac{y}{4} = \dfrac{1}{2} \\ \dfrac{x}{4} - \dfrac{y}{2} = -\dfrac{1}{4} \end{cases}$

Multiply each equation by its LCD to clear fractions.

$$\begin{cases} 12\left(-\dfrac{x}{3} + \dfrac{y}{4}\right) = 12\left(\dfrac{1}{2}\right) \\ 4\left(\dfrac{x}{4} - \dfrac{y}{2}\right) = 4\left(-\dfrac{1}{4}\right) \end{cases}$$

$$\begin{cases} -4x + 3y = 6 \\ x - 2y = -1 \end{cases}$$

Solve the second equation for x.

$$x - 2y = -1$$
$$x = 2y - 1$$

Replace x with $2y - 1$ in the first equation.

$$-4x + 3y = 6$$
$$-4(2y - 1) + 3y = 6$$
$$-8y + 4 + 3y = 6$$
$$-5y + 4 = 6$$
$$-5y = 2$$
$$y = -\frac{2}{5}$$

To find the x-coordinate, replace y with $-\dfrac{2}{5}$ in $x = 2y - 1$.

$$x = 2\left(-\frac{2}{5}\right) - 1 = -\frac{4}{5} - 1 = -\frac{4}{5} - \frac{5}{5} = -\frac{9}{5}$$

The solution is $\left(-\dfrac{9}{5}, -\dfrac{2}{5}\right)$.

6. $\begin{cases} 3x - y = 5 \\ 5x + y = 11 \end{cases}$

We add the equations.

$$\begin{array}{r} 3x - y = 5 \\ 5x + y = 11 \\ \hline 8x \quad\;\; = 16 \\ x = 2 \end{array}$$

Replace x with 2 in the second equation to find y.

$$5x + y = 11$$
$$5(2) + y = 11$$
$$10 + y = 11$$
$$y = 1$$

The solution is $(2, 1)$.

7. $\begin{cases} 3x - 2y = -6 \\ 4x + 5y = -8 \end{cases}$

We can eliminate y if we multiply both sides of the first equation by 5 and both sides of the second equation by 2.

$$\begin{cases} 5(3x - 2y) = 5(-6) \\ 2(4x + 5y) = 2(-8) \end{cases}$$

$$\begin{array}{r} \begin{cases} 15x - 10y = -30 \\ 8x + 10y = -16 \end{cases} \\ \hline 23x \qquad\;\; = -46 \\ x = -2 \end{array}$$

To find y, replace x with -2 in either equation.

$$4x + 5y = -8$$
$$4(-2) + 5y = -8$$
$$-8 + 5y = -8$$
$$5y = 0$$
$$y = 0$$

The solution is $(-2, 0)$.

8. $\begin{cases} 8x + y = 6 \\ 2x + \dfrac{y}{4} = -2 \end{cases}$

If we multiply the second equation by -4, the coefficients of x will be opposites.

$\begin{cases} 8x + y = 6 \\ -4\left(2x + \dfrac{y}{4}\right) = -4(-2) \end{cases}$

$\begin{cases} 8x + y = 6 \\ -8x - y = 8 \end{cases}$

$\overline{\qquad 0 = 14 \quad \text{False}}$

The system has no solution. The solution set is $\{\ \}$ or $\varnothing$.

9. $\begin{cases} -3x + 2y = -1 \\ 9x - 6y = 3 \end{cases}$

To eliminate x, we multiply both sides of the first equation by 3.

$\begin{cases} 3(-3x + 2y) = 3(-1) \\ 9x - 6y = 3 \end{cases}$

$\begin{cases} -9x + 6y = -3 \\ 9x - 6y = 3 \end{cases}$

$\overline{\qquad\quad 0 = 0 \quad \text{True}}$

There are an infinite number of solutions. The solution set is $\{(x, y) | -3x + 2y = -1\}$ or $\{(x, y) | 9x - 6y = 3\}$.

10. The break-even point is the solution of the system.

$\begin{cases} y = 17x \\ y = 6x + 8030 \end{cases}$

The company breaks even when 730 units are produced and sold.

Vocabulary and Readiness Check

1. A system with no solution has lines that are parallel. The correct graph is B.

2. A system with an infinite number of solutions has lines that are the same. The correct graph is C.

3. A system with solution $(1, -2)$ has lines that intersect at $(1, -2)$. The correct graph is A.

4. A system with solution $(-3, 0)$ has lines that intersect at $(-3, 0)$. The correct graph is D.

Exercise Set 4.1

2. $\begin{cases} x - y = -4 \\ 2x + 10y = 4 \end{cases}$

$x - y = -4$
$-3 - 1 \stackrel{?}{=} -4$
$\quad -4 = -4 \quad \text{True}$
$2x + 10y = 4$
$2(-3) + 10(1) \stackrel{?}{=} 4$
$\qquad\qquad 4 = 4 \quad \text{True}$

Yes, $(-3, 1)$ is a solution.

4. $\begin{cases} 2x - 5y = -2 \\ 3x + 4y = 4 \end{cases}$

$2x - 5y = -2$
$2(4) - 5(2) \stackrel{?}{=} -2$
$\qquad\quad -2 = -2 \quad \text{True}$
$3x + 4y = 4$
$3(4) + 4(2) \stackrel{?}{=} 4$
$\qquad\quad 20 = 4 \quad \text{False}$

No, $(4, 2)$ is not a solution.

6. $\begin{cases} 4x + 5y = -7 \\ -8x = 3y - 1 \end{cases}$

$4x + 5y = -7$
$4\left(\dfrac{3}{4}\right) + 5(-2) \stackrel{?}{=} -7$
$3 + (-10) \stackrel{?}{=} -7$
$\qquad\qquad -7 = -7 \quad \text{True}$
$-8x = 3y - 1$
$-8\left(\dfrac{3}{4}\right) \stackrel{?}{=} 3(-2) - 1$
$\qquad -6 \stackrel{?}{=} -6 - 1$
$\qquad -6 = -7 \quad \text{False}$

No, $\left(\dfrac{3}{4}, -2\right)$ is not a solution.

8. The solution appears to be $(2, -1)$.

The solution is $(2, -1)$.

10. The solution appears to be $(2.6, -2.8)$.

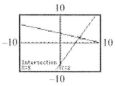

The solution is $(2.6, -2.8)$.

12. $\begin{cases} 2x - y = 8 \\ x + 3y = 11 \end{cases}$

Solve both equations for y.

$\begin{cases} y = 2x - 8 \\ y = \dfrac{11 - x}{3} \end{cases}$

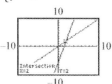

The solution is $(5, 2)$.

14. $\begin{cases} 4x - y = 6 \\ x - y = 0 \end{cases}$

Solve both equations for y.

$\begin{cases} y = 4x - 6 \\ y = x \end{cases}$

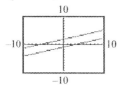

The solution is $(2, 2)$.

16. $\begin{cases} -x + 3y = 6 \\ 3x - 9y = 9 \end{cases}$

Solve both equations for y.

$\begin{cases} y = \dfrac{6 + x}{3} \\ y = \dfrac{9 - 3x}{-9} \end{cases}$

The solution set is $\varnothing$.

18. 0, 1, or 2. Answers may vary.

20. $\begin{cases} 5x + 2y = -17 \\ x = 3y \end{cases}$

Replace x with $3y$ in E1.

$5(3y) + 2y = -17$

$17y = -17$

$y = -1$

Replace y with -1 in E2.

$x = 3(-1) = -3$

The solution is $(-3, -1)$.

22. $\begin{cases} 3x - y = 6 \\ -4x + 2y = -8 \end{cases}$

Solve E1 for y: $y = 3x - 6$

Replace y with $3x - 6$ in E2.

$-4x + 2(3x - 6) = -8$

$-4x + 6x - 12 = -8$

$2x = 4$

$x = 2$

Replace x with 2 in E1.

$3(2) - y = 6$

$y = 0$

The solution is $(2, 0)$.

24. $\begin{cases} \dfrac{2}{5}x + \dfrac{1}{5}y = -1 \\ x + \dfrac{2}{5}y = -\dfrac{8}{5} \end{cases}$

Clear fractions by multiplying each equation by 5.

$\begin{cases} 2x + y = -5 \\ 5x + 2y = -8 \end{cases}$

Now solve E1 for y: $y = -2x - 5$.

Replace y with $-2x - 5$ in E2.

$5x + 2(-2x - 5) = -8$

$5x - 4x - 10 = -8$

$x = 2$

Replace x with 2 in equation $y = -2x - 5$.

$y = -2(2) - 5 = -9$

The solution is $(2, -9)$.

26. $\begin{cases} \dfrac{x}{8} - \dfrac{y}{2} = 1 \\ \dfrac{x}{3} - y = 2 \end{cases}$

Clear fractions by multiplying E1 by 8 and E2 by 3.

$\begin{cases} x - 4y = 8 \\ x - 3y = 6 \end{cases}$

Solve E1 for x.

$x = 4y + 8$

Replace x with $4y + 8$ in the equation $x - 3y = 6$.

$(4y + 8) - 3y = 6$

$y + 8 = 6$

$y = -2$

Replace y with -2 in equation $x = 4y + 8$.

$x = 4(-2) + 8 = 0$

The solution is $(0, -2)$.

28. $\begin{cases} -2x + 3y = 0 \\ 2x + 6y = 3 \end{cases}$

Multiply E1 by -2.

$\begin{cases} 4x - 6y = 0 \\ 2x + 6y = 3 \end{cases}$

E1 + E2: $\begin{array}{r} 4x - 6y = 0 \\ 2x + 6y = 3 \\ \hline 6x\qquad = 3 \\ x = \dfrac{1}{2} \end{array}$

Replace x with $\dfrac{1}{2}$ in E1.

$-2\left(\dfrac{1}{2}\right) + 3y = 0$

$3y = 1$

$y = \dfrac{1}{3}$

The solution is $\left(\dfrac{1}{2}, \dfrac{1}{3}\right)$.

30. $\begin{cases} 6x - y = -5 \\ 4x - 2y = 6 \end{cases}$

Multiply E1 by -2.

$\begin{cases} -12x + 2y = 10 \\ 4x - 2y = 6 \end{cases}$

Add these equations to get $-8x = 16$

$x = -2$.

Replace x with -2 in E1.

$6(-2) - y = -5$

$-12 - y = -5$

$y = -7$

The solution is $(-2, -7)$.

32. $\begin{cases} \dfrac{2}{3}x + \dfrac{1}{4}y = -\dfrac{3}{2} \\ \dfrac{1}{2}x - \dfrac{1}{4}y = -2 \end{cases}$

Clear fractions by multiplying E1 by 12 and E2 by 4.

$\begin{cases} 8x + 3y = -18 \\ 2x - y = -8 \end{cases}$

Multiply E2 by 3.

$\begin{cases} 8x + 3y = -18 \\ 6x - 3y = -24 \end{cases}$

Add these equations to get $14x = -42$

$x = -3$.

Replace x with -3 in the equation $2x - y = -8$.

$2(-3) - y = -8$

$-6 - y = -8$

$y = 2$

The solution is $(-3, 2)$.

34. $\begin{cases} 6x - 3y = -3 \\ 4x + 5y = -9 \end{cases}$

Multiply E1 by 5 and E2 by 3.

$\begin{cases} 30x - 15y = -15 \\ 12x + 15y = -27 \end{cases}$

Add these equations to get $42x = -42$

$x = -1$.

Replace x with -1 in E2.

$4(-1) + 5y = -9$

$5y = -5$

$y = -1$

The solution is $(-1, -1)$.

36. $\begin{cases} -x + 3y = 6 \\ 3x - 9y = 9 \end{cases}$

Multiply E1 by 3.

$\begin{cases} -3x + 9y = 18 \\ 3x - 9y = 9 \end{cases}$

Add these equations to get $0 = 27$, which is false. Inconsistent system; the solution set is $\varnothing$.

38. $\begin{cases} y = 2x - 5 \\ 8x - 4y = 20 \end{cases}$

$\begin{cases} -2x + y = -5 \\ 8x - 4y = 20 \end{cases}$

Multiply E1 by 4.

$\begin{cases} -8x + 4y = -20 \\ 8x - 4y = 20 \end{cases}$

Add these equations to get $0 = 0$, which is always true.

Dependent system; the solution set is $\{(x, y) \mid y = 2x - 5\}$.

40. $\begin{cases} x - 4y = -5 \\ -3x - 8y = 0 \end{cases}$

Multiply E1 by 3.

$\begin{cases} 3x - 12y = -15 \\ -3x - 8y = 0 \end{cases}$

Add these equations to get $-20y = -15$

$$y = \frac{3}{4}.$$

Replace y with $\frac{3}{4}$ in E1.

$x - 4\left(\dfrac{3}{4}\right) = -5$

$x - 3 = -5$

$x = -2$

The solution is $\left(-2, \dfrac{3}{4}\right)$.

42. $\begin{cases} 2x - y = 8 \\ x + 3y = 11 \end{cases}$

Multiply E1 by 3.

$\begin{cases} 6x - 3y = 24 \\ x + 3y = 11 \end{cases}$

Add these equations to get $7x = 35$

$x = 5.$

Replace x with 5 in E1.

$2(5) - y = 8$

$y = 2$

The solution is $(5, 2)$.

44. $\begin{cases} \dfrac{3}{4}x - \dfrac{1}{2}y = -\dfrac{1}{2} \\ x + y = -\dfrac{3}{2} \end{cases}$

Clear fractions by multiplying E1 by 4 and E2 by 2.

$\begin{cases} 3x - 2y = -2 \\ 2x + 2y = -3 \end{cases}$

Add these equations to get $5x = -5$

$x = -1.$

Replace x with -1 in the equation $2x + 2y = -3$.

$2(-1) + 2y = -3$

$2y = -1$

$y = -\dfrac{1}{2}$

The solution is $\left(-1, -\dfrac{1}{2}\right)$.

46. $\begin{cases} x = 3y - 1 \\ 2x - 6y = -2 \end{cases}$

Replace x with $3y - 1$ in E2.

$2(3y - 1) - 6y = -2$

$6y - 2 - 6y = -2$

$-2 = -2$ True

Dependent system; the solution set is $\{(x, y) | x = 3y - 1\}$.

48. $\begin{cases} 3x + 6y = 15 \\ 2x + 4y = 3 \end{cases}$

Multiply E1 by -2, E2 by 3, and add.

$-6x - 12y = -30$

$\underline{6x + 12y = 9}$

$0 = -21$ False

Inconsistent system; the solution set is $\varnothing$.

50. $\begin{cases} 3x + 4y = 0 \\ 7x = 3y \end{cases}$

$\begin{cases} 3x + 4y = 0 \\ 7x - 3y = 0 \end{cases}$

Multiply E1 by 3, E2 by 4, and add.

$9x + 12y = 0$

$\underline{28x - 12y = 0}$

$37x = 0$

$x = 0$

Replace x with 0 in the equation $7x = 3y$.

$7(0) = 3y$

$0 = 3y$

$y = 0$

The solution is $(0, 0)$.

52. $\begin{cases} 3x + 4y = 2 \\ 2x + 5y = -1 \end{cases}$

Multiply E1 by 2 and E2 by -3.

$\begin{cases} 6x + 8y = 4 \\ -6x - 15y = 3 \end{cases}$

Add these equations to get $-7y = 7$

$y = -1.$

Replace y with -1 in E1.

$3x + 4(-1) = 2$

$3x = 6$

$x = 2$

The solution is $(2, -1)$.

54. $\begin{cases} y = \dfrac{1}{7}x + 3 \\ x - 7y = -21 \end{cases}$

Replace y with $\dfrac{1}{7}x + 3$ in E2.

$x - 7\left(\dfrac{1}{7}x + 3\right) = -21$

$x - x - 21 = -21$

$-21 = -21$ True

The system is dependent. The solution set is

$\left\{ (x,\ y) \middle| y = \dfrac{1}{7}x + 3 \right\}.$

56. $\begin{cases} x = \dfrac{1}{5}y \\ x - y = -4 \end{cases}$

Multiply E1 by 5.

$\begin{cases} 5x = y \\ x - y = -4 \end{cases}$

Replace y with $5x$ in E2.

$x - (5x) = -4$

$-4x = -4$

$x = 1$

Replace x with 1 in the equation $5x = y$ to get y
$= 5(1) = 5$. The solution is (1, 5).

58. $\begin{cases} x = 3y + 4 \\ -y = 5 \end{cases}$

E2 yields $y = -5$.
Replace y with -5 in E1.

$x = 3(-5) + 4 = -11$

The solution is (–11, –5).

60. $\begin{cases} \dfrac{y}{5} = \dfrac{8 - x}{2} \\ x = \dfrac{2y - 8}{3} \end{cases}$

Multiply E1 by 10 and E2 by 3.

$\begin{cases} 2y = 40 - 5x \\ 3x = 2y - 8 \end{cases}$

$\begin{cases} 5x + 2y = 40 \\ 3x - 2y = -8 \end{cases}$

Add these equations to get $8x = 32$
$x = 4.$

Replace x with 4 in the equation $2y = 40 - 5x$.

$2y = 40 - 5(4)$

$2y = 20$

$y = 10$

The solution is (4, 10).

62. $\begin{cases} 2x - 5y = 12 \\ -4x + 10y = 20 \end{cases}$

Multiply E1 by 2.

$\begin{cases} 4x - 10y = 24 \\ -4x + 10y = 20 \end{cases}$

Add to get $0 = 44$ which is false.
Inconsistent system; the solution set is $\varnothing$.

64. $\begin{cases} \dfrac{1}{2}x - \dfrac{1}{3}y = -3 \\ \dfrac{1}{8}x + \dfrac{1}{6}y = 0 \end{cases}$

Multiply E1 by 6 and E2 by 24.

$\begin{cases} 3x - 2y = -18 \\ 3x + 4y = 0 \end{cases}$

Multiply E1 by 2 and add to E2.
$\quad\begin{aligned} 6x - 4y &= -36 \\ 3x + 4y &= 0 \\ \hline 9x \quad\ \ &= -36 \\ x &= -4 \end{aligned}$

Replace x with –4 in the equation $3x + 4y = 0$.

$3(-4) + 4y = 0$

$-12 + 4y = 0$

$4y = 12$

$y = 3$

The solution is (–4, 3).

66. $\begin{cases} -0.7x + 0.6y = 1.3 \\ 0.5x - 0.3y = -0.8 \end{cases}$

Multiply both equations by 10.

$\begin{cases} -7x + 6y = 13 \\ 5x - 3y = -8 \end{cases}$

Multiply E2 by 2.

$\begin{cases} -7x + 6y = 13 \\ 10x - 6y = -16 \end{cases}$

Add these equations to get $3x = -3$
$x = -1.$

Replace x with –1 in the equation $-7x + 6y = 13$.

$-7(-1) + 6y = 13$

$7 + 6y = 13$

$6y = 6$

$y = 1$

The solution is (–1, 1).

68. $\begin{cases} x - 3y = -5.3 \\ 6.3x + 6y = 3.96 \end{cases}$

Multiply E1 by 2.

$\begin{cases} 2x - 6y = -10.6 \\ 6.3x + 6y = 3.96 \end{cases}$

Add these equations to get $8.3x = -6.64$

$$x = -\frac{6.64}{8.3} = -0.8.$$

Replace x with -0.8 in the equation
$x - 3y = -5.3$.

$-0.8 - 3y = -5.3$

$-3y = -4.5$

$y = 1.5$

The solution is $(-0.8, 1.5)$.

70. $x + 2y - z = 7$

$2 + 2(-3) - 3 \overset{?}{=} 7$

$-7 = 7$

False

72. $-4x + y - 8z = 4$

$-4(1) + 0 - 8(-1) \overset{?}{=} 4$

$-4 + 8 \overset{?}{=} 4$

$4 = 4$

True

74. $\begin{array}{r} x + 4y - 5z = 20 \\ 2x - 4y - 2z = -17 \\ \hline 3x \quad\quad - 7z = 3 \end{array}$

76. $\begin{array}{r} -9x - 8y - z = 31 \\ 9x + 4y - z = 12 \\ \hline -4y - 2z = 43 \end{array}$

78. Demand is greater than supply because the line representing demand is above that for supply.

80. For x-values greater than 5.

82. 1875 tubes must be sold to break even.

84. It loses money because cost is greater than revenue at $x = 1000$.

86. The company loses money for x-values less than 1875.

88. Answers may vary.

90. $\begin{cases} y = 230x + 8146 \\ y = 611x + 7378 \end{cases}$

a. The slope is the number of books (in thousands) added to the libraries each year.

b. Substitute $230x + 8146$ for y in the second equation.

$230x + 8146 = 611x + 7378$

$-381x = -768$

$$x = \frac{-768}{-381} \approx 2.016$$

Replace x with 2.016 in the first equation.

$y = 230(2.016) + 8146 = 8609.68$

The solution is $(2, 8610)$.

c. In year 2 (2004), the two libraries had the same number of books, about 8610 thousand.

92. $\begin{cases} x + \dfrac{2}{y} = 7 \\ 3x + \dfrac{3}{y} = 6 \end{cases}$

Replacing $\dfrac{1}{y}$ with b, we have

$\begin{cases} x + 2b = 7 \\ 3x + 3b = 6 \end{cases}$

Multiply E1 by -3 and add to E2 to get

$-3b = -15$

$b = 5$

Replace b with 5 in the equation $x + 2b = 7$.

$x + 2(5) = 7$

$x = -3$

Since $b = 5$, $y = \dfrac{1}{5}$.

The solution is $\left(-3, \dfrac{1}{5} \right)$.

94. $\begin{cases} \dfrac{2}{x} + \dfrac{3}{y} = 5 \\ \dfrac{5}{x} - \dfrac{3}{y} = 2 \end{cases}$

Replace $\dfrac{1}{x}$ with a and $\dfrac{1}{y}$ with b.

$\begin{cases} 2a + 3b = 5 \\ 5a - 3b = 2 \end{cases}$

Add these new equations to get $7a = 7$
$$a = 1.$$
Replace a with 1 in the equation $2a + 3b = 5$.
$$2(1) + 3b = 5$$
$$3b = 3$$
$$b = 1$$
Since $a = b = 1$, $x = y = 1$.
The solution is $(1, 1)$.

96.
$$\begin{cases} \dfrac{3}{x} - \dfrac{2}{y} = -18 \\ \dfrac{2}{x} + \dfrac{3}{y} = 1 \end{cases}$$

Replace $\dfrac{1}{x}$ with a and $\dfrac{1}{y}$ with b.
$$\begin{cases} 3a - 2b = -18 \\ 2a + 3b = 1 \end{cases}$$
Multiply E1 by 3 and E2 by 2 to obtain
$$\begin{cases} 9a - 6b = -54 \\ 4a + 6b = 2 \end{cases}$$
Add these equations to get $13a = -52$
$$a = -4.$$
Replace a with -4 in the equation $2a + 3b = 1$.
$$2(-4) + 3b = 1$$
$$3b = 9$$
$$b = 3$$
Since $a = -4$, $x = -\dfrac{1}{4}$. Similarly, $y = \dfrac{1}{3}$. The

solution is $\left(-\dfrac{1}{4}, \dfrac{1}{3} \right)$.

98.
$$\begin{cases} \dfrac{5}{x} + \dfrac{7}{y} = 1 \\ -\dfrac{10}{x} - \dfrac{14}{y} = 0 \end{cases}$$

Replace $\dfrac{1}{x}$ with a and $\dfrac{1}{y}$ with b.
$$\begin{cases} 5a + 7b = 1 \\ -10a - 14b = 0 \end{cases}$$
Multiply E1 by 2 and add to E2 to get
$$\begin{array}{r} 10a + 14b = 2 \\ -10a - 14b = 0 \\ \hline 0 = 2 \ \text{False} \end{array}$$
This system is inconsistent. The solution set is $\varnothing$.

Section 4.2

Practice Exercises

1.
$$\begin{cases} 3x + 2y - z = 0 \quad (1) \\ x - y + 5z = 2 \quad (2) \\ 2x + 3y + 3z = 7 \quad (3) \end{cases}$$

Multiply equation (2) by 2 and add to equation (1) to eliminate y.
$$\begin{cases} 3x + 2y - z = 0 \\ 2(x - y + 5z) = 2(2) \end{cases}$$
$$\begin{array}{r} 3x - 2y \ \ - z = 0 \\ 2x - 2y + 10z = 4 \\ \hline 5x \quad\quad + 9z = 4 \quad (4) \end{array}$$
Multiply equation (2) by 3 and add to equation (3) to eliminate y again.
$$\begin{cases} 3(x - y + 5z) = 3(2) \\ 2x + 3y + 3z = 7 \end{cases}$$
$$\begin{array}{r} 3x - 3y + 15z = 6 \\ 2x + 3y \ \ + 3z = 7 \\ \hline 5x + \quad 18z = 13 \quad (5) \end{array}$$
Multiply equation (4) by -1 and add to equation (5) to eliminate x.
$$\begin{cases} -1(5x + 9z) = -1(4) \\ 5x + 18z = 13 \end{cases}$$
$$\begin{array}{r} -5x \ \ - 9z = -4 \\ 5x + 18z = 13 \\ \hline 9z = 9 \\ z = 1 \end{array}$$
Replace z with 1 in equation (4) or (5).
$$5x + 9z = 4$$
$$5x + 9(1) = 4$$
$$5x = -5$$
$$x = -1$$
Replace x with -1 and z with 1 in equation (1), (2), or (3).
$$x - y + 5z = 2$$
$$-1 - y + 5(1) = 2$$
$$-y + 4 = 2$$
$$-y = -2$$
$$y = 2$$
The solution is $(-1, 2, 1)$. To check, let $x = -1$, $y = 2$, and $z = 1$ in all three original equations of the system.

2. $\begin{cases} 6x - 3y + 12z = 4 & (1) \\ -6x + 4y - 2z = 7 & (2) \\ -2x + y - 4z = 3 & (3) \end{cases}$

Multiply equation (3) by 3 and add to equation (1) to eliminate x.

$\begin{cases} 6x - 3y + 12z = 4 \\ 3(-2x + y - 4z) = 3(3) \end{cases}$

$\begin{cases} 6x - 3y + 12z = 4 \\ -6x + 3y - 12z = 9 \end{cases}$

$\overline{ \quad 0 = 13 \quad \text{False}}$

Since the statement is false, this system is inconsistent and has no solution. The solution set is $\{ \ \}$ or $\varnothing$.

3. $\begin{cases} 3x + 4y = 0 & (1) \\ 9x - 4z = 6 & (2) \\ -2y + 7z = 1 & (3) \end{cases}$

Equation (2) has no term containing the variable y. Eliminate y using equations (1) and (3). Multiply equation (3) by 2 and add to equation (1).

$\begin{cases} 3x + 4y = 0 \\ 2(-2y + 7z) = 2(1) \end{cases}$

$\begin{cases} 3x + 4y = 0 \\ -4y + 14z = 2 \end{cases}$

$\overline{3x + 14z = 2 \quad (4)}$

Multiply equation (4) by -3 and add to equation (2) to eliminate x.

$\begin{cases} 9x - 4z = 6 \\ -3(3x + 14z) = -3(2) \end{cases}$

$\begin{cases} 9x - 4z = 6 \\ -9x - 52z = -6 \end{cases}$

$\overline{ -56z = 0}$

$z = 0$

Replace z with 0 in equation (2) and solve for x.
$9x - 4z = 6$
$9x - 4(0) = 6$
$9x = 6$
$x = \dfrac{6}{9} = \dfrac{2}{3}$

Replace z with 0 in equation (3) and solve for y.
$-2y + 7z = 1$
$-2y + 7(0) = 1$
$-2y = 1$
$y = -\dfrac{1}{2}$

The solution is $\left(\dfrac{2}{3}, -\dfrac{1}{2}, 0 \right)$.

4. $\begin{cases} 2x + y - 3z = 6 & (1) \\ x + \dfrac{1}{2}y - \dfrac{3}{2}z = 3 & (2) \\ -4x - 2y + 6z = -12 & (3) \end{cases}$

Multiply both sides of equation (2) by 2 to eliminate fractions, and multiply both sides of equation (3) by $-\dfrac{1}{2}$ since all coefficients in equation (3) are divisible by 2 and the coefficient of x is negative. The resulting system is

$\begin{cases} 2x + y - 3z = 6 \\ 2x + y - 3z = 6 \\ 2x + y - 3z = 6 \end{cases}$

Since the three equations are identical, there are infinitely many solutions of the system. The equations are dependent. The solution set can be written as $\{(x, y, z) | 2x + y - 3z = 6\}$.

5. $\begin{cases} x + 2y + 4z = 16 & (1) \\ x + 2z = -4 & (2) \\ y - 3z = 30 & (3) \end{cases}$

Solve equation (2) for x and equation (3) for y.
$\begin{aligned} x + 2z &= -4 & y - 3z &= 30 \\ x &= -2z - 4 & y &= 3z + 30 \end{aligned}$

Substitute $-2z - 4$ for x and $3z + 30$ for y in equation (1) and solve for z.
$$x + 2y + 4z = 16$$
$$(-2z - 4) + 2(3z + 30) + 4z = 16$$
$$-2z - 4 + 6z + 60 + 4z = 16$$
$$8z + 56 = 16$$
$$8z = -40$$
$$z = -5$$
Use $x = -2z - 4$ to find x:
$x = -2(-5) - 4 = 10 - 4 = 6$.
Use $y = 3z + 30$ to find y:
$y = 3(-5) + 30 = -15 + 30 = 15$.
The solution is $(6, 15, -5)$.

Exercise Set 4.2

2. a. $\quad x + y + z = -1$
$\qquad 2 + 1 + (-4) \overset{?}{=} -1$
$\qquad\qquad\qquad -1 = -1$
$\qquad$ a is true.

b. $\quad x - y - z = -3$
$\qquad 2 - 1 - (-4) \overset{?}{=} -3$
$\qquad\qquad\qquad\quad 5 = -3$
$\qquad$ b is false.

c.
$$2x - y + z = -1$$
$$2(2) - 1 + (-4) \stackrel{?}{=} -1$$
$$-1 = -1$$
c is true.

d.
$$-x - 3y - z = -1$$
$$-2 - 3(1) - (-4) \stackrel{?}{=} -1$$
$$-1 = -1$$
d is true.

Equations a, c, and d.

4. No; answers may vary

6.
$$\begin{cases} x + y - z = -1 & (1) \\ -4x - y + 2z = -7 & (2) \\ 2x - 2y - 5z = 7 & (3) \end{cases}$$
Add E1 and E2.
$$-3x + z = -8$$
Multiply E1 by 2 and add to E3 to get
$$4x - 7z = 5$$
Solve the new system:
$$\begin{cases} -3x + z = -8 \\ 4x - 7z = 5 \end{cases}$$
Multiply the first equation by 7.
$$\begin{cases} -21x + 7z = -56 \\ 4x - 7z = 5 \end{cases}$$
Add the equations to get $-17x = -51$
$$x = 3.$$
Replace x with 3 in the equation $-3x + z = -8$.
$$-3(3) + z = -8$$
$$z = 1$$
Replace x with 3 and z with 1 in E1.
$$3 + y - 1 = -1$$
$$y = -3$$
The solution is $(3, -3, 1)$.

8.
$$\begin{cases} 5x = 5 & (1) \\ 2x + y = 4 & (2) \\ 3x + y - 4z = -15 & (3) \end{cases}$$
Solve E1 for x: $x = 1$
Replace x with 1 in E2.
$$2(1) + y = 4$$
$$y = 2$$
Replace x with 1 and y with 2 in E3.
$$3(1) + 2 - 4z = -15$$
$$5 - 4z = -15$$
$$-4z = -20$$
$$z = 5$$
The solution is $(1, 2, 5)$.

10.
$$\begin{cases} 2x - 3y + z = 5 & (1) \\ x + y + z = 0 & (2) \\ 4x + 2y + 4z = 4 & (3) \end{cases}$$
Multiply E2 by -1 and add to E1.
$$\begin{aligned} -x - y - z &= 0 \\ 2x - 3y + z &= 5 \\ \hline x - 4y &= 5 \quad (4) \end{aligned}$$
Multiply E2 by -4 and add to E3.
$$\begin{aligned} -4x - 4y - 4z &= 0 \\ 4x + 2y + 4z &= 4 \\ \hline -2y &= 4 \\ y &= -2 \end{aligned}$$
Replace y with -2 in E4.
$$x - 4(-2) = 5$$
$$x + 8 = 5$$
$$x = -3$$
Replace x with -3 and y with -2 in E2.
$$-3 + (-2) + z = 0$$
$$-5 + z = 0$$
$$z = 5$$
The solution is $(-3, -2, 5)$.

12.
$$\begin{cases} 3x + y - 2z = 2 & (1) \\ -6x - 2y + 4z = -2 & (2) \\ 9x + 3y - 6z = 6 & (3) \end{cases}$$
Multiply E1 by 2 and add to E2.
$$\begin{aligned} 6x + 2y - 4z &= 4 \\ -6x - 2y + 4z &= -2 \\ \hline 0 &= 2 \quad \text{False} \end{aligned}$$
Inconsistent system; the solution set is $\varnothing$.

14.
$$\begin{cases} 5y - 7z = 14 & (1) \\ 2x + y + 4z = 10 & (2) \\ 2x + 6y - 3z = 30 & (3) \end{cases}$$
Multiply E2 by -1 and add to E3.
$$\begin{aligned} -2x - y - 4z &= -10 \\ 2x + 6y - 3z &= 30 \\ \hline 5y - 7z &= 20 \quad (4) \end{aligned}$$
Multiply E4 by -1 and add to E1.
$$\begin{aligned} -5y + 7z &= -20 \\ 5y - 7z &= 14 \\ \hline 0 &= -6 \quad \text{False} \end{aligned}$$
Inconsistent system; the solution set is $\varnothing$.

16. $\begin{cases} x - 5y \quad\quad = 0 & (1) \\ x \quad\quad - z = 0 & (2) \\ -x \quad\quad + 5z = 0 & (3) \end{cases}$

Add E2 and E3.

$4z = 0$

$z = 0$

Replace z with 0 in E2.

$x - 0 = 0$

$x = 0$

Replace x with 0 in E1.

$0 - 5y = 0$

$y = 0$

The solution is $(0, 0, 0)$.

18. $\begin{cases} x + 2y \quad\quad = 6 & (1) \\ 7x + 3y + z = -33 & (2) \\ x \quad\quad - z = 16 & (3) \end{cases}$

Add E2 and E3.

$8x + 3y = -17$ (4)

Multiply E1 by -8 and to E4.

$-8x - 16y = -48$

$\underline{\quad 8x + 3y = -17 \quad}$

$-13y = -65$

$y = 5$

Replace y with 5 in E1.

$x + 2(5) = 6$

$x + 10 = 6$

$x = -4$

Replace x with -4 in E3.

$-4 - z = 16$

$z = -20$

The solution is $(-4, 5, -20)$.

20. $\begin{cases} 5x + y + 3z = 1 & (1) \\ x - y + 3z = -7 & (2) \\ -x + y \quad\quad = 1 & (3) \end{cases}$

Add E2 and E3.

$3z = -6$ or $z = -2$

Add E1 to E2.

$6x + 6z = -6$

$x + z = -1$

Replace z with -2 in this equation.

$x + (-2) = -1$ so $x = 1$

Replace x with 1 and z with -2 in E1.

$5(1) + y + 3(-2) = 1$

$y - 1 = 1$

$y = 2$

The solution is $(1, 2, -2)$.

22. $\begin{cases} 4x - y + 3z = 10 & (1) \\ x + y - z = 5 & (2) \\ 8x - 2y + 6z = 10 & (3) \end{cases}$

Multiply E1 by -2 and add to E3.

$-8x + 2y - 6z = -20$

$\underline{\quad 8x - 2y + 6z = 10 \quad}$

$0 = -10$ False

Inconsistent system; the solution set is $\varnothing$.

24. $\begin{cases} 4x + y - z = 8 & (1) \\ x - y + 2z = 3 & (2) \\ 3x - y + z = 6 & (3) \end{cases}$

Add E1 and E2.

$5x + z = 11$ (4)

Add E1 and E3.

$7x = 14$ or $x = 2$

Replace x with 2 in E4.

$5(2) + z = 11$

$z = 1$

Replace x with 2 and z with 1 in E1.

$4(2) + y - 1 = 8$

$y + 7 = 8$

$y = 1$

The solution is $(2, 1, 1)$.

26. $\begin{cases} -6x + 12y + 3z = -6 & (1) \\ 2x - 4y - z = 2 & (2) \\ -x + 2y + \dfrac{z}{2} = -1 & (3) \end{cases}$

Multiply E3 by 2 and add to E2.

$-2x + 4y + z = -2$

$\underline{\quad 2x - 4y - z = 2 \quad}$

$0 = 0$

The system is dependent. The solution set is $\{(x, y, z) | 2x - 4y - z = 2\}$.

28. $\begin{cases} 7x + 4y \quad\quad = 10 & (1) \\ x - 4y + 2z = 6 & (2) \\ y - 2z = -1 & (3) \end{cases}$

Add E1 to E2.

$8x + 2z = 16$ (4)

Add 4 times E3 to E2.

$4y - 8z = -4$

$\underline{\quad x - 4y + 2z = 6 \quad}$

$x \quad\quad - 6z = 2$ (5)

Add 3 times E4 to E5.

$$24x + 6z = 48$$
$$\underline{x - 6z = 2}$$
$$25x \quad\quad = 50$$
$$x = 2$$

Replace x with 2 in E5.
$$2 - 6z = 2$$
$$-6z = 0$$
$$z = 0$$

Replace z with 0 in E3 to get $y = -1$. The solution is $(2, -1, 0)$.

30. $\begin{cases} 3x - 3y + z = -1 & (1) \\ 3x - y - z = 3 & (2) \\ -6x + y + 2z = -6 & (3) \end{cases}$

Add E1 and E2.
$$6x - 4y = 2 \text{ or } 3x - 2y = 1 \quad (4)$$

Add twice E2 to E3.
$$6x - 2y - 2z = 6$$
$$\underline{-6x + y + 2z = -6}$$
$$-y \quad\quad = 0$$
$$y = 0$$

Replace y with 0 in E4.
$$3x - 2(0) = 1$$
$$3x = 1$$
$$x = \frac{1}{3}$$

Replace x with $\dfrac{1}{3}$ and y with 0 in E1.

$$3\left(\frac{1}{3}\right) - 3(0) + z = -1$$
$$1 + z = -1$$
$$z = -2$$

The solution is $\left(\dfrac{1}{3}, 0, -2\right)$.

32. $\begin{cases} \dfrac{1}{3}x - \dfrac{1}{4}y + z = -9 & (1) \\ \dfrac{1}{2}x - \dfrac{1}{3}y - \dfrac{1}{4}z = -6 & (2) \\ x - \dfrac{1}{2}y - z = -8 & (3) \end{cases}$

Multiply E1 and E2 by 12, and multiply E3 by 2.
$\begin{cases} 4x - 3y + 12z = -108 & (4) \\ 6x - 4y - 3z = -72 & (5) \\ 2x - y - 2z = -16 & (6) \end{cases}$

Add -3 times E6 to E4.

$$-6x + 3y + 6z = 48$$
$$\underline{4x - 3y + 12z = -108}$$
$$-2x \quad\quad + 18z = -60 \quad (7)$$

Add -4 times E6 to E5.
$$-8x + 4y + 8z = 64$$
$$\underline{6x - 4y - 3z = -72}$$
$$-2x \quad\quad + 5z = -8 \quad (8)$$

Add -1 times E7 to E8.
$$2x - 18z = 60$$
$$\underline{-2x + 5z = -8}$$
$$-13z = 52$$
$$z = -4$$

Replace z with -4 in E8.
$$-2x + 5(-4) = -8$$
$$-2x = 12$$
$$x = -6$$

Replace x with -6 and z with -4 in E6.
$$2(-6) - y - 2(-4) = -16$$
$$-4 - y = -16$$
$$y = 12$$

The solution is $(-6, 12, -4)$.

34. Let $x = $ the first number, then
$x + 5 = $ the second number.
$$2x + 5(x + 5) = 53$$
$$2x + 5x + 25 = 53$$
$$7x = 28$$
$$x = 4$$
$$x + 5 = 4 + 5 = 9$$
The numbers are 4 and 9.

36. $7(2x - 1) + 4 = 11(3x - 2)$
$$14x - 7 + 4 = 33x - 22$$
$$-19x = -19$$
$$x = 1$$

38. $z - 3(z + 7) = 6(2z + 1)$
$$z - 3z - 21 = 12z + 6$$
$$-2z - 21 = 12z + 6$$
$$-14z = 27$$
$$z = -\frac{27}{14}$$

40. Answers may vary

42. Answers may vary

44. $\begin{cases} x + 3y + z = -3 & (1) \\ -x + y + 2z = -14 & (2) \\ 3x + 2y - z = 12 & (3) \end{cases}$

Add E1 and E3.

$4x + 5y = 9$ (4)

Add –2 times E1 to E2.

$-2x - 6y - 2z = 6$

$\underline{-x + y + 2z = -14}$

$-3x - 5y \quad\quad = -8$ (5)

Add E4 and E5 to get $x = 1$.

Replace x with 1 in E4.

$4(1) + 5y = 9$

$\quad\quad 5y = 5$

$\quad\quad y = 1$

Replace x and y with 1 in E1.

$1 + 3(1) + z = -3$

$\quad z + 4 = -3$

$\quad\quad z = -7$

The solution is (1, 1, –7), and

$$\frac{x}{2} + \frac{y}{3} + \frac{z}{9} = \frac{1}{2} + \frac{1}{3} - \frac{7}{9}$$

$$= \frac{9}{18} + \frac{6}{18} - \frac{14}{18}$$

$$= \frac{1}{18}.$$

46. $\begin{cases} 5x + 4y \quad\quad\quad = 29 \ (1) \\ \quad\quad y + z - w = -2 \ (2) \\ 5x \quad\quad + z \quad\quad = 23 \ (3) \\ \quad\quad y - z + w = 4 \quad (4) \end{cases}$

Add E2 and E4.

$2y = 2$ or $y = 1$

Replace y with 1 in E1.

$5x + 4(1) = 29$

$\quad\quad 5x = 25$

$\quad\quad x = 5$

Replace x with 5 in E3.

$5(5) + z = 23$

$\quad\quad z = -2$

Replace y with 1 and z with –2 in E4.

$1 - (-2) + w = 4$

$\quad\quad\quad w = 1$

The solution is (5, 1, –2, 1).

48. $\begin{cases} 2x \quad\quad - z \quad\quad = -1 \ (1) \\ \quad\quad y + z + w = 9 \quad (2) \\ \quad\quad y \quad - 2w = -6 \ (3) \\ x + y \quad\quad\quad = 3 \quad (4) \end{cases}$

Solve E2 for w.

$w = 9 - y - z$ (5)

Substitute into E3.

$y - 2(9 - y - z) = -6$

$\quad\quad 3y + 2z = 12$ (6)

A new system is

$\begin{cases} 2x \quad\quad - z = -1 \ (7) \\ \quad\quad 3y + 2z = 12 \ (8) \\ x + y \quad\quad = 3 \quad (9) \end{cases}$

Add 2 times E7 and E8.

$4x \quad\quad - 2z = -2$

$\underline{\quad\quad 3y + 2z = 12}$

$4x + 3y \quad\quad = 10$ (10)

Add –4 times E9 to E10.

$-4x - 4y = -12$

$\underline{4x + 3y = 10}$

$\quad\quad - y = -2$

$\quad\quad\quad y = 2$

Replace y with 2 in E9.

$x + 2 = 3$

$\quad\quad x = 1$

Replace x with 1 in E7.

$2(1) - z = -1$

$\quad\quad 3 = z$

Replace y with 2 and z with 3 in E5.

$w = 9 - 2 - 3 = 4$

The solution is (1, 2, 3, 4).

50. Infinite number of solutions

Section 4.3

Practice Exercises

1. a. We are given a system of equations.

$\begin{cases} y = -0.16x + 113.9 \\ y = 1.06x + 62.3 \end{cases}$

We want to know the year x in which the pounds y are the same. Since both equations are solved for y, we use the substitution method. Substitute $-0.16x + 113.9$ for y in the second equation.

$-0.16x + 113.9 = 1.06x + 62.3$

$\quad\quad -1.22x = -51.6$

$$x = \frac{-51.6}{-1.22} \approx 42.30$$

Since we are only asked to give the year, we need only solve for x. The consumption of red meat and poultry will be the same about 42.30 years after 1995, or in about 2037.

b. Yes; answers may vary.

2. Let x = first number

y = second number

"A first number is five more than a second number" is translated as $x = y + 5$. "Twice the first number is 2 less than 3 times the second

number" is translated as $2x = 3y - 2$.
We solve the following system.
$$\begin{cases} x = y + 5 \\ 2x = 3y - 2 \end{cases}$$
Since the first equation is solved for x, we use substitution. Substitute $y + 5$ for x in the second equation.
$$2(y + 5) = 3y - 2$$
$$2y + 10 = 3y - 2$$
$$12 = y$$
Replace y with 12 in the equation $x = y + 5$ and solve for x.
$$x = 12 + 5 = 17$$
The numbers are 12 and 17.

3. Let x = speed of the V150
y = speed of the Atlantique
We summarize the information in a chart. Both trains have traveled two hours.

	Rate	•	Time	=	Distance
V150	x		2		$2x$
Atlantique	y		2		$2y$

The trains are 2150 kilometers apart, so the sum of the distances is 2150: $2x + 2y = 2150$.

The V150 is 75 kph faster than the Atlantique: $x = y + 75$.

We solve the following system.
$$\begin{cases} 2x + 2y = 2150 \\ x = y + 75 \end{cases}$$
Since the second equation is solved for x, we use substitution. Substitute $y + 75$ for x in the first equation.
$$2(y + 75) + 2y = 2150$$
$$2y + 150 + 2y = 2150$$
$$4y + 150 = 2150$$
$$4y = 2000$$
$$y = 500$$
To find x, we replace y with 500 in the second equation.
$$x = 500 + 75 = 575$$
The speed of the V150 is 575 kph, and the speed of the Atlantique is 500 kph.

4. Let x = amount of 99% acid
y = amount of water (0%)
Both x and y are measured in liters. We use a table to organize the given data.

	Amount	Acid Strength	Amount of Pure Acid
99% acid	x	99%	$0.99x$
Water	y	0%	$0y$

The amount of 99% acid and water combined must equal 1 liter, so $x + y = 1$.
The amount of pure acid in the mixture must equal the sum of the amounts of pure acid in the 99% acid and in the water, so
$0.99x + 0y = 0.05(1)$, which simplifies to
$0.99x = 0.05$.
We solve the following system.
$$\begin{cases} x + y = 1 \\ 0.99x = 0.05 \end{cases}$$
Since the second equation does not contain y, we solve it for x.
$$0.99x = 0.05$$
$$x = \frac{0.05}{0.99} \approx 0.05$$
To find y, we replace x with 0.05 in the first equation.
$$x + y = 1$$
$$0.05 + y = 1$$
$$y = 0.95$$
The teacher should use 0.05 liter of the 99% HCL solution and 0.95 liter of water.

5. Let x = the number of packages.
The firm charges the customer $4.50 for each package, so the revenue equation is $R(x) = 4.5x$.
Each package costs $2.50 to produce and the equipment costs $3000, so the cost equation is $C(x) = 2.5x + 3000$.
Since the break-even point is when $R(x) = C(x)$, we solve the equation $4.5x = 2.5x + 3000$.
$$4.5x = 2.5x + 3000$$
$$2x = 3000$$
$$x = 1500$$
The company must sell 1500 packages to break even.

6. Let x = measure of smallest angle
y = measure of largest angle
z = measure of third angle
The sum of the measures is 180°:
$x + y + z = 180$.

The measure of the largest angle is 40° more than the measure of the smallest angle:
$y = x + 40$.

The measure of the remaining angle is $20°$ more than the measure of the smallest angle:
$y = x + 20$.
We solve the following system.
$$\begin{cases} x + y + z = 1180 \\ y = x + 40 \\ z = x + 20 \end{cases}$$
We substitute $x + 40$ for y and $x + 20$ for z in the first equation.
$$x + (x + 40) + (x + 20) = 180$$
$$3x + 60 = 180$$
$$3x = 120$$
$$x = 40$$
Then $y = x + 40 = 40 + 40 = 80$ and
$z = x + 20 = 40 + 20 = 60$.
The angle measures are $40°$, $60°$, and $80°$.

Exercise Set 4.3

2. Let x = the first number, and
y = the second number.
$$\begin{cases} 3x - y = 8 & (1) \\ x + y = 12 & (2) \end{cases}$$
Add E1 and E2.
$$4x = 20$$
$$x = 5$$
Replace x with 5 in E2.
$$5 + y = 12$$
$$y = 7$$
The numbers are 5 and 7.

4. Let x = number in inline skating, and
y = number in skateboarding.
$$\begin{cases} x + y = 25.1 & (1) \\ y = 2x - 14.2 & (2) \end{cases}$$
Replace y with $2x - 14.2$ in E1.
$$x + (2x - 14.2) = 25.1$$
$$3x - 14.2 = 25.1$$
$$3x = 39.3$$
$$x = 13.1$$
Replace x with 13.1 in E2.
$$y = 2(13.1) - 14.2 = 26.2 - 14.2 = 12$$
There were 13.1 million participants in inline skating and 12.0 million in skateboarding.

6. Let r = rowing speed in still water, and
c = speed of the current.
$$\begin{cases} r + c = 10.6 & (1) \\ r - c = 6.8 & (2) \end{cases}$$
Add E1 and E2.

$$2r = 17.4$$
$$r = 8.7$$
Replace r with 8.7 in E1.
$$8.7 + c = 10.6$$
$$c = 1.9$$
Rowing speed in still water: 8.7 km/hr
Speed of the current: 1.9 km/hr.

8. Let x = millimeters of 5% solution, and
y = millimeters of 25% solution.
$$\begin{cases} x + y = 500 & (1) \\ 0.05x + 0.25y = 0.20(500) & (2) \end{cases}$$
Multiply E2 by 100.
$$\begin{cases} x + y = 500 \\ 5x + 25y = 10,000 \end{cases}$$
Multiply E1 by -5 and add to E2.
$$-5x - 5y = -2500$$
$$\underline{5x + 25y = 10,000}$$
$$20y = 7500$$
$$y = 375$$
Replace y with 375 in E1.
$$x + 375 = 500$$
$$x = 125$$
5% solution: 125 ml
25% solution: 375 ml

10. Let x = number of volumes in the Harvard library and
y = number of volumes in the Cornell library.
$$\begin{cases} x = 2y + 266,791 \\ x + y = 23,199,904 \end{cases}$$
Substitute $2y + 266,791$ for x in E2.
$$(2y + 266,791) + y = 23,199,904$$
$$3y + 266,791 = 23,199,904$$
$$3y = 22,933,113$$
$$y = 7,644,371$$
Replace y with 7,644,371 in E1.
$$x = 2(7,644,371) + 266,791 = 15,555,533$$
There were 15,555,533 volumes in the Harvard library and 7,644,371 in the Cornell library.

12. Let s = number of student tickets, and
n = number of nonstudent tickets.
$$\begin{cases} s + n = 311 & (1) \\ 0.50s + 1.50n = 385.50 & (2) \end{cases}$$
Multiply E2 by 10.
$$\begin{cases} s + n = 311 & (1) \\ 5s + 15n = 3855 & (2) \end{cases}$$
Multiply E1 by -5 and add to E2.

$-5s - 5n = -1555$

$5s + 15n = 3855$

$\overline{10n = 2300}$

$n = 230$

Replace n with 230 in E1.

$s + 230 = 311$

$s = 81$

Student tickets: 81

Nonstudent tickets: 230.

14. Let x = the first number, and
y = the second number.
$$\begin{cases} 2x + y = 42 & (1) \\ x - y = -6 & (2) \end{cases}$$
Add E1 and E2 to get $3x = 36$
$x = 12$.
Substitute this value for x in E1.
$2(12) + y = 42$
$24 + y = 42$
$y = 18$
The numbers are 12 and 18.

16. **a.** $\begin{cases} y = -x + 54.2 & (1) \\ y = x + 45.8 & (2) \end{cases}$

Substitute $x + 45.8$ for y in E1.
$x + 45.8 = -x + 54.2$
$2x = 8.4$
$x = 4.2$
$2000 + 4 = 2004$
The year would be 2004.

b. No

18. Let m = pounds of M & M's, and
t = pounds of trail mix.
$$\begin{cases} 2m + 1.5t = 1.8(50) & (1) \\ m + t = 50 & (2) \end{cases}$$
Multiply E2 by -2 and add to E1.
$2m + 1.5t = 90$
$\underline{-2m - 2t = -100}$
$-0.5t = -10$
$t = 20$
Replace t with 20 in E2.
$m + 20 = 50$
$m = 30$
M & M's: 30 lb.
Trail mix: 20 lb.

20. Let x = the speed of one cyclist, and
y = the speed of the other cyclist.
$$\begin{cases} x = y + 4 & (1) \\ 4x + 4y = 112 & (2) \end{cases}$$
Substitute $y + 4$ for x in E2.
$4(y + 4) + 4y = 112$
$8y + 16 = 108$
$8y = 96$
$y = 12$
Replace y with 12 in E1.
$x = 12 + 4 = 16$
The cyclists are traveling at 12 mph and 16 mph.

22. $\begin{cases} y = -0.40x + 15.9 \\ y = 0.14x + 11.9 \end{cases}$
Substitute $0.14x + 11.9$ for y in E1.
$0.14x + 11.9 = -0.40x + 15.9$
$0.54x = 4$
$x = \dfrac{4}{0.54} \approx 7.4$
The year would be 1987.

24. Let x = amount of weekly sales, and
y = earnings.
$$\begin{cases} y = 200 + 0.05x & (1) \\ y = 0.15x & (2) \end{cases}$$
Replace y with $0.15x$ in E1.
$0.15x = 200 + 0.05x$
$0.10x = 200$
$ = 2000$
His weekly sales must be $2000.

26. Let x = cost for templates, y = cost for pencils,
and z = cost for pads
$$\begin{cases} z = 3y & (1) \\ 3x + y = 6.45 & (2) \\ 2z + 4y = 7.50 & (3) \end{cases}$$
Substitute $3y$ for z in E3.
$2(3y) + 4y = 7.50$
$10y = 7.50$
$y = 0.75$
Replace y with 0.75 in E1 and E2.
$z = 3(0.75) = 2.25$ and
$3x + 0.75 = 6.45$
$3x = 5.7$
$x = 1.9$
Templates: $1.90 each
Pencils: $0.75 each
Pads: $2.25 each

28. $\begin{cases} x+2y=180 \\ y+(3x-10)=180, \text{ or} \end{cases}$

$\begin{cases} x+2y=180 \quad (1) \\ 3x+y=190 \quad (2) \end{cases}$

Multiply E1 by –3 and add to E2.
$-3x-6y=-540$
$\underline{\quad 3x+y=190}$
$-5y=-350$
$y=70$

Replace y with 70 in E1.
$x+2(70)=180$
$x+140=180$
$x=40$

The value of x is 40° and the value of y is 70°.

30. $C(x)=12x+15,000$
$R(x)=32x$
$32x=12x+15,000$
$20x=15,000$
$x=750$
750 units

32. $C(x)=0.8x+900$
$R(x)=2x$
$2x=0.8x+900$
$1.2x=900$
$x=750$
750 units

34. $C(x)=105x+70,000$
$R(x)=245x$
$245x=105x+70,000$
$140x=70,000$
$x=500$
500 units

36. a. $R(x)=31x$

b. $C(x)=15x+500$

c. $R(x)=C(x)$
$31x=15x+500$
$16x=500$
$x=31.25,$ or 32 baskets

38. Let x = liters of 25% solution,
y = liters of 40% solution, and
z = liters of 50% solution.

$\begin{cases} x+y+z=200 \\ 0.25x+0.40y+0.50z=0.32(200) \\ x=2y \end{cases}$

Multiply E2 by 100.

$\begin{cases} x+y+z=200 \quad (1) \\ 25x+40y+50z=6400 \quad (2) \\ x=2y \quad (3) \end{cases}$

Replace x with $2y$ in E1 and E2 and simplify.
$\begin{cases} 3y+z=200 \quad (4) \\ 90y+50z=6400 \quad (5) \end{cases}$

Multiply E4 by –50 and add to E5.
$-150y-50z=-10,000$
$\underline{\quad 90y+50z=6400}$
$-60y \qquad =-3600 \quad (5)$
$y=60$

Replace y with 60 in E4 and E3.
$3(60)+z=200$ and $x=2y$
$180+z=200 \qquad x=2(60)$
$z=20 \qquad x=120$

25% solution: 120 L
40% solution: 60 L
50% solution: 20 L

40. Let x = measure of smallest angle,
y = measure of largest, and
z = measure of remaining side.
$\begin{cases} x+y+z=180 \quad (1) \\ y=x+90 \quad (2) \\ z=x+30 \quad (3) \end{cases}$

Substitute $y=x+90$ and $z=x+30$ in E1.
$x+(x+90)+(x+30)=180$
$3x+120=180$
$3x=60$
$x=20$

Replace x with 20 in E2 and E3.
$y=20+90=110$ and $z=20+30=50$

The measures are 20°, 50°, and 110°.

42. Let o = the ones digit, t = the tens digit and
h = the hundreds digit.
$\begin{cases} h+t+o=15 \quad (1) \\ t=2h \quad (2) \\ o=h-1 \quad (3) \end{cases}$

Substitute $t=2h$ and $o=h-1$ into E1.

$h + (2h) + (h - 1) = 15$

$4h - 1 = 15$

$4h = 16$

$h = 4$

Use this value in E2 and E3.

$t = 2(4) = 8$

$o = 4 - 1 = 3$

The number is 483.

44. Let x = number of free throws,

y = number of two-point field goals, and

z = number of three-point field goals

$$\begin{cases} x + 2y + 3z = 654 \\ x = y - 3 \\ z = \dfrac{1}{5}y - 27 \end{cases}$$

Rewrite the system in a more convenient form.

$$\begin{cases} x + 2y + 3z = 654 & (1) \\ x - y = -3 & (2) \\ -y + 5z = -135 & (3) \end{cases}$$

Multiply E2 by -1 and add to E1.

$x + 2y + 3z = 654$

$\underline{-x + y = 3}$

$ 3y + 3z = 657 \quad (4)$

Multiply E3 by 3 and add to E4.

$-3y + 15z = -405$

$\underline{3y + 3z = 657}$

$ 18z = 252$

$ z = 14$

Replace z with 14 in E3.

$-y + 5(14) = -135$

$ -y + 70 = -135$

$ 205 = y$

Replace y with 205 in E2.

$x - 205 = -3$

$ x = 202$

He made 202 free throws, 205 two-point field goals, and 14 three-point field goals.

46. $\begin{cases} x + y + z + 72 = 360 \\ y + (z - 13) = 180 \\ x + (z + 15) = 180 \end{cases}$

$\begin{cases} x + y + z = 288 & (1) \\ y + z = 193 & (2) \\ x + z = 165 & (3) \end{cases}$

Multiply E2 by -1 and add to E1.

$x + y + z = 288$

$\underline{ -y - z = -193}$

$x = 95$

Use this value in E3.

$95 + z = 165$

$ z = 70$

Replace z with 70 in E2.

$y + 70 = 193$

$ y = 123$

$x = 95$, $y = 123$, and $z = 70$.

48. $\begin{cases} 2x + y + 3z = 7 & (1) \\ -4x + y + 2z = 4 & (2) \end{cases}$

Multiply E1 by 2 and add to E2.

$4x + 2y + 6z = 14$

$\underline{-4x + y + 2z = 4}$

$ 3y + 8z = 18$

$3y + 8z = 18$

50. $\begin{cases} 2x - 3y + 2z = 5 & (1) \\ x - 9y + z = -1 & (2) \end{cases}$

Multiply E1 by -3 and add to E2.

$-6x + 9y - 6z = -15$

$\underline{x - 9y + z = -1}$

$-5x - 5z = -16$

$-5x - 5z = -16$

52. a. Let x = median earnings for male mail carriers and

y = median earnings for female mail carriers.

$\begin{cases} x = y + 126 \\ y = 0.86x \end{cases}$

Substitute $y + 126$ for x in the second equation.

$y = 0.86(y + 126)$

$y = 0.86y + 1008.36$

$0.14y = 108.36$

$y = 774$

Female mail carriers earned \$774. (Males earn \$900.)

b. Let x = median earnings for female lawyers and y = median earnings for male lawyers.

$\begin{cases} x = y - 540 \\ y = 1.4x \end{cases}$

Substitute $1.4x$ for y in the first equation.

$x = 1.4x - 540$

$-0.4x = -540$

$x = 1350$

Female lawyers earned \$1350. (Males earned \$1890.)

c. Male lawyers earned the most. Female mail carriers earned the least.

54. $y = ax^2 + bx + c$

$(1, 6):\ 6 = a + b + c$ (1)
$(-1, -2): -2 = a - b + c$ (2)
$(0, -1): -1 = c$ (3)

Substitute $c = -1$ in E1 and E2 to obtain

$$\begin{cases} a + b = 7 & \text{(from E1)} \\ a - b = -1 & \text{(from E2)} \end{cases}$$

Add these equations.
$2a = 6$
$a = 3$
Replace a with 3 in $a + b = 7$.
$3 + b = 7$ so $b = 4$
Therefore, $a = 3$, $b = 4$, and $c = -1$.

56. $y = ax^2 + bx + c$

$(0, 1065):\ 1065 = c$ (1)
$(1, 1070):\ 1070 = a + b + c$ (2)
$(3, 1175):\ 1175 = 9a + 3b + c$ (3)

Substitute $c = 1065$ in E2 and E3 to obtain

$$\begin{cases} a + b = 5 & \text{(from E2)} \\ 9a + b = 105 & \text{(from E3)} \end{cases}$$

Multiply the first equation by -1 and add to the second equation.

$$\begin{array}{r} -3a - 3b = -15 \\ \underline{9a + 3b = 110} \\ 6a \quad\;\; = 95 \end{array}$$

$$a = \frac{95}{6} = 15\frac{5}{6}$$

Replace a with $15\frac{5}{6}$ in $a + b = 5$.

$$\frac{95}{6} + b = 5$$

$$b = -\frac{65}{6} = -10\frac{5}{6}$$

So, $a = 15\frac{5}{6}$, $b = -10\frac{5}{6}$, and $c = 1065$.

The year 2009 is represented by $x = 9$.

$$y = 15\frac{5}{6}x^2 - 10\frac{5}{6}x + 1065$$

$$y = 15\frac{5}{6}(9)^2 - 10\frac{5}{6}(9) + 1065$$

$$y = 2250 \text{ students}$$

Integrated Review

1. A system with solution $(1, 2)$ has lines that intersect at $(1, 2)$. The correct graph is C.

2. A system with solution $(-2, 3)$ has lines that intersect at $(-2, 3)$. The correct graph is D.

3. A system with no solution has lines that are parallel. The correct graph is A.

4. A system with an infinite number of solutions has lines that are the same. The correct graph is B.

5. $\begin{cases} x + y = 4 & (1) \\ \quad\;\; y = 3x & (2) \end{cases}$

   Substitute $y = 3x$ in E1.
   $x + (3x) = 4$
   $4x = 4$
   $x = 1$
   Replace x with 1 in E2.
   $y = 3x = 3(1) = 3$
   The solution is $(1, 3)$.

6. $\begin{cases} x - y = -4 & (1) \\ \quad\;\; y = 4x & (2) \end{cases}$

   Substitute $y = 4x$ in E1.
   $x - (4x) = -4$
   $-3x = -4$
   $x = \dfrac{4}{3}$

   Replace x with $\dfrac{4}{3}$ in E2.

   $$y = 4x = 4\left(\frac{4}{3}\right) = \frac{16}{3}$$

   The solution is $\left(\dfrac{4}{3}, \dfrac{16}{3}\right)$.

7. $\begin{cases} x + y = 1 & (1) \\ x - 2y = 4 & (2) \end{cases}$

   Multiply E1 by -1 and add to E2.

   $$\begin{array}{r} -x - y = -1 \\ \underline{x - 2y = 4} \\ -3y = 3 \\ y = -1 \end{array}$$

   Replace y with -1 in E1.

$$x + (-1) = 1$$
$$x - 1 = 1$$
$$x = 2$$

The solution is $(2, -1)$.

8. $\begin{cases} 2x - y = 8 & (1) \\ x + 3y = 11 & (2) \end{cases}$

Multiply E1 by 3 and add to E2.

$$6x - 3y = 24$$
$$\underline{x + 3y = 11}$$
$$7x \quad\quad = 35$$
$$x = 5$$

Replace x with 5 in E1.

$$2(5) - y = 8$$
$$10 - y = 8$$
$$y = 2$$

The solution is $(5, 2)$.

9. $\begin{cases} 2x + 5y = 8 & (1) \\ 6x + y = 10 & (2) \end{cases}$

Multiply E2 by -5 and add to E1.

$$2x + 5y = 8$$
$$\underline{-30x - 5y = -50}$$
$$-28x \quad\quad = -42$$
$$x = \frac{3}{2}$$

Replace x with $\frac{3}{2}$ in E2.

$$6\left(\frac{3}{2}\right) + y = 10$$
$$9 + y = 8$$
$$y = 1$$

The solution is $\left(\frac{3}{2}, 1\right)$.

10. $\begin{cases} \frac{1}{8}x - \frac{1}{2}y = -\frac{5}{8} & (1) \\ -3x - 8y = 0 & (2) \end{cases}$

Multiply E1 by -16 and add to E2.

$$-2x + 8y = 10$$
$$\underline{-3x - 8y = 0}$$
$$-5x \quad\quad = 10$$
$$x = -2$$

Replace x with -2 in E2.

$$-3(-2) - 8y = 0$$
$$6 - 8y = 0$$
$$-8y = -6$$
$$y = \frac{-6}{-8} = \frac{3}{4}$$

The solution is $\left(-2, \frac{3}{4}\right)$.

11. $\begin{cases} 4x - 7y = 7 & (1) \\ 12x - 21y = 24 & (2) \end{cases}$

Multiply E1 by -3 and add to E2.

$$-12x + 21y = -21$$
$$\underline{12x - 21y = 24}$$
$$0 = 3 \quad \text{False}$$

The system is inconsistent. The solution set is $\varnothing$.

12. $\begin{cases} 2x - 5y = 3 & (1) \\ -4x + 10y = -6 & (2) \end{cases}$

Multiply E1 by 2 and add to E2.

$$4x - 10y = 6$$
$$\underline{-4x + 10y = -6}$$
$$0 = 0 \quad \text{True}$$

The system is dependent. The solution set is $\{(x, y) | 2x - 5y = 3\}$.

13. $\begin{cases} y = \frac{1}{3}x \\ 5x - 3y = 4 \end{cases}$

Substitute $\frac{1}{3}x$ for y in E2.

$$5x - 3\left(\frac{1}{3}x\right) = 4$$
$$5x - x = 4$$
$$4x = 4$$
$$x = 1$$

Replace x with 1 in E1.

$$y = \frac{1}{3}(1) = \frac{1}{3}$$

The solution is $\left(1, \frac{1}{3}\right)$.

14. $\begin{cases} y = \frac{1}{4}x \\ 2x - 4y = 3 \end{cases}$

Substitute $\frac{1}{4}x$ for y in E2.

$$2x - 4\left(\frac{1}{4}x\right) = 3$$
$$2x - x = 3$$
$$x = 3$$

Replace x with 3 in E1.

$$y = \frac{1}{4}(3) = \frac{3}{4}$$

The solution is $\left(3, \dfrac{3}{4}\right)$.

15. $\begin{cases} x + y = 2 \quad (1) \\ -3y + z = -7 \quad (2) \\ 2x + y - z = -1 \quad (3) \end{cases}$

Add E2 and E3.

$$2x - 2y = -8 \text{ or } x - y = -4 \quad (4)$$

Add E1 and E4.

$$2x = -2$$
$$x = -1$$

Replace x with -1 in E1.

$$-1 + y = 2$$
$$y = 3$$

Replace y with 3 in E2.

$$-3(3) + z = -7$$
$$-9 + z = -7$$
$$z = 2$$

The solution is $(-1, 3, 2)$.

16. $\begin{cases} y + 2z = -3 \quad (1) \\ x - 2y = 7 \quad (2) \\ 2x - y + z = 5 \quad (3) \end{cases}$

Multiply E2 by -2 and add to E3.

$$\begin{array}{r} -2x + 4y = -14 \\ 2x - y + z = 5 \\ \hline 3y + z = -9 \quad (4) \end{array}$$

Multiply E4 by -2 and add to E1.

$$\begin{array}{r} -6y - 2z = 18 \\ y + 2z = -3 \\ \hline -5y = 15 \\ y = -3 \end{array}$$

Replace y with -3 in E4.

$$3(-3) + z = -9$$
$$z = 0$$

Replace y with -3 in E2.

$$x - 2(-3) = 7$$
$$x + 6 = 7$$
$$x = 1$$

The solution is $(1, -3, 0)$.

17. $\begin{cases} 2x + 4y - 6z = 3 \quad (1) \\ -x + y - z = 6 \quad (2) \\ x + 2y - 3z = 1 \quad (3) \end{cases}$

Multiply E3 by -2 and add to E1.

$$\begin{array}{r} -2x - 4y + 6z = -2 \\ 2x + 4y - 6z = 3 \\ \hline 0 = 1 \text{ False} \end{array}$$

The system is inconsistent. The solution set is $\varnothing$.

18. $\begin{cases} x - y + 3z = 2 \quad (1) \\ -2x + 2y - 6z = -4 \quad (2) \\ 3x - 3y + 9z = 6 \quad (3) \end{cases}$

Multiply E1 by 2 and add to E2.

$$\begin{array}{r} 2x - 2y + 6z = 4 \\ -2x + 2y - 6z = -4 \\ \hline 0 = 0 \text{ True} \end{array}$$

The system is dependent. The solution set is $\{(x, y) \mid x - y + 3z = 2\}$.

19. $\begin{cases} x + y - 4z = 5 \quad (1) \\ x - y + 2z = -2 \quad (2) \\ 3x + 2y + 4z = 18 \quad (3) \end{cases}$

Add E1 and E2.

$$2x - 2z = 3 \quad (4)$$

Multiply E2 by 2 and add to E3.

$$\begin{array}{r} 2x - 2y + 4z = -4 \\ 3x + 2y + 4z = 18 \\ \hline 5x + 8z = 14 \quad (5) \end{array}$$

Multiply E4 by 4 and add to E5.

$$\begin{array}{r} 8x - 8z = 12 \\ 5x + 8z = 14 \\ \hline 13x = 26 \\ x = 2 \end{array}$$

Replace x with 2 in E4.

$$2(2) - 2z = 3$$
$$-2z = -1$$
$$z = \frac{1}{2}$$

Replace x with 2 and z with $\dfrac{1}{2}$ in E1.

$$2 + y - 4\left(\frac{1}{2}\right) = 5$$
$$2 + y - 2 = 5$$
$$y = 5$$

The solution is $\left(2, 5, \dfrac{1}{2}\right)$.

20. $\begin{cases} 2x - y + 3z = 2 & (1) \\ x + y - 6z = 0 & (2) \\ 3x + 4y - 3z = 6 & (3) \end{cases}$

Add E1 and E3.

$5x + 3y = 8 \quad (4)$

Multiply E1 by 2 and add to E2.

$4x - 2y + 6z = 4$

$\underline{x + \ y - 6z = 0}$

$5x - y \qquad = 4 \quad (5)$

Multiply E5 by 3 and add to E4.

$15x - 3y = 12$

$\underline{5x + 3y = 8}$

$20x \qquad = 20$

$x = 1$

Replace x with 1 in E5.

$5(1) - y = 4$

$-y = -1$

$y = 1$

Replace both x and y with 1 in E1.

$2(1) - 1 + 3z = 2$

$1 + 3z = 2$

$3z = 1$

$z = \dfrac{1}{3}$

The solution is $\left(1, 1, \dfrac{1}{3}\right)$.

21. Let x = the first number and
y = the second number.

$\begin{cases} x = y - 8 & (1) \\ 2x = y + 11 & (2) \end{cases}$

Substitute $x = y - 8$ in E2.

$2(y - 8) = y + 11$

$2y - 16 = y + 11$

$y = 27$

Replace y with 27 in E1.

$x = 27 - 8 = 19$

The numbers are 19 and 27.

22. Let x = measure of the two smallest angles,
y = measure of the third angle, and
z = measure of the fourth angle.

$\begin{cases} 2x + y + z = 360 \\ y = x + 30 \\ z = x + 50 \end{cases}$

Substitute $y = x + 30$ and $z = x + 50$ in the first equation.

$2x + (x + 30) + (x + 50) = 360$

$4x + 80 = 360$

$4x = 280$

$x = 70$

so $y = 70 + 30 = 100$ and $z = 70 + 50 = 120$

The two smallest angles are $70°$, the third angle is $100°$, and the fourth angle is $120°$.

Section 4.4

Practice Exercises

1. $\begin{cases} x + 4y = -2 \\ 3x - y = 7 \end{cases}$

The corresponding matrix is $\begin{bmatrix} 1 & 4 & | & -2 \\ 3 & -1 & | & 7 \end{bmatrix}$. The element in the first row, first column is already 1. Multiply row 1 by -3 and add to row 2 to get a 0 below the 1.

$\begin{bmatrix} 1 & 4 & | & -2 \\ -3(1)+3 & -3(4)+(-1) & | & -3(-2)+7 \end{bmatrix}$

$\begin{bmatrix} 1 & 4 & | & -2 \\ 0 & -13 & | & 13 \end{bmatrix}$

We change -13 to a 1 by dividing row 2 by -13.

$\begin{bmatrix} 1 & 4 & | & -2 \\ 0 & \frac{-13}{-13} & | & \frac{13}{-13} \end{bmatrix}$

$\begin{bmatrix} 1 & 4 & | & -2 \\ 0 & 1 & | & -1 \end{bmatrix}$

The last matrix corresponds to $\begin{cases} x + 4y = -2 \\ \qquad y = -1 \end{cases}$

To find x, we let $y = -1$ in the first equation.

$x + 4y = -2$

$x + 4(-1) = -2$

$x - 4 = -2$

$x = 2$

The solution is $(2, -1)$.

2. $\begin{cases} x - 3y = 3 \\ -2x + 6y = 4 \end{cases}$

The corresponding matrix is $\begin{bmatrix} 1 & -3 & | & 3 \\ -2 & 6 & | & 4 \end{bmatrix}$. The element in the first row, first column is already 1. Multiply row 1 by 2 and add to row 2 to get a 0 below the 1.

$\begin{bmatrix} 1 & -3 & | & 3 \\ 2(1)+(-2) & 2(-3)+6 & | & 2(3)+4 \end{bmatrix}$

$\begin{bmatrix} 1 & -3 & | & 3 \\ 0 & 0 & | & 10 \end{bmatrix}$

The corresponding system is $\begin{cases} x - 3y = 3 \\ \qquad 0 = 10 \end{cases}$

The equation $0 = 10$ is false. Hence, the system is inconsistent and has no solution. The solution set is $\varnothing$.

3. $\begin{cases} x + 3y - z = 0 \\ 2x + y + 3z = 5 \\ -x - 2y + 4z = 7 \end{cases}$

The corresponding matrix is $\begin{bmatrix} 1 & 3 & -1 & | & 0 \\ 2 & 1 & 3 & | & 5 \\ -1 & -2 & 4 & | & 7 \end{bmatrix}$.

The element in the first row, first column is already 1. Multiply row 1 by -2 and add to row 2 to get a 0 below the 1 in row 2. Add row 1 to row 3 to get a 0 below the 1 in row 3.

$\begin{bmatrix} 1 & 3 & -1 & | & 0 \\ -2(1)+2 & -2(3)+1 & -2(-1)+3 & | & -2(0)+5 \\ 1+(-1) & 3+(-2) & -1+4 & | & 0+7 \end{bmatrix}$

$\begin{bmatrix} 1 & 3 & -1 & | & 0 \\ 0 & -5 & 5 & | & 5 \\ 0 & 1 & 3 & | & 7 \end{bmatrix}$

Now we want a 1 where the -5 is now. Interchange rows 2 and 3.

$\begin{bmatrix} 1 & 3 & -1 & | & 0 \\ 0 & 1 & 3 & | & 7 \\ 0 & -5 & 5 & | & 5 \end{bmatrix}$

Now we want a 0 below the 1. Multiply row 2 by 5 and add to row 3.

$\begin{bmatrix} 1 & 3 & -1 & | & 0 \\ 0 & 1 & 3 & | & 7 \\ 5(0)+0 & 5(1)+(-5) & 5(3)+5 & | & 5(7)+5 \end{bmatrix}$

$\begin{bmatrix} 1 & 3 & -1 & | & 0 \\ 0 & 1 & 3 & | & 7 \\ 0 & 0 & 20 & | & 40 \end{bmatrix}$

Finally, divide row 3 by 20.

$\begin{bmatrix} 1 & 3 & -1 & | & 0 \\ 0 & 1 & 3 & | & 7 \\ 0 & 0 & \frac{20}{20} & | & \frac{40}{20} \end{bmatrix}$

$\begin{bmatrix} 1 & 3 & -1 & | & 0 \\ 0 & 1 & 3 & | & 7 \\ 0 & 0 & 1 & | & 2 \end{bmatrix}$

This matrix corresponds to the system

$\begin{cases} x + 3y - z = 0 \\ \quad y + 3z = 7 \\ \qquad\quad z = 2 \end{cases}$

The z-coordinate is 2. Replace z with 2 in the second equation and solve for y.

$y + 3z = 7$
$y + 3(2) = 7$
$y + 6 = 7$
$y = 1$

To find x, we let $z = 2$ and $y = 1$ in the first equation.

$x + 3y - z = 0$
$x + 3(1) - 2 = 0$
$x + 1 = 0$
$x = -1$

The solution is $(-1, 1, 2)$.

4. The augmented matrix from Practice 1 is $\begin{bmatrix} 1 & 4 & | & -2 \\ 3 & -1 & | & 7 \end{bmatrix}$.

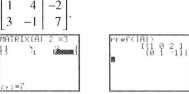

This corresponds to the system

$\begin{cases} 1x + 0y = 2 \\ 0x + 1y = -1 \end{cases}$ or $\begin{cases} x = 2 \\ y = -1 \end{cases}$.

The solution of the system is $(2, -1)$.

5. The augmented matrix from Practice 3 is $\begin{bmatrix} 1 & 3 & -1 & | & 0 \\ 2 & 1 & 3 & | & 5 \\ -1 & -2 & 4 & | & 7 \end{bmatrix}$.

This corresponds to the system

$\begin{cases} 1x + 0y + 0z = -1 \\ 0x + 1y + 0z = 1 \\ 0x + 0y + 1z = 2 \end{cases}$ or $\begin{cases} x = -1 \\ y = 1 \\ z = 2 \end{cases}$.

The solution of the system is $(-1, 1, 2)$.

Vocabulary and Readiness Check

1. A <u>matrix</u> is a rectangular array of numbers.

2. Each of the numbers in a matrix is called an element.

3. The numbers aligned horizontally in a matrix are in the same row.

4. The numbers aligned vertically in a matrix are in the same column.

5. Any two columns may be interchanged. false

6. Any two rows may be interchanged. true

7. The elements in a row may be added to their corresponding elements in another row. true

8. The elements of a column may be multiplied by any nonzero number. false

Exercise Set 4.4

2. $\begin{cases} 2x - y = 8 \\ x + 3y = 11 \end{cases}$

$$\begin{bmatrix} 2 & -1 & | & 8 \\ 1 & 3 & | & 11 \end{bmatrix}$$

Interchange R1 and R2.

$$\begin{bmatrix} 1 & 3 & | & 11 \\ 2 & -1 & | & 8 \end{bmatrix}$$

Multiply R1 by -2 and add to R2.

$$\begin{bmatrix} 1 & 3 & | & 11 \\ 0 & -7 & | & -14 \end{bmatrix}$$

Divide R2 by -7.

$$\begin{bmatrix} 1 & 3 & | & 11 \\ 0 & 1 & | & 2 \end{bmatrix}$$

This corresponds to $\begin{cases} x + 3y = 11 \\ y = 2 \end{cases}$.

$x + 3(2) = 11$
$ x = 5$
The solution is (5, 2).

4. $\begin{cases} 4x - y = 5 \\ 3x + 3y = 0 \end{cases}$

$$\begin{bmatrix} 4 & -1 & | & 5 \\ 3 & 3 & | & 0 \end{bmatrix}$$

Interchange R1 and R2.

$$\begin{bmatrix} 3 & 3 & | & 0 \\ 4 & -1 & | & 5 \end{bmatrix}$$

Divide R1 by 3.

$$\begin{bmatrix} 1 & 1 & | & 0 \\ 4 & -1 & | & 5 \end{bmatrix}$$

Multiply R1 by -4 and add to R2.

$$\begin{bmatrix} 1 & 1 & | & 0 \\ 0 & -5 & | & 5 \end{bmatrix}$$

Divide R2 by -5.

$$\begin{bmatrix} 1 & 1 & | & 0 \\ 0 & 1 & | & -1 \end{bmatrix}$$

This corresponds to $\begin{cases} x + y = 0 \\ y = -1 \end{cases}$.

$x + (-1) = 0$
$ x = 1$
The solution is $(1, -1)$.

6. $\begin{cases} -x + 3y = 6 \\ 3x - 9y = 9 \end{cases}$

$$\begin{bmatrix} -1 & 3 & | & 6 \\ 3 & -9 & | & 9 \end{bmatrix}$$

Multiply R1 by 3 and add to R2.

$$\begin{bmatrix} -1 & 3 & | & 6 \\ 0 & 0 & | & 27 \end{bmatrix}$$

This corresponds to $\begin{cases} -x + 3y = 6 \\ 0 = 27 \end{cases}$.

This is an inconsistent system. The solution set is $\varnothing$.

8. $\begin{cases} 9x - 3y = 6 \\ -18x + 6y = -12 \end{cases}$

$$\begin{bmatrix} 9 & -3 & | & 6 \\ -18 & 6 & | & -12 \end{bmatrix}$$

Multiply R1 by 2 and add to R2.

$$\begin{bmatrix} 9 & -3 & | & 6 \\ 0 & 0 & | & 0 \end{bmatrix}$$

This corresponds to $\begin{cases} 9x - 3y = 6 \\ 0 = 0 \end{cases}$.

This is a dependent system. The solution set is $\{(x, y)| 9x - 3y = 6\}$.

10. $\begin{cases} 5x = 5 \\ 2x + y = 4 \\ 3x + y - 5z = -15 \end{cases}$

$$\begin{bmatrix} 5 & 0 & 0 & | & 5 \\ 2 & 1 & 0 & | & 4 \\ 3 & 1 & -5 & | & -15 \end{bmatrix}$$

Divide R1 by 5.

$$\begin{bmatrix} 1 & 0 & 0 & | & 1 \\ 2 & 1 & 0 & | & 4 \\ 3 & 1 & -5 & | & -15 \end{bmatrix}$$

Multiply R1 by −2 and add to R2.
Multiply R1 by −3 and add to R3.

$$\begin{bmatrix} 1 & 0 & 0 & | & 1 \\ 0 & 1 & 0 & | & 2 \\ 0 & 1 & -5 & | & -18 \end{bmatrix}$$

Multiply R2 by −1 and add to R3.

$$\begin{bmatrix} 1 & 0 & 0 & | & 1 \\ 0 & 1 & 0 & | & 2 \\ 0 & 0 & -5 & | & -20 \end{bmatrix}$$

Divide R3 by −5.

$$\begin{bmatrix} 1 & 0 & 0 & | & 1 \\ 0 & 1 & 0 & | & 2 \\ 0 & 0 & 1 & | & 4 \end{bmatrix}$$

This corresponds to $\begin{cases} x = 1 \\ y = 2. \\ z = 4 \end{cases}$

The solution is $(1, 2, 4)$.

12. $\begin{cases} 4y + 3z = -2 \\ 5x - 4y = 1 \\ -5x + 4y + z = -3 \end{cases}$

$$\begin{bmatrix} 0 & 4 & 3 & | & -2 \\ 5 & -4 & 0 & | & 1 \\ -5 & 4 & 1 & | & -3 \end{bmatrix}$$

Interchange R1 and R2.

$$\begin{bmatrix} 5 & -4 & 0 & | & 1 \\ 0 & 4 & 3 & | & -2 \\ -5 & 4 & 1 & | & -3 \end{bmatrix}$$

Add R1 and R3.

$$\begin{bmatrix} 5 & -4 & 0 & | & 1 \\ 0 & 4 & 3 & | & -2 \\ 0 & 0 & 1 & | & -2 \end{bmatrix}$$

Divide R2 by 4.

$$\begin{bmatrix} 5 & -4 & 0 & | & 1 \\ 0 & 1 & \frac{3}{4} & | & -\frac{1}{2} \\ 0 & 0 & 1 & | & -2 \end{bmatrix}$$

This corresponds to $\begin{cases} 5x - 4y = 1 \\ y + \dfrac{3}{4}z = -\dfrac{1}{2}. \\ z = -2 \end{cases}$

$$y + \frac{3}{4}(-2) = -\frac{1}{2}$$
$$y - \frac{3}{2} = -\frac{1}{2}$$
$$y = 1$$
$$5x - 4(1) = 1$$
$$5x = 5$$
$$x = 1$$

The solution is $(1, 1, -2)$.

14. $\begin{cases} 3y = 6 \\ x + y = 7 \end{cases}$

$$\begin{bmatrix} 0 & 3 & | & 6 \\ 1 & 1 & | & 7 \end{bmatrix}$$

Interchange R1 and R2.

$$\begin{bmatrix} 1 & 1 & | & 7 \\ 0 & 3 & | & 6 \end{bmatrix}$$

Divide R2 by 3.

$$\begin{bmatrix} 1 & 1 & | & 7 \\ 0 & 1 & | & 2 \end{bmatrix}$$

This corresponds to $\begin{cases} x + y = 7 \\ y = 2 \end{cases}$.

$$x + 2 = 7$$
$$x = 5$$

The solution is $(5, 2)$.

16. $\begin{cases} x + 2y + z = 5 \\ x - y - z = 3 \\ y + z = 2 \end{cases}$

$$\begin{bmatrix} 1 & 2 & 1 & | & 5 \\ 1 & -1 & -1 & | & 3 \\ 0 & 1 & 1 & | & 2 \end{bmatrix}$$

Multiply R1 by −1 and add to R2.

$$\begin{bmatrix} 1 & 2 & 1 & | & 5 \\ 0 & -3 & -2 & | & -2 \\ 0 & 1 & 1 & | & 2 \end{bmatrix}$$

Interchange R2 and R3.

$$\begin{bmatrix} 1 & 2 & 1 & | & 5 \\ 0 & 1 & 1 & | & 2 \\ 0 & -3 & -2 & | & -2 \end{bmatrix}$$

Multiply R2 by 3 and add to R3.

$$\begin{bmatrix} 1 & 2 & 1 & | & 5 \\ 0 & 1 & 1 & | & 2 \\ 0 & 0 & 1 & | & 4 \end{bmatrix}$$

This corresponds to $\begin{cases} x+2y+z=5 \\ \quad\;\; y+z=2. \\ \qquad\quad z=4 \end{cases}$

$y+4=2$
$\quad y=-2$
$x+2(-2)+4=5$
$\qquad\quad x=5$
The solution is $(5, -2, 4)$.

18. $\begin{cases} 4x-y=9 \\ 2x+3y=-27 \end{cases}$

$\begin{bmatrix} 4 & -1 & | & 9 \\ 2 & 3 & | & -27 \end{bmatrix}$

Divide R1 by 4.

$\begin{bmatrix} 1 & -\frac{1}{4} & | & \frac{9}{4} \\ 2 & 3 & | & -27 \end{bmatrix}$

Multiply R1 by -2 and add to R2.

$\begin{bmatrix} 1 & -\frac{1}{4} & | & \frac{9}{4} \\ 0 & \frac{7}{2} & | & -\frac{63}{2} \end{bmatrix}$

Multiply R2 by $\frac{2}{7}$.

$\begin{bmatrix} 1 & -\frac{1}{4} & | & \frac{9}{4} \\ 0 & 1 & | & -9 \end{bmatrix}$

This corresponds to $\begin{cases} x-\dfrac{1}{4}y=\dfrac{9}{4} \\ \qquad\quad y=-9 \end{cases}$.

$x-\dfrac{1}{4}(-9)=\dfrac{9}{4}$
$\qquad x+\dfrac{9}{4}=\dfrac{9}{4}$
$\qquad\qquad x=0$
The solution is $(0, -9)$.

20. $\begin{cases} 2x-5y=12 \\ -4x+10y=20 \end{cases}$

$\begin{bmatrix} 2 & -5 & | & 12 \\ -4 & 10 & | & 20 \end{bmatrix}$

Multiply R1 by 2 and add to R2.

$\begin{bmatrix} 2 & -5 & | & 12 \\ 0 & 0 & | & 44 \end{bmatrix}$

This corresponds to $\begin{cases} 2x-5y=12 \\ \qquad\;\; 0=44 \end{cases}$.

This is an inconsistent system. The solution set is $\varnothing$.

22. $\begin{cases} 5y-7z=14 \\ 2x+y+4z=10 \\ 2x+6y-3z=30 \end{cases}$

$\begin{bmatrix} 0 & 5 & -7 & | & 14 \\ 2 & 1 & 4 & | & 10 \\ 2 & 6 & -3 & | & 30 \end{bmatrix}$

Interchange R1 and R2.

$\begin{bmatrix} 2 & 1 & 4 & | & 10 \\ 0 & 5 & -7 & | & 14 \\ 2 & 6 & -3 & | & 30 \end{bmatrix}$

Divide R1 by 2.

$\begin{bmatrix} 1 & \frac{1}{2} & 2 & | & 5 \\ 0 & 5 & -7 & | & 14 \\ 2 & 6 & -3 & | & 30 \end{bmatrix}$

Multiply R1 by -2 and add to R3.

$\begin{bmatrix} 1 & \frac{1}{2} & 2 & | & 5 \\ 0 & 5 & -7 & | & 14 \\ 0 & 5 & -7 & | & 20 \end{bmatrix}$

Multiply R2 by -1 and add to R3.

$\begin{bmatrix} 1 & \frac{1}{2} & 2 & | & 5 \\ 0 & 5 & -7 & | & 14 \\ 0 & 0 & 0 & | & 6 \end{bmatrix}$

This corresponds to $\begin{cases} x+\dfrac{1}{2}y+2z=5 \\ \qquad 5y-7z=14. \\ \qquad\qquad\;\; 0=6 \end{cases}$

This is an inconsistent system. The solution set is $\varnothing$.

24. $\begin{cases} x+y+z=9 \\ 3x-y+z=-1 \\ -2x+2y-3z=-2 \end{cases}$

$\begin{bmatrix} 1 & 1 & 1 & | & 9 \\ 3 & -1 & 1 & | & -1 \\ -2 & 2 & -3 & | & -2 \end{bmatrix}$

Multiply R1 by -3 and add to R2.
Multiply R1 by 2 and add to R3.

$\begin{bmatrix} 1 & 1 & 1 & | & 9 \\ 0 & -4 & -2 & | & -28 \\ 0 & 4 & -1 & | & 16 \end{bmatrix}$

Add R2 to R3.

$\begin{bmatrix} 1 & 1 & 1 & | & 9 \\ 0 & -4 & -2 & | & -28 \\ 0 & 0 & -3 & | & -12 \end{bmatrix}$

Divide R2 by –3.

$$\begin{bmatrix} 1 & 1 & 1 & | & 9 \\ 0 & -4 & -2 & | & -28 \\ 0 & 0 & 1 & | & 4 \end{bmatrix}$$

This corresponds to $\begin{cases} x+y+z=9 \\ -4y-2z=-28. \\ \qquad\qquad z=4 \end{cases}$

$$-4y-2(4)=-28$$
$$-4y=-20$$
$$y=5$$
$$x+5+4=9$$
$$x+9=9$$
$$x=0$$

The solution is (0, 5, 4).

26. No vertical line intersects the graph more than once. It is the graph of a function.

28. Vertical lines can be drawn that intersect the graph more than once. It is not the graph of a function.

30. $(2)(-8)-(-4)(1)=-16+4=-12$

32. $(-7)(3)-(-2)(-6)=-21-12=-33$

34. $(5)(6)-(10)(10)=30-100=-70$

36. $\begin{cases} x-6=0 \\ 2x-3y=1 \end{cases}$

Rewrite the first equation before identifying the corresponding matrix.

$$\begin{cases} x \qquad\quad=6 \\ 2x-3y=1 \end{cases}$$

The last number in the first row should be 6. The correct matrix is (b).

38. $\begin{cases} y=455x+14,123 \\ y=-776x+15,985 \end{cases}$

Substitute $455x + 14{,}123$ for y in the second equation.

$$455x+14,123=-776x+15,985$$
$$1231x=1862$$
$$x=\frac{1862}{1231}\approx 1.5$$

The last year was 1 year after 2001, or 2002.

Section 4.5

Practice Exercises

1. $\begin{cases} 4x \ge y \\ x+3y \ge 6 \end{cases}$

Graph both inequalities on the same set of axes. The solution is the intersection of the solution regions.
For $4x \ge y$, the boundary line is the graph of
$4x = y$. The boundary line is solid since the inequality means $4x > y$ or $4x = y$. The test point $(1, 0)$ satisfies the inequality, so we shade the half-plane that includes $(1, 0)$.
For $x+3y \ge 6$, sketch the solid boundary line
$x + 3y = 6$. The test point $(0, 0)$ does not satisfy the inequality, so shade the half-plane that does not include $(0, 0)$.
The solution of the system is the darker shaded region. This solution includes parts of both boundary lines.

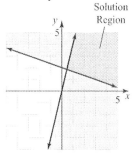

2. $\begin{cases} x-y<1 \\ \quad\; y<4 \\ 3x+y>-3 \end{cases}$

Graph all three inequalities on the same set of axes. All boundary lines are dashed since the inequality symbols are < and >. The solution set of the system is the shaded region. The boundary lines are not a part of the solution.

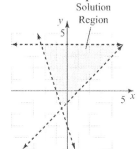

3. $\begin{cases} -2x+5y \le 10 \\ \quad\quad x \le 4 \\ \quad\quad x \ge 0 \\ \quad\quad y \ge 0 \end{cases}$

Graph the inequalities on the same set of axes. The intersection of the inequalities is the solution region. It is the only shaded region in this graph and includes the portion of all four boundary lines that border the shaded region.

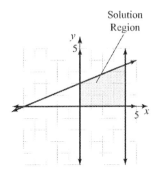

Vocabulary and Readiness Check

1. Two or more linear inequalities form a <u>system</u> of linear inequalities.

2. An ordered pair that satisfies each inequality in a system is a <u>solution</u> of the system.

3. The point where two boundary lines intersect is a <u>corner</u> point.

4. The solution region of a system of inequalities consists of the <u>intersection</u> of the solution regions of the inequalities in the system.

Exercise Set 4.5

2. $\begin{cases} y \ge x-3 \\ y \ge -1-x \end{cases}$

Graph both inequalities on the same set of axes. The solution is the intersection of the solution regions. The solution of the system is the darker shaded region. This solution includes parts of both boundary lines.

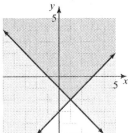

4. $\begin{cases} y \le 2x+1 \\ y > x+2 \end{cases}$

Graph both inequalities on the same set of axes. The solution is the intersection of the solution regions. The solution of the system is the darker shaded region. This solution includes the part of the solid boundary line that borders the region but not the dashed boundary line or the point where the boundary lines intersect.

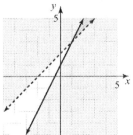

6. $\begin{cases} y \le 2x+4 \\ y \ge -x-5 \end{cases}$

Graph both inequalities on the same set of axes. The solution is the intersection of the solution regions. The solution of the system is the darker shaded region. This solution includes parts of both boundary lines.

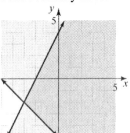

8. $\begin{cases} y \ge x-5 \\ y \le -3x+3 \end{cases}$

Graph both inequalities on the same set of axes. The solution is the intersection of the solution regions. The solution of the system is the darker shaded region. This solution includes parts of both boundary lines.

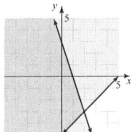

10. $\begin{cases} -2x < y \\ x + 2y < 3 \end{cases}$

Graph both inequalities on the same set of axes. The solution is the intersection of the solution regions. The solution of the system is the darker shaded region. This solution does not include any portion of the boundary lines.

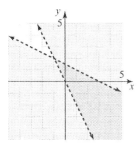

12. $\begin{cases} x \ge -3 \\ y \ge -2 \end{cases}$

Graph both inequalities on the same set of axes. The solution is the intersection of the solution regions. The solution of the system is the darker shaded region. This solution includes parts of both boundary lines.

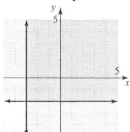

14. $\begin{cases} y > 2 \\ x \ge -1 \end{cases}$

Graph both inequalities on the same set of axes. The solution is the intersection of the solution regions. The solution of the system is the darker shaded region. This solution includes the part of the solid boundary line that borders the region but not the dashed boundary line or the point where the boundary lines intersect.

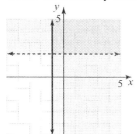

16. $\begin{cases} y + 2x \le 0 \\ 5x + 3y \ge -2 \\ y \le 4 \end{cases}$

Graph all three inequalities on the same set of axes. The solution set of the system is the shaded region. The parts of the boundary lines that border the shaded region are part of the solution.

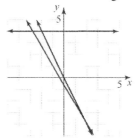

18. $\begin{cases} 4x - y \ge -2 \\ 2x + 3y \le -8 \\ y \ge -5 \end{cases}$

Graph all three inequalities on the same set of axes. The solution set of the system is the shaded region. The parts of the boundary lines that border the shaded region are part of the solution.

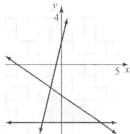

20. $\begin{cases} 3x + y \le 4 \\ x \le 4 \\ x \ge 0 \\ y \ge 0 \end{cases}$

Graph the inequalities on the same set of axes. The intersection of the inequalities is the solution region. It is the only shaded region in this graph and includes the portion of all four boundary lines that border the shaded region.

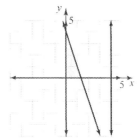

22. $\begin{cases} y > 5 \\ x < 3 \end{cases}$

Both boundary lines should be dashed. The region including (0, 6) should be shaded since (0, 6) satisfies both inequalities. The correct graph is A.

24. $\begin{cases} y > 5 \\ x \geq 3 \end{cases}$

The boundary line $x = 3$ should be solid. The correct graph is B.

26. $(-5)^3 = (-5)(-5)(-5) = -125$

28. $\left(\dfrac{3}{4}\right)^3 = \dfrac{3}{4} \cdot \dfrac{3}{4} \cdot \dfrac{3}{4} = \dfrac{3 \cdot 3 \cdot 3}{4 \cdot 4 \cdot 4} = \dfrac{27}{64}$

30. $5^2 - 11 + 3(-5) = 25 - 11 + 3(-5)$
$$= 25 - 11 + (-15)$$
$$= 25 - 11 - 15$$
$$= 14 - 15$$
$$= -1$$

32. $(-12)^2 + (-1)(2) - 6 = 144 + (-1)(2) - 6$
$$= 144 + (-2) - 6$$
$$= 144 - 2 - 6$$
$$= 142 - 6$$
$$= 136$$

34. $\begin{cases} x \leq 5 \\ x \leq 3 \end{cases}$

Every x-value that satisfies $x \leq 3$ also satisfies $x \leq 5$. The solution of the system is the region described by $x \leq 3$.

36. a. The sum of x and y must be less than or equal to 8, and x must be less than 3. Furthermore, neither x nor y can be negative. The system is
$$\begin{cases} x + y \leq 8 \\ x \quad\; < 3 \\ x \quad\; \geq 0 \\ \quad\; y \geq 0 \end{cases}$$

b.

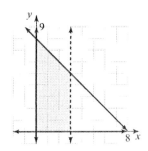

Chapter 4 Vocabulary Check

1. Two or more linear equations in two variables form a <u>system of equations</u>.

2. A <u>solution</u> of a system of two equations in two variables is an ordered pair that makes both equations true.

3. A <u>consistent</u> system of equations has at least one solution.

4. If a matrix has the same number of rows and columns, it is called a <u>square</u> matrix.

5. An <u>inconsistent</u> system of equations has no solution.

6. A <u>matrix</u> is a rectangular array of numbers.

Chapter 4 Review

1. $\begin{cases} 3x + 10y = 1 \quad (1) \\ x + 2y = -1 \quad (2) \end{cases}$

(1)

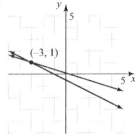

(2) From E2: $x = -2y - 1$

Replace x with $-2y - 1$ in E1.
$$3(-2y - 1) + 10y = 1$$
$$-6y - 3 + 10y = 1$$
$$4y = 4$$
$$y = 1$$

Replace y with 1 in the equation $x = -2y - 1$.
$$x = -2(1) - 1 = -3$$
The solution is $(-3, 1)$.

(3) Multiply E2 by –3 and add to E1.

$$3x + 10y = 1$$
$$\underline{-3x - 6y = 3}$$
$$4y = 4$$
$$y = 1$$

Replace y with 1 in E2.

$$x + 2(1) = -1$$
$$x + 2 = -1$$
$$x = -3$$

The solution is $(-3, 1)$.

2. $\begin{cases} y = \dfrac{1}{2}x + \dfrac{2}{3} & (1) \\ 4x + 6y = 4 & (2) \end{cases}$

(1)

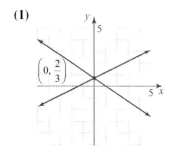

(2) Replace y with $\dfrac{1}{2}x + \dfrac{2}{3}$ in E2.

$$4x + 6\left(\frac{1}{2}x + \frac{2}{3}\right) = 4$$
$$4x + 3x + 4 = 4$$
$$x = 0$$

Replace x with 0 in E1.

$$y = \frac{1}{2}(0) + \frac{2}{3} = \frac{2}{3}$$

The solution is $\left(0, \dfrac{2}{3}\right)$.

(3) Rewrite the system: $\begin{cases} -\dfrac{1}{2}x + y = \dfrac{2}{3} \\ 4x + 6y = 4 \end{cases}$.

Multiply the first equation by –6.

$$\begin{cases} 3x - 6y = -4 \\ 4x + 6y = 4 \end{cases}$$

Add these equations.

$$7x = 0$$
$$x = 0$$

Replace x with 0 in second equation.

$$4(0) + 6y = 4$$
$$6y = 4$$
$$y = \frac{4}{6} = \frac{2}{3}$$

The solution is $\left(0, \dfrac{2}{3}\right)$.

3. $\begin{cases} 2x - 4y = 22 & (1) \\ 5x - 10y = 15 & (2) \end{cases}$

(1)

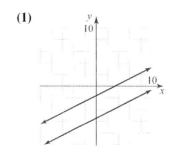

(2) Solve E1 for x.

$$2x - 4y = 22$$
$$2x = 4y + 22$$
$$x = 2y + 11$$

Replace x with $2y + 11$ in E2.

$$5(2y + 11) - 10y = 15$$
$$10y + 55 - 10y = 15$$
$$55 = 15 \text{ False}$$

This is an inconsistent system. The solution is $\varnothing$.

(3) Multiply E1 by 5 and E2 by –2.

$$\begin{cases} 10x - 20y = 110 \\ -10x + 20y = -30 \end{cases}$$

Add these equations.

$$10x - 20y = 110$$
$$\underline{-10x + 20y = -30}$$
$$0 = 80 \text{ False}$$

This is an inconsistent system. The solution is $\varnothing$.

4. $\begin{cases} 3x - 6y = 12 & (1) \\ 2y = x - 4 & (2) \end{cases}$

(1)

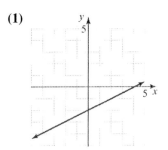

(2) Solve E2 for x.

$x = 2y + 4$

Replace x with $2y + 4$ in E1.

$3(2y + 4) - 6y = 12$

$6y + 12 - 6y = 12$

$\qquad 12 = 12$ True

This is a dependent system. The solution is $\{(x, y) | 3x - 6y = 12\}$.

(3) $\begin{cases} 3x - 6y = 12 & (1) \\ -x + 2y = -4 & (2) \end{cases}$

Multiply E2 by 3.

$\begin{cases} 3x - 6y = 12 \\ -3x + 6y = -12 \end{cases}$

Add these equations.

$\quad 3x - 6y = 12$

$\underline{-3x + 6y = -12}$

$\qquad\qquad 0 = 0$ True

This is a dependent system. The solution is $\{(x, y) | 3x - 6y = 12\}$.

5. $\begin{cases} \dfrac{1}{2}x - \dfrac{3}{4}y = -\dfrac{1}{2} & (1) \\ \dfrac{1}{8}x + \dfrac{3}{4}y = \dfrac{19}{8} & (2) \end{cases}$

(1)

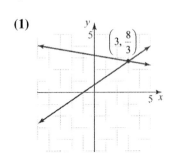

(2) Clear fractions by multiplying E1 by 4 and E2 by 8.

$\begin{cases} 2x - 3y = -2 & (1) \\ x + 6y = 19 & (2) \end{cases}$

Solve the new E2 for x.

$x = -6y + 19$

Replace x with $-6y + 19$ in new E1.

$2(-6y + 19) - 3y = -2$

$-12y + 38 - 3y = -2$

$\qquad\qquad -15y = -40$

$\qquad\qquad\qquad y = \dfrac{-40}{-15} = \dfrac{8}{3}$

Replace y with $\dfrac{8}{3}$ in the equation

$x = -6y + 19$.

$x = -6\left(\dfrac{8}{3}\right) + 19$

$x = -16 + 19$

$x = 3$

The solution is $\left(3, \dfrac{8}{3}\right)$.

(3) Add the equations.

$\dfrac{1}{2}x - \dfrac{3}{4}y = -\dfrac{1}{2}$

$\underline{\dfrac{1}{8}x + \dfrac{3}{4}y = \dfrac{19}{8}}$

$\dfrac{5}{8}x \qquad\quad = \dfrac{15}{8}$

$\qquad 5x = 15$

$\qquad\; x = 3$

Replace x with 3 in E1.

$\dfrac{1}{2}(3) - \dfrac{3}{4}y = -\dfrac{1}{2}$

$\qquad -\dfrac{3}{4}y = -2$

$\qquad\quad -3y = -8$

$\qquad\qquad y = \dfrac{8}{3}$

The solution is $\left(3, \dfrac{8}{3}\right)$.

6. $\begin{cases} y = 32x & (1) \\ y = 15x + 25,500 & (2) \end{cases}$

Multiply E1 by -1 and add to E2.

$-y = -32$

$\underline{y = 15x + 25,500}$

$0 = -17x + 25,500$

$17x = 25,500$

$x = 1500$

Replace x with 1500 in E1.

$y = 32(1500) = 48,000$

The number of backpacks that the company must sell is 1500.

7. $\begin{cases} x + z = 4 & (1) \\ 2x - y = 4 & (2) \\ x + y - z = 0 & (3) \end{cases}$

Adding E2 and E3 gives $3x - z = 4$ (4)

Adding E1 and E4 gives $4x = 8$ or $x = 2$

Replace x with 2 in E1.

$2 + z = 4$

$z = 2$

Replace x with 2 and z with 2 in E3.

$2 + y - 2 = 0$

$y = 0$

The solution is (2, 0, 2).

8. $\begin{cases} 2x + 5y = 4 & (1) \\ x - 5y + z = -1 & (2) \\ 4x - z = 11 & (3) \end{cases}$

Add E2 and E3.

$5x - 5y = 10$ (4)

Add E1 and E4.

$7x = 14$

$x = 2$

Replace x with 2 in E1.

$2(2) + 5y = 4$

$4 + 5y = 4$

$5y = 0$

$y = 0$

Replace x with 2 in E3.

$4(2) - z = 11$

$8 - z = 11$

$z = -3$

The solution is (2, 0, -3).

9. $\begin{cases} 4y + 2z = 5 & (1) \\ 2x + 8y = 5 & (2) \\ 6x + 4z = 1 & (3) \end{cases}$

Multiply E1 by -2 and add to E2.

$-8y - 4z = -10$

$\underline{2x + 8y = 5}$

$2x - 4z = -5$ (4)

Add E3 and E4.

$8x = -4$

$x = -\dfrac{1}{2}$

Replace x with $-\dfrac{1}{2}$ in E2.

$2\left(-\dfrac{1}{2}\right) + 8y = 5$

$-1 + 8y = 5$

$8y = 6$

$y = \dfrac{3}{4}$

Replace x with $-\dfrac{1}{2}$ in E3.

$6\left(-\dfrac{1}{2}\right) + 4z = 1$

$-3 + 4z = 1$

$4z = 4$

$z = 1$

The solution is $\left(-\dfrac{1}{2}, \dfrac{3}{4}, 1\right)$.

10. $\begin{cases} 5x + 7y = 9 & (1) \\ 14y - z = 28 & (2) \\ 4x + 2z = -4 & (3) \end{cases}$

Dividing E3 by 2 gives $2x + z = -2$.

Add this equation to E2.

$2x + z = -2$

$\underline{ 14y - z = 28}$

$2x + 14y = 26$ or $x + 7y = 13$ (4)

Multiply E4 by -1 and add to E1.

$-x - 7y = -13$

$\underline{5x + 7y = 9}$

$4x = -4$

$x = -1$

Replace x with -1 in E4.

$-1 + 7y = 13$

$7y = 14$

$y = 2$

Replace x with -1 in E3.

$4(-1) + 2z = -4$

$-4 + 2z = -4$

$2z = 0$

$z = 0$

The solution is (-1, 2, 0).

11. $\begin{cases} 3x - 2y + 2z = 5 & (1) \\ -x + 6y + z = 4 & (2) \\ 3x + 14y + 7z = 20 & (3) \end{cases}$

Multiply E2 by 3 and add to E1.

$$\begin{array}{r} 3x - 2y + 2z = 5 \\ -3x + 18y + 3z = 12 \\ \hline 16y + 5z = 17 \quad (4) \end{array}$$

Multiply E3 by –1 and add to E1.

$$\begin{array}{r} 3x - 2y + 2z = 5 \\ -3x - 14y - 7z = -20 \\ \hline -16y - 5z = -15 \quad (5) \end{array}$$

Add E4 and E5.

$$\begin{array}{r} 16y + 5z = 17 \\ -16y - 5z = -15 \\ \hline 0 = 2 \quad \text{False} \end{array}$$

The system is inconsistent. The solution is $\varnothing$.

12. $\begin{cases} x + 2y + 3z = 11 & (1) \\ y + 2z = 3 & (2) \\ 2x + 2z = 10 & (3) \end{cases}$

Multiply E2 by –2 and add to E1.

$$\begin{array}{r} x + 2y + 3z = 11 \\ -2y - 4z = -6 \\ \hline x - z = 5 \quad (4) \end{array}$$

Multiply E4 by 2 and add to E3.

$$\begin{array}{r} 2x + 2z = 10 \\ 2x - 2z = 10 \\ \hline 4x = 20 \\ x = 5 \end{array}$$

Replace x with 5 in E3.

$$2(5) + 2z = 10$$
$$10 + 2z = 10$$
$$2z = 0$$
$$z = 0$$

Replace z with 0 in E2.

$$y + 2(0) = 3$$
$$y + 0 = 3$$
$$y = 3$$

The solution is (5, 3, 0).

13. $\begin{cases} 7x - 3y + 2z = 0 & (1) \\ 4x - 4y - z = 2 & (2) \\ 5x + 2y + 3z = 1 & (3) \end{cases}$

Multiply E2 by 2 and add to E1.

$$\begin{array}{r} 7x - 3y + 2z = 0 \\ 8x - 8y - 2z = 4 \\ \hline 15x - 11y = 4 \quad (4) \end{array}$$

Multiply E2 by 3 and add to E3.

$$\begin{array}{r} 12x - 12y - 3z = 6 \\ 5x + 2y + 3z = 1 \\ \hline 17x - 10y = 7 \quad (5) \end{array}$$

Solve the new system.

$\begin{cases} 15x - 11y = 4 & (4) \\ 17x - 10y = 7 & (5) \end{cases}$

Multiply E4 by –10, multiply E5 by 11, and add.

$$\begin{array}{r} -150x + 110y = -40 \\ 187x - 110y = 77 \\ \hline 37x = 37 \\ x = 1 \end{array}$$

Replace x with 1 in E4.

$$15(1) - 11y = 4$$
$$15 - 11y = 4$$
$$-11y = -11$$
$$y = 1$$

Replace x with 1 and y with 1 in E1.

$$7(1) - 3(1) + 2z = 0$$
$$4 + 2z = 0$$
$$2z = -4$$
$$z = -2$$

The solution is (1, 1, –2).

14. $\begin{cases} x - 3y - 5z = -5 & (1) \\ 4x - 2y + 3z = 13 & (2) \\ 5x + 3y + 4z = 22 & (3) \end{cases}$

Multiply E1 by –4 and add to E2.

$$\begin{array}{r} -4x + 12y + 20z = 20 \\ 4x - 2y + 3z = 13 \\ \hline 10y + 23z = 33 \quad (4) \end{array}$$

Multiply E1 by –5 and add to E3.

$$\begin{array}{r} -5x + 15y + 25z = 25 \\ 5x + 3y + 4z = 22 \\ \hline 18y + 29z = 47 \quad (5) \end{array}$$

Solve the new system.

$\begin{cases} 10y + 23z = 33 & (4) \\ 18y + 29z = 47 & (5) \end{cases}$

Multiply E4 by 9, multiply E5 by –5 and add.

$$\begin{array}{r} 90y + 207z = 297 \\ -90y - 145z = -235 \\ \hline 62z = 62 \\ z = 1 \end{array}$$

Replace z with 1 in E4.

$$10y + 23(1) = 33$$
$$10y = 10$$
$$y = 1$$

Replace y with 1 and z with 1 in E1.

$$x - 3(1) - 5(1) = -5$$
$$x - 8 = -5$$
$$x = 3$$
The solution is (3, 1, 1).

15. Let x = the first number, y = the second number, and z = the third number.
$$\begin{cases} x + y + z = 98 & (1) \\ x + y = z + 2 & (2) \\ y = 4x & (3) \end{cases}$$
Replace y with $4x$ in E1 and E2.
$$x + 4x + z = 98$$
$$5x + z = 98 \quad (4)$$
$$x + 4x = z + 2$$
$$5x - z = 2 \quad (5)$$
Add E4 and E5.
$$5x + z = 98$$
$$\underline{5x - z = 2}$$
$$10x = 100$$
$$x = 10$$
Replace x with 10 in E3.
$$y = 4(10) = 40$$
Replace x with 10 and y with 40 in E2.
$$10 + 40 = z + 2$$
$$50 = z + 2$$
$$48 = z$$
The numbers are 10, 40, and 48.

16. Let x = the first number and y = the second number.
$$\begin{cases} x = 3y & (1) \\ 2(x + y) = 168 & (2) \end{cases}$$
Replace x with $3y$ in E2.
$$2(3y + y) = 168$$
$$8y = 168$$
$$y = 21$$
Replace y with 21 in E1.
$$x = 3(21) = 63$$
The numbers are 63 and 21.

17. Let x = speed of first car and y = speed of the second car.
$$\begin{cases} 4x + 4y = 492 & (1) \\ y = x + 7 & (2) \end{cases}$$
Replace y with $x + 7$ in E1.
$$4x + 4(x + 7) = 492$$
$$8x + 28 = 492$$
$$8x = 464$$
$$x = 58$$
Replace x with 58 in E2.

$$y = 58 + 7 = 65$$
The cars are going 58 and 65 miles per hour.

18. Let w = the width of the foundation and l = the length of the foundation.
$$\begin{cases} l = 3w & (1) \\ 2w + 2l = 296 & (2) \end{cases}$$
Replace l with $3w$ in E2.
$$2w + 2(3w) = 296$$
$$2w + 6w = 296$$
$$8w = 296$$
$$w = 37$$
Replace w with 37 in E1.
$$l = 3(37) = 111$$
The foundation is 37 feet wide and 111 feet long.

19. Let x = liters of 10% solution and y = liters of 60% solution.
$$\begin{cases} x + y = 50 & (1) \\ 0.10x + 0.60y = 0.40(50) & (2) \end{cases}$$
Solve E1 for y.
$$y = 50 - x$$
Replace y with $50 - x$ in E2.
$$0.10x + 0.60(50 - x) = 0.40(50)$$
$$10[0.10x + 0.60(50 - x)] = 10[0.40(50)]$$
$$x + 6(50 - x) = 4(50)$$
$$x + 300 - 6x = 200$$
$$-5x = -100$$
$$x = 20$$
Replace x with 20 in the equation $y = 50 - x$.
$$y = 50 - 20 = 30$$
He should use 20 liters of 10% solution and 30 liters of 60% solution.

20. Let c = pounds of chocolate used, n = pounds of nuts used, and r = pounds of raisins used.
$$\begin{cases} r = 2n & (1) \\ c + n + r = 45 & (2) \\ 3.00c + 2.70n + 2.25r = 2.80(45) & (3) \end{cases}$$
Replace r with $2n$ in E2.
$$c + n + 2n = 45$$
$$c + 3n = 45$$
$$c = -3n + 45$$
Replace r with $2n$ and c with $-3n + 45$ in E3.
$$3.00(-3n + 45) + 2.70n + 2.25(2n) = 126$$
$$-9n + 135 + 2.7n + 4.5n = 126$$
$$-1.8n + 135 = 126$$
$$-1.8n = -9$$
$$n = 5$$
Replace n with 5 in E1.

$r = 2(5) = 10$

Replace n with 5 and r with 10 in E2.

$c + 5 + 10 = 45$

$c + 15 = 45$

$c = 30$

She should use 30 pounds of creme-filled chocolates, 5 pounds of chocolate-covered nuts, and 10 pounds of chocolate-covered raisins.

21. Let $x =$ the number of pennies, $y =$ the number of nickels, and $z =$ the number dimes.

$$\begin{cases} x + y + z = 53 & (1) \\ 0.01x + 0.05y + 0.10z = 2.77 & (2) \\ y = z + 4 & (3) \end{cases}$$

Clear the decimals from E2 by multiplying by 100.

$x + 5y + 10z = 277$ (4)

Replace y with $z + 4$ in E1.

$x + z + 4 + z = 53$

$x + 2z = 49$ (5)

Replace y with $z + 4$ in E4.

$x + 5(z + 4) + 10z = 277$

$x + 15z = 257$ (6)

Solve the new system.

$$\begin{cases} x + 2z = 49 & (5) \\ x + 15z = 257 & (6) \end{cases}$$

Multiply E5 by -1 and add to E6.

$\begin{array}{r} -x - 2z = -49 \\ x + 15z = 257 \\ \hline 13z = 208 \end{array}$

$z = 16$

Replace z with 16 in E3.

$x + 2(16) = 49$

$x + 32 = 49$

$x = 17$

Replace z with 16 in E3.

$y = 16 + 4 = 20$

He has 17 pennies, 20 nickels, and 16 dimes in his jar.

22. Let $l =$ rate of interest on the larger investment and $s =$ the rate of interest on the smaller investment, both expressed as decimals.

$$\begin{cases} 10,000l + 4000s = 1250 & (1) \\ l = s + 0.02 & (2) \end{cases}$$

Replace l with $s + 0.02$ in E1.

$10,000(s + 0.02) + 4000s = 1250$

$10,000s + 200 + 4000s = 1250$

$14,000s = 1050$

$s = \dfrac{1050}{14,000} = 0.075$

and $l = 0.075 + 0.02 = 0.095$.

The interest rate on the larger investment is 9.5% and the rate on the smaller investment is 7.5%.

23. Let $x =$ length of the equal side and $y =$ length of the third side.

$$\begin{cases} 2x + y = 73 & (1) \\ y = x + 7 & (2) \end{cases}$$

Replace y with $x + 7$ in E1.

$2x + x + 7 = 73$

$3x = 66$

$x = 22$

Replace x with 22 in E2.

$y = 22 + 7 = 29$

Two sides of the triangle have length 22 cm and the third side has length 29 cm.

24. Let $f =$ the first number, $s =$ the second number, and $t =$ the third number.

$$\begin{cases} f + s + t = 295 & (1) \\ f = s + 5 & (2) \\ f = 2t & (3) \end{cases}$$

Solve E2 for s and E3 for t.

$s = f - 5$

$t = \dfrac{f}{2}$

Replace s with $f - 5$ and t with $\dfrac{f}{2}$ in E1.

$f + f - 5 + \dfrac{f}{2} = 295$

$\dfrac{5}{2}f = 300$

$f = 120$

Replace f with 300 in the equation $s = f - 5$.

$s = 120 - 5 = 115$

Replace f with 120 the equation $\dfrac{f}{2}$.

$t = \dfrac{120}{2} = 60$

The first number is 120, the second number is 115, and the third number is 60.

25. $\begin{cases} 3x + 10y = 1 \\ x + 2y = -1 \end{cases}$

$\begin{bmatrix} 3 & 10 & | & 1 \\ 1 & 2 & | & -1 \end{bmatrix}$

Interchange R1 and R2.

$\begin{bmatrix} 1 & 2 & | & -1 \\ 3 & 10 & | & 1 \end{bmatrix}$

Multiply R1 by -3 and add to R2.

$\begin{bmatrix} 1 & 2 & | & -1 \\ 0 & 4 & | & 4 \end{bmatrix}$

Divide R2 by 4.

$\begin{bmatrix} 1 & 2 & | & -1 \\ 0 & 1 & | & 1 \end{bmatrix}$

This corresponds to $\begin{cases} x + 2y = -1 \\ y = 1 \end{cases}$.

$x + 2(1) = -1$
$x = -3$
The solution is $(-3, 1)$.

26. $\begin{cases} 3x - 6y = 12 \\ 2y = x - 4 \end{cases}$, or $\begin{cases} 3x - 6y = 12 \\ -x + 2y = -4 \end{cases}$

$\begin{bmatrix} 3 & -6 & | & 12 \\ -1 & 2 & | & -4 \end{bmatrix}$

Divide R1 by 3.

$\begin{bmatrix} 1 & -2 & | & 4 \\ -1 & 2 & | & -4 \end{bmatrix}$

Add R1 to R2.

$\begin{bmatrix} 1 & -2 & | & 4 \\ 0 & 0 & | & 0 \end{bmatrix}$

This corresponds to $\begin{cases} x - 2y = 4 \\ 0 = 0 \end{cases}$.

This is a dependent system. The solution is
$\{(x, y) | x - 2y = 4\}$.

27. $\begin{cases} 3x - 2y = -8 \\ 6x + 5y = 11 \end{cases}$

$\begin{bmatrix} 3 & -2 & | & -8 \\ 6 & 5 & | & 11 \end{bmatrix}$

Divide R1 by 3.

$\begin{bmatrix} 1 & -\frac{2}{3} & | & -\frac{8}{3} \\ 6 & 5 & | & 11 \end{bmatrix}$

Multiply R1 by -6 and add to R2.

$\begin{bmatrix} 1 & -\frac{2}{3} & | & -\frac{8}{3} \\ 0 & 9 & | & 27 \end{bmatrix}$

Divide R2 by 9.

$\begin{bmatrix} 1 & -\frac{2}{3} & | & -\frac{8}{3} \\ 0 & 1 & | & 3 \end{bmatrix}$

This corresponds to $\begin{cases} x - \frac{2}{3}y = -\frac{8}{3} \\ y = 3 \end{cases}$.

$x - \frac{2}{3}(3) = -\frac{8}{3}$

$x - 2 = -\frac{8}{3}$

$x = -\frac{2}{3}$

The solution is $\left(-\frac{2}{3}, 3\right)$.

28. $\begin{cases} 6x - 6y = -5 \\ 10x - 2y = 1 \end{cases}$

$\begin{bmatrix} 6 & -6 & | & -5 \\ 10 & -2 & | & 1 \end{bmatrix}$

Divide R1 by 6.

$\begin{bmatrix} 1 & -1 & | & -\frac{5}{6} \\ 10 & -2 & | & 1 \end{bmatrix}$

Multiply R1 by -10 and add to R2.

$\begin{bmatrix} 1 & -1 & | & -\frac{5}{6} \\ 0 & 8 & | & \frac{28}{3} \end{bmatrix}$

Divide R2 by 8.

$\begin{bmatrix} 1 & -1 & | & -\frac{5}{6} \\ 0 & 1 & | & \frac{7}{6} \end{bmatrix}$

Add R2 to R1.

$\begin{bmatrix} 1 & 0 & | & \frac{1}{3} \\ 0 & 1 & | & \frac{7}{6} \end{bmatrix}$

This corresponds to $\begin{cases} x = \frac{1}{3} \\ y = \frac{7}{6} \end{cases}$. The solution is

$\left(\frac{1}{3}, \frac{7}{6}\right)$.

29. $\begin{cases} 3x - 6y = 0 \\ 2x + 4y = 5 \end{cases}$

$\begin{bmatrix} 3 & -6 & | & 0 \\ 2 & 4 & | & 5 \end{bmatrix}$

Divide R1 by 3.

$\begin{bmatrix} 1 & -2 & | & 0 \\ 2 & 4 & | & 5 \end{bmatrix}$

Multiply R1 by –2 and add to R2.

$$\begin{bmatrix} 1 & -2 & | & 0 \\ 0 & 8 & | & 5 \end{bmatrix}$$

Divide R2 by 8.

$$\begin{bmatrix} 1 & -2 & | & 0 \\ 0 & 1 & | & \frac{5}{8} \end{bmatrix}$$

This corresponds to $\begin{cases} x - 2y = 0 \\ \quad\quad y = \dfrac{5}{8} \end{cases}$.

$$x - 2\left(\frac{5}{8}\right) = 0$$
$$x - \frac{5}{4} = 0$$
$$x = \frac{5}{4}$$

The solution is $\left(\dfrac{5}{4}, \dfrac{5}{8}\right)$.

30. $\begin{cases} 5x - 3y = 10 \\ -2x + y = -1 \end{cases}$

$$\begin{bmatrix} 5 & -3 & | & 10 \\ -2 & 1 & | & -1 \end{bmatrix}$$

Divide R1 by 5.

$$\begin{bmatrix} 1 & -\frac{3}{5} & | & 2 \\ -2 & 1 & | & -1 \end{bmatrix}$$

Multiply R1 by 2 and add to R2.

$$\begin{bmatrix} 1 & -\frac{3}{5} & | & 2 \\ 0 & -\frac{1}{5} & | & 3 \end{bmatrix}$$

Multiply R2 by –5.

$$\begin{bmatrix} 1 & -\frac{3}{5} & | & 2 \\ 0 & 1 & | & -15 \end{bmatrix}$$

This corresponds to $\begin{cases} x - \dfrac{3}{5}y = 2 \\ \quad\quad y = -15 \end{cases}$.

$$x - \frac{3}{5}(-15) = 2$$
$$x + 9 = 2$$
$$x = -7$$

The solution is (–7, –15).

31. $\begin{cases} 0.2x - 0.3y = -0.7 \\ 0.5x + 0.3y = 1.4 \end{cases}$

$$\begin{bmatrix} 0.2 & -0.3 & | & -0.7 \\ 0.5 & 0.3 & | & 1.4 \end{bmatrix}$$

Multiply both rows by 10 to clear decimals.

$$\begin{bmatrix} 2 & -3 & | & -7 \\ 5 & 3 & | & 14 \end{bmatrix}$$

Divide R1 by 2.

$$\begin{bmatrix} 1 & -\frac{3}{2} & | & -\frac{7}{2} \\ 5 & 3 & | & 14 \end{bmatrix}$$

Multiply R1 by –5 and add to R2.

$$\begin{bmatrix} 1 & -\frac{3}{2} & | & -\frac{7}{2} \\ 0 & \frac{21}{2} & | & \frac{63}{2} \end{bmatrix}$$

Multiply R2 by $\dfrac{2}{21}$.

$$\begin{bmatrix} 1 & -\frac{3}{2} & | & -\frac{7}{2} \\ 0 & 1 & | & 3 \end{bmatrix}$$

This corresponds to $\begin{cases} x - \dfrac{3}{2}y = -\dfrac{7}{2} \\ \quad\quad y = 3 \end{cases}$.

$$x - \frac{3}{2}(3) = -\frac{7}{2}$$
$$x - \frac{9}{2} = -\frac{7}{2}$$
$$x = 1$$

The solution is (1, 3).

32. $\begin{cases} 3x + 2y = 8 \\ 3x - y = 5 \end{cases}$

$$\begin{bmatrix} 3 & 2 & | & 8 \\ 3 & -1 & | & 5 \end{bmatrix}$$

Divide R1 by 3.

$$\begin{bmatrix} 1 & \frac{2}{3} & | & \frac{8}{3} \\ 3 & -1 & | & 5 \end{bmatrix}$$

Multiply R1 by –3 and add to R2.

$$\begin{bmatrix} 1 & \frac{2}{3} & | & \frac{8}{3} \\ 0 & -3 & | & -3 \end{bmatrix}$$

Divide R2 by –3.

$$\begin{bmatrix} 1 & \frac{2}{3} & | & \frac{8}{3} \\ 0 & 1 & | & 1 \end{bmatrix}$$

This corresponds to $\begin{cases} x + \dfrac{2}{3}y = \dfrac{8}{3} \\ \quad\quad y = 1 \end{cases}$.

$$x + \frac{2}{3}(1) = \frac{8}{3}$$
$$x = 2$$

The solution is (2, 1).

33. $\begin{cases} x \quad\; + z = 4 \\ 2x - y \quad\;\; = 0 \\ x + y - z = 0 \end{cases}$

$$\begin{bmatrix} 1 & 0 & 1 & | & 4 \\ 2 & -1 & 0 & | & 0 \\ 1 & 1 & -1 & | & 0 \end{bmatrix}$$

Multiply R1 by –2 and add to R2. Multiply R1 by –1 and add to R3.

$$\begin{bmatrix} 1 & 0 & 1 & | & 4 \\ 0 & -1 & -2 & | & -8 \\ 0 & 1 & -2 & | & -4 \end{bmatrix}$$

Multiply R2 by –1.

$$\begin{bmatrix} 1 & 0 & 1 & | & 4 \\ 0 & 1 & 2 & | & 8 \\ 0 & 1 & -2 & | & -4 \end{bmatrix}$$

Multiply R2 by –1 and add to R3.

$$\begin{bmatrix} 1 & 0 & 1 & | & 4 \\ 0 & 1 & 2 & | & 8 \\ 0 & 0 & -4 & | & -12 \end{bmatrix}$$

Divide R3 by –4.

$$\begin{bmatrix} 1 & 0 & 1 & | & 4 \\ 0 & 1 & 2 & | & 8 \\ 0 & 0 & 1 & | & 3 \end{bmatrix}$$

This corresponds to $\begin{cases} x + z = 4 \\ y + 2z = 8 \\ \quad\;\; z = 3 \end{cases}$.

$$y + 2(3) = 8$$
$$y + 6 = 8$$
$$y = 2$$
$$x + 3 = 4$$
$$x = 1$$

The solution is (1, 2, 3).

34. $\begin{cases} 2x + 5y \quad\;\; = 4 \\ x - 5y + z = -1 \\ 4x \quad\;\; - z = 11 \end{cases}$

$$\begin{bmatrix} 2 & 5 & 0 & | & 4 \\ 1 & -5 & 1 & | & -1 \\ 4 & 0 & -1 & | & 11 \end{bmatrix}$$

Interchange R1 and R2.

$$\begin{bmatrix} 1 & -5 & 1 & | & -1 \\ 2 & 5 & 0 & | & 4 \\ 4 & 0 & -1 & | & 11 \end{bmatrix}$$

Multiply R1 by –2 and add to R2. Multiply R1 by –4 and add to R3.

$$\begin{bmatrix} 1 & -5 & 1 & | & -1 \\ 0 & 15 & -2 & | & 6 \\ 0 & 20 & -5 & | & 15 \end{bmatrix}$$

Divide R2 by 15.

$$\begin{bmatrix} 1 & -5 & 1 & | & -1 \\ 0 & 1 & -\frac{2}{15} & | & \frac{2}{5} \\ 0 & 20 & -5 & | & 15 \end{bmatrix}$$

Multiply R2 by –20 and add to R3.

$$\begin{bmatrix} 1 & -5 & 1 & | & -1 \\ 0 & 1 & -\frac{2}{15} & | & \frac{2}{5} \\ 0 & 0 & -\frac{7}{3} & | & 7 \end{bmatrix}$$

Multiply R3 by $-\frac{3}{7}$.

$$\begin{bmatrix} 1 & -5 & 1 & | & -1 \\ 0 & 1 & -\frac{2}{15} & | & \frac{2}{5} \\ 0 & 0 & 1 & | & -3 \end{bmatrix}$$

This corresponds to $\begin{cases} x - 5y + z = -1 \\ y - \frac{2}{15}z = \frac{2}{5} \\ \quad\quad z = -3 \end{cases}$.

$$y - \frac{2}{15}(-3) = \frac{2}{5}$$
$$y + \frac{2}{5} = \frac{2}{5}$$
$$y = 0$$
$$x - 5(0) + (-3) = -1$$
$$x - 3 = -1$$
$$x = 2$$

The solution is (2, 0, –3).

35. $\begin{cases} 3x - y \quad\;\; = 11 \\ x \quad\; + 2z = 13 \\ y - z = -7 \end{cases}$

$$\begin{bmatrix} 3 & -1 & 0 & | & 11 \\ 1 & 0 & 2 & | & 13 \\ 0 & 1 & -1 & | & -7 \end{bmatrix}$$

Interchange R1 and R2.

$$\begin{bmatrix} 1 & 0 & 2 & | & 13 \\ 3 & -1 & 0 & | & 11 \\ 0 & 1 & -1 & | & -7 \end{bmatrix}$$

Interchange R2 and R3.

$$\begin{bmatrix} 1 & 0 & 2 & | & 13 \\ 0 & 1 & -1 & | & -7 \\ 3 & -1 & 0 & | & 11 \end{bmatrix}$$

Multiply R1 by –3 and add to R3.

$$\begin{bmatrix} 1 & 0 & 2 & | & 13 \\ 0 & 1 & -1 & | & -7 \\ 0 & -1 & -6 & | & -28 \end{bmatrix}$$

Add R2 to R3.

$$\begin{bmatrix} 1 & 0 & 2 & | & 13 \\ 0 & 1 & -1 & | & -7 \\ 0 & 0 & -7 & | & -35 \end{bmatrix}$$

Divide R3 by –7.

$$\begin{bmatrix} 1 & 0 & 2 & | & 13 \\ 0 & 1 & -1 & | & -7 \\ 0 & 0 & 1 & | & 5 \end{bmatrix}$$

This corresponds to $\begin{cases} x + 2z = 13 \\ y - z = -7 \\ z = 5 \end{cases}$.

$$y - 5 = -7$$
$$y = -2$$
$$x + 2(5) = 13$$
$$x = 3$$

The solution is $(3, -2, 5)$.

36. $\begin{cases} 5x + 7y + 3z = 9 \\ 14y - z = 28 \\ 4x + 2z = -4 \end{cases}$

$$\begin{bmatrix} 5 & 7 & 3 & | & 9 \\ 0 & 14 & -1 & | & 28 \\ 4 & 0 & 2 & | & -4 \end{bmatrix}$$

Divide R1 by 5.

$$\begin{bmatrix} 1 & \frac{7}{5} & \frac{3}{5} & | & \frac{9}{5} \\ 0 & 14 & -1 & | & 28 \\ 4 & 0 & 2 & | & -4 \end{bmatrix}$$

Multiply R1 by –4 and add to R3.

$$\begin{bmatrix} 1 & \frac{7}{5} & \frac{3}{5} & | & \frac{9}{5} \\ 0 & 14 & -1 & | & 28 \\ 0 & -\frac{28}{5} & -\frac{2}{5} & | & -\frac{56}{5} \end{bmatrix}$$

Divide R2 by 14.

$$\begin{bmatrix} 1 & \frac{7}{5} & \frac{3}{5} & | & \frac{9}{5} \\ 0 & 1 & -\frac{1}{14} & | & 2 \\ 0 & -\frac{28}{5} & -\frac{2}{5} & | & -\frac{56}{5} \end{bmatrix}$$

Multiply R2 by $\frac{28}{5}$ and add to R3.

$$\begin{bmatrix} 1 & \frac{7}{5} & \frac{3}{5} & | & \frac{9}{5} \\ 0 & 1 & -\frac{1}{14} & | & 2 \\ 0 & 0 & -\frac{4}{5} & | & 0 \end{bmatrix}$$

Multiply R3 by $-\frac{5}{4}$.

$$\begin{bmatrix} 1 & \frac{7}{5} & \frac{3}{5} & | & \frac{9}{5} \\ 0 & 1 & -\frac{1}{14} & | & 2 \\ 0 & 0 & 1 & | & 0 \end{bmatrix}$$

This corresponds to $\begin{cases} x + \dfrac{7}{5}y + \dfrac{3}{5}z = \dfrac{9}{5} \\ y - \dfrac{1}{14}z = 2 \\ z = 0 \end{cases}$.

$$y - \frac{1}{14}(0) = 2$$
$$y = 2$$
$$x + \frac{7}{5}(2) + \frac{3}{5}(0) = \frac{9}{5}$$
$$x + \frac{14}{5} = \frac{9}{5}$$
$$x = -1$$

The solution is $(-1, 2, 0)$.

37. $\begin{cases} 7x - 3y + 2z = 0 \\ 4x - 4y - z = 2 \\ 5x + 2y + 3z = 1 \end{cases}$

$$\begin{bmatrix} 7 & -3 & 2 & | & 0 \\ 4 & -4 & -1 & | & 2 \\ 5 & 2 & 3 & | & 1 \end{bmatrix}$$

Interchange R1 and R2.

$$\begin{bmatrix} 4 & -4 & -1 & | & 2 \\ 7 & -3 & 2 & | & 0 \\ 5 & 2 & 3 & | & 1 \end{bmatrix}$$

Divide R1 by 4.

$$\begin{bmatrix} 1 & -1 & -\frac{1}{4} & | & \frac{1}{2} \\ 7 & -3 & 2 & | & 0 \\ 5 & 2 & 3 & | & 1 \end{bmatrix}$$

Multiply R1 by –7 and add to R2. Multiply R1 by –5 and add to R3.

$$\begin{bmatrix} 1 & -1 & -\frac{1}{4} & | & \frac{1}{2} \\ 0 & 4 & \frac{15}{4} & | & -\frac{7}{2} \\ 0 & 7 & \frac{17}{4} & | & -\frac{3}{2} \end{bmatrix}$$

Divide R2 by 4.

$$\begin{bmatrix} 1 & -1 & -\frac{1}{4} & | & \frac{1}{2} \\ 0 & 1 & \frac{15}{16} & | & -\frac{7}{8} \\ 0 & 7 & \frac{17}{4} & | & -\frac{3}{2} \end{bmatrix}$$

Multiply R2 by –7 and add to R3.

$$\begin{bmatrix} 1 & -1 & -\frac{1}{4} & \Big| & \frac{1}{2} \\ 0 & 1 & \frac{15}{16} & \Big| & -\frac{7}{8} \\ 0 & 0 & -\frac{37}{16} & \Big| & -\frac{37}{8} \end{bmatrix}$$

Multiply R3 by $-\dfrac{16}{37}$.

$$\begin{bmatrix} 1 & -1 & -\frac{1}{4} & \Big| & \frac{1}{2} \\ 0 & 1 & \frac{15}{16} & \Big| & -\frac{7}{8} \\ 0 & 0 & 1 & \Big| & -2 \end{bmatrix}$$

This corresponds to $\begin{cases} x - y - \dfrac{1}{4}z = \dfrac{1}{2} \\ y + \dfrac{15}{16}z = -\dfrac{7}{8} \\ z = -2 \end{cases}$.

$$y + \frac{15}{16}(-2) = -\frac{7}{8}$$
$$y - \frac{15}{8} = -\frac{7}{8}$$
$$y = 1$$

$$x - 1 - \frac{1}{4}(-2) = \frac{1}{2}$$
$$x - 1 + \frac{1}{2} = \frac{1}{2}$$
$$x = 1$$

The solution is $(1, 1, -2)$.

38. $\begin{cases} x + 2y + 3z = 14 \\ \quad\;\; y + 2z = 3 \\ 2x \qquad\; - 2z = 10 \end{cases}$

$$\begin{bmatrix} 1 & 2 & 3 & \big| & 14 \\ 0 & 1 & 2 & \big| & 3 \\ 2 & 0 & -2 & \big| & 10 \end{bmatrix}$$

Multiply R1 by –2 and add to R3.

$$\begin{bmatrix} 1 & 2 & 3 & \big| & 14 \\ 0 & 1 & 2 & \big| & 3 \\ 0 & -4 & -8 & \big| & -18 \end{bmatrix}$$

Multiply R2 by 4 and add to R3.

$$\begin{bmatrix} 1 & 2 & 3 & \big| & 14 \\ 0 & 1 & 2 & \big| & 3 \\ 0 & 0 & 0 & \big| & -6 \end{bmatrix}$$

This corresponds to $\begin{cases} x + 2y + 3z = 14 \\ \quad\;\; y + 2z = 3 \\ \qquad\qquad 0 = -6 \end{cases}$.

This system is inconsistent. The solution is $\varnothing$.

39. $\begin{cases} y \ge 2x - 3 \\ y \le -2x + 1 \end{cases}$

Graph both inequalities on the same set of axes. The solution is the intersection of the solution regions. The solution of the system is the darker shaded region. This solution includes parts of both boundary lines.

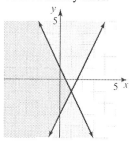

40. $\begin{cases} y \le -3x - 3 \\ y \le 2x + 7 \end{cases}$

Graph both inequalities on the same set of axes. The solution is the intersection of the solution regions. The solution of the system is the darker shaded region. This solution includes parts of both boundary lines.

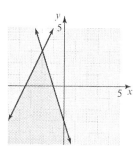

41. $\begin{cases} x + 2y > 0 \\ x - y \le 6 \end{cases}$

Graph both inequalities on the same set of axes. The solution is the intersection of the solution regions. The solution of the system is the darker shaded region. This solution includes the part of the solid boundary line that borders the region but not the dashed boundary line or the point where the boundary lines intersect.

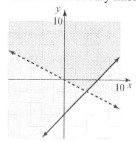

42. $\begin{cases} x - 2y \geq 7 \\ x + y \leq -5 \end{cases}$

Graph both inequalities on the same set of axes. The solution is the intersection of the solution regions. The solution of the system is the darker shaded region. This solution includes parts of both boundary lines.

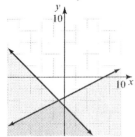

43. $\begin{cases} 3x - 2y \leq 4 \\ 2x + y \geq 5 \\ y \leq 4 \end{cases}$

Graph all three inequalities on the same set of axes. The solution set of the system is the shaded region. The parts of the boundary lines that border the shaded region are part of the solution.

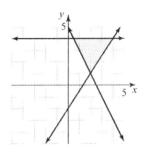

44. $\begin{cases} 4x - y \leq 0 \\ 3x - 2y \geq -5 \\ y \geq -4 \end{cases}$

Graph all three inequalities on the same set of axes. The solution set of the system is the shaded region. The parts of the boundary lines that border the shaded region are part of the solution.

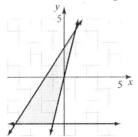

45. $\begin{cases} x + 2y \leq 5 \\ x \leq 2 \\ x \geq 0 \\ y \geq 0 \end{cases}$

Graph the inequalities on the same set of axes. The intersection of the inequalities is the solution region. It is the only shaded region in this graph and includes the portion of all four boundary lines that border the shaded region.

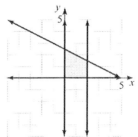

46. $\begin{cases} x + 3y \leq 7 \\ y \leq 5 \\ x \geq 0 \\ y \geq 0 \end{cases}$

Graph the inequalities on the same set of axes. The intersection of the inequalities is the solution region. It is the only shaded region in this graph and includes the portion of all four boundary lines that border the shaded region.

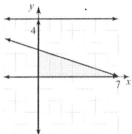

47. $\begin{cases} y = x - 5 \\ y = -2x + 2 \end{cases}$

We substitute $x - 5$ for y in the second equation.
$$x - 5 = -2x + 2$$
$$3x = 7$$
$$x = \frac{7}{3}$$

Replace x with $\frac{7}{3}$ in the first equation.

$$y = \frac{7}{3} - 5 = \frac{7}{3} - \frac{15}{3} = -\frac{8}{3}$$

The solution is $\left(\frac{7}{3}, \ -\frac{8}{3} \right)$.

48. $\begin{cases} \dfrac{2}{5}x + \dfrac{3}{4}y = 1 \\ x + 3y = -2 \end{cases}$

Multiply both sides of the first equation by 20 to eliminate fractions.

$\begin{cases} 20\left(\dfrac{2}{5}x + \dfrac{3}{4}y\right) = 20(1) \\ x + 3y = -2 \end{cases}$

$\begin{cases} 8x + 15y = 20 \\ x + 3y = -2 \end{cases}$

Multiply both sides of the second equation by -5 and add to the first equation to eliminate y.

$\begin{array}{r} 8x + 15y = 20 \\ \underline{-5x - 15y = 10} \\ 3x = 30 \\ x = 10 \end{array}$

To find y, replace x with 10 in the second equation.

$\begin{aligned} 10 + 3y &= -2 \\ 3y &= -12 \\ y &= -4 \end{aligned}$

The solution is $(10, -4)$.

49. $\begin{cases} 5x - 2y = 10 \\ x = \dfrac{2}{5}y + 2 \end{cases}$

Multiply both sides of the second equation by 5.

$\begin{cases} 5x - 2y = 10 \\ 5x = 5\left(\dfrac{2}{5}y + 2\right) \end{cases}$

$\begin{cases} 5x - 2y = 10 \\ 5x = 2y + 10 \end{cases}$

Subtract $2y$ from both sides of the second equation.

$\begin{cases} 5x - 2y = 10 \\ 5x - 2y = 10 \end{cases}$

The equations are the same. The system has an infinite number of solutions. The solution set can be written as $\{(x, y) \mid 5x - 2y = 10\}$.

50. $\begin{cases} x - 4y = 4 \\ \dfrac{1}{8}x - \dfrac{1}{2}y = 3 \end{cases}$

Multiply the second by -8 and add to the first equation to eliminate x.

$\begin{cases} x - 4y = 4 \\ -x + 4y = -24 \end{cases}$

The equation $0 = -20$ is false. The system has no solution. The solution set is $\{\ \}$ or $\varnothing$.

51. $\begin{cases} x - 3y + 2z = 0 \\ 9y - z = 22 \\ 5x + 3z = 10 \end{cases}$

The corresponding matrix is $\begin{bmatrix} 1 & -3 & 2 & | & 0 \\ 0 & 9 & -1 & | & 22 \\ 5 & 0 & 3 & | & 10 \end{bmatrix}$

Multiply row 1 by -5 and add to row 3.

$\begin{bmatrix} 1 & -3 & 2 & | & 0 \\ 0 & 9 & -1 & | & 22 \\ 0 & 15 & -7 & | & 10 \end{bmatrix}$

Divide row 2 by 9.

$\begin{bmatrix} 1 & -3 & 2 & | & 0 \\ 0 & 1 & -\frac{1}{9} & | & \frac{22}{9} \\ 0 & 15 & -7 & | & 10 \end{bmatrix}$

Multiply row 2 by -15 and add to row 3.

$\begin{bmatrix} 1 & -3 & 2 & | & 0 \\ 0 & 1 & -\frac{1}{9} & | & \frac{22}{9} \\ 0 & 0 & -\frac{48}{9} & | & -\frac{240}{9} \end{bmatrix}$

Multiply row 3 by $-\dfrac{9}{48}$.

$\begin{bmatrix} 1 & -3 & 2 & | & 0 \\ 0 & 1 & -\frac{1}{9} & | & \frac{22}{9} \\ 0 & 0 & 1 & | & 5 \end{bmatrix}$

This matrix represents the system

$\begin{cases} x - 3y + 2z = 0 \\ y - \dfrac{1}{9}z = \dfrac{22}{9}. \\ z = 5 \end{cases}$

Replace z with 5 in the second equation to find y.

$y - \dfrac{1}{9}(5) = \dfrac{22}{9}$

$y = \dfrac{22}{9} + \dfrac{5}{9} = \dfrac{27}{9} = 3$

Replace y with 3 and z with 5 in the first equation to find x.

$\begin{aligned} x - 3(3) + 2(5) &= 0 \\ x - 9 + 10 &= 0 \\ x + 1 &= 0 \\ x &= -1 \end{aligned}$

The solution is $(-1, 3, 5)$.

52. Let $x =$ the first number
$y =$ the second number
We solve the system

$$\begin{cases} x = 3y - 5 \\ x + y = 127 \end{cases}$$

We substitute $3y - 5$ for x in the second equation.

$$(3y - 5) + y = 127$$
$$4y - 5 = 127$$
$$4y = 132$$
$$y = 33$$

We replace y with 33 in the first equation to find x.

$$x = 3(33) - 5 = 99 - 5 = 94$$

The numbers are 33 and 94.

53. Let x = length of the shortest side
y = length of the second side
z = length of the third side
We solve the system

$$\begin{cases} x + y + z = 126 \\ y = 2x \\ z = x + 14 \end{cases}$$

We substitute $2x$ for y and $x + 14$ for z in the first equation.

$$x + 2x + (x + 14) = 126$$
$$4x + 14 = 126$$
$$4x = 112$$
$$x = 28$$

Now we find y and z.

$$y = 2x = 2(28) = 56$$
$$z = x + 14 = 28 + 14 = 42$$

The lengths are 28 units, 42 units, and 56 units.

54. $$\begin{cases} y \le 3x - \dfrac{1}{2} \\ 3x + 4y \ge 6 \end{cases}$$

Graph both inequalities on the same set of axes. The solution is the intersection of the solution regions. The solution of the system is the darker shaded region. This solution includes parts of both boundary lines.

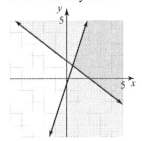

55. We solve the system

$$\begin{cases} y = -443x + 2584 \\ y = 500x + 551 \end{cases}$$

We substitute $-443x + 2584$ for y in the second equation.

$$-443x + 2584 = 500x + 551$$
$$-994x = -2033$$
$$x = \frac{-2033}{-994} \approx 2.05$$

The amount spent on VCR decks and DVD players was the same about 2 years after 1998, or in 2000.

Chapter 4 Test

1. $$\begin{cases} 2x - y = -1 & (1) \\ 5x + 4y = 17 & (2) \end{cases}$$

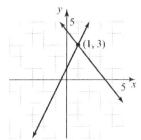

By elimination:
Multiply E1 by 4 and add it to E2.

$$8x - 4y = -4$$
$$\underline{5x + 4y = 17}$$
$$13x = 13$$
$$x = 1$$

Replace x with 1 in E2.

$$5(1) + 4y = 17$$
$$4y = 12$$
$$y = 3$$

The solution is (1, 3).

2. $$\begin{cases} 7x - 14y = 5 & (1) \\ x = 2y & (2) \end{cases}$$

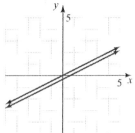

By substitution:
Replace x with $2y$ in E1.

$$7(2y) - 14y = 5$$
$$14y - 14y = 5$$
$$0 = 5 \ \text{False}$$

The system is inconsistent. The solution set is $\varnothing$.

3. $\begin{cases} 4x - 7y = 29 \\ 2x + 5y = -11 \end{cases}$

Multiply E2 by -2 and add to E1.

$$\begin{array}{r} -4x - 10y = 22 \\ 4x - 7y = 29 \\ \hline -17y = 51 \\ y = -3 \end{array}$$

Replace y with -3 in E1.

$$4x - 7(-3) = 29$$
$$4x + 21 = 29$$
$$4x = 8$$
$$x = 2$$

The solution is $(2, -3)$.

4. $\begin{cases} 15x + 6y = 15 \\ 10x + 4y = 10 \end{cases}$

Divide E1 by 3 and E2 by 2.

$$\begin{cases} 5x + 2y = 5 \\ 5x + 2y = 5 \end{cases}$$

The system is dependent. The solution is $\{(x, y) | 10x + 4y = 10\}$.

5. $\begin{cases} 2x - 3y \quad\;\; = 4 \quad (1) \\ \quad\;\; 3y + 2z = 2 \quad (2) \\ x \quad\quad\;\; - z = -5 \quad (3) \end{cases}$

Add E1 and E2.

$2x + 2z = 6$ or $x + z = 3$ (4)

Add E3 and E4.

$$\begin{array}{r} x + z = 3 \\ x - z = -5 \\ \hline 2x \quad\;\; = -2 \\ x = -1 \end{array}$$

Replace x with -1 in E3.

$$-1 - z = -5$$
$$-z = -4 \text{ so } z = 4$$

Replace x with -1 in E1.

$$2(-1) - 3y = 4$$
$$-2 - 3y = 4$$
$$-3y = 6$$
$$y = -2$$

The solution is $(-1, -2, 4)$.

6. $\begin{cases} 3x - 2y - z = -1 \quad (1) \\ 2x - 2y \quad\;\; = 4 \quad (2) \\ 2x \quad\;\; - 2z = -12 \quad (3) \end{cases}$

Multiply E2 by -1 and add to E1.

$$\begin{array}{r} 3x - 2y - z = -1 \\ -2x + 2y \quad\quad = -4 \\ \hline x \quad\quad\;\; - z = -5 \quad (4) \end{array}$$

Multiply E4 by -2 and add to E3.

$$\begin{array}{r} 2x - 2z = -12 \\ -2x + 2z = 10 \\ \hline 0 = -2 \text{ False} \end{array}$$

The system is inconsistent. The solution set is $\varnothing$.

7. $\begin{cases} \dfrac{x}{2} + \dfrac{y}{4} = -\dfrac{3}{4} \\ x + \dfrac{3}{4}y = -4 \end{cases}$

Clear fractions by multiplying both equations by 4.

$$\begin{cases} 2x + y = -3 \quad (1) \\ 4x + 3y = -16 \quad (2) \end{cases}$$

Multiply E1 by -2 and add to E2.

$$\begin{array}{r} -4x - 2y = 6 \\ 4x + 3y = -16 \\ \hline y = -10 \end{array}$$

Replace y with -10 in E1.

$$2x + (-10) = -3$$
$$2x = 7 \text{ so } x = \frac{7}{2}$$

The solution is $\left(\dfrac{7}{2}, -10 \right)$.

8. $\begin{cases} x - y = -2 \\ 3x - 3y = -6 \end{cases}$

$$\begin{bmatrix} 1 & -1 & | & -2 \\ 3 & -3 & | & -6 \end{bmatrix}$$

Multiply R1 by -3 and add to R2.

$$\begin{bmatrix} 1 & -1 & | & -2 \\ 0 & 0 & | & 0 \end{bmatrix}$$

This corresponds to $\begin{cases} x - y = -2 \\ 0 = 0 \end{cases}$.

This is a dependent system. The solution is $\{(x, y) | x - y = -2\}$.

9. $\begin{cases} x + 2y = -1 \\ 2x + 5y = -5 \end{cases}$

$$\begin{bmatrix} 1 & 2 & | & -1 \\ 2 & 5 & | & -5 \end{bmatrix}$$

Multiply R1 by -2 and add to R2.

$$\begin{bmatrix} 1 & 2 & | & -1 \\ 0 & 1 & | & -3 \end{bmatrix}$$

This corresponds to $\begin{cases} x + 2y = -1 \\ y = -3 \end{cases}$.

$$x + 2(-3) = -1$$
$$x - 6 = -1$$
$$x = 5$$

The solution is (5, –3).

10. $\begin{cases} x - y - z = 0 \\ 3x - y - 5z = -2 \\ 2x + 3y = -5 \end{cases}$

$$\begin{bmatrix} 1 & -1 & -1 & | & 0 \\ 3 & -1 & -5 & | & -2 \\ 2 & 3 & 0 & | & -5 \end{bmatrix}$$

Multiply R1 by –3 and add to R2. Multiply R1 by –2 and add to R3.

$$\begin{bmatrix} 1 & -1 & -1 & | & 0 \\ 0 & 2 & -2 & | & -2 \\ 0 & 5 & 2 & | & -5 \end{bmatrix}$$

Divide R2 by 2.

$$\begin{bmatrix} 1 & -1 & -1 & | & 0 \\ 0 & 1 & -1 & | & -1 \\ 0 & 5 & 2 & | & -5 \end{bmatrix}$$

Multiply R2 by –5 and add to R3.

$$\begin{bmatrix} 1 & -1 & -1 & | & 0 \\ 0 & 1 & -1 & | & -1 \\ 0 & 0 & 7 & | & 0 \end{bmatrix}$$

Divide R3 by 7.

$$\begin{bmatrix} 1 & -1 & -1 & | & 0 \\ 0 & 1 & -1 & | & -1 \\ 0 & 0 & 1 & | & 0 \end{bmatrix}$$

This corresponds to $\begin{cases} x - y - z = 0 \\ y - z = -1. \\ z = 0 \end{cases}$

$$y - 0 = -1$$
$$y = -1$$
$$x - (-1) - 0 = 0$$
$$x + 1 = 0$$
$$x = -1$$

The solution is (–1, –1, 0).

11. Let x = double occupancy rooms and y = single occupancy rooms.

$$\begin{cases} x + y = 80 \quad (1) \\ 90x + 80y = 6930 \quad (2) \end{cases}$$

Multiply E1 by –80 and add to E2.

$$-80x - 80y = -6400$$
$$\underline{90x + 80y = 6930}$$
$$10x = 530$$
$$x = 53$$

Replace x with 53 in E1.

$$53 + y = 80$$
$$y = 27$$

53 double-occupancy and 27 single-occupancy rooms are occupied.

12. Let x = gallons of 10% solution and y = gallons of 20% solution.

$$\begin{cases} x + y = 20 \quad (1) \\ 0.10x + 0.20y = 0.175(20) \quad (2) \end{cases}$$

Multiply E1 by –0.10 add to E2.

$$-0.10x - 0.10y = -2.0$$
$$\underline{0.10x + 0.20y = 3.5}$$
$$0.10y = 1.5$$
$$y = 15$$

Replace y with 15 in E1.

$$x + 15 = 20$$
$$x = 5$$

They should use 5 gallons of 10% fructose solution and 15 gallons of the 20% solution.

13. $R(x) = 4x$ and $C(x) = 1.5x + 2000$

Break even occurs when $R(x) = C(x)$.

$$4x = 1.5x + 2000$$
$$2.5x = 2000$$
$$x = 800$$

The company must sell 800 packages to break even.

14. Let x = measure of the smallest angle. Then the largest angle has a measure of $5x - 3$, and the remaining angle has a measure of $2x - 1$. The sum of the three angles must add to 180°:

$$a + b + c = 180$$
$$x + (5x - 3) + (2x - 1) = 180$$
$$x + 5x - 3 + 2x - 1 = 180$$
$$8x - 4 = 180$$
$$8x = 184$$
$$x = 23$$
$$5x - 3 = 5(23) - 3 = 115 - 3 = 112$$
$$2x - 1 = 2(23) - 1 = 46 - 1 = 45$$

The angle measures are 23°, 45°, and 112°.

15. $\begin{cases} 2y - x \geq 1 \\ x + y \geq -4 \\ y \leq 2 \end{cases}$

Graph all three inequalities on the same set of axes. The solution set of the system is the shaded region. The parts of the boundary lines that border the shaded region are part of the solution.

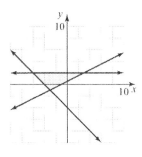

Chapter 4 Cumulative Review

1. a. Since 3 is a natural number, the statement is true.

  b. Since 7 is not one of the three numbers listed in the set, the statement is true.

2. a. Since 7 is not an element of the second set, the first set is not a subset of the second set. The statement is false.

  b. Since all three numbers in the first set are also elements of the second set, the first set is a subset of the second set. The statement is true.

3. a. $11 + 2 - 7 = 13 - 7 = 6$

  b. $-5 - 4 + 2 = -9 + 2 = -7$

4. a. $-7 - (-2) = -7 + 2 = -5$

  b. $14 - 38 = -24$

5. a. The opposite of 4 is –4.

  b. The opposite of $\dfrac{3}{7}$ is $-\dfrac{3}{7}$.

  c. The opposite of –11.2 is 11.2.

6. a. The reciprocal of 5 is $\dfrac{1}{5}$.

  b. The reciprocal of $-\dfrac{2}{3}$ is $-\dfrac{3}{2}$.

7. a. $3(2x + y) = 6x + 3y$

  b. $-(3x - 1) = -3x + 1$

  c. $0.7a(b - 2) = 0.7ab - 1.4a$

8. a. $7(3x - 2y + 4) = 21x - 14y + 28$

  b. $-(-2s - 3t) = 2s + 3t$

9. a. $3x - 5x + 4 = (3 - 5)x + 4 = -2x + 4$

  b. $7yz + yz = (7 + 1)yz = 8yz$

  c. $4z + 6.1 = 4z + 6.1$

10. a. $5y^2 - 1 + 2(y^2 + 2) = 5y^2 - 1 + 2y^2 + 4$
$$= 7y^2 + 3$$

  b. $(7.8x - 1.2) - (5.6x - 2.4)$
$$= 7.8x - 1.2 - 5.6x + 2.4$$
$$= 2.2x + 1.2$$

11. $-4x - 1 + 5x = 9x + 3 - 7x$
$$x - 1 = 2x + 3$$
$$-x = 4$$
$$x = -4$$

12. $8y - 14 = 6y - 14$
$$2y = 0$$
$$y = 0$$

13. $0.3x + 0.1 = 0.27x - 0.02$
$$0.03x = -0.12$$
$$x = -4$$

14. $2(m - 6) - m = 4(m - 3) - 3m$
$$2m - 12 - m = 4m - 12 - 3m$$
$$m - 12 = m - 12$$
$$0 = 0 \quad \text{Always True}$$
The solution is all real numbers.

15. Let x = length of the third side, then
$2x + 12$ = length of the two equal sides.
$$x + (2x + 12) + (2x + 12) = 149$$
$$5x + 24 = 149$$
$$5x = 125$$
$$x = 25$$
$$2(25) + 12 = 50 + 12 = 62$$
The sides are 25 cm, 62 cm, and 62 cm.

16. Let x = measure of the equal angles,
$x + 10$ = measure of the third angle, and
$\dfrac{1}{2}x$ = measure of the fourth angle.

$$x+x+(x+10)+\frac{1}{2}x=360$$
$$\frac{7}{2}x+10=360$$
$$\frac{7}{2}x=350$$
$$7x=700$$
$$x=100$$
$$x+10=100+10=110$$
$$\frac{1}{2}x=\frac{1}{2}(100)=50$$

The measure of the angles are $100°$, $100°$, $110°$, and $50°$.

17. $3x+4 \geq 2x-6$
$x \geq -10$

-10

18. $5(2x-1) > -5$
$10x-5 > -5$
$10x > 0$
$x > 0$
$(0, \infty)$

19. $2 < 4-x < 7$
$-2 < -x < 3$
$2 > x > -3$
$-3 < x < 2$
$(-3, 2)$

20. $-1 < \dfrac{-2x-1}{3} < 1$
$3(-1) < 3\left[\dfrac{-2x-1}{3}\right] < 3(1)$
$-3 < -2x-1 < 3$
$-2 < -2x < 4$
$1 > x > -2$
$-2 < x < 1$
$(-2, 1)$

21. $|2x|+5=7$
$|2x|=2$
$2x=2$ or $2x=-2$
$x=1$ or $x=-1$
The solution set is $\{-1, 1\}$.

22. $|x-5|=4$
$x-5=4$ or $x-5=-4$
$x=9$ or $x=1$
The solution set is $\{1, 9\}$.

23. $|m-6| < 2$
$-2 < m-6 < 2$
$4 < m < 8$
$(4, 8)$

24. $|2x+1| > 5$
$2x+1 < -5$ or $2x+1 > 5$
$2x < -6$ or $2x > 4$
$x < -3$ or $x > 2$
$(-\infty, -3) \cup (2, \infty)$

25.

a. $(2, -1)$ is in Quadrant IV.

b. $(0, 5)$ is on the y-axis.

c. $(-3, 5)$ is in Quadrant II.

d. $(-2, 0)$ is on the x-axis.

e. $\left(-\dfrac{1}{2}, -4\right)$ is in Quadrant III.

f. $(1.5, 1.5)$ is in Quadrant I.

26. a. $(-1, -5)$ is in Quadrant III.

b. $(4, -2)$ is in Quadrant IV.

c. $(0, 2)$ is on the y-axis.

27. No; for the input $x = 4$, there are two outputs, $y = \pm 2$.

28. $-2x + \dfrac{1}{2}y = -2,$ or $y = 4x - 4$

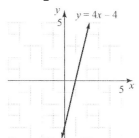

29. $f(x) = 7x^2 - 3x + 1,\ g(x) = 3x - 2,\ h(x) = x^2$

    a. $f(1) = 7(1)^2 - 3(1) + 1 = 7 - 3 + 1 = 5$

    b. $g(1) = 3(1) - 2 = 3 - 2 = 1$

    c. $h(-2) = (-2)^2 = 4$

30. $f(x) = 3x^2$

    a. $f(5) = 3(5)^2 = 3(25) = 75$

    b. $f(-2) = 3(-2)^2 = 3(4) = 12$

31. $g(x) = 2x + 1$ and $f(x) = 2x$

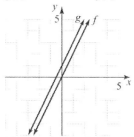

The graph of *g* is the graph of *f* shifted 1 unit up.

32. $m = \dfrac{9 - 6}{0 - (-2)} = \dfrac{3}{2}$

33. $3x - 4y = 4$
$$-4y = -3x + 4$$
$$y = \dfrac{3}{4}x - 1$$
$$m = \dfrac{3}{4},\ \ y\text{-intercept} = (0, -1)$$

34. $y = 2$
$$m = 0,\ \ y\text{-intercept} = (0, 2)$$

35. a. $3x + 7y = 4$
$$7y = -3x + 4$$
$$y = -\dfrac{3}{7}x + \dfrac{4}{7}$$
$$m = -\dfrac{3}{7}$$
$$6x + 14y = 7$$
$$14y = -6x + 7$$
$$y = -\dfrac{3}{7}x + \dfrac{1}{2}$$
$$m = -\dfrac{3}{7}$$
Parallel, since the slopes are equal.

  b. $-x + 3y = 2$
$$3y = x + 2$$
$$y = \dfrac{1}{3}x + \dfrac{2}{3}$$
$$m = \dfrac{1}{3}$$
$$2x + 6y = 5$$
$$6y = -2x + 5$$
$$y = -\dfrac{1}{3}x + \dfrac{5}{6}$$
$$m = -\dfrac{1}{3}$$
Neither, since the slopes are not equal and their product is not -1.

  c. $2x - 3y = 12$
$$-3y = -2x + 12$$
$$y = \dfrac{2}{3}x - 4$$
$$m = \dfrac{2}{3}$$
$$6x + 4y = 16$$
$$4y = -6x + 16$$
$$y = -\dfrac{3}{2}x + 4$$
$$m = -\dfrac{3}{2}$$
Perpendicular, since the product of the slopes is -1.

36. $y - (-9) = \dfrac{1}{5}(x - 0)$
$$y + 9 = \dfrac{1}{5}x$$
$$y = \dfrac{1}{5}x - 9$$

37. $m = \dfrac{-5-0}{-4-4} = \dfrac{-5}{-8} = \dfrac{5}{8}$

$y - 0 = \dfrac{5}{8}(x-4)$

$y = \dfrac{5}{8}x - \dfrac{5}{2}$

$f(x) = \dfrac{5}{8}x - \dfrac{5}{2}$

38. $f(x) = \dfrac{1}{2}x - \dfrac{1}{3}$ or $y = \dfrac{1}{2}x - \dfrac{1}{3}$

$m = \dfrac{1}{2}$ so $m_\perp = -2$

$y - 6 = -2[x - (-2)]$

$y - 6 = -2(x+2)$

$y - 6 = -2x - 4$

$y = -2x + 2$

39. $3x \ge y$, or $y \le 3x$

Graph the boundary line $y = 3x$ with a solid line because the inequality symbol is $\le$.

Test: (0, 1)

$3x \ge y$

$3(0) \ge 1$

$0 \ge 1$ False

Shade the half-plane that does not contain (0, 1).

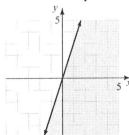

40. $x \ge 1$

Graph the boundary line $x = 1$ with a solid line because the inequality symbol is $\ge$.

Shade the half-plane that does not contain (0, 0).

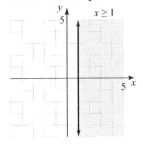

41. a. $\begin{cases} -x + y = 2 \\ 2x - y = -3 \end{cases}$

$-(-1) + 1 = 2$

$1 + 1 = 2$

$2 = 2$ True

$2(-1) - (1) = -3$

$-2 - 1 = -3$

$-3 = -3$ True

Yes, (–1, 1) is a solution.

b. $\begin{cases} 5x + 3y = -1 \\ x - y = 1 \end{cases}$

$5(-2) + 3(3) = -1$

$-10 + 9 = -1$

$-1 = -1$ True

$-2 - 3 = -1$

$-5 = -1$ False

No, (–2, 3) is not a solution.

42. $\begin{cases} 5x + y = -2 & (1) \\ 4x - 2y = -10 & (2) \end{cases}$

Multiply E1 by 2 and add to E2.

$10x + 2y = -4$

$\underline{4x - 2y = -10}$

$14x \qquad = -14$

$x = -1$

Replace x with –1 in E1.

$5(-1) + y = -2$

$-5 + y = -2$

$y = 3$

The solution is (–1, 3).

43. $\begin{cases} 3x - y + z = -15 & (1) \\ x + 2y - z = 1 & (2) \\ 2x + 3y - 2z = 0 & (3) \end{cases}$

Add E1 and E2.

$4x + y = -14$ (4)

Multiply E1 by 2 and add to E3.

$6x - 2y + 2z = -30$

$\underline{2x + 3y - 2z = 0}$

$8x + y \qquad = -30$ (5)

Solve the new system:

$\begin{cases} 4x + y = -14 & (4) \\ 8x + y = -30 & (5) \end{cases}$

Multiply E4 by –1 and add to E5.

$-4x - y = 14$

$\underline{8x + y = -30}$

$4x \qquad = -16$

$x = -4$

Replace x with -4 in E4.

$4(-4) + y = -14$

$-16 + y = -14$

$y = 2$

Replace x with -4 and y with 2 in E1.

$3(-4) - (2) + z = -15$

$-12 - 2 + z = -15$

$-14 + z = -15$

$z = -1$

The solution is $(-4, 2, -1)$.

44. $\begin{cases} x - 2y + z = 0 & (1) \\ 3x - y - 2z = -15 & (2) \\ 2x - 3y + 3z = 7 & (3) \end{cases}$

Multiply E1 by 2 and add to E2.

$2x - 4y + 2z = 0$

$\underline{3x - y - 2z = -15}$

$5x - 5y \quad\quad = -15$ or $x - y = -3$ (4)

Multiply E1 by -3 and add to E3.

$-3x + 6y - 3z = 0$

$\underline{2x - 3y + 3z = 7}$

$-x + 3y \quad\quad = 7$ (5)

Add E4 and E5.

$2y = 4$

$y = 2$

Replace y with 2 in E4.

$x - 2 = -3$

$x = -1$

Replace x with -1 and y with 2 in E1.

$-1 - 2(2) + z = 0$

$-5 + z = 0$

$z = 5$

The solution is $(-1, 2, 5)$.

45. $\begin{cases} x + 3y = 5 \\ 2x - y = -4 \end{cases}$

$\begin{bmatrix} 1 & 3 & | & 5 \\ 2 & -1 & | & -4 \end{bmatrix}$

Multiply R1 by -2 and add to R2.

$\begin{bmatrix} 1 & 3 & | & 5 \\ 0 & -7 & | & -14 \end{bmatrix}$

Divide R2 by -7.

$\begin{bmatrix} 1 & 3 & | & 5 \\ 0 & 1 & | & 2 \end{bmatrix}$

This corresponds to $\begin{cases} x + 3y = 5 \\ \quad\quad y = 2 \end{cases}$.

$x + 3(2) = 5$

$x + 6 = 5$

$x = -1$

The solution is $(-1, 2)$.

46. $\begin{cases} -6x + 8y = 0 & (1) \\ 9x - 12y = 2 & (2) \end{cases}$

Divide E1 by -2 and E2 by 3.

$\begin{cases} 3x - 4y = 0 \\ 3x - 4y = \dfrac{2}{3} \end{cases}$

This system is inconsistent. The solution set is $\varnothing$.

Chapter 5

Practice Exercises

1. a. $3^4 \cdot 3^2 = 3^{4+2} = 3^6$

   b. $x^5 \cdot x^2 = x^{5+2} = x^7$

   c. $y \cdot y^3 \cdot y^5 = (y^1 \cdot y^3) \cdot y^5 = y^4 \cdot y^5 = y^9$

2. a. $(5z^3)(7z) = 5(7)z^3 z^1 = 35z^4$

   b. $(-4.1t^5 q^3)(5tq^5) = -4.1(5)t^5 t^1 q^3 q^5$
$$= -20.5t^6 q^8$$

3. a. $5^0 = 1$

   b. $-5^0 = -(5^0) = -(1) = -1$

   c. $(3x - 8)^0 = 1$

   d. $3x^0 = 3(1) = 3$

4. a. $\dfrac{z^8}{z^3} = z^{8-3} = z^5$

   b. $\dfrac{3^9}{3^3} = 3^{9-3} = 3^6$

   c. $\dfrac{45x^7}{5x^3} = 9x^{7-3} = 9x^4$

   d. $\dfrac{24a^{14}b^6}{18a^7 b^6} = \dfrac{4}{3}a^{14-7}b^{6-6}$
$$= \dfrac{4}{3}a^7 b^0$$
$$= \dfrac{4}{3}a^7 \text{ or } \dfrac{4a^7}{3}$$

5. a. $6^{-2} = \dfrac{1}{6^2} = \dfrac{1}{36}$

   b. $(-2)^{-6} = \dfrac{1}{(-2)^6} = \dfrac{1}{64}$

   c. $3x^{-5} = 3 \cdot \dfrac{1}{x^5} = \dfrac{3}{x^5}$

   d. $(5y)^{-1} = \dfrac{1}{(5y)^1} = \dfrac{1}{5y}$

   e. $\dfrac{k^4}{k^{11}} = k^{4-11} = k^{-7} = \dfrac{1}{k^7}$

   f. $\dfrac{5^3}{5^5} = 5^{3-5} = 5^{-2} = \dfrac{1}{5^2} = \dfrac{1}{25}$

   g. $5^{-1} + 2^{-2} = \dfrac{1}{5^1} + \dfrac{1}{2^2} = \dfrac{1}{5} + \dfrac{1}{4} = \dfrac{4}{20} + \dfrac{5}{20} = \dfrac{9}{20}$

   h. $\dfrac{1}{z^{-8}} = \dfrac{1}{\frac{1}{z^8}} = 1 \div \dfrac{1}{z^8} = 1 \cdot \dfrac{z^8}{1} = z^8$

6. a. $\dfrac{z^{-8}}{z^3} = z^{-8-3} = z^{-11} = \dfrac{1}{z^{11}}$

   b. $\dfrac{7t^3}{t^{-5}} = 7 \cdot t^{3-(-5)} = 7t^8$

   c. $\dfrac{3^{-2}}{3^{-4}} = 3^{-2-(-4)} = 3^{-2+4} = 3^2 = 9$

   d. $\dfrac{5a^{-5}b^3}{15a^2 b^{-4}} = \dfrac{a^{-5-2}b^{3-(-4)}}{3} = \dfrac{a^{-7}b^7}{3} = \dfrac{b^7}{3a^7}$

   e. $\dfrac{(2x^{-5})(x^6)}{x^5} = \dfrac{2x^{-5+6}}{x^5}$
$$= \dfrac{2x^1}{x^5}$$
$$= 2x^{1-5}$$
$$= 2x^{-4}$$
$$= \dfrac{2}{x^4}$$

7. a. $x^{3a} \cdot x^4 = x^{3a+4}$

   b. $\dfrac{x^{3t-2}}{x^{t-3}} = x^{(3t-2)-(t-3)} = x^{3t-2-t+3} = x^{2t+1}$

8. a. Move the decimal point until the number is between 1 and 10. The decimal point is moved 4 places and the original number is 10 or greater, so the count is positive 4.

$$65,000 = 6.5 \times 10^4$$

b. Move the decimal point until the number is between 1 and 10. The decimal point is moved 5 places and the original number is less than 1, so the count is -5.

$$0.000038 = 3.8 \times 10^{-5}$$

9. a. Since the exponent is positive, move the decimal point 5 places to the right.

$$6.2 \times 10^5 = 620,000$$

b. Since the exponent is negative, more the decimal point 2 places to the left.

$$3.109 \times 10^{-2} = 0.03109$$

Vocabulary and Readiness Check

1. $9x^5$; base x

2. yz^5; base z

3. -3^5; base 3

4. $(-3)^5$; base -3

5. $(y^7)^5$; base y^7

6. $9 \cdot 2^5$; base 2

7. $5x^{-1}y^{-2} = \dfrac{5}{xy^2}$

8. $7xy^{-4} = \dfrac{7x}{y^4}$

9. $a^2 b^{-1} c^{-5} = \dfrac{a^2}{bc^5}$

10. $a^{-4}b^2 c^{-6} = \dfrac{b^2}{a^4 c^6}$

11. $\dfrac{y^{-2}}{x^{-4}} = \dfrac{x^4}{y^2}$

12. $\dfrac{x^{-7}}{z^{-3}} = \dfrac{z^3}{x^7}$

Exercise Set 5.1

2. $3^3 \cdot 3^5 = 3^{3+5} = 3^8$

4. $a^2 \cdot a^9 = a^{2+9} = a^{11}$

6. $n \cdot n^{10} \cdot n^{12} = n^{1+10+12} = n^{23}$

8. $(-7xy)(7y) = -7(7) \cdot x \cdot y^{1+1} = -49xy^2$

10. $(-6a^2 b^3)(-3ab^3) = 18a^{2+1}b^{3+3} = 18a^3 b^6$

12. $(-9)^0 = 1$

14. $(3x-1)^0 = 1$

16. $-5x^0 = -5 \cdot 1 = -5$

18. $8x^0 + 1 = 8 \cdot 1 + 1 = 8 + 1 = 9$

20. $\dfrac{x^9}{x^4} = x^{9-4} = x^5$

22. $-\dfrac{16x^5}{8x} = -2x^{5-1} = -2x^4$

24. $\dfrac{a^{12}b^2}{a^9 b} = a^{12-9}b^{2-1} = a^3 b^1 = a^3 b$

26. $\dfrac{24a^{10}b^{11}}{10ab^3} = \dfrac{12a^{10-1}b^{11-3}}{5} = \dfrac{12}{5}a^9 b^8$

28. $\dfrac{49a^3 bc^{14}}{-7abc^8} = -7a^{3-1}b^{1-1}c^{14-8}$
$$= -7a^2 b^0 c^6$$
$$= -7a^2 c^6$$

30. $2^{-3} = \dfrac{1}{2^3} = \dfrac{1}{8}$

32. $(-6)^{-2} = \dfrac{1}{(-6)^2} = \dfrac{1}{36}$

34. $\dfrac{z}{z^3} = z^{1-3} = z^{-2} = \dfrac{1}{z^2}$

36. $10b^{-1} = \dfrac{10}{b^1} = \dfrac{10}{b}$

38. $\dfrac{p^{-13}}{q^{-3}} = \dfrac{q^3}{p^{13}}$

40. $\dfrac{z^{-12}}{z^{10}} = z^{-12-10} = z^{-22} = \dfrac{1}{z^{22}}$

42. $\dfrac{3s^3}{15s^{-3}} = \dfrac{s^{3-(-3)}}{5} = \dfrac{s^6}{5}$

44. $\dfrac{y^{-7}y}{y^8} = \dfrac{y^{-7+1}}{y^8} = \dfrac{y^{-6}}{y^8} = y^{-6-8} = y^{-14} = \dfrac{1}{y^{14}}$

46. $\dfrac{18ab^{-6}}{3a^{-3}b^6} = 6a^{1-(-3)}b^{-6-6} = 6a^4b^{-12} = \dfrac{6a^4}{b^{12}}$

48. $\dfrac{(30z^2)(z^5)}{55z^{-4}} = \dfrac{6z^{2+5}}{11z^{-4}} = \dfrac{6z^{7-(-4)}}{11} = \dfrac{6z^{11}}{11}$

50. $-3y \cdot -9y^4 = -3 \cdot (-9)y^{1+4} = 27y^5$

52. $y^6 \cdot y \cdot y^9 = y^{6+1+9} = y^{16}$

54. $-3z^4 \cdot 10z^7 = -3 \cdot 10z^{4+7} = -30z^{11}$

56. $4y^0 - (4y)^0 = 4 \cdot 1 - 1 = 4 - 1 = 3$

58. $\dfrac{x^{11}}{x^{20}} = x^{11-20} = x^{-9} = \dfrac{1}{x^9}$

60. $4^0 + 4x^0 = 1 + 4 \cdot 1 = 1 + 4 = 5$

62. $\dfrac{y^{-6}}{y^{-9}} = y^{-6-(-9)} = y^3$

64. $1^{-3} - 4^{-2} = \dfrac{1}{1^3} - \dfrac{1}{4^2} = \dfrac{16}{16} - \dfrac{1}{16} = \dfrac{15}{16}$

66. $(4x)^{-1} = \dfrac{1}{(4x)^1} = \dfrac{1}{4x}$

68. $\dfrac{x^{-5}}{x^3} = x^{-5-3} = x^{-8} = \dfrac{1}{x^8}$

70. $\dfrac{a^{-5}b^7}{a^{-2}b^{-3}} = a^{-5-(-2)}b^{7-(-3)} = a^{-3}b^{10} = \dfrac{b^{10}}{a^3}$

72. $(-6a^4b)(2b^3)(-3ab^6)$
$= -6(2)(-3)a^4 \cdot a \cdot b \cdot b^3 \cdot b^6$
$= 36a^{4+1} \cdot b^{1+3+6}$
$= 36a^5b^{10}$

74. $5^{-2} \cdot y = \dfrac{y}{5^2} = \dfrac{y}{25}$

76. $\dfrac{10^{25}}{10^{23}} = 10^{25-23} = 10^2 = 100$

78. $\dfrac{13^{-10}}{13^{-9}} = 13^{-10-(-9)} = 13^{-10+9} = 13^{-1} = \dfrac{1}{13}$

80. $\dfrac{11^{-9}b^3}{11^{-7}b^{-4}} = 11^{-9-(-7)}b^{3-(-4)}$
$= 11^{-9+7}b^{3+4}$
$= 11^{-2}b^7$
$= \dfrac{b^7}{11^2}$
$= \dfrac{b^7}{121}$

82. $\dfrac{30x^{-7}yz^{-14}}{3xyz} = \dfrac{30}{3} \cdot x^{-7-1}y^{1-1}z^{-14-1}$
$= 10x^{-8}y^0z^{-15}$
$= \dfrac{10}{x^8z^{15}}$

84. $y^{2p} \cdot y^{9p} = y^{2p+9p} = y^{11p}$

86. $\dfrac{y^{4p-2}}{y^{3p}} = y^{4p-2-3p} = y^{p-2}$

88. $x^{9y} \cdot x^{-7y} = x^{9y-7y} = x^{2y}$

90. $\dfrac{y^6}{y^{4z}} = y^{6-4z}$

92. $\dfrac{z^{5x} \cdot z^{x-7}}{z^x} = \dfrac{z^{6x-7}}{z^x} = z^{(6x-7)-x} = z^{5x-7}$

94. $678,000 = 6.78 \times 10^5$

96. $0.007613 = 7.613 \times 10^{-3}$

98. $36,800,000 = 3.68 \times 10^7$

100. $0.00084 = 8.4 \times 10^{-4}$

102. $98,700,000,000 = 9.87 \times 10^{10}$

104. $170,000 = 1.7 \times 10^5$

106. $61,049,000 = 6.1049 \times 10^7$

108. $27,000,000 = 2.7 \times 10^7$

110. $0.0000164 = 1.64 \times 10^{-5}$

112. $2.7 \times 10^{-5} = 0.000027$

114. $6.378 \times 10^8 = 637,800,000$

116. $7.6 \times 10^4 = 76,000$

118. $1.66 \times 10^{-5} = 0.0000166$

120. $8.007 \times 10^8 = 800,700,000$

122. $3.949 \times 10^6 = 3,949,000$

124. $1.2 \times 10^9 = 1,200,000,000$

126. $5^2 \cdot 2^2 = 25 \cdot 4 = 100$

128. $\dfrac{3^3}{4^3} = \dfrac{27}{64}$

130. $(2^2)^3 = 4^3 = 64$

132. Answers may vary

134. Answers may vary

136. All are equal to 36,000. **b** is written in scientific notation.

138. 5^{10}

140. 5^{-9}

Section 5.2

Practice Exercises

1. a. $(z^3)^5 = z^{3 \cdot 5} = z^{15}$

   b. $(5^2)^2 = 5^{2 \cdot 2} = 5^4 = 625$

   c. $(3^{-1})^3 = 3^{-1 \cdot 3} = 3^{-3} = \dfrac{1}{3^3} = \dfrac{1}{27}$

   d. $(x^{-4})^{-6} = x^{-4(-6)} = x^{24}$

2. a. $(2x^3)^5 = 2^5 \cdot (x^3)^5 = 2^5 \cdot x^{3 \cdot 5} = 32x^{15}$

   b. $\left(\dfrac{3}{5}\right)^2 = \dfrac{3^2}{5^2} = \dfrac{9}{25}$

   c. $\left(\dfrac{2a^5}{b^7}\right)^4 = \dfrac{(2a^5)^4}{(b^7)^4} = \dfrac{2^4 \cdot (a^5)^4}{(b^7)^4} = \dfrac{16a^{20}}{b^{28}}$

   d. $\left(\dfrac{3^{-2}}{x}\right)^{-1} = \dfrac{(3^{-2})^{-1}}{x^{-1}} = \dfrac{3^2}{x^{-1}} = 9x$

   e. $(a^{-2}b^{-5}c^4)^{-2} = (a^{-2})^{-2} \cdot (b^{-5})^{-2} \cdot (c^4)^{-2}$
$$= a^4 b^{10} c^{-8}$$
$$= \dfrac{a^4 b^{10}}{c^8}$$

3. a. $(3ab^{-5})^{-3} = 3^{-3} a^{-3} (b^{-5})^{-3}$
$$= 3^{-3} a^{-3} b^{15}$$
$$= \dfrac{b^{15}}{3^3 a^3}$$
$$= \dfrac{b^{15}}{27a^3}$$

b. $\left(\dfrac{y^{-7}}{y^{-4}}\right)^{-5} = \dfrac{(y^{-7})^{-5}}{(y^{-4})^{-5}}$

$\qquad = \dfrac{y^{35}}{y^{20}}$

$\qquad = y^{35-20}$

$\qquad = y^{15}$

c. $\left(\dfrac{3}{8}\right)^{-2} = \dfrac{3^{-2}}{8^{-2}} = \dfrac{8^2}{3^2} = \dfrac{64}{9}$

d. $\dfrac{9^{-2}a^{-4}b^3}{a^2 b^{-5}} = 9^{-2}\left(\dfrac{a^{-4}}{a^2}\right)\left(\dfrac{b^3}{b^{-5}}\right)$

$\qquad = 9^{-2}a^{-4-2}b^{3-(-5)}$

$\qquad = 9^{-2}a^{-6}b^8$

$\qquad = \dfrac{b^8}{9^2 a^6}$

$\qquad = \dfrac{b^8}{81a^6}$

4. a. $\left(\dfrac{5a^4 b}{a^{-8}c}\right)^{-3} = \left(\dfrac{5a^{12}b}{c}\right)^{-3}$

$\qquad = \dfrac{5^{-3}a^{-36}b^{-3}}{c^{-3}}$

$\qquad = \dfrac{c^3}{5^3 a^{36}b^3}$

$\qquad = \dfrac{c^3}{125a^{36}b^3}$

b. $\left(\dfrac{2x^4}{5y^{-2}}\right)^3\left(\dfrac{x^{-4}}{10y^{-2}}\right)^{-1} = \dfrac{8x^{12}}{125y^{-6}}\cdot\dfrac{x^4}{10^{-1}y^2}$

$\qquad = \dfrac{8\cdot 10 \cdot x^{12}x^4 y^6}{125y^2}$

$\qquad = \dfrac{16x^{16}y^4}{25}$

5. a. $x^{-2a}(3x^a)^3 = x^{-2a}\cdot 3^3 \cdot x^{a\cdot 3}$

$\qquad = 27x^{-2a+3a}$

$\qquad = 27x^a$

b. $\dfrac{(y^{3b})^3}{y^{4b-3}} = \dfrac{y^{9b}}{y^{4b-3}}$

$\qquad = y^{9b-(4b-3)}$

$\qquad = y^{9b-4b+3}$

$\qquad = y^{5b+3}$

6. a. $(3.4\times 10^4)(5\times 10^{-7})$

$\qquad = 3.4\times 5\times 10^4 \times 10^{-7}$

$\qquad = 17.0\times 10^{-3}$

$\qquad = (1.7\times 10^1)\times 10^{-3}$

$\qquad = 1.7\times 10^{-2}$

b. $\dfrac{5.6\times 10^8}{4\times 10^{-2}} = \left(\dfrac{5.6}{4}\right)\left(\dfrac{10^8}{10^{-2}}\right)$

$\qquad = 1.4\times 10^{8-(-2)}$

$\qquad = 1.4\times 10^{10}$

7. $\dfrac{2400\times 0.0000014}{800}$

$\qquad = \dfrac{(2.4\times 10^3)(1.4\times 10^{-6})}{8\times 10^2}$

$\qquad = \dfrac{2.4(1.4)}{8}\cdot\dfrac{10^3\cdot 10^{-6}}{10^2}$

$\qquad = 0.42\times 10^{-5}$

$\qquad = (4.2\times 10^{-1})\times 10^{-5}$

$\qquad = 4.2\times 10^{-6}$

Vocabulary and Readiness Check

1. $(x^4)^5 = x^{4(5)} = x^{20}$

2. $(5^6)^2 = 5^{6(2)} = 5^{12}$

3. $x^4 \cdot x^5 = x^{4+5} = x^9$

4. $x^7 \cdot x^8 = x^{7+8} = x^{15}$

5. $(y^6)^7 = y^{6(7)} = y^{42}$

6. $(x^3)^4 = x^{3(4)} = x^{12}$

7. $(z^4)^9 = z^{4(9)} = z^{36}$

8. $(z^3)^7 = z^{3(7)} = z^{21}$

9. $(z^{-6})^{-3} = z^{-6(-3)} = z^{18}$

10. $(y^{-4})^{-2} = y^{-4(-2)} = y^8$

Exercise Set 5.2

2. $(2^{-2})^2 = 2^{-2(2)} = 2^{-4} = \dfrac{1}{2^4} = \dfrac{1}{16}$

4. $(y^7)^{-3} = y^{7(-3)} = y^{-21} = \dfrac{1}{y^{21}}$

6. $(z^{-1})^{10} = z^{-1(10)} = z^{-10} = \dfrac{1}{z^{10}}$

8. $(4x^3yz)^2 = 4^2(x^3)^2 y^2 z^2$
$= 16x^{3(2)} y^2 z^2$
$= 16x^6 y^2 z^2$

10. $\left(\dfrac{3a^{-4}}{b^7}\right)^3 = \dfrac{3^3(a^{-4})^3}{(b^7)^3}$
$= \dfrac{27a^{-4(3)}}{b^{7(3)}}$
$= \dfrac{27a^{-12}}{b^{21}}$
$= \dfrac{27}{a^{12}b^{21}}$

12. $(6x^{-6}y^7z^0)^{-2} = 6^{-2}(x^{-6})^{-2}(y^7)^{-2}(z^0)^{-2}$
$= \dfrac{x^{12}y^{-14}z^0}{6^2}$
$= \dfrac{x^{12}}{36y^{14}}$

14. $\left(\dfrac{a^{-2}b^{-5}}{c^{-11}}\right)^{-6} = \dfrac{(a^{-2})^{-6}(b^{-5})^{-6}}{(c^{-11})^{-6}} = \dfrac{a^{12}b^{30}}{c^{66}}$

16. $\left(\dfrac{a^{-4}}{a^{-5}}\right)^{-2} = \dfrac{(a^{-4})^{-2}}{(a^{-5})^{-2}}$
$= \dfrac{a^8}{a^{10}}$
$= a^{8-10}$
$= a^{-2}$
$= \dfrac{1}{a^2}$

18. $\left(\dfrac{2a^{-2}b^5}{4a^2b^7}\right)^{-2} = \left(\dfrac{1}{2a^4b^2}\right)^{-2}$
$= \dfrac{(1)^{-2}}{(2)^{-2}(a^4)^{-2}(b^2)^{-2}}$
$= \dfrac{(2)^2}{(1)^2 a^{-8}b^{-4}}$
$= 4a^8b^4$

20. $\dfrac{4^{-1}x^2yz}{x^{-2}yz^3} = \dfrac{x^{2-(-2)}y^0z^{1-3}}{4^1} = \dfrac{x^4z^{-2}}{4} = \dfrac{x^4}{4z^2}$

22. $\left(\dfrac{6p^6}{p^{12}}\right)^2 = \dfrac{6^2 p^{12}}{p^{24}}$
$= 36p^{12-24}$
$= 36p^{-12}$
$= \dfrac{36}{p^{12}}$

24. $(-8y^3xa^{-2})^{-3} = (-8)^{-3}(y^3)^{-3}x^{-3}(a^{-2})^{-3}$
$= \dfrac{y^{-9}a^6}{(-8)^3 x^3}$
$= \dfrac{a^6}{-512x^3y^9}$
$= -\dfrac{a^6}{512x^3y^9}$

26. $\left(\dfrac{x^{-2}y^{-2}}{a^{-3}}\right)^{-7} = \dfrac{(x^{-2})^{-7}(y^{-2})^{-7}}{(a^{-3})^{-7}} = \dfrac{x^{14}y^{14}}{a^{21}}$

28. $(8^2)^{-1} = 8^{2(-1)} = 8^{-2} = \dfrac{1}{8^2} = \dfrac{1}{64}$

30. $(y^{-4})^5 = y^{-4(5)} = y^{-20} = \dfrac{1}{y^{20}}$

32. $\left(\dfrac{4}{3}\right)^2 = \dfrac{4^2}{3^2} = \dfrac{16}{9}$

34. $(-8x^3)^2 = (-8)^2(x^3)^2 = 64x^6$

36. $(-4^{-6}y^{-6})^{-4} = (-4^{-6})^{-4}(y^{-6})^{-4} = 4^{24}y^{24}$

38. $\left(\dfrac{7^{-3}}{ab^2}\right)^{-2} = \dfrac{(7^{-3})^{-2}}{a^{-2}(b^2)^{-2}} = \dfrac{7^6}{a^{-2}b^{-4}} = 7^6 a^2 b^4$

40. $\left(\dfrac{1}{8}\right)^{-2} = \dfrac{1^{-2}}{8^{-2}} = \dfrac{8^2}{1^2} = 64$

42. $\left(\dfrac{8^{-3}}{y^2}\right)^{-2} = \dfrac{8^{-3(-2)}}{y^{2(-2)}} = \dfrac{8^6}{y^{-4}} = 8^6 y^4$

44. $\dfrac{2(y^3)^{-3}}{y^{-3}} = \dfrac{2y^{-9}}{y^{-3}} = 2y^{-9-(-3)} = 2y^{-6} = \dfrac{2}{y^6}$

46. $\left(\dfrac{n^5}{2m^{-2}}\right)^{-4} = \dfrac{(n^5)^{-4}}{2^{-4}(m^{-2})^{-4}}$
$= \dfrac{2^4 n^{-20}}{m^8}$
$= \dfrac{16}{n^{20}m^8}$

48. $\dfrac{2^{-3}m^{-4}n^{-5}}{5^{-2}m^{-5}n} = \dfrac{5^2 m^{-4-(-5)}n^{-5-1}}{2^3}$
$= \dfrac{25mn^{-6}}{8}$
$= \dfrac{25m}{8n^6}$

50. $(5xy)^3(z^{-2})^{-3} = 5^3 x^3 y^3 z^{-2(-3)} = 125x^3 y^3 z^6$

52. $2(y^2 b)^{-4} = 2y^{2(-4)}b^{-4} = 2y^{-8}b^{-4} = \dfrac{2}{y^8 b^4}$

54. $\dfrac{7^{-1}a^{-3}b^5}{a^2 b^{-2}} = \dfrac{a^{-3-2}b^{5-(-2)}}{7^1} = \dfrac{a^{-5}b^7}{7} = \dfrac{b^7}{7a^5}$

56. $\left(\dfrac{3z^{-2}}{y}\right)^2 \left(\dfrac{9y^{-4}}{z^{-3}}\right)^{-1} = \dfrac{3^2 z^{-2(2)} 9^{-1} y^{-4(-1)}}{y^2 z^{-3(-1)}}$
$= \dfrac{9z^{-4}y^4}{9^1 y^2 z^3}$
$= z^{-4-3}y^{4-2}$
$= z^{-7}y^2$
$= \dfrac{y^2}{z^7}$

58. $(x^{2b+7})^2 = x^{(2b+7)\cdot 2} = x^{4b+14}$

60. $\dfrac{x^{-5y+2}x^{2y}}{x} = \dfrac{x^{-5y+2+2y}}{x}$
$= \dfrac{x^{-3y+2}}{x}$
$= x^{-3y+2-1}$
$= x^{-3y+1}$

62. $(c^{2a+3})^3 = c^{(2a+3)\cdot 3} = c^{6a+9}$

64. $\dfrac{(y^{4a})^7}{y^{2a-1}} = \dfrac{y^{28a}}{y^{2a-1}} = y^{28a-(2a-1)} = y^{26a+1}$

66. $\left(\dfrac{3y^{5a}}{y^{-a+1}}\right)^2 = \dfrac{3^2 y^{5a(2)}}{y^{(-a+1)\cdot 2}}$
$= \dfrac{9y^{10a}}{y^{-2a+2}}$
$= 9y^{10a-(-2a+2)}$
$= 9y^{12a-2}$

68. $\dfrac{16x^{-5-3a}y^{-2a-b}}{2x^{-5+3b}y^{-2b-a}}$
$= \left(\dfrac{16}{2}\right)\left(\dfrac{x^{-5-3a}}{x^{-5+3b}}\right)\left(\dfrac{y^{-2a-b}}{y^{-2b-a}}\right)$
$= 8x^{-5-3a-(-5+3b)}y^{-2a-b-(-2b-a)}$
$= 8x^{-5-3a+5-3b}y^{-2a-b+2b+a}$
$= 8x^{-3a-3b}y^{b-a}$

70. $(3.6 \times 10^{-12})(6 \times 10^9) = 3.6 \times 6 \times 10^{-12+9}$
$$= 21.6 \times 10^{-3}$$
$$= 2.16 \times 10^1 \times 10^{-3}$$
$$= 2.16 \times 10^{-2}$$

72. $(3 \times 10^{-7})^3 = 3^3 \times 10^{-7(3)}$
$$= 27 \times 10^{-21}$$
$$= 2.7 \times 10^1 \times 10^{-21}$$
$$= 2.7 \times 10^{-20}$$

74. $\dfrac{1.2 \times 10^9}{2 \times 10^{-5}} = \dfrac{1.2}{2} \times 10^{9-(-5)}$
$$= 0.6 \times 10^{14}$$
$$= 6 \times 10^{-1} \times 10^{14}$$
$$= 6 \times 10^{13}$$

76. $\dfrac{0.00048}{0.0016} = \dfrac{4.8 \times 10^{-4}}{1.6 \times 10^{-3}}$
$$= \dfrac{4.8}{1.6} \times 10^{-4-(-3)}$$
$$= 3 \times 10^{-1}$$

78. $\dfrac{0.0003 \times 0.0024}{0.0006 \times 20} = \dfrac{3 \times 10^{-4} \times 2.4 \times 10^{-3}}{6 \times 10^{-4} \times 2 \times 10^1}$
$$= \dfrac{7.2 \times 10^{-7}}{12 \times 10^{-3}}$$
$$= \dfrac{7.2}{12} \times 10^{-7-(-3)}$$
$$= 0.6 \times 10^{-4}$$
$$= 6 \times 10^{-1} \times 10^{-4}$$
$$= 6 \times 10^{-5}$$

80. $\dfrac{0.00016 \times 300}{0.064 \times 100} = \dfrac{1.6 \times 10^{-4} \times 3 \times 10^2}{6.4 \times 10^{-2} \times 1 \times 10^2}$
$$= \dfrac{4.8 \times 10^{-2}}{6.4 \times 10^0}$$
$$= 0.75 \times 10^{-2}$$
$$= 7.5 \times 10^{-1} \times 10^{-2}$$
$$= 7.5 \times 10^{-3}$$

82. $\dfrac{0.00072 \times 0.003}{0.00024} = \dfrac{7.2 \times 10^{-4} \times 3 \times 10^{-3}}{2.4 \times 10^{-4}}$
$$= \dfrac{21.6 \times 10^{-7}}{2.4 \times 10^{-4}}$$
$$= 9 \times 10^{-7-(-4)}$$
$$= 9 \times 10^{-3}$$

84. $\dfrac{0.0007 \times 11,000}{0.001 \times 0.0001} = \dfrac{7 \times 10^{-4} \times 1.1 \times 10^4}{1 \times 10^{-3} \times 1 \times 10^{-4}}$
$$= \dfrac{7.7 \times 10^0}{1 \times 10^{-7}}$$
$$= 7.7 \times 10^{0-(-7)}$$
$$= 7.7 \times 10^7$$

86. $\dfrac{(2.6 \times 10^{-3})(4.8 \times 10^{-4})}{1.3 \times 10^{-12}} = \dfrac{12.48 \times 10^{-7}}{1.3 \times 10^{-12}}$
$$= 9.6 \times 10^{-7-(-12)}$$
$$= 9.6 \times 10^5$$

88. $(4 \times 10^{-2})(6.452 \times 10^{-4}) = 25.808 \times 10^{-6}$
$$= 2.5808 \times 10^1 \times 10^{-6}$$
$$= 2.5808 \times 10^{-5}$$
The area is 2.5808×10^{-5} square meter.

90. $-5y + 4y - 18 - y = -2y - 18$

92. $-3x - (4x - 2) = -3x - 4x + 2 = -7x + 2$

94. $3(z - 4) - 2(3z + 1) = 3z - 12 - 6z - 2$
$$= -3z - 14$$

96. $\left(\dfrac{2x^{-2}}{y}\right)^3 = \dfrac{2^3 x^{-2(3)}}{y^3} = \dfrac{8x^{-6}}{y^3} = \dfrac{8}{x^6 y^3}$
The volume is $\dfrac{8}{x^6 y^3}$ cubic meters.

98. $D = \dfrac{500,000}{250}$
$$= \dfrac{5 \times 10^5}{2.5 \times 10^2}$$
$$= 2 \times 10^{5-2}$$
$$= 2 \times 10^3$$
Its density is 2×10^3 pounds per cubic feet.

100. $a^{-1} = a^1$

$\dfrac{1}{a} = a$

$1 = a^2$

$(1)^2 = 1$ and $(-1)^2 = 1$

Yes; $a = 1$ and $a = -1$.

102. No; answers may vary

104. $\dfrac{1.855 \times 10^{12}}{2.98 \times 10^8} = \dfrac{1.855}{2.98} \times 10^{12-8}$

$= 0.6225 \times 10^4$

$= 6225$

The average value of imports is \$6225 per person.

106. No; answers may vary

108. $\dfrac{4.21 \times 10^8}{4.8 \times 10^7} = \dfrac{4.21}{4.8} \times 10^{8-7} = 0.88 \times 10^1 = 8.8$

The square footage of office space in New York is 8.8 times larger than that in Dallas.

Section 5.3

Practice Exercises

1. a. $4x^5$: The exponent on x is 5, so the degree of the term is 5.

   b. $-4^3 y^3$: The exponent on y is 3, so the degree of the term is 3.

   c. The degree of z, or z^1, is 1.

   d. $65a^3 b^7 c$: The degree is the sum of the exponents on the variables, or $3 + 7 + 1 = 11$.

   e. The degree of 36, which can be written as $36x^0$, is 0.

2.

	Polynomial	Degree	Classification
a.	$3x^4 + 2x^2 - 3$	4	trinomial
b.	$9abc^3$	5	monomial
c.	$8x^5 + 5x^3$	5	binomial

3.

Term	Degree
$2x^3 y$	4
$-3x^3 y^2$	5
$-9y^5$	5
9.6	0

The largest degree of any term is 5, so the degree of this polynomial is 5.

4. a. Substitute -1 for x and simplify.

$P(x) = -5x^2 + 2x - 8$

$P(-1) = -5(-1)^2 + 2(-1) - 8$

$= -5 - 2 - 8$

$= -15$

   b. Substitute 3 for x and simplify.

$P(x) = -5x^2 + 2x - 8$

$P(3) = -5(3)^2 + 2(3) - 8$

$= -45 + 6 - 8$

$= -47$

5. a. $P(t) = -16t^2 + 290$

Let $t = 0$: $P(0) = -16(0)^2 + 290 = 290$

Let $t = 2$: $P(2) = -16(2)^2 + 290 = 226$

The height of the object at $t = 0$ second is 290 feet and the height at $t = 2$ seconds is 226 feet.

   b.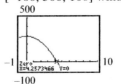

Since $P(4) = 34$ and $P(5) = -110$, and 34 is closer to 0 than -110, the object hits the ground after 4 seconds, to the nearest second.

   c. Graph y_1 in a $[-1, 10, 1]$ by $[-100, 500, 100]$ window.

To the nearest tenth, the object hits the ground after 4.3 seconds.

6. a. $8x^4 - 5x^4 - 5x = (8-5)x^4 - 5x$
$$= 3x^4 - 5x$$

b. $4ab - 5b + 3ab + 2b$
$$= 4ab + 3ab - 5b + 2b$$
$$= (4+3)ab + (-5+2)b$$
$$= 7ab - 3b$$

7. a. $(3a^4b - 5ab^2 + 7) + (9ab^2 - 12)$
$$= 3a^4b - 5ab^2 + 7 + 9ab^2 - 12$$
$$= 3a^4b - 5ab^2 + 9ab^2 + 7 - 12$$
$$= 3a^4b + 4ab^2 - 5$$

b. $(2x^5 - 3y + x - 6) + (4y - 2x - 3)$
$$= 2x^5 - 3y + x - 6 + 4y - 2x - 3$$
$$= 2x^5 - 3y + 4y + x - 2x - 6 - 3$$
$$= 2x^5 + y - x - 9$$

8. $(5x^3 - 3x^2 - 9x - 8) + (x^3 + 9x^2 + 2x)$
$$= 5x^3 + x^3 - 3x^2 + 9x^2 - 9x + 2x - 8$$
$$= 6x^3 + 6x^2 - 7x - 8$$

9. $(13a^4 - 7a^3 - 9) - (-2a^4 + 8a^3 - 12)$
$$= 13a^4 - 7a^3 - 9 + 2a^4 - 8a^3 + 12$$
$$= 13a^4 + 2a^4 - 7a^3 - 8a^3 - 9 + 12$$
$$= 15a^4 - 15a^3 + 3$$

10. $(11x^2y^2 - 7xy^2) - (5x^2y^2 - 3xy^2 + 5y^3)$
$$= 11x^2y^2 - 7xy^2 - 5x^2y^2 + 3xy^2 - 5y^3$$
$$= 6x^2y^2 - 4xy^2 - 5y^3$$

11. The degree of $f(x)$ is 3, which means that its graph has the shape of **C**.

12. a. The y-intercept is $(0, -12)$. Since the degree of the function $f(x) = x^2 - x - 12$ is 2, the graph is U-shaped. Since the coefficient of x^2 is 1, the graph opens upward.

b. The y-intercept is $(0, 6)$. Since the degree of the function $g(x) = -3x^2 + 5x + 6$ is 2, the graph is U-shaped. Since the coefficient of x^2 is -3, the graph opens downward.

c. The y-intercept is $(0, 4)$. Since the degree of $h(x) = x^3 + 4$ is 3, the graph is S-shaped.

d. The y-intercept is $(0, -1)$. Since the degree of $f(x) = -x^3 + 2x^2 - 5x - 1$ is 3, the graph is S-shaped.

Vocabulary and Readiness Check

1. The numerical factor of a term is the <u>coefficient</u>.

2. A <u>polynomial</u> is a finite sum of terms in which all variables are raised to nonnegative integer powers and no variables appear in any denominator.

3. A <u>binomial</u> is a polynomial with 2 terms.

4. A <u>monomial</u> is a polynomial with 1 term.

5. A <u>trinomial</u> is a polynomial with 3 terms.

6. The degree of a term is the sum of the exponents on the <u>variables</u> in the term.

7. The <u>degree</u> of a polynomial is the largest degree of all its terms.

8. <u>Like</u> terms contain the same variables raised to the same powers.

9. $5x + x = 6x$

10. $5x - x = 4x$

11. $y + y = 2y$

12. $z^2 + z^2 = 2z^2$

13. $7xy^2 - y^2 = 7xy^2 - y^2$

14. $x^3 - 9x^3 = -8x^3$

Exercise Set 5.3

2. 7 has degree 0.

4. $-z^3$ has degree 3.

6. $12x^3z$ has degree $3 + 1 = 4$.

8. $-9^{11}y^5$ has degree 5 (note: the degree on the *variable* is 5).

10. $9.11r^2st^{12}$ has degree $2 + 1 + 12 = 15$.

12. $7x - 0.8$ has degree 1 and is a binomial.

14. $5x^2 - 3x - 2$ has degree 3 and is a trinomial.

16. -7^5abc has degree $1 + 1 + 1 = 3$ and is a monomial.

18.

Term	Degree
$-2x^2y$	3
$-3y^2$	2
$4x$	1
y^5	5

$-2x^2y - 3y^2 + 4x + y^5$ has degree 5 and is none of these.

20. $Q(x) = 5x^2 - 1$

$Q(4) = 5(4)^2 - 1 = 5(16) - 1 = 80 - 1 = 79$

22. $P(x) = x^2 + x + 1$

$P(-4) = (-4)^2 + (-4) + 1 = 13$

24. $P(x) = x^2 + x + 1$

$P\left(\dfrac{1}{2}\right) = \left(\dfrac{1}{2}\right)^2 + \left(\dfrac{1}{2}\right) + 1$

$= \dfrac{1}{4} + \dfrac{1}{2} + 1$

$= \dfrac{1}{4} + \dfrac{2}{4} + \dfrac{4}{4}$

$= \dfrac{7}{4}$

26. $P(t) = -16t^2 + 1125$

$P(4) = -16(4)^2 + 1125 = 869$ feet

28. $\quad P(t) = -16t^2 + 1125$

$0 = -16t^2 + 1125$

$-1125 = -16t^2$

$70.3125 = t^2$

$8 \approx t$

It will hit the ground in approximately 8 seconds.

30. $-x + 3x = 2x$

32. $-8y + 9y + 4y^2 = 4y^2 + y$

34. $-8xy^2 + 4x - x + 2xy^2 = -6xy^2 + 3x$

36. $-a^2 + 18ab - 2b^2 + 14a^2 - 12ab - b^2$

$= 13a^2 + 6ab - 3b^2$

38. $(x^2 + 4x - 7) + (8x^2 + 9x - 7) = 9x^2 + 13x - 14$

40. $\begin{array}{r} 4x^3 - 6x^2 + 5x + 7 \\ + \quad\ 2x^2 + 6x - 3 \\ \hline 4x^3 - 4x^2 + 11x + 4 \end{array}$

42. $\begin{array}{r} -2x^2 + 3x - 9 \\ + \quad\quad (2x - 3) \\ \hline -2x^2 + 5x - 12 \end{array}$

44. $(2x^2 + 3x + 12) - (5x - 7)$

$= 2x^2 + 3x + 12 - 5x + 7$

$= 2x^2 - 2x + 19$

46. $(xy + x - 3) - (xy + x - y)$

$= xy + x - 3 - xy - x + y$

$= y - 3$

48. $\begin{array}{r} -3x^2 - 4x + 8 \\ -5x - 12 \\ \hline -3x^2 - 9x - 4 \end{array}$

50. $(3x^2 - 2x) + (5x^2 - 9x) = 8x^2 - 11x$

52. $(4x - 4) - (-x - 4) = 4x - 4 + x + 4 = 5x$

54. $(9xyz + 4x - y) + (-9xyz - 3x + y + 2) = x + 2$

56. $(3x^2 + 6xy + 3y^2) - (8x^2 - 6xy - y^2)$
$= 3x^2 + 6xy + 3y^2 - 8x^2 + 6xy + y^2$
$= -5x^2 + 12xy + 4y^2$

58. $(3x^2 - 4x + 5) - (x - 4) = 3x^2 - 4x + 5 - x + 4$
$= 3x^2 - 5x + 9$

60. $(5x^2 - 6) + (2x^2 - 4x + 8)$
$= 5x^2 - 6 + 2x^2 - 4x + 8$
$= 7x^2 - 4x + 2$

62. $(5x^2 + x + 9) - (2x^2 - 9)$
$= 5x^2 + x + 9 - 2x^2 + 9$
$= 3x^2 + x + 18$

64. $(5y^2 - 2y + 4) + (3y + 7) = 5y^2 + y + 11$

66. $(-3x^2y + 4) - (-7x^2y - 8y)$
$= -3x^2y + 4 + 7x^2y + 8y$
$= 4x^2y + 8y + 4$

68. $\quad -4x^3 + 4x^2 - 4x$
$\quad \underline{-2x^3 + 2x^2 - 3x}$
$\quad -6x^3 + 6x^2 - 7x$

70. $\quad 9x^2 + 9x - 4$
$\quad \underline{7x^2 - 3x - 4}$
$\quad 16x^2 + 6x - 8$

72. $\quad \dfrac{2}{5}a^2 \qquad\qquad - ab + \dfrac{4}{3}b^2$
$\qquad \underline{\quad \dfrac{1}{5}a^2b \;\; - ab + \dfrac{5}{6}b^2}$
$\quad \dfrac{2}{5}a^2 + \dfrac{1}{5}a^2b - 2ab + \dfrac{13}{6}b^2$

74. $\quad 5y^4 - 7y^2 + x^2 - 3$
$\quad \underline{-3y^4 + 2y^2 \qquad\;\; + 4}$
$\quad 2y^4 - 5y^2 + x^2 + 1$

76. $(3x^2 - 2x - x^3 + 2) + (5x^2 - 8x - x^3 + 4)$
$= -2x^3 + 8x^2 - 10x + 6$
Now subtract $(9x + 8)$.
$(-2x^3 + 8x^2 - 10x + 6) - (9x + 8)$
$= -2x^3 + 8x^2 - 10x + 6 - 9x - 8$
$= -2x^3 + 8x^2 - 19x - 2$

78. $\qquad\qquad 8x^4 - 14x^2 + 6$
$\quad \underline{-12x^6 - 21x^4 - 9x^2 \qquad}$
$\quad -12x^6 - 13x^4 - 23x^2 + 6$

80. $\quad \dfrac{3}{16}x^2 + \dfrac{5}{8}x - \dfrac{1}{4}$
$\quad \underline{-\dfrac{5}{16}x^2 + \dfrac{3}{8}x - \dfrac{3}{4}}$
$\quad -\dfrac{1}{8}x^2 \;\; + x - 1$

82. $2(4)(8.5) + 2(4)(4) + 2(8.5)(4) = 168$
The surface area is 168 square inches.
$202 - 168 = 34$
Using this box saves 34 square inches.

84. $P(t) = -16t^2 + 25t + 984$

  a. $P(1) = -16(1)^2 + 25(1) + 984 = 993$ feet

  b. $P(3) = -16(3)^2 + 25(3) + 984 = 915$ feet

  c. $P(5) = -16(5)^2 + 25(5) + 984 = 709$ feet

  d. $P(8) = 160$ and $P(9) = -87$
    The object hits the ground in approximately 9 seconds.

86. $C(20,000) = 0.8(20,000) + 10,000$
$\qquad\qquad\quad\; = 26,000$
The total cost is \$26,000.

88. $P(x) = 2x - (0.8x + 10,000)$
$P(x) = 2x - 0.8x - 10,000$
$P(x) = 1.2x - 10,000$

90. B: The degree of $h(x)$ is 3, so the graph has the shape of B or D. The coefficient of x^3 is a positive number, so the graph has the shape of B.

92. C: The degree of $F(x)$ is 2, so the graph has the shape of A or C. The coefficient of x^2 is a negative number, so the graph has the shape of C.

94. $-7(2z - 6y) = -14z + 42y$

96. $5(-3y^2 - 2y + 7) = -15y^2 - 10y + 35$

98. The opposite of $-y^5 + 10y^3 - 2.3$ is
$-(-y^5 + 10y^3 - 2.3) = y^5 - 10y^3 + 2.3$; d

100. $(12x - 1.7) + (15x + 6.2) = 12x - 1.7 + 15x + 6.2$
$= 27x + 4.5$

102. Answers may vary

104. Answers may vary

106. $(9y^{5a} - 4y^{3a} + 1.5y) - (6y^{5a} - y^{3a} + 4.7y)$
$= 9y^{5a} - 4y^{3a} + 1.5y - 6y^{5a} + y^{3a} - 4.7y$
$= 9y^{5a} - 6y^{5a} - 4y^{3a} + y^{3a} + 1.5y - 4.7y$
$= 3y^{5a} - 3y^{3a} - 3.2y$

108. $(14z^{5x} + 3z^{2x} + z) - (2z^{5x} - 10z^{2x} + 3z)$
$= 14z^{5x} + 3z^{2x} + z - 2z^{5x} + 10z^{2x} - 3z$
$= 14z^{5x} - 2z^{5x} + 3z^{2x} + 10z^{2x} + z - 3z$
$= 12z^{5x} + 13z^{2x} - 2z$

110. $(z + 2) + (2z^2 + z) + (z^3 - 4z + 1)$
$= z + 2 + 2z^2 + z + z^3 - 4z + 1$
$= z^3 + 2z^2 - 2z + 3$
The perimeter is $(z^3 + 2z^2 - 2z + 3)$ units.

112. $R(x) + P(x) = (5x^2 - 7) + (3x + 3)$
$= 5x^2 + 3x - 4$

114. $P(x) - Q(x) = (3x + 3) - (4x^2 - 6x + 3)$
$= 3x + 3 - 4x^2 + 6x - 3$
$= -4x^2 + 9x$

116. $-5[P(x)] - Q(x) = -5(3x + 3) - (4x^2 - 6x + 3)$
$= -15x - 15 - 4x^2 + 6x - 3$
$= -4x^2 - 9x - 18$

118. $2[Q(x)] + 7[R(x)]$
$= 2(4x^2 - 6x + 3) + 7(5x^2 - 7)$
$= 8x^2 - 12x + 6 + 35x^2 - 49$
$= 43x^2 - 12x - 43$

120. $P(x) = 8x + 3$

  a. $P(a) = 8a + 3$

  b. $P(-x) = 8(-x) + 3 = -8x + 3$

  c. $P(x + h) = 8(x + h) + 3 = 8x + 8h + 3$

122. $P(x) = -4x$

  a. $P(a) = -4a$

  b. $P(-x) = -4(-x) = 4x$

  c. $P(x + h) = -4(x + h) = -4x - 4h$

124. $P(x) = 3x - 2$

  a. $P(a) = 3a - 2$

  b. $P(-x) = 3(-x) - 2 = -3x - 2$

  c. $P(x + h) = 3(x + h) - 2 = 3x + 3h - 2$

126. $f(x) = -61x^2 - 5530x + 585,753$

  a. 2003 means that $x = 1$.
  $f(1) = -61(1)^2 - 5530(1) + 585,753$
  $= 580,162$ students

  b. 2005 means that $x = 3$.
  $f(3) = -61(3)^2 - 5530(3) + 585,753$
  $= 568,614$ students

  c. 2010 means that $x = 8$.
  $f(8) = -61(8)^2 - 5530(8) + 585,753$
  $= 537,609$ students

128. $f(x) = -14x^2 + 269.2x + 7414.2$

    a. 2004 means that $x = 2$.
$$f(2) = -14(2)^2 + 269.2(2) + 7414.2$$
$$= 7896.6 \text{ thousand}$$
$$\text{or } 7,896,600 \text{ volumes}$$

    b. 2008 means that $x = 6$.
$$f(6) = -14(6)^2 + 269.2(6) + 7414.2$$
$$= 8525.4 \text{ thousand}$$
$$\text{or } 8,525,400 \text{ volumes}$$

130. $f(x) = 873x^2 - 4104x + 40,263$

    a. 2001 means that $x = 0$.
$$f(0) = 873(0)^2 - 4104(0) + 40,263$$
$$= 40,263 \text{ cases}$$

    b. 2003 means that $x = 2$.
$$f(2) = 873(2)^2 - 4104(2) + 40,263$$
$$= 35,547 \text{ cases}$$

    c. 2005 means that $x = 4$.
$$f(4) = 873(4)^2 - 4104(4) + 40,263$$
$$= 37,815 \text{ cases}$$

    d. The number of cases decreased, then increased.

Section 5.4

Practice Exercises

  1. a. $(3x^4)(2x^2) = 3(2)(x^4)(x^2) = 6x^6$

    b. $(-5m^4 np^3)(-8mnp^5)$
$$= -5(-8)(m^4 m)(n \cdot n)(p^3 p^5)$$
$$= 40m^5 n^2 p^8$$

  2. a. $3x(7x - 1) = 3x(7x) + 3x(-1)$
$$= 21x^2 - 3x$$

    b. $-5a^2(3a^2 - 6a + 5)$
$$= -5a^2(3a^2) + (-5a^2)(-6a)$$
$$+ (-5a^2)(5)$$
$$= -15a^4 + 30a^3 - 25a^2$$

    c. $-mn^3(5m^2 n^2 + 2mn - 5m)$
$$= -mn^3(5m^2 n^2) + (-mn^3)(2mn)$$
$$+ (-mn^3)(-5m)$$
$$= -5m^3 n^5 - 2m^2 n^4 + 5m^2 n^3$$

  3. a. $(x + 5)(2x + 3) = x(2x + 3) + 5(2x + 3)$
$$= 2x^2 + 3x + 10x + 15$$
$$= 2x^2 + 13x + 15$$

    b. $(3x - 1)(x^2 - 6x + 2)$
$$= 3x(x^2 - 6x + 2) + (-1)(x^2 - 6x + 2)$$
$$= 3x^3 - 18x^2 + 6x - x^2 + 6x - 2$$
$$= 3x^3 - 19x^2 + 12x - 2$$

  4.
$$\begin{array}{r} x^2 - 4x - 5 \\ 3x^2 + 2 \\ \hline 2x^2 - 8x - 10 \\ 3x^4 - 12x^3 - 15x^2 \\ \hline 3x^4 - 12x^3 - 13x^2 - 8x - 10 \end{array}$$

  5. $(x - 5)(x + 3)$
$$= x \cdot x + 3 \cdot x + (-5)x + (-5)(3)$$
$$= x^2 + 3x - 5x - 15$$
$$= x^2 - 2x - 15$$

  6. a. $(3x - 5)(2x - 7)$
$$= 3x(2x) + 3x(-7) + (-5)(2x)$$
$$+ (-5)(-7)$$
$$= 6x^2 - 21x - 10x + 35$$
$$= 6x^2 - 31x + 35$$

    b. $(2x^2 - 3y)(4x^2 + y)$
$$= 8x^4 + 2x^2 y - 12x^2 y - 3y^2$$
$$= 8x^4 - 10x^2 y - 3y^2$$

  7. a. $(x + 6)^2 = x^2 + 2 \cdot x \cdot 6 + 6^2$
$$= x^2 + 12x + 36$$

    b. $(x - 2)^2 = x^2 - 2 \cdot x \cdot 2 + 2^2$
$$= x^2 - 4x + 4$$

    c. $(3x + 5y)^2$
$$= (3x)^2 + 2(3x)(5y) + (5y)^2$$
$$= 9x^2 + 30xy + 25y^2$$

d. $(3x^2 - 8b)^2$

$= (3x^2)^2 - 2(3x^2)(8b) + (8b)^2$

$= 9x^4 - 48x^2b + 64b^2$

8. a. $(x - 7)(x + 7) = x^2 - 7^2 = x^2 - 49$

b. $(2a + 5)(2a - 5) = (2a)^2 - 5^2$

$= 4a^2 - 25$

c. $\left(5x^2 + \dfrac{1}{4}\right)\left(5x^2 - \dfrac{1}{4}\right) = (5x^2)^2 - \left(\dfrac{1}{4}\right)^2$

$= 25x^4 - \dfrac{1}{16}$

d. $(a^3 - 4b^2)(a^3 + 4b^2) = (a^3)^2 - (4b^2)^2$

$= a^6 - 16b^4$

9. $[2 + (3x - y)]^2$

$= 2^2 + 2(2)(3x - y) + (3x - y)^2$

$= 4 + 4(3x - y) + (3x)^2 - 2(3x) \cdot y + y^2$

$= 4 + 12x - 4y + 9x^2 - 6xy + y^2$

10. $[(3x - y) - 5][(3x - y) + 5]$

$= (3x - y)^2 - 5^2$

$= (3x)^2 - 2(3x)(y) + y^2 - 25$

$= 9x^2 - 6xy + y^2 - 25$

11. $(x + 4)(x - 4)(x^2 - 16)$

$= (x^2 - 16)(x^2 - 16)$

$= (x^2 - 16)^2$

$= x^4 - 32x^2 + 256$

12. $f(x) = x^2 - 3x + 5$

$f(h + 1) = (h + 1)^2 - 3(h + 1) + 5$

$= h^2 + 2h + 1 - 3h - 3 + 5$

$= h^2 - h + 3$

Vocabulary and Readiness Check

1. $(6x^3)\left(\dfrac{1}{2}x^3\right) = \underline{3x^6}$

2. $(x + 7)^2 = \underline{x^2 + 14x + 49}$

3. $(x + 7)(x - 7) = \underline{x^2 - 49}$

4. The product of $(3x - 1)(4x^2 - 2x + 1)$ is a polynomial of degree 3.

5. If $f(x) = x^2 + 1$ then $f(a + 1) = \underline{(a + 1)^2 + 1}$.

6. $[x + (2y + 1)]^2$

$= \underline{[x + (2y + 1)][x + (2y + 1)]}$

Exercise Set 5.4

2. $(-6a)(4a) = -6 \cdot 4a^2 = -24a^2$

4. $5x(6x - 4) = 5x(6x) - 5x(4) = 30x^2 - 20x$

6. $-8y(6xy + 4x) = -8y(6xy) - 8y(4x)$

$= -48xy^2 - 32xy$

8. $-6b^2z(z^2a + baz - 3b)$

$= -6b^2z^3a - 6b^3az^2 + 18b^3z$

10. $(y + 5)(3y - 2) = 3y^2 - 2y + 15y - 10$

$= 3y^2 + 13y - 10$

12. $(a + 2)(3a^2 - a + 5)$

$= a(3a^2 - a + 5) + 2(3a^2 - a + 5)$

$= 3a^3 - a^2 + 5a + 6a^2 - 2a + 10$

$= 3a^3 + 5a^2 + 3a + 10$

14.

$$\begin{array}{r} 2z - 4 \\ 6z - 2 \\ \hline -4z + 8 \\ 12z^2 - 24z \\ \hline 12z^2 - 28z + 8 \end{array}$$

16.

$$\begin{array}{r} 2x^2 - 3x - 4 \\ \times \quad\quad x + 5 \\ \hline 10x^2 - 15x - 20 \\ 2x^3 - 3x^2 - 4x \quad\quad \\ \hline 2x^3 + 7x^2 - 19x - 20 \end{array}$$

18. $(c - 3)(c + 1) = c^2 + c - 3c - 3$

$= c^2 - 2c - 3$

20. $(2n-9m)(n-7m)$

$= 2n^2 - 14mn - 9mn + 63m^2$

$= 2n^2 - 23mn + 63m^2$

22. $(5d-3)(d+6) = 5d^2 + 30d - 3d - 18$

$\qquad = 5d^2 + 27d - 18$

24. $\left(2x - \dfrac{1}{3}\right)\left(2x + \dfrac{1}{3}\right) = 4x^2 + \dfrac{2}{3}x - \dfrac{2}{3}x - \dfrac{1}{9}$

$\qquad\qquad = 4x^2 - \dfrac{1}{9}$

26. $(4x^2 - 5y^2)(x^2 - 2y^2)$

$= 4x^4 - 8x^2 y^2 - 5x^2 y^2 + 10y^4$

$= 4x^4 - 13x^2 y^2 + 10y^4$

28. $(x-5)^2 = x^2 - 2(x)(5) + 5^2$

$\qquad = x^2 - 10x + 25$

30. $(7x-9)(7x+9) = (7x)^2 - 9^2 = 49x^2 - 81$

32. $(4x-z)^2 = (4x)^2 - 2(4x)(z) + z^2$

$\qquad = 16x^2 - 8xz + z^2$

34. $(2x-4y)(2x+4y) = (2x)^2 - (4y)^2 = 4x^2 - 16y^2$

36. $[5 - (3b-3)]^2$

$= 5^2 - 2(5)(3b-3) + (3b-3)^2$

$= 25 - 10(3b-3) + (3b)^2 - 2(3b)(3) + 3^2$

$= 25 - 30b + 30 + 9b^2 - 18b + 9$

$= 9b^2 - 48b + 64$

38. $[(2y+5) + 6][(2y+5) - 6]$

$= (2y+5)^2 - 6^2$

$= (2y)^2 + 2(2y)(5) + 5^2 - 36$

$= 4y^2 + 20y + 25 - 36$

$= 4y^2 + 20y - 11$

40. $[(2a^2 + 4a) + 1]^2$

$= (2a^2 + 4a)^2 + 2(2a^2 + 4a)(1) + 1^2$

$= 4a^4 + 2(2a^2)(4a) + 16a^2 + 4a^2 + 8a + 1$

$= 4a^4 + 8a(2a^2) + 20a^2 + 8a + 1$

$= 4a^4 + 16a^3 + 20a^2 + 8a + 1$

42. Answers may vary; possible answer:

$(a+b)(a-b) = a^2 - b^2$ has only two terms.

44. $(z-y)(z+y)(z^2 - y^2) = (z^2 - y^2)(z^2 - y^2)$

$\qquad\qquad = (z^2)^2 - 2z^2 y^2 + (y^2)^2$

$\qquad\qquad = z^4 - 2z^2 y^2 + y^4$

46. $(x-1)^4 = (x-1)^2 (x-1)^2$

$\qquad = (x^2 - 2x + 1)(x^2 - 2x + 1)$

$$
\begin{array}{r}
x^2 - 2x + 1 \\
\times \quad x^2 - 2x + 1 \\
\hline
x^2 - 2x + 1 \\
-2x^3 + 4x^2 - 2x \\
x^4 - 2x^3 + x^2 \\
\hline
x^4 - 4x^3 + 6x^2 - 4x + 1
\end{array}
$$

48. $(x+3)(x-3)(x^2 + 9) = (x^2 - 9)(x^2 + 9)$

$\qquad\qquad = (x^2)^2 - 9^2$

$\qquad\qquad = x^4 - 81$

50. $(4x-5)(5x+6) = 20x^2 + 24x - 25x - 30$

$\qquad = 20x^2 - x - 30$

52. $(3y^3 - 1)(3y^3 - 6y + 1)$

$= 3y^3(3y^3 - 6y + 1) - 1(3y^3 - 6y + 1)$

$= 9y^6 - 18y^4 + 3y^3 - 3y^3 + 6y - 1$

$= 9y^6 - 18y^4 + 6y - 1$

54. $(4x+1)(4x-1) = (4x)^2 - 1^2 = 16x^2 - 1$

56.
$$
\begin{array}{r}
6x^2 + 2x - 1 \\
\times \quad 3x - 6 \\
\hline
-36x^2 - 12x + 6 \\
18x^3 + 6x^2 - 3x \\
\hline
18x^3 - 30x^2 - 15x + 6
\end{array}
$$

58. $\left(4y - \dfrac{1}{3}\right)\left(3y - \dfrac{1}{8}\right) = 12y^2 - \dfrac{1}{2}y - y + \dfrac{1}{24}$

$\qquad\qquad = 12y^2 - \dfrac{3}{2}y + \dfrac{1}{24}$

60. $(4x+7)^2 = (4x)^2 + 2(4x)(7) + 7^2$

$\qquad = 16x^2 + 56x + 49$

62. $(3x+2y)(3x-2y) = (3x)^2 - (2y)^2 = 9x^2 - 4y^2$

64. $7x^2 y^3(-3ax-4xy+z)$
$= -21ax^3 y^3 - 28x^3 y^4 + 7x^2 y^3 z$

66. $(2x-3)(x+1) = 2x^2 + 2x - 3x - 3$
$\qquad\qquad = 2x^2 - x - 3$

68. $(3xy-2b)(3xy+2b) = (3xy)^2 - (2b)^2$
$\qquad\qquad\qquad = 9x^2 y^2 - 4b^2$

70. $(x+2)^2 = x^2 + 2(x)(2) + 4 = x^2 + 4x + 4$

72. $(4x+6)^2 = (4x)^2 + 2(4x)(6) + 6^2$
$\qquad\qquad = 16x^2 + 48x + 36$

74. $(c-8)(c+2) = c^2 + 2c - 8c - 16 = c^2 - 6c - 16$

76. $(z+2)(z-3)(2z+1)$
$= (z^2 - 3z + 2z - 6)(2z+1)$
$= (z^2 - z - 6)(2z+1)$
$= 2z(z^2 - z - 6) + 1(z^2 - z - 6)$
$= 2z^3 - 2z^2 - 12z + z^2 - z - 6$
$= 2z^3 - z^2 - 13z - 6$

78.
$$
\begin{array}{r}
4x^2 + 4x - 4 \\
\times \quad 4x^2 + 4x - 4 \\
\hline
-16x^2 - 16x + 16 \\
16x^3 + 16x^2 - 16x \\
16x^4 + 16x^3 - 16x^2 \\
\hline
16x^4 + 32x^3 - 16x^2 - 32x + 16
\end{array}
$$

80. $(2x-1)(5x^2 - x - 2)$
$= 10x^3 - 2x^2 - 4x - 5x^2 + x + 2$
$= 10x^3 - 7x^2 - 3x + 2$

82. $f(x) = x^2 - 3x$
$f(c) = c^2 - 3c$

84. $f(x) = x^2 - 3x$
$f(a+5) = (a+5)^2 - 3(a+5)$
$\qquad = a^2 + 10a + 25 - 3a - 15$
$\qquad = a^2 + 7a + 10$

86. $f(x) = x^2 - 3x$
$f(a-b) = (a-b)^2 - 3(a-b)$
$\qquad = a^2 - 2ab + b^2 - 3a + 3b$

88. $y = \dfrac{3}{2}x - 1$
$m = \dfrac{3}{2}$

90. $x + 7y = 2$
$7y = -x + 2$
$y = -\dfrac{1}{7}x + \dfrac{2}{7}$
$m = -\dfrac{1}{7}$

92. Since any vertical line crosses the graph at most once, it is a function.

94. $2x + 3x(12-x) = 2x + 36x - 3x^2 = 38x - 3x^2$

96. Answers may vary

98. $g(x) = x^2 + 2x + 1$

   a. $g(a+h) = (a+h)^2 + 2(a+h) + 1$
$\qquad\qquad = a^2 + 2ah + h^2 + 2a + 2h + 1$

   b. $g(a) = a^2 + 2a + 1$

   c. $g(a+h) - g(a)$
$\qquad = a^2 + 2ah + h^2 + 2a + 2h + 1 - (a^2 + 2a + 1)$
$\qquad = 2ah + h^2 + 2h$

100. $-3yz^n(2y^3 z^{2n} - 1) = -6y^4 z^{3n} + 3yz^n$

102. $(x^a + y^{2b})(x^a - y^{2b}) = (x^a)^2 - (y^{2b})^2$
$\qquad\qquad\qquad = x^{2a} - y^{4b}$

104. Volume $= \pi r^2 h$
$\qquad = \pi(y-3)^2(7y)$
$\qquad = \pi(y^2 - 6y + 9)(7y)$
$\qquad = \pi(7y^3 - 42y^2 + 63y)$ cu. cm

106. $\text{Area} = (x-7)(2x+x) - \dfrac{1}{2}(2x)(x-7)$

$\qquad\qquad = (x-7)(3x) - x(x-7)$

$\qquad\qquad = 3x^2 - 21x - x^2 + 7x$

$\qquad\qquad = (2x^2 - 14x) \text{ square units}$

108. When multiplying two binomials. (Answers may vary)

110. $P(x) \cdot Q(x) = (5x)(x^2 - 2) = 5x^3 - 10x$

112. $[R(x)]^2 = (x+5)^2 = x^2 + 10x + 25$

114. $P(x) \cdot R(x) \cdot Q(x) = (5x)(x+5)(x^2 - 2)$

$\qquad\qquad\qquad = 5x(x^3 - 2x + 5x^2 - 10)$

$\qquad\qquad\qquad = 5x(x^3 + 5x^2 - 2x - 10)$

$\qquad\qquad\qquad = 5x^4 + 25x^3 - 10x^2 - 50x$

Section 5.5

Practice Exercises

1. $32x^4 y^2 = 2 \cdot 2 \cdot 2 \cdot 2 \cdot 2 \cdot x^4 \cdot y \cdot y$

$48x^3 y = 2 \cdot 2 \cdot 2 \cdot 2 \cdot 3 \cdot x^3 \cdot y$

$24y^2 = 2 \cdot 2 \cdot 2 \cdot 3 \cdot y \cdot y$

$\text{GCF} = 2 \cdot 2 \cdot 2 \cdot y = 8y$

2. a. The GCF of $6x^2$, 9, and $15x$ is 3.

$6x^2 + 9 + 15x = 3(2x^2) + 3(3) + 3(5x)$

$\qquad\qquad\qquad = 3(2x^2 + 3 + 5x)$

  b. There is no common factor of the terms $3x$ and $-8y^3$ other than 1 (or -1).

$3x - 8y^3$

  c. The GCF of $8a^4$ and $-2a^3$ is $2a^3$.

$8a^4 - 2a^3 = 2a^3 \cdot 4a - 2a^3 \cdot 1$

$\qquad\qquad = 2a^3(4a - 1)$

3. Factor out the GCF of the two terms, $8x^3 y^2$.

$64x^5 y^2 - 8x^3 y^2 = 8x^3 y^2 \cdot 8x^2 - 8x^3 y^2 \cdot 1$

$\qquad\qquad\qquad = 8x^3 y^2 (8x^2 - 1)$

4. Factor out the GCF of the three terms, $-xy^2$.

$-9x^4 y^2 + 5x^2 y^2 + 7xy^2$

$= -xy^2 \cdot 9x^3 - xy^2(-5x) - xy^2(-7)$

$= -xy^2(9x^3 - 5x - 7)$

5. The GCF is $(x + 4)$.

$3(x+4) + 5b(x+4) = (x+4)(3 + 5b)$

6. $8b(a^3 + 2y) - (a^3 + 2y)$

$= 8b(a^3 + 2y) - 1(a^3 + 2y)$

$= (a^3 + 2y)(8b - 1)$

7. $xy + 2y - 10 - 5x = (xy + 2y) + (-10 - 5x)$

$\qquad\qquad\qquad = y(x+2) - 5(2+x)$

$\qquad\qquad\qquad = y(x+2) - 5(x+2)$

$\qquad\qquad\qquad = (x+2)(y-5)$

8. $a^3 + 2a^2 + 5a + 10 = (a^3 + 2a^2) + (5a + 10)$

$\qquad\qquad\qquad\qquad = a^2(a+2) + 5(a+2)$

$\qquad\qquad\qquad\qquad = (a+2)(a^2 + 5)$

9. $x^2 y^2 + 3y^2 - 5x^2 - 15$

$= (x^2 y^2 + 3y^2) + (-5x^2 - 15)$

$= y^2(x^2 + 3) - 5(x^2 + 3)$

$= (x^2 + 3)(y^2 - 5)$

10. $pq + 3p - q - 3 = (pq + 3p) + (-q - 3)$

$\qquad\qquad\qquad = p(q+3) - 1(q+3)$

$\qquad\qquad\qquad = (q+3)(p-1)$

Vocabulary and Readiness Check

1. The reverse of multiplying is <u>factoring</u>.

2. The greatest common factor (GCF) of x^7, x^3, x^5 is <u>x^3</u>.

3. In general, the GCF of a list of common variables raised to powers is the <u>least</u> exponent in the list.

4. Factoring means writing as a <u>product</u>.

5. True or false: A factored form of $2xy^3 + 10xy$ is $2xy \cdot y^2 + 2xy \cdot 5$. <u>false</u>

6. True or false: A factored form of $x^3 - 6x^2 + x$ is $x(x^2 - 6x)$. <u>false</u>

7. True or false: A factored form of $5x - 5y + x^3 - x^2y$ is $5(x-y) + x^2(x-y)$. <u>false</u>

8. True or false: A factored form of $5x - 5y + x^3 - x^2y$ is $(x-y)(5+x^2)$. <u>true</u>

9. $6 = 2 \cdot 3$
$12 = 2 \cdot 2 \cdot 3$
GCF $= 2 \cdot 3 = 6$

10. $9 = 3 \cdot 3$
$27 = 3 \cdot 3 \cdot 3$
GCF $= 3 \cdot 3 = 9$

11. $15x = 3 \cdot 5 \cdot x$
$10 = 2 \cdot 5$
GCF $= 5$

12. $9x = 3 \cdot 3 \cdot x$
$12 = 2 \cdot 2 \cdot 3$
GCF $= 3$

13. $13x = 13 \cdot x$
$2x = 2 \cdot x$
GCF $= x$

14. $4y = 4 \cdot y$
$5y = 5 \cdot y$
GCF $= y$

15. $7x = 7 \cdot x$
$14x = 2 \cdot 7 \cdot x$
GCF $= 7x$

16. $8z = 2 \cdot 2 \cdot 2 \cdot z$
$4z = 2 \cdot 2 \cdot z$
GCF $= 2 \cdot 2 \cdot z = 4z$

Exercise Set 5.5

2. GCF $= b^2$

4. GCF $= xy^2$

6. GCF $= 4xy^2$

8. GCF $= 3y^2z^3$

10. $21x + 14 = 7 \cdot 3x + 7 \cdot 2 = 7(3x + 2)$

12. $3z - 21xz^4 = 3z(1) - 3z(7xz^3) = 3z(1 - 7xz^3)$

14. $9x + 3x^2 - 6x^3 = 3x(3) + 3x(x) - 3x(2x^2)$
$\qquad = 3x(3 + x - 2x^2)$

16. $12a^3b - 6ab + 18ab^2 - 18a^2b$
$= 6ab(2a^2) - 6ab(1) + 6ab(3b) - 6ab(3a)$
$= 6ab(2a^2 - 1 + 3b - 3a)$

18. $2(x-4) + 3y(x-4) = (x-4)(2+3y)$

20. $x(y-2) + (y-2) = (y-2)(x+1)$

22. $4x(2y+3) - 5(2y+3) = (2y+3)(4x-5)$

24. Answers may vary; one example:
$5x^2y^3 + 10x^3y^4 + 15x^5y^6$.

26. $ab + 2a + 5b + 10 = a(b+2) + 5(b+2)$
$\qquad\qquad\qquad\quad = (a+5)(b+2)$

28. $bc + 8b - 3c - 24 = b(c+8) - 3(c+8)$
$\qquad\qquad\qquad\quad = (b-3)(c+8)$

30. $12xy - 18x - 10y + 15 = 6x(2y-3) - 5(2y-3)$
$\qquad\qquad\qquad\qquad\quad = (6x-5)(2y-3)$

32. $20xy - 15x - 4y + 3 = 5x(4y-3) - (4y-3)$
$\qquad\qquad\qquad\qquad = (5x-1)(4y-3)$

34. $6x^2 - 8 = 2(3x^2) - 2(4) = 2(3x^2 - 4)$

36. $x^4 - 4x^3 = x^3 \cdot x - x^3 \cdot 4 = x^3(x-4)$

38. $12b^4 + 3b^2 = 3b^2 \cdot 4b^2 + 3b^2 \cdot 1 = 3b^2(4b^2 + 1)$

40. $-18xy^3 + 27x^4y$
$= 9xy(-2y^2) + 9xy(3x^3)$
$= 9xy(-2y^2 + 3x^3)$ or $-9xy(2y^2 - 3x^3)$

42. $10ef - 20e^2f^3 + 30e^3f$
$= 10ef(1) - 10ef(2ef^2) + 10ef(3e^2)$
$= 10ef(1 - 2ef^2 + 3e^2)$

44. $4a^2b^2c - 6ab^2c - 4ac + 8a$

$= 2a(2ab^2c) - 2a(3b^2c) - 2a(2c) + 2a(4)$

$= 2a(2ab^2c - 3b^2c - 2c + 4)$

46. $8y(z + 8) - 3(z + 8) = (z + 8)(8y - 3)$

48. $15xy + 20x + 6y + 8 = 5x(3y + 4) + 2(3y + 4)$

$= (5x + 2)(3y + 4)$

50. $xy + 4y - 3x - 12 = y(x + 4) - 3(x + 4)$

$= (y - 3)(x + 4)$

52. $16ab - 8a - 6b + 3 = 8a(2b - 1) - 3(2b - 1)$

$= (8a - 3)(2b - 1)$

54. $20xy + 8x + 5y + 2$

$= 4x(5y + 2) + 1(5y + 2)$

$= (5y + 2)(4x + 1)$

56. $3a(b - 4) - (b - 4) = (3a - 1)(b - 4)$

58. $12x^4y^2 - 16x^3y^3 = 4x^3y^2 \cdot 3x - 4x^3y^2 \cdot 4y$

$= 4x^3y^2(3x - 4y)$

60. $3x^2 + 12x + 4xy + 16y = 3x(x + 4) + 4y(x + 4)$

$= (x + 4)(3x + 4y)$

62. $4x^2 + 2xy - 10x - 5y = 2x(2x + y) - 5(2x + y)$

$= (2x - 5)(2x + y)$

64. $x^3 + 4x^2 + 3x + 12 = x^2(x + 4) + 3(x + 4)$

$= (x^2 + 3)(x + 4)$

66. $x^3 - 2x^2 - 3x + 6 = x^2(x - 2) - 3(x - 2)$

$= (x^2 - 3)(x - 2)$

68. $(7y)(-2y^3) = 7(-2)y \cdot y^3 = -14y^4$

70. $(-2y^3)^4 = (-2)^4(y^3)^4 = 16y^{12}$

72. $(x - 7)(x - 1) = x^2 - 1x - 7x + 7 = x^2 - 8x + 7$

74. $(x - 4)(x + 2) = x^2 + 2x - 4x - 8 = x^2 - 2x - 8$

76. $(s + 8)(s + 10) = s^2 + 10s + 8s + 80$

$= s^2 + 18s + 80$

78. c is correct.

   a. $-1(x^4 + 5x^3 + x^2) = -x^4 - 5x^3 - x^2$

   b. $x^2(x^2 + 5x^3 - x^2) = x^4 + 5x^5 - x^4$

   c. $x^2(x^2 + 5x - 1) = x^4 + 5x^3 - x^2$

   d. $5x^2(x^2 + 5x - 5) = 5x^4 + 25x^3 - 25x^2$

80. $4\pi r^2 + \dfrac{4}{3}\pi r^3 = 4\pi r^2 \cdot 1 + 4\pi r^2 \cdot \dfrac{1}{3}r$

$= 4\pi r^2\left(1 + \dfrac{1}{3}r\right)$

82. $x^2 + 4(10x) = x^2 + 40x = x(x + 40)$ sq in.

84. Answers may vary

86. Answers may vary

88. $IR_1 + IR_2 = E$

$I(R_1 + R_2) = E$

90. $x^{3n} - 2x^{2n} + 5x^n$

$= x^n \cdot x^{2n} - x^n \cdot 2x^n + x^n \cdot 5$

$= x^n(x^{2n} - 2x^n + 5)$

92. $6x^{8a} - 2x^{5a} - 4x^{3a} = 2x^{3a}(3x^{5a} - x^{2a} - 2)$

94. $h(t) = -16t^2 + 64t$

   a. $h(t) = -16t(t - 4)$

   b. $h(1) = -16(1)^2 + 64(1) = 48$

$h(1) = -16(1)(1 - 4) = 48$ feet

   c. Answers may vary

Section 5.6

Practice Exercises

1. Find two integers whose product is 6 and whose sum is 5. Since our integers must have a positive product and a positive sum, look for positive factors.

Positive Factors of 6	Sum of Factors
1, 6	$1 + 6 = 7$
3, 2	$3 + 2 = 5$ (correct)

$$x^2 + 5x + 6 = (x+3)(x+2)$$

2. Find two integers whose product is 24 and whose sum is -11. Since our integers must have a positive product and a negative sum, look for negative factors.

Negative Factors of 24	Sum of Factors
$-1, -24$	$-1 + (-24) = -25$
$-2, -12$	$-2 + (-12) = -14$
$-3, -8$	$-3 + (-8) = -11$ (correct)
$-4, -6$	$-4 + (-6) = -10$

$$x^2 - 11x + 24 = (x-3)(x-8)$$

3. $3x^3 - 9x^2 - 30x = 3x(x^2 - 3x - 10)$

Find two integers whose product is -10 and whose sum is -3. The numbers are -5 and 2.

$$\begin{aligned} 3x^3 - 9x^2 - 30x &= 3x(x^2 - 3x - 10) \\ &= 3x(x-5)(x+2) \end{aligned}$$

4. $2b^2 - 18b - 22 = 2(b^2 - 9b - 11)$

Find two integers whose product is -11 and whose sum is -9.

Factors	Sum
$-1, 11$	10
$1, -11$	-10

Neither of the pairs has a sum of -9, so no further factoring is possible.

$$2b^2 - 18b - 22 = 2(b^2 - 9b - 11)$$

5. Factors of $2x^2$: $2x \cdot x$

Factors of 6: $1 \cdot 6$ and $2 \cdot 3$

$(2x + 6)(x + 1) \Rightarrow 2x + 6x = 8x$ (incorrect middle term)

$(2x + 1)(x + 6) \Rightarrow 12x + x = 13x$ (correct middle term)

$(2x + 2)(x + 3) \Rightarrow 6x + 2x = 8x$ (incorrect middle term)

$(2x + 3)(x + 2) \Rightarrow 4x + 3x = 7x$ (incorrect middle term)

$$2x^2 + 13x + 6 = (2x+1)(x+6)$$

6. Factors of $4x^2$: $4x \cdot x$ and $2x \cdot 2x$

Factors of -6: $-6 \cdot 1$, $6 \cdot -1$, $2 \cdot -3$, $-2 \cdot 3$

$(4x - 6)(x + 1) \Rightarrow 4x - 6x = -2x$ (incorrect)

$(4x + 6)(x - 1) \Rightarrow -4x + 6x = 2x$ (incorrect)

$(4x + 2)(x - 3) \Rightarrow -12x + 2x = -10x$ (incorrect)

$(4x - 3)(x + 2) \Rightarrow 8x - 3x = 5x$ (correct)

$$4x^2 + 5x - 6 = (4x-3)(x+2)$$

7. $18b^4 - 57b^3 + 30b^2 = 3b^2(6b^2 - 19b + 10)$

Factors of $6b^2$: $2b \cdot 3b$, $6b \cdot b$

Negative factors of 10: $-1 \cdot -10$, $-5 \cdot -2$

$(2b - 1)(3b - 10) \Rightarrow -20b - 3b = -23b$ (incorrect)

$(2b - 10)(3b - 1) \Rightarrow -2b - 30b = -32b$ (incorrect)

$(2b - 5)(3b - 2) \Rightarrow -4b - 15b = -19b$ (correct)

$$\begin{aligned} 18b^4 - 57b^3 + 30b^2 &= 3b^2(6b^2 - 19b + 10) \\ &= 3b^2(2b-5)(3b-2) \end{aligned}$$

8. No greatest common factor can be factored out.

Factors of $25x^2$: $25x \cdot x$, $5x \cdot 5x$

Factors of $4y^2$: $4y \cdot y$, $2y \cdot 2y$

Try possible combinations.

$$\begin{aligned} 25x^2 + 20xy + 4y^2 &= (5x+2y)(5x+2y) \\ &= (5x+2y)^2 \end{aligned}$$

9. $20x^2 + 23x + 6$

$a = 20$, $b = 23$, $c = 6$

Find two numbers whose product is $a \cdot c = 20 \cdot 6 = 120$, and whose sum is b, 23. The two numbers are 8 and 15.

$$\begin{aligned} 20x^2 + 23x + 6 &= 20x^2 + 8x + 15x + 6 \\ &= 4x(5x+2) + 3(5x+2) \\ &= (5x+2)(4x+3) \end{aligned}$$

10. $15x^2 + 4x - 3$

$a = 15$, $b = 4$, $c = -3$

Find two numbers whose product is $a \cdot c = 15(-3) = -45$ and whose sum is b, 4. The two numbers are 9 and -5.

$$\begin{aligned} 15x^2 + 4x - 3 &= 15x^2 + 9x - 5x - 3 \\ &= 3x(5x+3) - 1(5x+3) \\ &= (5x+3)(3x-1) \end{aligned}$$

11. Let $y = x + 1$.

$$3(x+1)^2 - 7(x+1) - 20 = 3y^2 - 7y - 20$$
$$= (3y+5)(y-4)$$

Replace y with $x + 1$.

$$(3y+5)(y-4) = [3(x+1)+5][(x+1)-4]$$
$$= (3x+3+5)(x+1-4)$$
$$= (3x+8)(x-3)$$

Thus, $3(x+1)^2 - 7(x+1) - 20 = (3x+8)(x-3)$.

12. Let $y = x^2$.

$$6x^4 - 11x^2 - 10 = 6y^2 - 11y - 10$$
$$= (3y+2)(2y-5)$$

Replace y with x^2.

$$(3y+2)(2y-5) = (3x^2+2)(2x^2-5)$$

Vocabulary and Readiness Check

1. $10 = 2 \cdot 5$
$7 = 2 + 5$
2 and 5

2. $12 = 2 \cdot 2 \cdot 3 = 2 \cdot 6$
$8 = 2 + 6$
2 and 6

3. $24 = 2 \cdot 2 \cdot 2 \cdot 3 = 8 \cdot 3$
$11 = 8 + 3$
8 and 3

4. $30 = 2 \cdot 3 \cdot 5 = 10 \cdot 3$
$13 = 10 + 3$
10 and 3

Exercise Set 5.6

2. $x^2 + 9x + 20 = (x+5)(x+4)$

4. $x^2 - 12x + 27 = (x-3)(x-9)$

6. $x^2 + 3x - 54 = (x-6)(x+9)$

8. $x^2 - 9x - 36 = (x+3)(x-12)$

10. Note that the GCF is y^2.

$$x^2y^2 + 4xy^2 + 3y^2 = y^2(x^2+4x+3)$$
$$= y^2(x+1)(x+3)$$

12. Note that the GCF is 5.

$$5x^2 - 45x + 70 = 5(x^2-9x+14)$$
$$= 5(x-7)(x-2)$$

14. Since the zeros of the polynomial are -2 and 1, factors of the polynomial are $(x + 2)$ and $(x - 1)$.

16. Since the zeros of the polynomial are -1 and -5, factors of the polynomial are $(x + 1)$ and $(x + 5)$.

18. $3x^2 + 8x + 4 = (3x+2)(x+2)$

20. $3x^2 - 19x + 20 = (3x-4)(x-5)$

22. $6x^2 + 13x + 8$ is prime.

24. $25x^2 - 30x + 9 = (5x-3)^2$

26. Note that the GCF is 3.

$$12y^2 - 48y + 45 = 3(4y^2-16y+15)$$
$$= 3(2y-3)(2y-5)$$

28. Note that the GCF is z.

$$2x^2z + 5xz - 12z = z(2x^2+5x-12)$$
$$= z(2x-3)(x+4)$$

30. $6x^2 + 11xy + 4y^2 = (3x+4y)(2x+y)$

32. Note that the GCF is y, so that

$$24y^3 - 2y^2 - y = y(24y^2-2y-1).$$

$ac = -24$; the two numbers are 4 and -6.

$$24y^3 - 2y^2 - y = y(24y^2+4y-6y-1)$$
$$= y[4y(6y+1)-1(6y+1)]$$
$$= y(6y+1)(4y-1)$$

34. $3x^2 + 14x + 15$; $ac = 45$ so the two numbers are 5 and 9.

$$3x^2 + 14x + 15 = 3x^2 + 5x + 9x + 15$$
$$= x(3x+5) \div 3(3x+5)$$
$$= (3x+5)(x+3)$$

36. Let $y = x^2$. Then we have

$$x^4 - x^2 - 20 = y^2 - y - 20 = (y-5)(y+4).$$

This yields $(x^2-5)(x^2+4)$.

38. Let $y = 3x - 1$. Then we have
$$(3x-1)^2 + 5(3x-1) + 6 = y^2 + 5y + 6$$
$$= (y+2)(y+3).$$
This yields
$$[(3x-1)+2][(3x-1)+3]$$
$$= (3x+1)(3x+2).$$

40. Let $y = x^3$. Then we have
$$x^6 - 4x^3 - 12 = y^2 - 4y - 12$$
$$= (y-6)(y+2).$$
This yields $(x^3 - 6)(x^3 + 2)$.

42. Let $y = 3c + 6$. Then we have
$$(3c+6)^2 + 12(3c+6) - 28 = y^2 + 12y - 28$$
$$= (y+14)(y-2).$$
This yields
$$[(3c+6)+14][(3c+6)-2] = (3c+20)(3c+4).$$

44. $x^2 - 48x - 100 = (x+2)(x-50)$

46. $x^2 - 15x + 54 = (x-9)(x-6)$

48. $8x^2 - 8x + 2 = 2(4x^2 - 4x + 1)$
$$= 2(2x-1)(2x-1)$$
$$= 2(2x-1)^2$$

50. $5x^2 - 14x - 3 = (5x+1)(x-3)$

52. $12x^2 - 17x + 6 = (4x-3)(3x-2)$

54. $20x^5 + 54x^4 + 10x^3 = 2x^3(10x^2 + 27x + 5)$
$$= 2x^3(2x+5)(5x+1)$$

56. $a^2 - 2ab - 15b^2 = (a+3b)(a-5b)$

58. $x^2 + 4x - 5 = (x-1)(x+5)$

60. $2x^2 + 16xy + 32y^2 = 2(x^2 + 8xy + 16y^2)$
$$= 2(x+4y)(x+4y)$$
$$= 2(x+4y)^2$$

62. $x^2 + 6x + 8 = (x+2)(x+4)$

64. Let $y = x + 3$. Then
$$3(x+3)^2 + 2(x+3) - 5$$
$$= 3y^2 + 2y - 5$$
$$= (3y+5)(y-1)$$
$$= [3(x+3)+5][(x+3)-1]$$
$$= (3x+9+5)(x+3-1)$$
$$= (3x+14)(x+2)$$

66. $4x^2 - 39x + 27 = (4x-3)(x-9)$

68. Let $y = x^2$. Then
$$x^4 - 5x^2 + 6 = y^2 - 5y + 6$$
$$= (y-2)(y-3)$$
$$= (x^2-2)(x^2-3)$$

70. $12x^3 + x^2 - x = x(12x^2 + x - 1)$
$$= x(4x-1)(3x+1)$$

72. $16y^2 + 6yx - 27x^2 = (8y-9x)(2y+3x)$

74. $4x^2 + 6x + 9$; this polynomial is prime.

76. $5xy^2 - 9xy + 4x = x(5y^2 - 9y + 4)$
$$= x(5y-4)(y-1)$$

78. $3x^2 + 6x - 45 = 3(x^2 + 2x - 15)$
$$= 3(x+5)(x-3)$$

80. Let $y = x - 3$. Then
$$(x-3)^2 - 2(x-3) - 8$$
$$= y^2 - 2y - 8$$
$$= (y-4)(y+2)$$
$$= [(x-3)-4][(x-3)+2]$$
$$= (x-7)(x-1)$$

82. Let $y = x^3$. Then
$$3x^6 - 14x^3 + 8 = 3y^2 - 14y + 8$$
$$= (3y-2)(y-4)$$
$$= (3x^3-2)(x^3-4)$$

84. $36xy^2 - 48xyz^2 + 16xz^4$
$$= 4x(9y^2 - 12yz^2 + 4z^4)$$
$$= 4x(3y-2z^2)(3y-2z^2)$$
$$= 4x(3y-2z^2)^2$$

86. $3x^2y^3 + 6x^2y^2 - 45x^2y = 3x^2y(y^2 + 2y - 15)$
$$= 3x^2y(y-3)(y+5)$$

88. $x^2 + 6xy + 8y^2 = (x+2y)(x+4y)$

90. $(x-4)(x+4) = x^2 - 4^2 = x^2 - 16$

92. $(3x+5)^2 = (3x)^2 + 2(3x)(5) + 5^2$
$$= 9x^2 + 30x + 25$$

94. $(y+1)(y^2 - y + 1) = y(y^2 - y + 1) + 1(y^2 - y + 1)$
$$= y^3 - y^2 + y + y^2 - y + 1$$
$$= y^3 + 1$$

96. ± 9 and ± 3; ± 9 arise from the pairs 10 and -1 and -10 and 1. ± 3 arise from the pairs 5 and -2 and -5 and 2.

98. From 97 we know:
$V(x) = x^3 + 2x^2 - 8x$
$V(x) = x(x+4)(x-2)$
$V(5) = 5(5+4)(5-2)$
$V(5) = 5(9)(3)$
The width is 3 inches and the length is 9 inches.

100. $h(t) = -16t^2 + 64t + 960$

    a. $h(0) = -16(0)^2 + 64(0) + 960 = 960$ ft

        $h(3) = -16(3)^2 + 64(3) + 960$
             $= -16(9) + 192 + 960$
             $= -144 + 192 + 960$
             $= 1008$ ft

        $h(6) = -16(6)^2 + 64(6) + 960$
             $= -16(36) + 384 + 960$
             $= -576 + 384 + 960$
             $= 768$ ft

        $h(9) = -16(9)^2 + 64(9) + 960$
             $= -16(81) + 576 + 960$
             $= -1296 + 576 + 960$
             $= 240$ ft

    b. Answers may vary

    c. $h(t) = -16t^2 + 64t + 960$
            $= -16(t^2 - 4t - 60)$
            $= -16(t-10)(t+6)$

102. $x^{2n} - 7x^n + 12 = (x^n - 3)(x^n - 4)$

104. $x^{2n} + 7x^n - 18 = (x^n - 2)(x^n + 9)$

106. $3x^{2n} - 8x^n + 4 = (3x^n - 2)(x^n - 2)$

108. $9x^{2n} + 24x^n + 16 = (3x^n + 4)(3x^n + 4)$
$$= (3x^n + 4)^2$$

Section 5.7

Practice Exercises

1. $b^2 + 16b + 64 = b^2 + 2(b)(8) + 8^2 = (b+8)^2$

2. $45x^2b - 30xb + 5b = 5b(9x^2 - 6x + 1)$
$$= 5b[(3x)^2 - 2(3x)(1) + 1^2]$$
$$= 5b(3x-1)^2$$

3. a. $x^2 - 16 = x^2 - 4^2 = (x+4)(x-4)$

    b. $25b^2 - 49 = (5b)^2 - 7^2 = (5b-7)(5b+7)$

    c. $45 - 20x^2 = 5(9 - 4x^2)$
               $= 5[3^2 - (2x)^2]$
               $= 5(3 - 2x)(3 + 2x)$

    d. $y^2 - \dfrac{1}{81} = y^2 - \left(\dfrac{1}{9}\right)^2 = \left(y - \dfrac{1}{9}\right)\left(y + \dfrac{1}{9}\right)$

4. a. $x^4 - 10,000 = (x^2)^2 - 100^2$
                     $= (x^2 + 100)(x^2 - 100)$
                     $= (x^2 + 100)(x+10)(x-10)$

    b. $(x+2)^2 - 49 = (x+2)^2 - 7^2$
                    $= [(x+2)+7][(x+2)-7]$
                    $= (x+2+7)(x+2-7)$
                    $= (x+9)(x-5)$

5. $m^2 + 6m + 9 - n^2 = (m^2 + 6m + 9) - n^2$
$$= (m+3)^2 - n^2$$
$$= [(m+3)+n][(m+3)-n]$$
$$= (m+3+n)(m+3-n)$$

6. $x^3 + 64 = x^3 + 4^3$
$$= (x+4)(x^2 - x \cdot 4 + 4^2)$$
$$= (x+4)(x^2 - 4x + 16)$$

7. $a^3 + 8b^3 = a^3 + (2b)^3$
$$= (a+2b)[a^2 - a(2b) + (2b)^2]$$
$$= (a+2b)(a^2 - 2ab + 4b^2)$$

8. $27 - y^3 = 3^3 - y^3$
$$= (3-y)(3^2 + 3 \cdot y + y^2)$$
$$= (3-y)(9 + 3y + y^2)$$

9. $b^3 x^2 - 8x^2 = x^2(b^3 - 8)$
$$= x^2(b^3 - 2^3)$$
$$= x^2(b-2)(b^2 + b \cdot 2 + 2^2)$$
$$= x^2(b-2)(b^2 + 2b + 4)$$

Vocabulary and Readiness Check

1. $81y^2 = (9y)^2$

2. $4z^2 = (2z)^2$

3. $64x^6 = (8x^3)^2$

4. $49y^6 = (7y^3)^2$

5. $125 = 5^3$

6. $216 = 6^3$

7. $8x^3 = (2x)^3$

8. $27y^3 = (3y)^3$

9. $64y^6 = (4x^2)^3$

10. $x^3 y^6 = (xy^2)^3$

Exercise Set 5.7

2. $x^2 - 10x + 25 = x^2 - 2 \cdot x \cdot 5 + 5^2 = (x-5)^2$

4. $25x^2 + 10x + 1 = (5x)^2 + 2 \cdot 5x \cdot 1 + 1^2$
$$= (5x+1)^2$$

6. $x^3 + 14x^2 + 49x = x(x^2 + 14x + 49)$
$$= x(x+7)^2$$

8. $32x^2 - 16xy + 2y^2 = 2(16x^2 - 8xy + y^2)$
$$= 2(4x - y)^2$$

10. $y^2 - 100 = y^2 - 10^2 = (y+10)(y-10)$

12. $16x^2 - y^2 = (4x)^2 - y^2 = (4x+y)(4x-y)$

14. $(x-1)^2 - z^2 = [(x-1) + z][(x-1) - z]$
$$= (x-1+z)(x-1-z)$$

16. $4x^2 - 36 = 4(x^2 - 9) = 4(x+3)(x-3)$

18. $y^3 + 1 = y^3 + 1^3 = (y+1)(y^2 - y + 1)$

20. $x^3 - 8 = x^3 - 2^3 = (x-2)(x^2 + 2x + 4)$

22. $r^3 + 125 = r^3 + 5^3 = (r+5)(r^2 - 5r + 25)$

24. $64 - p^3 = 4^3 - p^3 = (4-p)(16 + 4p + p^2)$

26. $8ab^3 + 27a^4 = a(8b^3 + 27a^3)$
$$= a[(2b)^3 + (3a)^3]$$
$$= a(2b+3a)(4b^2 - 6ab + 9a^2)$$

28. $54y^3 - 128 = 2(27y^3 - 64)$
$$= 2[(3y)^3 - 4^3]$$
$$= 2(3y - 4)(9y^2 + 12y + 16)$$

30. $x^2 + 12x + 36 - y^2 = (x+6)^2 - y^2$
$$= (x+6+y)(x+6-y)$$

32. $x^2 - 18x + 81 - y^2 = (x-9)^2 - y^2$
$$= (x-9+y)(x-9-y)$$

34. $9y^2 + 12y + 4 - x^2 = (3y+2)^2 - x^2$
$$= (3y+2+x)(3y+2-x)$$

36. $25x^2 - 4 = (5x)^2 - 2^2 = (5x+2)(5x-2)$

38. $x^2 - 18x + 81 = x^2 - 2 \cdot x \cdot 9 + 9^2 = (x-9)^2$

40. $x^4 - 256 = (x^2 + 16)(x^2 - 16)$
$$= (x^2 + 16)(x + 4)(x - 4)$$

42. $x^2 + 14x + 49 - 9y^2 = (x + 7)^2 - (3y)^2$
$$= (x + 7 + 3y)(x + 7 - 3y)$$

44. $(3x + y)^2 - 25 = (3x + y)^2 - 5^2$
$$= (3x + y + 5)(3x + y - 5)$$

46. $8 - a^3 = 2^3 - a^3 = (2 - a)(4 + 2a + a^2)$

48. $x^3 + 216 = x^3 + 6^3 = (x + 6)(x^2 - 6x + 36)$

50. $16x^2 + 25$ is prime.

52. $9a^2 - 30a + 25 = (3a)^2 - 2 \cdot 3a \cdot 5 + 5^2$
$$= (3a - 5)^2$$

54. $12xy^2 - 108x = 12x(y^2 - 9)$
$$= 12x(y + 3)(y - 3)$$

56. $27x^3 - y^3 = (3x)^3 - y^3$
$$= (3x - y)(9x^2 + 3xy + y^2)$$

58. $x^3 - y^6 = x^3 - (y^2)^3$
$$= (x - y^2)(x^2 + xy^2 + y^4)$$

60. $x^2 + 20x + 100 - x^4$
$$= (x + 10)^2 - (x^2)^2$$
$$= (x + 10 + x^2)(x + 10 - x^2)$$

62. $x^2 y^9 + x^2 y^3 = x^2 y^3 (y^6 + 1)$
$$= x^2 y^3 [(y^2)^3 + 1^3]$$
$$= x^2 y^3 (y^2 + 1)(y^4 - y^2 + 1)$$

64. $(x + y)^3 + 27$
$$= (x + y)^3 + 3^3$$
$$= [(x + y) + 3][(x + y)^2 - 3(x + y) + 9]$$
$$= (x + y + 3)(x^2 + 2xy + y^2 - 3x - 3y + 9)$$

66. $(4x + 2)^3 - 125$
$$= (4x + 2)^3 - 5^3$$
$$= [(4x + 2) - 5][(4x + 2)^2 + 5(4x + 2) + 25]$$
$$= (4x - 3)(16x^2 + 16x + 4 + 20x + 10 + 25)$$
$$= (4x - 3)(16x^2 + 36x + 39)$$

68. $x + 7 = 0$
$$x = -7$$

70. $5x - 15 = 0$
$$5x = 15$$
$$x = 3$$

72. $3x = 0$
$$x = 0$$

74. $-4x - 16 = 0$
$$-4x = 16$$
$$x = -4$$

76. No; $x^3 - y^3$ can be factored further.
$$x^2 y^2 (x^3 - y^3) = x^2 y^2 (x - y)(x^2 + xy + y^2)$$

78. Yes; $9z(x^2 + 4)$ is factored completely.

80. Area $= x^2 - y^2 = (x + y)(x - y)$ sq units

82. Volume $= \pi x^2 h - \pi y^2 h$
$$= \pi h(x^2 - y^2)$$
$$= \pi h(x + y)(x - y) \text{ cubic units}$$

84. $\frac{1}{2} \cdot b = \frac{1}{2} \cdot 10 = 5$ so $c = 5^2 = 25$

86. $\frac{1}{2} \cdot b = \frac{1}{2}(-2) = -1$ so $c = (-1)^2 = 1$

88. $\frac{1}{2} \cdot c = \frac{c}{2}$ so $\left(\frac{c}{2}\right)^2 = 36$
$$\frac{c^2}{4} = 36$$
$$c^2 = 144$$
$$c = \pm 12$$

90. $x^{2n} - 25 = (x^n)^2 - 5^2 = (x^n + 5)(x^n - 5)$

92. $36x^{2n} - 49 = (6x^n)^2 - 7^2 = (6x^n + 7)(6x^n - 7)$

94. $x^{4n} - 16 = (x^{2n})^2 - 4^2$

$$= (x^{2n} + 4)(x^{2n} - 4)$$
$$= (x^{2n} + 4)[(x^n)^2 - 2^2]$$
$$= (x^{2n} + 4)(x^n + 2)(x^n - 2)$$

Integrated Review

Practice Exercises

1. a. $12x^2 y - 3xy = 3xy(4x) + 3xy(-1)$
$$= 3xy(4x - 1)$$

b. $49x^2 - 4 = (7x)^2 - 2^2 = (7x + 2)(7x - 2)$

c. $5x^2 + 2x - 3 = (5x - 3)(x + 1)$

d. $3x^2 + 6 + x^3 + 2x = 3(x^2 + 2) + x(x^2 + 2)$
$$= (x^2 + 2)(3 + x)$$

e. $4x^2 + 20x + 25 = (2x)^2 + 2 \cdot 2x \cdot 5 + 5^2$
$$= (2x + 5)^2$$

f. $b^2 + 100$ cannot be factored.

2. a. $64x^3 + y^3 = (4x)^3 + y^3$
$$= (4x + y)[(4x)^2 - 4x \cdot y + y^2]$$
$$= (4x + y)(16x^2 - 4xy + y^2)$$

b. $7x^2 y^2 - 63y^4 = 7y^2(x^2 - 9y^2)$
$$= 7y^2[x^2 - (3y)^2]$$
$$= 7y^2(x - 3y)(x + 3y)$$

c. $3x^2 + 12x + 12 - 3b^2$
$$= 3(x^2 + 4x + 4 - b^2)$$
$$= 3[(x + 2)^2 - b^2]$$
$$= 3(x + 2 + b)(x + 2 - b)$$

d. $x^5 y^4 + 27x^2 y$
$$= x^2 y(x^3 y^3 + 27)$$
$$= x^2 y[(xy)^3 + 3^3]$$
$$= x^2 y(xy + 3)(x^2 y^2 - 3xy + 9)$$

e. $(x + 7)^2 - 81y^2 = (x + 7)^2 - (9y)^2$
$$= (x + 7 + 9y)(x + 7 - 9y)$$

Integrated Review Exercise Set

1. $(-y^2 + 6y - 1) + (3y^2 - 4y - 10)$
$$= -y^2 + 6y - 1 + 3y^2 - 4y - 10$$
$$= 2y^2 + 2y - 11$$

2. $(5z^4 - 6z^2 + z + 1) - (7z^4 - 2z + 1)$
$$= 5z^4 - 6z^2 + z + 1 - 7z^4 + 2z - 1$$
$$= -2z^4 - 6z^2 + 3z$$

3. $(x^2 - 6x + 2) - (x - 5) = x^2 - 6x + 2 - x + 5$
$$= x^2 - 7x + 7$$

4. $(2x^2 + 6x - 5) + (5x^2 - 10x) = 7x^2 - 4x - 5$

5. $(5x - 3)^2 = (5x)^2 - 2(5x)(3) + 3^2$
$$= 25x^2 - 30x + 9$$

6. $\dfrac{5x^2 - 14x - 3}{5x + 1} = \dfrac{(x - 3)(5x + 1)}{5x + 1} = x - 3$

7.

$$
\begin{array}{r}
2x^3 - 4x^2 + 5x - 3 \\
x+2 \overline{\smash{\big)}\ 2x^4 + 0x^3 - 3x^2\ \ +5x\ -2} \\
\underline{2x^4 + 4x^3} \\
-4x^3 - 3x^2 \\
\underline{-4x^3 - 8x^2} \\
5x^2\ \ +5x \\
\underline{5x^2 + 10x} \\
-5x\ \ -2 \\
\underline{-5x - 10} \\
8
\end{array}
$$

$$92x^4 - 3x^2 + 5x - 2) \div (x + 2)$$
$$= 2x^3 - 4x^2 + 5x - 5 + \frac{8}{x + 2}$$

8.

$$
\begin{array}{r}
x^2 - 3x - 2 \\
\times \qquad\qquad 4x - 1 \\
\hline
-x^2 + 3x + 2 \\
4x^3 - 12x^2 - 8x \\
\hline
4x^3 - 13x^2 - 5x + 2
\end{array}
$$

9. $x^2 - 8x + 16 - y^2 = (x - 4)^2 - y^2$
$$= (x - 4 + y)(x - 4 - y)$$

10. $12x^2 - 22x - 20 = 2(6x^2 - 11x - 10)$
$$= 2(3x+2)(2x-5)$$

11. $x^4 - x = x(x^3 - 1) = x(x-1)(x^2 + x + 1)$

12. Let $y = 2x + 1$. Then
$$(2x+1)^2 - 3(2x+1) + 2$$
$$= y^2 - 3y + 2$$
$$= (y-2)(y-1)$$
$$= [(2x+1)-2][(2x+1)-1]$$
$$= (2x-1)(2x)$$
$$= 2x(2x-1)$$

13. $14x^2y - 2xy = 2xy(7x - 1)$

14. $24ab^2 - 6ab = 6ab(4b - 1)$

15. $4x^2 - 16 = 4(x^2 - 4) = 4(x+2)(x-2)$

16. $9x^2 - 81 = 9(x^2 - 9) = 9(x+3)(x-3)$

17. $3x^2 - 8x - 11 = (3x-11)(x+1)$

18. $5x^2 - 2x - 3 = (5x+3)(x-1)$

19. $4x^2 + 8x - 12 = 4(x^2 + 2x - 3)$
$$= 4(x+3)(x-1)$$

20. $6x^2 - 6x - 12 = 6(x^2 - x - 2)$
$$= 6(x-2)(x+1)$$

21. $4x^2 + 36x + 81 = (2x)^2 + 2 \cdot 2x \cdot 9 + 9^2$
$$= (2x+9)^2$$

22. $25x^2 + 40x + 16 = (5x)^2 + 2 \cdot 5x \cdot 4 + 4^2$
$$= (5x+4)^2$$

23. $8x^3 + 125y^3 = (2x)^3 + (5y)^3$
$$= (2x+5y)(4x^2 - 10xy + 25y^2)$$

24. $27x^3 - 64y^3 = (3x)^3 - (4y)^3$
$$= (3x-4y)(9x^2 + 12xy + 16y^2)$$

25. $64x^2y^3 - 8x^2 = 8x^2(8y^3 - 1)$
$$= 8x^2[(2y)^3 - 1^3]$$
$$= 8x^2(2y-1)(4y^2 + 2y + 1)$$

26. $27x^5y^4 - 216x^2y$
$$= 27x^2y(x^3y^3 - 8)$$
$$= 27x^2y[(xy)^3 - 2^3]$$
$$= 27x^2y(xy-2)(x^2y^2 + 2xy + 4)$$

27. $(x+5)^3 + y^3$
$$= [(x+5)+y][(x+5)^2 - (x+5)y + y^2]$$
$$= (x+y+5)(x^2 + 10x + 25 - xy - 5y + y^2)$$
$$= (x+y+5)(x^2 + 10x - xy - 5y + y^2 + 25)$$

28. $(y-1)^3 + 27x^3$
$$= (y-1)^3 + (3x)^3$$
$$= [(y-1)+3x][(y-1)^2 - (y-1)(3x) + (3x)^2]$$
$$= (y-1+3x)(y^2 - 2y + 1 - 3xy + 3x + 9x^2)$$

29. Let $y = 5a - 3$. Then
$$(5a-3)^2 - 6(5a-3) + 9 = y^2 - 6y + 9$$
$$= (y-3)(y-3)$$
$$= (y-3)^2$$
$$= [(5a-3)-3]^2$$
$$= (5a-6)^2$$

30. Let $y = 4r + 1$. Then
$$(4r+1)^2 + 8(4r+1) + 16 = y^2 + 8y + 16$$
$$= (y+4)(y+4)$$
$$= (y+4)^2$$
$$= [(4r+1)+4]^2$$
$$= (4r+5)^2$$

31. $7x^2 - 63x = 7x(x - 9)$

32. $20x^2 + 23x + 6 = (4x+3)(5x+2)$

33. $ab - 6a + 7b - 42 = a(b-6) + 7(b-6)$
$$= (a+7)(b-6)$$

34. $20x^2 - 220x + 600 = 20(x^2 - 11x + 30)$
$$= 20(x-6)(x-5)$$

35. $x^4 - 1 = (x^2)^2 - 1^2$
$$= (x^2 + 1)(x^2 - 1)$$
$$= (x^2 + 1)(x + 1)(x - 1)$$

36. $15x^2 - 20x = 5x(3x - 4)$

37. $10x^2 - 7x - 33 = (5x - 11)(2x + 3)$

38. $45m^3 n^3 - 27m^2 n^2 = 9m^2 n^2 (5mn - 3)$

39. $5a^3 b^3 - 50a^3 b = 5a^3 b(b^2 - 10)$

40. $x^4 + x = x(x^3 + 1)$
$$= x(x^3 + 1^3)$$
$$= x(x + 1)(x^2 - x + 1)$$

41. $16x^2 + 25$ is a prime polynomial.

42. $20x^3 + 20y^3 = 20(x^3 + y^3)$
$$= 20(x + y)(x^2 - xy + y^2)$$

43. $10x^3 - 210x^2 + 1100x = 10x(x^2 - 21x + 110)$
$$= 10x(x - 11)(x - 10)$$

44. $9y^2 - 42y + 49 = (3y)^2 - 2 \cdot 3y \cdot 7 + 7^2$
$$= (3y - 7)^2$$

45. $64a^3 b^4 - 27a^3 b$
$$= a^3 b(64b^3 - 27)$$
$$= a^3 b[(4b)^3 - 3^3]$$
$$= a^3 b(4b - 3)(16b^2 + 12b + 9)$$

46. $y^4 - 16 = (y^2)^2 - 4^2$
$$= (y^2 + 4)(y^2 - 4)$$
$$= (y^2 + 4)(y + 2)(y - 2)$$

47. $2x^3 - 54 = 2(x^3 - 27)$
$$= 2(x^3 - 3^3)$$
$$= 2(x - 3)(x^2 + 3x + 9)$$

48. $2sr + 10s - r - 5 = 2s(r + 5) - 1(r + 5)$
$$= (2s - 1)(r + 5)$$

49. $3y^5 - 5y^4 + 6y - 10 = y^4(3y - 5) + 2(3y - 5)$
$$= (y^4 + 2)(3y - 5)$$

50. $64a^2 + b^2$ is a prime polynomial.

51. $100z^3 + 100 = 100(z^3 + 1)$
$$= 100(z + 1)(z^2 - z + 1)$$

52. $250x^4 - 16x = 2x(125x^3 - 8)$
$$= 2x[(5x)^3 - 2^3]$$
$$= 2x(5x - 2)(25x^2 + 10x + 4)$$

53. $4b^2 - 36b + 81 = (2b)^2 - 2 \cdot 2b \cdot 9 + 9^2$
$$= (2b - 9)^2$$

54. $2a^5 - a^4 + 6a - 3 = a^4(2a - 1) + 3(2a - 1)$
$$= (a^4 + 3)(2a - 1)$$

55. Let $x = y - 6$. Then
$$(y - 6)^2 + 3(y - 6) + 2 = x^2 + 3x + 2$$
$$= (x + 2)(x + 1)$$
$$= [(y - 6) + 2][(y - 6) + 1]$$
$$= (y - 4)(y - 5)$$

56. Let $x = c + 2$. Then
$$(c + 2)^2 - 6(c + 2) + 5 = x^2 - 6x + 5$$
$$= (x - 5)(x - 1)$$
$$= [(c + 2) - 5][(c + 2) - 1]$$
$$= (c - 3)(c + 1)$$

57. Area $= 3^2 - 4x^2 = 3^2 - (2x)^2 = (3 + 2x)(3 - 2x)$

Section 5.8

Practice Exercises

1. $(x + 8)(x - 5) = 0$
$x + 8 = 0$ or $x - 5 = 0$
$x = -8$ or $x = 5$
Both solutions check. The solution set is $\{-8, 5\}$.

2. $3x^2 + 10x - 8 = 0$
$(3x - 2)(x + 4) = 0$
$3x - 2 = 0$ or $x + 4 = 0$
$3x = 2$
$x = \dfrac{2}{3}$ or $x = -4$
Both solutions check. The solution set is
$\left\{ -4, \dfrac{2}{3} \right\}$.

3.
$$x(3x+14) = -8$$
$$3x^2 + 14x = -8$$
$$3x^2 + 14x + 8 = 0$$
$$(3x+2)(x+4) = 0$$
$$3x+2 = 0 \quad \text{or} \quad x+4 = 0$$
$$3x = -2$$
$$x = -\frac{2}{3} \quad \text{or} \quad x = -4$$

The solutions are $-\dfrac{2}{3}$ and -4.

4.
$$8(x^2+3)+4 = -8x(x+3)+19$$
$$8x^2 + 24 + 4 = -8x^2 - 24x + 19$$
$$16x^2 + 24x + 9 = 0$$
$$(4x+3)(4x+3) = 0$$
$$4x+3 = 0 \quad \text{or} \quad 4x+3 = 0$$
$$4x = -3 \quad \text{or} \quad 4x = -3$$
$$x = -\frac{3}{4} \quad \text{or} \quad x = -\frac{3}{4}$$

The solution is $-\dfrac{3}{4}$.

5.
$$4x^2 = \frac{15}{2}x + 1$$
$$2(4x^2) = 2\left(\frac{15}{2}x + 1\right)$$
$$8x^2 = 15x + 2$$
$$8x^2 - 15x - 2 = 0$$
$$(8x+1)(x-2) = 0$$
$$8x+1 = 0 \quad \text{or} \quad x-2 = 0$$
$$8x = -1$$
$$x = -\frac{1}{8} \quad \text{or} \quad x = 2$$

The solutions are $-\dfrac{1}{8}$ and 2.

6.
$$x^3 = 2x^2 + 3x$$
$$x^3 - 2x^2 - 3x = 0$$
$$x(x^2 - 2x - 3) = 0$$
$$x(x-3)(x+1) = 0$$
$$x = 0 \quad \text{or} \quad x-3 = 0 \quad \text{or} \quad x+1 = 0$$
$$x = 3 \quad \text{or} \quad x = -1$$

The solutions are 0, 3, and -1.

7.
$$x^3 - 9x = 18 - 2x^2$$
$$x^3 + 2x^2 - 9x - 18 = 0$$
$$x^2(x+2) - 9(x+2) = 0$$
$$(x+2)(x^2 - 9) = 0$$
$$(x+2)(x+3)(x-3) = 0$$
$$x+2 = 0 \quad \text{or} \quad x+3 = 0 \quad \text{or} \quad x-3 = 0$$
$$x = -2 \quad \text{or} \quad x = -3 \quad \text{or} \quad x = 3$$

The solutions are 3, -3, and -2.

8. Let $h = 0$.
$$-16t^2 + 96t = 0$$
$$-16t(t-6) = 0$$
$$-16t = 0 \quad \text{or} \quad t-6 = 0$$
$$t = 0 \quad \text{or} \quad t = 6$$

The rocket will return to the ground in 6 seconds.

9. Let $x =$ first even integer, then $x + 2 =$ next even integer, and $x + 4 =$ third even integer.
$$x^2 + (x+2)^2 = (x+4)^2$$
$$x^2 + x^2 + 4x + 4 = x^2 + 8x + 16$$
$$x^2 - 4x - 12 = 0$$
$$(x-6)(x+2) = 0$$
$$x-6 = 0 \quad \text{or} \quad x+2 = 0$$
$$x = 6 \quad \text{or} \quad x = -2$$

Discard $x = -2$ since length cannot be negative. The legs are $x = 6$ units, $x + 2 = 8$ units, and $x + 4 = 10$ units.

10. The graph of $f(x) = (x-1)(x+3)$ has two x-intercepts, $(1, 0)$ and $(-3, 0)$, so the graph is C.
The graph of $g(x) = x(x+3)(x-2)$ has three x-intercepts, $(0, 0)$, $(-3, 0)$, and $(2, 0)$, so the graph is A.
The graph of $h(x) = (x-3)(x+2)(x-2)$ has three x-intercepts, $(3, 0)$, $(-2, 0)$, and $(2, 0)$, so the graph is B.

Vocabulary and Readiness Check

1.
$$(x-3)(x+5) = 0$$
$$x-3 = 0 \quad \text{or} \quad x+5 = 0$$
$$x = 3 \quad \text{or} \quad x = -5$$

The solutions are -5, 3.

2. $(y+5)(y+3)=0$
$\quad y+5=0 \quad$ or $\quad y+3=0$
$\qquad y=-5 \quad$ or $\qquad y=-3$
$\quad$ The solutions are $-5, -3$.

3. $(z-3)(z+7)=0$
$\quad z-3=0 \quad$ or $\quad z+7=0$
$\qquad z=3 \quad$ or $\qquad z=-7$
$\quad$ The solutions are $-7, 3$.

4. $(c-2)(c-4)=0$
$\quad c-2=0 \quad$ or $\quad c-4=0$
$\qquad c=2 \quad$ or $\qquad c=4$
$\quad$ The solutions are $2, 4$.

5. $x(x-9)=0$
$\quad x=0 \quad$ or $\quad x-9=0$
$\qquad\qquad\qquad x=9$
$\quad$ The solutions are $0, 9$.

6. $w(w+7)=0$
$\quad w=0 \quad$ or $\quad w+7=0$
$\qquad\qquad\qquad w=-7$
$\quad$ The solutions are $-7, 0$.

Exercise Set 5.8

2. $(5x+1)(x-2)=0$
$\quad 5x+1=0 \quad$ or $\quad x-2=0$
$\qquad 5x=-1 \quad$ or $\qquad x=2$
$\qquad x=-\dfrac{1}{5}$
$\quad$ The solutions are $-\dfrac{1}{5}, 2$.

4. $8(3x-4)(2x-7)=0$
$\quad 3x-4=0 \quad$ or $\quad 2x-7=0$
$\qquad 3x=4 \quad$ or $\qquad 2x=7$
$\qquad x=\dfrac{4}{3} \quad$ or $\qquad x=\dfrac{7}{2}$
$\quad$ The solutions are $\dfrac{4}{3}, \dfrac{7}{2}$.

6. $y^2-10y+24=0$
$\quad (y-6)(y-4)=0$
$\quad y-6=0 \quad$ or $\quad y-4=0$
$\qquad y=6 \quad$ or $\qquad y=4$
$\quad$ The solutions are $4, 6$.

8. $3y^2-y-14=0$
$\quad (3y-7)(y+2)=0$
$\quad 3y-7=0 \quad$ or $\quad y+2=0$
$\qquad 3y=7 \quad$ or $\qquad y=-2$
$\qquad y=\dfrac{7}{3}$
$\quad$ The solutions are $-2, \dfrac{7}{3}$.

10. $\qquad n^2+n=72$
$\qquad n^2+n-72=0$
$\qquad (n+9)(n-8)=0$
$\quad n+9=0 \quad$ or $\quad n-8=0$
$\qquad n=-9 \quad$ or $\qquad n=8$
$\quad$ The solutions are $-9, 8$.

12. $\qquad n(2n-3)=2$
$\qquad 2n^2-3n-2=0$
$\qquad (2n+1)(n-2)=0$
$\quad 2n+1=0 \quad$ or $\quad n-2=0$
$\qquad 2n=-1 \quad$ or $\qquad n=2$
$\qquad n=-\dfrac{1}{2}$
$\quad$ The solutions are $-\dfrac{1}{2}, 2$.

14. $n(3+n)=n^2+4n$
$\quad 3n+n^2=n^2+4n$
$\qquad -n=0$
$\qquad n=0$
$\quad$ The solution is 0.

16. $\dfrac{c^2}{20}-\dfrac{c}{4}+\dfrac{1}{5}=0$
$\quad c^2-5c+4=0$
$\quad (c-4)(c-1)=0$
$\quad c-4=0 \quad$ or $\quad c-1=0$
$\qquad c=4 \quad$ or $\qquad c=1$
$\quad$ The solutions are $1, 4$.

18. $\qquad \dfrac{y^2}{30}=\dfrac{y}{15}+\dfrac{1}{2}$
$\qquad y^2=2y+15$
$\quad y^2-2y-15=0$
$\quad (y-5)(y+3)=0$

$$y - 5 = 0 \text{ or } y + 3 = 0$$
$$y = 5 \text{ or } \quad y = -3$$
The solutions are –3, 5.

20.　$\dfrac{5x^2}{6} - \dfrac{7x}{2} + \dfrac{2}{3} = 0$

$$5x^2 - 21x + 4 = 0$$
$$(5x - 1)(x - 4) = 0$$
$$5x - 1 = 0 \text{ or } x - 4 = 0$$
$$5x = 1 \text{ or } \quad x = 4$$
$$x = \dfrac{1}{5}$$

The solutions are $\dfrac{1}{5}$, 4.

22.　$(4x + 9)(x - 4)(x + 1) = 0$

$$4x + 9 = 0 \quad \text{ or } x - 4 = 0 \text{ or } x + 1 = 0$$
$$4x = -9 \text{ or } \quad x = 4 \text{ or } \quad x = -1$$
$$x = -\dfrac{9}{4}$$

The solutions are $-\dfrac{9}{4}, -1, 4$.

24.　$n^3 = 16n$

$$n^3 - 16n = 0$$
$$n(n^2 - 16) = 0$$
$$n(n + 4)(n - 4) = 0$$
$$n = 0 \text{ or } n + 4 = 0 \quad \text{ or } n - 4 = 0$$
$$n = -4 \text{ or } \quad n = 4$$
The solutions are –4, 0, 4.

26.　$m^3 = m^2 + 12m$

$$m^3 - m^2 + 12m = 0$$
$$m(m^2 - m + 12) = 0$$
$$m(m - 4)(m + 3) = 0$$
$$m = 0 \quad \text{ or } m - 4 = 0 \text{ or } m + 3 = 0$$
$$m = 4 \text{ or } \quad m = -3$$
The solutions are –3, 0, 4.

28.　Answers may vary

30.　$(x + 4)(5x - 1) = 0$

$$x + 4 = 0 \quad \text{ or } 5x - 1 = 0$$
$$x = -4 \text{ or } \quad 5x = 1$$
$$x = \dfrac{1}{5}$$

The solutions are $-4, \dfrac{1}{5}$.

32.　$4x(2x + 3) = 0$

$$4x = 0 \text{ or } 2x + 3 = 0$$
$$x = 0 \text{ or } \quad 2x = -3$$
$$x = -\dfrac{3}{2}$$

The solutions are $-\dfrac{3}{2}$, 0.

34.　$x^2 + 6x - 7 = 0$

$$(x + 7)(x - 1) = 0$$
$$x + 7 = 0 \quad \text{ or } x - 1 = 0$$
$$x = -7 \text{ or } \quad x = 1$$
The solutions are –7, 1.

36.　$8x^2 + 13x + 5 = 0$

$$(8x + 5)(x + 1) = 0$$
$$8x + 5 = 0 \quad \text{ or } x + 1 = 0$$
$$8x = -5 \text{ or } \quad x = -1$$
$$x = -\dfrac{5}{8}$$

The solutions are $-1, -\dfrac{5}{8}$.

38.　$x^2 + 32 = 12x$

$$x^2 - 12x + 32 = 0$$
$$(x - 8)(x - 4) = 0$$
$$x - 8 = 0 \text{ or } x - 4 = 0$$
$$x = 8 \text{ or } \quad x = 4$$
The solutions are 4, 8.

40.　$9n^2 + 30n + 25 = 0$

$$(3n + 5)^2 = 0$$
$$3n + 5 = 0$$
$$3n = -5$$
$$n = -\dfrac{5}{3}$$

The solution is $-\dfrac{5}{3}$.

42.　$-2t^3 = 108t - 30t^2$

$$-2t^3 + 30t^2 - 108t = 0$$
$$-2t(t^2 - 15t + 54) = 0$$
$$2t(t - 9)(t - 6) = 0$$
$$t = 0 \text{ or } t = 9 \text{ or } t = 6$$
The solutions are 0, 6, 9.

44. $2r(r+3)(5r-4)=0$

$r=0$ or $r=-3$ or $r=\dfrac{4}{5}$

The solutions are $-3, 0, \dfrac{4}{5}$.

46. $3c^2-8c+2=c(3c-8)$

$3c^2-8c+2=3c^2-8c$

$\quad\quad\quad\quad 2=0$ False

No solution exists; $\varnothing$.

48. $(2x-1)(x+2)=-3$

$\quad 2x^2+3x-2=-3$

$\quad 2x^2+3x+1=0$

$\quad (2x+1)(x+1)=0$

$x=-\dfrac{1}{2}$ or $x=-1$

The solutions are $-1, -\dfrac{1}{2}$.

50. $\dfrac{x^2}{18}+\dfrac{x}{2}+1=0$

$x^2+9x+18=0$

$(x+6)(x+3)=0$

$x=-6$ or $x=-3$

The solutions are $-6, -3$.

52. $\dfrac{x^2}{10}+\dfrac{5}{2}=x$

$\quad x^2+25=10x$

$x^2-10x+25=0$

$\quad\quad (x-5)^2=0$

$\quad\quad\quad x-5=0$

$\quad\quad\quad\quad x=5$

The solution is 5.

54. $\quad\quad x^3+5x^2=x+5$

$\quad\quad x^3+5x^2-x-5=0$

$\quad x^2(x+5)-1(x+5)=0$

$\quad\quad (x^2-1)(x+5)=0$

$\quad (x+1)(x-1)(x+5)=0$

$x=-1$ or $x=1$ or $x=-5$

The solutions are $-5, -1, 1$.

56. $\quad\quad\quad\quad m^5=36m^3$

$\quad\quad\quad m^5-36m^3=0$

$\quad\quad\quad m^3(m^2-36)=0$

$\quad m^3(m+6)(m-6)=0$

$m=0$ or $m=-6$ or $m=6$

The solutions are $-6, 0, 6$.

58. $\quad\quad y^2+(y+2)^2=34$

$\quad y^2+y^2+4y+4=34$

$\quad\quad\quad 2y^2+4y-30=0$

$\quad\quad\quad 2(y^2+2y-15)=0$

$\quad\quad\quad 2(y+5)(y-3)=0$

$y=-5$ or $y=3$

The solutions are $-5, 3$.

60. $\quad\quad x^2(5x+3)=26x$

$\quad\quad\quad 5x^3+3x^2=26x$

$\quad\quad 5x^3+3x^2-26x=0$

$\quad\quad x(5x^2+3x-26)=0$

$\quad\quad x(5x+13)(x-2)=0$

$x=0$ or $x=-\dfrac{13}{5}$ or $x=2$

The solutions are $-\dfrac{13}{5}, 0, 2$.

62. $\quad\quad y^2=-5y$

$\quad y^2+5y=0$

$\quad y(y+5)=0$

$y=0$ or $y=-5$

The solutions are $-5, 0$.

64. $z^2-4z+10=z(z-5)$

$z^2-4z+10=z^2-5z$

$\quad\quad\quad\quad z=-10$

The solution is -10.

66. $7c-2(3c+1)=5(4-2c)$

$\quad 7c-6c-2=20-10c$

$\quad\quad\quad c-2=20-10c$

$\quad\quad\quad 11c=22$

$\quad\quad\quad\quad c=2$

The solution is 2.

68. $-4(a+1)-3a = -7(2a-3)$

$-4a-4-3a = -14a+21$

$-7a-4 = -14a+21$

$7a = 25$

$a = \dfrac{25}{7}$

The solution is $\dfrac{25}{7}$.

70. Answers may vary

72. Let x be one of the numbers and y be the other. Since $x+y=4$, we know that $y=4-x$. Then we have

$$xy = \frac{15}{4}$$

$$x(4-x) = \frac{15}{4}$$

$$4x-x^2-\frac{15}{4} = 0$$

$$16x-4x^2-15 = 0$$

$$4x^2-16x+15 = 0$$

$$(2x-3)(2x-5) = 0$$

$$2x-3 = 0 \quad \text{or} \quad 2x-5 = 0$$

$$x = \frac{3}{2} \quad \text{or} \quad x = \frac{5}{2}$$

The two solutions are $\dfrac{3}{2}$ and $\dfrac{5}{2}$.

74. Let h be the diagonal of the rectangle. By the Pythagorean theorem, we have

$$h^2 = 40^2 + 75^2$$

$$h^2 = 7225$$

$$h^2 - 7225 = 0$$

$$(h+85)(h-85) = 0$$

$$h = -85 \quad \text{or} \quad h = 85$$

Since h must be positive, we see that $h = 85$ feet. Therefore, she needs $85 \cdot 2 = 170$ feet.

76. Let x, $x+1$, and $x+2$ represent the three consecutive integers. Note that $x+2$, the largest of the three numbers, must be the hypotenuse. By the Pythagorean theorem,

$$x^2 + (x+1)^2 = (x+2)^2$$

$$x^2 + x^2 + 2x + 1 = x^2 + 4x + 4$$

$$2x^2 + 2x + 1 = x^2 + 4x + 4$$

$$x^2 - 2x - 3 = 0$$

$$(x-3)(x+1) = 0$$

$x = 3$ or $x = -1$

Disregard the negative since the length must be positive. The three numbers are 3, 4, and 5.

78. Let $x =$ one leg of a right triangle and $x+4 =$ the other leg of the right triangle.

$$20^2 = x^2 + (x+4)^2$$

$$400 = x^2 + x^2 + 8x + 16$$

$$400 = 2x^2 + 8x + 16$$

$$0 = 2x^2 + 8x - 384$$

$$0 = 2(x^2 + 4x - 192)$$

$$0 = 2(x+16)(x-12)$$

$x = -16$ or $x = 12$

Disregard the negative solution, we find that one leg of the right triangle is 12 ft and the other leg is 16 ft.

80. Let x be the width of the pine bark. Then the area of the garden with the pine bark is $(20+2x)(30+2x) = 4x^2 + 100x + 600$. The area of the garden itself is $(20)(30) = 600$. Thus,

$$(4x^2 + 100x + 600) - 600 = 336$$

$$4x^2 + 100x - 336 = 0$$

$$x^2 + 25x - 84 = 0$$

$$(x-3)(x+28) = 0$$

$x = 3$ or $x = -28$ (disregard)

The width should be 3 feet.

82. $h(t) = -16t^2 + 80t$

$$96 = -16t^2 + 80t$$

$$0 = -16t^2 + 80t - 96$$

$$0 = t^2 - 5t + 6$$

$$0 = (t-2)(t-3)$$

$t = 2$ or $t = 3$

2 sec (ascending) and 3 sec (descending).

84. Let $x =$ width and $3x - 1 =$ length.

$$x(3x-1) = 200$$

$$3x^2 - x - 200 = 0$$

$$(3x-25)(x+8) = 0$$

$$3x - 25 = 0 \quad \text{or} \quad x+8 = 0$$

$$x = \frac{25}{3} = 8\frac{1}{3} \quad \text{or} \quad x = -8$$

Disregard the negative.

$$3x - 1 = 3\left(\frac{25}{3}\right) - 1 = 24$$

The garden is 24 feet by $8\frac{1}{3}$ feet.

86.
$$0.5x^2 = 200$$
$$0.5x^2 - 200 = 0$$
$$5x^2 - 2000 = 0$$
$$x^2 - 400 = 0$$
$$(x + 20)(x - 20) = 0$$
$$x + 20 = 0 \quad \text{or} \quad x - 20 = 0$$
$$x = -20 \quad \text{or} \quad x = 20$$

Disregard the negative solution. A 20-inch square tier is needed.

88. $-16t^2 + 64t + 960 = 0$
$$-16(t^2 - 4t - 60) = 0$$
$$-16(t - 10)(t + 6) = 0$$
$$t - 10 = 0 \quad \text{or} \quad t + 6 = 0$$
$$t = 10 \quad \text{or} \quad t = -6$$

The object will hit the ground 10 seconds after being dropped.

90. D; x-intercepts $(-1, 0), (6, 0)$

92. A; x-intercepts $(-1, 0), (2, 0), (-5, 0)$

94. C; x-intercepts $\left(-\frac{1}{2}, 0\right), (4, 0)$

96. $(-4, 0), (0, 0), (3, 0)$; function, because any vertical line will cross only once.

98. $(-5, 0), (5, 0), (0, -4)$; function, because any vertical line will cross only once.

100. Answers may vary

102. $(4x - 5)(x + 7) = 0$
$$4x - 5 = 0 \quad \text{or} \quad x + 7 = 0$$
$$4x = 5 \quad \text{or} \quad x = -7$$
$$x = \frac{5}{4}$$

104.
$$3x^2 - 19x = 14$$
$$3x^2 - 19x - 14 = 0$$
$$(3x + 2)(x - 7) = 0$$
$$3x + 2 = 0 \quad \text{or} \quad x - 7 = 0$$
$$x = -\frac{2}{3} \quad \text{or} \quad x = 7$$

106. $(x^2 - 9)(x^2 + 8x + 16) = 0$
$$x^2 - 9 = 0 \quad \text{or} \quad x^2 + 8x + 16 = 0$$
$$(x + 3)(x - 3) = 0 \quad \text{or} \quad (x + 4)(x + 4) = 0$$
$$x = -3, x = 3, x = -4$$
The solutions are $-4, -3, 3$.

108. Answers may vary
Ex.: $(x - 5)(x - 3) = x^2 - 8x + 15 = 0$

110. Answers may vary
Ex.: $(x + 1)(x - 2) = x^2 - x - 2 = 0$

The Bigger Picture

1. $|7x - 3| = |5x - 9|$
$$7x - 3 = 5x + 9 \quad \text{or} \quad 7x - 3 = -(5x + 9)$$
$$2x = 12 \qquad\qquad\quad 7x - 3 = -5x - 9$$
$$x = 6 \qquad\qquad\qquad 12x = -6$$
$$x = -\frac{1}{2}$$

2. $\left|\dfrac{x + 2}{5}\right| < 1$
$$-1 < \frac{x + 2}{5} < 1$$
$$-5 < x + 2 < 5$$
$$-7 < x < 3$$
$$(-7, 3)$$

3. $3(x - 6) + 2 = 9 + 5(3x - 1)$
$$3x - 18 + 2 = 9 + 15x - 5$$
$$3x - 16 = 15x + 4$$
$$-12x = 20$$
$$x = -\frac{5}{3}$$

4. $(x - 6)(2x + 3) = 0$
$$x - 6 = 0 \quad \text{or} \quad 2x + 3 = 0$$
$$x = 6 \quad \text{or} \quad x = -\frac{3}{2}$$

5. $|-3x + 10| \geq -2$
The absolute value of any expression is always
≥ 0. Therefore, the solution is $(-\infty, \infty)$.

6. $|-2x - 5| = 11$
$$-2x - 5 = -11 \quad \text{or} \quad -2x - 5 = 11$$
$$-2x = -6 \quad \text{or} \quad -2x = 16$$
$$x = 3 \quad \text{or} \quad x = -8$$

7.
$$x(x - 7) = 30$$
$$x^2 - 7x = 30$$
$$x^2 - 7x - 30 = 0$$
$$(x + 3)(x - 10) = 0$$
$$x + 3 = 0 \quad \text{or} \quad x - 10 = 0$$
$$x = -3 \quad \text{or} \quad x = 10$$

8. $8x - 4 \geq 15x - 4$
$$-7x \geq 0$$
$$x \leq 0$$
The solution set is $(-\infty, 0]$.

Chapter 5 Vocabulary Check

1. A polynomial is a finite sum of terms in which
    all variables are raised to nonnegative integer
    powers and no variables appear in any
    denominator.

2. Factoring is the process of writing a polynomial
    as a product.

3. Exponents are used to write repeated factors in a
    more compact form.

4. The degree of a term is the sum of the exponents
    on the variables contained in the term.

5. A monomial is a polynomial with three terms.

6. If a is not 0, $a^0 = \underline{1}$.

7. A trinomial is a polynomial with three terms.

8. A polynomial equation of degree 2 is also called
    a quadratic equation.

9. A positive number is written in scientific
    notation if it is written as the product of a
    number a, such that $1 \leq a < 10$ and a power of
    10.

10. The degree of a polynomial is the largest degree
    of all of its terms.

11. A binomial is a polynomial with two terms.

12. If a and b are real numbers and $a \cdot b = \underline{0}$, then
    $a = 0$ and $b = 0$.

Chapter 5 Review

1. $(-2)^2 = (-2)(-2) = 4$

2. $(-3)^4 = (-3)(-3)(-3)(-3) = 81$

3. $-2^2 = -(2 \cdot 2) = -4$

4. $-3^4 = -(3 \cdot 3 \cdot 3 \cdot 3) = -81$

5. $8^0 = 1$

6. $-9^0 = -1$

7. $-4^{-2} = -\dfrac{1}{4^2} = -\dfrac{1}{16}$

8. $(-4)^2 = \dfrac{1}{(-4)^2} = \dfrac{1}{16}$

9. $-xy^2 \cdot y^3 \cdot xy^2z = -x^{1+1}y^{2+3+2}z = -x^2y^7z$

10. $(-4xy)(-3xy^2b) = (-4)(-3)x^{1+1}y^{1+2}b$
    $$= 12x^2y^3b$$

11. $a^{-14}a^5 = a^{-14+5} = a^{-9} = \dfrac{1}{a^9}$

12. $\dfrac{a^{16}}{a^{17}} = a^{16-17} = a^{-1} = \dfrac{1}{a}$

13. $\dfrac{x^{-7}}{x^4} = x^{-7-4} = x^{-11} = \dfrac{1}{x^{11}}$

14. $\dfrac{9a(a^{-3})}{18a^{15}} = \dfrac{a^{1-3-15}}{2} = \dfrac{a^{-17}}{2} = \dfrac{1}{2a^{17}}$

15. $\dfrac{y^{6p-3}}{y^{6p+2}} = y^{(6p-3)-(6p+2)}$

$\qquad = y^{6p-3-6p-2}$

$\qquad = y^{-5}$

$\qquad = \dfrac{1}{y^5}$

16. $36{,}890{,}000 = 3.689 \times 10^7$

17. $-0.000362 = -3.62 \times 10^{-4}$

18. $1.678 \times 10^{-6} = 0.000001678$

19. $4.1 \times 10^5 = 410{,}000$

20. $(8^5)^3 = 8^{5\cdot3} = 8^{15}$

21. $\left(\dfrac{a}{4}\right)^2 = \dfrac{a^2}{4^2} = \dfrac{a^2}{16}$

22. $(3x)^3 = 3^3 x^3 = 27x^3$

23. $(-4x)^{-2} = \dfrac{1}{(-4x)^2} = \dfrac{1}{(-4)^2 x^2} = \dfrac{1}{16x^2}$

24. $\left(\dfrac{6x}{5}\right)^2 = \dfrac{(6x)^2}{5^2} = \dfrac{36x^2}{25}$

25. $(8^6)^{-3} = 8^{6(-3)} = 8^{-18} = \dfrac{1}{8^{18}}$

26. $\left(\dfrac{4}{3}\right)^{-2} = \dfrac{4^{-2}}{3^{-2}} = \dfrac{3^2}{4^2} = \dfrac{9}{16}$

27. $(-2x^3)^{-3} = \dfrac{1}{(-2x^3)^3}$

$\qquad = \dfrac{1}{(-2)^3 (x^3)^3}$

$\qquad = \dfrac{1}{-8x^9}$

$\qquad = -\dfrac{1}{8x^9}$

28. $\left(\dfrac{8p^6}{4p^4}\right)^{-2} = (2p^2)^{-2} = 2^{-2}p^{-4} = \dfrac{1}{4p^4}$

29. $(-3x^{-2}y^2)^3 = (-3)^3 (x^{-2})^3 (y^2)^3$

$\qquad = -27x^{-6}y^6$

$\qquad = -\dfrac{27y^6}{x^6}$

30. $\left(\dfrac{x^{-5}y^{-3}}{z^3}\right)^{-5} = \dfrac{x^{25}y^{15}}{z^{-15}} = x^{25}y^{15}z^{15}$

31. $\dfrac{4^{-1}x^3 yz}{x^{-2}yx^4} = \dfrac{x^{3-(-2)-4}z}{4} = \dfrac{x^{3+2-4}z}{4} = \dfrac{xz}{4}$

32. $(5xyz)^{-4}(x^{-2})^{-3} = \dfrac{1}{(5xyz)^4}x^6$

$\qquad = \dfrac{x^6}{5^4 x^4 y^4 z^4}$

$\qquad = \dfrac{x^2}{625y^4 z^4}$

33. $\dfrac{2(3yz)^{-3}}{y^{-3}} = \dfrac{2(3)^{-3}y^{-3}z^{-3}}{y^{-3}} = \dfrac{2}{3^3 z^3} = \dfrac{2}{27z^3}$

34. $x^{4a}(3x^{5a})^3 = x^{4a}(3^3 x^{15a})$

$\qquad = 27x^{4a+15a}$

$\qquad = 27x^{19a}$

35. $\dfrac{4y^{3x-3}}{2y^{2x+4}} = 2y^{(3x-3)-(2x+4)}$

$\qquad = 2y^{3x-3-2x-4}$

$\qquad = 2y^{x-7}$

36. $\dfrac{(0.00012)(144{,}000)}{0.0003} = \dfrac{(1.2 \times 10^{-4})(1.44 \times 10^5)}{3 \times 10^{-4}}$

$\qquad = 0.576 \times 10^5$

$\qquad = 5.76 \times 10^4$

37. $\dfrac{(-0.00017)(0.00039)}{3000}$

$= \dfrac{(-1.7\times10^{-4})(3.9\times10^{-4})}{3\times10^3}$

$= -2.21\times10^{-4-4-3}$

$= -2.21\times10^{-11}$

38. $\dfrac{27x^{-5}y^5}{18x^{-6}y^2}\cdot\dfrac{x^4y^{-2}}{x^{-2}y^3} = \dfrac{3x^{-5+4}y^{5-2}}{2x^{-6-2}y^{2+3}}$

$= \dfrac{3x^{-1}y^3}{2x^{-8}y^5}$

$= \dfrac{3}{2}x^{-1-(-8)}y^{3-5}$

$= \dfrac{3}{2}x^7y^{-2}$

$= \dfrac{3x^7}{2y^2}$

39. $\dfrac{3x^5}{y^{-4}}\cdot\dfrac{(3xy^{-3})^{-2}}{(z^{-3})^{-4}} = \dfrac{3x^5\cdot3^{-2}x^{-2}y^6}{y^{-4}z^{12}}$

$= \dfrac{3^{1-2}x^{5-2}y^{6-(-4)}}{z^{12}}$

$= \dfrac{3^{-1}x^3y^{10}}{z^{12}}$

$= \dfrac{x^3y^{10}}{3z^{12}}$

40. $\dfrac{(x^w)^2}{(x^{w-4})^{-2}} = \dfrac{x^{2w}}{x^{-2(w-4)}}$

$= \dfrac{x^{2w}}{x^{-2w+8}}$

$= x^{2w-(-2w+8)}$

$= x^{4w-8}$

41. The degree of the polynomial $x^2y - 3xy^3z + 5x + 7y$ is the degree of the term $-3xy^3z$ which is 5.

42. $3x + 2$ has degree 1.

43. $4x + 8x - 6x^2 - 6x^2y = (4+8)x - 6x^2 - 6x^2y$
$= 12x - 6x^2 - 6x^2y$

44. $-8xy^3 + 4xy^3 - 3x^3y = (-8+4)xy^3 - 3x^3y$
$= -4xy^3 - 3x^3y$

45. $(3x+7y) + (4x^2-3x+7) + (y-1)$
$= 3x + 7y + 4x^2 - 3x + 7 + y - 1$
$= 4x^2 + (3-3)x + (7+1)y + (7-1)$
$= 4x^2 + 8y + 6$

46. $(4x^2 - 6xy + 9y^2) - (8x^2 - 6xy - y^2)$
$= 4x^2 - 6xy + 9y^2 - 8x^2 + 6xy + y^2$
$= (4-8)x^2 + (9+1)y^2$
$= -4x^2 + 10y^2$

47. $(3x^2 - 4b + 28) + (9x^2 - 30) - (4x^2 - 6b + 20)$
$= 3x^2 - 4b + 28 + 9x^2 - 30 - 4x^2 + 6b - 20$
$= (3+9-4)x^2 + (-4+6)b + (28-30-20)$
$= 8x^2 + 2b - 22$

48. $(9xy + 4x^2 + 18) + (7xy - 4x^3 - 9x)$
$= 9xy + 4x^2 + 18 + 7xy - 4x^3 - 9x$
$= -4x^3 + 4x^2 + (9+7)xy - 9x + 18$
$= -4x^3 + 4x^2 + 16xy - 9x + 18$

49. $(3x^2y - 7xy - 4) + (9x^2y + x) - (x - 7)$
$= 3x^2y - 7xy - 4 + 9x^2y + x - x + 7$
$= (3+9)x^2y - 7xy + (-4+7)$
$= 12x^2y - 7xy + 3$

50. $\begin{array}{r} x^2 - 5x + 7 \\ -\quad(x+4) \\ \hline x^2 - 6x + 3 \end{array}$

51. $\begin{array}{r} x^3 \quad\quad + 2xy^2 - y \\ +\quad (x - 4xy^2 \quad\;\; -7) \\ \hline x^3 + x - 2xy^2 - y - 7 \end{array}$

52. $P(6) = 9(6)^2 - 7(6) + 8 = 290$

53. $P(-2) = 9(-2)^2 - 7(-2) + 8 = 58$

54. $P(-3) = 9(-3)^2 - 7(-3) + 8 = 110$

55. $P(x) + Q(x) = (2x - 1) + (x^2 + 2x - 5)$
$$= 2x - 1 + x^2 + 2x - 5$$
$$= x^2 + 4x - 6$$

56. $2[P(x)] - Q(x) = 2(2x - 1) - (x^2 + 2x - 5)$
$$= 4x - 2 - x^2 - 2x + 5$$
$$= -x^2 + 2x + 3$$

57. $2(2x^2 y - 6x + 1) + 2(x^2 y + 5)$
$$= 4x^2 y - 12x + 2 + 2x^2 y + 10$$
$$= (6x^2 y - 12x + 12) \text{ cm}$$

58. $-6x(4x^2 - 6x + 1) = -24x^3 + 36x^2 - 6x$

59. $-4ab^2(3ab^3 + 7ab + 1)$
$$= -4ab^2(3ab^3) - 4ab^2(7ab) - 4ab^2(1)$$
$$= -12a^2 b^5 - 28a^2 b^3 - 4ab^2$$

60. $(x - 4)(2x + 9) = 2x^2 + 9x - 8x - 36$
$$= 2x^2 + x - 36$$

61. $(-3xa + 4b)^2 = (-3xa)^2 + 2(-3xa)(4b) + (4b)^2$
$$= 9x^2 a^2 - 24xab + 16b^2$$

62.
$$
\begin{array}{r}
9x^2 + 4x + 1 \\
4x - 3 \\
\hline
-27x^2 - 12x - 3 \\
36x^3 + 16x^2 \quad + 4x \\
\hline
36x^3 - 11x^2 \quad - 8x - 3
\end{array}
$$

63. $(5x - 9y)(3x + 9y) = 15x^2 + 45xy - 27xy + 81y^2$
$$= 15x^2 + 18xy - 81y^2$$

64. $\left(x - \dfrac{1}{3}\right)\left(x + \dfrac{2}{3}\right) = x^2 + \dfrac{2}{3}x - \dfrac{1}{3}x - \dfrac{1}{3}\left(\dfrac{2}{3}\right)$
$$= x^2 + \dfrac{1}{3}x - \dfrac{2}{9}$$

65. $(x^2 + 9x + 1)^2$
$$= (x^2 + 9x + 1)(x^2 + 9x + 1)$$
$$= x^2(x^2 + 9x + 1) + 9x(x^2 + 9x + 1) + 1(x^2 + 9x + 1)$$
$$= x^4 + 9x^3 + x^2 + 9x^3 + 81x^2 + 9x + x^2 + 9x + 1$$
$$= x^4 + 18x^3 + 83x^2 + 18x + 1$$

66. $(3x - y)^2 = (3x)^2 - 2(3x)y + y^2$
$$= 9x^2 - 6xy + y^2$$

67. $(4x + 9)^2 = (4x)^2 + 2(4x)(9) + 9^2$
$$= 16x^2 + 72x + 81$$

68. $(x + 3y)(x - 3y) = x^2 - (3y)^2 = x^2 - 9y^2$

69. $[4 + (3a - b)][4 - (3a - b)]$
$$= 4^2 - (3a - b)^2$$
$$= 16 - [(3a)^2 - 2(3a)b + b^2]$$
$$= 16 - (9a^2 - 6ab + b^2)$$
$$= 16 - 9a^2 + 6ab - b^2$$

70. $P(x) \cdot Q(x)$
$$= (2x - 1)(x^2 + 2x - 5)$$
$$= 2x(x^2 + 2x - 5) - 1(x^2 + 2x - 5)$$
$$= 2x^3 + 4x^2 - 10x - x^2 - 2x + 5$$
$$= 2x^3 + 3x^2 - 12x + 5$$

71. $\text{Area} = lw$
$$= (3y + 7z)(3y - 7z)$$
$$= (3y)^2 - (7z)^2$$
$$= (9y^2 - 49z^2) \text{ square units}$$

72. $4a^b(3a^{b+2} - 7) = 4a^b(3a^{b+2}) + 4a^b(-7)$
$$= 12a^{b+b+2} - 28a^b$$
$$= 12a^{2b+2} - 28a^b$$

73. $(4xy^z - b)^2 = (4xy^z)^2 - 2(4xy^z)b + b^2$
$$= 4^2 x^2 (y^z)^2 - 8xy^z b + b^2$$
$$= 16x^2 y^{2z} - 8xy^z b + b^2$$

74. $(3x^a - 4)(3x^a + 4) = (3x^a)^2 - 4^2$
$$= 3^2 (x^a)^2 - 16$$
$$= 9x^{2a} - 16$$

75. $16x^3 - 24x^2 = 8x^2(2x - 3)$

76. $36y - 24y^2 = 12y(3 - 2y)$

77. $6ab^2 + 8ab - 4a^2 b^2 = 2ab(3b + 4 - 2ab)$

78. $14a^2 b^2 - 21ab^2 + 7ab = 7ab(2ab - 3b + 1)$

79. $6a(a+3b)-5(a+3b)=(6a-5)(a+3b)$

80. $4x(x-2y)-5(x-2y)=(4x-5)(x-2y)$

81. $xy-6y+3x-18=y(x-6)+3(x-6)$
$\qquad = (y+3)(x-6)$

82. $ab-8b+4a-32=b(a-8)+4(a-8)$
$\qquad = (b+4)(a-8)$

83. $pq-3p-5q+15=p(q-3)-5(q-3)$
$\qquad = (p-5)(q-3)$

84. $x^3-x^2-2x+2=x^2(x-1)-2(x-1)$
$\qquad = (x^2-2)(x-1)$

85. Area $= 2xy-x^2 = x(2y-x)$ sq units

86. $x^2-14x-72=(x-18)(x+4)$

87. $x^2+16x-80=(x-4)(x+20)$

88. $2x^2-18x+28=2(x^2-9x+14)$
$\qquad = 2(x-7)(x-2)$

89. $3x^2+33x+54=3(x^2+11x+18)$
$\qquad = 3(x+9)(x+2)$

90. $2x^3-7x^2-9x=x(2x^2-7x-9)$
$\qquad = x(2x-9)(x+1)$

91. $3x^2+2x-16=(3x+8)(x-2)$

92. $6x^2+17x+10=(6x+5)(x+2)$

93. $15x^2-91x+6=(15x-1)(x-6)$

94. $4x^2+2x-12=2(2x^2+x-6)$
$\qquad = 2(2x-3)(x+2)$

95. $9x^2-12x-12=3(3x^2-4x-4)$
$\qquad = 3(3x+2)(x-2)$

96. $y^2(x+6)^2-2y(x+6)^2-3(x+6)^2$
$= (x+6)^2(y^2-2y-3)$
$= (x+6)^2(y-3)(y+1)$

97. Let $y=x+5$. Then
$(x+5)^2+6(x+5)+8=y^2+6y+8$
$\qquad = (y+4)(y+2)$
$\qquad = [(x+5)+4][(x+5)+2]$
$\qquad = (x+9)(x+7)$

98. $x^4-6x^2-16=(x^2-8)(x^2+2)$

99. $x^4+8x^2-20=(x^2+10)(x^2-2)$

100. $x^2-100=x^2-10^2=(x+10)(x-10)$

101. $x^2-81=x^2-9^2=(x+9)(x-9)$

102. $2x^2-32=2(x^2-16)$
$\qquad = 2(x^2-4^2)$
$\qquad = 2(x+4)(x-4)$

103. $6x^2-54=6(x^2-9)$
$\qquad = 6(x^2-3^2)$
$\qquad = 6(x+3)(x-3)$

104. $81-x^4=9^2-(x^2)^2$
$\qquad = (9+x^2)(9-x^2)$
$\qquad = (9+x^2)(3+x)(3-x)$

105. $16-y^4=4^2-(y^2)^2$
$\qquad = (4+y^2)(4-y^2)$
$\qquad = (4+y^2)(2+y)(2-y)$

106. $(y+2)^2-25=(y+2)^2-5^2$
$\qquad = [(y+2)+5][(y+2)-5]$
$\qquad = (y+7)(y-3)$

107. $(x-3)^2-16=(x-3)^2-4^2$
$\qquad = [(x-3)+4][(x-3)-4]$
$\qquad = (x+1)(x-7)$

108. $x^3+216=x^3+6^3$
$\qquad = (x+6)(x^2-6\cdot x+6^2)$
$\qquad = (x+6)(x^2-6x+36)$

109. $y^3 + 512 = y^3 + 8^3$

$\qquad = (y+8)(y^2 - 8 \cdot y + 8^2)$

$\qquad = (y+8)(y^2 - 8y + 64)$

110. $8 - 27y^3 = 2^3 - (3y)^3$

$\qquad = (2 - 3y)(4 + 2 \cdot 3y + (3y)^2)$

$\qquad = (2 - 3y)(4 + 6y + 9y^2)$

111. $1 - 64y^3 = 1^3 - (4y)^3$

$\qquad = (1 - 4y)(1^2 + 1 \cdot 4y + (4y)^2)$

$\qquad = (1 - 4y)(1 + 4y + 16y^2)$

112. $6x^4 y + 48xy = 6xy(x^3 + 8)$

$\qquad = 6xy(x^3 + 2^3)$

$\qquad = 6xy(x+2)(x^2 - 2x + 2^2)$

$\qquad = 6xy(x+2)(x^2 - 2x + 4)$

113. $2x^5 + 16x^2 y^3 = 2x^2(x^3 + 8y^3)$

$\qquad = 2x^2(x^3 + (2y)^3)$

$\qquad = 2x^2(x + 2y)(x^2 - x \cdot 2y + (2y)^2)$

$\qquad = 2x^2(x + 2y)(x^2 - 2xy + 4y^2)$

114. $x^2 - 2x + 1 - y^2 = (x^2 - 2x + 1) - y^2$

$\qquad = (x-1)^2 - y^2$

$\qquad = [(x-1)+y][(x-1)-y]$

$\qquad = (x-1+y)(x-1-y)$

115. $x^2 - 6x + 9 - 4y^2 = (x^2 - 6x + 9) - 4y^2$

$\qquad = (x-3)^2 - (2y)^2$

$\qquad = [(x-3)+2y][(x-3)-2y]$

$\qquad = (x-3+2y)(x-3-2y)$

116. $4x^2 + 12x + 9 = (2x+3)(2x+3)$

$\qquad = (2x+3)^2$

117. $16a^2 - 40ab + 25b^2 = (4a - 5b)(4a - 5b)$

$\qquad = (4a - 5b)^2$

118. Volume $= \pi R^2 h - \pi r^2 h$

$\qquad = \pi h(R^2 - r^2)$

$\qquad = \pi h(R + r)(R - r)$ cubic units

119. $(3x - 1)(x + 7) = 0$

$\quad 3x - 1 = 0$ or $x + 7 = 0$

$\quad x = \dfrac{1}{3}$ or $\quad x = -7$

The solutions are $-7, \dfrac{1}{3}$.

120. $3(x+5)(8x-3) = 0$

$\quad x + 5 = 0$ or $8x - 3 = 0$

$\quad x = -5$ or $\quad x = \dfrac{3}{8}$

The solutions are $-5, \dfrac{3}{8}$.

121. $5x(x - 4)(2x - 9) = 0$

$\quad 5x = 0$ or $x - 4 = 0$ or $2x - 9 = 0$

$\quad x = 0$ or $\quad x = 4$ or $\quad x = \dfrac{9}{2}$

The solutions are $0, 4, \dfrac{9}{2}$.

122. $6(x + 3)(x - 4)(5x + 1) = 0$

$\quad x + 3 = 0$ or $x - 4 = 0$ or $5x + 1 = 0$

$\quad x = -3$ or $\quad x = 4$ or $\quad 5x = -1$

$\qquad\qquad\qquad\qquad\qquad\qquad x = -\dfrac{1}{5}$

The solutions are $-\dfrac{1}{5}, -3, 4$.

123. $\qquad 2x^2 = 12x$

$\quad 2x^2 - 12x = 0$

$\quad 2x(x - 6) = 0$

$\quad 2x = 0$ or $x - 6 = 0$

$\quad x = 0$ or $\quad x = 6$

The solutions are $0, 6$.

124. $\qquad 4x^3 - 36x = 0$

$\qquad 4x(x^2 - 9) = 0$

$\quad 4x(x + 3)(x - 3) = 0$

$\quad 4x = 0$ or $x + 3 = 0$ or $x - 3 = 0$

$\quad x = 0$ or $\quad x = -3$ or $\quad x = 3$

The solutions are $-3, 0, 3$.

125.
$$(1-x)(3x+2) = -4x$$
$$3x+2-3x^2-2x = -4x$$
$$-3x^2+x+2 = -4x$$
$$-3x^2+5x+2 = 0$$
$$3x^2-5x-2 = 0$$
$$(3x+1)(x-2) = 0$$
$$3x+1 = 0 \quad \text{or} \quad x-2 = 0$$
$$3x = -1 \text{ or} \quad x = 2$$
$$x = -\frac{1}{3}$$

The solutions are $-\dfrac{1}{3}$, 2.

126.
$$2x(x-12) = -40$$
$$2x^2-24x = -40$$
$$2x^2-24x+40 = 0$$
$$2(x^2-12x+20) = 0$$
$$2(x-10)(x-2) = 0$$
$$x-10 = 0 \quad \text{or} \quad x-2 = 0$$
$$x = 10 \text{ or} \quad x = 2$$

The solutions are 2, 10.

127.
$$3x^2+2x = 12-7x$$
$$3x^2+9x-12 = 0$$
$$3(x^2+3x-4) = 0$$
$$3(x+4)(x-1) = 0$$
$$x+4 = 0 \quad \text{or} \quad x-1 = 0$$
$$x = -4 \text{ or} \quad x = 1$$

The solutions are –4, 1.

128.
$$2x^2+3x = 35$$
$$2x^2+3x-35 = 0$$
$$(2x-7)(x+5) = 0$$
$$2x-7 = 0 \quad \text{or} \quad x+5 = 0$$
$$2x = 7 \text{ or} \quad x = -5$$
$$x = \frac{7}{2}$$

The solutions are -5, $\dfrac{7}{2}$.

129.
$$x^3-18x = 3x^2$$
$$x^3-3x^2-18x = 0$$
$$x(x^2-3x-18) = 0$$
$$x(x-6)(x+3) = 0$$
$$x = 0 \quad \text{or} \quad x-6 = 0 \quad \text{or} \quad x+3 = 0$$
$$x = 6 \text{ or} \quad x = -3$$

The solutions are –3, 0, 6.

130.
$$19x^2-42x = -x^3$$
$$x^3+19x^2-42x = 0$$
$$x(x^2+19x-42) = 0$$
$$x(x+21)(x-2) = 0$$
$$x = 0 \quad \text{or} \quad x+21 = 0 \quad \text{or} \quad x-2 = 0$$
$$x = -21 \text{ or} \quad x = 2$$

The solutions are –21, 0, 2.

131.
$$12x = 6x^3+6x^2$$
$$-6x^3-6x^2+12x = 0$$
$$-6x(x^2+x-2) = 0$$
$$-6x(x+2)(x-1) = 0$$
$$-6x = 0 \quad \text{or} \quad x+2 = 0 \quad \text{or} \quad x-1 = 0$$
$$x = 0 \text{ or} \quad x = -2 \text{ or} \quad x = 1$$

The solutions are –2, 0, 1.

132.
$$8x^3+10x^2 = 3x$$
$$8x^3+10x^2-3x = 0$$
$$x(8x^2+10x-3) = 0$$
$$x(4x-1)(2x+3) = 0$$
$$x = 0 \quad \text{or} \quad 4x-1 = 0 \quad \text{or} \quad 2x+3 = 0$$
$$4x = 1 \text{ or} \quad 2x = -3$$
$$x = \frac{1}{4} \text{ or} \quad x = -\frac{3}{2}$$

The solutions are $-\dfrac{3}{2}$, 0, $\dfrac{1}{4}$.

133. Let x = the number. Then
$$x+2x^2 = 105$$
$$2x^2+x-105 = 0$$
$$(2x+15)(x-7) = 0$$
$$2x+15 = 0 \quad \text{or} \quad x-7 = 0$$
$$2x = -15 \text{ or} \quad x = 7$$
$$x = -\frac{15}{2}$$

The number is $-\dfrac{15}{2}$ or 7.

134. Let x = width; then $2x - 5$ = length.
$$x(2x - 5) = 33$$
$$2x^2 - 5x = 33$$
$$2x^2 - 5x - 33 = 0$$
$$(2x - 11)(x + 3) = 0$$
$$2x - 11 = 0 \quad \text{or} \quad x + 3 = 0$$
$$2x = 11 \quad \text{or} \qquad x = -3$$
$$x = \frac{11}{2}$$
Disregard the negative.
Width = $\dfrac{11}{2} = 5\dfrac{1}{2}$ m

Length = $2\left(\dfrac{11}{2}\right) - 5 = 6$ m

135. $h(t) = -16t^2 + 400$
$$0 = -16t^2 + 400$$
$$0 = -16(t^2 - 25)$$
$$0 = -16(t + 5)(t - 5)$$
$$t + 5 = 0 \quad \text{or} \quad t - 5 = 0$$
$$t = -5 \quad \text{or} \qquad t = 5$$
Disregard the negative. The stunt dummy will reach the ground after 5 seconds.

136. $P(t) = -16t^2 + 1053$

$P(1) = -16(1)^2 + 1053 = -16 + 1053 = 1037$

$P(8) = -16(8)^2 + 1053 = -1024 + 1053 = 29$

After 1 second, the object is at 1037 feet and after 8 seconds, the object is at 29 feet.

137. $(x + 5)(3x^2 - 2x + 1)$
$$= x(3x^2 - 2x + 1) + 5(3x^2 - 2x + 1)$$
$$= 3x^3 - 2x^2 + x + 15x^2 - 10x + 5$$
$$= 3x^3 + 13x^2 - 9x + 5$$

138. $(3x^2 + 4x - 1.2) - (5x^2 - x + 5.7)$
$$= 3x^2 + 4x - 1.2 - 5x^2 + x - 5.7$$
$$= -2x^2 + 5x - 6.9$$

139. $(3x^2 + 4x - 1.2) + (5x^2 - x + 5.7)$
$$= 3x^2 + 4x - 1.2 + 5x^2 - x + 5.7$$
$$= 8x^2 + 3x + 4.5$$

140. $\left(7ab - \dfrac{1}{2}\right)^2 = (7ab)^2 - 2(7ab)\left(\dfrac{1}{2}\right) + \left(\dfrac{1}{2}\right)^2$
$$= 49a^2b^2 - 7ab + \dfrac{1}{4}$$

141. $P(x) = -x^2 + x - 4$

$P(5) = -5^2 + 5 - 4 = -25 + 5 - 4 = -24$

142. $P(x) = -x^2 + x - 4$

$P(-2) = -(-2)^2 + (-2) - 4 = -4 - 2 - 4 = -10$

143. $12y^5 - 6y^4 = 6y^4(2y) + 6y^4(-1) = 6y^4(2y - 1)$

144. $x^2y + 4x^2 - 3y - 12 = x^2(y + 4) - 3(y + 4)$
$$= (y + 4)(x^2 - 3)$$

145. $6x^2 - 34x - 12 = 2(3x^2 - 17x - 6)$
$$= 2(3x + 1)(x - 6)$$

146. $y^2(4x + 3)^2 - 19y(4x + 3)^2 - 20(4x + 3)^2$
$$= (4x + 3)^2(y^2 - 19y - 20)$$
$$= (4x + 3)^2(y - 20)(y + 1)$$

147. $4z^7 - 49z^5 = z^5(4z^2 - 49)$
$$= z^5[(2z)^2 - 7^2]$$
$$= z^5(2z + 7)(2z - 7)$$

148. $5x^4 + 4x^2 - 9 = (x^2 - 1)(5x^2 + 9)$
$$= (x + 1)(x - 1)(5x^2 + 9)$$

149.
$$8x^2 = 24x$$
$$8x^2 - 24x = 0$$
$$8x(x - 3) = 0$$
$$8x = 0 \quad \text{or} \quad x - 3 = 0$$
$$x = 0 \quad \text{or} \qquad x = 3$$

150.
$$x(x - 11) = 26$$
$$x^2 - 11x = 26$$
$$x^2 - 11x - 26 = 0$$
$$(x + 2)(x - 13) = 0$$
$$x + 2 = 0 \quad \text{or} \quad x - 13 = 0$$
$$x = -2 \quad \text{or} \qquad x = 13$$

Chapter 5 Test

1. $(-9x)^{-2} = \dfrac{1}{(-9x)^2} = \dfrac{1}{81x^2}$

2. $-3xy^{-2}(4xy^2)z = -12x^{1+1}y^{-2+2}z = -12x^2z$

3. $\dfrac{6^{-1}a^2b^{-3}}{3^{-2}a^{-5}b^2} = \dfrac{3^2\,a^{2+5}}{6^1\,b^{2+3}} = \dfrac{9a^7}{6b^5} = \dfrac{3a^7}{2b^5}$

4. $\left(\dfrac{-xy^{-5}z}{xy^3}\right)^{-5} = \dfrac{-x^{-5}y^{25}z^{-5}}{x^{-5}y^{-15}}$

$\qquad = \dfrac{x^{-5+5}y^{25-(-15)}}{z^5}$

$\qquad = -\dfrac{y^{40}}{z^5}$

5. $630,000,000 = 6.3\times10^8$

6. $0.01200 = 1.2\times10^{-2}$

7. $5\times10^{-6} = 0.000005$

8. $\dfrac{(0.0024)(0.00012)}{0.00032} = \dfrac{(2.4\times10^{-3})(1.2\times10^{-4})}{3.2\times10^{-4}}$

$\qquad = \dfrac{(2.4)(1.2)}{3.2}\times10^{-3+(-4)-(-4)}$

$\qquad = 0.9\times10^{-3}$

$\qquad = 0.0009$

9. $(4x^3y - 3x - 4) - (9x^3y + 8x + 5)$

$\qquad = 4x^3y - 3x - 4 - 9x^3y - 8x - 5$

$\qquad = -5x^3y - 11x - 9$

10. $-3xy(4x + y) = -3xy(4x) - 3xy(y)$

$\qquad = -12x^2y - 3xy^2$

11. $(3x + 4)(4x - 7) = 12x^2 - 21x + 16x - 28$

$\qquad = 12x^2 - 5x - 28$

12. $(5a - 2b)(5a + 2b) = (5a)^2 - (2b)^2 = 25a^2 - 4b^2$

13. $(6m + n)^2 = (6m)^2 + 2(6m)n + n^2$

$\qquad = 36m^2 + 12mn + n^2$

14.

$$\begin{array}{r} x^2 - 6x + 4 \\ \times \qquad\quad 2x - 1 \\ \hline -x^2 + 6x - 4 \\ 2x^3 - 12x^2 + 8x \qquad \\ \hline 2x^3 - 13x^2 + 14x - 4 \end{array}$$

15. $16x^3y - 12x^2y^4 = 4x^2y(4x - 3y^3)$

16. $x^2 - 13x - 30 = (x - 15)(x + 2)$

17. $4y^2 + 20y + 25 = (2y + 5)(2y + 5)$

$\qquad = (2y + 5)^2$

18. $6x^2 - 15x - 9 = 3(2x^2 - 5x - 3)$

$\qquad = 3(2x + 1)(x - 3)$

19. $4x^2 - 25 = (2x)^2 - 5^2 = (2x + 5)(2x - 5)$

20. $x^3 + 64 = x^3 + 4^3 = (x + 4)(x^2 - 4x + 16)$

21. $3x^2y - 27y^3 = 3y(x^2 - 9y^2)$

$\qquad = 3y(x^2 - (3y)^2)$

$\qquad = 3y(x + 3y)(x - 3y)$

22. $6x^2 + 24 = 6(x^2 + 4)$

23. $16y^3 - 2 = 2(8y^3 - 1)$

$\qquad = 2((2y)^3 - 1^3)$

$\qquad = 2(2y - 1)(4y^2 + 2y + 1)$

24. $x^2y - 9y - 3x^2 + 27 = y(x^2 - 9) - 3(x^2 - 9)$

$\qquad = (x^2 - 9)(y - 3)$

$\qquad = (x + 3)(x - 3)(y - 3)$

25.

$\qquad 3n(7n - 20) = 96$

$\qquad 21n^2 - 60n = 96$

$\qquad 21n^2 - 60n - 96 = 0$

$\qquad 3(7n^2 - 20n - 32) = 0$

$\qquad 3(7n + 8)(n - 4) = 0$

$$7n + 8 = 0 \quad \text{or} \quad n - 4 = 0$$
$$7n = -8 \quad \text{or} \quad n = 4$$
$$n = -\frac{8}{7}$$

The solutions are $-\frac{8}{7}$, 4.

26. $(x+2)(x-2) = 5(x+4)$

$$x^2 - 4 = 5x + 20$$
$$x^2 - 5x - 24 = 0$$
$$(x-8)(x+3) = 0$$
$$x - 8 = 0 \quad \text{or} \quad x + 3 = 0$$
$$x = 8 \quad \text{or} \quad x = -3$$

The solutions are 8, –3.

27. $\quad 2x^3 + 5x^2 - 8x - 20 = 0$

$$x^2(2x+5) - 4(2x+5) = 0$$
$$(2x+5)(x^2-4) = 0$$
$$(2x+5)(x+2)(x-2) = 0$$

$$2x + 5 = 0 \quad \text{or} \quad x + 2 = 0 \quad \text{or} \quad x - 2 = 0$$
$$2x = -5 \quad \text{or} \quad x = -2 \quad \text{or} \quad x = 2$$
$$x = -\frac{5}{2}$$

The solutions are $-\frac{5}{2}, -2, 2$.

28. Area $= x^2 - (2y)^2$
$$= (x+2y)(x-2y) \text{ square units}$$

29. $h(t) = -16t^2 + 96t + 880$

a. $\quad -16(1)^2 + 96(1) + 880 = -16 + 96 + 880$
$$= 960 \text{ feet}$$

b. $\quad -16(5.1)^2 + 96(5.1) + 880$
$$= -416.16 + 489.6 + 880$$
$$= 953.44 \text{ feet}$$

c. $\qquad\qquad 0 = -16t^2 + 96t + 880$
$$16t^2 - 96t - 880 = 0$$
$$16(t^2 - 6t - 55) = 0$$
$$(t-11)(t+5) = 0$$
$$t - 11 = 0 \quad \text{or} \quad t + 5 = 0$$
$$t = 11 \quad \text{or} \quad t = -5$$

Disregard the negative. The pebble will hit the ground in 11 seconds.

Chapter 5 Cumulative Review

1. a. $\sqrt[3]{27} = 3$ since $3^3 = 27$.

   b. $\sqrt[5]{1} = 1$ since $1^5 = 1$.

   c. $\sqrt[4]{16} = 2$ since $2^4 = 16$.

2. a. $\sqrt[3]{64} = 4$ since $4^3 = 64$.

   b. $\sqrt[4]{81} = 3$ since $3^4 = 81$.

   c. $\sqrt[5]{32} = 2$ since $2^5 = 32$.

3. $2(x-3) = 5x - 9$
$$2x - 6 = 5x - 9$$
$$-3x = -3$$
$$x = 1$$

The solution is 1.

4. $\qquad 0.3y + 2.4 = 0.1y + 4$
$$10(0.3y + 2.4) = 10(0.1y + 4)$$
$$3y + 24 = y + 40$$
$$2y = 16$$
$$y = 8$$

The solution is 8.

5. $\quad A = 10,000\left(1 + \dfrac{0.05}{4}\right)^{4(3)}$
$$= 10,000(1.0125)^{12}$$
$$= 10,000(1.160754518)$$
$$= 11,607.54518$$

There will be $11,607.55 in the account.

6. The area of the room is
$2(14 \cdot 8) + 2(18 \cdot 8) = 512$ sq ft. Two coats means
$2 \cdot 512 = 1024$ sq ft of wall needs paint.

$$\frac{1}{400} = \frac{x}{1024}$$
$$1024\left(\frac{1}{400}\right) = 1024\left(\frac{x}{512}\right)$$
$$2.56 = x$$
$$x \approx 3$$

3 gallons of paint are needed.

7. a. $\dfrac{1}{4}x \le \dfrac{3}{8}$

$8\left(\dfrac{1}{4}x\right) \le 8\left(\dfrac{3}{8}\right)$

$2x \le 3$

$x \le \dfrac{3}{2}$

$\left\{ x \,\middle|\, x \le \dfrac{3}{2} \right\}$ or $\left(-\infty, \dfrac{3}{2}\right]$

$\dfrac{3}{2}$

b. $-2.3x < 6.9$

$10(-2.3x) < 10(6.9)$

$-23x < 69$

$\dfrac{-23x}{-23} > \dfrac{69}{-23}$

$x > -3$

$\{x \mid x > -3\}$ or $(-3, \infty)$

-3

8. $x + 2 \le \dfrac{1}{4}(x - 7)$

$4(x + 2) \le 4\left[\dfrac{1}{4}(x - 7)\right]$

$4x + 8 \le x - 7$

$3x \le -15$

$x \le -5$

$\{x \mid x \le -5\}$ or $(-\infty, -5]$

-5

9. $-1 \le \dfrac{2x}{3} + 5 \le 2$

$3(-1) \le 3\left(\dfrac{2x}{3} + 5\right) \le 3(2)$

$-3 \le 2x + 15 \le 6$

$-18 \le 2x \le -9$

$-9 \le x \le -\dfrac{9}{2}$

$\left[-9, -\dfrac{9}{2}\right]$

10. $-\dfrac{1}{3} < \dfrac{3x + 1}{6} \le \dfrac{1}{3}$

$6\left(-\dfrac{1}{3}\right) < 6\left(\dfrac{3x + 1}{6}\right) \le 6\left(\dfrac{1}{3}\right)$

$-2 < 3x + 1 \le 2$

$-3 < 3x \le 1$

$-1 < x \le \dfrac{1}{3}$

$\left(-1, \dfrac{1}{3}\right]$

11. $|y| = 0$

$y = 0$

The solution is 0.

12. $8 + |4c| = 24$

$|4c| = 16$

$4c = 16$ or $4c = -16$

$c = 4$ or $c = -4$

The solutions are –4, 4.

13. $\left|2x - \dfrac{1}{10}\right| < -13$ is impossible; $\varnothing$.

14. $|5x - 1| + 9 > 5$

$|5x - 1| > -4$ is always true.

$(-\infty, \infty)$

15. $y = \dfrac{1}{3}x$

16. $y = 3x$

17. $f(x) = \begin{cases} 2x+3 & \text{if } x \le 0 \\ -x-1 & \text{if } x > 0 \end{cases}$

$f(2) = -2 - 1 = -3: (2, -3)$

$f(-6) = 2(-6) + 3 = -9: (-6, -9)$

$f(0) = 2(0) + 3 = 3: (0, 3)$

18. $f(x) = 3x^2 + 2x + 3$

$\begin{aligned} f(-3) &= 3(-3)^2 + 2(-3) + 3 \\ &= 3(9) - 6 + 3 \\ &= 27 - 6 + 3 \\ &= 24 \end{aligned}$

19. $x = 2$

20. $y - 5 = 0$

     $y = 5$

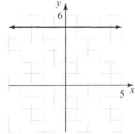

21. $y = 2$

This is a horizontal line.

$m = 0$

22. $f(x) = -2x - 3$

     $m = -2$

23. $y = 3$

24. $x = -3$

25. $x + \dfrac{1}{2}y \ge -4 \qquad \text{or } y \le -2$

     $\dfrac{1}{2}y \ge -x - 4 \quad \text{or } y \le -2$

       $y \ge -2x - 8 \text{ or } y \le -2$

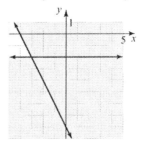

26. $y - 3 = 0[x - (-2)]$

     $y - 3 = 0$

       $y = 3$

27. $\begin{cases} 2x + 4y = -6 & (1) \\ x = 2y - 5 & (2) \end{cases}$

Substitute $2y - 5$ for x in E1.

$2(2y - 5) + 4y = -6$

   $4y - 10 + 4y = -6$

         $8y = 4$

          $y = \dfrac{1}{2}$

Substitute $\dfrac{1}{2}$ for y in E2.

$x = 2\left(\dfrac{1}{2}\right) - 5 = 1 - 5 = -4$

The solution is $\left(-4, \dfrac{1}{2}\right)$.

28. $\begin{cases} 4x - 2y = 8 & (1) \\ y = 3x - 6 & (2) \end{cases}$

Substitute $3x - 6$ for y in E1.

$4x - 2(3x - 6) = 8$

  $4x - 6x + 12 = 8$

        $-2x = -4$

           $x = 2$

Substitute 2 for x in E2.

$y = 3(2) - 6 = 6 - 6 = 0$

The solution is $(2, 0)$.

29. $\begin{cases} 2x + 4y = 1 & (1) \\ 4x - 4z = -1 & (2) \\ y - 4z = -3 & (3) \end{cases}$

Multiply E2 by -1 and add to E3.

$$-4x \quad\quad + 4z = 1$$
$$\underline{\quad\quad y - 4z = -3}$$
$$-4x + y \quad\quad = -2 \quad (4)$$

Muliply E1 by 2 and add to E4.
$$4x + 8y = 2$$
$$\underline{-4x \; + y = -2}$$
$$9y = 0$$
$$y = 0$$

Replace y with 0 in E1.
$$2x + 4(0) = 1$$
$$2x = 1$$
$$x = \frac{1}{2}$$

Replace y with 0 in E3.
$$y - 4z = -3$$
$$-4z = -3$$
$$z = \frac{3}{4}$$

The solution is $\left(\dfrac{1}{2}, 0, \dfrac{3}{4}\right)$.

30. $\begin{cases} x + y - \dfrac{3}{2}z = \dfrac{1}{2} & (1) \\ -y - 2z = 14 & (2) \\ x - \dfrac{2}{3}y = -\dfrac{1}{3} & (3) \end{cases}$

Multiply E1 by 2 and E3 by 3 to clear fractions.
$$\begin{cases} 2x + 2y - 3z = 1 & (1) \\ -y - 2z = 14 & (2) \\ 3x - 2y = -1 & (3) \end{cases}$$

Add E1 and E3.
$$5x - 3z = 0 \quad (4)$$
Multiply E2 by 2 and add to E1.
$$-2y - 4z = 28$$
$$\underline{2x + 2y - 3z = 1}$$
$$2x \quad\quad - 7z = 29 \quad (5)$$

Solve the new system $\begin{cases} 5x - 3z = 0 & (4) \\ 2x - 7z = 29 & (5) \end{cases}$.

Multiply E4 by –2, multiply E5 by 5, and add.
$$-10x + 6z = 0$$
$$\underline{10x - 35z = 145}$$
$$-29z = 145$$
$$z = -5$$

Replace z with –5 in E4.
$$5x - 3(-5) = 0$$
$$5x + 15 = 0$$
$$5x = -15$$
$$x = -3$$

Replace z with –5 in E2.

$$-y - 2(-5) = 14$$
$$-y + 10 = 14$$
$$-y = 4$$
$$y = -4$$

The solution is (–3, –4, –5).

31. Let x = the first number and y = the second number.
$$\begin{cases} x = y - 4 & (1) \\ 4x = 2y + 6 & (2) \end{cases}$$

Multiply E1 by –4 and add to E2.
$$-4x = -4y + 16$$
$$\underline{4x = 2y + 6}$$
$$0 = -2y + 22$$
$$2y = 22$$
$$y = 11$$

Replace y with 11 in E1.
$$x = 11 - 4 = 7$$
The numbers are 7 and 11.

32. Let x = ounces of 20% solution and y = ounces of 60% solution.
$$\begin{cases} x + y = 50 & (1) \\ 0.20x + 0.60y = 50(0.30) & (2) \end{cases}$$

Multiply E2 by 100 to clear decimals.
$$\begin{cases} x + y = 50 & (1) \\ 20x + 60y = 1500 & (2) \end{cases}$$

Multiply E1 by –20 and add to E2.
$$-20x - 20y = -1000$$
$$\underline{20x + 60y = 1500}$$
$$40y = 500$$
$$y = \frac{500}{40} = 12.5$$

Replace y with 12.5 in E1.
$$x + 12.5 = 50$$
$$x = 37.5$$
You should mix 37.5 ounces of the 20% solution and 12.5 ounces of the 60% solution.

33. $\begin{cases} 2x - y = 3 \\ 4x - 2y = 5 \end{cases}$

$$\begin{bmatrix} 2 & -1 & | & 3 \\ 4 & -2 & | & 5 \end{bmatrix}$$

Divide R1 by 2.
$$\begin{bmatrix} 1 & -\frac{1}{2} & | & \frac{3}{2} \\ 4 & -2 & | & 5 \end{bmatrix}$$

Multiply R1 by –4 and add to R2.
$$\begin{bmatrix} 1 & -\frac{1}{2} & | & \frac{3}{2} \\ 0 & 0 & | & -1 \end{bmatrix}$$

This corresponds to $\begin{cases} x - \dfrac{1}{2}y = \dfrac{3}{2} \\ 0 = -1 \end{cases}$. The last

equation is impossible. The system is inconsistent. The solution set is $\varnothing$.

34. $\begin{cases} 4y = 8 \\ x + y = 7 \end{cases}$

$\begin{bmatrix} 0 & 4 & | & 8 \\ 1 & 1 & | & 7 \end{bmatrix}$

Interchange R1 and R2.

$\begin{bmatrix} 1 & 1 & | & 7 \\ 0 & 4 & | & 8 \end{bmatrix}$

Divide R2 by 4.

$\begin{bmatrix} 1 & 1 & | & 7 \\ 0 & 1 & | & 2 \end{bmatrix}$

This corresponds to $\begin{cases} x + y = 7 \\ y = 2 \end{cases}$.

Replace y with 2 in the equation $x + y = 7$.
$x + 2 = 7$
$\quad x = 5$
The solution is $(5, 2)$.

35. Let x = measure of smallest angle, then
$x + 80$ = measure of largest angle, and
$x + 10$ = measure of remaining angle.
$x + (x + 80) + (x + 10) = 180$
$\qquad 3x + 90 = 180$
$\qquad\qquad 3x = 90$
$\qquad\qquad\quad x = 30$
$x + 80 = 110$
$x + 10 = 40$
The angles measure $30°$, $110°$, and $40°$.

36. $m = \dfrac{1}{2}$, y-intercept $(0, 5)$, $b = 5$
$\quad y = mx + b$
$\quad y = \dfrac{1}{2}x + 5$
$\quad f(x) = \dfrac{1}{2}x + 5$

37. a. $730,000 = 7.3 \times 10^5$

b. $0.00000104 = 1.04 \times 10^{-6}$

38. a. $8,250,000 = 8.25 \times 10^6$

b. $0.0000346 = 3.46 \times 10^{-5}$

39. a. $(2x^0 y^{-3})^{-2} = 2^{-2}(1)^{-2}(y^{-3})^{-2} = \dfrac{y^6}{2^2} = \dfrac{y^6}{4}$

b. $\left(\dfrac{x^{-5}}{x^{-2}}\right)^{-3} = \dfrac{(x^{-5})^{-3}}{(x^{-2})^{-3}} = \dfrac{x^{15}}{x^6} = x^{15-6} = x^9$

c. $\left(\dfrac{2}{7}\right)^{-2} = \dfrac{2^{-2}}{7^{-2}} = \dfrac{7^2}{2^2} = \dfrac{49}{4}$

d. $\dfrac{5^{-2}x^{-3}y^{11}}{x^2 y^{-5}} = \dfrac{x^{-3-2}y^{11-(-5)}}{5^2}$

$= \dfrac{x^{-5}y^{16}}{25}$

$= \dfrac{y^{16}}{25x^5}$

40. a. $(4a^{-1}b^0)^{-3} = 4^{-3}(a^{-1})^{-3}(1)^{-3} = \dfrac{a^3}{4^3} = \dfrac{a^3}{64}$

b. $\left(\dfrac{a^{-6}}{a^{-8}}\right)^{-2} = \dfrac{(a^{-6})^{-2}}{(a^{-8})^{-2}}$

$= \dfrac{a^{12}}{a^{16}}$

$= a^{12-16}$

$= a^{-4}$

$= \dfrac{1}{a^4}$

c. $\left(\dfrac{2}{3}\right)^{-3} = \dfrac{2^{-3}}{3^{-3}} = \dfrac{3^3}{2^3} = \dfrac{27}{8}$

d. $\dfrac{3^{-2}a^{-2}b^{12}}{a^4 b^{-5}} = \dfrac{a^{-2-4}b^{12-(-5)}}{3^2}$

$= \dfrac{a^{-6}b^{17}}{9}$

$= \dfrac{b^{17}}{9a^6}$

41. The degree is the degree of the term $x^2 y^2$, which is $2 + 2 = 4$.

42. $(3x^2 - 2x) - (5x^2 + 3x) = 3x^2 - 2x - 5x^2 - 3x$
$\qquad\qquad = -2x^2 - 5x$

43. a. $(2x^3)(5x^6) = 2(5)x^{3+6} = 10x^9$

   b. $(7y^4z^4)(-xy^{11}z^5) = -7xy^{4+11}z^{4+5}$
$$= -7xy^{15}z^9$$

44. a. $(3y^6)(4y^2) = 3(4)y^{6+2} = 12y^8$

   b. $(6a^3b^2)(-a^2bc^4) = -6a^{3+2}b^{2+1}c^4$
$$= -6a^5b^3c^4$$

45. $17x^3y^2 - 34x^4y^2 = 17x^3y^2(1-2x)$

46. $12x^3y - 3xy^3 = 3xy(4x^2 - y^2)$
$$= 3xy((2x)^2 - y^2)$$
$$= 3xy(2x + y)(2x - y)$$

47. $x^2 + 10x + 16 = (x+8)(x+2)$

48. $5a^2 + 14a - 3 = (5a-1)(a+3)$

49. $2x^2 + 9x - 5 = 0$
$(2x-1)(x+5) = 0$
$2x-1 = 0$ or $x+5 = 0$
   $2x = 1$ or $x = -5$
   $x = \dfrac{1}{2}$

The solution is $-5, \dfrac{1}{2}$.

50. $3x^2 - 10x - 8 = 0$
$(3x+2)(x-4) = 0$
$3x+2 = 0$ or $x-4 = 0$
   $3x = -2$ or $x = 4$
   $x = -\dfrac{2}{3}$

The solution is $-\dfrac{2}{3}, 4$.

Chapter 6

Section 6.1

Practice Exercises

1. a. The denominator of $f(x)$ is never 0.
Domain: $\{x | x \text{ is a real number}\}$

b. Undefined values when
$x + 3 = 0$, or $x = -3$
Domain: $\{x | x \text{ is a real number and } x \neq -3\}$

c. Undefined values when
$$x^2 - 5x + 6 = 0$$
$$(x - 3)(x - 2) = 0$$
$x - 3 = 0$ or $x - 2 = 0$
$\quad x = 3$ or $\quad\quad x = 2$
Domain:
$\{x | x \text{ is a real number and } x \neq 2, x \neq 3\}$

2. a. $x + 3 = 0$
$\quad\quad x = -3$
Domain: $\{x | x \text{ is a real number and } x \neq -3\}$

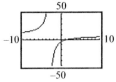

b. $3x^2 - 8x + 5 = 0$
$(3x - 5)(x - 1) = 0$
$3x - 5 = 0$ or $x - 1 = 0$
$\quad 3x = 5$ or $\quad\quad x = 1$
$\quad\quad x = \dfrac{5}{3}$
Domain:
$\left\{ x \middle| x \text{ is a real number and } x \neq 1, \ x \neq \dfrac{5}{3} \right\}$

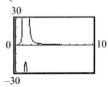

3. a. $\dfrac{5z^4}{10z^5 - 5z^4} = \dfrac{5z^4 \cdot 1}{5z^4 \left(2z - 1\right)}$
$\quad\quad = 1 \cdot \dfrac{1}{2z - 1} = \dfrac{1}{2z - 1}$

b. $\dfrac{5x^2 + 13x + 6}{6x^2 + 7x - 10} = \dfrac{(5x + 3)(x + 2)}{(6x - 5)(x + 2)}$
$\quad\quad = \dfrac{5x + 3}{6x - 5} \cdot 1$
$\quad\quad = \dfrac{5x + 3}{6x - 5}$

4. a. $\dfrac{x + 3}{3 + x} = \dfrac{x + 3}{x + 3} = 1$

b. $\dfrac{3 - x}{x - 3} = \dfrac{-1(-3 + x)}{x - 3} = \dfrac{-1(x - 3)}{x - 3} = \dfrac{-1}{1} = -1$

5. $\dfrac{20 - 5x^2}{x^2 + x - 6} = \dfrac{5(4 - x^2)}{(x + 3)(x - 2)}$
$\quad\quad = \dfrac{5(2 + x)(2 - x)}{(x + 3)(x - 2)}$
$\quad\quad = \dfrac{5(2 + x) \cdot (-1)(x - 2)}{(x + 3)(x - 2)}$
$\quad\quad = -\dfrac{5(2 + x)}{x + 3}$

6. a. $\dfrac{x^3 + 64}{4 + x} = \dfrac{(x + 4)(x^2 - 4x + 16)}{x + 4}$
$\quad\quad = x^2 - 4x + 16$

b. $\dfrac{5z^2 + 10}{z^3 - 3z^2 + 2z - 6} = \dfrac{5(z^2 + 2)}{(z^3 - 3z^2) + (2z - 6)}$
$\quad\quad = \dfrac{5(z^2 + 2)}{z^2(z - 3) + 2(z - 3)}$
$\quad\quad = \dfrac{5(z^2 + 2)}{(z - 3)(z^2 + 2)}$
$\quad\quad = \dfrac{5}{z - 3}$

7. a. $\dfrac{2 + 5n}{3n} \cdot \dfrac{6n + 3}{5n^2 - 3n - 2}$
$\quad = \dfrac{2 + 5n}{3n} \cdot \dfrac{3(2n + 1)}{(5n + 2)(n - 1)}$
$\quad = \dfrac{2n + 1}{n(n - 1)}$

b. $\dfrac{x^3-8}{-6x+12}\cdot\dfrac{6x^2}{x^2+2x+4}$

$=\dfrac{(x-2)(x^2+2x+4)}{-6(x-2)}\cdot\dfrac{6x^2}{x^2+2x+4}$

$=\dfrac{(x-2)(x^2+2x+4)\cdot 6\cdot x^2}{-1\cdot 6(x-2)(x^2+2x+4)}$

$=\dfrac{x^2}{-1}$

$=-x^2$

8. a. $\dfrac{6y^3}{3y^2-27}\div\dfrac{42}{3-y}=\dfrac{6y^3}{3y^2-27}\cdot\dfrac{3-y}{42}$

$=\dfrac{6y^3(3-y)}{3(y+3)(y-3)\cdot 42}$

$=\dfrac{6y^3\cdot(-1)(y-3)}{3(y+3)(y-3)\cdot 6\cdot 7}$

$=-\dfrac{y^3}{21(y+3)}$

b. $\dfrac{10x^2+23x-5}{5x^2-51x+10}\div\dfrac{2x^2+9x+10}{7x^2-68x-20}$

$=\dfrac{10x^2+23x-5}{5x^2-51x+10}\cdot\dfrac{7x^2-68x-20}{2x^2+9x+10}$

$=\dfrac{(5x-1)(2x+5)}{(5x-1)(x-10)}\cdot\dfrac{(7x+2)(x-10)}{(2x+5)(x+2)}$

$=\dfrac{7x+2}{x+2}$

9. $\dfrac{x^2-16}{(x-4)^2}\cdot\dfrac{5x-20}{3x}\div\dfrac{x^2+x-12}{x}$

$=\dfrac{x^2-16}{(x-4)^2}\cdot\dfrac{5x-20}{3x}\cdot\dfrac{x}{x^2+x-12}$

$=\dfrac{(x+4)(x-4)}{(x-4)(x-4)}\cdot\dfrac{5(x-4)}{3x}\cdot\dfrac{x}{(x+4)(x-3)}$

$=\dfrac{5}{3(x-3)}$

10. a. $C(100)=\dfrac{3.2(100)+400}{100}=\dfrac{720}{100}=7.2$

　　　$7.20 per tee shirt

b. $C(1000)=\dfrac{3.2(1000)+400}{1000}=\dfrac{3600}{1000}=3.6$

　　　$3.60 per tee shirt

Vocabulary and Readiness Check

1. A <u>rational</u> expression is an expression that can be written as the quotient $\dfrac{P}{Q}$ of two polynomials P and Q as long as $Q\neq 0$.

2. A rational expression is undefined if the denominator is <u>0</u>.

3. The <u>domain</u> of the rational function $f(x)=\dfrac{2}{x}$ is $\{x|x$ is a real number and $x\neq 0\}$.

4. A rational expression is <u>simplified</u> if the numerator and denominator have no common factors other than 1 or -1.

5. The expression $\dfrac{x^2+2}{2+x^2}$ simplifies to <u>1</u>.

6. The expression $\dfrac{y-z}{z-y}$ simplifies to <u>-1</u>.

7. For a rational expression, $-\dfrac{a}{b}=\dfrac{-a}{b}=\dfrac{a}{-b}$.

8. The statement $\dfrac{a-6}{a+2}=\dfrac{-(a-6)}{-(a+2)}=\dfrac{-a+6}{-a-2}$ is true.

9. $\dfrac{x}{5}\cdot\dfrac{y}{2}=\dfrac{xy}{10}$

10. $\dfrac{y}{6}\cdot\dfrac{z}{5}=\dfrac{yz}{30}$

11. $\dfrac{2}{x}\cdot\dfrac{y}{3}=\dfrac{2y}{3x}$

12. $\dfrac{a}{5}\cdot\dfrac{7}{b}=\dfrac{7a}{5b}$

13. $\dfrac{m}{6}\cdot\dfrac{m}{6}=\dfrac{m^2}{36}$

14. $\dfrac{9}{x}\cdot\dfrac{8}{x}=\dfrac{72}{x^2}$

Exercise Set 6.1

2. 2 is never 0, so the domain of $g(x) = \dfrac{4-3x}{2}$ is

$\{x|x \text{ is a real number}\}$.

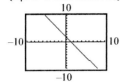

4. $3t = 0$

$t = 0$

The domain of $v(t) = \dfrac{5t+t^2}{3t}$ is

$\{t|t \text{ is a real number and } t \neq 0\}$.

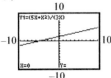

6. $-2 + x = 0$

$x = 2$

The domain of $f(x) = \dfrac{-4x}{-2+x}$ is

$\{x|x \text{ is a real number and } x \neq 2\}$.

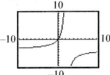

8. $2x + 5 = 0$

$2x = -5$

$x = -\dfrac{5}{2}$

The domain of $g(x) = \dfrac{-2}{2x+5}$ is

$\left\{x \middle| x \text{ is a real number and } x \neq -\dfrac{5}{2}\right\}$.

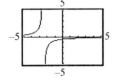

10. $2x^2 - 14x + 20 = 0$

$2(x^2 - 7x + 10) = 0$

$2(x-2)(x-5) = 0$

$x - 2 = 0 \quad \text{or} \quad x - 5 = 0$

$\quad x = 2 \quad \text{or} \quad\quad x = 5$

The domain of $h(x) = \dfrac{5-3x}{2x^2-14x+20}$ is

$\{x|x \text{ is a real number and } x \neq 2,\ x \neq 5\}$.

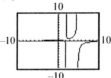

12. $x^2 - 7x = 0$

$x(x-7) = 0$

$x = 0 \quad \text{or} \quad x - 7 = 0$

$x = 0 \quad \text{or} \quad\quad x = 7$

The domain of $R(x) = \dfrac{5}{x^2-7x}$ is

$\{x|x \text{ is a real number and } x \neq 0,\ x \neq 7\}$.

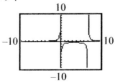

14. $\dfrac{3x-6x^2}{3x} = \dfrac{3x(1-2x)}{3x} = 1-2x$

16. $\dfrac{x^2-25}{5+x} = \dfrac{(x+5)(x-5)}{5+x} = \dfrac{(x+5)(x-5)}{x+5} = x-5$

18. $\dfrac{6y-18}{2y-6} = \dfrac{6(y-3)}{2(y-3)} = 3$

20. $\dfrac{x^2-8x+16}{x-4} = \dfrac{(x-4)(x-4)}{x-4} = x-4$

22. $\dfrac{x-4}{4-x} = \dfrac{x-4}{-1(-4+x)} = \dfrac{x-4}{-1(x-4)} = -1$

24.
$$\frac{x^2 - y^2}{y - x} = \frac{(x-y)(x+y)}{y-x}$$
$$= \frac{(x-y)(x+y)}{-1(-y+x)}$$
$$= \frac{(x-y)(x+y)}{-1(x-y)}$$
$$= -(x+y)$$

26.
$$\frac{3x^2 - 11x + 10}{x^2 - 7x + 10} = \frac{(3x-5)(x-2)}{(x-2)(x-5)} = \frac{3x-5}{x-5}$$

28.
$$\frac{4x+4}{x^3+1} = \frac{4(x+1)}{(x+1)(x^2-x+1)} = \frac{4}{x^2-x+1}$$

30.
$$\frac{2x^2 - x - 3}{2x^3 - 3x^2 + 2x - 3} = \frac{(2x-3)(x+1)}{x^2(2x-3)+1(2x-3)}$$
$$= \frac{(2x-3)(x+1)}{(x^2+1)(2x-3)}$$
$$= \frac{x+1}{x^2+1}$$

32.
$$\frac{8x^3 - 27}{4x^2 + 6x + 9} = \frac{(2x-3)(4x^2+6x+9)}{4x^2+6x+9} = 2x - 3$$

34.
$$\frac{10-2x}{7} \cdot \frac{14}{5x-25} = \frac{2(5-x)}{7} \cdot \frac{2 \cdot 7}{5(x-5)}$$
$$= \frac{-2(x-5)}{7} \cdot \frac{2 \cdot 7}{5(x-5)}$$
$$= -\frac{4}{5}$$

36.
$$\frac{a-5b}{a^2+ab} \cdot \frac{b^2-a^2}{10b-2a} = \frac{a-5b}{a(a+b)} \cdot \frac{(b+a)(b-a)}{2(5b-a)}$$
$$= \frac{a-5b}{a(a+b)} \cdot \frac{-(a+b)(a-b)}{-2(a-5b)}$$
$$= \frac{a-b}{2a}$$

38.
$$\frac{2x^2-2}{10x+30} \cdot \frac{12x+36}{3x-3}$$
$$= \frac{2(x^2-1)}{10(x+3)} \cdot \frac{12(x+3)}{3(x-1)}$$
$$= \frac{2(x+1)(x-1)}{2 \cdot 5(x+3)} \cdot \frac{2 \cdot 2 \cdot 3(x+3)}{3(x-1)}$$
$$= \frac{4(x+1)}{5}$$

40.
$$\frac{x^2-3x+9}{5x^2-20x-105} \cdot \frac{x^2-49}{x^3+27}$$
$$= \frac{x^2-3x+9}{5(x^2-4x-21)} \cdot \frac{(x+7)(x-7)}{(x+3)(x^2-3x+9)}$$
$$= \frac{x^2-3x+9}{5(x-7)(x+3)} \cdot \frac{(x+7)(x-7)}{(x+3)(x^2-3x+9)}$$
$$= \frac{x+7}{5(x+3)^2}$$

42.
$$\frac{4a^2-8a}{ab-2b+3a-6} \cdot \frac{8b+24}{3a+6}$$
$$= \frac{4a(a-2)}{b(a-2)+3(b-2)} \cdot \frac{8(b+3)}{3(a+2)}$$
$$= \frac{4a(a-2)}{(a-2)(b+3)} \cdot \frac{8(b+3)}{3(a+2)}$$
$$= \frac{32a}{3(a+2)}$$

44.
$$\frac{2x^2+12x-32}{x^2+16x+64} \cdot \frac{x^2+10x+16}{x^2-3x-10}$$
$$= \frac{2(x^2+6x-16)}{(x+8)(x+8)} \cdot \frac{(x+2)(x+8)}{(x-5)(x+2)}$$
$$= \frac{2(x+8)(x-2)}{(x+8)(x+8)} \cdot \frac{(x+2)(x+8)}{(x-5)(x+2)}$$
$$= \frac{2(x-2)}{x-5}$$

46.
$$\frac{7}{3x} \div \frac{14-7x}{18-9x} = \frac{7}{3x} \cdot \frac{18-9x}{14-7x}$$
$$= \frac{7}{3x} \cdot \frac{9(2-x)}{7(2-x)}$$
$$= \frac{7}{3x} \cdot \frac{3 \cdot 3(2-x)}{7(2-x)}$$
$$= \frac{3}{x}$$

48.
$$\frac{6a^2b^2}{a^2-4} \div \frac{3ab^2}{a-2} = \frac{6a^2b^2}{a^2-4} \cdot \frac{a-2}{3ab^2}$$
$$= \frac{2 \cdot 3 \cdot a^2b^2}{(a-2)(a+2)} \cdot \frac{a-2}{3ab^2}$$
$$= \frac{2a}{a+2}$$

50.
$$\frac{x^2-4}{3x+6} \div \frac{2x^2-8x+8}{x^2+4x+4} = \frac{x^2-4}{3x+6} \cdot \frac{x^2+4x+4}{2x^2-8x+8}$$
$$= \frac{(x+2)(x-2)}{3(x+2)} \cdot \frac{(x+2)(x+2)}{2(x^2-4x+4)}$$
$$= \frac{(x+2)(x-2)}{3(x+2)} \cdot \frac{(x+2)(x+2)}{2(x-2)(x-2)}$$
$$= \frac{(x+2)^2}{6(x-2)}$$

52.
$$\frac{a^2-a-6}{a^2-81} \div \frac{a^2-7a-18}{4a+36} = \frac{a^2-a-6}{a^2-81} \cdot \frac{4a+36}{a^2-7a-18}$$
$$= \frac{(a-3)(a+2)}{(a+9)(a-9)} \cdot \frac{4(a+9)}{(a-9)(a+2)}$$
$$= \frac{4(a-3)}{(a-9)^2}$$

54.
$$\frac{x^2-3x}{x^3-27} \div \frac{2x}{2x^2+6x+18} = \frac{x^2-3x}{x^3-27} \cdot \frac{2x^2+6x+18}{2x}$$
$$= \frac{x(x-3)}{(x-3)(x^2+3x+9)} \cdot \frac{2(x^2+3x+9)}{2x}$$
$$= 1$$

56.
$$\frac{2a^2-2b^2}{a^3+a^2b+a+b} \div \frac{6a^2}{a^3+a} = \frac{2a^2-2b^2}{a^3+a^2b+a+b} \cdot \frac{a^3+a}{6a^2}$$
$$= \frac{2(a^2-b^2)}{a^2(a+b)+1(a+b)} \cdot \frac{a(a^2+1)}{2\cdot3\cdot a^2}$$
$$= \frac{2(a-b)(a+b)}{(a+b)(a^2+1)} \cdot \frac{a(a^2+1)}{2\cdot3\cdot a^2}$$
$$= \frac{a-b}{3a}$$

58.
$$\frac{x^2-4}{9} \cdot \frac{x^2-6x+9}{x^2-5x+6} = \frac{(x-2)(x+2)}{9} \cdot \frac{(x-3)(x-3)}{(x-2)(x-3)}$$
$$= \frac{(x-3)(x+2)}{9}$$

60.
$$\frac{4a+36}{a^2-7a-18} \div \frac{a^2-a-6}{a^2-81} = \frac{4a+36}{a^2-7a-18} \cdot \frac{a^2-81}{a^2-a-6}$$
$$= \frac{4(a+9)}{(a-9)(a+2)} \cdot \frac{(a-9)(a+9)}{(a-3)(a+2)}$$
$$= \frac{4(a+9)^2}{(a+2)^2(a-3)}$$

62.
$$\frac{m^3-n^3}{m-n} = \frac{(m-n)(m^2+mn+n^2)}{m-n}$$
$$= m^2+mn+n^2$$

64. $\dfrac{4}{x} \cdot \dfrac{3xy}{x^2} \div \dfrac{6x^2}{x^4} = \dfrac{4}{x} \cdot \dfrac{3xy}{x^2} \cdot \dfrac{x^4}{6x^2} = \dfrac{12x^5 y}{6x^5} = 2y$

66. $\dfrac{x^2 + x - 2}{3y^2 - 5y - 2} \cdot \dfrac{12y^2 + y - 1}{x^2 + 4x - 5} \div \dfrac{8y^2 - 6y + 1}{5y^2 - 9y - 2} = \dfrac{x^2 + x - 2}{3y^2 - 5y - 2} \cdot \dfrac{12y^2 + y - 1}{x^2 + 4x - 5} \cdot \dfrac{5y^2 - 9y - 2}{8y^2 - 6y + 1}$

$$= \dfrac{(x+2)(x-1)}{(3y+1)(y-2)} \cdot \dfrac{(4y-1)(3y+1)}{(x-1)(x+5)} \cdot \dfrac{(5y+1)(y-2)}{(2y-1)(4y-1)}$$

$$= \dfrac{(x+2)(5y+1)}{(x+5)(2y-1)}$$

68. $\dfrac{5a^2 - 20}{3a^2 - 12a} \div \left(\dfrac{a^3 + 2a^2}{2a^2 - 8a} \cdot \dfrac{9a^3 + 6a^2}{2a^2 - 4a} \right) = \dfrac{5(a^2 - 4)}{3a(a-4)} \div \left(\dfrac{a^2(a+2)}{2a(a-4)} \cdot \dfrac{3a^2(3a+2)}{2a(a-2)} \right)$

$$= \dfrac{5(a+2)(a-2)}{3a(a-4)} \div \dfrac{3a^2(a+2)(3a+2)}{4(a-2)(a-4)}$$

$$= \dfrac{5(a+2)(a-2)}{3a(a-4)} \cdot \dfrac{4(a-2)(a-4)}{3a^2(a+2)(3a+2)}$$

$$= \dfrac{20(a-2)^2}{9a^3(3a+2)}$$

70. $\dfrac{3x^4 - 10x^2 - 8}{x - 2} \cdot \dfrac{3x + 6}{15x^2 + 10} = \dfrac{(3x^2 + 2)(x^2 - 4)}{x - 2} \cdot \dfrac{3(x + 2)}{5(3x^2 + 2)}$

$$= \dfrac{3(x+2)(x-2)(x+2)}{5(x-2)}$$

$$= \dfrac{3(x+2)^2}{5}$$

72. $f(x) = \dfrac{x - 2}{-5 + x}$

$f(-5) = \dfrac{-5 - 2}{-5 + (-5)} = \dfrac{-7}{-10} = \dfrac{7}{10}$

$f(0) = \dfrac{0 - 2}{-5 + 0} = \dfrac{-2}{-5} = \dfrac{2}{5}$

$f(10) = \dfrac{10 - 2}{-5 + 10} = \dfrac{8}{5}$

74. $s(t) = \dfrac{t^3 + 1}{t^2 + 1}$

$s(-1) = \dfrac{(-1)^3 + 1}{(-1)^2 + 1} = \dfrac{-1 + 1}{1 + 1} = \dfrac{0}{2} = 0$

$s(1) = \dfrac{1^3 + 1}{1^2 + 1} = \dfrac{1 + 1}{1 + 1} = \dfrac{2}{2} = 1$

$s(2) = \dfrac{2^3 + 1}{2^2 + 1} = \dfrac{8 + 1}{4 + 1} = \dfrac{9}{5}$

76. $f(x) = \dfrac{100,000x}{100 - x}$

    a. $f(20) = \dfrac{100,000(20)}{100 - 20}$

                $= \dfrac{2,000,000}{80}$

                $= 25,000$

        It costs \$25,000 to remove 20% of the pollutants from the bayou.

    b. $f(60) = \dfrac{100,000(60)}{100 - 60}$

                $= \dfrac{6,000,000}{40}$

                $= 150,000$

        $f(80) = \dfrac{100,000(80)}{100 - 80}$

                $= \dfrac{8,000,000}{20}$

                $= 400,000$

        The cost of removing 60% of the pollutants from the bayou is \$150,000, and the cost of removing 80% of the pollutants from the bayou is \$400,000.

    c. $f(90) = \dfrac{100,000(90)}{100 - 90}$

                $= \dfrac{9,000,000}{10}$

                $= \$900,000$

        $f(95) = \dfrac{100,000(95)}{100 - 95}$

                $= \dfrac{9,500,000}{5}$

                $= \$1,900,000$

        $f(99) = \dfrac{100,000(99)}{100 - 99}$

                $= \dfrac{9,900,000}{1}$

                $= \$9,900,000$

        answers may vary

    d. $100 - x = 0$

              $-x = -100$

                 $x = 100$

        The domain of f is $\{x | x \text{ is a real number and } x \neq 100\}$.

78. $\dfrac{4}{10} - \dfrac{7}{10} = -\dfrac{3}{10}$

80. $\dfrac{5}{13} + \dfrac{2}{7} = \dfrac{35}{91} + \dfrac{26}{91} = \dfrac{61}{91}$

82. $\dfrac{2}{9} - \dfrac{1}{6} + \dfrac{2}{3} = \dfrac{4}{18} - \dfrac{3}{18} + \dfrac{12}{18} = \dfrac{13}{18}$

84. a. $\dfrac{2-x}{-x} = \dfrac{-(-2+x)}{-x} = \dfrac{-2+x}{x}$

    b. $-\dfrac{2-x}{x} = \dfrac{-(2-x)}{x} = \dfrac{-2+x}{x}$

    c. $\dfrac{x-2}{x} = \dfrac{-2+x}{x}$

    d. $\dfrac{x-2}{-x} = \dfrac{-2+x}{-x} \neq \dfrac{-2+x}{x}$

86. No; answers may vary

88. $A = \dfrac{1}{2} b \cdot h$

      $= \dfrac{1}{2} \left(\dfrac{5y}{6x} \right) \left(\dfrac{4x}{10y^2} \right)$

      $= \dfrac{1}{2} \cdot \dfrac{5y}{2 \cdot 3x} \cdot \dfrac{2 \cdot 2x}{5 \cdot 2y^2}$

      $= \dfrac{1}{2 \cdot 3y}$

      $= \dfrac{1}{6y}$

    The area is $\dfrac{1}{6y}$ square inches.

90. $\dfrac{15x^3}{y^2} \div 5x = \dfrac{15x^3}{y^2} \cdot \dfrac{1}{5x}$

                  $= \dfrac{5 \cdot 3x^3}{y^2} \cdot \dfrac{1}{5x}$

                  $= \dfrac{3x^2}{y^2}$

    Each person will receive $\dfrac{3x^2}{y^2}$ dollars.

92. Answers may vary

94. Answers may vary

96. Answers may vary

98. $f(x) = \dfrac{1}{x}$

x	$\frac{1}{4}$	$\frac{1}{2}$	1	2	4
y	4	2	1	$\frac{1}{2}$	$\frac{1}{4}$

x	-4	-2	-1	$-\frac{1}{2}$	$-\frac{1}{4}$
y	$-\frac{1}{4}$	$-\frac{1}{2}$	-1	-2	-4

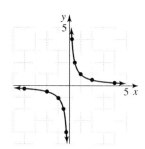

100. $\dfrac{x^{2n} + 4x^n + 4}{4x - 3} \cdot \dfrac{8x^2 - 6x}{x^n + 2}$

$= \dfrac{(x^n + 2)^2 \cdot 2x(4x - 3)}{(4x - 3)(x^n + 2)}$

$= 2x(x^n + 2)$

102. $\dfrac{y^{4n} - 16}{y^{2n} + 4} \cdot \dfrac{6y}{y^n + 2}$

$= \dfrac{(y^{2n} + 4)(y^{2n} - 4)}{y^{2n} + 4} \cdot \dfrac{6y}{y^n + 2}$

$= \dfrac{6y(y^{2n} - 4)}{y^n + 2}$

$= \dfrac{6y(y^n + 2)(y^n - 2)}{y^n + 2}$

$= 6y(y^n - 2)$

104. $\dfrac{y^{2n} + 7y^n + 10}{10} \div \dfrac{y^{2n} + 4y^n + 4}{5y^n + 25}$

$= \dfrac{y^{2n} + 7y^n + 10}{10} \cdot \dfrac{5y^n + 25}{y^{2n} + 4y^n + 4}$

$= \dfrac{(y^n + 5)(y^n + 2)}{10} \cdot \dfrac{5(y^n + 5)}{(y^n + 2)(y^n + 2)}$

$= \dfrac{(y^n + 5)^2}{2(y^n + 2)}$

Section 6.2

Practice Exercises

1. a. $\dfrac{9}{11z^2} + \dfrac{x}{11z^2} = \dfrac{9 + x}{11z^2}$

b. $\dfrac{x}{8} + \dfrac{5x}{8} = \dfrac{x + 5x}{8} = \dfrac{6x}{8} = \dfrac{3x}{4}$

c. $\dfrac{x^2}{x + 4} - \dfrac{16}{x + 4} = \dfrac{x^2 - 16}{x + 4}$

$= \dfrac{(x + 4)(x - 4)}{x + 4}$

$= x - 4$

d. $\dfrac{z}{2a^2} - \dfrac{z + 3}{2a^2} = \dfrac{z - (z + 3)}{2a^2}$

$= \dfrac{z - z - 3}{2a^2}$

$= \dfrac{-3}{2a^2}$

2. a. $\dfrac{7}{6x^3 y^5}, \dfrac{2}{9x^2 y^4}$

We factor each denominator.

$6x^3 y^5 = 2 \cdot 3 \cdot x^3 \cdot y^5$

$9x^2 y^4 = 3^2 \cdot x^2 \cdot y^4$

$\text{LCD} = 2 \cdot 3^2 \cdot x^3 \cdot y^5 = 18x^3 y^5$

b. $\dfrac{11}{x - 2}, \dfrac{x}{x - 3}$

The denominators $x - 2$ and $x - 3$ do not factor further.

$\text{LCD} = (x - 2)(x - 3)$

c. $\dfrac{b + 2}{b^2 - 16}, \dfrac{8}{b^2 - 8b + 16}, \dfrac{5b}{2b^2 - 5b - 12}$

We factor each denominator.

$b^2 - 16 = (b - 4)(b + 4)$

$b^2 - 8b + 16 = (b - 4)(b - 4)$

$2b^2 - 5b - 12 = (2b + 3)(b - 4)$

$\text{LCD} = (b - 4)^2 (b + 4)(2b + 3)$

d. $\dfrac{y}{y^2-9}, \dfrac{3}{12-4y}$

We factor each denominator.

$y^2-9=(y-3)(y+3)$

$12-4y=4(3-y)=4(-1)(y-3)$

$\text{LCD}=-4(y-3)(y+3)$

3. a. The LCD is $5p^4q$.

$$\dfrac{4}{p^3q}+\dfrac{3}{5p^4q}=\dfrac{4\cdot 5p}{p^3q\cdot 5p}+\dfrac{3}{5p^4q}$$

$$=\dfrac{20p}{5p^4q}+\dfrac{3}{5p^4q}$$

$$=\dfrac{20p+3}{5p^4q}$$

b. The LCD is the product of the two denominators: $(y+3)(y-3)$.

$$\dfrac{4}{y+3}+\dfrac{5y}{y-3}=\dfrac{4\cdot(y-3)}{(y+3)\cdot(y-3)}+\dfrac{5y\cdot(y+3)}{(y-3)\cdot(y+3)}$$

$$=\dfrac{4y-12}{(y+3)(y-3)}+\dfrac{5y^2+15y}{(y+3)(y-3)}$$

$$=\dfrac{4y-12+5y^2+15y}{(y+3)(y-3)}$$

$$=\dfrac{5y^2+19y-12}{(y+3)(y-3)}$$

c. The LCD is either $z-5$ or $5-z$.

$$\dfrac{3z-18}{z-5}-\dfrac{3}{5-z}=\dfrac{3z-18}{z-5}-\dfrac{3}{-1(z-5)}$$

$$=\dfrac{3z-18}{z-5}-\dfrac{-1\cdot 3}{z-5}$$

$$=\dfrac{3z-18-(-3)}{z-5}$$

$$=\dfrac{3z-18+3}{z-5}$$

$$=\dfrac{3z-15}{z-5}$$

$$=\dfrac{3(z-5)}{z-5}$$

$$=3$$

4. $\dfrac{t}{t^2-25} - \dfrac{3}{t^2-3t-10} = \dfrac{t}{(t+5)(t-5)} - \dfrac{3}{(t-5)(t+2)}$

The LCD is $(t+5)(t-5)(t+2)$.

$$\dfrac{t}{(t+5)(t-5)} - \dfrac{3}{(t-5)(t+2)} = \dfrac{t\cdot(t+2)}{(t+5)(t-5)\cdot(t+2)} - \dfrac{3\cdot(t+5)}{(t-5)(t+2)\cdot(t+5)}$$

$$= \dfrac{t^2+2t}{(t+5)(t-5)(t+2)} - \dfrac{3t+15}{(t+5)(t-5)(t+2)}$$

$$= \dfrac{t^2+2t-3t-15}{(t+5)(t-5)(t+2)}$$

$$= \dfrac{t^2-t-15}{(t+5)(t-5)(t+2)}$$

5. $\dfrac{2x+3}{3x^2-5x-2} + \dfrac{x-6}{6x^2-13x-5} = \dfrac{2x+3}{(3x+1)(x-2)} + \dfrac{x-6}{(3x+1)(2x-5)}$

The LCD is $(3x+1)(x-2)(2x-5)$.

$$= \dfrac{(2x+3)\cdot(2x-5)}{(3x+1)(x-2)\cdot(2x-5)} + \dfrac{(x-6)\cdot(x-2)}{(3x+1)(2x-5)\cdot(x-2)}$$

$$= \dfrac{4x^2-4x-15}{(3x+1)(x-2)(2x-5)} + \dfrac{x^2-8x+12}{(3x+1)(x-2)(2x-5)}$$

$$= \dfrac{4x^2-4x-15+x^2-8x+12}{(3x+1)(x-2)(2x-5)}$$

$$= \dfrac{5x^2-12x-3}{(3x+1)(x-2)(2x-5)}$$

6. $\dfrac{2}{x-2} + \dfrac{3x}{x^2-x-2} - \dfrac{1}{x+1} = \dfrac{2}{x-2} + \dfrac{3x}{(x-2)(x+1)} - \dfrac{1}{x+1}$

The LCD is $(x-2)(x-1)$.

$$= \dfrac{2\cdot(x+1)}{(x-2)\cdot(x+1)} + \dfrac{3x}{(x-2)(x+1)} - \dfrac{1\cdot(x-2)}{(x+1)\cdot(x-2)}$$

$$= \dfrac{2x+2}{(x-2)(x+1)} + \dfrac{3x}{(x-2)(x+1)} - \dfrac{x-2}{(x-2)(x+1)}$$

$$= \dfrac{2x+2+3x-x+2}{(x-2)(x+1)}$$

$$= \dfrac{4x+4}{(x-2)(x+1)}$$

$$= \dfrac{4(x+1)}{(x-2)(x+1)}$$

$$= \dfrac{4}{x-2}$$

Vocabulary and Readiness Check

1. The denominators must be the same before performing the operations of addition and subtraction (<u>a, b</u>).

2. To perform the operation of division (<u>d</u>), you multiply the first rational expression by the reciprocal of the second rational expression.

3. Numerator times numerator all over denominator times denominator is multiplication (<u>c</u>).

4. The operations of addition and multiplication (<u>a, c</u>) are commutative (order doesn't matter).

5. Addition: $\dfrac{5}{y} + \dfrac{7}{y} = \dfrac{12}{y}$

6. Subtraction: $\dfrac{5}{y} - \dfrac{7}{y} = -\dfrac{2}{y}$

7. Multiplication: $\dfrac{5}{y} \cdot \dfrac{7}{y} = \dfrac{35}{y^2}$

8. Division: $\dfrac{5}{y} \div \dfrac{7}{y} = \dfrac{5}{y} \cdot \dfrac{y}{7} = \dfrac{5}{7}$

9. $\dfrac{5}{2x} - \dfrac{x+1}{2x} = \dfrac{5-(x+1)}{2x} = \dfrac{-x+4}{2x}$

10. $\dfrac{9}{5x} - \dfrac{6-x}{5x} = \dfrac{9-(6-x)}{5x} = \dfrac{x+3}{5x}$

11. $\dfrac{y+11}{y-2} - \dfrac{y-5}{y-2} = \dfrac{y+11-(y-5)}{y-2} = \dfrac{16}{y-2}$

12. $\dfrac{z-1}{z+6} - \dfrac{z+4}{z+6} = \dfrac{z-1-(z+4)}{z+6} = \dfrac{-5}{z+6}$

Exercise Set 6.2

2. $\dfrac{4}{x^2 y} + \dfrac{2}{x^2 y} = \dfrac{4+2}{x^2 y} = \dfrac{6}{x^2 y}$

4. $\dfrac{x}{5-x} + \dfrac{7}{5-x} = \dfrac{x+7}{5-x}$

6. $\dfrac{x^2}{x+6} - \dfrac{36}{x+6} = \dfrac{x^2-36}{x+6} = \dfrac{(x+6)(x-6)}{x+6} = x-6$

8. $\dfrac{5x+2}{x^2+2x-8} + \dfrac{2-4x}{x^2+2x-8} = \dfrac{5x+2+2-4x}{x^2+2x-8}$

        $= \dfrac{x+4}{x^2+2x-8}$

        $= \dfrac{x+4}{(x+4)(x-2)}$

        $= \dfrac{1}{x-2}$

10. $\dfrac{x+4}{4x} - \dfrac{x-4}{4x} = \dfrac{x+4-x+4}{4x} = \dfrac{8}{4x} = \dfrac{2}{x}$

12. $5y = 5y$

    $4y^2 = 2 \cdot 2 y^2$

    $\text{LCD} = 2 \cdot 2 \cdot 5 \cdot y^2 = 20y^2$

14. $2x = 2x$

    $2 + x = 2 + x$

    $\text{LCD} = 2x(2 + x)$

16. $2x - 1 = 2x - 1$

    $2x + 1 = 2x + 1$

    $\text{LCD} = (2x - 1)(2x + 1)$

18. $3a + 9 = 3(a + 3)$

    $5a - 15 = 5(a - 3)$

    $\text{LCD} = 3 \cdot 5(a + 3)(a - 3) = 15(a + 3)(a - 3)$

20. $a^2 + 8a + 16 = (a + 4)^2$

    $a^2 + a - 12 = (a + 4)(a - 3)$

    $\text{LCD} = (a + 4)^2 (a - 3)$

22. $x^2 - 25 = (x + 5)(x - 5)$

    $50 - 10x = 10(5 - x) = -10(x - 5)$

    $x = x$

    $\text{LCD} = -10x(x + 5)(x - 5)$

24. $\dfrac{10}{7x} + \dfrac{5}{2x} = \dfrac{10 \cdot 2}{7x(2)} + \dfrac{5(7)}{2x(7)} = \dfrac{20}{14x} + \dfrac{35}{14x} = \dfrac{55}{14x}$

26. $\dfrac{4}{11x^4} - \dfrac{1}{4x^2} = \dfrac{4 \cdot 4}{11x^4 \cdot 4} - \dfrac{1 \cdot 11x^2}{4x^2 \cdot 11x^2}$

$\quad\quad\quad\quad\quad = \dfrac{16}{44x^4} - \dfrac{11x^2}{44x^4}$

$\quad\quad\quad\quad\quad = \dfrac{16 - 11x^2}{44x^4}$

28. $\dfrac{x-1}{x-5} - \dfrac{x+2}{x+5} = \dfrac{(x-1)(x+5)}{(x-5)(x+5)} - \dfrac{(x+2)(x-5)}{(x+5)(x-5)}$

$\quad\quad\quad\quad\quad = \dfrac{x^2+4x-5}{(x-5)(x+5)} - \dfrac{x^2-3x-10}{(x-5)(x+5)}$

$\quad\quad\quad\quad\quad = \dfrac{x^2+4x-5-x^2+3x+10}{(x-5)(x+5)}$

$\quad\quad\quad\quad\quad = \dfrac{7x+5}{(x-5)(x+5)}$

30. $\dfrac{4x-2}{(x-5)(x+4)} - \dfrac{2}{x+4}$

$\quad = \dfrac{4x-2}{(x-5)(x+4)} - \dfrac{2(x-5)}{(x+4)(x-5)}$

$\quad = \dfrac{4x-2}{(x-5)(x+4)} - \dfrac{2x-10}{(x-5)(x+4)}$

$\quad = \dfrac{4x-2-2x+10}{(x-5)(x+4)}$

$\quad = \dfrac{2x+8}{(x-5)(x+4)}$

$\quad = \dfrac{2(x+4)}{(x-5)(x+4)}$

$\quad = \dfrac{2}{x-5}$

32. $\dfrac{1}{a-3} - \dfrac{1}{3-a} = \dfrac{1}{a-3} - \dfrac{1}{-(-3+a)}$

$\quad\quad\quad\quad\quad = \dfrac{1}{a-3} - \dfrac{-1}{a-3}$

$\quad\quad\quad\quad\quad = \dfrac{2}{a-3}$

34. $\dfrac{5}{1-x} - \dfrac{1}{x-1} = \dfrac{5}{-1(-1+x)} - \dfrac{1}{x-1}$

$\quad\quad\quad\quad\quad = \dfrac{-5}{x-1} - \dfrac{1}{x-1}$

$\quad\quad\quad\quad\quad = \dfrac{-5-1}{x-1}$

$\quad\quad\quad\quad\quad = \dfrac{-6}{x-1}$

$\quad\quad\quad\quad\quad = -\dfrac{6}{x-1}$

36. $\dfrac{3}{5-x} + \dfrac{x+2}{x-5} = \dfrac{3}{-(-5+x)} + \dfrac{x+2}{x-5}$

$\quad\quad\quad\quad\quad = \dfrac{-3}{x-5} + \dfrac{x+2}{x-5}$

$\quad\quad\quad\quad\quad = \dfrac{-3+x+2}{x-5}$

$\quad\quad\quad\quad\quad = \dfrac{x-1}{x-5}$

38. $\dfrac{x+2}{x^2-36} - \dfrac{x}{x^2+9x+18}$

$\quad = \dfrac{x+2}{(x+6)(x-6)} - \dfrac{x}{(x+6)(x+3)}$

$\quad = \dfrac{(x+2)(x+3)}{(x+6)(x-6)(x+3)} - \dfrac{x(x-6)}{(x+6)(x+3)(x-6)}$

$\quad = \dfrac{x^2+5x+6}{(x+6)(x-6)(x+3)} - \dfrac{x^2-6x}{(x+6)(x-6)(x+3)}$

$\quad = \dfrac{x^2+5x+6-x^2+6x}{(x+6)(x-6)(x+3)}$

$\quad = \dfrac{11x+6}{(x+6)(x-6)(x+3)}$

40. $\dfrac{x+3}{5x^2+12x+4} + \dfrac{6}{x^2-x-6}$

$\quad = \dfrac{x+3}{(5x+2)(x+2)} + \dfrac{6}{(x-3)(x+2)}$

$\quad = \dfrac{(x+3)(x-3)}{(5x+2)(x+2)(x-3)} + \dfrac{6(5x+2)}{(x-3)(x+2)(5x+2)}$

$\quad = \dfrac{x^2-9}{(5x+2)(x+2)(x-3)} + \dfrac{30x+12}{(5x+2)(x+2)(x-3)}$

$\quad = \dfrac{x^2-9+30x+12}{(5x+2)(x+2)(x-3)}$

$\quad = \dfrac{x^2+30x+3}{(5x+2)(x+2)(x-3)}$

42. $\dfrac{a}{a^2+10a+25}-\dfrac{4-a}{a^2+6a+5}$

$=\dfrac{a}{(a+5)(a+5)}-\dfrac{4-a}{(a+5)(a+1)}$

$=\dfrac{a(a+1)}{(a+5)(a+5)(a+1)}-\dfrac{(4-a)(a+5)}{(a+5)(a+1)(a+5)}$

$=\dfrac{a^2+a}{(a+5)^2(a+1)}-\dfrac{-a^2-a+20}{(a+5)^2(a+1)}$

$=\dfrac{a^2+a+a^2+a-20}{(a+5)^2(a+1)}$

$=\dfrac{2a^2+2a-20}{(a+5)^2(a+1)}$

$=\dfrac{2(a^2+a-10)}{(a+5)^2(a+1)}$

44. $\dfrac{x}{x^2-7x+6}-\dfrac{x+4}{3x^2-2x-1}$

$=\dfrac{x}{(x-6)(x-1)}-\dfrac{x+4}{(3x+1)(x-1)}$

$=\dfrac{x(3x+1)}{(x-6)(x-1)(3x+1)}-\dfrac{(x+4)(x-6)}{(3x+1)(x-1)(x-6)}$

$=\dfrac{3x^2+x}{(3x+1)(x-6)(x-1)}-\dfrac{x^2-2x-24}{(3x+1)(x-6)(x-1)}$

$=\dfrac{3x^2+x-x^2+2x+24}{(3x+1)(x-6)(x-1)}$

$=\dfrac{2x^2+3x+24}{(3x+1)(x-6)(x-1)}$

46. $\dfrac{9x+2}{3x^2-2x-8}+\dfrac{7}{3x^2+x-4}$

$=\dfrac{9x+2}{(3x+4)(x-2)}+\dfrac{7}{(3x+4)(x-1)}$

$=\dfrac{(9x+2)(x-1)}{(3x+4)(x-2)(x-1)}+\dfrac{7(x-2)}{(3x+4)(x-2)(x-1)}$

$=\dfrac{9x^2-7x-2}{(3x+4)(x-2)(x-1)}+\dfrac{7x-14}{(3x+4)(x-2)(x-1)}$

$=\dfrac{9x^2-7x-2+7x-14}{(3x+4)(x-2)(x-1)}$

$=\dfrac{9x^2-16}{(3x+4)(x-2)(x-1)}$

$=\dfrac{(3x+4)(3x-4)}{(3x+4)(x-2)(x-1)}$

$=\dfrac{3x-4}{(x-2)(x-1)}$

48. $\dfrac{7}{2xy^4}+\dfrac{1}{2xy^4}=\dfrac{8}{2xy^4}=\dfrac{4}{xy^4}$

50. $\dfrac{17x+4}{4x}-\dfrac{17x-4}{4x}=\dfrac{17x+4-17x+4}{4x}=\dfrac{8}{4x}=\dfrac{2}{x}$

52. $\dfrac{10}{3x-3}+\dfrac{1}{7x-7}=\dfrac{10}{3(x-1)}+\dfrac{1}{7(x-1)}$

$=\dfrac{10\cdot7}{3(x-1)\cdot7}+\dfrac{1\cdot3}{7(x-1)\cdot3}$

$=\dfrac{70}{21(x-1)}+\dfrac{3}{21(x-1)}$

$=\dfrac{73}{21(x-1)}$

54. $\dfrac{-3}{2a+8}-\dfrac{8}{a^2+4a}=\dfrac{-3}{2(a+4)}-\dfrac{8}{a(a+4)}$

$=\dfrac{-3\cdot a}{2(a+4)\cdot a}-\dfrac{8\cdot2}{a(a+4)\cdot2}$

$=\dfrac{-3a}{2a(a+4)}-\dfrac{16}{2a(a+4)}$

$=\dfrac{-3a-16}{2a(a+4)}$

56. $\dfrac{x}{25-x^2}+\dfrac{2}{3x-15}$

$=\dfrac{x}{-(x^2-25)}+\dfrac{2}{3(x-5)}$

$=\dfrac{-x}{(x-5)(x+5)}+\dfrac{2}{3(x-5)}$

$=\dfrac{-x\cdot3}{(x-5)(x+5)\cdot3}+\dfrac{2(x+5)}{3(x-5)(x+5)}$

$=\dfrac{-3x}{3(x-5)(x+5)}+\dfrac{2x+10}{3(x-5)(x+5)}$

$=\dfrac{-3x+2x+10}{3(x-5)(x+5)}$

$=\dfrac{-x+10}{3(x-5)(x+5)}$

58.
$$\frac{3z}{z^2-9}-\frac{2}{3-z}=\frac{3z}{(z+3)(z-3)}-\frac{2}{-(z-3)}$$
$$=\frac{3z}{(z+3)(z-3)}-\frac{-2}{z-3}$$
$$=\frac{3z}{(z+3)(z-3)}-\frac{-2(z+3)}{(z-3)(z+3)}$$
$$=\frac{3z}{(z+3)(z-3)}-\frac{-2z-6}{(z+3)(z-3)}$$
$$=\frac{3z+2z+6}{(z-3)(z+3)}$$
$$=\frac{5z+6}{(z-3)(z+3)}$$

60.
$$\frac{2x}{3x^2-13x+4}+\frac{5}{x^2-2x-8}=\frac{2x}{(3x-1)(x-4)}+\frac{5}{(x-4)(x+2)}$$
$$=\frac{2x(x+2)}{(3x-1)(x-4)(x+2)}+\frac{5(3x-1)}{(x-4)(x+2)(3x-1)}$$
$$=\frac{2x^2+4x}{(3x-1)(x-4)(x+2)}+\frac{15x-5}{(3x-1)(x-4)(x+2)}$$
$$=\frac{2x^2+4x+15x-5}{(3x-1)(x-4)(x+2)}$$
$$=\frac{2x^2+19x-5}{(3x-1)(x-4)(x+2)}$$

62.
$$\frac{5}{3x-6}-\frac{x}{x-2}+\frac{3+2x}{5x-10}=\frac{5}{3(x-2)}-\frac{x}{x-2}+\frac{3+2x}{5(x-2)}$$
$$=\frac{5\cdot5}{3(x-2)\cdot5}-\frac{x\cdot3\cdot5}{(x-2)\cdot3\cdot5}+\frac{(3+2x)\cdot3}{5(x-2)\cdot3}$$
$$=\frac{25}{15(x-3)}-\frac{15x}{15(x-2)}+\frac{9+6x}{15(x-2)}$$
$$=\frac{25-15x+9+6x}{15(x-2)}$$
$$=\frac{34-9x}{15(x-2)}$$

64.
$$\frac{x+2}{x^2-2x-3}+\frac{x}{x-3}-\frac{x}{x+1}=\frac{x+2}{(x-3)(x+1)}+\frac{x}{x-3}-\frac{x}{x+1}$$
$$=\frac{x+2}{(x-3)(x+1)}+\frac{x(x+1)}{(x-3)(x+1)}-\frac{x(x-3)}{(x-3)(x+1)}$$
$$=\frac{x+2}{(x-3)(x+1)}+\frac{x^2+x}{(x-3)(x+1)}-\frac{x^2-3x}{(x-3)(x+1)}$$
$$=\frac{x+2+x^2+x-x^2+3x}{(x-3)(x+1)}$$
$$=-\frac{5x+2}{(x-3)(x+1)}$$

66. $\dfrac{3}{x^2-9} - \dfrac{x}{x^2-6x+9} + \dfrac{1}{x+3} = \dfrac{3}{(x+3)(x-3)} - \dfrac{x}{(x-3)^2} + \dfrac{1}{x+3}$

$$= \dfrac{3(x-3)}{(x+3)(x-3)^2} - \dfrac{x(x+3)}{(x-3)^2(x+3)} + \dfrac{1(x-3)^2}{(x+3)(x-3)^2}$$

$$= \dfrac{3x-9}{(x+3)(x-3)^2} - \dfrac{x^2+3x}{(x+3)(x-3)^2} + \dfrac{x^2-6x+9}{(x+3)(x-3)^2}$$

$$= \dfrac{3x-9-x^2-3x+x^2-6x+9}{(x+3)(x-3)^2}$$

$$= \dfrac{-6x}{(x+3)(x-3)^2}$$

68. $\left(\dfrac{1}{2} + \dfrac{2}{x}\right) - \left(\dfrac{1}{2} - \dfrac{1}{x}\right) = \left(\dfrac{x}{2x} + \dfrac{4}{2x}\right) - \left(\dfrac{x}{2x} - \dfrac{2}{2x}\right)$

$$= \left(\dfrac{x+4}{2x}\right) - \left(\dfrac{x-2}{2x}\right)$$

$$= \dfrac{x+4-x+2}{2x}$$

$$= \dfrac{6}{2x}$$

$$= \dfrac{3}{x}$$

70. $\left(\dfrac{2}{3} - \dfrac{1}{x}\right) \div \left(\dfrac{3}{x} + \dfrac{1}{2}\right) = \left(\dfrac{2x}{3x} - \dfrac{3}{3x}\right) \div \left(\dfrac{3 \cdot 2}{2x} + \dfrac{x}{2x}\right)$

$$= \left(\dfrac{2x-3}{3x}\right) \div \left(\dfrac{6+x}{2x}\right)$$

$$= \dfrac{2x-3}{3x} \cdot \dfrac{2x}{x+6}$$

$$= \dfrac{2(2x-3)}{3(x+6)}$$

72. $\left(\dfrac{x+2}{2x} - \dfrac{x-2}{2x}\right) \cdot \left(\dfrac{5x}{4}\right)^2 = \left(\dfrac{x+2-x+2}{2x}\right) \cdot \left(\dfrac{5^2 x^2}{4^2}\right)$

$$= \left(\dfrac{4}{2x}\right) \cdot \left(\dfrac{25x^2}{4^2}\right)$$

$$= \dfrac{25x}{2 \cdot 4}$$

$$= \dfrac{25x}{8}$$

74. $\left(\dfrac{2x}{3}\right)^2 \cdot \left(\dfrac{3}{x}\right)^2 = \dfrac{2^2 x^2}{3^2} \cdot \dfrac{3^2}{x^2} = 2^2 = 4$

76. $\dfrac{x}{2x+2} \div \left(\dfrac{x}{x+1} + \dfrac{x}{x-1} \right)$

$= \dfrac{x}{2(x+1)} \div \left(\dfrac{x(x-1)}{(x+1)(x-1)} + \dfrac{x(x+1)}{(x-1)(x+1)} \right)$

$= \dfrac{x}{2(x+1)} \div \left(\dfrac{x^2-x}{(x+1)(x-1)} + \dfrac{x^2+x}{(x+1)(x-1)} \right)$

$= \dfrac{x}{2(x+1)} \div \left(\dfrac{x^2-x+x^2+x}{(x+1)(x-1)} \right)$

$= \dfrac{x}{2(x+1)} \div \dfrac{2x^2}{(x+1)(x-1)}$

$= \dfrac{x}{2(x+1)} \cdot \dfrac{(x+1)(x-1)}{2x^2}$

$= \dfrac{x-1}{2 \cdot 2x}$

$= \dfrac{x-1}{4x}$

78. $\dfrac{1}{x+1} \cdot \left(\dfrac{5}{x} + \dfrac{2}{x-3} \right) = \dfrac{1}{x+1} \cdot \left(\dfrac{5(x-3)}{x(x-3)} + \dfrac{2x}{(x-3)x} \right)$

$= \dfrac{1}{x+1} \cdot \left(\dfrac{5x-15}{x(x-3)} + \dfrac{2x}{x(x-3)} \right)$

$= \dfrac{1}{x+1} \cdot \left(\dfrac{5x-15+2x}{x(x-3)} \right)$

$= \dfrac{1}{x+1} \cdot \left(\dfrac{7x-15}{x(x-3)} \right)$

$= \dfrac{7x-15}{x(x-3)(x+1)}$

80. $14\left(\dfrac{1}{7} + \dfrac{3}{14} \right) = 14\left(\dfrac{1}{7} \right) + 14\left(\dfrac{3}{14} \right) = 2 + 3 = 5$

82. $5y^2 \left(\dfrac{1}{y^2} - \dfrac{1}{5} \right) = 5y^2 \cdot \dfrac{1}{y^2} - 5y^2 \cdot \dfrac{1}{5} = 5 - y^2$

84. $\sqrt{25} = 5$ because $5^2 = 25$.

86. $\sqrt[3]{27} = 3$ because $3^3 = 27$.

88. $\sqrt[4]{16} = 2$ because $2^4 = 16$.

90. $a^2 + b^2 = c^2$

$7^2 + 24^2 = c^2$

$49 + 576 = c^2$

$625 = c^2$

$c = 25$ feet

92. $\dfrac{7}{x+7} - \dfrac{x+3}{x+7} = \dfrac{7-x-3}{x+7} = \dfrac{4-x}{x+7} = \dfrac{-x+4}{x+7}$

The denominator should be $x + 7$, not $(x+7)^2$.

94. $P = \dfrac{5}{x-1} + \dfrac{3x}{x-1} + \dfrac{x^2-8}{x-1} + \dfrac{x^2-2x}{x-1}$

$= \dfrac{5+3x+x^2-8+x^2-2x}{x-1}$

$= \dfrac{2x^2+x-3}{x-1}$

$= \dfrac{(2x+3)(x-1)}{x-1}$

$= 2x+3$

The perimeter is $(2x + 3)$ centimeters.

96. Answers may vary

98. Answers may vary

100. Answers may vary

102. $y^{-1} + (4y)^{-1} = \dfrac{1}{y} + \dfrac{1}{4y} = \dfrac{4}{4y} + \dfrac{1}{4y} = \dfrac{5}{4y}$

104. $(4x)^{-2} - (3x)^{-1} = \dfrac{1}{(4x)^2} - \dfrac{1}{3x}$

$= \dfrac{3x}{(4x)^2 \cdot 3x} - \dfrac{(4x)^2}{3x(4x)^2}$

$= \dfrac{3x}{3x(4x)^2} - \dfrac{16x^2}{3x(4x)^2}$

$= \dfrac{3x-16x^2}{3x(16x^2)}$

$= \dfrac{x(3-16x)}{48x^3}$

$= \dfrac{3-16x}{48x^2}$

106.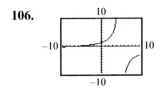

Section 6.3

Practice Exercises

1. a. $\dfrac{\frac{5k}{36m}}{\frac{15k}{9}} = \dfrac{5k}{36m} \div \dfrac{15k}{9}$

$= \dfrac{5k}{36m} \cdot \dfrac{9}{15k}$

$= \dfrac{5k \cdot 9}{36m \cdot 15k}$

$= \dfrac{1}{12m}$

b. $\dfrac{\frac{8x}{x-4}}{\frac{3}{x+4}} = \dfrac{8x}{x-4} \div \dfrac{3}{x+4}$

$= \dfrac{8x}{x-4} \cdot \dfrac{x+4}{3}$

$= \dfrac{8x(x+4)}{3(x-4)}$

c. $\dfrac{\frac{5}{a}+\frac{b}{a^2}}{\frac{5a}{b^2}+\frac{1}{b}} = \dfrac{\frac{5\cdot a}{a\cdot a}+\frac{b}{a^2}}{\frac{5a}{b^2}+\frac{1\cdot b}{b\cdot b}}$

$= \dfrac{\frac{5a+b}{a^2}}{\frac{5a+b}{b^2}}$

$= \dfrac{5a+b}{a^2} \cdot \dfrac{b^2}{5a+b}$

$= \dfrac{b^2(5a+b)}{a^2(5a+b)}$

$= \dfrac{b^2}{a^2}$

2. a. The LCD is $(x-4)(x+4)$.

$\dfrac{\frac{8x}{x-4}}{\frac{3}{x+4}} = \dfrac{\left(\frac{8x}{x-4}\right)\cdot(x-4)(x+4)}{\left(\frac{3}{x+4}\right)\cdot(x-4)(x+4)}$

$= \dfrac{8x(x+4)}{3(x-4)}$

b. The LCD is a^2b^2.

$\dfrac{\frac{b}{a^2}+\frac{1}{a}}{\frac{a}{b^2}+\frac{1}{b}} = \dfrac{\left(\frac{b}{a^2}+\frac{1}{a}\right)\cdot a^2b^2}{\left(\frac{a}{b^2}+\frac{1}{b}\right)\cdot a^2b^2}$

$= \dfrac{\frac{b}{a^2}\cdot a^2b^2 + \frac{1}{a}\cdot a^2b^2}{\frac{a}{b^2}\cdot a^2b^2 + \frac{1}{b}\cdot a^2b^2}$

$= \dfrac{b^3+ab^2}{a^3+a^2b}$

$= \dfrac{b^2(b+a)}{a^2(a+b)}$

$= \dfrac{b^2}{a^2}$

3. $\dfrac{3x^{-1}+x^{-2}y^{-1}}{y^{-2}+xy^{-1}} = \dfrac{\frac{3}{x}+\frac{1}{x^2y}}{\frac{1}{y^2}+\frac{x}{y}}$

The LCD is x^2y^2.

$= \dfrac{\left(\frac{3}{x}+\frac{1}{x^2y}\right)\cdot x^2y^2}{\left(\frac{1}{y^2}+\frac{x}{y}\right)\cdot x^2y^2}$

$= \dfrac{\frac{3}{x}\cdot x^2y^2 + \frac{1}{x^2y}\cdot x^2y^2}{\frac{1}{y^2}\cdot x^2y^2 + \frac{x}{y}\cdot x^2y^2}$

$= \dfrac{3xy^2+y}{x^2+x^3y}$ or $\dfrac{y(3xy+1)}{x^2(1+xy)}$

4. $\dfrac{(3x)^{-1}-2}{5x^{-1}+2} = \dfrac{\frac{1}{3x}-2}{\frac{5}{x}+2}$

$= \dfrac{\left(\frac{1}{3x}-2\right)\cdot 3x}{\left(\frac{5}{x}+2\right)\cdot 3x}$

$= \dfrac{\frac{1}{3x}\cdot 3x - 2\cdot 3x}{\frac{5}{x}\cdot 3x + 2\cdot 3x}$

$= \dfrac{1-6x}{15+6x}$

Vocabulary and Readiness Check

1. $\dfrac{\frac{7}{x}}{\frac{1}{x}+\frac{z}{x}} = \dfrac{x\left(\frac{7}{x}\right)}{x\left(\frac{1}{x}\right)+x\left(\frac{z}{x}\right)} = \dfrac{7}{1+z}$

2. $\dfrac{\frac{x}{4}}{\frac{x^2}{2}+\frac{1}{4}} = \dfrac{4\left(\frac{x}{4}\right)}{4\left(\frac{x^2}{2}\right)+4\left(\frac{1}{4}\right)} = \dfrac{x}{2x^2+1}$

3. $x^{-2} = \dfrac{1}{\underline{x^2}}$

4. $y^{-3} = \dfrac{1}{\underline{y^3}}$

5. $2x^{-1} = \dfrac{2}{\underline{x}}$

6. $(2x)^{-1} = \dfrac{1}{\underline{2x}}$

7. $(9y)^{-1} = \dfrac{1}{\underline{9y}}$

8. $9y^{-2} = \dfrac{9}{\underline{y^2}}$

Exercise Set 6.3

2. $\dfrac{\frac{15}{2x}}{\frac{5}{6x}} = \dfrac{15}{2x} \cdot \dfrac{6x}{5} = \dfrac{90x}{10x} = 9$

4. $\dfrac{2+\frac{1}{7}}{3-\frac{4}{7}} = \dfrac{7\left(2+\frac{1}{7}\right)}{7\left(3-\frac{4}{7}\right)} = \dfrac{14+1}{21-4} = \dfrac{15}{17}$

6. $\dfrac{\frac{x}{x+2}}{\frac{2}{x+2}} = \dfrac{x}{x+2} \cdot \dfrac{x+2}{2} = \dfrac{x}{2}$

8. $\dfrac{5-\frac{3}{x}}{x+\frac{2}{3x}} = \dfrac{3x\left(5-\frac{3}{x}\right)}{3x\left(x+\frac{2}{3x}\right)} = \dfrac{15x-9}{3x^2+2} = \dfrac{3(5x-3)}{3x^2+2}$

10. $\dfrac{\frac{x^2-9y^2}{xy}}{\frac{1}{y}-\frac{3}{x}} = \dfrac{xy\left(\frac{x^2-9y^2}{xy}\right)}{xy\left(\frac{1}{y}-\frac{3}{x}\right)}$

$= \dfrac{x^2-9y^2}{x-3y}$

$= \dfrac{(x+3y)(x-3y)}{x-3y}$

$= x+3y$

12. $\dfrac{\frac{x+3}{12}}{\frac{4x-5}{15}} = \dfrac{x+3}{12} \cdot \dfrac{15}{4x-5} = \dfrac{5(x+3)}{4(4x-5)}$

14. $\dfrac{\frac{2}{x^2}+\frac{1}{x}}{\frac{4}{x^2}-\frac{1}{x}} = \dfrac{x^2\left(\frac{2}{x^2}+\frac{1}{x}\right)}{x^2\left(\frac{4}{x^2}-\frac{1}{x}\right)} = \dfrac{2+x}{4-x}$

16. $\dfrac{\frac{1}{y}+\frac{3}{y^2}}{y+\frac{27}{y^2}} = \dfrac{y^2\left(\frac{1}{y}+\frac{3}{y^2}\right)}{y^2\left(y+\frac{27}{y^2}\right)}$

$= \dfrac{y+3}{y^3+27}$

$= \dfrac{y+3}{(y+3)(y^2-3y+9)}$

$= \dfrac{1}{y^2-3y+9}$

18. $\dfrac{\frac{3}{x-4}-\frac{2}{4-x}}{\frac{2}{x-4}-\frac{2}{x}} = \dfrac{\frac{3}{x-4}-\frac{-2}{x-4}}{\frac{2x-2(x-4)}{x(x-4)}}$

$= \dfrac{\frac{5}{x-4}}{\frac{2x-2x+8}{x(x-4)}}$

$= \dfrac{5}{x-4} \cdot \dfrac{x(x-4)}{8}$

$= \dfrac{5x}{8}$

20.
$$\frac{\frac{5}{a+2}-\frac{1}{a-2}}{\frac{3}{2+a}+\frac{6}{2-a}}=\frac{\frac{5}{a+2}-\frac{1}{a-2}}{\frac{3}{a+2}+\frac{-6}{a-2}}$$

$$=\frac{\frac{5(a-2)-1(a+2)}{(a+2)(a-2)}}{\frac{3(a-2)-6(a+2)}{(a+2)(a-2)}}$$

$$=\frac{\frac{5a-10-a-2}{(a+2)(a-2)}}{\frac{3a-6-6a-12}{(a+2)(a-2)}}$$

$$=\frac{4a-12}{(a+2)(a-2)}\cdot\frac{(a+2)(a-2)}{-3a-18}$$

$$=\frac{4(a-3)}{(a+2)(a-2)}\cdot\frac{(a+2)(a-2)}{-3(a+6)}$$

$$=-\frac{4(a-3)}{3(a+6)}$$

22.
$$\frac{2+\frac{1}{x}}{4x-\frac{1}{x}}=\frac{\left(2+\frac{1}{x}\right)\cdot x}{\left(4x-\frac{1}{x}\right)\cdot x}$$

$$=\frac{2x+1}{4x^2-1}$$

$$=\frac{2x+1}{(2x+1)(2x-1)}$$

$$=\frac{1}{2x-1}$$

24.
$$\frac{1-\frac{2}{x}}{x-\frac{4}{x}}=\frac{\left(1-\frac{2}{x}\right)\cdot x}{\left(x-\frac{4}{x}\right)\cdot x}$$

$$=\frac{x-2}{x^2-4}$$

$$=\frac{x-2}{(x-2)(x+2)}$$

$$=\frac{1}{x+2}$$

26.
$$\frac{\frac{7y}{x^2+xy}}{\frac{y^2}{x^2}}=\frac{7y}{x^2+xy}\div\frac{y^2}{x^2}$$

$$=\frac{7y}{x^2+xy}\cdot\frac{x^2}{y^2}$$

$$=\frac{7y}{x(x+y)}\cdot\frac{x^2}{y^2}$$

$$=\frac{7x}{y(x+y)}$$

28.
$$\frac{\frac{5}{x^2}-\frac{2}{x}}{\frac{1}{x}+2}=\frac{\left(\frac{5}{x^2}-\frac{2}{x}\right)x^2}{\left(\frac{1}{x}+2\right)x^2}=\frac{5-2x}{x+2x^2}=\frac{5-2x}{x(1+2x)}$$

30.
$$\frac{\frac{x}{4}-\frac{4}{x}}{1-\frac{4}{x}}=\frac{\left(\frac{x}{4}-\frac{4}{x}\right)4x}{\left(1-\frac{4}{x}\right)4x}$$

$$=\frac{x^2-16}{4x-16}$$

$$=\frac{(x+4)(x-4)}{4(x-4)}$$

$$=\frac{x+4}{4}$$

32.
$$\frac{\frac{x+3}{x^2-9}}{1+\frac{1}{x-3}}=\frac{\frac{x+3}{x^2-9}}{\frac{x-3}{x-3}+\frac{1}{x-3}}$$

$$=\frac{\frac{x+3}{x^2-9}}{\frac{x-3+1}{x-3}}$$

$$=\frac{x+3}{(x+3)(x-3)}\cdot\frac{x-3}{x-2}$$

$$=\frac{1}{x-2}$$

34.
$$\frac{\frac{2}{x+2}+\frac{6}{x+7}}{\frac{4x+13}{x^2+9x+14}}=\frac{\frac{2(x+7)+6(x+2)}{(x+2)(x+7)}}{\frac{4x+13}{x^2+9x+14}}$$

$$=\frac{\frac{2x+14+6x+12}{(x+2)(x+7)}}{\frac{4x+13}{x^2+9x+14}}$$

$$=\frac{8x+26}{(x+2)(x+7)}\cdot\frac{x^2+9x+14}{4x+13}$$

$$=\frac{2(4x+13)}{(x+2)(x+7)}\cdot\frac{(x+2)(x+7)}{4x+13}$$

$$=2$$

36.
$$\frac{a^{-3}+b^{-1}}{a^{-2}}=\frac{\frac{1}{a^3}+\frac{1}{b}}{\frac{1}{a^2}}=\frac{a^3b\left(\frac{1}{a^3}+\frac{1}{b}\right)}{a^3b\left(\frac{1}{a^2}\right)}=\frac{b+a^3}{ab}$$

38.
$$\frac{x^{-1}+y^{-1}}{3x^{-2}+5y^{-2}}=\frac{\frac{1}{x}+\frac{1}{y}}{\frac{3}{x^2}+\frac{5}{y^2}}$$
$$=\frac{x^2y^2\left(\frac{1}{x}+\frac{1}{y}\right)}{x^2y^2\left(\frac{3}{x^2}+\frac{5}{y^2}\right)}$$
$$=\frac{xy^2+x^2y}{3y^2+5x^2}$$
$$=\frac{xy(y+x)}{3y^2+5x^2}$$

40.
$$\frac{x^{-2}}{x+3x^{-1}}=\frac{\frac{1}{x^2}}{x+\frac{3}{x}}$$
$$=\frac{x^2\left(\frac{1}{x^2}\right)}{x^2\left(x+\frac{3}{x}\right)}$$
$$=\frac{1}{x^3+3x}$$
$$=\frac{1}{x(x^2+3)}$$

42.
$$\frac{a^{-1}-4}{4+a^{-1}}=\frac{\frac{1}{a}-4}{4+\frac{1}{a}}=\frac{a\left(\frac{1}{a}-4\right)}{a\left(4+\frac{1}{a}\right)}=\frac{1-4a}{4a+1}$$

44.
$$\frac{5x^{-2}-3y^{-1}}{x^{-1}+y^{-1}}=\frac{\frac{5}{x^2}-\frac{3}{y}}{\frac{1}{x}+\frac{1}{y}}$$
$$=\frac{x^2y\left(\frac{5}{x^2}-\frac{3}{y}\right)}{x^2y\left(\frac{1}{x}+\frac{1}{y}\right)}$$
$$=\frac{5y-3x^2}{xy+x^2}$$
$$=\frac{5y-3x^2}{x(y+x)}$$

46.
$$\frac{a^{-1}+2a^{-2}}{2a^{-1}+(2a)^{-1}}=\frac{\frac{1}{a}+\frac{2}{a^2}}{\frac{2}{a}+\frac{1}{2a}}$$
$$=\frac{2a^2\left(\frac{1}{a}+\frac{2}{a^2}\right)}{2a^2\left(\frac{2}{a}+\frac{1}{2a}\right)}$$
$$=\frac{2a+4}{4a+a}$$
$$=\frac{2a+4}{5a}\text{ or }\frac{2(a+2)}{5a}$$

48.
$$\frac{x^{-2}y^{-2}}{5x^{-1}+2y^{-1}}=\frac{\frac{1}{x^2y^2}}{\frac{5}{x}+\frac{2}{y}}$$
$$=\frac{x^2y^2\left(\frac{1}{x^2y^2}\right)}{x^2y^2\left(\frac{5}{x}+\frac{2}{y}\right)}$$
$$=\frac{1}{5xy^2+2x^2y}$$
$$=\frac{1}{xy(5y+2x)}$$

50.
$$\frac{3x^{-1}+3y^{-1}}{4x^{-2}-9y^{-2}}=\frac{\frac{3}{x}+\frac{3}{y}}{\frac{4}{x^2}-\frac{9}{y^2}}$$
$$=\frac{x^2y^2\left(\frac{3}{x}+\frac{3}{y}\right)}{x^2y^2\left(\frac{4}{x^2}-\frac{9}{y^2}\right)}$$
$$=\frac{3xy^2+3x^2y}{4y^2-9x^2}$$
$$=\frac{3xy(y+x)}{(2y+3x)(2y-3x)}$$

52.
$$\frac{-36xb^3}{9xb^2}=\frac{9xb^2\cdot(-4b)}{9xb^2\cdot1}=-4b$$

54.
$$\frac{48x^3y^2}{-4xy}=\frac{4xy\cdot12x^2y}{4xy\cdot(-1)}=-12x^2y$$

56. $|2y+1|=1$
$$2y+1=-1\quad\text{or}\quad2y+1=1$$
$$2y=-2\quad\text{or}\quad\quad2y=0$$
$$y=-1\quad\text{or}\quad\quad\quad y=0$$
The solution set is $\{-1,0\}$.

58. $\dfrac{\frac{a}{7}}{\frac{b}{13}} = \dfrac{a}{7} \div \dfrac{b}{13} = \dfrac{a}{7} \cdot \dfrac{13}{b}$

Both b and d are equivalent to the original expression.

60. $\dfrac{E}{\frac{I}{9}} = I \div \dfrac{I}{9} = E \cdot \dfrac{9}{I} = \dfrac{9E}{I}$

62. Answers may vary

64. $\dfrac{(x+2)^{-1}+(x-2)^{-1}}{(x^2-4)^{-1}} = \dfrac{\frac{1}{x+2}+\frac{1}{x-2}}{\frac{1}{x^2-4}}$

$= \dfrac{(x^2-4)\left(\frac{1}{x+2}+\frac{1}{x-2}\right)}{(x^2-4)\left(\frac{1}{x^2-4}\right)}$

$= \dfrac{(x-2)+(x+2)}{1}$

$= 2x$

66. $\dfrac{x}{1-\frac{1}{1-\frac{1}{x}}} = \dfrac{x}{1-\frac{1}{\frac{x-1}{x}}}$

$= \dfrac{x}{1-\frac{x}{x-1}}$

$= \dfrac{(x-1)(x)}{(x-1)\left(1-\frac{x}{x-1}\right)}$

$= \dfrac{x(x-1)}{x-1-x}$

$= \dfrac{x(x-1)}{-1}$

$= -x(x-1)$

68. $\dfrac{\frac{2}{x^2}-\frac{1}{xy}-\frac{1}{y^2}}{\frac{1}{x^2}-\frac{3}{xy}+\frac{2}{y^2}} = \dfrac{x^2y^2\left(\frac{2}{x^2}-\frac{1}{xy}-\frac{1}{y^2}\right)}{x^2y^2\left(\frac{1}{x^2}-\frac{3}{xy}+\frac{2}{y^2}\right)}$

$= \dfrac{2y^2-xy-x^2}{y^2-3xy+2x^2}$

$= \dfrac{(2y+x)(y-x)}{(y-2x)(y-x)}$

$= \dfrac{2y+x}{y-2x}$

70. $\dfrac{9x^{-1}-5(x-y)^{-1}}{4(x-y)^{-1}} = \dfrac{\frac{9}{x}-\frac{5}{x-y}}{\frac{4}{x-y}}$

$= \dfrac{\frac{9(x-y)-5x}{x(x-y)}}{\frac{4}{x-y}}$

$= \dfrac{\frac{9x-9y-5x}{x(x-y)}}{\frac{4}{x-y}}$

$= \dfrac{4x-9y}{x(x-y)} \cdot \dfrac{x-y}{4}$

$= \dfrac{4x-9y}{4x}$

72. $f(x) = \dfrac{5}{x}$

    a. $f(a+h) = \dfrac{5}{a+h}$

    b. $f(a) = \dfrac{5}{a}$

    c. $\dfrac{f(a+h)-f(a)}{h} = \dfrac{\frac{5}{a+h}-\frac{5}{a}}{h}$

    d. $\dfrac{\frac{5}{a+h}-\frac{5}{a}}{h} = \dfrac{a(a+h)\left(\frac{5}{a+h}-\frac{5}{a}\right)}{ah(a+h)}$

$= \dfrac{5a-5(a+h)}{ah(a+h)}$

$= \dfrac{5a-5a-5h}{ah(a+h)}$

$= \dfrac{-5h}{ah(a+h)}$

$= \dfrac{-5}{a(a+h)}$

74. $f(x) = \dfrac{2}{x^2}$

    a. $f(a+h) = \dfrac{2}{(a+h)^2}$

    b. $f(a) = \dfrac{2}{a^2}$

c. $\dfrac{f(a+h)-f(a)}{h}=\dfrac{\frac{2}{(a+h)^2}-\frac{2}{a^2}}{h}$

d. $\dfrac{\frac{2}{(a+h)^2}-\frac{2}{a^2}}{h}=\dfrac{a^2(a+h)^2\left(\frac{2}{(a+h)^2}-\frac{2}{a^2}\right)}{a^2(a+h)^2\cdot h}$

$=\dfrac{2a^2-2(a+h)^2}{a^2h(a+h)^2}$

$=\dfrac{2a^2-2(a^2+2ah+h^2)}{a^2h(a+h)^2}$

$=\dfrac{2a^2-2a^2-4ah-2h^2}{a^2h(a+h)^2}$

$=\dfrac{-4ah-2h^2}{a^2h(a+h)^2}$

$=\dfrac{-2h(2a+h)}{a^2h(a+h)^2}$

$=\dfrac{-2(2a+h)}{a^2(a+h)^2}$

Section 6.4

Practice Exercises

1. $\dfrac{18a^3-12a^2+30a}{6a}=\dfrac{18a^3}{6a}-\dfrac{12a^2}{6a}+\dfrac{30a}{6a}$

$=3a^2-2a+5$

2. $\dfrac{5a^3b^4-8a^2b^3+ab^2-8b}{ab^2}$

$=\dfrac{5a^3b^4}{ab^2}-\dfrac{8a^2b^3}{ab^2}+\dfrac{ab^2}{ab^2}-\dfrac{8b}{ab^2}$

$=5a^2b^2-8ab+1-\dfrac{8}{ab}$

3.
$$
\begin{array}{r}
3x-2 \\
x+3\overline{)3x^2+7x-6} \\
\underline{3x^2+9x} \\
-2x-6 \\
\underline{-2x-6} \\
0
\end{array}
$$
Answer: $3x-2$

4.
$$
\begin{array}{r}
3x-2 \\
2x-1\overline{)6x^2-7x+2} \\
\underline{6x^2-3x} \\
-4x+2 \\
\underline{-4x+2} \\
0
\end{array}
$$
Answer: $3x-2$

5.
$$
\begin{array}{r}
5x^2-6x+8 \\
x+3\overline{)5x^3+9x^2-10x+30} \\
\underline{5x^3+15x^2} \\
-6x^2-10x \\
\underline{-6x^2-18x} \\
8x+30 \\
\underline{8x+24} \\
6
\end{array}
$$
Answer: $5x^2-6x+8+\dfrac{6}{x+3}$

6.
$$
\begin{array}{r}
2x^2+3x-2 \\
x^2+0x+1\overline{)2x^4+3x^3+0x^2-5x+2} \\
\underline{2x^4+0x^3+2x^2} \\
3x^3-2x^2-5x \\
\underline{3x^3+0x^2+3x} \\
-2x^2-8x+2 \\
\underline{-2x^2+0x-2} \\
-8x+4
\end{array}
$$
Answer: $2x^2+3x-2+\dfrac{-8x+4}{x^2+1}$

7.
$$
\begin{array}{r}
16x^2+20x+25 \\
4x-5\overline{)64x^3+0x^2+0x-125} \\
\underline{64x^3-80x^2} \\
80x^2+0x \\
\underline{80x^2-100x} \\
100x-125 \\
\underline{100x-125} \\
0
\end{array}
$$
Answer: $16x^2+20x+25$

8. Since $x - c = x - 1$, c is 1.

$$\begin{array}{r|rrrr} 1 & 4 & -3 & 6 & 5 \\ & & 4 & 1 & 7 \\ \hline & 4 & 1 & 7 & 12 \end{array}$$

$$4x^2 + x + 7 + \frac{12}{x-1}$$

9. Since $x - c = x + 3 = x - (-3)$, c is -3.

$$\begin{array}{r|rrrrr} -3 & 1 & 3 & -5 & 6 & 12 \\ & & -3 & 0 & 15 & -63 \\ \hline & 1 & 0 & -5 & 21 & -51 \end{array}$$

$$x^3 - 5x + 21 - \frac{51}{x+3}$$

10. a. $P(x) = x^3 - 5x - 2$

$$\begin{aligned} P(2) &= 2^3 - 5(2) - 2 \\ &= 8 - 10 - 2 \\ &= -4 \end{aligned}$$

b. Since $x - c = x - 2$, c is 2.

$$\begin{array}{r|rrrr} 2 & 1 & 0 & -5 & -2 \\ & & 2 & 4 & -2 \\ \hline & 1 & 2 & -1 & -4 \end{array}$$

The remainder is -4.

11. $\begin{array}{r|rrrrrr} 3 & 2 & -18 & 0 & 90 & 59 & 0 \\ & & 6 & -36 & -108 & -54 & 15 \\ \hline & 2 & -12 & -36 & -18 & 5 & 15 \end{array}$

$$P(3) = 15$$

Exercise Set 6.4

2. $\dfrac{6x^4 - 3x^3}{3x^2} = \dfrac{6x^4}{3x^2} - \dfrac{3x^3}{3x^2} = 2x^2 - x$

4. $\dfrac{4x^3 y + 12x^2 y^2 - 4xy^3}{4xy}$

$$= \frac{4x^3 y}{4xy} + \frac{12x^2 y^2}{4xy} - \frac{4xy^3}{4xy}$$

$$= x^2 + 3xy - y^2$$

6. $\dfrac{6x^5 y + 75x^4 y - 24x^3 y^2}{3x^4 y}$

$$= \frac{6x^5 y}{3x^4 y} + \frac{75x^4 y}{3x^4 y} - \frac{24x^3 y^2}{3x^4 y}$$

$$= 2x + 25 - \frac{8y}{x}$$

8.

$$\begin{array}{r} y+2 \\ y+5 \overline{\smash{\big)}\, y^2 + 7y + 10} \\ \underline{y^2 + 5y } \\ 2y + 10 \\ \underline{2y + 10} \\ 0 \end{array}$$

$$\frac{y^2 + 7y + 10}{y+5} = y + 2$$

10.

$$\begin{array}{r} 3x + 4 \\ x+5 \overline{\smash{\big)}\, 3x^2 + 19x + 20} \\ \underline{3x^2 + 15x } \\ 4x + 20 \\ \underline{4x + 20} \\ 0 \end{array}$$

$$\frac{3x^2 + 19x + 20}{x+5} = 3x + 4$$

12.

$$\begin{array}{r} 2x + \frac{1}{3} \\ 3x-9 \overline{\smash{\big)}\, 6x^2 - 17x - 3} \\ \underline{6x^2 - 18x } \\ x - 3 \\ \underline{x - 3} \\ 0 \end{array}$$

$$\frac{6x^2 - 17x - 3}{3x - 9} = 2x + \frac{1}{3}$$

14.

$$\begin{array}{r} 2x^2 + \frac{1}{2}x + 3 \\ 4x+8 \overline{\smash{\big)}\, 8x^3 + 18x^2 + 16x + 24} \\ \underline{8x^3 + 16x^2 } \\ 2x^2 + 16x \\ \underline{2x^2 + 4x} \\ 12x + 24 \\ \underline{12x + 24} \\ 0 \end{array}$$

$$\frac{8x^3 + 18x^2 + 16x + 24}{4x + 8} = 2x^2 + \frac{1}{2}x + 3$$

16.

$$\begin{array}{r} 5x^2 +2 \\ 2x-3\overline{\smash{\big)}\,10x^3-15x^2+4x-6} \\ \underline{10x^3-15x^2} \\ 4x-6 \\ \underline{4x-6} \\ 0 \end{array}$$

$$\frac{4x-15x^2+10x^3-6}{2x-3}=5x^2+2$$

18.

$$\begin{array}{r} 2x^3-6x^2+7x-18 \\ x^2+0x-3\overline{\smash{\big)}\,2x^5-6x^4+x^3+0x^2-4x+3} \\ \underline{2x^5+0x^4-6x^3} \\ -6x^4+7x^3+0x^2 \\ \underline{-6x^4+0x^3+18x^2} \\ 7x^3-18x^2-4x \\ \underline{7x^3+0x^2-21x} \\ -18x^2+17x+3 \\ \underline{-18x^2+0x+54} \\ 17x-51 \end{array}$$

$$\frac{2x^5-6x^4+x^3-4x+3}{x^2-3}$$
$$=2x^3-6x^2+7x-18+\frac{17x-51}{x^2-3}$$

20.

$$\begin{array}{r} x^3+\frac{7}{3}x^2+7x+22 \\ x-3\overline{\smash{\big)}\,x^4-\frac{2}{3}x^3+0x^2+x+0} \\ \underline{x^4-3x^3} \\ \frac{7}{3}x^3+0x^2 \\ \underline{\frac{7}{3}x^3-7x^2} \\ 7x^2+x \\ \underline{7x^2-21x} \\ 22x+0 \\ \underline{22x-66} \\ 66 \end{array}$$

$$\frac{x^4-\frac{2}{3}x^3+x}{x-3}=x^3+\frac{7}{3}x^2+7x+22+\frac{66}{x-3}$$

22. $x-2=x-c$ where $c=2$.

$$\begin{array}{r|rrr} 2 & 1 & -14 & 24 \\ & & 2 & -24 \\ \hline & 1 & -12 & 0 \end{array}$$

$$\frac{x^2-14x+24}{x-2}=x-12$$

24. $x+4=x-c$ where $c=-4$.

$$\begin{array}{r|rrr} -4 & 1 & 12 & 32 \\ & & -4 & -32 \\ \hline & 1 & 8 & 0 \end{array}$$

$$\frac{x^2+12x+32}{x+4}=x+8$$

26. $x+5=x-c$ where $c=-5$.

$$\begin{array}{r|rrrr} -5 & 1 & 6 & 4 & -7 \\ & & -5 & -5 & 5 \\ \hline & 1 & 1 & -1 & -2 \end{array}$$

$$\frac{x^3+6x^2+4x-7}{x+5}=x^2+x-1-\frac{2}{x+5}$$

28. $x-1=x-c$ where $c=1$.

$$\begin{array}{r|rrr} 1 & 3 & 0 & -4 \\ & & 3 & 3 \\ \hline & 3 & 3 & -1 \end{array}$$

$$\frac{3x^2-4}{x-1}=3x+3-\frac{1}{x-1}$$

30.

$$\frac{15x^3y-5x^2y+10xy^2}{5x^2y}=\frac{15x^3y}{5x^2y}-\frac{5x^2y}{5x^2y}+\frac{10xy^2}{5x^2y}$$
$$=3x-1+\frac{2y}{x}$$

32.

$$\begin{array}{r} 4x^2 \qquad\quad +1 \\ 5x-2\overline{\smash{)}20x^3-8x^2+5x-5} \\ \underline{20x^3-8x^2} \\ 5x-5 \\ \underline{5x-2} \\ -3 \end{array}$$

$$\frac{20x^3-8x^2+5x-5}{5x-2}=4x^2+1-\frac{3}{5x-2}$$

34. $x+2$ has the form $x-c$, where $c=-2$, so synthetic division can be used.

$$3x^3+4x-10=3x^3+0x^2+4x-10$$

$$\begin{array}{r|rrrr} -2 & 3 & 0 & 4 & -10 \\ & & -6 & 12 & -32 \\ \hline & 3 & -6 & 16 & -42 \end{array}$$

$$\frac{3x^3+4x-10}{x+2}=3x^2-6x+16-\frac{42}{x+2}$$

36. $x+2$ has the form $x-c$, where $c=-2$, so synthetic division can be used.

$$\begin{array}{r|rrrrr} -2 & 3 & 5 & -1 & 1 & -2 \\ & & -6 & 2 & -2 & 2 \\ \hline & 3 & -1 & 1 & -1 & 0 \end{array}$$

$$\frac{3x^4+5x^3-x^2+x-2}{x+2}=3x^3-x^2+x-1$$

38. $x-2$ has the form $x-c$, where $c=2$, so synthetic division can be used.

$$4x^3+x^4-x^2-16x-4=x^4+4x^3-x^2-16x-4$$

$$\begin{array}{r|rrrrr} 2 & 1 & 4 & -1 & -16 & -4 \\ & & 2 & 12 & 22 & 12 \\ \hline & 1 & 6 & 11 & 6 & 8 \end{array}$$

$$\frac{4x^3+x^4-x^2-16x-4}{x-2}$$
$$=x^3+6x^2+11x+6+\frac{8}{x-2}$$

40. $y+\dfrac{2}{3}$ has the form $x-c$, where $c=-\dfrac{2}{3}$, so synthetic division can be used.

$$\begin{array}{r|rrrr} -\frac{2}{3} & 9 & 9 & -1 & 2 \\ & & -6 & -2 & 2 \\ \hline & 9 & 3 & -3 & 4 \end{array}$$

$$\frac{9y^3+9y^2-y+2}{y+\frac{2}{3}}=9y^2+3y-3+\frac{4}{y+\frac{2}{3}}$$

42. $y-2$ has the form $x-c$, where $c=2$, so synthetic division can be used.

$$\begin{array}{r|rrrr} 2 & 1 & 0 & 0 & -8 \\ & & 2 & 4 & 8 \\ \hline & 1 & 2 & 4 & 0 \end{array}$$

$$\frac{y^3-8}{y-2}=y^2+2y+4$$

44.
$$\frac{x^6y^6-x^3y^3z+7x^3y}{-7yz^2}$$
$$=\frac{x^6y^6}{-7yz^2}-\frac{x^3y^3z}{-7yz^2}+\frac{7x^3y}{-7yz^2}$$
$$=-\frac{x^6y^5}{7z^2}+\frac{x^3y^2}{7z}-\frac{x^3}{z^2}$$

46. $5x^4-5x^2+10x^3-10x$
$$=5x^4+10x^3-5x^2-10x+0$$

$$\begin{array}{r} x^3 \qquad\qquad -x \\ 5x+10\overline{\smash{)}5x^4+10x^3-5x^2-10x+0} \\ \underline{5x^4+10x^3} \\ -5x^2-10x \\ \underline{-5x^2-10x} \\ 0 \end{array}$$

$$(5x^4-5x^2+10x^3-10x)\div(5x+10)=x^3-x$$

48.
$$\begin{array}{r|rrrr} 2 & 1 & 5 & -4 & -6 \\ & & 2 & 14 & 20 \\ \hline & 1 & 7 & 10 & 14 \end{array}$$

Thus, $P(2)=14$.

50.

$$\begin{array}{r|rrrr} -2 & 4 & 5 & -6 & -4 \\ & & -8 & 6 & 0 \\ \hline & 4 & -3 & 0 & -4 \end{array}$$

Thus, $P(-2) = -4$.

52.

$$\begin{array}{r|rrrrr} -2 & 1 & 0 & -3 & -2 & 5 \\ & & -2 & 4 & -2 & 8 \\ \hline & 1 & -2 & 1 & -4 & 13 \end{array}$$

Thus, $P(-2) = 13$.

54.

$$\begin{array}{r|rrrrr} \frac{1}{2} & 4 & -2 & 1 & -1 & -4 \\ & & 2 & 0 & \frac{1}{2} & -\frac{1}{4} \\ \hline & 4 & 0 & 1 & -\frac{1}{2} & -\frac{17}{4} \end{array}$$

Thus, $P\left(\dfrac{1}{2}\right) = -\dfrac{17}{4}$.

56.

$$\begin{array}{r|rrrrrr} \frac{2}{3} & 1 & 0 & -2 & 4 & -5 & 6 \\ & & \frac{2}{3} & \frac{4}{9} & -\frac{28}{27} & \frac{160}{81} & -\frac{490}{243} \\ \hline & 1 & \frac{2}{3} & -\frac{14}{9} & \frac{80}{27} & -\frac{245}{81} & \frac{968}{243} \end{array}$$

Thus, $P\left(\dfrac{2}{3}\right) = \dfrac{968}{243}$.

58.
$$4 - 2x = 17 - 5x$$
$$3x = 13$$
$$x = \frac{13}{3}$$

The solution is $\dfrac{13}{3}$.

60.
$$5x^2 + 10x = 15$$
$$5x^2 + 10x - 15 = 0$$
$$5(x^2 + 2x - 3) = 0$$
$$2(x+3)(x-1) = 0$$
$$x + 3 = 0 \quad \text{or} \quad x - 1 = 0$$
$$x = -3 \quad \text{or} \quad x = 1$$
The solutions are -3, 1.

62.
$$\frac{2x}{9} + 1 = \frac{7}{9}$$
$$9\left(\frac{2x}{9} + 1\right) = 9\left(\frac{7}{9}\right)$$
$$2x + 9 = 7$$
$$2x = -2$$
$$x = -1$$
The solution is -1.

64. $8y^3 + 1 = (2y)^3 + 1^3 = (2y+1)(4y^2 - 2y + 1)$

66. $a^3 - 27 = a^3 - 3^3 = (a-3)(a^2 + 3a + 9)$

68. $x^2 - x + xy - y = x(x-1) + y(x-1)$
$$= (x-1)(x+y)$$

70. $2x^3 - 32x = 2x(x^2 - 16)$
$$= 2x(x+4)(x-4)$$

72. $(x^4 - 6) \div (x^3 + 3x - 1)$ is not a candidate for synthetic division since $x^3 + 3x - 1$ does not have the form $x - c$.

74. $(3x^2 + 7x - 1) \div \left(x - \dfrac{1}{3}\right)$ is a candidate for synthetic division since $x - \dfrac{1}{3}$ is in the form $x - c$, where $c = \dfrac{1}{3}$.

76. The degree of the remainder must be less than that of the divisor, or 1 in this case. The choice is b.

78.
$$\frac{12x^5 - 48x^3 + 3}{6} = \frac{12x^5}{6} - \frac{48x^3}{6} + \frac{3}{6}$$
$$= 2x^5 - 8x^3 + \frac{1}{2}$$

The length of each side is $\left(2x^5 - 8x^3 + \dfrac{1}{2}\right)$ miles.

80.

$$\begin{array}{r}
x - 5 \\
2x - 7 \overline{\smash{)}\, 2x^2 - 17x + 35} \\
\underline{2x^2 - 7x } \\
-10x + 35 \\
\underline{-10x + 35} \\
0
\end{array}$$

The height is $(x - 5)$ centimeters.

82. $V = lwh$ so $w = \dfrac{V}{lh}$

$$= \frac{x^4 + 6x^3 - 7x^2}{x^2(x+7)}$$

$$= \frac{x^4 + 6x^3 - 7x^2}{x^3 + 7x^2}$$

$$
\begin{array}{r}
x - 1 \\
x^3 + 7x^2 \overline{\smash{\big)}\ x^4 + 6x^3 - 7x^2} \\
\underline{x^4 + 7x^3} \\
-x^3 - 7x^2 \\
\underline{-x^3 - 7x^2} \\
0
\end{array}
$$

The width is $(x - 1)$ meters.

84.
$$
\begin{array}{r}
2x^2 + \frac{1}{2}x \ - 5 \\
x + 2 \overline{\smash{\big)}\ 2x^3 + \frac{9}{2}x^2 - 4x - 10} \\
\underline{2x^3 + 4x^2} \\
\frac{1}{2}x^2 - 4x \\
\underline{\frac{1}{2}x^2 + \ x} \\
-5x - 10 \\
\underline{-5x - 10} \\
0
\end{array}
$$

Answer: $2x^2 + \dfrac{1}{2}x - 5$

86.
$$
\begin{array}{r}
x^3 - \frac{1}{4}x^2 \ \ + \frac{1}{2} \\
2x + 1 \overline{\smash{\big)}\ 2x^4 + \frac{1}{2}x^3 - \frac{1}{4}x^2 + x + 0} \\
\underline{2x^4 \ + x^3} \\
-\frac{1}{2}x^3 - \frac{1}{4}x^2 \\
\underline{-\frac{1}{2}x^3 - \frac{1}{4}x^2} \\
x + 0 \\
x + \frac{1}{2} \\
\underline{\phantom{x + \frac{1}{2}}} \\
-\frac{1}{2}
\end{array}
$$

Answer:

$$x^3 - \frac{1}{4}x^2 + \frac{1}{2} + \frac{-\frac{1}{2}}{2x+1} = x^3 - \frac{1}{4}x^2 + \frac{1}{2} - \frac{1}{2(2x+1)}$$

88.
$$
\begin{array}{r}
3x^4 \qquad\qquad - 2x \\
3x + 2 \overline{\smash{\big)}\ 9x^5 + 6x^4 + 0x^3 - 6x^2 - 4x + \ 0} \\
\underline{9x^5 + 6x^4} \\
-6x^2 - 4x \\
\underline{-6x^2 - 4x} \\
0
\end{array}
$$

Answer: $3x^4 - 2x$

90. $\dfrac{f(x)}{g(x)} = \dfrac{12x^4 - 9x^3 + 3x - 1}{3x}$

$$= \frac{12x^4}{3x} - \frac{9x^3}{3x} + \frac{3x}{3x} - \frac{1}{3x}$$

$$= 4x^3 - 3x^2 + 1 - \frac{1}{3x}$$

Setting the denominator equal to 0, we get
$3x = 0$
$x = 0.$

Thus, $x = 0$ is not in the domain of $\dfrac{f(x)}{g(x)}$.

92. $\dfrac{f(x)}{g(x)} = \dfrac{2x^3 - 4x^2 + 1}{x + 3}$

$$
\begin{array}{r}
2x^2 - 10x + 30 \\
x + 3 \overline{\smash{\big)}\ 2x^3 - 4x^2 + \ 0x + 1} \\
\underline{2x^3 + 6x^2} \\
-10x^2 + \ 0x \\
\underline{-10x^2 - 30x} \\
30x + \ 1 \\
\underline{30x + 90} \\
-89
\end{array}
$$

Therefore, $\dfrac{f(x)}{g(x)} = \dfrac{2x^3 - 4x^2 + 1}{x + 3}$

$$= 2x^2 - 10x + 30 - \frac{89}{x+3}$$

Setting the denominator equal to 0, we get
$x + 3 = 0$
$x = -3.$

Thus, $x = -3$ is not in the domain of $\dfrac{f(x)}{g(x)}$.

94. Answers may vary

96. Answers may vary

98.

$$
\begin{array}{r|rrrr}
2 & 1 & -2 & -3 & 6 \\
  &   & 2 & 0 & -6 \\
\hline
  & 1 & 0 & -3 & 0
\end{array}
$$

Remainder = 0. Therefore,

$x^3 - 2x^2 - 3x + 6 = (x-2)(x^2 - 3)$.

100. $(2x^2 + 5x - 6)(x - 5) + 3$

$= 2x^3 - 10x^2 + 5x^2 - 25x - 6x + 30 + 3$

$= 2x^3 - 5x^2 - 31x + 33$

102. a. $m(x) = \dfrac{P(x)}{R(x)}$

$= \dfrac{-7x^3 + 94x^2 - 76x + 59}{939x - 194}$

b. $m(10) = \dfrac{-7(10)^3 + 94(10)^2 - 76(10) + 59}{939(10) - 194}$

$= \dfrac{1699}{9196}$

≈ 0.18

The profit margin will be 0.18 in 2010.

Section 6.5

Practice Exercises

1. The LCD is 8.

$$\frac{5x}{4} - \frac{3}{2} = \frac{7x}{8}$$

$$8\left(\frac{5x}{4} - \frac{3}{2}\right) = 8\left(\frac{7x}{8}\right)$$

$$8 \cdot \frac{5x}{4} - 8 \cdot \frac{3}{2} = 8 \cdot \frac{7x}{8}$$

$$10x - 12 = 7x$$

$$3x = 12$$

$$x = 4$$

2. The LCD of the denominators x, $5x$, and 5 is $5x$.

$$\frac{6}{x} - \frac{x+9}{5x} = \frac{2}{5}$$

$$5x\left(\frac{6}{x} - \frac{x+9}{5x}\right) = 5x\left(\frac{2}{5}\right)$$

$$5x \cdot \frac{6}{x} - 5x \cdot \frac{x+9}{5x} = 5x \cdot \frac{2}{5}$$

$$30 - (x + 9) = 2x$$

$$30 - x - 9 = 2x$$

$$21 = 3x$$

$$7 = x$$

3. The LCD is $x + 3$.

$$\frac{x-5}{x+3} = \frac{2(x-1)}{x+3}$$

$$(x+3) \cdot \frac{x-5}{x+3} = (x+3) \cdot \frac{2(x-1)}{x+3}$$

$$x - 5 = 2(x-1)$$

$$x - 5 = 2x - 2$$

$$-3 = x$$

The number -3 makes the denominator $x + 3$ equal to 0, so it is not a solution. The solution set is { } or $\varnothing$.

4. The LCD is $x(5x - 1)$.

$$\frac{5x}{5x-1} + \frac{1}{x} = \frac{1}{5x-1}$$

$$x(5x-1) \cdot \frac{5x}{5x-1} + x(5x-1) \cdot \frac{1}{x} = x(5x-1) \cdot \frac{1}{5x-1}$$

$$x(5x) + (5x-1) = x$$

$$5x^2 + 5x - 1 - x = 0$$

$$5x^2 + 4x - 1 = 0$$

$$(5x - 1)(x + 1) = 0$$

$$5x - 1 = 0 \ \text{ or } \ x + 1 = 0$$

$$x = \frac{1}{5} \ \text{ or } \quad x = -1$$

The number $\dfrac{1}{5}$ makes the denominator $5x - 1$ equal 0, so it is not a solution. The solution is -1.

5. $x^2 - 4 = (x + 2)(x - 2)$

The LCD is $(x + 2)(x - 2)$.

$$\frac{2}{x-2} - \frac{5+2x}{x^2-4} = \frac{x}{x+2}$$

$$(x+2)(x-2) \cdot \frac{2}{x-2} - (x+2)(x-2) \cdot \frac{5+2x}{(x+2)(x-2)}$$

$$= (x+2)(x-2) \cdot \frac{x}{x+2}$$

$$2(x+2) - (5+2x) = x(x-2)$$

$$2x + 4 - 5 - 2x = x^2 - 2x$$

$$x^2 - 2x + 1 = 0$$

$$(x - 1)(x - 1) = 0$$

$$x - 1 = 0$$

$$x = 1$$

Since 1 does not make any denominator 0, the solution is 1.

6. $2z^2 - z - 6 = (2z + 3)(z - 2)$

$z^2 - 2z = z(z - 2)$

The LCD is $3z(2z + 3)(z - 2)$.

$$\frac{z}{2z^2 - z - 6} - \frac{1}{3z} = \frac{2}{z^2 - 2z}$$

$$\frac{z}{(2z + 3)(z - 2)} - \frac{1}{3z} = \frac{2}{z(z - 2)}$$

$$3z(2z+3)(z-2) \cdot \frac{z}{(2z+3)(z-2)} - 3z(2z+3)(z-2) \cdot \frac{1}{3z} = 3z(2z+3)(z-2) \cdot \frac{2}{z(z-2)}$$

$$3z(z) - (2z+3)(z-2) = 2 \cdot 3(2z+3)$$

$$3z^2 - (2z^2 - z - 6) = 12z + 18$$

$$3z^2 - 2z^2 + z + 6 = 12z + 18$$

$$z^2 + z + 6 = 12z + 18$$

$$z^2 - 11z - 12 = 0$$

$$(z - 12)(z + 1) = 0$$

$z - 12 = 0$ or $z + 1 = 0$

$z = 12$ or $z = -1$

Neither 12 nor –1 makes any denominator 0, so they are both solutions. The solutions are 12 and –1.

Vocabulary and Readiness Check

1. The LCD of $\dfrac{x}{7}, \dfrac{x}{2}$, and $\dfrac{1}{2}$ is <u>14</u>.

2. The LCD of $\dfrac{9}{x+1}, \dfrac{5}{(x+1)^2}$, and $\dfrac{x}{x+1}$ is $\underline{(x+1)^2}$.

3. The LCD of $\dfrac{7}{x-4}, \dfrac{x}{x^2 - 16} = \dfrac{x}{(x+4)(x-4)}$, and $\dfrac{1}{x+4}$ is <u>(x + 4)(x − 4)</u>.

4. The LCD of $3 = \dfrac{3}{1}, \dfrac{1}{x-5}$, and $\dfrac{2}{x^2 - 5x} = \dfrac{2}{x(x-5)}$ is <u>x(x − 5)</u>.

Exercise Set 6.5

2. $x = \dfrac{x}{2} - 4$

$2(x) = 2\left(\dfrac{x}{2} - 4\right)$

$2x = x - 8$

$x = -8$

4.

$$\frac{x}{2} = \frac{21}{10} - \frac{x}{5}$$

$$10\left(\frac{x}{2}\right) = 10\left(\frac{21}{10} - \frac{x}{5}\right)$$

$$5x = 21 - 2x$$

$$7x = 21$$

$$x = 3$$

6.

$$\frac{5}{3x} + 1 = \frac{7}{6}$$

$$6x\left(\frac{5}{3x} + 1\right) = 6x\left(\frac{7}{6}\right)$$

$$10 + 6x = 7x$$

$$10 = x$$

8.

$$\frac{x^2 - 14}{2x} = \frac{5}{2x}$$

$$2x\left(\frac{x^2 - 14}{2x}\right) = 2x\left(-\frac{5}{2x}\right)$$

$$x^2 - 14 = -5$$

$$x^2 - 9 = 0$$

$$(x+3)(x-3) = 0$$

$$x+3 = 0 \quad \text{or} \quad x-3 = 0$$

$$x = -3 \quad \text{or} \qquad x = 3$$

10.

$$\frac{x-7}{x-1} = \frac{11}{x-1}$$

$$(x-1) \cdot \frac{x-7}{x-1} = (x-1) \cdot \frac{11}{x-1}$$

$$x - 7 = 11$$

$$x = 18$$

12.

$$\frac{1}{x-1} + \frac{1}{x+1} = \frac{2}{x^2 - 1}$$

$$\frac{1}{x-1} + \frac{1}{x+1} = \frac{2}{(x+1)(x-1)}$$

$$(x-1)(x+1)\left(\frac{1}{x-1} + \frac{1}{x+1}\right) = (x-1)(x+1)\left(\frac{2}{(x-1)(x+1)}\right)$$

$$1(x+1) + 1(x-1) = 2$$

$$x + 1 + x - 1 = 2$$

$$2x = 2$$

$$x = 1$$

which we discard as extraneous. No solution, or $\varnothing$.

14.

$$\frac{6}{x+3} = \frac{4}{x-3}$$

$$(x+3)(x-3) \cdot \frac{6}{x+3} = (x+3)(x-3) \cdot \frac{4}{x-3}$$

$$6(x-3) = 4(x+3)$$

$$6x-18 = 4x+12$$

$$2x = 30$$

$$x = 15$$

16.

$$\frac{4x^2-24x}{3x^2-x-2} + \frac{3}{3x+2} = \frac{-4}{x-1}$$

$$\frac{4x^2-24x}{(3x+2)(x-1)} + \frac{3}{3x+2} = \frac{-4}{x-1}$$

$$(3x+2)(x-1)\left[\frac{4x^2-24x}{(3x+2)(x-1)} + \frac{3}{3x+2}\right] = (3x+2)(x-1) \cdot \frac{-4}{x-1}$$

$$(4x^2-24x)+3(x-1) = -4(3x+2)$$

$$4x^2-24x+3x-3 = -12x-8$$

$$4x^2-9x+5 = 0$$

$$(4x-5)(x-1) = 0$$

$$4x-5 = 0 \text{ or } x-1 = 0$$

$$4x = 5 \text{ or } x = 1$$

$$x = \frac{5}{4}$$

We discard 1 as extraneous.

$$x = \frac{5}{4}$$

18.

$$\frac{3}{2x+3} - \frac{1}{2x-3} = \frac{4}{4x^2-9}$$

$$\frac{3}{2x+3} - \frac{1}{2x-3} = \frac{4}{(2x+3)(2x-3)}$$

$$(2x+3)(2x-3)\left[\frac{3}{2x+3} - \frac{1}{2x-3}\right] = (2x+3)(2x-3) \cdot \frac{4}{(2x+3)(2x-3)}$$

$$3(2x-3)-1(2x+3) = 4$$

$$6x-9-2x-3 = 4$$

$$4x-12 = 4$$

$$4x = 16$$

$$x = 4$$

20.

$$\frac{2}{x^2 - 4} = \frac{1}{2x - 4}$$

$$\frac{2}{(x+2)(x-2)} = \frac{1}{2(x-2)}$$

$$2(x+2)(x-2) \cdot \frac{2}{(x+2)(x-2)} = 2(x+2)(x-2) \cdot \frac{1}{2(x-2)}$$

$$2(2) = 1(x+2)$$

$$4 = x + 2$$

$$2 = x$$

which we discard as extraneous. No solution, or $\varnothing$.

22.

$$\frac{12}{3x^2 + 12x} = 1 - \frac{1}{x+4}$$

$$\frac{12}{3x(x+4)} = 1 - \frac{1}{x+4}$$

$$3x(x+4) \cdot \frac{12}{3x(x+4)} = 3x(x+4)\left[1 - \frac{1}{x+4}\right]$$

$$12 = 1 \cdot 3x(x+4) - 1(3x)$$

$$12 = 3x^2 + 12x - 3x$$

$$0 = 3x^2 + 9x - 12$$

$$0 = 3(x^2 + 3x - 4)$$

$$0 = 3(x+4)(x-1)$$

$$x + 4 = 0 \quad \text{or} \quad x - 1 = 0$$

$$x = -4 \quad \text{or} \quad x = 1$$

We discard -4 as extraneous.

$$x = 1$$

24.

$$\frac{2}{x} = \frac{10}{5}$$

$$5x\left(\frac{2}{x}\right) = 5x\left(\frac{10}{5}\right)$$

$$10 = 10x$$

$$1 = x$$

26.

$$7 + \frac{6}{a} = 5$$

$$a\left(7 + \frac{6}{a}\right) = a(5)$$

$$7a + 6 = 5a$$

$$2a = -6$$

$$a = -3$$

28.
$$\frac{x^2+6}{x}+5=\frac{2(x+3)}{x}$$

$$x\left(\frac{x^2+6}{x}+5\right)=x\left[\frac{2(x+3)}{x}\right]$$

$$x^2+6+5x=2x+6$$

$$x^2+3x=0$$

$$x(x+3)=0$$

$$x=0 \ \text{ or } \ x=-3$$

We discard 0 as extraneous.

$$x=-3$$

30.
$$\frac{2}{x-5}+\frac{1}{2x}=\frac{5}{3x^2-15x}$$

$$\frac{2}{x-5}+\frac{1}{2x}=\frac{5}{3x(x-5)}$$

$$6x(x-5)\left[\frac{2}{x-5}+\frac{1}{2x}\right]=6x(x-5)\cdot\frac{5}{3x(x-5)}$$

$$6x\cdot2+3(x-5)\cdot1=2\cdot5$$

$$12x+3x-15=10$$

$$15x=25$$

$$x=\frac{25}{15}=\frac{5}{3}$$

32.
$$\frac{x}{4}+\frac{5}{x}=3$$

$$4x\left(\frac{x}{4}+\frac{5}{x}\right)=4x(3)$$

$$x^2+20=12x$$

$$x^2-12x+20=0$$

$$(x-10)(x-2)=0$$

$$x=10 \ \text{ or } \ x=2$$

34.
$$1-\frac{5}{y+7}=\frac{4}{y+7}$$

$$(y+7)\left(1-\frac{5}{y+7}\right)=(y+7)\cdot\frac{4}{y+7}$$

$$y+7-5=4$$

$$y+2=4$$

$$y=2$$

36.
$$\frac{6x+7}{2x+9} = \frac{5}{3}$$
$$3(2x+9) \cdot \frac{6x+7}{2x+9} = 3(2x+9) \cdot \frac{5}{3}$$
$$3(6x+7) = 5(2x+9)$$
$$18x+21 = 10x+45$$
$$8x = 24$$
$$x = 3$$

38.
$$\frac{2x+1}{4-x} = \frac{9}{4-x}$$
$$(4-x) \cdot \frac{2x+1}{4-x} = (4-x) \cdot \frac{9}{4-x}$$
$$2x+1 = 9$$
$$2x = 8$$
$$x = 4$$
which we discard as extraneous. No solution, or $\varnothing$.

40.
$$\frac{12}{9-a^2} + \frac{3}{3+a} = \frac{2}{3-a}$$
$$\frac{12}{(3+a)(3-a)} + \frac{3}{3+a} = \frac{2}{3-a}$$
$$(3+a)(3-a)\left[\frac{12}{(3+a)(3-a)} + \frac{3}{3+a}\right] = (3+a)(3-a) \cdot \frac{2}{3-a}$$
$$12 + 3(3-a) = 2(3+a)$$
$$12 + 9 - 3a = 6 + 2a$$
$$21 - 3a = 6 + 2a$$
$$-5a = -15$$
$$a = 3$$
which we discard as extraneous. No solution, or $\varnothing$.

42.
$$2 + \frac{3}{x} = \frac{2x}{x+3}$$
$$x(x+3)\left(2 + \frac{3}{x}\right) = x(x+3)\left(\frac{2x}{x+3}\right)$$
$$2x(x+3) + 3(x+3) = x(2x)$$
$$2x^2 + 6x + 3x + 9 = 2x^2$$
$$9x + 9 = 0$$
$$9x = -9$$
$$x = -1$$

44.
$$\frac{36}{x^2-9}+1=\frac{2x}{x+3}$$
$$\frac{36}{(x+3)(x-3)}+1=\frac{2x}{x+3}$$
$$(x+3)(x-3)\left[\frac{36}{(x+3)(x-3)}+1\right]=(x+3)(x-3)\cdot\frac{2x}{x+3}$$
$$36+1(x+3)(x-3)=2x(x-3)$$
$$36+x^2-9=2x^2-6x$$
$$0=x^2-6x-27$$
$$0=(x+3)(x-9)$$
$x=-3$ or $x=9$
We discard 3 as extraneous.
$x=9$

46.
$$\frac{x^2-20}{x^2-7x+12}=\frac{3}{x-3}+\frac{5}{x-4}$$
$$\frac{x^2-20}{(x-4)(x-3)}=\frac{3}{x-3}+\frac{5}{x-4}$$
$$(x-4)(x-3)\cdot\frac{x^2-20}{(x-4)(x-3)}=(x-4)(x-3)\left[\frac{3}{x-3}+\frac{5}{x-4}\right]$$
$$x^2-20=3(x-4)+5(x-3)$$
$$x^2-20=3x-12+5x-15$$
$$x^2-8x+7=0$$
$$(x-7)(x-1)=0$$
$x=7$ or $x=1$

48.
$$\frac{3}{2x-5}+\frac{2}{2x+3}=0$$
$$(2x-5)(2x+3)\left[\frac{3}{2x-5}+\frac{2}{2x+3}\right]=(2x-5)(2x+3)\cdot0$$
$$3(2x+3)+2(2x-5)=0$$
$$6x+9+4x-10=0$$
$$10x-1=0$$
$$10x=1$$
$$x=\frac{1}{10}$$

50. Let $x=$ 1st integer. Then $x+1=$ next integer.
$$x+(x+1)=147$$
$$2x+1=147$$
$$2x=146$$
$$x=73$$
$$x+1=73+1=74$$
The integers are 73 and 74.

52. Let n = the number. Then $\dfrac{1}{n}$ = its reciprocal.

$$n + \frac{1}{n} = \frac{5}{2}$$
$$2n\left(n + \frac{1}{n}\right) = 2n\left(\frac{5}{2}\right)$$
$$2n^2 + 2 = 5n$$
$$2n^2 - 5n + 2 = 0$$
$$(2n - 1)(n - 2) = 0$$
$$n = \frac{1}{2} \text{ or } \quad n = 2$$

The numbers are $\dfrac{1}{2}$ and 2.

54. 94% (reading from the graph)

56. 46% (reading from the graph)

58. Answers may vary

60. $f(x) = 3.3 + \dfrac{5400}{x}$

$$5.10 = 3.3 + \frac{5400}{x}$$
$$1.8 = \frac{5400}{x}$$
$$1.8x = 5400$$
$$x = 3000$$

3000 game disks

62. $\quad x^{-2} - 19x^{-1} + 48 = 0$

$$\frac{1}{x^2} - \frac{19}{x} + 48 = 0$$
$$x^2\left(\frac{1}{x^2} - \frac{19}{x} + 48\right) = x^2 \cdot 0$$
$$1 - 19x + 48x^2 = 0$$
$$48x^2 - 19x + 1 = 0$$
$$(16x - 1)(3x - 1) = 0$$
$$x = \frac{1}{16} \text{ or } x = \frac{1}{3}$$

64. $p^{-2} + 4p^{-1} - 5 = 0$

$$\frac{1}{p^2} + \frac{4}{p} - 5 = 0$$

$$p^2\left(\frac{1}{p^2} + \frac{4}{p} - 5\right) = p^2 \cdot 0$$

$$1 + 4p - 5p^2 = 0$$

$$5p^2 - 4p - 1 = 0$$

$$(5p+1)(p-1) = 0$$

$$p = -\frac{1}{5} \text{ or } p = 1$$

66.
$$\frac{1.4}{x-2.6} = \frac{-3.5}{x+7.1}$$

$$(x-2.6)(x+7.1)\cdot\frac{1.4}{x-2.6} = (x-2.6)(x+7.1)\cdot\frac{-3.5}{x+7.1}$$

$$1.4(x+7.1) = -3.5(x-2.6)$$

$$1.4x + 9.94 = -3.5x + 9.1$$

$$4.9x = -0.84$$

$$x \approx -0.17$$

68. $\dfrac{10.6}{y} - 14.7 = \dfrac{9.92}{3.2} + 7.6$

$$\frac{10.6}{y} - 14.7 = 10.7$$

$$\frac{10.6}{y} = 25.4$$

$$y\cdot\frac{10.6}{y} = y\cdot 25.4$$

$$10.6 = 25.4y$$

$$0.42 \approx y$$

70. $(x-1)^2 + 3(x-1) + 2 = 0$

Let $u = x - 1$.

$$u^2 + 3u + 2 = 0$$

$$(u+2)(u+1) = 0$$

$$u = -2 \text{ or } u = -1$$

$$x-1 = -2 \text{ or } x-1 = -1$$

$$x = -1 \text{ or } x = 0$$

72. $\left(\dfrac{3}{x-1}\right)^2 + 2\left(\dfrac{3}{x-1}\right) + 1 = 0$

Let $u = \dfrac{3}{x-1}$.

$$u^2 + 2u + 1 = 0$$
$$(u+1)^2 = 0$$
$$u + 1 = 0$$
$$u = -1$$
$$\frac{3}{x-1} = -1$$
$$3 = -1(x-1)$$
$$3 = -x + 1$$
$$x = -2$$

74.

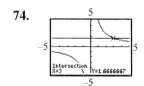

76.

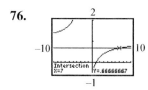

The Bigger Picture

1. $|-7x + 1| < 15$
$$-15 < -7x + 1 < 15$$
$$-16 < -7x < 14$$
$$\frac{16}{7} > x > -2$$

The solution set is $\left(-2, \dfrac{16}{7}\right)$.

2. $|-7x + 1| = 15$

$$-7x + 1 = 15 \quad \text{or} \quad -7x + 1 = -15$$
$$-7x = 14 \qquad\qquad -7x = -16$$
$$x = -2 \qquad\qquad\quad x = \frac{16}{7}$$

The solution set is $\left\{-2, \dfrac{16}{7}\right\}$.

3. $\qquad x^2 - 121 = 0$
$$(x-11)(x+11) = 0$$
$$x - 11 = 0 \quad \text{or} \quad x + 11 = 0$$
$$x = 11 \quad \text{or} \qquad x = -11$$

The solution set is $\{11, -11\}$.

4. $x^2 + x - 2 = (x+2)(x-1)$

The LCD is $(x + 2)(x - 1)$.

$$\frac{8}{x+2} - \frac{3}{x-1} = \frac{x+6}{x^2+x-2}$$

$$(x+2)(x-1)\cdot\frac{8}{x+2} - (x+2)(x-1)\cdot\frac{3}{x-1} = (x+2)(x-1)\cdot\frac{x+6}{(x+2)(x-1)}$$

$$8(x-1) - 3(x+2) = x+6$$
$$8x - 8 - 3x - 6 = x+6$$
$$5x - 14 = x+6$$
$$4x - 14 = 6$$
$$4x = 20$$
$$x = 5$$

The solution set is $\{5\}$.

5. $9x + 6 = 4x - 2$

$$9x = 4x - 8$$
$$5x = -8$$
$$x = -\frac{8}{5}$$

The solution set is $\left\{-\dfrac{8}{5}\right\}$.

6. $3x \le 6$　or　$-x \ge 5$

$x \le 2$　or　$x \le -5$

$(-\infty, 2] \cup (-\infty, -5] = (-\infty, 2]$

The solution set is $(-\infty, 2]$.

7. $3x \le 6$　and　$-x \ge 5$

$x \le 2$　and　$x \le -5$

$(-\infty, 2] \cap (-\infty, -5] = (-\infty, -5]$

The solution set is $(-\infty, -5]$.

8. $-9 \le -3x + 21 < 0$

$$-30 \le -3x < -21$$
$$10 \ge x > 7$$

The solution set is $(7, 10]$.

9. $\left|\dfrac{2x-1}{5}\right| > 7$

$\dfrac{2x-1}{5} > 7$　or　$\dfrac{2x-1}{5} < -7$

$2x - 1 > 35$　or　$2x - 1 < -35$

$2x > 36$　or　$2x < -34$

$x > 18$　or　$x < -17$

$(18, \infty) \cup (-\infty, -17)$

The solution set is $(-\infty, -17) \cup (18, \infty)$.

10.
$$15x^3 - 16x^2 = 7x$$
$$15x^3 - 16x^2 - 7x = 0$$
$$x(15x^2 - 16x - 7) = 0$$
$$x(3x+1)(5x-7) = 0$$
$$x = 0 \quad \text{or} \quad 3x+1 = 0 \quad \text{or} \quad 5x-7 = 0$$
$$x = 0 \quad \text{or} \quad 3x = -1 \quad \text{or} \quad 5x = 7$$
$$x = 0 \quad \text{or} \quad x = -\frac{1}{3} \quad \text{or} \quad x = \frac{7}{5}$$

The solution set is $\left\{ 0, -\dfrac{1}{3}, \dfrac{7}{5} \right\}$.

Integrated Review

1. $\dfrac{x}{2} = \dfrac{1}{8} + \dfrac{x}{4}$

The LCD is 8.

$$8 \cdot \frac{x}{2} = 8 \cdot \frac{1}{8} + 8 \cdot \frac{x}{4}$$
$$4x = 1 + 2x$$
$$2x = 1$$
$$x = \frac{1}{2}$$

The solution set is $\left\{ \dfrac{1}{2} \right\}$.

2. $\dfrac{x}{4} = \dfrac{3}{2} + \dfrac{x}{10}$

The LCD is 20.

$$20 \cdot \frac{x}{4} = 20 \cdot \frac{3}{2} + 20 \cdot \frac{x}{10}$$
$$5x = 30 + 2x$$
$$3x = 30$$
$$x = 10$$

The solution set is $\{10\}$.

3. $\dfrac{1}{8} + \dfrac{x}{4} = \dfrac{1}{8} + \dfrac{x}{4} \cdot \dfrac{2}{2} = \dfrac{1}{8} + \dfrac{2x}{8} = \dfrac{1+2x}{8}$

4. $\dfrac{3}{2} + \dfrac{x}{10} = \dfrac{5}{5} \cdot \dfrac{3}{2} + \dfrac{x}{10} = \dfrac{15}{10} + \dfrac{x}{10} = \dfrac{15+x}{10}$

5. $\dfrac{4}{x+2} - \dfrac{2}{x-1} = \dfrac{4}{x+2} \cdot \dfrac{x-1}{x-1} - \dfrac{2}{x-1} \cdot \dfrac{x+2}{x+2}$

$$= \frac{4(x-1)}{(x+2)(x-1)} - \frac{2(x+2)}{(x+2)(x+1)}$$
$$= \frac{4x-4-2x-4}{(x+2)(x-1)}$$
$$= \frac{2x-8}{(x+2)(x-1)}$$
$$= \frac{2(x-4)}{(x+2)(x-1)}$$

6. $\dfrac{5}{x-2} - \dfrac{10}{x+4} = \dfrac{5}{x-2} \cdot \dfrac{x+4}{x+4} - \dfrac{10}{x+4} \cdot \dfrac{x-2}{x-2}$

$$= \frac{5(x+4)}{(x-2)(x+4)} - \frac{10(x-2)}{(x-2)(x+4)}$$
$$= \frac{5x+20-10x+20}{(x-2)(x+4)}$$
$$= \frac{-5x+40}{(x-2)(x+4)}$$
$$= \frac{-5(x-8)}{(x-2)(x+4)} \quad \text{or} \quad -\frac{5(x-8)}{(x-2)(x+4)}$$

7. $\dfrac{4}{x+2} = \dfrac{2}{x-1}$

The LCD is $(x+2)(x-1)$.

$$(x+2)(x-1) \cdot \frac{4}{x+2} = (x+2)(x-1) \cdot \frac{2}{x-1}$$
$$4(x-1) = 2(x+2)$$
$$4x-4 = 2x+4$$
$$4x = 2x+8$$
$$2x = 8$$
$$x = 4$$

The solution set is $\{4\}$.

8. $\dfrac{5}{x-2} = \dfrac{10}{x+4}$

The LCD is $(x-2)(x+4)$.

$$(x-2)(x+4) \cdot \frac{5}{x-2} = (x-2)(x+4) \cdot \frac{10}{x+4}$$
$$5(x+4) = 10(x-2)$$
$$5x+20 = 10x-20$$
$$5x = 10x-40$$
$$-5x = -40$$
$$x = 8$$

The solution set is $\{8\}$.

9. $x^2 - 4 = (x+2)(x-2)$

The LCD is $(x + 2)(x - 2)$.

$$\frac{2}{x^2-4} = \frac{1}{x+2} - \frac{3}{x-2}$$

$$(x+2)(x-2)\cdot\frac{2}{x^2-4} = (x+2)(x-2)\cdot\frac{1}{x+2} - (x+2)(x-2)\cdot\frac{3}{x-2}$$

$$2 = (x-2) - 3(x+2)$$
$$2 = x - 2 - 3x - 6$$
$$2 = -2x - 8$$
$$2x = -10$$
$$x = -5$$

The solution set is $\{-5\}$.

10. $x^2 - 25 = (x+5)(x-5)$

The LCD is $(x + 5)(x - 5)$.

$$\frac{3}{x^2-25} = \frac{1}{x+5} + \frac{2}{x-5}$$

$$(x+5)(x-5)\cdot\frac{3}{(x+5)(x-5)} = (x+5)(x-5)\cdot\frac{1}{x+5} + (x+5)(x-5)\cdot\frac{2}{x-5}$$

$$3 = (x-5) + 2(x+5)$$
$$3 = x - 5 + 2x + 10$$
$$3 = 3x + 5$$
$$-2 = 3x$$
$$-\frac{2}{3} = x$$

The solution set is $\left\{-\dfrac{2}{3}\right\}$.

11. $\dfrac{5}{x^2-3x} + \dfrac{4}{2x-6} = \dfrac{5}{x(x-3)} + \dfrac{4}{2(x-3)}$

$$= \frac{5}{x(x-3)}\cdot\frac{2}{2} + \frac{4}{2(x-3)}\cdot\frac{x}{x}$$

$$= \frac{10}{2x(x-3)} + \frac{4x}{2x(x-3)}$$

$$= \frac{4x+10}{2x(x-3)}$$

$$= \frac{2(2x+5)}{2x(x-3)}$$

$$= \frac{2x+5}{x(x-3)}$$

12. $\dfrac{5}{x^2-3x} \div \dfrac{4}{2x-6} = \dfrac{5}{x^2-3x}\cdot\dfrac{2x-6}{4}$

$$= \frac{5}{x(x-3)}\cdot\frac{2(x-3)}{4}$$

$$= \frac{5}{2x}$$

13. $x^2 - 1 = (x-1)(x+1)$

The LCD is $(x-1)(x+1)$.

$$\frac{x-1}{x+1} + \frac{x+7}{x-1} = \frac{4}{x^2-1}$$

$$(x-1)(x+1) \cdot \frac{x-1}{x+1} + (x-1)(x+1) \cdot \frac{x+7}{x-1} = (x-1)(x+1) \cdot \frac{4}{(x-1)(x+1)}$$

$$(x-1)(x-1) + (x+1)(x+7) = 4$$

$$x^2 - 2x + 1 + x^2 + 8x + 7 = 4$$

$$2x^2 + 6x + 8 = 4$$

$$2x^2 + 6x + 4 = 0$$

$$2(x^2 + 3x + 2) = 0$$

$$2(x+1)(x+2) = 0$$

$$x+1 = 0 \quad \text{or} \quad x+2 = 0$$
$$x = -1 \quad \text{or} \quad x = -2$$

The number -1 makes the denominator $x + 1$ equal to 0, so it is not a solution. The solution set is $\{-2\}$.

14.
$$\left(1 - \frac{y}{x}\right) \div \left(1 - \frac{x}{y}\right) = \left(\frac{x}{x} - \frac{y}{x}\right) \div \left(\frac{y}{y} - \frac{x}{y}\right)$$

$$= \left(\frac{x-y}{x}\right) \div \left(\frac{y-x}{y}\right)$$

$$= \frac{x-y}{x} \cdot \frac{y}{y-x}$$

$$= \frac{x-y}{x} \cdot \frac{y}{-(x-y)}$$

$$= -\frac{y}{x}$$

15.
$$\frac{a^2-9}{a-6} \cdot \frac{a^2-5a-6}{a^2-a-6} = \frac{(a+3)(a-3)}{a-6} \cdot \frac{(a-6)(a+1)}{(a-3)(a+2)}$$

$$= \frac{(a+3)(a+1)}{a+2}$$

16.
$$\frac{2}{a-6} + \frac{3a}{a^2-5a-6} - \frac{a}{5a+5} = \frac{2}{a-6} + \frac{3a}{(a-6)(a+1)} - \frac{a}{5(a+1)}$$

$$= \frac{2}{a-6} \cdot \frac{5(a+1)}{5(a+1)} + \frac{3a}{(a-6)(a+1)} \cdot \frac{5}{5} - \frac{a}{5(a+1)} \cdot \frac{a-6}{a-6}$$

$$= \frac{10a+10}{5(a+1)(a-6)} + \frac{15a}{5(a+1)(a-6)} - \frac{a^2-6a}{5(a+1)(a-6)}$$

$$= \frac{10a+10+15a-a^2+6a}{5(a+1)(a-6)}$$

$$= \frac{-a^2+31a+10}{5(a+1)(a-6)}$$

17. $\dfrac{2x+3}{3x-2} = \dfrac{4x+1}{6x+1}$

The LCD is $(3x-2)(6x+1)$.

$$(3x-2)(6x+1)\cdot\dfrac{2x+3}{3x-2} = (3x-2)(6x+1)\cdot\dfrac{4x+1}{6x+1}$$

$$(6x+1)(2x+3) = (3x-2)(4x+1)$$

$$12x^2+18x+2x+3 = 12x^2+3x-8x-2$$

$$12x^2+20x+3 = 12x^2-5x-2$$

$$20x+3 = -5x-2$$

$$25x+3 = -2$$

$$25x = -5$$

$$x = -\dfrac{5}{25}$$

$$x = -\dfrac{1}{5}$$

The solution set is $\left\{-\dfrac{1}{5}\right\}$.

18. The LCD is $2x(4x+1)$.

$$\dfrac{5x-3}{2x} = \dfrac{10x+3}{4x+1}$$

$$2x(4x+1)\cdot\dfrac{5x-3}{2x} = 2x(4x+1)\cdot\dfrac{10x+3}{4x+1}$$

$$(4x+1)(5x-3) = 2x(10x+3)$$

$$20x^2-12x+5x-3 = 20x^2+6x$$

$$20x^2-7x-3 = 20x^2+6x$$

$$-7x-3 = 6x$$

$$-3 = 13x$$

$$-\dfrac{3}{13} = x$$

The solution set is $\left\{-\dfrac{3}{13}\right\}$.

19. $\dfrac{a}{9a^2-1} + \dfrac{2}{6a-2} = \dfrac{a}{(3a-1)(3a+1)} + \dfrac{2}{2(3a-1)}$

$$= \dfrac{a}{(3a-1)(3a+1)}\cdot\dfrac{2}{2} + \dfrac{2}{2(3a-1)}\cdot\dfrac{(3a+1)}{(3a+1)}$$

$$= \dfrac{2a}{2(3a-1)(3a+1)} + \dfrac{6a+2}{2(3a-1)(3a+1)}$$

$$= \dfrac{8a+2}{2(3a-1)(3a+1)}$$

$$= \dfrac{2(4a+1)}{2(3a-1)(3a+1)}$$

$$= \dfrac{4a+1}{(3a-1)(3a+1)}$$

20. $\dfrac{3}{4a-8} - \dfrac{a+2}{a^2-2a} = \dfrac{3}{4(a-2)} - \dfrac{a+2}{a(a-2)}$

$$= \dfrac{3}{4(a-2)} \cdot \dfrac{a}{a} - \dfrac{a+2}{a(a-2)} \cdot \dfrac{4}{4}$$

$$= \dfrac{3a}{4a(a-2)} - \dfrac{4(a+2)}{4a(a-2)}$$

$$= \dfrac{3a}{4a(a-2)} - \dfrac{4a+8}{4a(a-2)}$$

$$= \dfrac{3a-4a-8}{4a(a-2)}$$

$$= \dfrac{-a-8}{4a(a-2)}$$

$$= -\dfrac{a+8}{4a(a-2)}$$

21. The LCD is x^2.

$$-\dfrac{3}{x^2} - \dfrac{1}{x} + 2 = 0$$

$$x^2 \cdot -\dfrac{3}{x^2} - x^2 \cdot \dfrac{1}{x} + x^2 \cdot 2 = 0$$

$$-3 - x + 2x^2 = 0$$

$$2x^2 - x - 3 = 0$$

$$(2x-3)(x+1) = 0$$

$2x - 3 = 0$ or $x + 1 = 0$

    $2x = 3$ or $x = -1$

     $x = \dfrac{3}{2}$ or $x = -1$

The solution set is $\left\{-1, \dfrac{3}{2}\right\}$.

22. $\dfrac{x}{2x+6} + \dfrac{5}{x^2-9} = \dfrac{x}{2(x+3)} + \dfrac{5}{(x-3)(x+3)}$

$$= \dfrac{x}{2(x+3)} \cdot \dfrac{x-3}{x-3} + \dfrac{5}{(x-3)(x+3)} \cdot \dfrac{2}{2}$$

$$= \dfrac{x(x-3)}{2(x+3)(x-3)} + \dfrac{10}{2(x+3)(x-3)}$$

$$= \dfrac{x^2-3x}{2(x+3)(x-3)} + \dfrac{10}{2(x+3)(x-3)}$$

$$= \dfrac{x^2-3x+10}{2(x+3)(x-3)}$$

23. $\dfrac{x-8}{x^2-x-2}+\dfrac{2}{x-2}=\dfrac{x-8}{(x-2)(x+1)}+\dfrac{2}{x-2}$

$\qquad\qquad =\dfrac{x-8}{(x-2)(x+1)}+\dfrac{2}{x-2}\cdot\dfrac{x+1}{x+1}$

$\qquad\qquad =\dfrac{x-8}{(x-2)(x+1)}+\dfrac{2x+2}{(x-2)(x+1)}$

$\qquad\qquad =\dfrac{x-8+2x+2}{(x-2)(x+1)}$

$\qquad\qquad =\dfrac{3x-6}{(x-2)(x+1)}$

$\qquad\qquad =\dfrac{3(x-2)}{(x-2)(x+1)}$

$\qquad\qquad =\dfrac{3}{x+1}$

24. $x^2-x-2=(x-2)(x+1)$

The LCD is $(x-2)(x+1)$.

$$\dfrac{x-8}{x^2-x-2}+\dfrac{2}{x-2}=\dfrac{3}{x+1}$$

$$(x-2)(x+1)\cdot\dfrac{x-8}{(x-2)(x+1)}+(x-2)(x+1)\cdot\dfrac{2}{x-2}=(x-2)(x+1)\cdot\dfrac{3}{x+1}$$

$$(x-8)+2(x+1)=3(x-2)$$

$$x-8+2x+2=3x-6$$

$$3x-6=3x-6$$

$$-6=-6\quad\text{True}$$

The solution set is
$\{x|x$ is a real number and $x\neq 2,\ x\neq -1\}$.

25. The LCD is a.

$$\dfrac{3}{a}-5=\dfrac{7}{a}-1$$

$$a\cdot\dfrac{3}{a}-a\cdot 5=a\cdot\dfrac{7}{a}-a\cdot 1$$

$$3-5a=7-a$$

$$3=7+4a$$

$$-4=4a$$

$$-1=a$$

The solution set is $\{-1\}$.

26.
$$\frac{7}{3z-9}+\frac{5}{z}=\frac{7}{3(z-3)}+\frac{5}{z}$$
$$=\frac{7}{3(z-3)}\cdot\frac{z}{z}+\frac{5}{z}\cdot\frac{3(z-3)}{3(z-3)}$$
$$=\frac{7z}{3z(z-3)}+\frac{15(z-3)}{3z(z-3)}$$
$$=\frac{7z+15z-45}{3z(z-3)}$$
$$=\frac{22z-45}{3z(z-3)}$$

27. a. $\dfrac{x}{5}-\dfrac{x}{4}+\dfrac{1}{10}$ is an expression.

b. The first step to simplify this expression is to write each rational expression term so that the denominator is the LCD, 20.

c.
$$\frac{x}{5}-\frac{x}{4}+\frac{1}{10}=\frac{x}{5}\cdot\frac{4}{4}-\frac{x}{4}\cdot\frac{5}{5}+\frac{1}{10}\cdot\frac{2}{2}$$
$$=\frac{4x}{20}-\frac{5x}{20}+\frac{2}{20}$$
$$=\frac{4x-5x+2}{20}$$
$$=\frac{-x+2}{20}$$

28. a. $\dfrac{x}{5}-\dfrac{x}{4}=\dfrac{1}{10}$ is an equation.

b. The first step to solve this equation is to clear the equation of fractions by multiplying each term by the LCD, 20.

c.
$$\frac{x}{5}-\frac{x}{4}=\frac{1}{10}$$
$$20\cdot\frac{x}{5}-20\cdot\frac{x}{4}=20\cdot\frac{1}{10}$$
$$4x-5x=2$$
$$-x=2$$
$$x=-2$$
The solution set is $\{-2\}$.

29. $\dfrac{\triangle+\square}{\triangle}=\dfrac{\triangle}{\triangle}+\dfrac{\square}{\triangle}=1+\dfrac{\square}{\triangle}$

b is the correct answer.

30. $\dfrac{\triangle}{\square}+\dfrac{\square}{\triangle}=\dfrac{\triangle}{\square}\cdot\dfrac{\triangle}{\triangle}+\dfrac{\square}{\triangle}\cdot\dfrac{\square}{\square}$
$$=\frac{\triangle\triangle}{\square\triangle}+\frac{\square\square}{\square\triangle}$$
$$=\frac{\triangle\triangle+\square\square}{\square\triangle}$$

d is the correct answer.

31. $\dfrac{\triangle}{\square}\cdot\dfrac{\bigcirc}{\square}=\dfrac{\triangle\bigcirc}{\square\square}$

d is the correct answer.

32. $\dfrac{\triangle}{\square}\div\dfrac{\bigcirc}{\triangle}=\dfrac{\triangle}{\square}\cdot\dfrac{\triangle}{\bigcirc}=\dfrac{\triangle\triangle}{\square\bigcirc}$

a is the correct answer.

33. $\dfrac{\frac{\triangle+\square}{\bigcirc}}{\frac{\triangle}{\bigcirc}}=\dfrac{\triangle+\square}{\bigcirc}\div\dfrac{\triangle}{\bigcirc}=\dfrac{\triangle+\square}{\bigcirc}\cdot\dfrac{\bigcirc}{\triangle}=\dfrac{\triangle+\square}{\triangle}$

d is the correct answer.

Section 6.6

Practice Exercises

1. abc is the LCD.
$$\frac{1}{a}-\frac{1}{b}=\frac{1}{c}$$
$$abc\left(\frac{1}{a}-\frac{1}{b}\right)=abc\left(\frac{1}{c}\right)$$
$$abc\left(\frac{1}{a}\right)-abc\left(\frac{1}{b}\right)=abc\left(\frac{1}{c}\right)$$
$$bc-ac=ab$$
$$bc=ab+ac$$
$$bc=a(b+c)$$
$$\frac{bc}{b+c}=a$$

2. Let n = the number.
$$\frac{3+n}{11-n}=\frac{5}{2}$$
$$2(11-n)\cdot\frac{3+n}{11-n}=2(11-n)\cdot\frac{5}{2}$$
$$2(3+n)=5(11-n)$$
$$6+2n=55-5n$$
$$7n=49$$
$$n=7$$
The number is 7.

3. Let x = the number of homes heated by fuel oil.

$$\frac{1}{12} = \frac{x}{36,000}$$

$$12x = 1 \cdot 36,000$$

$$x = \frac{36,000}{12}$$

$$x = 3000$$

3000 homes in the community are heated by fuel oil.

4. Let t = the time it takes them to clean the cages together.

	Time	Part done in one hour
Elissa	3	$\frac{1}{3}$
Bill	2	$\frac{1}{2}$
Together	t	$\frac{1}{t}$

$$\frac{1}{3} + \frac{1}{2} = \frac{1}{t}$$

$$6t\left(\frac{1}{3} + \frac{1}{2}\right) = 6t\left(\frac{1}{t}\right)$$

$$2t + 3t = 6$$

$$5t = 6$$

$$t = \frac{6}{5} \text{ or } 1\frac{1}{5}$$

Elissa and Bill can clean the cages in $1\frac{1}{5}$ hours if they work together.

5. Let x = the speed of the wind.

	Distance $(r \cdot t)$	Rate	Time
Tailwind	$450 + x$	$450 + x$	1
Headwind	$\frac{5}{4}(450 - x)$	$450 - x$	$1\frac{1}{4} = \frac{5}{4}$

$$450 + x = \frac{5}{4}(450 - x)$$

$$4 \cdot (450 + x) = 4 \cdot \frac{5}{4}(450 - x)$$

$$1800 + 4x = 5(450 - x)$$

$$1800 + 4x = 2250 - 5x$$

$$9x = 450$$

$$x = 50$$

The wind speed is 50 mph.

Exercise Set 6.6

2.
$$V = \frac{1}{3}\pi r^2 h$$

$$3V = \pi r^2 h$$

$$\frac{3V}{\pi r^2} = \frac{\pi r^2 h}{\pi r^2}$$

$$\frac{3V}{\pi r^2} = h$$

4.
$$P = 1 - \frac{C}{S}$$

$$P - 1 = -\frac{C}{S}$$

$$S(P - 1) = S\left(-\frac{C}{S}\right)$$

$$S(P - 1) = -C$$

$$S = \frac{-C}{P - 1}$$

$$S = \frac{C}{1 - P}$$

6.
$$\frac{1}{R} = \frac{1}{R_1} + \frac{1}{R_2}$$

$$RR_1R_2 \cdot \frac{1}{R} = RR_1R_2\left(\frac{1}{R_1} + \frac{1}{R_2}\right)$$

$$R_1R_2 = RR_2 + RR_1$$

$$R_1R_2 - RR_1 = RR_2$$

$$R_1(R_2 - R) = RR_2$$

$$R_1 = \frac{RR_2}{R_2 - R}$$

8.
$$S = \frac{n(a + L)}{2}$$

$$2S = n(a + L)$$

$$2S = na + nL$$

$$2S - nL = na$$

$$\frac{2S - nL}{n} = a$$

10.
$$A = \frac{h(a+b)}{2}$$
$$2A = h(a+b)$$
$$\frac{2A}{a+b} = h$$

12.
$$H = \frac{kA(T_1 - T_2)}{L}$$
$$LH = kA(T_1 - T_2)$$
$$\frac{LH}{kA} = T_1 - T_2$$
$$T_2 = T_1 - \frac{LH}{kA}$$
$$T_2 = \frac{kAT_1 - LH}{kA}$$

14.
$$I = \frac{E}{R+r}$$
$$I(R+r) = E$$
$$IR + Ir = E$$
$$Ir = E - IR$$
$$r = \frac{E - IR}{I}$$

16.
$$S = \frac{a_1 - a_n r}{1-r}$$
$$S(1-r) = a_1 - a_n r$$
$$S(1-r) + a_n r = a_1$$

18.
$$F = \frac{-GMm}{r^2}$$
$$Fr^2 = -GMm$$
$$-\frac{Fr^2}{Gm} = M$$

20. Let n = the number. Then
$$\frac{1}{n} = \text{the reciprocal of the number.}$$
$$\frac{n}{9\left(\frac{1}{n}\right)} = 1$$
$$n = \frac{9}{n}$$
$$n^2 = 9$$
$$n^2 - 9 = 0$$
$$(n+3)(n-3) = 0$$
$$n = -3 \text{ or } n = 3$$
The number is either -3 or 3.

22. Let x = the number.
$$\frac{13-x}{8+x} = \frac{2}{5}$$
$$5(13-x) = 2(8+x)$$
$$65 - 5x = 16 + 2x$$
$$-7x = -49$$
$$x = 7$$
The number is 7.

24. Let d = distance in 10 hours.
$$\frac{20}{8} = \frac{d}{10}$$
$$8d = 20(10)$$
$$8d = 200$$
$$d = 25$$
The camel can travel 25 miles.

26. Let m = the number of men.
$$\frac{42.8}{50} = \frac{m}{353,496}$$
$$50m = 42.8(353,496)$$
$$50m = 15,129,628.8$$
$$m = 302,592.576$$
There were 302,593 men.

28. Let x = time for Steve to work alone.
$$\frac{1}{x} + \frac{1}{6} = \frac{1}{4}$$
$$12x\left(\frac{1}{x} + \frac{1}{6}\right) = 12x\left(\frac{1}{4}\right)$$
$$12 + 2x = 3x$$
$$12 = x$$
It would take Steve 12 hours.

30. Let x = time with both printers operating.
$$\frac{1}{4} + \frac{2}{4} = \frac{1}{x}$$
$$\frac{3}{4} = \frac{1}{x}$$
$$3x = 4$$
$$x = \frac{4}{3} = 1\frac{1}{3}$$
It will take $1\frac{1}{3}$ hours.

32. Let r = the speed of the truck. Then $3r$ = the speed of the plane.

$$t_{\text{truck}} = t_{\text{plane}} + 6$$

$$\frac{450}{r} = \frac{450}{3r} + 6$$

$$3r \cdot \frac{450}{r} = 3r\left(\frac{450}{3r} + 6\right)$$

$$1350 = 450 + 18r$$

$$900 = 18r$$

$$50 = r$$

The speed of the truck is 50 mph.

34. Let c = speed of the current.

$$t_{\text{upstream}} = t_{\text{downstream}}$$

$$\frac{54}{24 - c} = \frac{90}{24 + c}$$

$$54(24 + c) = 90(24 - c)$$

$$1296 + 54c = 2160 - 90c$$

$$144c = 864$$

$$c = 6$$

The speed of the current is 6 mph.

36. Let x = the first odd integer. Then $x + 2$ = the next odd integer.

$$\frac{1}{x} + \frac{1}{x+2} = \frac{20}{99}$$

$$99x(x+2)\left(\frac{1}{x} + \frac{1}{x+2}\right) = 99x(x+2) \cdot \frac{20}{99}$$

$$99(x+2) + 99x = 20x(x+2)$$

$$99x + 198 + 99x = 20x^2 + 40x$$

$$198x + 198 = 20x^2 + 40x$$

$$20x^2 - 158x - 198 = 0$$

$$10x^2 - 79x - 99 = 0$$

$$(10x + 11)(x - 9) = 0$$

$$10x + 11 = 0 \quad \text{or} \quad x - 9 = 0$$

$$10x = -11 \quad \text{or} \qquad x = 9$$

$$x = -\frac{11}{10}$$

$-\dfrac{11}{10}$ is not an integer.

$x + 2 = 9 + 2 = 11$

The integers are 9 and 11.

38. Let t = time for Dick to do the job alone.

$$\frac{1}{5} + \frac{1}{t} = \frac{1}{2} \cdot$$

$$10t\left(\frac{1}{5} + \frac{1}{t}\right) = 10t \cdot \frac{1}{2}$$

$$2t + 10 = 5t$$

$$10 = 3t$$

$$t = \frac{10}{3} = 3\frac{1}{3}$$

It will take Dick $3\dfrac{1}{3}$ hours to do the job alone.

40. Let r = the speed of the walker. Then $r + 10$ = the speed of the biker.

$$t_{\text{walker}} = t_{\text{bicker}}$$

$$\frac{6}{r} = \frac{26}{r + 10}$$

$$6(r + 10) = 26r$$

$$6r + 60 = 26r$$

$$60 = 20r$$

$$3 = r$$

$r + 10 = 3 + 10 = 13$

The bicyclist speed was 13 mph.

42. Let t = time to travel 300 feet.

$$\frac{88}{3} = \frac{300}{t}$$

$$88t = 900$$

$$t = \frac{900}{88} \approx 10.22727273$$

It would take 10.2 seconds.

44. Let t = time to empty a full tank working together.

$$-\frac{1}{1.5} + \frac{1}{1} = \frac{1}{t}$$

$$1.5t\left(-\frac{1}{1.5} + \frac{1}{1}\right) = 1.5t \cdot \frac{1}{t}$$

$$-t + 1.5t = 1.5$$

$$0.5t = 1.5$$

$$t = 3$$

It would take 3 hours to empty the tank if both pipes are open.

46. Let d = the distance.

$$t_{\text{rocket 1}} = \frac{1}{4} + t_{\text{rocket 2}}$$

$$\frac{d}{9000} = \frac{1}{4} + \frac{d}{10,000}$$

$$90,000\left(\frac{d}{9000}\right) = 90,000\left(\frac{1}{4} + \frac{d}{10,000}\right)$$

$$10d = 22,500 + 9d$$

$$d = 22,500$$

They are an equal distance from the earth at 22,500 miles.

48. Let r = the flatland rate. Then
$r - 20$ = the mountain rate.

$$t_{\text{flatland}} = t_{\text{mountain}}$$

$$\frac{300}{r} = \frac{180}{r-20}$$

$$300(r-20) = 180r$$

$$300r - 6000 = 180r$$

$$120r = 6000$$

$$r = 50$$

$r - 20 = 50 - 20 = 30$
The flatland rate was 50 mph and the mountain rate was 30 mph.

50. Let d = denominator. Then
$d - 4$ = the numerator, and
$\dfrac{d-4}{d}$ = the fraction. Now

$$\frac{(d-4)+2}{d+2} = \frac{2}{3}$$

$$\frac{d-2}{d+2} = \frac{2}{3}$$

$$3(d-2) = 2(d+2)$$

$$3d - 6 = 2d + 4$$

$$d = 10$$

Thus, $\dfrac{d-4}{d} = \dfrac{10-4}{10} = \dfrac{6}{10}$ is the fraction.

52. Let t = time if both worked together.

$$\frac{1}{6} + \frac{1}{4} = \frac{1}{t}$$

$$12t\left(\frac{1}{6} + \frac{1}{4}\right) = 12t \cdot \frac{1}{t}$$

$$2t + 3t = 12$$

$$5t = 12$$

$$t = \frac{12}{5} = 2.4$$

The labor estimate would be 2.4($45) = $108.

54. Let t = time to paint the house working together.

$$\frac{1}{4} + \frac{1}{5} = \frac{1}{t}$$

$$20t\left(\frac{1}{4} + \frac{1}{5}\right) = 20t \cdot \frac{1}{t}$$

$$5t + 4t = 20$$

$$9t = 20$$

$$t = \frac{20}{9} = 2\frac{2}{9}$$

It would take them $2\dfrac{2}{9}$ days.

56. Let r = the speed in still water.

$$t_{\text{downstream}} = t_{\text{upstream}}$$

$$\frac{9}{r+6} = \frac{3}{r-6}$$

$$9(r-6) = 3(r+6)$$

$$9r - 54 = 3r + 18$$

$$6r = 72$$

$$r = 12$$

Thus, $t = t_{\text{downstream}} + t_{\text{upstream}}$

$$= \frac{9}{12+6} + \frac{3}{12-6}$$

$$= \frac{1}{2} + \frac{1}{2}$$

$$= 1$$

It takes him 1 hour to cover the 12 miles.

58. Let x = time with both scanners operating.

$$\frac{1}{3} + \frac{1}{5} = \frac{1}{x}$$

$$15x \cdot \frac{1}{3} + 15x \cdot \frac{1}{5} = 15x \cdot \frac{1}{x}$$

$$5x + 3x = 15$$

$$8x = 15$$

$$x = \frac{15}{8} = 1\frac{7}{8}$$

It will take $1\dfrac{7}{8}$ hours.

60. Let m = the number of movies that were rated PG-13.

$$\frac{13}{20} = \frac{m}{599}$$

$$20m = 13 \cdot 599$$

$$20m = 7787$$

$$m = \frac{7787}{20} = 389.35$$

Approximately 389 movies would be PG-13.

62. $\dfrac{x}{5} = \dfrac{x+2}{3}$

$5(x+2) = 3x$

$5x + 10 = 3x$

$10 = -2x$

$-5 = x$

64. $\dfrac{x-3}{2} = \dfrac{x-5}{6}$

$6(x-3) = 2(x-5)$

$6x - 18 = 2x - 10$

$4x = 8$

$x = 2$

66. $\dfrac{705w}{h^2} = 25$

$\dfrac{705w}{68^2} = 25$

$\dfrac{705w}{4624} = 25$

$705w = 25(4624)$

$705w = 115,600$

$w \approx 163.9716312$

The person should weigh 164 pounds.

68. $h = \dfrac{a}{1 - \frac{s}{770}} = \dfrac{329.63}{1 - \frac{50}{770}}$

$= \dfrac{329.63}{\frac{770-50}{770}}$

$= \dfrac{329.63}{\frac{720}{770}}$

$= \dfrac{329.63(770)}{720}$

≈ 352.52

The pitch is higher, closer to the musical note F.

70. $\dfrac{1}{R} = \dfrac{1}{R_1} + \dfrac{1}{R_2}$

$\dfrac{1}{R} = \dfrac{1}{12} + \dfrac{1}{12}$

$\dfrac{1}{R} = \dfrac{1}{6}$

$R = 6$

6 ohms

Section 6.7

Practice Exercises

1. $y = kx$

$20 = k(15)$

$\dfrac{4}{3} = k$

$k = \dfrac{4}{3}; \; y = \dfrac{4}{3}x$

2. $d = kw$

$9 = k(36)$

$\dfrac{1}{4} = k$

$d = \dfrac{1}{4}w$

$d = \dfrac{1}{4}(75)$

$d = \dfrac{75}{4}$ inches or $18\dfrac{3}{4}$ inches

3. $b = \dfrac{k}{a}$

$5 = \dfrac{k}{9}$

$k = 45; \; b = \dfrac{45}{a}$

4. $P = \dfrac{k}{V}$

$350 = \dfrac{k}{2.8}$

$980 = k$

$P = \dfrac{980}{V}$

$P = \dfrac{980}{1.5}$

$P = 653\dfrac{1}{3}$ kilopascals

5. $A = kap$

6. $y = \dfrac{k}{x^3}$

$\dfrac{1}{2} = \dfrac{k}{2^3}$

$\dfrac{1}{2} = \dfrac{k}{8}$

$4 = k$

$k = 4; \quad y = \dfrac{4}{x^3}$

7. $y = \dfrac{kz}{x^3}$

$15 = \dfrac{k \cdot 5}{3^3}$

$81 = k$

$k = 81; \quad y = \dfrac{81z}{x^3}$

Vocabulary and Readiness Check

1. $y = 5x$ represents direct variation.

2. $y = \dfrac{700}{x}$ represents inverse variation.

3. $y = 5xz$ represents joint variation.

4. $y = \dfrac{1}{2}abc$ represents joint variation.

5. $y = \dfrac{9.1}{x}$ represents inverse variation.

6. $y = 2.3x$ represents direct variation.

7. $y = \dfrac{2}{3}x$ represents direct variation.

8. $y = 3.1st$ represents joint variation.

Exercise Set 6.7

2. $y = kx$

$5 = k(30)$

$k = \dfrac{1}{6}$

$y = \dfrac{1}{6}x$

4. $y = kx$

$12 = k(8)$

$y = \dfrac{3}{2}$

$y = \dfrac{3}{2}x$

6. $y = kx$

$11 = k\left(\dfrac{1}{3}\right)$

$k = 33$

$y = 33x$

8. $y = kx$

$0.4 = k(2.5)$

$k = 0.16$

$y = 0.16x$

10. $d = k\sqrt{e}$

$7.4 = k\sqrt{36}$

$7.4 = k \cdot 6$

$k = \dfrac{37}{30}$

$d = \dfrac{37}{30}\sqrt{e} = \dfrac{37}{30}\sqrt{64} \approx 9.9$

The person can see 9.9 miles.

12. $V = kT$

$20 = k(300)$

$k = \dfrac{20}{300} = \dfrac{1}{15}$

$V = \dfrac{1}{15}T = \dfrac{1}{15}(360) = 24$

The new volume is 24 cubic meters.

14. $y = \dfrac{k}{x}$

$20 = \dfrac{k}{9}$

$k = 180$

$y = \dfrac{180}{x}$

16.
$$y = \frac{k}{x}$$
$$63 = \frac{k}{3}$$
$$k = 189$$
$$y = \frac{189}{x}$$

18.
$$y = \frac{k}{x}$$
$$\frac{1}{10} = \frac{k}{40}$$
$$k = 4$$
$$y = \frac{4}{x}$$

20.
$$y = \frac{k}{x}$$
$$0.6 = \frac{k}{0.3}$$
$$k = 0.18$$
$$y = \frac{0.18}{x}$$

22.
$$w = \frac{k}{d^2}$$
$$160 = \frac{k}{(4000)^2}$$
$$k = 2,560,000,000$$
$$w = \frac{2,560,000,000}{d^2} = \frac{2,560,000,000}{(4200)^2} \approx 145$$
The person will weigh 145 pounds.

24.
$$C = \frac{k}{n}$$
$$1.20 = \frac{k}{4000}$$
$$k = 4800$$
$$C = \frac{4800}{n} = \frac{4800}{6000} = 0.8 = 0.80$$
The cost per disk is $0.80.

26.
$$W = \frac{k}{h^2}$$
$$2 = \frac{k}{8^2}$$
$$k = 128$$
$$W = \frac{128}{h^2} = \frac{128}{10^2} = 1.28$$
It can hold 1.28 tons.

28. $P = kRS^2$

30. $a = kbc$

32.
$$y = kx^3$$
$$32 = k(4)^3$$
$$32 = 64k$$
$$k = \frac{1}{2}$$
$$y = \frac{1}{2}x^3$$

34.
$$y = k\sqrt{x}$$
$$2.1 = k\sqrt{9}$$
$$2.1 = 3k$$
$$k = 0.7$$
$$y = 0.7\sqrt{x}$$

36.
$$y = \frac{k}{x^2}$$
$$0.011 = \frac{k}{10^2}$$
$$k = 1.1$$
$$y = \frac{1.1}{x^2}$$

38.
$$y = kxz^2$$
$$360 = k(4)(3)^2$$
$$360 = k \cdot 4 \cdot 9$$
$$360 = 36k$$
$$k = 10$$
$$y = 10xz^2$$

40.
$$C = kwt$$
$$60 = k(200)(2)$$
$$60 = 400k$$
$$k = 0.15$$
$$C = 0.15wt = 0.15(240)(3) = 108$$
The workers can make 108 cars.

42. $F = kAs$

$20 = k(12)(10)$

$20 = 120k$

$k = \dfrac{1}{6}$

$F = \dfrac{1}{6}As = \dfrac{1}{6}(8)(12) = 16$

The force is 16 pounds.

44. $h = ksd^3$

$40 = k(120)(2)^3$

$40 = k(120)(8)$

$40 = 960k$

$k = \dfrac{40}{960} = \dfrac{1}{24}$

$h = \dfrac{1}{24}sd^3 = \dfrac{1}{24}(80)(3)^3 = \dfrac{1}{24}\cdot 80\cdot 27 = 90$

It can transmit 90 horsepower.

46. p varies directly as q is written as $p = kq$.

48. y varies inversely as x is written as $y = \dfrac{k}{x}$.

50. y varies jointly as q, r, and t is written as $y = kqrt$.

52. y varies inversely as a^4 is written as $y = \dfrac{k}{a^4}$.

54. y varies directly as a^5 and inversely as b is written as $y = \dfrac{ka^5}{b}$.

56. $r = 6$ cm

$C = 2\pi r = 2\pi(6) = 12\pi$ cm

$A = \pi r^2 = \pi(6)^2 = 36\pi$ sq cm

58. $r = 7$ m

$C = 2\pi r = 2\pi(7) = 14\pi$ m

$A = \pi r^2 = \pi(7)^2 = 49\pi$ sq m

60. $\sqrt{36} = 6$

62. $\sqrt{4} = 2$

64. $\sqrt{\dfrac{1}{25}} = \dfrac{1}{5}$

66. $\sqrt{\dfrac{25}{121}} = \dfrac{5}{11}$

68. $y = \dfrac{0.6}{x}$ is an example of inverse variation; b.

70. $xy = \dfrac{2}{11}$ or $y = \dfrac{2}{11x}$ is an example of inverse variation; b.

72. $V_1 = khr^2$

$V_2 = k\left(\dfrac{1}{2}h\right)(2r)^2$

$\quad = k\left(\dfrac{1}{2}h\right)(4r^2)$

$\quad = 2(khr^2)$

$\quad = 2V_1$

It is multiplied by 2.

74. $y_1 = kx^2$

$y_2 = k(2x)^2 = k(4x^2) = 4(kx^2) = 4y_1$

It is multiplied by 4.

76.

x	$\frac{1}{4}$	$\frac{1}{2}$	1	2	4
$y = \frac{1}{x}$	4	2	1	$\frac{1}{2}$	$\frac{1}{4}$

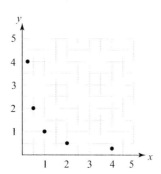

78.

x	$\frac{1}{4}$	$\frac{1}{2}$	1	2	4
$y = \frac{5}{x}$	20	10	5	$\frac{5}{2}$	$\frac{5}{4}$

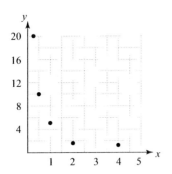

Chapter 6 Vocabulary Check

1. A rational expression whose numerator, denominator, or both contain one or more rational expressions is called a <u>complex fraction</u>.

2. To divide a polynomial by a polynomial other than a monomial, we use <u>long division</u>.

3. In the equation $y = kx$, y varies <u>directly</u> as x.

4. In the equation $y = \dfrac{k}{x}$, y varies <u>inversely</u> as x.

5. The <u>least common denominator</u> of a list of rational expressions is a polynomial of least degree whose factors include the denominator factors in the list.

6. When a polynomial is to be divided by a binomial of the form $x - c$, a shortcut process called <u>synthetic division</u> may be used.

7. In the equation $y = kxz$, y varies <u>jointly</u> as x and z.

8. The expressions $(x - 5)$ and $(5 - x)$ are called <u>opposites</u>.

9. A <u>rational expression</u> is an expression that can be written as the quotient $\dfrac{P}{Q}$ of two polynomials P and Q as long as Q is not 0.

10. Which is an expression and which is an equation? An example of an <u>equation</u> is $\dfrac{2}{x} + \dfrac{2}{x^2} = 7$ and an example of an <u>expression</u> is $\dfrac{2}{x} + \dfrac{5}{x^2}$.

Chapter 6 Review

1. 7 is never 0 so the domain of $f(x) = \dfrac{3 - 5x}{7}$ is $\{x | x \text{ is a real number}\}$.

2. 11 is never 0 so the domain of $g(x) = \dfrac{2x + 4}{11}$ is $\{x | x \text{ is a real number}\}$.

3. $x - 5 = 0$
   $x = 5$

   The domain of $F(x) = \dfrac{-3x^2}{x - 5}$ is $\{x | x \text{ is a real number and } x \neq 5\}$.

4. $3x - 12 = 0$
   $3x = 12$
   $x = 4$

   The domain of $h(x) = \dfrac{4x}{3x - 12}$ is $\{x | x \text{ is a real number and } x \neq 4\}$.

5. $x^2 + 8x = 0$
   $x(x + 8) = 0$
   $x = 0 \quad \text{or} \quad x + 8 = 0$
   $x = 0 \quad \text{or} \quad x = -8$

   The domain of $f(x) = \dfrac{x^3 + 2}{x^2 + 8x}$ is $\{x | x \text{ is a real number and } x \neq 0, x \neq -8\}$.

6. $3x^2 - 48 = 0$
   $3(x^2 - 16) = 0$
   $3(x + 4)(x - 4) = 0$
   $x + 4 = 0 \quad \text{or} \quad x - 4 = 0$
   $x = -4 \quad \text{or} \quad x = 4$

   The domain of $G(x) = \dfrac{20}{3x^2 - 48}$ is $\{x | x \text{ is a real number and } x \neq -4, x \neq 4\}$.

7. $\dfrac{x - 12}{12 - x} = \dfrac{x - 12}{-(x - 12)} = -1$

8. $\dfrac{5x - 15}{25x - 75} = \dfrac{5(x - 3)}{25(x - 3)} = \dfrac{5}{25} = \dfrac{1}{5}$

9. $\dfrac{2x}{2x^2 - 2x} = \dfrac{2x}{2x(x - 1)} = \dfrac{1}{x - 1}$

10. $\dfrac{x+7}{x^2-49} = \dfrac{x+7}{(x-7)(x+7)} = \dfrac{1}{x-7}$

11. $\dfrac{2x^2+4x-30}{x^2+x-20} = \dfrac{2(x^2+2x-15)}{(x+5)(x-4)}$
$= \dfrac{2(x+5)(x-3)}{(x+5)(x-4)}$
$= \dfrac{2(x-3)}{x-4}$

12. $C(x) = \dfrac{35x+4200}{x}$

a. $C(50) = \dfrac{35(50)+4200}{50}$
$= \dfrac{1750+4200}{50}$
$= \dfrac{5950}{50}$
$= 119$
The average cost is $119.

b. $C(100) = \dfrac{35(100)+4200}{100}$
$= \dfrac{3500+4200}{100}$
$= \dfrac{7700}{100}$
$= 77$
The average cost is $77.

c. It will decrease.

13. $\dfrac{4-x}{5} \cdot \dfrac{15}{2x-8} = \dfrac{4-x}{5} \cdot \dfrac{5\cdot3}{2(x-4)}$
$= \dfrac{-1(x-4)}{5} \cdot \dfrac{5\cdot3}{2(x-4)}$
$= -\dfrac{3}{2}$

14. $\dfrac{x^2-6x+9}{2x^2-18} \cdot \dfrac{4x+12}{5x-15}$
$= \dfrac{(x-3)(x-3)}{2(x^2-9)} \cdot \dfrac{4(x+3)}{5(x-3)}$
$= \dfrac{(x-3)(x-3)}{2(x-3)(x+3)} \cdot \dfrac{4(x+3)}{5(x-3)}$
$= \dfrac{4}{10}$
$= \dfrac{2}{5}$

15. $\dfrac{a-4b}{a^2+ab} \cdot \dfrac{b^2-a^2}{8b-2a}$
$= \dfrac{a-4b}{a(a+b)} \cdot \dfrac{(b-a)(b+a)}{2(4b-a)}$
$= \dfrac{-(4b-a)}{a(a+b)} \cdot \dfrac{(a-b)(a+b)}{2(4b-a)}$
$= \dfrac{a-b}{2a}$

16. $\dfrac{x^2-x-12}{2x^2-32} \cdot \dfrac{x^2+8x+16}{3x^2+21x+36}$
$= \dfrac{(x-4)(x+3)}{2(x^2-16)} \cdot \dfrac{(x+4)(x+4)}{3(x^2+7x+12)}$
$= \dfrac{(x-4)(x+3)}{2(x-4)(x+4)} \cdot \dfrac{(x+4)(x+4)}{3(x+4)(x+3)}$
$= \dfrac{1}{2\cdot3}$
$= \dfrac{1}{6}$

17. $\dfrac{4x+8y}{3} \div \dfrac{5x+10y}{9} = \dfrac{4x+8y}{3} \cdot \dfrac{9}{5x+10y}$
$= \dfrac{4(x+2y)}{3} \cdot \dfrac{3\cdot3}{5(x+2y)}$
$= \dfrac{12}{5}$

18. $\dfrac{x^2-25}{3} \div \dfrac{x^2-10x+25}{x^2-x-20}$
$= \dfrac{x^2-25}{3} \cdot \dfrac{x^2-x-20}{x^2-10x+25}$
$= \dfrac{(x+5)(x-5)}{3} \cdot \dfrac{(x-5)(x+4)}{(x-5)(x-5)}$
$= \dfrac{(x+5)(x+4)}{3}$

19. $\dfrac{a-4b}{a^2+ab} \div \dfrac{20b-5a}{b^2-a^2}$

$= \dfrac{a-4b}{a^2+ab} \cdot \dfrac{b^2-a^2}{20b-5a}$

$= \dfrac{a-4b}{a(a+b)} \cdot \dfrac{(b+a)(b-a)}{5(4b-a)}$

$= \dfrac{a-4b}{a(a+b)} \cdot \dfrac{-(a+b)(a-b)}{-5(a-4b)}$

$= \dfrac{a-b}{5a}$

20. $\dfrac{3x+3}{x-1} \div \dfrac{x^2-6x-7}{x^2-1} = \dfrac{3x+3}{x-1} \cdot \dfrac{x^2-1}{x^2-6x-7}$

$= \dfrac{3(x+1)}{x-1} \cdot \dfrac{(x+1)(x-1)}{(x-7)(x+1)}$

$= \dfrac{3(x+1)}{x-7}$

21. $\dfrac{2x-x^2}{x^3-8} \div \dfrac{x^2}{x^2+2x+4}$

$= \dfrac{2x-x^2}{x^3-8} \cdot \dfrac{x^2+2x+4}{x^2}$

$= \dfrac{x(2-x)}{(x-2)(x^2+2x+4)} \cdot \dfrac{x^2+2x+4}{x^2}$

$= \dfrac{-x(x-2)}{(x-2)(x^2+2x+4)} \cdot \dfrac{x^2+2x+4}{x^2}$

$= -\dfrac{1}{x}$

22. $\dfrac{5x-15}{3-x} \cdot \dfrac{x+2}{10x+20} \cdot \dfrac{x^2-9}{x^2-x-6}$

$= \dfrac{5(x-3)}{-(x-3)} \cdot \dfrac{x+2}{10(x+2)} \cdot \dfrac{(x+3)(x-3)}{(x-3)(x+2)}$

$= -\dfrac{x+3}{2(x+2)}$

23. $4x^2y^5 = 2 \cdot 2x^2y^5$

$10x^2y^4 = 2 \cdot 5x^2y^4$

$6y^4 = 2 \cdot 3y^4$

The LCD is $2 \cdot 2 \cdot 5 \cdot 3x^2y^5 = 60x^2y^5$.

24. The LCD is $2x(x-2)$.

25. The LCD is $5x(x-5)$.

26. $5x^3 = 5 \cdot x^3$

$x^2+3x-28 = (x+7)(x-4)$

$10x^2-30x = 10x(x-3) = 2 \cdot 5 \cdot x \cdot (x-3)$

The LCD is

$2 \cdot 5 \cdot x^3 \cdot (x-4)(x+7)(x-3)$

$= 10x^3(x-4)(x+7)(x-3)$.

27. $\dfrac{4}{x-4} + \dfrac{x}{x-4} = \dfrac{4+x}{x-4}$

28. $\dfrac{4}{3x^2} + \dfrac{2}{3x^2} = \dfrac{4+2}{3x^2} = \dfrac{6}{3x^2} = \dfrac{2}{x^2}$

29. $\dfrac{1}{x-2} - \dfrac{1}{4-2x} = \dfrac{1}{x-2} - \dfrac{1}{2(2-x)}$

$= \dfrac{1}{x-2} - \dfrac{-1}{2(x-2)}$

$= \dfrac{1}{x-2} \cdot \dfrac{2}{2} - \dfrac{-1}{2(x-2)}$

$= \dfrac{2}{2(x-2)} - \dfrac{-1}{2(x-2)}$

$= \dfrac{2+1}{2(x-2)}$

$= \dfrac{3}{2(x-2)}$

30. $\dfrac{1}{10-x} + \dfrac{x-1}{x-10} = \dfrac{-1}{x-10} + \dfrac{x-1}{x-10}$

$= \dfrac{-1+x-1}{x-10}$

$= \dfrac{x-2}{x-10}$

31.
$$\frac{x}{9-x^2} - \frac{2}{5x-15} = \frac{-x}{x^2-9} - \frac{2}{5x-15}$$
$$= \frac{-x}{(x-3)(x+3)} - \frac{2}{5(x-3)}$$
$$= \frac{-x}{(x-3)(x+3)} \cdot \frac{5}{5} - \frac{2}{5(x-3)} \cdot \frac{x+3}{x+3}$$
$$= \frac{-5x}{5(x-3)(x+3)} - \frac{2(x+3)}{5(x-3)(x+3)}$$
$$= \frac{-5x-2(x+3)}{5(x-3)(x+3)}$$
$$= \frac{-5x-2x-6}{5(x-3)(x+3)}$$
$$= \frac{-7x-6}{5(x-3)(x+3)}$$

32.
$$2x+1-\frac{1}{x-3} = 2x \cdot \frac{x-3}{x-3} + 1 \cdot \frac{x-3}{x-3} - \frac{1}{x-3}$$
$$= \frac{2x^2-6x}{x-3} + \frac{x-3}{x-3} - \frac{1}{x-3}$$
$$= \frac{2x^2-6x+x-3-1}{x-3}$$
$$= \frac{2x^2-5x-4}{x-3}$$

33.
$$\frac{2}{a^2-2a+1} + \frac{3}{a^2-1} = \frac{2}{(a-1)(a-1)} + \frac{3}{(a+1)(a-1)}$$
$$= \frac{2}{(a-1)(a-1)} \cdot \frac{a+1}{a+1} + \frac{3}{(a+1)(a-1)} \cdot \frac{(a-1)}{(a-1)}$$
$$= \frac{2(a+1)}{(a-1)^2(a+1)} + \frac{3(a-1)}{(a-1)^2(a+1)}$$
$$= \frac{2a+2}{(a-1)^2(a+1)} + \frac{3a-3}{(a-1)^2(a+1)}$$
$$= \frac{2a+2+3a-3}{(a-1)^2(a+1)}$$
$$= \frac{5a-1}{(a-1)^2(a+1)}$$

34.
$$\frac{x}{9x^2+12x+16} - \frac{3x+4}{27x^3-64} = \frac{x}{9x^2+12x+16} - \frac{3x+4}{(3x-4)(9x^2+12x+16)}$$
$$= \frac{x}{9x^2+12x+16} \cdot \frac{3x-4}{3x-4} - \frac{3x+4}{(3x-4)(9x^2+12x+16)}$$
$$= \frac{3x^2-4x-3x-4}{(3x-4)(9x^2+12x+16)}$$
$$= \frac{3x^2-7x-4}{(3x-4)(9x^2+12x+16)}$$

35. $\dfrac{2}{x-1}-\dfrac{3x}{3x-3}+\dfrac{1}{2x-2}$

$=\dfrac{2}{x-1}-\dfrac{3x}{3(x-1)}+\dfrac{1}{2(x-1)}$

$=\dfrac{2}{x-1}\cdot\dfrac{6}{6}-\dfrac{3x}{3(x-1)}\cdot\dfrac{2}{2}+\dfrac{1}{2(x-1)}\cdot\dfrac{3}{3}$

$=\dfrac{12}{6(x-1)}-\dfrac{6x}{6(x-1)}+\dfrac{3}{6(x-1)}$

$=\dfrac{12-6x+3}{6(x-1)}$

$=\dfrac{15-6x}{6(x-1)}$

$=\dfrac{3(5-2x)}{6(x-1)}$

$=\dfrac{5-2x}{2(x-1)}$

36. Perimeter $=\dfrac{1}{x}+\dfrac{1}{x}+\dfrac{1}{x}+\dfrac{2}{x}+\dfrac{2}{x}+\dfrac{3}{2x}+\dfrac{5}{2x}$

$=\dfrac{7}{x}+\dfrac{8}{2x}$

$=\dfrac{7}{x}\cdot\dfrac{2}{2}+\dfrac{8}{2x}$

$=\dfrac{14}{2x}+\dfrac{8}{2x}$

$=\dfrac{14+8}{2x}$

$=\dfrac{22}{2x}$

$=\dfrac{11}{x}$

37. $\dfrac{1-\frac{3x}{4}}{2+\frac{x}{4}}=\dfrac{4\left(1-\frac{3x}{4}\right)}{4\left(2+\frac{x}{4}\right)}=\dfrac{4-3x}{8+x}$

38. $\dfrac{\frac{x^2}{15}}{\frac{x+1}{5x}}=\dfrac{x^2}{15}\div\dfrac{x+1}{5x}=\dfrac{x^2}{15}\cdot\dfrac{5x}{x+1}=\dfrac{x^3}{3(x+1)}$

39. $\dfrac{2-\frac{3}{2x}}{x-\frac{2}{5x}}=\dfrac{10x\left(2-\frac{3}{2x}\right)}{10x\left(x-\frac{2}{5x}\right)}$

$=\dfrac{20x-15}{10x^2-4}$

$=\dfrac{5(4x-3)}{2(5x^2-2)}$

40. $\dfrac{1+\frac{x}{y}}{\frac{x^2}{y^2}-1}=\dfrac{y^2\left(1+\frac{x}{y}\right)}{y^2\left(\frac{x^2}{y^2}-1\right)}$

$=\dfrac{y^2+xy}{x^2-y^2}$

$=\dfrac{y(y+x)}{(x+y)(x-y)}$

$=\dfrac{y}{x-y}$

41. $\dfrac{\frac{5}{x}+\frac{1}{xy}}{\frac{3}{x^2}}=\dfrac{x^2y\left(\frac{5}{x}+\frac{1}{xy}\right)}{x^2y\left(\frac{3}{x^2}\right)}=\dfrac{5xy+x}{3y}=\dfrac{x(5y+1)}{3y}$

42. $\dfrac{\frac{x}{3}-\frac{3}{x}}{1+\frac{3}{x}}=\dfrac{3x\left(\frac{x}{3}-\frac{3}{x}\right)}{3x\left(1+\frac{3}{x}\right)}$

$=\dfrac{x^2-9}{3x+9}$

$=\dfrac{(x+3)(x-3)}{3(x+3)}$

$=\dfrac{x-3}{3}$

43. $\dfrac{\frac{1}{x-1}+1}{\frac{1}{x+1}-1}=\dfrac{(x+1)(x-1)\left(\frac{1}{x-1}+1\right)}{(x+1)(x-1)\left(\frac{1}{x+1}-1\right)}$

$=\dfrac{x+1+(x+1)(x-1)}{x-1-(x+1)(x-1)}$

$=\dfrac{x+1+x^2-1}{x-1-x^2+1}$

$=\dfrac{x+x^2}{x-x^2}$

$=\dfrac{x(1+x)}{x(1-x)}$

$=\dfrac{1+x}{1-x}$

44.
$$\frac{\frac{x-3}{x+3}+\frac{x+3}{x-3}}{\frac{x-3}{x+3}-\frac{x+3}{x-3}} = \frac{(x-3)(x+3)\left(\frac{x-3}{x+3}+\frac{x+3}{x-3}\right)}{(x-3)(x+3)\left(\frac{x-3}{x+3}-\frac{x+3}{x-3}\right)}$$

$$=\frac{(x-3)^2+(x+3)^2}{(x-3)^2-(x+3)^2}$$

$$=\frac{x^2-6x+9+x^2+6x+9}{x^2-6x+9-(x^2+6x+9)}$$

$$=\frac{2x^2+18}{x^2-6x+9-x^2-6x-9}$$

$$=\frac{2(x^2+9)}{-12x}$$

$$=-\frac{x^2+9}{6x}$$

45. $f(a+h) = \dfrac{3}{a+h}$

46. $f(a) = \dfrac{3}{a}$

47. $\dfrac{f(a+h)-f(a)}{h} = \dfrac{\frac{3}{a+h}-\frac{3}{a}}{h}$

48. $\dfrac{f(a+h)-f(a)}{h} = \dfrac{\frac{3}{a+h}-\frac{3}{a}}{h}$

$$=\frac{\left(\frac{3}{a+h}-\frac{3}{a}\right)\cdot a(a+h)}{h\cdot a(a+h)}$$

$$=\frac{3a-3(a+h)}{h\cdot a(a+h)}$$

$$=\frac{3a-3a-3h}{h\cdot a(a+h)}$$

$$=\frac{-3h}{h\cdot a(a+h)}$$

$$=\frac{-3}{a(a+h)}$$

49. $\dfrac{4xy+2x^2-9}{4xy} = \dfrac{4xy}{4xy}+\dfrac{2x^2}{4xy}-\dfrac{9}{4xy}$

$$=1+\frac{x}{2y}-\frac{9}{4xy}$$

50. $\dfrac{12xb^2+16xb^4}{4xb^3} = \dfrac{12xb^2}{4xb^3}+\dfrac{16xb^4}{4xb^3}$

$$=\frac{3}{b}+4b$$

51.
$$
\begin{array}{r}
3x^3+9x^2+2x+6 \\
x-3\overline{\smash{\big)}\,3x^4+0x^3-25x^2+0x-20} \\
\underline{3x^4-9x^3} \\
9x^3-25x^2 \\
\underline{9x^3-27x^2} \\
2x^2+0x \\
\underline{2x^2-6x} \\
6x-20 \\
\underline{6x-18} \\
-2
\end{array}
$$

Answer: $3x^3+9x^2+2x+6-\dfrac{2}{x-3}$

52.
$$
\begin{array}{r}
2x^3-4x^2+7x-9 \\
x+2\overline{\smash{\big)}\,2x^4+0x^3-x^2+5x-12} \\
\underline{2x^4+4x^3} \\
-4x^3-x^2 \\
\underline{-4x^3-8x^2} \\
7x^2+5x \\
\underline{7x^2+14x} \\
-9x-12 \\
\underline{-9x-18} \\
6
\end{array}
$$

Answer: $2x^3-4x^2+7x-9+\dfrac{6}{x+2}$

53.
$$
\begin{array}{r}
x^2-1 \\
2x+3\overline{\smash{\big)}\,2x^3+3x^2-2x+2} \\
\underline{2x^3+3x^2} \\
-2x+2 \\
\underline{-2x-3} \\
5
\end{array}
$$

Answer: $x^2-1+\dfrac{5}{2x+3}$

54.
$$x^2 + x + 2 \overline{\smash{\big)}\ 3x^4 + 5x^3 + 7x^2 + 3x - 2} \quad \frac{3x^2 + 2x - 1}{}$$
$$\underline{3x^4 + 3x^3 + 6x^2}$$
$$2x^3 + x^2 + 3x$$
$$\underline{2x^3 + 2x^2 + 4x}$$
$$-x^2 - x - 2$$
$$\underline{-x^2 - x - 2}$$
$$0$$

Answer: $3x^2 + 2x - 1$

55.

$$2 \,\vert\, \begin{array}{cccc} 3 & 0 & 12 & -4 \\ & 6 & 12 & 48 \\ \hline 3 & 6 & 24 & 44 \end{array}$$

Answer: $3x^2 + 6x + 24 + \dfrac{44}{x-2}$

56.

$$-1 \,\vert\, \begin{array}{cccccc} 1 & 0 & 0 & 0 & 0 & -1 \\ & -1 & 1 & -1 & 1 & -1 \\ \hline 1 & -1 & 1 & -1 & 1 & -2 \end{array}$$

Answer: $x^4 - x^3 + x^2 - x + 1 - \dfrac{2}{x+1}$

57.

$$3 \,\vert\, \begin{array}{cccc} 1 & 0 & 0 & -81 \\ & 3 & 9 & 27 \\ \hline 1 & 3 & 9 & -54 \end{array}$$

Answer: $x^2 + 3x + 9 - \dfrac{54}{x-3}$

58.

$$-2 \,\vert\, \begin{array}{ccccc} 3 & 0 & -2 & 0 & 10 \\ & -6 & 12 & -20 & 40 \\ \hline 3 & -6 & 10 & -20 & 50 \end{array}$$

Answer: $3x^3 - 6x^2 + 10x - 20 + \dfrac{50}{x+2}$

59.

$$4 \,\vert\, \begin{array}{cccccc} 3 & 0 & 0 & 0 & -9 & 7 \\ & 12 & 48 & 192 & 768 & 3036 \\ \hline 3 & 12 & 48 & 192 & 759 & 3043 \end{array}$$

Thus, $P(4) = 3043$.

60.

$$-5 \,\vert\, \begin{array}{cccccc} 3 & 0 & 0 & 0 & -9 & 7 \\ & -15 & 75 & -375 & 1875 & -9330 \\ \hline 3 & -15 & 75 & -375 & 1866 & -9323 \end{array}$$

Thus, $P(-5) = -9323$.

61.

$$-\tfrac{1}{2} \,\vert\, \begin{array}{cccccc} 3 & 0 & 0 & 0 & -9 & 7 \\ & -\tfrac{3}{2} & \tfrac{3}{4} & -\tfrac{3}{8} & \tfrac{3}{16} & \tfrac{141}{32} \\ \hline 3 & -\tfrac{3}{2} & \tfrac{3}{4} & -\tfrac{3}{8} & -\tfrac{141}{16} & \tfrac{365}{32} \end{array}$$

Thus, $P\left(-\dfrac{1}{2}\right) = \dfrac{365}{32}$.

62.

$$3 \,\vert\, \begin{array}{ccccc} 1 & -1 & -6 & -6 & 18 \\ & 3 & 6 & 0 & -18 \\ \hline 1 & 2 & 0 & -6 & 0 \end{array}$$

length $= (x^3 + 2x^2 - 6)$ miles

63. The LCD is $3x$.

$$\frac{3}{x} + \frac{1}{3} = \frac{5}{x}$$
$$3x\left(\frac{3}{x} + \frac{1}{3}\right) = 3x\left(\frac{5}{x}\right)$$
$$3x\left(\frac{3}{x}\right) + 3x\left(\frac{1}{3}\right) = 3x\left(\frac{5}{x}\right)$$
$$9 + x = 15$$
$$x = 6$$

The solution set is $\{6\}$.

64. The LCD is $2(5x - 9)$.

$$\frac{2x+3}{5x-9} = \frac{3}{2}$$
$$2(5x-9) \cdot \frac{2x+3}{5x-9} = 2(5x-9) \cdot \frac{3}{2}$$
$$2(2x+3) = (5x-9) \cdot 3$$
$$4x + 6 = 15x - 27$$
$$6 = 11x - 27$$
$$33 = 11x$$
$$3 = x$$

The solution set is $\{3\}$.

65. The LCD is $(x - 2)(x + 2)$.

$$\frac{1}{x-2} - \frac{3x}{x^2-4} = \frac{2}{x+2}$$

$$(x-2)(x+2)\left(\frac{1}{x-2} - \frac{3x}{x^2-4}\right) = (x-2)(x+2)\left(\frac{2}{x+2}\right)$$

$$(x-2)(x+2) \cdot \frac{1}{x-2} - (x-2)(x+2) \cdot \frac{3x}{(x+2)(x-2)} = (x-2)(x+2) \cdot \frac{2}{x+2}$$

$$(x+2) - 3x = 2(x-2)$$

$$-2x + 2 = 2x - 4$$

$$-4x + 2 = -4$$

$$-4x = -6$$

$$x = \frac{-6}{-4} = \frac{3}{2}$$

The solution set is $\left\{\dfrac{3}{2}\right\}$.

66. The LCD is $7x$.

$$\frac{7}{x} - \frac{x}{7} = 0$$

$$7x\left(\frac{7}{x} - \frac{x}{7}\right) = 7x(0)$$

$$7x\left(\frac{7}{x}\right) - 7x\left(\frac{x}{7}\right) = 0$$

$$49 - x^2 = 0$$

$$(7-x)(7+x) = 0$$

$$7 - x = 0 \quad \text{or} \quad 7 + x = 0$$

$$7 = x \quad \text{or} \qquad x = -7$$

The solution set is $\{-7, 7\}$.

67. $\dfrac{5}{x^2-7x} + \dfrac{4}{2x-14} = \dfrac{5}{x(x-7)} + \dfrac{4}{2(x-7)}$

$$= \frac{5}{x(x-7)} \cdot \frac{2}{2} + \frac{4}{2(x-7)} \cdot \frac{x}{x}$$

$$= \frac{10}{2x(x-7)} + \frac{4x}{2x(x-7)}$$

$$= \frac{10+4x}{2x(x-7)}$$

$$= \frac{2(5+2x)}{2x(x-7)}$$

$$= \frac{5+2x}{x(x-7)}$$

68. The LCD is x^2.

$$3 - \frac{5}{x} - \frac{2}{x^2} = 0$$

$$x^2\left(3 - \frac{5}{x} - \frac{2}{x^2}\right) = x^2(0)$$

$$x^2 \cdot 3 - x^2\left(\frac{5}{x}\right) - x^2\left(\frac{2}{x^2}\right) = 0$$

$$3x^2 - 5x - 2 = 0$$

$$(3x+1)(x-2) = 0$$

$$3x+1 = 0 \quad \text{or} \quad x-2 = 0$$

$$3x = -1 \quad \text{or} \quad x = 2$$

$$x = -\frac{1}{3} \quad \text{or} \quad x = 2$$

The solution set is $\left\{-\frac{1}{3}, 2\right\}$.

69. $\dfrac{4}{3-x} - \dfrac{7}{2x-6} + \dfrac{5}{x}$

$= \dfrac{-4}{x-3} - \dfrac{7}{2(x-3)} + \dfrac{5}{x}$

$= \dfrac{-4}{x-3} \cdot \dfrac{2x}{2x} - \dfrac{7}{2(x-3)} \cdot \dfrac{x}{x} + \dfrac{5}{x} \cdot \dfrac{2(x-3)}{2(x-3)}$

$= \dfrac{-8x}{2x(x-3)} - \dfrac{7x}{2x(x-3)} + \dfrac{10x-30}{2x(x-3)}$

$= \dfrac{-8x - 7x + 10x - 30}{2x(x-3)}$

$= \dfrac{-5x-30}{2x(x-3)}$

$= \dfrac{-5(x+6)}{2x(x-3)}$

70. $A = \dfrac{h(a+b)}{2}$

$2A = h(a+b)$

$\dfrac{2A}{h} = a+b$

$a = \dfrac{2A}{h} - b$

71.

$$\frac{1}{R} = \frac{1}{R_1} + \frac{1}{R_2}$$

$$RR_1R_2\left(\frac{1}{R}\right) = RR_1R_2\left(\frac{1}{R_1}\right) + RR_1R_2\left(\frac{1}{R_2}\right)$$

$$R_1R_2 = RR_2 + RR_1$$

$$R_1R_2 - RR_2 = RR_1$$

$$R_2(R_1 - R) = RR_1$$

$$R_2 = \frac{RR_1}{R_1 - R}$$

72.

$$I = \frac{E}{R+r}$$

$$I(R+r) = E$$

$$R + r = \frac{E}{I}$$

$$R = \frac{E}{I} - r$$

73.

$$A = P + Prt$$

$$A - P = Prt$$

$$\frac{A-P}{Pt} = r \text{ or } r = \frac{A-P}{Pt}$$

74.

$$H = \frac{kA(T_1 - T_2)}{L}$$

$$HL = kA(T_1 - T_2)$$

$$\frac{HL}{k(T_1 - T_2)} = A \text{ or } A = \frac{HL}{k(T_1 - T_2)}$$

75. Let $x =$ the number.

$$x + 2\left(\frac{1}{x}\right) = 3$$

$$x\left[x + 2\left(\frac{1}{x}\right)\right] = x \cdot 3$$

$$x^2 + 2 = 3x$$

$$x^2 - 3x + 2 = 0$$

$$(x-1)(x-2) = 0$$

$$x - 1 = 0 \quad \text{or} \quad x - 2 = 0$$

$$x = 1 \quad \text{or} \quad x = 2$$

The numbers are 1 and 2.

76. Let x = the number.

$$\frac{3+x}{7+2x} = \frac{10}{21}$$
$$21(3+x) = 10(7+2x)$$
$$63+21x = 70+20x$$
$$63+1x = 70$$
$$x = 7$$

The number is 7.

77. Let x = amount of time required for all three boys to paint the fence together.

$$\frac{1}{4}+\frac{1}{5}+\frac{1}{6} = \frac{1}{x}$$
$$60x\cdot\frac{1}{4}+60x\cdot\frac{1}{5}+60x\cdot\frac{1}{6} = 60x\cdot\frac{1}{x}$$
$$15x+12x+10x = 60$$
$$37x = 60$$
$$x = \frac{60}{37} = 1\frac{23}{37}$$

It will take $1\frac{23}{37}$ hours for all three boys to paint the fence together.

78. Let x = amount of time it takes Tom to type the mailing labels when working alone.

$$\frac{1}{6}+\frac{1}{x} = \frac{1}{4}$$
$$12x\cdot\frac{1}{6}+12x\cdot\frac{1}{x} = 12x\cdot\frac{1}{4}$$
$$2x+12 = 3x$$
$$12 = x$$

It takes Tom 12 hours to complete the task alone.

79. Let x = the speed of the current.

	distance =	rate	· time
Upstream	72	$32-x$	$\frac{72}{32-x}$
Downstream	120	$32+x$	$\frac{120}{32+x}$

$$\frac{72}{32-x} = \frac{120}{32+x}$$
$$72(32+x) = 120(32-x)$$
$$2304+72x = 3840-120x$$
$$72x = 1536-120x$$
$$192x = 1536$$
$$x = 8$$

The speed of the current is 8 mph.

80. Let x = the speed of the walker.

	distance =	rate	· time
Jogger	14	$x+3$	$\frac{14}{x+3}$
Walker	8	x	$\frac{8}{x}$

$$\frac{14}{x+3} = \frac{8}{x}$$
$$14x = 8(x+3)$$
$$14x = 8x+24$$
$$6x = 24$$
$$x = 4$$

The speed of the walker is 4 mph.

81. $A = kB$

$$6 = k(14)$$
$$k = \frac{6}{14} = \frac{3}{7}$$
$$A = \frac{3}{7}B = \frac{3}{7}(21) = 9$$

82. $P = \frac{K}{V}$

$$1250 = \frac{K}{2}$$
$$K = 2500$$
$$P = \frac{2500}{V}$$
$$800 = \frac{2500}{V}$$
$$800V = 2500$$
$$V = 3.125$$

When the pressure is 800 kilopascals, the volume is 3.125 cubic meters.

83. $\dfrac{22x+8}{11x+4} = \dfrac{2(11x+4)}{11x+4} = 2$

84.
$$\frac{xy-3x+2y-6}{x^2+4x+4} = \frac{x(y-3)+2(y-3)}{(x+2)(x+2)}$$
$$= \frac{(x+2)(y-3)}{(x+2)(x+2)}$$
$$= \frac{y-3}{x+2}$$

85. $\dfrac{2}{5x} \div \dfrac{4-18x}{6-27x} = \dfrac{2}{5x} \cdot \dfrac{6-27x}{4-18x}$

$\qquad = \dfrac{2}{5x} \cdot \dfrac{3(2-9x)}{2(2-9x)}$

$\qquad = \dfrac{3}{5x}$

86. $\dfrac{7x+28}{2x+4} \div \dfrac{x^2+2x-8}{x^2-2x-8}$

$\quad = \dfrac{7x+28}{2x+4} \cdot \dfrac{x^2-2x-8}{x^2+2x-8}$

$\quad = \dfrac{7(x+4)}{2(x+2)} \cdot \dfrac{(x-4)(x+2)}{(x+4)(x-2)}$

$\quad = \dfrac{7(x-4)}{2(x-2)}$

87. $\dfrac{5a^2-20}{a^3+2a^2+a+2} \div \dfrac{7a}{a^3+a}$

$\quad = \dfrac{5a^2-20}{a^3+2a^2+a+2} \cdot \dfrac{a^3+a}{7a}$

$\quad = \dfrac{5(a^2-4)}{a^2(a+2)+1(a+2)} \cdot \dfrac{a(a^2+1)}{7a}$

$\quad = \dfrac{5(a+2)(a-2)}{(a+2)(a^2+1)} \cdot \dfrac{a(a^2+1)}{7a}$

$\quad = \dfrac{5(a-2)}{7}$

88. $\dfrac{4a+8}{5a^2-20} \cdot \dfrac{3a^2-6a}{a+3} \div \dfrac{2a^2}{5a+15}$

$\quad = \dfrac{4a+8}{5a^2-20} \cdot \dfrac{3a^2-6a}{a+3} \cdot \dfrac{5a+15}{2a^2}$

$\quad = \dfrac{4(a+2)}{5(a^2-4)} \cdot \dfrac{3a(a-2)}{a+3} \cdot \dfrac{5(a+3)}{2a^2}$

$\quad = \dfrac{4(a+2)}{5(a-2)(a+2)} \cdot \dfrac{3a(a-2)}{a+3} \cdot \dfrac{5(a+3)}{2a^2}$

$\quad = \dfrac{6}{a}$

89. $\dfrac{7}{2x} + \dfrac{5}{6x} = \dfrac{7}{2x} \cdot \dfrac{3}{3} + \dfrac{5}{6x}$

$\qquad = \dfrac{21}{6x} + \dfrac{5}{6x}$

$\qquad = \dfrac{21+5}{6x}$

$\qquad = \dfrac{26}{6x}$

$\qquad = \dfrac{13}{3x}$

90. $\dfrac{x-2}{x+1} - \dfrac{x-3}{x-1} = \dfrac{x-2}{x+1} \cdot \dfrac{x-1}{x-1} - \dfrac{x-3}{x-1} \cdot \dfrac{x+1}{x+1}$

$\qquad = \dfrac{(x-2)(x-1)}{(x+1)(x-1)} - \dfrac{(x-3)(x+1)}{(x+1)(x-1)}$

$\qquad = \dfrac{x^2-3x+2}{(x+1)(x-1)} - \dfrac{x^2-2x-3}{(x+1)(x-1)}$

$\qquad = \dfrac{x^2-3x+2-x^2+2x+3}{(x+1)(x-1)}$

$\qquad = \dfrac{-x+5}{(x+1)(x-1)}$

91. $\dfrac{2x+1}{x^2+x-6} + \dfrac{2-x}{x^2+x-6} = \dfrac{2x+1+2-x}{x^2+x-6}$

$\qquad = \dfrac{x+3}{x^2+x-6}$

$\qquad = \dfrac{x+3}{(x+3)(x-2)}$

$\qquad = \dfrac{1}{x-2}$

92. $\dfrac{2}{x^2-16}-\dfrac{3x}{x^2+8x+16}+\dfrac{3}{x+4}=\dfrac{2}{(x+4)(x-4)}-\dfrac{3x}{(x+4)^2}+\dfrac{3}{x+4}$

$$=\dfrac{2}{(x+4)(x-4)}\cdot\dfrac{x+4}{x+4}-\dfrac{3x}{(x+4)^2}\cdot\dfrac{x-4}{x-4}+\dfrac{3}{x+4}\cdot\dfrac{(x+4)(x-4)}{(x+4)(x-4)}$$

$$=\dfrac{2x+8}{(x+4)^2(x-4)}-\dfrac{3x^2-12x}{(x+4)^2(x-4)}+\dfrac{3x^2-48}{(x+4)^2(x-4)}$$

$$=\dfrac{2x+8-3x^2+12x+3x^2-48}{(x+4)^2(x-4)}$$

$$=\dfrac{14x-40}{(x+4)^2(x-4)}$$

$$=\dfrac{2(7x-20)}{(x+4)^2(x-4)}$$

93. $\dfrac{\frac{1}{x}-\frac{2}{3x}}{\frac{5}{2x}-\frac{1}{3}}=\dfrac{6x\left(\frac{1}{x}-\frac{2}{3x}\right)}{6x\left(\frac{5}{2x}-\frac{1}{3}\right)}=\dfrac{6-4}{15-2x}=\dfrac{2}{15-2x}$

94. $\dfrac{2}{1-\frac{2}{x}}=\dfrac{x(2)}{x\left(1-\frac{2}{x}\right)}=\dfrac{2x}{x-2}$

95. $\dfrac{\frac{x^2+5x-6}{4x+3}}{\frac{(x+6)^2}{8x+6}}=\dfrac{x^2+5x-6}{4x+3}\div\dfrac{(x+6)^2}{8x+6}$

$$=\dfrac{x^2+5x-6}{4x+3}\cdot\dfrac{8x+6}{(x+6)^2}$$

$$=\dfrac{(x+6)(x-1)}{4x+3}\cdot\dfrac{2(4x+3)}{(x+6)^2}$$

$$=\dfrac{2(x-1)}{x+6}$$

96. $\dfrac{\frac{3}{x-1}-\frac{2}{1-x}}{\frac{2}{x-1}-\frac{2}{x}}=\dfrac{\frac{3}{x-1}-\frac{-2}{x-1}}{\frac{2}{x-1}-\frac{2}{x}}$

$$=\dfrac{(x)(x-1)\left(\frac{3}{x-1}-\frac{-2}{x-1}\right)}{(x)(x-1)\left(\frac{2}{x-1}-\frac{2}{x}\right)}$$

$$=\dfrac{3x+2x}{2x-2(x-1)}$$

$$=\dfrac{5x}{2x-2x+2}$$

$$=\dfrac{5x}{2}$$

97. $4 + \dfrac{8}{x} = 8$

The LCD is x.

$$x(4) + x\left(\dfrac{8}{x}\right) = x(8)$$
$$4x + 8 = 8x$$
$$8 = 4x$$
$$x = 2$$

The solution set is $\{2\}$.

98. $\dfrac{x-2}{x^2 - 7x + 10} = \dfrac{1}{5x - 10} - \dfrac{1}{x - 5}$

$$\dfrac{x-2}{(x-2)(x-5)} = \dfrac{1}{5(x-2)} - \dfrac{1}{x-5}$$

The LCD is $5(x-2)(x-5)$.

$$5(x-2)(x-5) \cdot \dfrac{x-2}{(x-2)(x-5)} = 5(x-2)(x-5) \cdot \dfrac{1}{5(x-2)} - 5(x-2)(x-5) \cdot \dfrac{1}{x-5}$$
$$5(x-2) = (x-5) - 5(x-2)$$
$$5x - 10 = x - 5 - 5x + 10$$
$$5x - 10 = -4x + 5$$
$$9x - 10 = 5$$
$$9x = 15$$
$$x = \dfrac{15}{9} = \dfrac{5}{3}$$

The solution set is $\left\{\dfrac{5}{3}\right\}$.

99. Let x be the numerator of a fraction. Then $x + 2$ is the denominator.

$$\dfrac{x-3}{x+2+5} = \dfrac{2}{3}$$
$$\dfrac{x-3}{x+7} = \dfrac{2}{3}$$
$$3(x-3) = 2(x+7)$$
$$3x - 9 = 2x + 14$$
$$x - 9 = 14$$
$$x = 23$$
$$x + 2 = 23 + 2 = 25$$

The fraction is $\dfrac{23}{25}$.

100. Let x be the first even integer and $x + 2$ be the next consecutive even integer.

$$\frac{1}{x} + \frac{1}{x+2} = -\frac{9}{40}$$

$$40x(x+2) \cdot \frac{1}{x} + 40x(x+2) \cdot \frac{1}{x+2} = 40x(x+2) \cdot \frac{-9}{40}$$

$$40(x+2) + 40x = -9x(x+2)$$

$$40x + 80 + 40x = -9x^2 - 18x$$

$$80x + 80 = -9x^2 - 18x$$

$$9x^2 + 98x + 80 = 0$$

$$(9x+8)(x+10) = 0$$

$$9x + 8 = 0 \quad \text{or} \quad x + 10 = 0$$

$$9x = -8 \quad \text{or} \quad x = -10$$

$$x = -\frac{8}{9} \quad \text{or} \quad x = -10$$

$-\dfrac{8}{9}$ is not an integer.

$x + 2 = -10 + 2 = -8$

The two integers are -10 and -8.

101. Let x = time it takes to empty a full tank if both pipes are open.

$$-\frac{1}{2.5} + \frac{1}{2} = \frac{1}{x}$$

$$(2.5)(2x) \cdot -\frac{1}{2.5} + (2.5)(2x) \cdot \frac{1}{2} = (2.5)(2x) \cdot \frac{1}{x}$$

$$-2x + 2.5x = 5$$

$$0.5x = 5$$

$$x = 10$$

It takes 10 hours to empty a full tank if both pipes are open.

102. Let x = the speed of the car and
$x + 430$ = the speed of the jet.

	distance	=	rate	·	time
Car	210		x		$\frac{210}{x}$
Jet	1715		$x + 430$		$\frac{1715}{x+430}$

$$\frac{210}{x} = \frac{1715}{x+430}$$

$$210(x+430) = 1715x$$

$$210x + 90,300 = 1715x$$

$$90,300 = 1505x$$

$$60 = x$$

$x + 430 = 60 + 430 = 490$

The speed of the jet is 490 mph.

103. One train traveled 382 miles in 6 hours and the second train traveled $382 - 112 = 270$ miles in 6 hours.

Recall $D = rt$ or $r = \dfrac{D}{t}$.

$r = \dfrac{382}{6} = 63\dfrac{2}{3}$ $\qquad$ $r = \dfrac{270}{6} = 45$

The speeds of the trains are $63\dfrac{2}{3}$ mph and 45 mph.

104. $C = \dfrac{k}{D}$

$12 = \dfrac{k}{8}$

$96 = k$

$C = \dfrac{96}{D} = \dfrac{96}{24} = 4$

105. $A = kr^2$

$36\pi = k(3)^2$

$36\pi = 9k$

$k = 4\pi$

$A = 4\pi r^2$

$A = 4\pi(4)^2 = 4\pi \cdot 16 = 64\pi$

The surface area is 64π square inches.

106.

$$
\begin{array}{r}
3x^3 + 13x^2 + 51x + 204 \\
x-4\overline{\smash{\big)}\,3x^4 + x^3 - x^2 + 0x - 2} \\
\underline{3x^4 - 12x^3} \\
13x^3 - x^2 \\
\underline{13x^3 - 52x^2} \\
51x^2 + 0x \\
\underline{51x^2 - 204x} \\
204x - 2 \\
\underline{204x - 816} \\
814
\end{array}
$$

$3x^3 + 13x^2 + 51x + 204 + \dfrac{814}{x-4}$

Chapter 6 Test

1. $1 - x = 0$

$ 1 = x$

The domain of $f(x) = \dfrac{5x^2}{1-x}$ is

$\{x|x$ is a real number and $x \neq 1\}$.

2. $x^2 + 4x + 3 = 0$

$(x+3)(x+1) = 0$

$x + 3 = 0$ $\quad$ or $\quad$ $x + 1 = 0$

$ x = -3$ $\quad$ or $\qquad$ $x = -1$

The domain of $g(x) = \dfrac{9x^2 - 9}{x^2 + 4x + 3}$ is

$\{x|x$ is a real number and $x \neq -3,\ x \neq -1\}$.

3. $\dfrac{7x - 21}{24 - 8x} = \dfrac{7(x-3)}{8(3-x)} = \dfrac{7(x-3)}{-8(x-3)} = -\dfrac{7}{8}$

4. $\dfrac{x^2 - 4x}{x^2 + 5x - 36} = \dfrac{x(x-4)}{(x+9)(x-4)} = \dfrac{x}{x+9}$

5. $\dfrac{x^3 - 8}{x - 2} = \dfrac{x^3 - 2^3}{x - 2}$

$ = \dfrac{(x-2)(x^2 + 2x + 4)}{x - 2}$

$ = x^2 + 2x + 4$

6. $\dfrac{2x^3 + 16}{6x^2 + 12x} \cdot \dfrac{5}{x^2 - 2x + 4}$

$= \dfrac{2(x^3 + 8)}{6x(x+2)} \cdot \dfrac{5}{x^2 - 2x + 4}$

$= \dfrac{2(x+2)(x^2 - 2x + 4)}{6x(x+2)} \cdot \dfrac{5}{x^2 - 2x + 4}$

$= \dfrac{5}{3x}$

7. $\dfrac{5}{4x^3} + \dfrac{7}{4x^3} = \dfrac{5+7}{4x^3} = \dfrac{12}{4x^3} = \dfrac{3}{x^3}$

8. $\dfrac{3x^2 - 12}{x^2 + 2x - 8} \div \dfrac{6x + 18}{x + 4}$

$= \dfrac{3x^2 - 12}{x^2 + 2x - 8} \cdot \dfrac{x + 4}{6x + 18}$

$= \dfrac{3(x^2 - 4)}{(x+4)(x-2)} \cdot \dfrac{x + 4}{6(x+3)}$

$= \dfrac{3(x+2)(x-2)}{(x+4)(x-2)} \cdot \dfrac{(x+4)}{6(x+3)}$

$= \dfrac{x + 2}{2(x+3)}$

9. $\dfrac{4x-12}{2x-9} \div \dfrac{3-x}{4x^2-81} \cdot \dfrac{x+3}{5x+15} = \dfrac{4x-12}{2x-9} \cdot \dfrac{4x^2-81}{3-x} \cdot \dfrac{x+3}{5x+15}$

$$= \dfrac{4(x-3)}{2x-9} \cdot \dfrac{(2x+9)(2x-9)}{-(x-3)} \cdot \dfrac{x+3}{5(x+3)}$$

$$= \dfrac{4(2x+9)}{-5}$$

$$= -\dfrac{4(2x+9)}{5}$$

10. $\dfrac{3+2x}{10-x} + \dfrac{13+x}{x-10} = \dfrac{-(3+2x)}{x-10} + \dfrac{13+x}{x-10}$

$$= \dfrac{-3-2x+13+x}{x-10}$$

$$= \dfrac{-x+10}{x-10}$$

$$= -\dfrac{x-10}{x-10}$$

$$= -1$$

11. $\dfrac{2x^2+7}{2x^4-18x^2} - \dfrac{6x+7}{2x^4-18x^2} = \dfrac{2x^2+7-6x-7}{2x^4-18x^2}$

$$= \dfrac{2x^2-6x}{2x^4-18x^2}$$

$$= \dfrac{2x(x-3)}{2x^2(x^2-9)}$$

$$= \dfrac{2x(x-3)}{2x^2(x-3)(x+3)}$$

$$= \dfrac{1}{x(x+3)}$$

12. $\dfrac{3}{x^2-x-6} + \dfrac{2}{x^2-5x+6} = \dfrac{3}{(x-3)(x+2)} + \dfrac{2}{(x-3)(x-2)}$

$$= \dfrac{3}{(x-3)(x+2)} \cdot \dfrac{x-2}{x-2} + \dfrac{2}{(x-3)(x-2)} \cdot \dfrac{x+2}{x+2}$$

$$= \dfrac{3(x-2)}{(x-3)(x+2)(x-2)} + \dfrac{2(x+2)}{(x-3)(x+2)(x-2)}$$

$$= \dfrac{3x-6}{(x-3)(x+2)(x-2)} + \dfrac{2x+4}{(x-3)(x+2)(x-2)}$$

$$= \dfrac{3x-6+2x+4}{(x-3)(x+2)(x-2)}$$

$$= \dfrac{5x-2}{(x-3)(x+2)(x-2)}$$

13. $3x - 21 = 3(x - 7)$
$2x - 14 = 2(x - 7)$
The LCD is $3 \cdot 2(x - 7) = 6(x - 7)$.

$$\frac{5}{x-7} - \frac{2x}{3x-21} + \frac{x}{2x-14} = \frac{5}{x-7} \cdot \frac{6}{6} - \frac{2x}{3(x-7)} \cdot \frac{2}{2} + \frac{x}{2(x-7)} \cdot \frac{3}{3}$$
$$= \frac{30}{6(x-7)} - \frac{4x}{6(x-7)} + \frac{3x}{6(x-7)}$$
$$= \frac{30 - 4x + 3x}{6(x-7)}$$
$$= \frac{30 - x}{6(x-7)}$$

14.
$$\frac{3x}{5} \cdot \left(\frac{5}{x} - \frac{5}{2x} \right) = \frac{3x}{5} \cdot \left(\frac{5}{x} \cdot \frac{2}{2} - \frac{5}{2x} \right)$$
$$= \frac{3x}{5} \left(\frac{10}{2x} - \frac{5}{2x} \right)$$
$$= \frac{3x}{5} \left(\frac{10 - 5}{2x} \right)$$
$$= \frac{3x}{5} \left(\frac{5}{2x} \right)$$
$$= \frac{3}{2}$$

15.
$$\frac{\frac{5}{x} - \frac{7}{3x}}{\frac{9}{8x} - \frac{1}{x}} = \frac{24x\left(\frac{5}{x} - \frac{7}{3x}\right)}{24x\left(\frac{9}{8x} - \frac{1}{x}\right)} = \frac{120 - 56}{27 - 24} = \frac{64}{3}$$

16.
$$\frac{\frac{x^2-5x+6}{x+3}}{\frac{x^2-4x+4}{x^2-9}} = \frac{x^2-5x+6}{x+3} \div \frac{x^2-4x+4}{x^2-9}$$
$$= \frac{x^2-5x+6}{x+3} \cdot \frac{x^2-9}{x^2-4x+4}$$
$$= \frac{(x-3)(x-2)}{x+3} \cdot \frac{(x+3)(x-3)}{(x-2)(x-2)}$$
$$= \frac{(x-3)^2}{x-2}$$

17.
$$\frac{4x^2y + 9x + 3xz}{3xz} = \frac{4x^2y}{3xz} + \frac{9x}{3xz} + \frac{3xz}{3xz}$$
$$= \frac{4xy}{3z} + \frac{3}{z} + 1$$

18.

$$\begin{array}{r} 2x^2 - x - 2 \\ 2x+1\overline{)4x^3 + 0x^2 - 5x + 0} \\ \underline{4x^3 + 2x^2} \\ -2x^2 - 5x \\ \underline{-2x^2 - x} \\ -4x + 0 \\ \underline{-4x - 2} \\ 2 \end{array}$$

Answer: $2x^2 - x - 2 + \dfrac{2}{2x+1}$

19.

$$\begin{array}{r|rrrrr} -3 & 4 & -3 & 0 & -1 & -1 \\ & & -12 & 45 & -135 & 408 \\ \hline & 4 & -15 & 45 & -136 & 407 \end{array}$$

Answer: $4x^3 - 15x^2 + 45x - 136 + \dfrac{407}{x+3}$

20.

$$\begin{array}{r|rrrrr} -2 & 4 & 0 & 7 & -2 & -5 \\ & & -8 & 16 & -46 & 96 \\ \hline & 4 & -8 & 23 & -48 & 91 \end{array}$$

Thus, $P(-2) = 91$.

21. The LCD is $x - 4$.

$$\frac{x}{x-4} = 3 - \frac{4}{x-4}$$
$$(x-4)\frac{x}{x-4} = (x-4)\cdot 3 - (x-4)\cdot\frac{4}{x-4}$$
$$x = 3(x-4) - 4$$
$$x = 3x - 12 - 4$$
$$x = 3x - 16$$
$$-2x = -16$$
$$x = 8$$

The solution set is $\{8\}$.

22.

$$\frac{3}{x+2} - \frac{1}{5x} = \frac{2}{5x^2 + 10x}$$
$$\frac{3}{x+2} - \frac{1}{5x} = \frac{2}{5x(x+2)}$$
$$5x(x+2)\left(\frac{3}{x+2} - \frac{1}{5x}\right) = 5x(x+2)\cdot\frac{2}{5x(x+2)}$$
$$3(5x) - 1(x+2) = 2$$
$$15x - x - 2 = 2$$
$$14x = 4$$
$$x = \frac{4}{14} = \frac{2}{7}$$

The solution set is $\left\{\dfrac{2}{7}\right\}$.

23.

$$\frac{x^2+8}{x} - 1 = \frac{2(x+4)}{x}$$
$$x\left(\frac{x^2+8}{x} - 1\right) = x\left(\frac{2(x+4)}{x}\right)$$
$$(x^2+8) - x = 2(x+4)$$
$$x^2 - x + 8 = 2x + 8$$
$$x^2 - 3x = 0$$
$$x(x-3) = 0$$
$$x = 0 \ \text{ or } \ x - 3 = 0$$
$$x = 3$$

Discard the answer 0 as extraneous.
The solution set is $\{3\}$.

24.

$$\frac{x+b}{a} = \frac{4x-7a}{b}$$
$$ab\left(\frac{x+b}{a}\right) = ab\left(\frac{4x-7a}{b}\right)$$
$$b(x+b) = a(4x-7a)$$
$$xb + b^2 = 4ax - 7a^2$$
$$b^2 + 7a^2 = 4ax - xb$$
$$b^2 + 7a^2 = x(4a-b)$$
$$x = \frac{b^2 + 7a^2}{4a-b}$$

25. Let $x = $ the number.

$$(x+1)\cdot\frac{2}{x} = \frac{12}{5}$$
$$\frac{2(x+1)}{x} = \frac{12}{5}$$
$$\frac{2x+2}{x} = \frac{12}{5}$$
$$5(2x+2) = 12x$$
$$10x + 10 = 12x$$
$$10 = 2x$$
$$5 = x$$

The number is 5.

26. Let t = time to weed garden together.

Note that 1 hr and 30 min = $\dfrac{3}{2}$ hours.

$$\dfrac{1}{2}+\dfrac{1}{3}=\dfrac{1}{\dfrac{3}{2}}$$

$$\dfrac{1}{2}+\dfrac{2}{3}=\dfrac{1}{t}$$

$$6t\left(\dfrac{1}{2}+\dfrac{2}{3}\right)=6t\left(\dfrac{1}{t}\right)$$

$$3t+4t=6$$

$$7t=6$$

$$t=\dfrac{6}{7}$$

It takes them $\dfrac{6}{7}$ hour.

27. $W=\dfrac{k}{V}$

$$20=\dfrac{k}{12}$$

$$k=20(12)=240$$

$$W=\dfrac{240}{V}=\dfrac{240}{15}=16$$

28. $Q=kRS^2$

$$24=k(3)(4)^2$$

$$24=48k$$

$$k=\dfrac{24}{48}=\dfrac{1}{2}$$

$$Q=\dfrac{1}{2}RS^2=\dfrac{1}{2}(2)(3)^2=9$$

29. $S=k\sqrt{d}$

$$160=k\sqrt{400}$$

$$160=20k$$

$$k=\dfrac{160}{20}=8$$

$$S=8\sqrt{d}$$

$$128=8\sqrt{d}$$

$$\sqrt{d}=\dfrac{128}{8}$$

$$\sqrt{d}=16$$

$$d=256$$

The height of the cliff is 256 feet.

Chapter 6 Cumulative Review

1. a. $8x$

b. $8x+3$

c. $x\div(-7)$ or $\dfrac{x}{-7}$

d. $2x-1\dfrac{6}{10}=2x-1.6$

e. $x-6$

f. $2(4+x)$

2. a. $x-\dfrac{1}{3}$

b. $5x-6$

c. $8x+3$

d. $\dfrac{7}{2-x}$

3. $\dfrac{y}{3}-\dfrac{y}{4}=\dfrac{1}{6}$

$$12\left(\dfrac{y}{3}-\dfrac{y}{4}\right)=12\left(\dfrac{1}{6}\right)$$

$$4y-3y=2$$

$$y=2$$

4. $\dfrac{x}{7}+\dfrac{x}{5}=\dfrac{12}{5}$

$$35\left(\dfrac{x}{7}+\dfrac{x}{5}\right)=35\left(\dfrac{12}{5}\right)$$

$$5x+7x=84$$

$$12x=84$$

$$x=7$$

5.

X	W1
-4	-20
10	-12.22
32	0
70	21.111
100	37.778

Y₁⊟5/9(X-32)

Fahrenheit	−4	10	32	70	100
Celsius	−20	−12.22	0	21.11	37.78

6. Let x = score on final exam.

$$\frac{78+65+82+79+2x}{6} \geq 78$$

$$\frac{304+2x}{6} \geq 78$$

$$6\left(\frac{304+2x}{6}\right) \geq 6(78)$$

$$304+2x \geq 468$$

$$2x \geq 164$$

$$x \geq 82$$

The minimum score she can make on her final is 82.

7. $\left|\dfrac{3x+1}{2}\right| = -2$ is impossible. The solution set is $\varnothing$.

8. $\left|\dfrac{2x-1}{3}\right| + 6 = 3$

$\left|\dfrac{2x-1}{3}\right| = -3,$ which is impossible.

The solution set is $\varnothing$.

9. $\left|\dfrac{2(x+1)}{3}\right| \leq 0$

$$\frac{2(x+1)}{3} = 0$$

$$2(x+1) = 0$$

$$2x+2 = 0$$

$$2x = -2$$

$$x = -1$$

The solution is -1.

10. $\left|\dfrac{3(x-1)}{4}\right| \geq 2$

$$\frac{3(x-1)}{4} \leq -2 \quad \text{or} \quad \frac{3(x-1)}{4} \geq 2$$

$$\frac{3x-3}{4} \leq -2 \quad \text{or} \quad \frac{3x-3}{4} \geq 2$$

$$3x-3 \leq -8 \quad \text{or} \quad 3x-3 \geq 8$$

$$3x \leq -5 \quad \text{or} \quad 3x \geq 11$$

$$x \leq -\frac{5}{3} \quad \text{or} \quad x \geq \frac{11}{3}$$

$$\left(-\infty, -\frac{5}{3}\right] \cup \left[\frac{11}{3}, \infty\right)$$

11. $y = -2x+3$

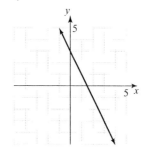

12. $y = -x+3$

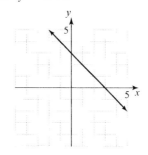

13. a. Function

b. Not a function

c. Function

14. $f(x) = -x^2 + 3x - 2$

a. $f(0) = -(0)^2 + 3(0) - 2 = -2$

b. $f(-3) = -(-3)^2 + 3(-3) - 2$
$$= -9 - 9 - 2$$
$$= -20$$

c. $f\left(\dfrac{1}{3}\right) = -\left(\dfrac{1}{3}\right)^2 + 3\left(\dfrac{1}{3}\right) - 2$

$$= -\frac{1}{9} + 1 - 2$$

$$= -\frac{1}{9} + \frac{9}{9} - \frac{18}{9}$$

$$= \frac{-1+9-18}{9}$$

$$= -\frac{10}{9}$$

15. $x - 3y = 6$

Let $y = 0$.

$x - 3(0) = 6$

$\quad\quad x = 6$

Plot $(6, 0)$.

Let $x = 0$.

$0 - 3y = 6$

$\quad -3y = 6$

$\quad\quad y = -2$

Plot $(0, -2)$.

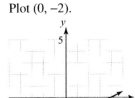

16. $3x - y = 6$

Let $y = 0$.

$3x - 0 = 6$

$\quad 3x = 6$

$\quad\quad x = 2$

Plot $(2, 0)$.

Let $x = 0$.

$3(0) - y = 6$

$\quad\quad -y = 6$

$\quad\quad\quad y = -6$

Plot $(0, -6)$.

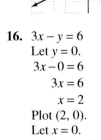

17. $y - (-5) = -3(x - 1)$

$\quad y + 5 = -3x + 3$

$\quad\quad\quad y = -3x - 2$

18. $y - 3 = \dfrac{1}{2}\big(x - (-1)\big)$

$\quad y - 3 = \dfrac{1}{2}(x + 1)$

$\quad y - 3 = \dfrac{1}{2}x + \dfrac{1}{2}$

$\quad\quad\quad y = \dfrac{1}{2}x + \dfrac{1}{2} + 3$

$\quad\quad\quad y = \dfrac{1}{2}x + \dfrac{7}{2}$

$\quad f(x) = \dfrac{1}{2}x + \dfrac{7}{2}$

19. $x \geq 1$ and $y \geq 2x - 1$

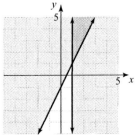

The solution region is the overlap, which has darker shading, along with its boundary.

20. $2x + y \leq 4$ or $y > 2$

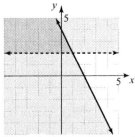

The solution region consists of all shaded regions and the boundary where the boundary line is solid.

21. $\begin{cases} 3x - 2y = 10 & (1) \\ 4x - 3y = 15 & (2) \end{cases}$

Multiply E1 by -4 and E2 by 3, and add.

$-12x + 8y = -40$

$\underline{\;\;12x - 9y = 45\;\;}$

$\quad\quad\quad -y = 5$

$\quad\quad\quad\quad y = -5$

Replace y with -5 in E1.

$$3x - 2(-5) = 10$$
$$3x + 10 = 10$$
$$3x = 0$$
$$x = 0$$

The solution is $(0, -5)$.

22. $\begin{cases} -2x + 3y = 6 & (1) \\ 3x - y = 5 & (2) \end{cases}$

Solve E2 for y:

$y = 3x - 5$

Replace y with $3x - 5$ in E1.

$$-2x + 3(3x - 5) = 6$$
$$-2x + 9x - 15 = 6$$
$$7x = 21$$
$$x = 3$$

Replace x with 3 in the equation $y = 3x - 5$.

$$y = 3(3) - 5 = 9 - 5 = 4$$

The solution is $(3, 4)$.

23. $\begin{cases} 2x - 4y + 8z = 2 & (1) \\ -x - 3y + z = 11 & (2) \\ x - 2y + 4z = 0 & (3) \end{cases}$

Add E2 and E3.

$-5y + 5z = 11$ (4)

Multiply E2 by 2 and add to E1.

$$-2x - 6y + 2z = 22$$
$$\underline{2x - 4y + 8z = 2}$$
$$-10y + 10z = 24 \ (5)$$

Solve the new system.

$\begin{cases} -5y + 5z = 11 & (4) \\ -10y + 10z = 24 & (5) \end{cases}$

Multiply E4 by -2 and add to E5.

$$10y - 10z = -22$$
$$\underline{-10y + 10z = 24}$$
$$0 = 2, \text{ which is impossible.}$$

The solution is $\varnothing$.

24. $\begin{cases} 2x - 2y + 4z = 6 & (1) \\ -4x - y + z = -8 & (2) \\ 3x - y + z = 6 & (3) \end{cases}$

Multiply E2 by -1 and add to E3.

$$4x + y - z = 8$$
$$\underline{3x - y + z = 6}$$
$$7x = 14$$
$$x = 2$$

Multiply E2 by -2 and add to E1.

$$8x + 2y - 2z = 16$$
$$\underline{2x - 2y + 4z = 6}$$
$$10x + 2z = 22 \text{ or } 5x + z = 11$$

Replace x with 2 in the equation $5x + z = 11$.

$$5(2) + z = 11$$
$$10 + z = 11$$
$$z = 1$$

Replace x with 2 and z with 1 in E3.

$$3(2) - y + 1 = 6$$
$$7 - y = 6$$
$$-y = -1$$
$$y = 1$$

The solution is $(2, 1, 1)$.

25. Let x = measure of the smallest angle,
y = measure of the largest angle and,
z = measure of the remaining angle.

$\begin{cases} x + y + z = 180 & (1) \\ y = x + 80 & (2) \\ z = x + 10 & (3) \end{cases}$

Substitute $x + 80$ for y and $x + 10$ for z in E1.

$$x + (x + 80) + (x + 10) = 180$$
$$3x + 90 = 180$$
$$3x = 90$$
$$x = 30$$

Replace x with 30 in E2 and E3.

$$y = 30 + 80 = 110$$
$$z = 30 + 10 = 40$$

The angles measure $30°$, $110°$, and $40°$.

26. Let x = the price of a ream of paper and
y = the price of a box of manila folders.

$\begin{cases} 3x + 2y = 21.90 & (1) \\ 5x + y = 24.25 & (2) \end{cases}$

Multiply E2 by -2 and add to E1.

$$-10x - 2y = -48.50$$
$$\underline{3x + 2y = 21.90}$$
$$-7x = -26.60$$
$$x = 3.80$$

Replace x with 3.80 in E2.

$$5(3.80) + y = 24.25$$
$$19 + y = 24.25$$
$$y = 5.25$$

A ream of paper cost \$3.80 and a box of manila folders cost \$5.25.

27. $\begin{cases} x + 2y + z = 2 \\ -2x - y + 2z = 5 \\ x + 3y - 2z = -8 \end{cases}$

$\begin{bmatrix} 1 & 2 & 1 & | & 2 \\ -2 & -1 & 2 & | & 5 \\ 1 & 3 & -2 & | & -8 \end{bmatrix}$

Multiply R1 by 2 and add to R2.
Multiply R1 by -1 and add to R3.

$$\begin{bmatrix} 1 & 2 & 1 & | & 2 \\ 0 & 3 & 4 & | & 9 \\ 0 & 1 & -3 & | & -10 \end{bmatrix}$$

Interchange R2 and R3.

$$\begin{bmatrix} 1 & 2 & 1 & | & 2 \\ 0 & 1 & -3 & | & -10 \\ 0 & 3 & 4 & | & 9 \end{bmatrix}$$

Multiply R2 by –3 and add to R3.

$$\begin{bmatrix} 1 & 2 & 1 & | & 2 \\ 0 & 1 & -3 & | & -10 \\ 0 & 0 & 13 & | & 39 \end{bmatrix}$$

Divide R3 by 13.

$$\begin{bmatrix} 1 & 2 & 1 & | & 2 \\ 0 & 1 & -3 & | & -10 \\ 0 & 0 & 1 & | & 3 \end{bmatrix}$$

This corresponds to $\begin{cases} x+2y+ \ z = 2 \\ \quad y-3z = -10 \\ \quad\quad\quad z = 3. \end{cases}$

$y-3z = -10$ and so $x+2(-1)+(3)=2$
$y-3(3) = -10$ $\quad\quad\quad x-2+3=2$
$y-9 = -10$ $\quad\quad\quad\quad x+1=2$
$y = -1$ $\quad\quad\quad\quad\quad x=1$

The solution is $(1, -1, 3)$.

28. $\begin{cases} x+ \ y+ \ z = 9 \\ 2x-2y+3z = 2 \\ -3x+ \ y- \ z = 1 \end{cases}$

$$\begin{bmatrix} 1 & 1 & 1 & | & 9 \\ 2 & -2 & 3 & | & 2 \\ -3 & 1 & -1 & | & 1 \end{bmatrix}$$

Multiply R1 by –2 and add to R2.
Multiply R1 by 3 and add to R3.

$$\begin{bmatrix} 1 & 1 & 1 & | & 9 \\ 0 & -4 & 1 & | & -16 \\ 0 & 4 & 2 & | & 28 \end{bmatrix}$$

Divide R2 by –4.

$$\begin{bmatrix} 1 & 1 & 1 & | & 9 \\ 0 & 1 & -\frac{1}{4} & | & 4 \\ 0 & 4 & 2 & | & 28 \end{bmatrix}$$

Multiply R2 by –4 and add to R3.

$$\begin{bmatrix} 1 & 1 & 1 & | & 9 \\ 0 & 1 & -\frac{1}{4} & | & 4 \\ 0 & 0 & 3 & | & 12 \end{bmatrix}$$

Divide R3 by 3.

$$\begin{bmatrix} 1 & 1 & 1 & | & 9 \\ 0 & 1 & -\frac{1}{4} & | & 4 \\ 0 & 0 & 1 & | & 4 \end{bmatrix}$$

This corresponds to $\begin{cases} x+y+ \ z = 9 \\ \quad y-\frac{1}{4}z = 4 \\ \quad\quad\quad z = 4 \end{cases}$

$y-\frac{1}{4}(4) = 4$ $\quad\quad x+5+4=9$
$y-1 = 4$ and so $\quad x+9=9$
$y = 5$ $\quad\quad\quad\quad x = 0$

The solution is $(0, 5, 4)$.

29. a. $7^0 = 1$

b. $-7^0 = -1 \cdot 7^0 = -1 \cdot 1 = -1$

c. $(2x+5)^0 = 1$

d. $2x^0 = 2 \cdot x^0 = 2 \cdot 1 = 2$

30. a. $2^{-2} + 3^{-1} = \dfrac{1}{2^2} + \dfrac{1}{3}$

$\quad = \dfrac{1}{4} + \dfrac{1}{3}$

$\quad = \dfrac{3}{12} + \dfrac{4}{12}$

$\quad = \dfrac{7}{12}$

b. $-6a^0 = -6 \cdot a^0 = -6 \cdot 1 = -6$

c. $\dfrac{x^{-5}}{x^{-2}} = x^{-5-(-2)} = x^{-3} = \dfrac{1}{x^3}$

31. a. $x^{-b}(2x^b)^2 = \dfrac{2^2(x^b)^2}{x^b}$

$\quad = \dfrac{4x^{2b}}{x^b}$

$\quad = 4x^{2b-b}$

$\quad = 4x^b$

b. $\dfrac{(y^{3a})^2}{y^{a-6}} = \dfrac{y^{6a}}{y^{a-6}} = y^{6a-(a-6)} = y^{5a+6}$

32. a. $3x^{4a}(4x^{-a})^2 = 3x^{4a} \cdot 16x^{-2a}$

$\quad = 48x^{4a+(-2a)}$

$\quad = 48x^{2a}$

b. $\dfrac{(y^{4b})^3}{y^{2b-3}} = \dfrac{y^{12b}}{y^{2b-3}}$

$= y^{12b-(2b-3)}$

$= y^{12b-2b+3}$

$= y^{10b+3}$

33. a. $3x^2$ has degree = 2.

b. $-2^3 x^5 = -8x^5$ has degree = 5.

c. y has degree = 1.

d. $12x^2 yz^3$ has degree = 2 + 1 + 3 = 6.

e. 5 has degree = 0.

34. $(2x^2 + 8x - 3) - (2x - 7)$

$= 2x^2 + 8x - 3 - 2x + 7$

$= 2x^2 + 6x + 4$

35. $[3 + (2a + b)]^2$

$= 3^2 + 2(3)(2a + b) + (2a + b)^2$

$= 9 + 6(2a + b) + (4a^2 + 2(2a)b + b^2)$

$= 9 + 12a + 6b + 4a^2 + 4ab + b^2$

36. $[4 + (3x - y)]^2$

$= 4^2 + 2(4)(3x - y) + (3x - y)^2$

$= 16 + 8(3x - y) + (9x^2 - 2(3x)y + y^2)$

$= 16 + 24x - 8y + 9x^2 - 6xy + y^2$

37. $ab - 6a + 2b - 12 = a(b - 6) + 2(b - 6)$

$= (b - 6)(a + 2)$

38. $xy + 2x - 5y - 10 = x(y + 2) - 5(y + 2)$

$= (y + 2)(x - 5)$

39. $2n^2 - 38n + 80 = 2(n^2 - 19n + 40)$

40. $6x^2 - x - 35 = (2x - 5)(3x + 7)$

41. $x^2 + 4x + 4 - y^2 = (x^2 + 4x + 4) - y^2$

$= (x + 2)^2 - y^2$

$= [(x + 2) + y][(x + 2) - y]$

$= (x + 2 + y)(x + 2 - y)$

42. $4x^2 - 4x + 1 - 9y^2$

$= (4x^2 - 4x + 1) - 9y^2$

$= (2x - 1)^2 - (3y)^2$

$= [(2x - 1) + 3y][(2x - 1) - 3y]$

$= (2x - 1 + 3y)(2x - 1 - 3y)$

43. $(x + 2)(x - 6) = 0$

$x + 2 = 0$ or $x - 6 = 0$

$x = -2$ or $x = 6$

The solutions are −2 and 6.

44. $2x(3x + 1)(x - 3) = 0$

$x = 0$ or $3x + 1 = 0$ or $x - 3 = 0$

$3x = -1$ or $x = 3$

$x = -\dfrac{1}{3}$

The solutions are $-\dfrac{1}{3}, 0, 3$.

45. a. $\dfrac{2x^2}{10x^3 - 2x^2} = \dfrac{2x^2}{2x^2(5x - 1)} = \dfrac{1}{5x - 1}$

b. $\dfrac{9x^2 + 13x + 4}{8x^2 + x - 7} = \dfrac{(9x + 4)(x + 1)}{(8x - 7)(x + 1)} = \dfrac{9x + 4}{8x - 7}$

46. a. Domain: $(-\infty, \infty)$; Range: $[-4, \infty)$

b. x-intercepts: (−2, 0), (2, 0)
y-intercept: (0, −4)

c. There is no such point.

d. The point with the least y-value is (0, −4).

e. −2, 2

f. x-values between $x = -2$ and $x = 2$

g. The solutions are −2 and 2.

47. $\dfrac{5k}{k^2-4}-\dfrac{2}{k^2+k-2}$

$=\dfrac{5k}{(k+2)(k-2)}-\dfrac{2}{(k+2)(k-1)}$

$=\dfrac{5k(k-1)-2(k-2)}{(k+2)(k-2)(k-1)}$

$=\dfrac{5k^2-5k-2k+4}{(k+2)(k-2)(k-1)}$

$=\dfrac{5k^2-7k+4}{(k+2)(k-2)(k-1)}$

48. $\dfrac{5a}{a^2-4}-\dfrac{3}{2-a}=\dfrac{5a}{(a+2)(a-2)}+\dfrac{3}{a-2}$

$=\dfrac{5a+3(a+2)}{(a+2)(a-2)}$

$=\dfrac{5a+3a+6}{(a+2)(a-2)}$

$=\dfrac{8a+6}{(a+2)(a-2)}$

49. $\dfrac{3}{x}-\dfrac{x+21}{3x}=\dfrac{5}{3}$

$3x\left(\dfrac{3}{x}-\dfrac{x+21}{3x}\right)=3x\left(\dfrac{5}{3}\right)$

$9-(x+21)=5x$

$9-x-21=5x$

$-x-12=5x$

$-12=6x$

$-2=x$

The solution is -2.

50. $\dfrac{3x-4}{2x}=-\dfrac{8}{x}$

$x(3x-4)=-8(2x)$

$3x^2-4x=-16x$

$3x^2+12x=0$

$3x(x+4)=0$

$3x=0$ or $x+4=0$

$x=0$ or $\quad x=-4$

Discard the answer 0 as extraneous. The solution is -4.

Chapter 7

Section 7.1

Practice Exercises

1. a. $\sqrt{49} = 7$ because $7^2 = 49$ and 7 is not negative.

b. $\sqrt{\dfrac{0}{1}} = \sqrt{0} = 0$ because $0^2 = 0$ and 0 is not negative.

c. $\sqrt{\dfrac{16}{81}} = \dfrac{4}{9}$ because $\left(\dfrac{4}{9}\right)^2 = \dfrac{16}{81}$ and $\dfrac{4}{9}$ is not negative.

d. $\sqrt{0.64} = 0.8$ because $(0.8)^2 = 0.64$.

e. $\sqrt{z^8} = z^4$ because $(z^4)^2 = z^8$.

f. $\sqrt{16b^4} = 4b^2$ because $(4b^2)^2 = 16b^4$.

g. $-\sqrt{36} = -6$. The negative in front of the radical indicates the negative square root of 36.

h. $\sqrt{-36}$ is not a real number.

2. $\sqrt{45} \approx 6.708$

Since $36 < 45 < 49$, then $\sqrt{36} < \sqrt{45} < \sqrt{49}$, or $6 < \sqrt{45} < 7$. The approximation is between 6 and 7 and thus is reasonable.

3. a. $\sqrt[3]{-1} = -1$ because $(-1)^3 = -1$.

b. $\sqrt[3]{27} = 3$ because $3^3 = 27$.

c. $\sqrt[3]{\dfrac{27}{64}} = \dfrac{3}{4}$ because $\left(\dfrac{3}{4}\right)^3 = \dfrac{27}{64}$.

d. $\sqrt[3]{x^{12}} = x^4$ because $(x^4)^3 = x^{12}$.

e. $\sqrt[3]{-8x^3} = -2x$ because $(-2x)^3 = -8x^3$.

4. a. $\sqrt[4]{10,000} = 10$ because $10^4 = 10,000$ and 10 is positive.

b. $\sqrt[5]{-1} = -1$ because $(-1)^5 = -1$.

c. $-\sqrt{81} = -9$ because -9 is the opposite of $\sqrt{81}$.

d. $\sqrt[4]{-625}$ is not a real number. There is no real number that, when raised to the fourth power, is -625.

e. $\sqrt[3]{27x^9} = 3x^3$ because $(3x^3)^3 = 27x^9$.

5. a. $\sqrt{(-4)^2} = |-4| = 4$

b. $\sqrt{x^{14}} = |x^7|$

c. $\sqrt[4]{(x+7)^4} = |x+7|$

d. $\sqrt[3]{(-7)^3} = -7$

e. $\sqrt[5]{(3x-5)^5} = 3x-5$

f. $\sqrt{49x^2} = 7|x|$

g. $\sqrt{x^2 + 4x + 4} = \sqrt{(x+2)^2} = |x+2|$

6. $f(x) = \sqrt{x+5}$, $g(x) = \sqrt[3]{x-3}$

a. $f(11) = \sqrt{11+5} = \sqrt{16} = 4$

b. $f(-1) = \sqrt{-1+5} = \sqrt{4} = 2$

c. $g(11) = \sqrt[3]{11-3} = \sqrt[3]{8} = 2$

d. $g(-5) = \sqrt[3]{-5-3} = \sqrt[3]{-8} = -2$

7. $h(x) = \sqrt{x+2}$
Find the domain.
$x + 2 \geq 0$
$\quad x \geq -2$
The domain of $h(x)$ is $\{x \mid x \geq -2\}$.

x	$h(x) = \sqrt{x+2}$
-2	0
-1	1
1	$\sqrt{1+2} = \sqrt{3} \approx 1.7$
2	2
7	3

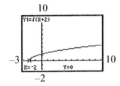

8. $f(x) = \sqrt[3]{x} - 4$

The domain is the set of all real numbers.

x	$f(x) = \sqrt[3]{x} - 4$
0	-4
1	-3
-1	-5
6	$\sqrt[3]{6} - 4 \approx 1.8 - 4 = -2.2$
-6	$\sqrt[3]{-6} - 4 \approx -1.8 - 4 = -5.8$
8	-2
-8	-6

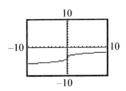

Vocabulary and Readiness Check

1. In the expression $\sqrt[n]{a}$, the n is called the <u>index</u>, the $\sqrt{}$ is called the <u>radical sign</u>, and a is called the <u>radicand</u>.

2. If $\sqrt{a}$ is the positive square root of a, $a \neq 0$, then $-\sqrt{a}$ is the negative square root of a.

3. The square root of a negative number <u>is not</u> a real number.

4. Numbers such as 1, 4, 9, and 25 are called perfect <u>squares</u> where numbers such as 1, 8, 27, and 125 are called perfect <u>cubes</u>.

5. The domain of the function $f(x) = \sqrt{x}$ is $[0, \infty)$.

6. The domain of the function $f(x) = \sqrt[3]{x}$ is $(-\infty, \infty)$.

7. If $f(16) = 4$, the corresponding ordered pair is $(16, 4)$.

8. If $g(-8) = -2$, the corresponding ordered pair is $(-8, -2)$.

9. The radical that is not a real number is $\sqrt{-10}$, choice d.

10. The radicals that simplify to 3 are $\sqrt{9}$ and $\sqrt[3]{27}$, choices a and c.

11. The radical that simplifies to -3 is $\sqrt[3]{-27}$, choice d.

12. The radical that does not simplify to a whole number is $\sqrt{8}$, choice c.

Exercise Set 7.1

2. $\sqrt{400} = 20$ because $20^2 = 400$.

4. $\sqrt{\dfrac{9}{25}} = \dfrac{3}{5}$ because $\left(\dfrac{3}{5}\right)^2 = \dfrac{9}{25}$.

6. $\sqrt{0.04} = 0.2$ because $(0.2)^2 = 0.04$.

8. $-\sqrt{9} = -3$ because $3^2 = 9$.

10. $\sqrt{x^{16}} = x^8$ because $(x^8)^2 = x^{16}$.

12. $\sqrt{64y^{20}} = 8y^{10}$ because $(8y^{10})^2 = 64y^{20}$.

14. $\sqrt{11} \approx 3.317$

Since $9 < 11 < 16$, then $\sqrt{9} < \sqrt{11} < \sqrt{16}$, or $3 < \sqrt{11} < 4$. The approximation is between 3 and 4 and thus is reasonable.

16. $\sqrt{56} \approx 7.483$

Since $49 < 56 < 64$, then $\sqrt{49} < \sqrt{56} < \sqrt{64}$; or $7 < \sqrt{56} < 8$. The approximation is between 7 and 8 and thus is reasonable.

18. $\sqrt{300} \approx 17.321$

Since $289 < 300 < 324$, then $\sqrt{289} < \sqrt{300} < \sqrt{324}$, or $17 < \sqrt{300} < 18$. The approximation is between 17 and 18 and thus is reasonable.

20. $\sqrt[3]{27} = 3$ because $3^3 = 27$.

22. $\sqrt[3]{\dfrac{27}{64}} = \dfrac{3}{4}$ because $\left(\dfrac{3}{4}\right)^3 = \dfrac{27}{64}$.

24. $\sqrt[3]{-125} = -5$ because $(-5)^3 = -125$.

26. $\sqrt[3]{x^{15}} = x^5$ because $(x^5)^3 = x^{15}$.

28. $\sqrt[3]{-64x^6} = -4x^2$ because $(-4x^2)^3 = -64x^6$.

30. $\sqrt[5]{-243} = -3$ because $(-3)^5 = -243$.

32. $\sqrt{-16}$ is not a real number. There is no real number that, when squared, is -16.

34. $\sqrt[5]{-1} = -1$ because $(-1)^5 = -1$.

36. $\sqrt[4]{x^{20}} = x^5$ because $(x^5)^4 = x^{20}$.

38. $\sqrt[5]{-32x^{15}} = -2x^3$ because $(-2x^3)^5 = -32x^{15}$.

40. $\sqrt[4]{81x^4} = 3x$ because $(3x)^4 = 81x^4$.

42. $\sqrt{256x^8} = 16x^4$ because $(16x^4)^2 = 256x^8$.

44. $\sqrt{(-7)^2} = |-7| = 7$

46. $\sqrt[5]{(-7)^5} = -7$

48. $\sqrt[4]{16x^4} = 4|x|$

50. $\sqrt[5]{x^5} = x$

52. $\sqrt{(y-6)^2} = |y-6|$

54. $\sqrt{x^2 - 8x + 16} = \sqrt{(x-4)^2} = |x-4|$

56. $-\sqrt[3]{125} = -5$

58. $\sqrt{16x^8} = 4x^4$

60. $\sqrt[3]{y^{12}} = y^4$

62. $\sqrt{9x^4 y^6} = 3x^2 y^3$

64. $\sqrt[3]{-8a^{21}b^6} = -2a^7 b^2$

66. $\sqrt[4]{x^8 y^{12}} = x^2 y^3$

68. $\sqrt[5]{-243z^{15}} = -3z^3$

70. $\sqrt{\dfrac{4}{81}} = \dfrac{2}{9}$

72. $\sqrt{\dfrac{y^{10}}{9x^6}} = \dfrac{y^5}{3x^3}$

74. $-\sqrt[3]{\dfrac{64a^3}{b^9}} = -\dfrac{4a}{b^3}$

76. $\sqrt[4]{\dfrac{y^4}{81x^4}} = \dfrac{y}{3x}$

78. $g(x) = \sqrt[3]{x-8}$
$g(0) = \sqrt[3]{0-8} = \sqrt[3]{-8} = -2$

80. $f(x) = \sqrt{2x+3}$
$f(-1) = \sqrt{2(-1)+3} = \sqrt{1} = 1$

82. $f(x) = \sqrt{2x+3}$
$f(3) = \sqrt{2(3)+3} = \sqrt{9} = 3$

84. $g(x) = \sqrt[3]{x-8}$
$g(1) = \sqrt[3]{1-8} = \sqrt[3]{-7}$

86. $f(x) = \sqrt{x} - 2$

This is the graph of $\sqrt{x}$ shifted down 2 units; A.

$x \geq 0$

Domain: $[0, \infty)$

88. $f(x) = \sqrt{x+1}$

This is the graph of $\sqrt{x}$ shifted left 1 unit; B.

$x + 1 \geq 0$

$\quad x \geq -1$

Domain: $[-1, \infty)$

90. $f(x) = \sqrt[3]{x} - 2$

This is the graph of $\sqrt[3]{x}$ shifted down 2 units; C.

Domain: $(-\infty, \infty)$

92. $g(x) = \sqrt[3]{x+1}$

This is the graph of $\sqrt[3]{x}$ shifted left 1 unit; D.

Domain: $(-\infty, \infty)$

94. $(4y^6 z^7)^3 = 4^3 y^{6 \cdot 3} z^{7 \cdot 3} = 64 y^{18} z^{21}$

96. $(-14a^5 bc^2)(2abc^4) = -14(2)a^{5+1} b^{1+1} c^{2+4}$
$\qquad = -28a^6 b^2 c^6$

98. $\dfrac{(2a^{-1}b^2)^3}{(8a^2 b)^{-2}} = \dfrac{8a^{-3}b^6}{8^{-2} a^{-4} b^{-2}}$

$\qquad = \dfrac{8^2 \cdot 8ab^8}{1}$

$\qquad = 64(8)ab^8$

$\qquad = 512ab^8$

100. $\sqrt[3]{-17}$ is a real number.

102. $\sqrt[15]{-17}$ is a real number.

104. Answers may vary

106. $900 < 1000 < 1600$ so $\sqrt{900} < \sqrt{1000} < \sqrt{1600}$, or $30 < \sqrt{1000} < 40$. Thus $\sqrt{1000}$ is between 30 and 40. Therefore, the answer is **b.**

108. $\sqrt{20} \approx 4$ and $\sqrt{8} \approx 3$ so the length is $\sqrt{20} + \sqrt{8} \approx 4 + 3 = 7$. Therefore, the answer is **c.**

110. $B = \sqrt{\dfrac{hw}{3131}} = \sqrt{\dfrac{74 \cdot 225}{3131}}$

$\qquad = \sqrt{\dfrac{16{,}650}{3131}}$

$\qquad \approx 2.31$ sq meters

112. $v = \sqrt{\dfrac{2Gm}{r}}$

$\qquad = \sqrt{\dfrac{2(6.67 \times 10^{-11})(5.97 \times 10^{24})}{6.37 \times 10^6}}$

$\qquad = \sqrt{\dfrac{2(6.67)(5.97)}{6.37} \times 10^{-11+24-6}}$

$\qquad = \sqrt{12.50232339 \times 10^7}$

$\qquad = \sqrt{125{,}023{,}233.9} = 11{,}181$ m per sec

Section 7.2

Practice Exercises

1. a. $36^{1/2} = \sqrt{36} = 6$

b. $1000^{1/3} = \sqrt[3]{1000} = 10$

c. $x^{1/5} = \sqrt[5]{x}$

d. $1^{1/4} = \sqrt[4]{1} = 1$

e. $-64^{1/2} = -\sqrt{64} = -8$

f. $(125x^9)^{1/3} = \sqrt[3]{125x^9} = 5x^3$

g. $(3x)^{1/4} = \sqrt[4]{3x}$

2. a. $16^{3/2} = \left(\sqrt{16}\right)^3 = 4^3 = 64$

b. $-1^{3/5} = -\left(\sqrt[5]{1}\right)^3 = -(1)^3 = -1$

c. $-(81)^{3/4} = -\left(\sqrt[4]{81}\right)^3 = -(3)^3 = -27$

d. $\left(\dfrac{1}{25}\right)^{3/2} = \left(\sqrt{\dfrac{1}{25}}\right)^3 = \left(\dfrac{1}{5}\right)^3 = \dfrac{1}{125}$

e. $(3x+2)^{5/9} = \sqrt[9]{(3x+2)^5}$

3. a. $9^{-3/2} = \dfrac{1}{9^{3/2}} = \dfrac{1}{\left(\sqrt{9}\right)^3} = \dfrac{1}{3^3} = \dfrac{1}{27}$

b. $(-64)^{-2/3} = \dfrac{1}{(-64)^{2/3}} = \dfrac{1}{\left(\sqrt[3]{-64}\right)^2} = \dfrac{1}{(-4)^2} = \dfrac{1}{16}$

4. a. $y^{2/3} \cdot y^{8/3} = y^{(2/3+8/3)} = y^{10/3}$

b. $x^{3/5} \cdot x^{1/4} = x^{3/5+1/4} = x^{12/20+5/20} = x^{17/20}$

c. $\dfrac{9^{2/7}}{9^{9/7}} = 9^{2/7-9/7} = 9^{-7/7} = 9^{-1} = \dfrac{1}{9}$

d. $b^{4/9} \cdot b^{-2/9} = b^{4/9+(-2/9)} = b^{2/9}$

e. $\dfrac{\left(3x^{1/4}y^{-2/3}\right)^4}{x^4 y} = \dfrac{3^4 (x^{1/4})^4 (y^{-2/3})^4}{x^4 y}$

$= \dfrac{81xy^{-8/3}}{x^4 y}$

$= 81x^{1-4} y^{-8/3-3/3}$

$= 81x^{-3} y^{-11/3}$

$= \dfrac{81}{x^3 y^{11/3}}$

5. a. $x^{3/5}(x^{1/3} - x^2) = x^{3/5} x^{1/3} - x^{3/5} x^2$

$= x^{(3/5+1/3)} - x^{(3/5+2)}$

$= x^{(9/15+5/15)} - x^{(3/5+10/5)}$

$= x^{14/15} - x^{13/5}$

b. $(x^{1/2} + 6)(x^{1/2} - 2)$

$= x^{2/2} - 2x^{1/2} + 6x^{1/2} - 12$

$= x + 4x^{1/2} - 12$

6. $2x^{-1/5} - 7x^{4/5} = (x^{-1/5})(2) - (x^{-1/5})(7x^{5/5})$

$= x^{-1/5}(2 - 7x)$

7. a. $\sqrt[9]{x^3} = x^{3/9} = x^{1/3} = \sqrt[3]{x}$

b. $\sqrt[4]{36} = 36^{1/4} = (6^2)^{1/4} = 6^{2/4} = 6^{1/2} = \sqrt{6}$

c. $\sqrt[8]{a^4 b^2} = (a^4 b^2)^{1/8}$

$= a^{4/8} b^{2/8}$

$= a^{2/4} b^{1/4}$

$= (a^2 b)^{1/4}$

$= \sqrt[4]{a^2 b}$

8. a. $\sqrt[3]{x} \cdot \sqrt[4]{x} = x^{1/3} \cdot x^{1/4}$

$= x^{1/3+1/4}$

$= x^{4/12+3/12}$

$= x^{7/12}$

$= \sqrt[12]{x^7}$

b. $\dfrac{\sqrt[3]{y}}{\sqrt[5]{y}} = \dfrac{y^{1/3}}{y^{1/5}}$

$= y^{1/3-1/5}$

$= y^{5/15-3/15}$

$= y^{2/15}$

$= \sqrt[15]{y^2}$

c. $\sqrt[3]{5} \cdot \sqrt{3} = 5^{1/3} \cdot 3^{1/2}$

$= 5^{2/6} \cdot 3^{3/6}$

$= (5^2 \cdot 3^3)^{1/6}$

$= \sqrt[6]{5^2 \cdot 3^3}$

$= \sqrt[6]{675}$

Vocabulary and Readiness Check

1. It is true that $9^{-1/2}$ is a positive number.

2. It is false that $9^{-1/2}$ is a whole number.

3. It is true that $\dfrac{1}{a^{-m/n}} = a^{m/n}$ (where $a^{m/n}$ is a nonzero real number).

4. To simplify $x^{2/3} \cdot x^{1/5}$, <u>add</u> the exponents.

5. To simplify $(x^{2/3})^{1/5}$, <u>multiply</u> the exponents.

6. To simplify $\dfrac{x^{2/3}}{x^{1/5}}$, <u>subtract</u> the exponents.

7. $4^{1/2} = 2$, A

8. $-4^{1/2} = -2$, B

9. $(-4)^{1/2}$ is not a real number, C

10. $8^{1/3} = 2$, A

11. $-8^{1/3} = -2$, B

12. $(-8)^{1/3} = -2$, B

Exercise Set 7.2

2. $64^{1/3} = \sqrt[3]{64} = 4$

4. $8^{1/3} = \sqrt[3]{8} = 2$

6. $\left(\dfrac{1}{64}\right)^{1/2} = \sqrt{\dfrac{1}{64}} = \dfrac{1}{8}$

8. $81^{1/4} = \sqrt[4]{81} = 3$

10. $(2m)^{1/3} = \sqrt[3]{2m}$

12. $(16x^8)^{1/2} = \sqrt{16x^8} = 4x^4$

14. $-64^{1/2} = -\sqrt{64} = -8$

16. $(-32)^{1/5} = \sqrt[5]{-32} = -2$

18. $4^{5/2} = \left(\sqrt{4}\right)^5 = 2^5 = 32$

20. $(-8)^{4/3} = \left(\sqrt[3]{-8}\right)^4 = (-2)^4 = 16$

22. $(-9)^{3/2} = \left(\sqrt{-9}\right)^3$ is not a real number.

24. $2x^{3/5} = 2\sqrt[5]{x^3}$

26. $(x-4)^{3/4} = \sqrt[4]{(x-4)^3}$ or $\left(\sqrt[4]{x-4}\right)^3$

28. $\left(\dfrac{49}{25}\right)^{3/2} = \left(\sqrt{\dfrac{49}{25}}\right)^3 = \left(\dfrac{7}{5}\right)^3 = \dfrac{343}{125}$

30. $64^{-2/3} = \dfrac{1}{64^{2/3}} = \dfrac{1}{\left(\sqrt[3]{64}\right)^2} = \dfrac{1}{4^2} = \dfrac{1}{16}$

32. $(-8)^{-4/3} = \dfrac{1}{(-8)^{4/3}}$

$= \dfrac{1}{\left(\sqrt[3]{-8}\right)^4}$

$= \dfrac{1}{(-2)^4}$

$= \dfrac{1}{16}$

34. $(-16)^{-5/4} = \dfrac{1}{(-16)^{5/4}} = \dfrac{1}{\left(\sqrt[4]{-16}\right)^5}$ is not a real

number.

36. $y^{-1/6} = \dfrac{1}{y^{1/6}}$

38. $\dfrac{1}{n^{-8/9}} = n^{8/9}$

40. $\dfrac{2}{3y^{-5/7}} = \dfrac{2y^{5/7}}{3}$

42. $b^{9/5}b^{8/5} = b^{9/5+8/5} = b^{17/5}$

44. $y^{4/3} \cdot y^{-1/3} = y^{\frac{4}{3}+\left(-\frac{1}{3}\right)} = y^{3/3} = y$

46. $5^{1/2} \cdot 5^{1/6} = 5^{\frac{1}{2}+\frac{1}{6}} = 5^{\frac{3}{6}+\frac{1}{6}} = 5^{4/6} = 5^{2/3}$

48. $\dfrac{x^{3/4}}{x^{1/8}} = x^{\frac{3}{4}-\frac{1}{8}} = x^{\frac{6}{8}-\frac{1}{8}} = x^{5/8}$

50. $(32^{1/5}x^{2/3})^3 = 32^{3/5}x^{6/3}$

$= \left(\sqrt[5]{32}\right)^3 x^2$

$= 2^3 x^2$

$= 8x^2$

52. $\dfrac{a^{1/4}a^{-1/2}}{a^{2/3}} = a^{\frac{1}{4}-\frac{1}{2}-\frac{2}{3}}$

$\qquad = a^{\frac{3}{12}-\frac{6}{12}-\frac{8}{12}}$

$\qquad = a^{-11/12}$

$\qquad = \dfrac{1}{a^{11/12}}$

54. $\dfrac{y^{11/3}}{(y^5)^{1/3}} = \dfrac{y^{11/3}}{y^{5/3}} = y^{\frac{11}{3}-\frac{5}{3}} = y^{6/3} = y^2$

56. $\dfrac{(2x^{1/5})^4}{x^{3/10}} = \dfrac{2^4 x^{4/5}}{x^{3/10}}$

$\qquad = 16x^{\frac{4}{5}-\frac{3}{10}}$

$\qquad = 16x^{\frac{8}{10}-\frac{3}{10}}$

$\qquad = 16x^{5/10}$

$\qquad = 16x^{1/2}$

58. $\dfrac{(m^2 n)^{1/4}}{m^{-1/2}n^{5/8}} = \dfrac{m^{1/2}n^{1/4}}{m^{-1/2}n^{5/8}}$

$\qquad = m^{\frac{1}{2}-\left(-\frac{1}{2}\right)}n^{\frac{1}{4}-\frac{5}{8}}$

$\qquad = m^{\frac{2}{2}}n^{-\frac{3}{8}}$

$\qquad = \dfrac{m}{n^{3/8}}$

60. $\dfrac{(a^{-2}b^3)^{1/8}}{(a^{-3}b)^{-1/4}} = \dfrac{a^{-2/8}b^{3/8}}{a^{3/4}b^{-1/4}}$

$\qquad = a^{-\frac{2}{8}-\frac{3}{4}}b^{\frac{3}{8}-\left(-\frac{1}{4}\right)}$

$\qquad = a^{-\frac{2}{8}-\frac{6}{8}}b^{\frac{3}{8}+\frac{2}{8}}$

$\qquad = a^{-8/8}b^{5/8}$

$\qquad = \dfrac{b^{5/8}}{a}$

62. $x^{1/2}(x^{1/2}+x^{3/2}) = x^{1/2+1/2}+x^{1/2+3/2}$

$\qquad = x^1 + x^2$

$\qquad = x + x^2$

64. $3x^{1/2}(x+y) = 3x^{1/2+1}+3x^{1/2}y$

$\qquad = 3x^{3/2}+3x^{1/2}y$

66. $(y^{1/2}+5)(y^{1/2}+5) = (y^{1/2})^2 + 2(y^{1/2}\cdot 5)+5^2$

$\qquad\qquad\qquad\qquad\quad = y+10y^{1/2}+25$

68. $x^{5/2}-x^{3/2} = x^{3/2}\cdot x^{2/2}-x^{3/2}\cdot 1 = x^{3/2}(x-1)$

70. $x^{3/7}-2x^{2/7} = x^{2/7}\cdot x^{1/7}-x^{2/7}\cdot 2$

$\qquad\qquad\qquad = x^{2/7}(x^{1/7}-2)$

72. $x^{-3/4}+3x^{1/4} = x^{-3/4}(1)+x^{-3/4}(3x^{4/4})$

$\qquad\qquad\qquad = x^{-3/4}(1+3x)$

74. $\sqrt[9]{a^3} = a^{3/9} = a^{1/3} = \sqrt[3]{a}$

76. $\sqrt[4]{36} = 36^{1/4} = (6^2)^{1/4} = 6^{1/2} = \sqrt{6}$

78. $\sqrt[8]{4y^2} = (4y^2)^{1/8}$

$\qquad = (2^2)^{1/8}(y^{2/8})$

$\qquad = 2^{1/4}y^{1/4}$

$\qquad = (2y)^{1/4}$

$\qquad = \sqrt[4]{2y}$

80. $\sqrt[9]{y^6 z^3} = (y^6 z^3)^{1/9}$

$\qquad = y^{2/3}z^{1/3}$

$\qquad = (y^2 z^1)^{1/3}$

$\qquad = \sqrt[3]{y^2 z}$

82. $\sqrt[10]{a^5 b^5} = (a^5 b^5)^{1/10}$

$\qquad = a^{5/10}b^{5/10}$

$\qquad = a^{1/2}b^{1/2}$

$\qquad = (ab)^{1/2}$

$\qquad = \sqrt{ab}$

84. $\sqrt[8]{(y+1)^4} = (y+1)^{4/8} = (y+1)^{1/2} = \sqrt{y+1}$

86. $\sqrt[3]{y^2}\cdot\sqrt[6]{y} = y^{2/3}\cdot y^{1/6}$

$\qquad = y^{\frac{2}{3}+\frac{1}{6}}$

$\qquad = y^{\frac{4}{6}+\frac{1}{6}}$

$\qquad = y^{5/6}$

$\qquad = \sqrt[6]{y^5}$

88. $\dfrac{\sqrt[4]{a}}{\sqrt[5]{b}} = \dfrac{a^{1/4}}{a^{1/5}} = a^{\frac{1}{4}-\frac{1}{5}} = a^{\frac{5}{20}-\frac{4}{20}} = a^{1/20} = \sqrt[20]{a}$

90. $\sqrt[6]{y} \cdot \sqrt[3]{y} \cdot \sqrt[5]{y^2} = y^{1/6} y^{1/3} y^{2/5}$

$= y^{5/30} y^{10/30} y^{12/30}$

$= y^{27/30}$

$= y^{9/10}$

$= \sqrt[10]{y^9}$

92. $\dfrac{\sqrt[5]{b^2}}{\sqrt[10]{b^3}} = \dfrac{b^{2/5}}{b^{3/10}} = b^{\frac{2}{5} - \frac{3}{10}} = b^{\frac{4}{10} - \frac{3}{10}} = b^{1/10} = \sqrt[10]{b}$

94. $\sqrt[3]{5} \cdot \sqrt{2} = 5^{1/3} \cdot 2^{1/2}$

$= 5^{2/6} \cdot 2^{3/6}$

$= (5^2 \cdot 2^3)^{1/6}$

$= (200)^{1/6}$

$= \sqrt[6]{200}$

96. $\sqrt[4]{5} \cdot \sqrt[3]{x} = 5^{1/4} \cdot x^{1/3}$

$= 5^{3/12} \cdot x^{4/12}$

$= (5^3 \cdot x^4)^{1/12}$

$= (125x^4)^{1/12}$

$= \sqrt[12]{125x^4}$

98. $\sqrt[3]{b} \cdot \sqrt[5]{4a} = b^{1/3}(4a)^{1/5}$

$= b^{1/3} 4^{1/5} a^{1/5}$

$= b^{5/15} 4^{3/15} a^{3/15}$

$= (4^3 a^3 b^5)^{1/15}$

$= (64a^3b^5)^{1/15}$

$= \sqrt[15]{64a^3b^5}$

100. $20 = 4 \cdot 5$ where 4 is a perfect square.

102. $45 = 9 \cdot 5$ where 9 is a perfect square.

104. $56 = 8 \cdot 7$ where 8 is a perfect cube.

106. $80 = 8 \cdot 10$ where 8 is a perfect cube.

108. $B(w) = 70w^{3/4}$

$B(90) = 70(90)^{3/4}$

≈ 2045 calories

110. $f(x) = 33.3x^{4/5}$

$f(14) = 33.3(14)^{4/5}$

≈ 275.0 million subscriptions

112. $\square \cdot x^{1/8} = x^{4/8}$

$\square = \dfrac{x^{4/8}}{x^{1/8}}$

$\square = x^{4/8 - 1/8}$

$\square = x^{3/8}$

114. $\dfrac{\square}{y^{-3/4}} = y^{4/4}$

$y^{-3/4}\left(\dfrac{\square}{y^{-3/4}}\right) = y^{4/4} \cdot y^{-3/4}$

$\square = y^{4/4 - 3/4}$

$\square = y^{1/4}$

116. $20^{1/5} \approx 1.8206$

118. $76^{5/7} \approx 22.0515$

120. $(LC)^{-1/2} = \dfrac{1}{(LC)^{1/2}} = \dfrac{1}{\sqrt{LC}}$

Section 7.3

Practice Exercises

1. a. $\sqrt{5} \cdot \sqrt{7} = \sqrt{5 \cdot 7} = \sqrt{35}$

b. $\sqrt{13} \cdot \sqrt{z} = \sqrt{13z}$

c. $\sqrt[4]{125} \cdot \sqrt[4]{5} = \sqrt[4]{125 \cdot 5} = \sqrt[4]{625} = 5$

d. $\sqrt[3]{5y} \cdot \sqrt[3]{3x^2} = \sqrt[3]{5y \cdot 3x^2} = \sqrt[3]{15x^2 y}$

e. $\sqrt{\dfrac{5}{m}} \cdot \sqrt{\dfrac{t}{2}} = \sqrt{\dfrac{5}{m} \cdot \dfrac{t}{2}} = \sqrt{\dfrac{5t}{2m}}$

2. a. $\sqrt{\dfrac{36}{49}} = \dfrac{\sqrt{36}}{\sqrt{49}} = \dfrac{6}{7}$

b. $\sqrt{\dfrac{z}{16}} = \dfrac{\sqrt{z}}{\sqrt{16}} = \dfrac{\sqrt{z}}{4}$

c. $\sqrt[3]{\dfrac{125}{8}} = \dfrac{\sqrt[3]{125}}{\sqrt[3]{8}} = \dfrac{5}{2}$

d. $\sqrt[4]{\dfrac{5}{81x^8}} = \dfrac{\sqrt[4]{5}}{\sqrt[4]{81x^8}} = \dfrac{\sqrt[4]{5}}{3x^2}$

3. a. $\sqrt{98} = \sqrt{49 \cdot 2} = \sqrt{49} \cdot \sqrt{2} = 7\sqrt{2}$

b. $\sqrt[3]{54} = \sqrt[3]{27 \cdot 2} = \sqrt[3]{27} \cdot \sqrt[3]{2} = 3\sqrt[3]{2}$

c. The largest perfect square factor of 35 is 1, so $\sqrt{35}$ cannot be simplified further.

d. $\sqrt[4]{243} = \sqrt[4]{81 \cdot 3} = \sqrt[4]{81} \cdot \sqrt[4]{3} = 3\sqrt[4]{3}$

4. a. $\sqrt{36z^7} = \sqrt{36z^6 \cdot z} = \sqrt{36z^6} \cdot \sqrt{z} = 6z^3\sqrt{z}$

b. $\sqrt[3]{32p^4q^7} = \sqrt[3]{8 \cdot 4 \cdot p^3 \cdot p \cdot q^6 \cdot q}$
$= \sqrt[3]{8p^3q^6 \cdot 4pq}$
$= \sqrt[3]{8p^3q^6} \cdot \sqrt[3]{4pq}$
$= 2pq^2\sqrt[3]{4pq}$

c. $\sqrt[4]{16x^{15}} = \sqrt[4]{16 \cdot x^{12} \cdot x^3}$
$= \sqrt[4]{16x^{12}} \cdot \sqrt[4]{x^3}$
$= 2x^3\sqrt[4]{x^3}$

5. a. $\dfrac{\sqrt{80}}{\sqrt{5}} = \sqrt{\dfrac{80}{5}} = \sqrt{16} = 4$

b. $\dfrac{\sqrt{98z}}{3\sqrt{2}} = \dfrac{1}{3} \cdot \sqrt{\dfrac{98z}{2}}$
$= \dfrac{1}{3} \cdot \sqrt{49z}$
$= \dfrac{1}{3} \cdot \sqrt{49} \cdot \sqrt{z}$
$= \dfrac{1}{3} \cdot 7 \cdot \sqrt{z}$
$= \dfrac{7}{3}\sqrt{z}$

c. $\dfrac{5\sqrt[3]{40x^5y^7}}{\sqrt[3]{5y}} = 5 \cdot \sqrt[3]{\dfrac{40x^5y^7}{5y}}$
$= 5 \cdot \sqrt[3]{8x^5y^6}$
$= 5 \cdot \sqrt[3]{8x^3y^6 \cdot x^2}$
$= 5 \cdot \sqrt[3]{8x^3y^6} \cdot \sqrt[3]{x^2}$
$= 5 \cdot 2xy^2 \cdot \sqrt[3]{x^2}$
$= 10xy^2\sqrt[3]{x^2}$

d. $\dfrac{3\sqrt[5]{64x^9y^8}}{\sqrt[5]{x^{-1}y^2}} = 3 \cdot \sqrt[5]{\dfrac{64x^9y^8}{x^{-1}y^2}}$
$= 3 \cdot \sqrt[5]{64x^{10}y^6}$
$= 3 \cdot \sqrt[5]{32 \cdot x^{10} \cdot y^5 \cdot 2 \cdot y}$
$= 3 \cdot \sqrt[5]{32x^{10}y^5} \cdot \sqrt[5]{2y}$
$= 3 \cdot 2x^2y \cdot \sqrt[5]{2y}$
$= 6x^2y\sqrt[5]{2y}$

6. Let $(x_1,\, y_1) = (-3,\, 7)$ and $(x_2,\, y_2) = (-2,\, 3)$.
$d = \sqrt{(x_2 - x_1)^2 + (y_2 - y_1)^2}$
$= \sqrt{[-2 - (-3)]^2 + (3 - 7)^2}$
$= \sqrt{(1)^2 + (-4)^2}$
$= \sqrt{1 + 16}$
$= \sqrt{17} \approx 4.123$
The distance between the two points is exactly $\sqrt{17}$ units, or approximately 4.123 units.

7. Let $(x_1,\, y_1) = (5,\, -2)$ and $(x_2,\, y_2) = (8,\, -6)$.
$\text{midpoint} = \left(\dfrac{x_1 + x_2}{2}, \dfrac{y_1 + y_2}{2} \right)$
$= \left(\dfrac{5 + 8}{2}, \dfrac{-2 + (-6)}{2} \right)$
$= \left(\dfrac{13}{2}, \dfrac{-8}{2} \right)$
$= \left(\dfrac{13}{2}, -4 \right)$
The midpoint of the segment is $\left(\dfrac{13}{2}, -4 \right)$.

Vocabulary and Readiness Check

1. The <u>midpoint</u> of a line segment is a <u>point</u> exactly halfway between the two endpoints of the line segment.

2. The <u>distance</u> formula is
$$d = \sqrt{(x_2 - x_1)^2 + (y_2 - y_1)^2}.$$

3. The <u>midpoint</u> formula is $\left(\dfrac{x_1 + x_2}{2}, \dfrac{y_1 + y_2}{2} \right)$.

4. The statement $\sqrt[n]{a} \cdot \sqrt[n]{b} = \sqrt[n]{ab}$ is <u>true</u>.

5. The statement $\sqrt[3]{7} \cdot \sqrt[3]{11} = \sqrt[3]{18}$ is <u>false</u>.

6. The statement $\sqrt[3]{7} \cdot \sqrt{11} = \sqrt{77}$ is <u>false</u>.

7. The statement $\sqrt{x^7 y^8} = \sqrt{x^7} \cdot \sqrt{y^8}$ is <u>true</u>.

8. The statement $\dfrac{\sqrt[n]{a}}{\sqrt[n]{b}} = \sqrt[n]{\dfrac{a}{b}}$ is <u>true</u>.

9. The statement $\dfrac{\sqrt[3]{12}}{\sqrt[3]{4}} = \sqrt[3]{8}$ is <u>false</u>.

10. The statement $\dfrac{\sqrt[n]{x^7}}{\sqrt[n]{x}} = \sqrt[n]{x^6}$ is <u>true</u>.

Exercise Set 7.3

2. $\sqrt{11} \cdot \sqrt{10} = \sqrt{11 \cdot 10} = \sqrt{110}$

4. $\sqrt[4]{27} \cdot \sqrt[4]{3} = \sqrt[4]{27 \cdot 3} = \sqrt[4]{81} = 3$

6. $\sqrt[3]{10} \cdot \sqrt[3]{5} = \sqrt[3]{10 \cdot 5} = \sqrt[3]{50}$

8. $\sqrt{3y} \cdot \sqrt{5x} = \sqrt{3y \cdot 5x} = \sqrt{15xy}$

10. $\sqrt{\dfrac{6}{m}} \cdot \sqrt{\dfrac{n}{5}} = \sqrt{\dfrac{6}{m} \cdot \dfrac{n}{5}} = \sqrt{\dfrac{6n}{5m}}$

12. $\sqrt[4]{ab^2} \cdot \sqrt[4]{27ab} = \sqrt[4]{ab^2 \cdot 27ab} = \sqrt[4]{27a^2 b^3}$

14. $\sqrt{\dfrac{8}{81}} = \dfrac{\sqrt{8}}{\sqrt{81}} = \dfrac{\sqrt{4 \cdot 2}}{9} = \dfrac{\sqrt{4} \cdot \sqrt{2}}{9} = \dfrac{2\sqrt{2}}{9}$

16. $\sqrt{\dfrac{5}{121}} = \dfrac{\sqrt{5}}{\sqrt{121}} = \dfrac{\sqrt{5}}{11}$

18. $\sqrt[4]{\dfrac{y}{81x^4}} = \dfrac{\sqrt[4]{y}}{\sqrt[4]{81x^4}} = \dfrac{\sqrt[4]{y}}{3x}$

20. $\sqrt[3]{\dfrac{3}{64}} = \dfrac{\sqrt[3]{3}}{\sqrt[3]{64}} = \dfrac{\sqrt[3]{3}}{4}$

22. $\sqrt[4]{\dfrac{a^3}{81}} = \dfrac{\sqrt[4]{a^3}}{\sqrt[4]{81}} = \dfrac{\sqrt[4]{a^3}}{3}$

24. $\sqrt[3]{\dfrac{3}{8x^6}} = \dfrac{\sqrt[3]{3}}{\sqrt[3]{8x^6}} = \dfrac{\sqrt[3]{3}}{2x^2}$

26. $\sqrt{\dfrac{y^2 z}{36}} = \dfrac{\sqrt{y^2 z}}{\sqrt{36}} = \dfrac{\sqrt{y^2} \sqrt{z}}{6} = \dfrac{y\sqrt{z}}{6}$

28. $\sqrt{\dfrac{y^{10}}{9x^6}} = \dfrac{\sqrt{y^{10}}}{\sqrt{9x^6}} = \dfrac{y^5}{3x^3}$

30. $-\sqrt[3]{\dfrac{64a}{b^9}} = -\dfrac{\sqrt[3]{64a}}{\sqrt[3]{b^9}} = -\dfrac{\sqrt[3]{64} \cdot \sqrt[3]{a}}{b^3} = -\dfrac{4\sqrt[3]{a}}{b^3}$

32. $\sqrt{27} = \sqrt{9 \cdot 3} = \sqrt{9} \cdot \sqrt{3} = 3\sqrt{3}$

34. $\sqrt[3]{108} = \sqrt[3]{27 \cdot 4} = \sqrt[3]{27} \cdot \sqrt[3]{4} = 3\sqrt[3]{4}$

36. $3\sqrt{8} = 3\sqrt{4 \cdot 2} = 3\sqrt{4} \cdot \sqrt{2} = 3(2)\sqrt{2} = 6\sqrt{2}$

38. $\sqrt{20} = \sqrt{4 \cdot 5} = \sqrt{4} \cdot \sqrt{5} = 2\sqrt{5}$

40. $\sqrt{64y^9} = \sqrt{64y^8 \cdot y} = \sqrt{64y^8} \cdot \sqrt{y} = 8y^4 \sqrt{y}$

42. $\sqrt[3]{64y^9} = 4y^3$

44. $\sqrt[5]{32z^{12}} = \sqrt[5]{32z^{10} \cdot z^2}$
$$= \sqrt[5]{32z^{10}} \cdot \sqrt[5]{z^2}$$
$$= 2z^2 \sqrt[5]{z^2}$$

46. $\sqrt[3]{y^5} = \sqrt[3]{y^3 \cdot y^2} = y\sqrt[3]{y^2}$

48. $\sqrt{9x^5 y^7} = \sqrt{9x^4 y^6 \cdot xy}$
$$= \sqrt{9x^4 y^6} \cdot \sqrt{xy}$$
$$= 3x^2 y^3 \sqrt{xy}$$

50. $\sqrt[5]{-243z^9} = \sqrt[5]{-243z^5 \cdot z^4}$
$$= \sqrt[5]{-243z^5} \cdot \sqrt[5]{z^4}$$
$$= -3z\sqrt[5]{z^4}$$

52. $\sqrt[3]{40y^{10}} = \sqrt[3]{8y^9 \cdot 5y} = \sqrt[3]{8y^9} \cdot \sqrt[3]{5y} = 2y^3\sqrt[3]{5y}$

54. $-\sqrt{20ab^6} = -\sqrt{4b^6 \cdot 5a}$
$$= -\sqrt{4b^6} \cdot \sqrt{5a}$$
$$= -2b^3\sqrt{5a}$$

56. $\sqrt{12r^9s^{12}} = \sqrt{4r^8s^{12} \cdot 3r}$
$$= \sqrt{4r^8s^{12}} \cdot \sqrt{3r}$$
$$= 2r^4s^6\sqrt{3r}$$

58. $\sqrt[3]{8a^6b^9} = 2a^2b^3$

60. $\dfrac{\sqrt{45}}{\sqrt{9}} = \sqrt{\dfrac{45}{9}} = \sqrt{5}$

62. $\dfrac{\sqrt[3]{10}}{\sqrt[3]{2}} = \sqrt[3]{\dfrac{10}{2}} = \sqrt[3]{5}$

64. $\dfrac{7\sqrt[4]{162}}{\sqrt[4]{2}} = 7\sqrt[4]{\dfrac{162}{2}} = 7\sqrt[4]{81} = 7(3) = 21$

66. $\dfrac{\sqrt{a^7b^6}}{\sqrt{a^3b^2}} = \sqrt{\dfrac{a^7b^6}{a^3b^2}} = \sqrt{a^4b^4} = a^2b^2$

68. $\dfrac{\sqrt[3]{128x^3}}{-3\sqrt[3]{2x}} = -\dfrac{1}{3}\sqrt[3]{\dfrac{128x^3}{2x}} = -\dfrac{1}{3}\sqrt[3]{64x^2} = -\dfrac{4}{3}\sqrt[3]{x^2}$

70. $\dfrac{\sqrt{270y^2}}{5\sqrt{3y^{-4}}} = \dfrac{1}{5}\sqrt{\dfrac{270y^2}{3y^{-4}}}$
$$= \dfrac{1}{5}\sqrt{90y^6}$$
$$= \dfrac{1}{5}\sqrt{9y^6 \cdot 10}$$
$$= \dfrac{1}{5}(3y^3)\sqrt{10}$$
$$= \dfrac{3y^3}{5}\sqrt{10} \text{ or } \dfrac{3y^3\sqrt{10}}{5}$$

72. $\dfrac{\sqrt[5]{64x^{10}y^3}}{\sqrt[5]{2x^3y^{-7}}} = \sqrt[5]{\dfrac{64x^{10}y^3}{2x^3y^{-7}}}$
$$= \sqrt[5]{32x^7y^{10}}$$
$$= \sqrt[5]{32x^5y^{10} \cdot x^2}$$
$$= \sqrt[5]{32x^5y^{10}} \cdot \sqrt[5]{x^2}$$
$$= 2xy^2\sqrt[5]{x^2}$$

74. $(2, 3), (14, 8)$
$$d = \sqrt{(14-2)^2 + (8-3)^2}$$
$$= \sqrt{12^2 + 5^2}$$
$$= \sqrt{144 + 25}$$
$$= \sqrt{169}$$
$$= 13 \text{ units}$$

76. $(3, -2), (-4, 1)$
$$d = \sqrt{(-4-3)^2 + [1-(-2)]^2}$$
$$= \sqrt{(-7)^2 + 3^2}$$
$$= \sqrt{49 + 9}$$
$$= \sqrt{58} \approx 7.616 \text{ units}$$

78. $(-5, -2), (-6, -6)$
$$d = \sqrt{[-6-(-5)]^2 + [-6-(-2)]^2}$$
$$= \sqrt{(-1)^2 + (-4)^2}$$
$$= \sqrt{1 + 16}$$
$$= \sqrt{17} \approx 4.123 \text{ units}$$

80. $\left(-\sqrt{5}, 0\right), \left(0, \sqrt{7}\right)$
$$d = \sqrt{\left[0 - \left(-\sqrt{5}\right)\right]^2 + \left(\sqrt{7} - 0\right)^2}$$
$$= \sqrt{\left(\sqrt{5}\right)^2 + \left(\sqrt{7}\right)^2}$$
$$= \sqrt{5 + 7}$$
$$= \sqrt{12}$$
$$= 2\sqrt{3} \approx 3.464 \text{ units}$$

82. $(9.6, 2.5), (-1.9, -3.7)$
$$d = \sqrt{(-1.9-9.6)^2 + (-3.7-2.5)^2}$$
$$= \sqrt{(-11.5)^2 + (-6.2)^2}$$
$$= \sqrt{170.69} \approx 13.065 \text{ units}$$

84. $(3, 9)$, $(7, 11)$

$$\left(\frac{3+7}{2}, \frac{9+11}{2}\right) = \left(\frac{10}{2}, \frac{20}{2}\right) = (5, 10)$$

The midpoint of the segment is $(5, 10)$.

86. $(-3, -4)$, $(6, -8)$

$$\left(\frac{-3+6}{2}, \frac{-4+(-8)}{2}\right) = \left(\frac{3}{2}, \frac{-12}{2}\right) = \left(\frac{3}{2}, -6\right)$$

The midpoint of the segment is $\left(\frac{3}{2}, -6\right)$.

88. $(-2, 5)$, $(-1, 6)$

$$\left(\frac{-2+(-1)}{2}, \frac{5+6}{2}\right) = \left(-\frac{3}{2}, \frac{11}{2}\right)$$

The midpoint of the segment is $\left(-\frac{3}{2}, \frac{11}{2}\right)$.

90. $\left(-\frac{2}{5}, \frac{7}{15}\right)$, $\left(-\frac{2}{5}, -\frac{4}{15}\right)$

$$\left(\frac{-\frac{2}{5}+\left(-\frac{2}{5}\right)}{2}, \frac{\frac{7}{15}+\left(-\frac{4}{15}\right)}{2}\right) = \left(\frac{-\frac{4}{5}}{2}, \frac{\frac{3}{15}}{2}\right)$$

$$= \left(-\frac{2}{5}, \frac{1}{10}\right)$$

The midpoint of the segment is $\left(-\frac{2}{5}, \frac{1}{10}\right)$.

92. $\left(\sqrt{8}, -\sqrt{12}\right)$, $\left(3\sqrt{2}, 7\sqrt{3}\right)$

$$\left(\frac{\sqrt{8}+3\sqrt{2}}{2}, \frac{-\sqrt{12}+7\sqrt{3}}{2}\right)$$

$$= \left(\frac{2\sqrt{2}+3\sqrt{2}}{2}, \frac{-2\sqrt{3}+7\sqrt{3}}{2}\right)$$

$$= \left(\frac{5\sqrt{2}}{2}, \frac{5\sqrt{3}}{2}\right)$$

The midpoint of the segment is $\left(\frac{5\sqrt{2}}{2}, \frac{5\sqrt{3}}{2}\right)$.

94. $(-4.6, 2.1)$, $(-6.7, 1.9)$

$$\left(\frac{-4.6+(-6.7)}{2}, \frac{2.1+1.9}{2}\right) = \left(\frac{-11.3}{2}, \frac{4}{2}\right)$$

$$= (-5.65, 2)$$

The midpoint of the segment is $(-5.65, 2)$.

96. $(6x)(8x) = (6)(8)x \cdot x = 48x^2$

98. $(2x+3)+(x-5) = 2x+3+x-5$
$$= (2x+x)+(3-5)$$
$$= 3x+(-2)$$
$$= 3x-2$$

100. $(9y^2)(-8y^2) = 9(-8)y^2 \cdot y^2 = -72y^4$

102. $-3+x+5 = x+(-3+5) = x+2$

104. $(2x+1)^2 = (2x)^2 + 2(2x)(1) + 1^2$
$$= 4x^2 + 4x + 1$$

106. $\dfrac{\sqrt[4]{16}}{\sqrt{4}} = \dfrac{2}{2} = 1$

108. $\sqrt[6]{y^{48}} = y^8$

110. $\sqrt[3]{a^9 b^{21} c^3} = a^3 b^7 c$

112. $\sqrt[5]{x^{49}} = \sqrt[5]{x^{45} \cdot x^4} = \sqrt[5]{x^{45}} \cdot \sqrt[5]{x^4} = x^9 \sqrt[5]{x^4}$

114. $\sqrt[4]{p^{11} q^4 r^{45}} = \sqrt[4]{p^8 \cdot p^3 \cdot q^4 \cdot r^{44} \cdot r}$
$$= \sqrt[4]{p^8 q^4 r^{44} \cdot p^3 r}$$
$$= p^2 q r^{11} \sqrt[4]{p^3 r}$$

116. $A = \pi r \sqrt{r^2 + h^2}$

    a. $A = \pi(4)\sqrt{4^2 + 3^2}$
$$= 4\pi\sqrt{16+9}$$
$$= 4\pi\sqrt{25}$$
$$= 4\pi(5)$$
$$= 20\pi \text{ sq centimeters}$$

    b. $A = \pi(6.8)\sqrt{(6.8)^2 + (7.2)^2}$
$$= 6.8\pi\sqrt{46.24+51.84}$$
$$= 6.8\pi\sqrt{98.08}$$
$$\approx 211.57 \text{ sq feet}$$

118. $A = \pi r \sqrt{r^2 + h^2}$
$$= \pi(25,200)\sqrt{(25,200)^2 + (4190)^2}$$
$$= 25,200\pi\sqrt{652,596,100}$$
$$\approx 2,022,426,050 \text{ sq feet}$$

Section 7.4

Practice Exercises

1. a. $3\sqrt{17} + 5\sqrt{17} = (3+5)\sqrt{17} = 8\sqrt{17}$

   b. $7\sqrt[3]{5z} - 12\sqrt[3]{5z} = (7-12)\sqrt[3]{5z} = -5\sqrt[3]{5z}$

   c. $3\sqrt{2} + 5\sqrt[3]{2}$
This expression cannot be simplified since $3\sqrt{2}$ and $5\sqrt[3]{2}$ do not contain like radicals.

2. a. $\sqrt{24} + 3\sqrt{54} = \sqrt{4 \cdot 6} + 3\sqrt{9 \cdot 6}$
$$= \sqrt{4} \cdot \sqrt{6} + 3 \cdot \sqrt{9} \cdot \sqrt{6}$$
$$= 2 \cdot \sqrt{6} + 3 \cdot 3 \cdot \sqrt{6}$$
$$= 2\sqrt{6} + 9\sqrt{6}$$
$$= 11\sqrt{6}$$

   b. $\sqrt[3]{24} - 4\sqrt[3]{81} + \sqrt[3]{3}$
$$= \sqrt[3]{8} \cdot \sqrt[3]{3} - 4 \cdot \sqrt[3]{27} \cdot \sqrt[3]{3} + \sqrt[3]{3}$$
$$= 2 \cdot \sqrt[3]{3} - 4 \cdot 3 \cdot \sqrt[3]{3} + \sqrt[3]{3}$$
$$= 2\sqrt[3]{3} - 12\sqrt[3]{3} + \sqrt[3]{3}$$
$$= -9\sqrt[3]{3}$$

   c. $\sqrt{75x} - 3\sqrt{27x} + \sqrt{12x}$
$$= \sqrt{25} \cdot \sqrt{3x} - 3 \cdot \sqrt{9} \cdot \sqrt{3x} + \sqrt{4} \cdot \sqrt{3x}$$
$$= 5 \cdot \sqrt{3x} - 3 \cdot 3 \cdot \sqrt{3x} + 2 \cdot \sqrt{3x}$$
$$= 5\sqrt{3x} - 9\sqrt{3x} + 2\sqrt{3x}$$
$$= -2\sqrt{3x}$$

   d. $\sqrt{40} + \sqrt[3]{40} = \sqrt{4} \cdot \sqrt{10} + \sqrt[3]{8} \cdot \sqrt[3]{5}$
$$= 2\sqrt{10} + 2\sqrt[3]{5}$$

   e. $\sqrt[3]{81x^4} + \sqrt[3]{3x^4} = \sqrt[3]{27x^3} \cdot \sqrt[3]{3x} + \sqrt[3]{x^3} \cdot \sqrt[3]{3x}$
$$= 3x\sqrt[3]{3x} + x\sqrt[3]{3x}$$
$$= 4x\sqrt[3]{3x}$$

3. a. $\dfrac{\sqrt{28}}{3} - \dfrac{\sqrt{7}}{4} = \dfrac{2\sqrt{7}}{3} - \dfrac{\sqrt{7}}{4}$
$$= \dfrac{2\sqrt{7} \cdot 4}{3 \cdot 4} - \dfrac{\sqrt{7} \cdot 3}{4 \cdot 3}$$
$$= \dfrac{8\sqrt{7}}{12} - \dfrac{3\sqrt{7}}{12}$$
$$= \dfrac{5\sqrt{7}}{12}$$

   b. $\sqrt[3]{\dfrac{6y}{64}} + 3\sqrt[3]{6y} = \dfrac{\sqrt[3]{6y}}{\sqrt[3]{64}} + 3\sqrt[3]{6y}$
$$= \dfrac{\sqrt[3]{6y}}{4} + 3\sqrt[3]{6y}$$
$$= \dfrac{\sqrt[3]{6y}}{4} + \dfrac{3\sqrt[3]{6y} \cdot 4}{4}$$
$$= \dfrac{\sqrt[3]{6y}}{4} + \dfrac{12\sqrt[3]{6y}}{4}$$
$$= \dfrac{13\sqrt[3]{6y}}{4}$$

4. a. $\sqrt{5}(2 + \sqrt{15}) = \sqrt{5}(2) + \sqrt{5}(\sqrt{15})$
$$= 2\sqrt{5} + \sqrt{5 \cdot 15}$$
$$= 2\sqrt{5} + \sqrt{5 \cdot 5 \cdot 3}$$
$$= 2\sqrt{5} + 5\sqrt{3}$$

   b. $(\sqrt{2} - \sqrt{5})(\sqrt{6} + 2)$
$$= \sqrt{2} \cdot \sqrt{6} + \sqrt{2} \cdot 2 - \sqrt{5} \cdot \sqrt{6} - \sqrt{5} \cdot 2$$
$$= \sqrt{2 \cdot 2 \cdot 3} + 2\sqrt{2} - \sqrt{30} - 2\sqrt{5}$$
$$= 2\sqrt{3} + 2\sqrt{2} - \sqrt{30} - 2\sqrt{5}$$

   c. $(3\sqrt{z} - 4)(2\sqrt{z} + 3)$
$$= 3\sqrt{z}(2\sqrt{z}) + 3\sqrt{z}(3) - 4(2\sqrt{z}) - 4(3)$$
$$= 6 \cdot z + 9\sqrt{z} - 8\sqrt{z} - 12$$
$$= 6z + \sqrt{z} - 12$$

   d. $(\sqrt{6} - 3)^2 = (\sqrt{6} - 3)(\sqrt{6} - 3)$
$$= \sqrt{6}(\sqrt{6}) - \sqrt{6}(3) - 3(\sqrt{6}) - 3(-3)$$
$$= 6 - 3\sqrt{6} - 3\sqrt{6} + 9$$
$$= 6 - 6\sqrt{6} + 9$$
$$= 15 - 6\sqrt{6}$$

   e. $(\sqrt{5x} + 3)(\sqrt{5x} - 3)$
$$= \sqrt{5x} \cdot \sqrt{5x} - 3\sqrt{5x} + 3\sqrt{5x} - 3 \cdot 3$$
$$= 5x - 9$$

   f. $(\sqrt{x+2} + 3)^2 = (\sqrt{x+2})^2 + 2 \cdot \sqrt{x+2} \cdot 3 + 3^2$
$$= x + 2 + 6\sqrt{x+2} + 9$$
$$= x + 11 + 6\sqrt{x+2}$$

Vocabulary and Readiness Check

1. The terms $\sqrt{7}$ and $\sqrt[3]{7}$ are <u>unlike</u> terms.

2. The terms $\sqrt[3]{x^2 y}$ and $\sqrt[3]{yx^2}$ are <u>like</u> terms.

3. The terms $\sqrt[3]{abc}$ and $\sqrt[3]{cba}$ are <u>like</u> terms.

4. The terms $2x\sqrt{5}$ and $2x\sqrt{10}$ are <u>unlike</u> terms.

5. $2\sqrt{3} + 4\sqrt{3} = \underline{6\sqrt{3}}$

6. $5\sqrt{7} + 3\sqrt{7} = \underline{8\sqrt{7}}$

7. $8\sqrt{x} - \sqrt{x} = \underline{7\sqrt{x}}$

8. $3\sqrt{y} - \sqrt{y} = \underline{2\sqrt{y}}$

9. $7\sqrt[3]{x} + \sqrt[3]{x} = \underline{8\sqrt[3]{x}}$

10. $8\sqrt[3]{z} + \sqrt[3]{z} = \underline{9\sqrt[3]{z}}$

11. $\sqrt{11} + \sqrt[3]{11} = \underline{\sqrt{11} + \sqrt[3]{11}}$

12. $9\sqrt{13} - \sqrt[4]{13} = \underline{9\sqrt{13} - \sqrt[4]{13}}$

13. $8\sqrt[3]{2x} + 3\sqrt[3]{2x} - \sqrt[3]{2x} = \underline{10\sqrt[3]{2x}}$

14. $8\sqrt[3]{2x} + 3\sqrt[3]{2x^2} - \sqrt[3]{2x} = \underline{7\sqrt[3]{2x} + 3\sqrt[3]{2x^2}}$

Exercise Set 7.4

2. $\sqrt{27} - \sqrt{75} = \sqrt{9 \cdot 3} - \sqrt{25 \cdot 3}$
$= \sqrt{9} \cdot \sqrt{3} - \sqrt{25} \cdot \sqrt{3}$
$= 3\sqrt{3} - 5\sqrt{3}$
$= -2\sqrt{3}$

4. $3\sqrt{45x^3} + x\sqrt{5x} = 3\sqrt{9x^2 \cdot 5x} + x\sqrt{5x}$
$= 3\sqrt{9x^2} \cdot \sqrt{5x} + x\sqrt{5x}$
$= 3(3x)\sqrt{5x} + x\sqrt{5x}$
$= 9x\sqrt{5x} + x\sqrt{5x}$
$= 10x\sqrt{5x}$

6. $4\sqrt{32} - \sqrt{18} + 2\sqrt{128}$
$= 4\sqrt{16 \cdot 2} - \sqrt{9 \cdot 2} + 2\sqrt{64 \cdot 2}$
$= 4\sqrt{16} \cdot \sqrt{2} - \sqrt{9} \cdot \sqrt{2} + 2\sqrt{64} \cdot \sqrt{2}$
$= 4(4)\sqrt{2} - 3\sqrt{2} + 2(8)\sqrt{2}$
$= 16\sqrt{2} - 3\sqrt{2} + 16\sqrt{2}$
$= 29\sqrt{2}$

8. $2\sqrt[3]{3a^4} - 3a\sqrt[3]{81a} = 2\sqrt[3]{a^3 \cdot 3a} - 3a\sqrt[3]{27 \cdot 3a}$
$= 2\sqrt[3]{a^3} \cdot \sqrt[3]{3a} - 3a\sqrt[3]{27} \cdot \sqrt[3]{3a}$
$= 2a\sqrt[3]{3a} - 3a(3)\sqrt[3]{3a}$
$= 2a\sqrt[3]{3a} - 9a\sqrt[3]{3a}$
$= -7a\sqrt[3]{3a}$

10. $\sqrt{4x^7} + 9x^2\sqrt{x^3} - 5x\sqrt{x^5}$
$= \sqrt{4x^6 \cdot x} + 9x^2\sqrt{x^2 \cdot x} - 5x\sqrt{x^4 \cdot x}$
$= \sqrt{4x^6} \cdot \sqrt{x} + 9x^2\sqrt{x^2} \cdot \sqrt{x} - 5x\sqrt{x^4} \cdot \sqrt{x}$
$= 2x^3\sqrt{x} + 9x^2(x)\sqrt{x} - 5x(x^2)\sqrt{x}$
$= 2x^3\sqrt{x} + 9x^3\sqrt{x} - 5x^3\sqrt{x}$
$= 6x^3\sqrt{x}$

12. $\dfrac{\sqrt{3}}{2} + \dfrac{4\sqrt{3}}{3} = \dfrac{3\left(\sqrt{3}\right) + 2\left(4\sqrt{3}\right)}{6}$
$= \dfrac{3\sqrt{3} + 8\sqrt{3}}{6}$
$= \dfrac{11\sqrt{3}}{6}$

14. $\dfrac{2\sqrt[3]{4}}{7} - \dfrac{\sqrt[3]{4}}{14} = \dfrac{2\left(2\sqrt[3]{4}\right) - \sqrt[3]{4}}{14}$
$= \dfrac{4\sqrt[3]{4} - \sqrt[3]{4}}{14}$
$= \dfrac{3\sqrt[3]{4}}{14}$

16. $\dfrac{3x\sqrt{7}}{5} + \sqrt{\dfrac{7x^2}{100}} = \dfrac{3x\sqrt{7}}{5} + \dfrac{\sqrt{7x^2}}{\sqrt{100}}$
$= \dfrac{3x\sqrt{7}}{5} + \dfrac{x\sqrt{7}}{10}$
$= \dfrac{2\left(3x\sqrt{7}\right) + x\sqrt{7}}{10}$
$= \dfrac{6x\sqrt{7} + x\sqrt{7}}{10}$
$= \dfrac{7x\sqrt{7}}{10}$

18. $\sqrt{16} - 5\sqrt{10} + 7 = 4 - 5\sqrt{10} + 7 = 11 - 5\sqrt{10}$

20. $3\sqrt{7} - \sqrt[3]{x} + 4\sqrt{7} - 3\sqrt[3]{x} = 7\sqrt{7} - 4\sqrt[3]{x}$

22. $-\sqrt{75} + \sqrt{12} - 3\sqrt{3} = -\sqrt{25 \cdot 3} + \sqrt{4 \cdot 3} - 3\sqrt{3}$
$$= -5\sqrt{3} + 2\sqrt{3} - 3\sqrt{3}$$
$$= -6\sqrt{3}$$

24. $-2\sqrt[3]{108} - \sqrt[3]{32} = -2\sqrt[3]{27 \cdot 4} - \sqrt[3]{8 \cdot 4}$
$$= -2(3)\sqrt[3]{4} - 2\sqrt[3]{4}$$
$$= -6\sqrt[3]{4} - 2\sqrt[3]{4}$$
$$= -8\sqrt[3]{4}$$

26. $\sqrt{4x^7 y^5} + 9x^2\sqrt{x^3 y^5} - 5xy\sqrt{x^5 y^3}$
$$= \sqrt{4x^6 y^4 \cdot xy} + 9x^2\sqrt{x^2 y^4 \cdot xy}$$
$$\quad - 5xy\sqrt{x^4 y^2 \cdot xy}$$
$$= 2x^3 y^2\sqrt{xy} + 9x^2(xy^2)\sqrt{xy} - 5xy(x^2 y)\sqrt{xy}$$
$$= 2x^3 y^2\sqrt{xy} + 9x^3 y^2\sqrt{xy} - 5x^3 y^2\sqrt{xy}$$
$$= 6x^3 y^2\sqrt{xy}$$

28. $3\sqrt{8x^2 y^3} - 2x\sqrt{32y^3}$
$$= 3\sqrt{4x^2 y^2 \cdot 2y} - 2x\sqrt{16y^2 \cdot 2y}$$
$$= 3(2xy)\sqrt{2y} - 2x(4y)\sqrt{2y}$$
$$= 6xy\sqrt{2y} - 8xy\sqrt{2y}$$
$$= -2xy\sqrt{2y}$$

30. $2\sqrt[3]{24x^3 y^4} + 4x\sqrt[3]{81y^4}$
$$= 2\sqrt[3]{8x^3 y^3 \cdot 3y} + 4x\sqrt[3]{27y^3 \cdot 3y}$$
$$= 2(2xy)\sqrt[3]{3y} + 4x(3y)\sqrt[3]{3y}$$
$$= 4xy\sqrt[3]{3y} + 12xy\sqrt[3]{3y}$$
$$= 16xy\sqrt[3]{3y}$$

32. $3\sqrt[3]{5} + 4\sqrt{5} = 3\sqrt[3]{5} + 4\sqrt{5}$

34. $6\sqrt[3]{24x^3} - 2\sqrt[3]{81x^3} - x\sqrt[3]{3}$
$$= 6\sqrt[3]{8x^3 \cdot 3} - 2\sqrt[3]{27x^3 \cdot 3} - x\sqrt[3]{3}$$
$$= 6(2x)\sqrt[3]{3} - 2(3x)\sqrt[3]{3} - x\sqrt[3]{3}$$
$$= 12x\sqrt[3]{3} - 6x\sqrt[3]{3} - x\sqrt[3]{3}$$
$$= 5x\sqrt[3]{3}$$

36. $\dfrac{\sqrt{45}}{10} + \dfrac{7\sqrt{5}}{10} = \dfrac{\sqrt{9 \cdot 5}}{10} + \dfrac{7\sqrt{5}}{10}$
$$= \dfrac{3\sqrt{5} + 7\sqrt{5}}{10}$$
$$= \dfrac{10\sqrt{5}}{10}$$
$$= \sqrt{5}$$

38. $\dfrac{\sqrt[4]{48}}{5x} - \dfrac{2\sqrt[4]{3}}{10x} = \dfrac{\sqrt[4]{16 \cdot 3}}{5x} - \dfrac{2\sqrt[4]{3}}{10x}$
$$= \dfrac{2\sqrt[4]{3}}{5x} - \dfrac{\sqrt[4]{3}}{5x}$$
$$= \dfrac{2\sqrt[4]{3} - \sqrt[4]{3}}{5x}$$
$$= \dfrac{\sqrt[4]{3}}{5x}$$

40. $\dfrac{\sqrt{99}}{5x} - \sqrt{\dfrac{44}{x^2}} = \dfrac{\sqrt{9 \cdot 11}}{5x} - \dfrac{\sqrt{4 \cdot 11}}{x}$
$$= \dfrac{3\sqrt{11}}{5x} - \dfrac{2\sqrt{11}}{x}$$
$$= \dfrac{3\sqrt{11} - 5\left(2\sqrt{11}\right)}{5x}$$
$$= \dfrac{3\sqrt{11} - 10\sqrt{11}}{5x}$$
$$= -\dfrac{7\sqrt{11}}{5x}$$

42. $\dfrac{\sqrt[3]{3}}{10} + \sqrt[3]{\dfrac{24}{125}} = \dfrac{\sqrt[3]{3}}{10} + \dfrac{\sqrt[3]{8 \cdot 3}}{\sqrt[3]{125}}$
$$= \dfrac{\sqrt[3]{3}}{10} + \dfrac{2\sqrt[3]{3}}{5}$$
$$= \dfrac{\sqrt[3]{3} + 2\left(2\sqrt[3]{3}\right)}{10}$$
$$= \dfrac{\sqrt[3]{3} + 4\sqrt[3]{3}}{10}$$
$$= \dfrac{5\sqrt[3]{3}}{10}$$
$$= \dfrac{\sqrt[3]{3}}{2}$$

44.
$$\frac{\sqrt[3]{y^5}}{8} + \frac{5y\sqrt[3]{y^2}}{4} = \frac{\sqrt[3]{y^3 \cdot y^2}}{8} + \frac{5y\sqrt[3]{y^2}}{4}$$
$$= \frac{y\sqrt[3]{y^2}}{8} + \frac{5y\sqrt[3]{y^2}}{4}$$
$$= \frac{y\sqrt[3]{y^2} + 2\left(5y\sqrt[3]{y^2}\right)}{8}$$
$$= \frac{y\sqrt[3]{y^2} + 10y\sqrt[3]{y^2}}{8}$$
$$= \frac{11y\sqrt[3]{y^2}}{8}$$

46.
$$P = \sqrt{8} + \sqrt{32} + \sqrt{45}$$
$$= \sqrt{4 \cdot 2} + \sqrt{16 \cdot 2} + \sqrt{9 \cdot 5}$$
$$= 2\sqrt{2} + 4\sqrt{2} + 3\sqrt{5}$$
$$= 6\sqrt{2} + 3\sqrt{5}$$
$$= \left(6\sqrt{2} + 3\sqrt{5}\right) \text{ meters}$$

48.
$$\sqrt{5}\left(\sqrt{15} - \sqrt{35}\right) = \sqrt{5}\sqrt{15} - \sqrt{5}\sqrt{35}$$
$$= \sqrt{75} - \sqrt{175}$$
$$= \sqrt{25 \cdot 3} - \sqrt{25 \cdot 7}$$
$$= 5\sqrt{3} - 5\sqrt{7}$$

50.
$$\left(3x - \sqrt{2}\right)\left(3x - \sqrt{2}\right) = \left(3x - \sqrt{2}\right)^2$$
$$= (3x)^2 - 2(3x)\sqrt{2} + \left(\sqrt{2}\right)^2$$
$$= 9x^2 - 6x\sqrt{2} + 2$$

52.
$$\sqrt{5y}\left(\sqrt{y} + \sqrt{5}\right) = \sqrt{5y}\sqrt{y} + \sqrt{5y}\sqrt{5}$$
$$= \sqrt{5y^2} + \sqrt{25y}$$
$$= y\sqrt{5} + 5\sqrt{y}$$

54.
$$\left(8\sqrt{y} + z\right)\left(4\sqrt{y} - 1\right)$$
$$= 8\sqrt{y}\left(4\sqrt{y}\right) - 8\sqrt{y} + z\left(4\sqrt{y}\right) - z$$
$$= 32y - 8\sqrt{y} + 4z\sqrt{y} - z$$

56.
$$\left(\sqrt[3]{a} + 2\right)\left(\sqrt[3]{a} + 7\right)$$
$$= \sqrt[3]{a}\left(\sqrt[3]{a}\right) + \sqrt[3]{a} \cdot 7 + 2\sqrt[3]{a} + 2(7)$$
$$= \sqrt[3]{a^2} + 7\sqrt[3]{a} + 2\sqrt[3]{a} + 14$$
$$= \sqrt[3]{a^2} + 9\sqrt[3]{a} + 14$$

58.
$$\sqrt{5}\left(6 - \sqrt{5}\right) = \sqrt{5} \cdot 6 - \sqrt{5}\left(\sqrt{5}\right) = 6\sqrt{5} - 5$$

60.
$$\sqrt{3}\left(\sqrt{3} - 2\sqrt{5x}\right) = \sqrt{3}\sqrt{3} - \sqrt{3}\left(2\sqrt{5x}\right)$$
$$= 3 - 2\sqrt{15x}$$

62.
$$(\sqrt{6} - 4\sqrt{2})(3\sqrt{6} + \sqrt{2})$$
$$= \sqrt{6}(3\sqrt{6}) + \sqrt{6}\sqrt{2} - 4\sqrt{2}(3\sqrt{6}) - 4\sqrt{2}(\sqrt{2})$$
$$= 3 \cdot 6 + \sqrt{12} - 12\sqrt{12} - 4 \cdot 2$$
$$= 18 - 11\sqrt{12} - 8$$
$$= 10 - 11\sqrt{4 \cdot 3}$$
$$= 10 - 22\sqrt{3}$$

64.
$$(\sqrt{3x} + 2)(\sqrt{3x} - 2) = \left(\sqrt{3x}\right)^2 - 2^2 = 3x - 4$$

66.
$$\left(\sqrt{y} - 3x\right)^2 = \left(\sqrt{y}\right)^2 - 2\sqrt{y} \cdot (3x) + (3x)^2$$
$$= y - 6x\sqrt{y} + 9x^2$$

68.
$$(5\sqrt{7x} - \sqrt{2x})(4\sqrt{7x} + 6\sqrt{2x})$$
$$= 5\sqrt{7x}(4\sqrt{7x}) + 5\sqrt{7x}(6\sqrt{2x})$$
$$\quad - \sqrt{2x}(4\sqrt{7x}) - \sqrt{2x}(6\sqrt{2x})$$
$$= 20 \cdot 7x + 30\sqrt{14x^2} - 4\sqrt{14x^2} - 6 \cdot 2x$$
$$= 140x + 30x\sqrt{14} - 4x\sqrt{14} - 12x$$
$$= 128x + 26x\sqrt{14}$$

70.
$$\left(\sqrt[3]{3} + \sqrt[3]{2}\right)\left(\sqrt[3]{9} - \sqrt[3]{4}\right)$$
$$= \sqrt[3]{3}\left(\sqrt[3]{9}\right) + \sqrt[3]{3}\left(-\sqrt[3]{4}\right) + \sqrt[3]{2}\left(\sqrt[3]{9}\right) + \sqrt[3]{2}\left(-\sqrt[3]{4}\right)$$
$$= \sqrt[3]{27} - \sqrt[3]{12} + \sqrt[3]{18} - \sqrt[3]{8}$$
$$= 3 - \sqrt[3]{12} + \sqrt[3]{18} - 2$$
$$= 1 - \sqrt[3]{12} + \sqrt[3]{18}$$

72.
$$\left(\sqrt[3]{3x} + 2\right)\left(\sqrt[3]{9x^2} - 2\sqrt[3]{3x} + 4\right)$$
$$= \sqrt[3]{3x}\left(\sqrt[3]{9x^2}\right) - \sqrt[3]{3x}\left(2\sqrt[3]{3x}\right) + \sqrt[3]{3x}(4)$$
$$\quad + 2\left(\sqrt[3]{9x^2}\right) - 2\left(2\sqrt[3]{3x}\right) + 2(4)$$
$$= \sqrt[3]{27x^3} - 2\sqrt[3]{9x^2} + 4\sqrt[3]{3x} + 2\sqrt[3]{9x^2} - 4\sqrt[3]{3x} + 8$$
$$= 3x + 8$$

74.
$$\left(\sqrt{3x+1} + 2\right)^2 = \left(\sqrt{3x+1}\right)^2 + 2\sqrt{3x+1} \cdot 2 + 2^2$$
$$= (3x+1) + 4\sqrt{3x+1} + 4$$
$$= 3x + 4\sqrt{3x+1} + 5$$

76. $\left(\sqrt{x-6}-7\right)^2 = \left(\sqrt{x-6}\right)^2 - 2\sqrt{x-6}\cdot 7 + 7^2$

$$= (x-6) - 14\sqrt{x-6} + 49$$
$$= x - 14\sqrt{x-6} + 43$$

78. $\dfrac{8x-24y}{4} = \dfrac{8(x-3y)}{4} = 2(x-3y)$

80. $\dfrac{x^3-8}{4x-8} = \dfrac{(x-2)(x^2+2x+4)}{4(x-2)} = \dfrac{x^2+2x+4}{4}$

82. $\dfrac{14r-28r^2s^2}{7rs} = \dfrac{14r(1-2rs^2)}{7rs} = \dfrac{2(1-2rs^2)}{s}$

84. $\dfrac{-5+10\sqrt{7}}{5} = \dfrac{5\left(-1+2\sqrt{7}\right)}{5} = -1+2\sqrt{7}$

86. $A = \dfrac{1}{2}h(b+B)$

$$= \dfrac{1}{2}\left(6\sqrt{3}\right)\left(2\sqrt{63}+7\sqrt{7}\right)$$
$$= 3\sqrt{3}\left(2\sqrt{9\cdot7}+7\sqrt{7}\right)$$
$$= 3\sqrt{3}\left(6\sqrt{7}+7\sqrt{7}\right)$$
$$= 3\sqrt{3}\left(13\sqrt{7}\right)$$
$$= 39\sqrt{21}\ \text{square meters}$$

$P = 2\sqrt{63}+6\sqrt{3}+7\sqrt{7}+2\sqrt{27}$

$$= 2\sqrt{9\cdot7}+6\sqrt{3}+7\sqrt{7}+2\sqrt{9\cdot3}$$
$$= 6\sqrt{7}+6\sqrt{3}+7\sqrt{7}+6\sqrt{3}$$
$$= 13\sqrt{7}+12\sqrt{3}$$
$$= \left(13\sqrt{7}+12\sqrt{3}\right)\ \text{meters}$$

88. $\left(\sqrt{2}+\sqrt{3}-1\right)^2$

$$= \left[\left(\sqrt{2}+\sqrt{3}\right)-1\right]^2$$
$$= \left(\sqrt{2}+\sqrt{3}\right)^2 - 2\left(\sqrt{2}+\sqrt{3}\right)+1^2$$
$$= \left(\sqrt{2}\right)^2 + 2\sqrt{2}\sqrt{3}+\left(\sqrt{3}\right)^2 - 2\sqrt{2}-2\sqrt{3}+1$$
$$= 2+2\sqrt{6}+3-2\sqrt{2}-2\sqrt{3}+1$$
$$= 6+2\sqrt{6}-2\sqrt{2}-2\sqrt{3}$$

90. Answers may vary

Section 7.5

Practice Exercises

1. a. $\dfrac{5}{\sqrt{3}} = \dfrac{5\cdot\sqrt{3}}{\sqrt{3}\cdot\sqrt{3}} = \dfrac{5\sqrt{3}}{3}$

b. $\dfrac{3\sqrt{25}}{\sqrt{4x}} = \dfrac{3(5)}{2\sqrt{x}} = \dfrac{15}{2\sqrt{x}} = \dfrac{15\cdot\sqrt{x}}{2\sqrt{x}\cdot\sqrt{x}} = \dfrac{15\sqrt{x}}{2x}$

c. $\sqrt[3]{\dfrac{2}{9}} = \dfrac{\sqrt[3]{2}}{\sqrt[3]{9}} = \dfrac{\sqrt[3]{2}\cdot\sqrt[3]{3}}{\sqrt[3]{3^2}\cdot\sqrt[3]{3}} = \dfrac{\sqrt[3]{6}}{3}$

2. $\sqrt{\dfrac{3z}{5y}} = \dfrac{\sqrt{3z}}{\sqrt{5y}} = \dfrac{\sqrt{3z}\cdot\sqrt{5y}}{\sqrt{5y}\cdot\sqrt{5y}} = \dfrac{\sqrt{15yz}}{5y}$

3. $\dfrac{\sqrt[3]{z^2}}{\sqrt[3]{27x^4}} = \dfrac{\sqrt[3]{z^2}}{\sqrt[3]{27x^3}\cdot\sqrt[3]{x}}$

$$= \dfrac{\sqrt[3]{z^2}}{3x\sqrt[3]{x}}$$
$$= \dfrac{\sqrt[3]{z^2}\cdot\sqrt[3]{x^2}}{3x\sqrt[3]{x}\cdot\sqrt[3]{x^2}}$$
$$= \dfrac{\sqrt[3]{z^2x^2}}{3x\sqrt[3]{x^3}}$$
$$= \dfrac{\sqrt[3]{x^2z^2}}{3x^2}$$

4. a. $\dfrac{5}{3\sqrt{5}+2} = \dfrac{5\left(3\sqrt{5}-2\right)}{\left(3\sqrt{5}+2\right)\left(3\sqrt{5}-2\right)}$

$$= \dfrac{5\left(3\sqrt{5}-2\right)}{\left(3\sqrt{5}\right)^2 - 2^2}$$
$$= \dfrac{5\left(3\sqrt{5}-2\right)}{45-4}$$
$$= \dfrac{5\left(3\sqrt{5}-2\right)}{41}$$

b. $\dfrac{\sqrt{2}+5}{\sqrt{3}-\sqrt{5}} = \dfrac{\left(\sqrt{2}+5\right)\left(\sqrt{3}+\sqrt{5}\right)}{\left(\sqrt{3}-\sqrt{5}\right)\left(\sqrt{3}+\sqrt{5}\right)}$

$= \dfrac{\sqrt{2}\sqrt{3}+\sqrt{2}\sqrt{5}+5\sqrt{3}+5\sqrt{5}}{\left(\sqrt{3}\right)^2 - \left(\sqrt{5}\right)^2}$

$= \dfrac{\sqrt{6}+\sqrt{10}+5\sqrt{3}+5\sqrt{5}}{3-5}$

$= \dfrac{\sqrt{6}+\sqrt{10}+5\sqrt{3}+5\sqrt{5}}{-2}$

c. $\dfrac{3\sqrt{x}}{2\sqrt{x}+\sqrt{y}} = \dfrac{3\sqrt{x}\left(2\sqrt{x}-\sqrt{y}\right)}{\left(2\sqrt{x}+\sqrt{y}\right)\left(2\sqrt{x}-\sqrt{y}\right)}$

$= \dfrac{6\sqrt{x^2}-3\sqrt{xy}}{\left(2\sqrt{x}\right)^2 - \left(\sqrt{y}\right)^2}$

$= \dfrac{6x-3\sqrt{xy}}{4x-y}$

5. $\dfrac{\sqrt{32}}{\sqrt{80}} = \dfrac{\sqrt{16\cdot 2}}{\sqrt{16\cdot 5}} = \dfrac{4\sqrt{2}}{4\sqrt{5}} = \dfrac{\sqrt{2}}{\sqrt{5}} = \dfrac{\sqrt{2}\cdot\sqrt{2}}{\sqrt{5}\cdot\sqrt{2}} = \dfrac{2}{\sqrt{10}}$

6. $\dfrac{\sqrt[3]{5b}}{\sqrt[3]{2a}} = \dfrac{\sqrt[3]{5b}\cdot\sqrt[3]{25b^2}}{\sqrt[3]{2a}\cdot\sqrt[3]{25b^2}} = \dfrac{\sqrt[3]{125b^3}}{\sqrt[3]{50ab^2}} = \dfrac{5b}{\sqrt[3]{50ab^2}}$

7. $\dfrac{\sqrt{x}-3}{4} = \dfrac{\left(\sqrt{x}-3\right)\left(\sqrt{x}+3\right)}{4\left(\sqrt{x}+3\right)}$

$= \dfrac{\left(\sqrt{x}\right)^2 - (3)^2}{4\left(\sqrt{x}+3\right)}$

$= \dfrac{x-9}{4\left(\sqrt{x}+3\right)}$

Vocabulary and Readiness Check

1. The <u>conjugate</u> of $a+b$ is $a-b$.

2. The process of writing an equivalent expression, but without a radical in the denominator is called <u>rationalizing the denominator</u>.

3. The process of writing an equivalent expression, but without a radical in the numerator is called <u>rationalizing the numerator</u>.

4. To rationalize the denominator of $\dfrac{5}{\sqrt{3}}$, we multiply by $\dfrac{\sqrt{3}}{\sqrt{3}}$.

5. The conjugate of $\sqrt{2}+x$ is $\sqrt{2}-x$.

6. The conjugate of $\sqrt{3}+y$ is $\sqrt{3}-y$.

7. The conjugate of $5-\sqrt{a}$ is $5+\sqrt{a}$.

8. The conjugate of $6-\sqrt{b}$ is $6+\sqrt{b}$.

9. The conjugate of $-7\sqrt{5}+8\sqrt{x}$ is $-7\sqrt{5}-8\sqrt{x}$.

10. The conjugate of $-9\sqrt{2}-6\sqrt{y}$ is $-9\sqrt{2}+6\sqrt{y}$.

Exercise Set 7.5

2. $\dfrac{\sqrt{3}}{\sqrt{2}} = \dfrac{\sqrt{3}\cdot\sqrt{2}}{\sqrt{2}\cdot\sqrt{2}} = \dfrac{\sqrt{6}}{\sqrt{4}} = \dfrac{\sqrt{6}}{2}$

4. $\sqrt{\dfrac{1}{2}} = \dfrac{\sqrt{1}}{\sqrt{2}} = \dfrac{1\cdot\sqrt{2}}{\sqrt{2}\cdot\sqrt{2}} = \dfrac{\sqrt{2}}{\sqrt{4}} = \dfrac{\sqrt{2}}{2}$

6. $\sqrt{\dfrac{25}{y}} = \dfrac{\sqrt{25}}{\sqrt{y}} = \dfrac{5}{\sqrt{y}} = \dfrac{5\cdot\sqrt{y}}{\sqrt{y}\cdot\sqrt{y}} = \dfrac{5\sqrt{y}}{\sqrt{y^2}} = \dfrac{5\sqrt{y}}{y}$

8. $\dfrac{6}{\sqrt[3]{9}} = \dfrac{6\cdot\sqrt[3]{3}}{\sqrt[3]{3^2}\cdot\sqrt[3]{3}} = \dfrac{6\sqrt[3]{3}}{\sqrt[3]{3^3}} = \dfrac{6\sqrt[3]{3}}{3} = 2\sqrt[3]{3}$

10. $\dfrac{5}{\sqrt{27a}} = \dfrac{5}{3\sqrt{3a}} = \dfrac{5\cdot\sqrt{3a}}{3\sqrt{3a}\cdot\sqrt{3a}} = \dfrac{5\sqrt{3a}}{3\cdot 3a} = \dfrac{5\sqrt{3a}}{9a}$

12. $\dfrac{5}{\sqrt[3]{3y}} = \dfrac{5\cdot\sqrt[3]{9y^2}}{\sqrt[3]{3y}\cdot\sqrt[3]{9y^2}} = \dfrac{5\sqrt[3]{9y^2}}{\sqrt[3]{27y^3}} = \dfrac{5\sqrt[3]{9y^2}}{3y}$

14. $\dfrac{x}{\sqrt{5}} = \dfrac{x\cdot\sqrt{5}}{\sqrt{5}\cdot\sqrt{5}} = \dfrac{x\sqrt{5}}{5}$

16. $\dfrac{5}{\sqrt[3]{9}} = \dfrac{5\cdot\sqrt[3]{3}}{\sqrt[3]{9}\cdot\sqrt[3]{3}} = \dfrac{5\sqrt[3]{3}}{\sqrt[3]{27}} = \dfrac{5\sqrt[3]{3}}{3}$

18. $\dfrac{-5\sqrt{2}}{\sqrt{11}} = \dfrac{-5\sqrt{2}\cdot\sqrt{11}}{\sqrt{11}\cdot\sqrt{11}} = \dfrac{-5\sqrt{22}}{11}$

20. $\sqrt{\dfrac{13a}{2b}} = \dfrac{\sqrt{13a}}{\sqrt{2b}} = \dfrac{\sqrt{13a}\cdot\sqrt{2b}}{\sqrt{2b}\cdot\sqrt{2b}} = \dfrac{\sqrt{26ab}}{2b}$

22. $\sqrt[3]{\dfrac{7}{10}} = \dfrac{\sqrt[3]{7}}{\sqrt[3]{10}}\cdot\dfrac{\sqrt[3]{100}}{\sqrt[3]{100}} = \dfrac{\sqrt[3]{700}}{10}$

24. $\sqrt{\dfrac{11y}{45}} = \dfrac{\sqrt{11y}}{\sqrt{45}} = \dfrac{\sqrt{11y}}{3\sqrt{5}}\cdot\dfrac{\sqrt{5}}{\sqrt{5}} = \dfrac{\sqrt{55y}}{15}$

26. $\dfrac{1}{\sqrt{32x}} = \dfrac{1}{4\sqrt{2x}}\cdot\dfrac{\sqrt{2x}}{\sqrt{2x}} = \dfrac{\sqrt{2x}}{8x}$

28. $\dfrac{\sqrt[3]{3x}}{\sqrt[3]{4y^4}} = \dfrac{\sqrt[3]{3x}}{y\sqrt[3]{4y}}\cdot\dfrac{\sqrt[3]{2y^2}}{\sqrt[3]{2y^2}} = \dfrac{\sqrt[3]{6xy^2}}{y\cdot 2y} = \dfrac{\sqrt[3]{6xy^2}}{2y^2}$

30. $\sqrt[4]{\dfrac{1}{9}} = \dfrac{\sqrt[4]{1}}{\sqrt[4]{9}} = \dfrac{1}{\sqrt[4]{9}} = \dfrac{1\cdot\sqrt[4]{3^2}}{\sqrt[4]{3^2}\cdot\sqrt[4]{3^2}} = \dfrac{\sqrt[4]{9}}{3}$

32. $\sqrt[5]{\dfrac{32}{m^6n^{13}}} = \dfrac{\sqrt[5]{32}}{\sqrt[5]{m^6n^{13}}}$

$= \dfrac{2}{mn^2\sqrt[5]{mn^3}}$

$= \dfrac{2\cdot\sqrt[5]{m^4n^2}}{mn^2\sqrt[5]{mn^3}\cdot\sqrt[5]{m^4n^2}}$

$= \dfrac{2\sqrt[5]{m^4n^2}}{mn^2\cdot mn}$

$= \dfrac{2\sqrt[5]{m^4n^2}}{m^2n^3}$

34. $\dfrac{9y}{\sqrt[4]{4y^9}} = \dfrac{9y}{y^2\sqrt[4]{4y}}$

$= \dfrac{9y\cdot\sqrt[4]{2^2y^3}}{y^2\sqrt[4]{2^2y}\cdot\sqrt[4]{2^2y^3}}$

$= \dfrac{9y\sqrt[4]{4y^3}}{y^2\cdot 2y}$

$= \dfrac{9\sqrt[4]{4y^3}}{2y^2}$

36. $\dfrac{3}{\sqrt{7}-4} = \dfrac{3(\sqrt{7}+4)}{(\sqrt{7}-4)(\sqrt{7}+4)}$

$= \dfrac{3(\sqrt{7}+4)}{7-16}$

$= \dfrac{3(\sqrt{7}+4)}{-9}$

$= -\dfrac{\sqrt{7}+4}{3}$

38. $\dfrac{-8}{\sqrt{y}+4} = \dfrac{-8(\sqrt{y}-4)}{(\sqrt{y}+4)(\sqrt{y}-4)}$

$= \dfrac{-8(\sqrt{y}-4)}{y-16}$ or $\dfrac{32-8\sqrt{y}}{y-16}$

40. $\dfrac{\sqrt{3}+\sqrt{4}}{\sqrt{2}-\sqrt{3}} = \dfrac{\sqrt{3}+2}{\sqrt{2}-\sqrt{3}}$

$= \dfrac{(\sqrt{3}+2)(\sqrt{2}+\sqrt{3})}{(\sqrt{2}-\sqrt{3})(\sqrt{2}+\sqrt{3})}$

$= \dfrac{\sqrt{6}+3+2\sqrt{2}+2\sqrt{3}}{2-3}$

$= \dfrac{\sqrt{6}+3+2\sqrt{2}+2\sqrt{3}}{-1}$

$= -3-\sqrt{6}-2\sqrt{2}-2\sqrt{3}$

42. $\dfrac{2\sqrt{a}-3}{2\sqrt{a}+\sqrt{b}} = \dfrac{(2\sqrt{a}-3)(2\sqrt{a}-\sqrt{b})}{(2\sqrt{a}+\sqrt{b})(2\sqrt{a}-\sqrt{b})}$

$= \dfrac{4a-2\sqrt{ab}-6\sqrt{a}+3\sqrt{b}}{4a-b}$

44. $\dfrac{-3}{\sqrt{6}-2} = \dfrac{-3(\sqrt{6}+2)}{(\sqrt{6}-2)(\sqrt{6}+2)}$

$= \dfrac{-3(\sqrt{6}+2)}{6-4}$

$= \dfrac{-3(\sqrt{6}+2)}{2}$ or $\dfrac{-3\sqrt{6}-6}{2}$

46.
$$\frac{2\sqrt{a}}{2\sqrt{x}-\sqrt{y}} = \frac{2\sqrt{a}\left(2\sqrt{x}+\sqrt{y}\right)}{\left(2\sqrt{x}-\sqrt{y}\right)\left(2\sqrt{x}+\sqrt{y}\right)}$$
$$= \frac{2\sqrt{a}\left(2\sqrt{x}+\sqrt{y}\right)}{4x-y}$$
$$= \frac{4\sqrt{ax}+2\sqrt{ay}}{4x-y}$$

48.
$$\frac{4\sqrt{5}+\sqrt{2}}{2\sqrt{5}-\sqrt{2}} = \frac{\left(4\sqrt{5}+\sqrt{2}\right)\left(2\sqrt{5}+\sqrt{2}\right)}{\left(2\sqrt{5}-\sqrt{2}\right)\left(2\sqrt{5}+\sqrt{2}\right)}$$
$$= \frac{8(5)+4\sqrt{10}+2\sqrt{10}+2}{4(5)-2}$$
$$= \frac{42+6\sqrt{10}}{18}$$
$$= \frac{6\left(7+\sqrt{10}\right)}{18}$$
$$= \frac{7+\sqrt{10}}{3}$$

50. $\sqrt{\dfrac{3}{2}} = \dfrac{\sqrt{3}}{\sqrt{2}} = \dfrac{\sqrt{3}\cdot\sqrt{3}}{\sqrt{2}\cdot\sqrt{3}} = \dfrac{3}{\sqrt{6}}$

52. $\sqrt{\dfrac{12}{7}} = \dfrac{\sqrt{12}}{\sqrt{7}} = \dfrac{2\sqrt{3}}{\sqrt{7}} = \dfrac{2\sqrt{3}\cdot\sqrt{3}}{\sqrt{7}\cdot\sqrt{3}} = \dfrac{2\cdot 3}{\sqrt{21}} = \dfrac{6}{\sqrt{21}}$

54.
$$\frac{\sqrt{3x^5}}{6} = \frac{x^2\sqrt{3x}}{6}$$
$$= \frac{x^2\sqrt{3x}\cdot\sqrt{3x}}{6\cdot\sqrt{3x}}$$
$$= \frac{x^2\cdot 3x}{6\sqrt{3x}}$$
$$= \frac{3x^3}{6\sqrt{3x}}$$
$$= \frac{x^3}{2\sqrt{3x}}$$

56. $\dfrac{\sqrt[3]{4x}}{\sqrt[3]{z^4}} = \dfrac{\sqrt[3]{4x}}{z\sqrt[3]{z}} = \dfrac{\sqrt[3]{2^2 x}\cdot\sqrt[3]{2x^2}}{z\sqrt[3]{z}\cdot\sqrt[3]{2x^2}} = \dfrac{2x}{z\sqrt[3]{2x^2 z}}$

58. $\sqrt{\dfrac{3}{7}} = \dfrac{\sqrt{3}}{\sqrt{7}} = \dfrac{\sqrt{3}\cdot\sqrt{3}}{\sqrt{7}\cdot\sqrt{3}} = \dfrac{3}{\sqrt{21}}$

60. $\dfrac{\sqrt{y}}{7} = \dfrac{\sqrt{y}\cdot\sqrt{y}}{7\cdot\sqrt{y}} = \dfrac{y}{7\sqrt{y}}$

62. $\sqrt[3]{\dfrac{25}{2}} = \dfrac{\sqrt[3]{25}}{\sqrt[3]{2}} = \dfrac{\sqrt[3]{5^2}\cdot\sqrt[3]{5}}{\sqrt[3]{2}\cdot\sqrt[3]{5}} = \dfrac{5}{\sqrt[3]{10}}$

64. $\sqrt[3]{\dfrac{9y}{7}} = \dfrac{\sqrt[3]{9y}}{\sqrt[3]{7}} = \dfrac{\sqrt[3]{3^2 y}\cdot\sqrt[3]{3y^2}}{\sqrt[3]{7}\cdot\sqrt[3]{3y^2}} = \dfrac{3y}{\sqrt[3]{21y^2}}$

66.
$$\sqrt{\frac{8x^5 y}{2z}} = \sqrt{\frac{4x^5 y}{z}} = \frac{\sqrt{4x^5 y}}{\sqrt{z}}$$
$$= \frac{2x^2\sqrt{xy}}{\sqrt{z}}$$
$$= \frac{2x^2\sqrt{xy}\cdot\sqrt{xy}}{\sqrt{z}\cdot\sqrt{xy}}$$
$$= \frac{2x^2\cdot xy}{\sqrt{xyz}}$$
$$= \frac{2x^3 y}{\sqrt{xyz}}$$

68. Answers may vary

70.
$$\frac{\sqrt{15}+1}{2} = \frac{\left(\sqrt{15}+1\right)\left(\sqrt{15}-1\right)}{2\left(\sqrt{15}-1\right)}$$
$$= \frac{15-1}{2\left(\sqrt{15}-1\right)}$$
$$= \frac{14}{2\left(\sqrt{15}-1\right)}$$
$$= \frac{7}{\sqrt{15}-1}$$

72.
$$\frac{\sqrt{5}+2}{\sqrt{2}} = \frac{\left(\sqrt{5}+2\right)\left(\sqrt{5}-2\right)}{\sqrt{2}\left(\sqrt{5}-2\right)}$$
$$= \frac{5-4}{\sqrt{10}-2\sqrt{2}}$$
$$= \frac{1}{\sqrt{10}-2\sqrt{2}}$$

74. $\dfrac{5+\sqrt{2}}{\sqrt{2x}} = \dfrac{\left(5+\sqrt{2}\right)\left(5-\sqrt{2}\right)}{\sqrt{2x}\left(5-\sqrt{2}\right)}$

$= \dfrac{25-2}{5\sqrt{2x}-\sqrt{4x}}$

$= \dfrac{23}{5\sqrt{2x}-2\sqrt{x}}$

76. $\dfrac{\sqrt{8}-\sqrt{3}}{\sqrt{2}+\sqrt{3}} = \dfrac{\left(\sqrt{8}-\sqrt{3}\right)\left(\sqrt{8}+\sqrt{3}\right)}{\left(\sqrt{2}+\sqrt{3}\right)\left(\sqrt{8}+\sqrt{3}\right)}$

$= \dfrac{8-3}{\sqrt{16}+\sqrt{6}+\sqrt{24}+3}$

$= \dfrac{5}{4+\sqrt{6}+2\sqrt{6}+3}$

$= \dfrac{5}{7+3\sqrt{6}}$

78. $\dfrac{\sqrt{x}+\sqrt{y}}{\sqrt{x}-\sqrt{y}} = \dfrac{\left(\sqrt{x}+\sqrt{y}\right)\left(\sqrt{x}-\sqrt{y}\right)}{\left(\sqrt{x}-\sqrt{y}\right)\left(\sqrt{x}-\sqrt{y}\right)}$

$= \dfrac{x-y}{x-2\sqrt{xy}+y}$

80. $9x-4 = 7(x-2)$

$9x-4 = 7x-14$

$2x = -10$

$x = -5$

The solution is –5.

82. $(y+2)(5y+4) = 0$

$y+2 = 0$ or $5y+4 = 0$

$y = -2$ or $5y = -4$

$y = -\dfrac{4}{5}$

The solutions are $-2, -\dfrac{4}{5}$.

84. $\quad\quad\quad x^3 = x$

$x^3 - x = 0$

$x(x^2 - 1) = 0$

$x(x+1)(x-1) = 0$

$x = 0$ or $x+1 = 0$ or $x-1 = 0$

$\quad\quad\quad\quad\quad x = -1$ or $\quad x = 1$

The solutions are –1, 0, 1.

86. $\dfrac{5}{\sqrt{27}} = \dfrac{5}{\sqrt{27}} \cdot \dfrac{\sqrt{3}}{\sqrt{3}} = \dfrac{5\sqrt{3}}{\sqrt{81}} = \dfrac{5\sqrt{3}}{9}$

The smallest number is $\sqrt{3}$.

88. $r = \sqrt{\dfrac{3V}{7\pi}} = \dfrac{\sqrt{3V}}{\sqrt{7\pi}} = \dfrac{\sqrt{3V} \cdot \sqrt{3V}}{\sqrt{7\pi} \cdot \sqrt{3V}} = \dfrac{3V}{\sqrt{21\pi V}}$

90. Answers may vary

Integrated Review

1. $\sqrt{81} = 9$ because $9^2 = 81$.

2. $\sqrt[3]{-8} = -2$ because $(-2)^3 = -8$.

3. $\sqrt[4]{\dfrac{1}{16}} = \dfrac{1}{2}$ because $\left(\dfrac{1}{2}\right)^4 = \dfrac{1}{16}$.

4. $\sqrt{x^6} = x^3$ because $(x^3)^2 = x^6$.

5. $\sqrt[3]{y^9} = y^3$ because $(y^3)^3 = y^9$.

6. $\sqrt{4y^{10}} = 2y^5$ because $(2y^5)^2 = 4y^{10}$.

7. $\sqrt[5]{-32y^5} = -2y$ because $(-2y)^5 = -32y^5$.

8. $\sqrt[4]{81b^{12}} = 3b^3$ because $(3b^3)^4 = 81b^{12}$.

9. $36^{1/2} = \sqrt{36} = 6$

10. $(3y)^{1/4} = \sqrt[4]{3y}$

11. $64^{-2/3} = \dfrac{1}{\left(\sqrt[3]{64}\right)^2} = \dfrac{1}{4^2} = \dfrac{1}{16}$

12. $(x+1)^{3/5} = \sqrt[5]{(x+1)^3}$

13. $y^{-1/6} \cdot y^{7/6} = y^{-\frac{1}{6}+\frac{7}{6}} = y^{6/6} = y$

14. $\dfrac{(2x^{1/3})^4}{x^{5/6}} = 16x^{4/3}x^{-5/6}$

$= 16x^{\frac{8}{6}-\frac{5}{6}}$

$= 16x^{3/6}$

$= 16x^{1/2}$

15. $\dfrac{x^{1/4}x^{3/4}}{x^{-1/4}} = x^{\frac{1}{4}+\frac{3}{4}+\frac{1}{4}} = x^{5/4}$

16. $4^{1/3} \cdot 4^{2/5} = 4^{\frac{1}{3}+\frac{2}{5}} = 4^{\frac{5}{15}+\frac{6}{15}} = 4^{11/15}$

17. $\sqrt[3]{8x^6} = (8x^6)^{1/3} = (2^3 x^6)^{1/3} = 2^{3/3} x^{6/3} = 2x^2$

18. $\sqrt[12]{a^9 b^6} = (a^9 b^6)^{1/12}$
$\qquad = a^{9/12} b^{6/12}$
$\qquad = a^{3/4} b^{1/2}$
$\qquad = a^{3/4} b^{2/4}$
$\qquad = (a^3 b^2)^{1/4}$
$\qquad = \sqrt[4]{a^3 b^2}$

19. $\sqrt[4]{x} \cdot \sqrt{x} = x^{1/4} \cdot x^{1/2} = x^{\frac{1}{4}+\frac{2}{4}} = x^{3/4} = \sqrt[4]{x^3}$

20. $\sqrt{5} \cdot \sqrt[3]{2} = 5^{1/2} \cdot 2^{1/3}$
$\qquad = 5^{3/6} \cdot 2^{2/6}$
$\qquad = (5^3 \cdot 2^2)^{1/6}$
$\qquad = \sqrt[6]{5^3 \cdot 2^2}$
$\qquad = \sqrt[6]{500}$

21. $\sqrt{40} = \sqrt{4}\sqrt{10} = 2\sqrt{10}$

22. $\sqrt[4]{16x^7 y^{10}} = \sqrt[4]{16x^4 y^8}\,\sqrt[4]{x^3 y^2} = 2xy^2 \sqrt[4]{x^3 y^2}$

23. $\sqrt[3]{54x^4} = \sqrt[3]{27x^3}\,\sqrt[3]{2x} = 3x\sqrt[3]{2x}$

24. $\sqrt[5]{-64b^{10}} = \sqrt[5]{-32b^{10}}\,\sqrt[5]{2} = -2b^2 \sqrt[5]{2}$

25. $\sqrt{5} \cdot \sqrt{x} = \sqrt{5x}$

26. $\sqrt[3]{8x} \cdot \sqrt[3]{8x^2} = \sqrt[3]{64x^3} = 4x$

27. $\dfrac{\sqrt{98y^6}}{\sqrt{2y}} = \sqrt{\dfrac{98y^6}{2y}}$
$\qquad = \sqrt{49y^5}$
$\qquad = \sqrt{49y^4} \cdot \sqrt{y}$
$\qquad = 7y^2 \sqrt{y}$

28. $\dfrac{\sqrt[4]{48a^9 b^3}}{\sqrt[4]{ab^3}} = \sqrt[4]{\dfrac{48a^9 b^3}{ab^3}}$
$\qquad = \sqrt[4]{48a^8}$
$\qquad = \sqrt[4]{16a^8} \cdot \sqrt[4]{3}$
$\qquad = 2a^2 \sqrt[4]{3}$

29. $\sqrt{20} - \sqrt{75} + 5\sqrt{7} = \sqrt{4}\sqrt{5} - \sqrt{25}\sqrt{3} + 5\sqrt{7}$
$\qquad = 2\sqrt{5} - 5\sqrt{3} + 5\sqrt{7}$

30. $\sqrt[3]{54y^4} - y\sqrt[3]{16y} = \sqrt[3]{27y^3}\sqrt[3]{2y} - y\sqrt[3]{8}\sqrt[3]{2y}$
$\qquad = 3y\sqrt[3]{2y} - 2y\sqrt[3]{2y}$
$\qquad = y\sqrt[3]{2y}$

31. $\sqrt{3}\left(\sqrt{5} - \sqrt{2}\right) = \sqrt{3}\sqrt{5} - \sqrt{3}\sqrt{2} = \sqrt{15} - \sqrt{6}$

32. $\left(\sqrt{7} + \sqrt{3}\right)^2 = \left(\sqrt{7}\right)^2 + 2\sqrt{7}\sqrt{3} + \left(\sqrt{3}\right)^2$
$\qquad = 7 + 2\sqrt{21} + 3$
$\qquad = 10 + 2\sqrt{21}$

33. $\left(2x - \sqrt{5}\right)\left(2x + \sqrt{5}\right) = (2x)^2 - \left(\sqrt{5}\right)^2$
$\qquad = 4x^2 - 5$

34. $\left(\sqrt{x+1} - 1\right)^2 = \left(\sqrt{x+1}\right)^2 - 2\left(\sqrt{x+1}\right) + 1^2$
$\qquad = x + 1 - 2\sqrt{x+1} + 1$
$\qquad = x + 2 - 2\sqrt{x+1}$

35. $\sqrt{\dfrac{7}{3}} = \dfrac{\sqrt{7}}{\sqrt{3}} = \dfrac{\sqrt{7}}{\sqrt{3}} \cdot \dfrac{\sqrt{3}}{\sqrt{3}} = \dfrac{\sqrt{21}}{3}$

36. $\dfrac{5}{\sqrt[3]{2x^2}} = \dfrac{5}{\sqrt[3]{2x^2}} \cdot \dfrac{\sqrt[3]{4x}}{\sqrt[3]{4x}} = \dfrac{5\sqrt[3]{4x}}{\sqrt[3]{8x^3}} = \dfrac{5\sqrt[3]{4x}}{2x}$

37. $\dfrac{\sqrt{3}-\sqrt{7}}{2\sqrt{3}+\sqrt{7}}$

$= \dfrac{\sqrt{3}-\sqrt{7}}{2\sqrt{3}+\sqrt{7}} \cdot \dfrac{\left(2\sqrt{3}-\sqrt{7}\right)}{\left(2\sqrt{3}-\sqrt{7}\right)}$

$= \dfrac{\sqrt{3}\left(2\sqrt{3}\right)-\sqrt{3}\sqrt{7}-\sqrt{7}\left(2\sqrt{3}\right)+\sqrt{7}\sqrt{7}}{\left(2\sqrt{3}\right)^2-\left(\sqrt{7}\right)^2}$

$= \dfrac{6-\sqrt{21}-2\sqrt{21}+7}{12-7}$

$= \dfrac{13-3\sqrt{21}}{5}$

38. $\sqrt{\dfrac{7}{3}} = \dfrac{\sqrt{7}}{\sqrt{3}} = \dfrac{\sqrt{7}}{\sqrt{3}} \cdot \dfrac{\sqrt{7}}{\sqrt{7}} = \dfrac{7}{\sqrt{21}}$

39. $\sqrt[3]{\dfrac{9y}{11}} = \dfrac{\sqrt[3]{9y}}{\sqrt[3]{11}} = \dfrac{\sqrt[3]{9y}}{\sqrt[3]{11}} \cdot \dfrac{\sqrt[3]{3y^2}}{\sqrt[3]{3y^2}} = \dfrac{\sqrt[3]{27y^3}}{\sqrt[3]{31y^2}} = \dfrac{3y}{\sqrt[3]{33y^2}}$

40. $\dfrac{\sqrt{x}-2}{\sqrt{x}} = \dfrac{\sqrt{x}-2}{\sqrt{x}} \cdot \dfrac{\sqrt{x}+2}{\sqrt{x}+2}$

$= \dfrac{\left(\sqrt{x}\right)^2-2^2}{\sqrt{x}\sqrt{x}+2\sqrt{x}}$

$= \dfrac{x-4}{x+2\sqrt{x}}$

Section 7.6

Practice Exercises

1. $\sqrt{3x-5} = 7$

$\left(\sqrt{3x-5}\right)^2 = 7^2$

$3x-5 = 49$

$3x = 54$

$x = 18$

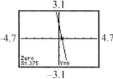

The solution is 18.

2. $\sqrt{3-2x}-4x = 0$

Graph $y_1 = \sqrt{3-2x}-4x$ in a decimal window.

The solution is 0.375, or $\dfrac{3}{8}$.

3. $\sqrt[3]{x-2}+1 = 3$

Graph $y_1 = \sqrt[3]{x-2}+1$ and $y_2 = 3$.

Check:

$\sqrt[3]{x-2}+1 = 3$

$\sqrt[3]{10-2}+1 \stackrel{?}{=} 3$

$\sqrt[3]{8}+1 \stackrel{?}{=} 3$

$2+1 = 3$

The solution is 10.

4. $\sqrt{16+x} = x-4$

$\left(\sqrt{16+x}\right)^2 = (x-4)^2$

$16+x = x^2-8x+16$

$x^2-9x = 0$

$x(x-9) = 0$

$x = 0 \text{ or } x-9 = 0$

$\hspace{3.5cm} x = 9$

Check 0:

$\sqrt{16+x} = x-4$

$\sqrt{16+0} \stackrel{?}{=} 0-4$

$\sqrt{16} \stackrel{?}{=} -4$

$4 \neq -4$

Check 9:

$\sqrt{16+x} = x-4$

$\sqrt{16+9} \stackrel{?}{=} 9-4$

$\sqrt{25} \stackrel{?}{=} 5$

$5 = 5$

0 does not check, so the only solution is 9.

5. Graph $y_1 = \sqrt{8x+1} + \sqrt{3x}$ and $y_2 = 2$.

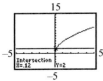

Now solve algebraically.

$$\sqrt{8x+1} + \sqrt{3x} = 2$$
$$\sqrt{8x+1} = 2 - \sqrt{3x}$$
$$\left(\sqrt{8x+1}\right)^2 = \left(2 - \sqrt{3x}\right)^2$$
$$8x+1 = 4 - 4\sqrt{3x} + 3x$$
$$4\sqrt{3x} = 3 - 5x$$
$$\left(4\sqrt{3x}\right)^2 = (3-5x)^2$$
$$16(3x) = 9 - 30x + 25x^2$$
$$25x^2 - 78x + 9 = 0$$
$$(25x - 3)(x - 3) = 0$$
$$25x - 3 = 0 \text{ or } x - 3 = 0$$
$$x = \frac{3}{25} \text{ or } \quad x = 3$$

From the graph, 3 does not check, so the only solution is $\frac{3}{25}$.

6. $a^2 + b^2 = c^2$
$$a^2 + 6^2 = 12^2$$
$$a^2 + 36 = 144$$
$$a^2 = 108$$
$$a = \pm\sqrt{108} = \pm\sqrt{36 \cdot 3} = \pm 6\sqrt{3}$$

Since a is a length, we will use the positive value only. The unknown leg is $6\sqrt{3}$ meters long.

7. Consider the base of the tank, and the plastic divider in the diagonal. Use the Pythagorean theorem to find l.

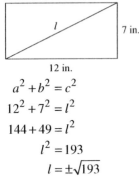

$$a^2 + b^2 = c^2$$
$$12^2 + 7^2 = l^2$$
$$144 + 49 = l^2$$
$$l^2 = 193$$
$$l = \pm\sqrt{193}$$

We will use the positive value because l represents length. The divider must be $\sqrt{193} \approx 13.89$ inches long.

Vocabulary and Readiness Check

1. A proposed solution that is not a solution of the original equation is called an <u>extraneous solution</u>.

2. The Pythagorean Theorem states that $a^2 + b^2 = c^2$ where a and b are the lengths of the <u>legs</u> of a <u>right</u> triangle and c is the length of the <u>hypotenuse</u>.

3. The square of $x - 5$, or $(x-5)^2 = \underline{x^2 - 10x + 25}$.

4. The square of $4 - \sqrt{7x}$, or
$$\left(4 - \sqrt{7x}\right)^2 = \underline{16 - 8\sqrt{7x} + 7x}.$$

Exercise Set 7.6

2. $\sqrt{3x} = 3$
$$\left(\sqrt{3x}\right)^2 = 3^2$$
$$3x = 9$$
$$x = 3$$
The solution is 3.

4. $\sqrt{x+1} = 5$
$$\left(\sqrt{x+1}\right)^2 = 5^2$$
$$x + 1 = 25$$
$$x = 24$$
The solution is 24.

6. $\sqrt{5x} = -5$
No solution since a principle square root does not yield a negative number.

8. $\sqrt{x-3} - 1 = 0$
$$\sqrt{x-3} = 1$$
$$\left(\sqrt{x-3}\right)^2 = 1^2$$
$$x - 3 = 1$$
$$x = 4$$
The solution is 4.

10. $\sqrt{3x+3} - 4 = 8$

$\qquad \sqrt{3x+3} = 12$

$\qquad \left(\sqrt{3x+3}\right)^2 = 12^2$

$\qquad 3x+3 = 144$

$\qquad 3x = 141$

$\qquad x = 47$

The solution is 47.

12. $\qquad \sqrt[3]{4x} = -2$

$\qquad \left(\sqrt[3]{4x}\right)^3 = (-2)^3$

$\qquad 4x = -8$

$\qquad x = -2$

The solution is –2.

14. $\sqrt[3]{2x-6} - 4 = 0$

$\qquad \sqrt[3]{2x-6} = 4$

$\qquad \left(\sqrt[3]{2x-6}\right)^3 = 4^3$

$\qquad 2x-6 = 64$

$\qquad 2x = 70$

$\qquad x = 35$

The solution is 35.

16. $\qquad \sqrt{2x-3} = 3-x$

$\qquad \left(\sqrt{2x-3}\right)^2 = (3-x)^2$

$\qquad 2x-3 = 9 - 6x + x^2$

$\qquad 0 = x^2 - 8x + 12$

$\qquad 0 = (x-6)(x-2)$

$x-6=0 \ \text{ or } \ x-2=0$

$\qquad x=6 \ \text{ or } \qquad x=2$

We discard 6 as extraneous. The solution is 2.

18. $2x + \sqrt{x+1} = 8$

$\qquad \sqrt{x+1} = 8 - 2x$

$\qquad \left(\sqrt{x+1}\right)^2 = (8-2x)^2$

$\qquad x+1 = 64 - 32x + 4x^2$

$\qquad 0 = 4x^2 - 33x + 63$

$\qquad 0 = (4x-21)(x-3)$

$4x-21=0 \quad \text{ or } \ x-3=0$

$\qquad x = \dfrac{21}{4} \ \text{ or } \qquad x=3$

We discard $\dfrac{21}{4}$ as extraneous. The solution is 3.

20. $\sqrt{x+3} + \sqrt{x-5} = 3$

$\qquad \left(\sqrt{x+3}\right)^2 = \left(3 - \sqrt{x-5}\right)^2$

$\qquad x+3 = 9 - 6\sqrt{x-5} + (x-5)$

$\qquad x+3 = x + 4 - 6\sqrt{x-5}$

$\qquad -1 = -6\sqrt{x-5}$

$\qquad (-1)^2 = \left(-6\sqrt{x-5}\right)^2$

$\qquad 1 = 36(x-5)$

$\qquad 1 = 36x - 180$

$\qquad 181 = 36x$

$\qquad \dfrac{181}{36} = x$

The solution is $\dfrac{181}{36}$.

22. $\qquad \sqrt{2x-4} - \sqrt{3x+4} = -2$

$\qquad \sqrt{2x-4} + 2 = \sqrt{3x+4}$

$\qquad \left(\sqrt{2x-4}+2\right)^2 = \left(\sqrt{3x+4}\right)^2$

$(2x-4) + 4\sqrt{2x-4} + 4 = 3x+4$

$\qquad 2x + 4\sqrt{2x-4} = 3x+4$

$\qquad 4\sqrt{2x-4} = x+4$

$\qquad \left(4\sqrt{2x-4}\right)^2 = (x+4)^2$

$\qquad 16(2x-4) = x^2 + 8x + 16$

$\qquad 32x - 64 = x^2 + 8x + 16$

$\qquad 0 = x^2 - 24x + 80$

$\qquad 0 = (x-4)(x-20)$

$x=4 \ \text{ or } \ x=20$

The solutions are 4 and 20.

24. $\qquad \sqrt{5x-4} = 9$

$\qquad \left(\sqrt{5x-4}\right)^2 = 9^2$

$\qquad 5x-4 = 81$

$\qquad 5x = 85$

$\qquad x = 17$

The solution is 17.

26. $\qquad -\sqrt{3x+9} = -12$

$\qquad \left(-\sqrt{3x+9}\right)^2 = (-12)^2$

$\qquad 3x+9 = 144$

$\qquad 3x = 135$

$\qquad x = 45$

The solution is 45.

28. $\sqrt{3x+1} - 2 = 0$

$\sqrt{3x+1} = 2$

$\left(\sqrt{3x+1}\right)^2 = 2^2$

$3x+1 = 4$

$3x = 3$

$x = 1$

The solution is 1.

30. $\sqrt[4]{2x-9} - 3 = 0$

$\sqrt[4]{2x-9} = 3$

$\left(\sqrt[4]{2x-9}\right)^4 = 3^4$

$2x-9 = 81$

$2x = 90$

$x = 45$

The solution is 45.

32. $\sqrt{3x+9} = 6$

$\left(\sqrt{3x+9}\right)^2 = 6^2$

$3x+9 = 36$

$3x = 27$

$x = 9$

The solution is 9.

34. $\sqrt[3]{3x} + 4 = 7$

$\sqrt[3]{3x} = 3$

$\left(\sqrt[3]{3x}\right)^3 = 3^3$

$3x = 27$

$x = 9$

The solution is 9.

36. $\sqrt[3]{x-4} - 5 = -7$

$\sqrt[3]{x-4} = -2$

$\left(\sqrt[3]{x-4}\right)^3 = (-2)^3$

$x-4 = -8$

$x = -4$

The solution is –4.

38. $\sqrt{3y+6} = \sqrt{7y-6}$

$\left(\sqrt{3y+6}\right)^2 = \left(\sqrt{7y-6}\right)^2$

$3y+6 = 7y-6$

$-4y = -12$

$x = 3$

The solution is 3.

40. $x - \sqrt{x-2} = 4$

$x-4 = \sqrt{x-2}$

$(x-4)^2 = \left(\sqrt{x-2}\right)^2$

$x^2 - 8x + 16 = x - 2$

$x^2 - 9x + 18 = 0$

$(x-6)(x-3) = 0$

$x = 6 \ \text{ or } \ x = 3$

We discard 3 as extraneous. The solution is 6.

42. $\sqrt[3]{-4x-3} = \sqrt[3]{-x-15}$

$\left(\sqrt[3]{-4x-3}\right)^3 = \left(\sqrt[3]{-x-15}\right)^3$

$-4x-3 = -x-15$

$-3x = -12$

$x = 4$

The solution is 4.

44. $\sqrt{2x-1} - 4 = -\sqrt{x-4}$

$\left(\sqrt{2x-1} - 4\right)^2 = \left(-\sqrt{x-4}\right)^2$

$(2x-1) - 8\sqrt{2x-1} + 16 = x - 4$

$x + 19 = 8\sqrt{2x-1}$

$(x+19)^2 = \left(8\sqrt{2x-1}\right)^2$

$x^2 + 38x + 361 = 64(2x-1)$

$x^2 + 38x + 361 = 128x - 64$

$x^2 - 90x + 425 = 0$

$(x-5)(x-85) = 0$

$x = 5 \ \text{ or } \ x = 85$

We discard 85 as extraneous. The solution is 5.

46. $\sqrt{7x-4} = \sqrt{4-7x}$

$\left(\sqrt{7x-4}\right)^2 = \left(\sqrt{4-7x}\right)^2$

$7x-4 = 4-7x$

$14x = 8$

$x = \dfrac{8}{14} = \dfrac{4}{7}$

The solution is $\dfrac{4}{7}$.

48.
$$\sqrt{x-2}+3=\sqrt{4x+1}$$
$$\left(\sqrt{x-2}+3\right)^2=\left(\sqrt{4x+1}\right)^2$$
$$(x-2)+6\sqrt{x-2}+9=4x+1$$
$$6\sqrt{x-2}=3x-6$$
$$2\sqrt{x-2}=x-2$$
$$\left(2\sqrt{x-2}\right)^2=(x-2)^2$$
$$4(x-2)=x^2-4x+4$$
$$4x-8=x^2-4x+4$$
$$0=x^2-8x+12$$
$$0=(x-6)(x-2)$$

$x=6$ or $x=2$
The solutions are 2 and 6.

50.
$$\sqrt{x+1}-\sqrt{x-1}=2$$
$$\sqrt{x+1}=2+\sqrt{x-1}$$
$$\left(\sqrt{x+1}\right)^2=\left(2+\sqrt{x-1}\right)^2$$
$$x+1=4+4\sqrt{x-1}+(x-1)$$
$$-2=4\sqrt{x-1}$$
$$(-2)^2=\left(4\sqrt{x-1}\right)^2$$
$$4=16(x-1)$$
$$4=16x-16$$
$$20=16x$$
$$x=\frac{20}{16}=\frac{5}{4}$$

We discard $\dfrac{5}{4}$ as extraneous so there is no solution.

52. Let c = length of the hypotenuse.
$$7^2+8^2=c^2$$
$$49+64=c^2$$
$$113=c^2$$
$$\sqrt{113}=\sqrt{c^2}$$
$$\sqrt{113}=c$$
$$c=\sqrt{113}\text{ inches}$$

54. Let b = length of the unknown leg.
$$4^2+b^2=7^2$$
$$16+b^2=49$$
$$b^2=33$$
$$\sqrt{b^2}=\sqrt{33}$$
$$b=\sqrt{33}\text{ cm}$$

56. Let c = length of the hypotenuse.
$$\left(5\sqrt{3}\right)^2+10^2=c^2$$
$$25(3)+100=c^2$$
$$175=c^2$$
$$\sqrt{175}=\sqrt{c^2}$$
$$\sqrt{25\cdot7}=c$$
$$c=5\sqrt{7}\approx13.2\text{ cm}$$

58. Let c = length of the hypotenuse.
$$(2.7)^2+(2.3)^2=c^2$$
$$7.29+5.29=c^2$$
$$12.58=c^2$$
$$\sqrt{12.58}=\sqrt{c^2}$$
$$c=\sqrt{12.58}\text{ in.}\approx3.5\text{ in.}$$

60. Let a = distance from base.
$$a^2+(2063)^2=(2382)^2$$
$$a^2=(2382)^2-(2063)^2$$
$$a^2=1,417,955$$
$$\sqrt{a^2}=\sqrt{1,417,955}$$
$$a\approx1191\text{ feet}$$

62. Let b = distance up the pole.
$$(15)^2+b^2=(30-2)^2$$
$$225+b^2=(28)^2$$
$$b^2=784-225$$
$$b^2=559$$
$$b=\sqrt{559}\text{ ft}\approx23.64\text{ ft}$$

64.
$$S(x)=\sqrt{10.5x}$$
$$=\sqrt{10.5(280)}$$
$$=\sqrt{2940}$$
$$=14\sqrt{15}\text{ mph}$$
$$\approx54.22\text{ mph}$$

66.
$$R = \sqrt{A^2 + B^2}$$
$$850 = \sqrt{600^2 + B^2}$$
$$850^2 = \left(\sqrt{600^2 + B^2}\right)^2$$
$$850^2 = 600^2 + B^2$$
$$B^2 = 850^2 - 600^2$$
$$= 722,500 - 360,000$$
$$= 362,500$$
$$B = \sqrt{362,500} = 50\sqrt{145} \approx 602.08 \text{ lb}$$

Tractor B is exerting approximately 602 pounds of force.

68.
$$S = 2\sqrt{I} - 9$$
$$15 = 2\sqrt{I} - 9$$
$$24 = 2\sqrt{I}$$
$$12 = \sqrt{I}$$
$$12^2 = \left(\sqrt{I}\right)^2$$
$$144 = I$$
The estimated IQ is 144.

70. $l = \dfrac{43 \text{ in.}}{1} \cdot \dfrac{1 \text{ ft}}{12 \text{ in.}} = \dfrac{43}{12} \text{ ft}$

$$P = 2\pi\sqrt{\dfrac{l}{32}} = 2\pi\sqrt{\dfrac{\frac{43}{12}}{32}} = 2\pi\sqrt{\dfrac{43}{384}} \approx 2.10 \text{ sec}$$

72.
$$P = 2\pi\sqrt{\dfrac{l}{32}}$$
$$3 = 2\pi\sqrt{\dfrac{l}{32}}$$
$$\dfrac{3}{2\pi} = \sqrt{\dfrac{l}{32}}$$
$$\left(\dfrac{3}{2\pi}\right)^2 = \left(\sqrt{\dfrac{l}{32}}\right)^2$$
$$\dfrac{9}{4\pi^2} = \dfrac{l}{32}$$
$$l = 32\left(\dfrac{9}{4\pi^2}\right) \approx 7.30 \text{ feet}$$

74. Answers may vary

76. $s = \dfrac{1}{2}(2 + 3 + 3) = \dfrac{1}{2}(8) = 4$
$$A = \sqrt{s(s-a)(s-b)(s-c)}$$
$$= \sqrt{4(4-2)(4-3)(4-3)}$$
$$= \sqrt{4(2)(1)(1)}$$
$$= \sqrt{8}$$
$$= 2\sqrt{2} \text{ sq cm} \approx 2.83 \text{ sq cm}$$

78. Answers may vary

80.
$$D(h) = 111.7\sqrt{h}$$
$$40 = 111.7\sqrt{h}$$
$$\dfrac{40}{111.7} = \sqrt{h}$$
$$\left(\dfrac{40}{111.7}\right)^2 = \left(\sqrt{h}\right)^2$$
$$0.1282370847 \approx h$$
$$h \approx 0.13 \text{ km}$$

82. Not a function; any vertical line to the right of the y-axis intersects the graph more than one time.

84. Not a function; the graph itself is a vertical line that intersects the graph more than one time.

86. Not a function; the y-axis is an example of a vertical line that intersects the graph more than one time.

88.
$$\dfrac{\frac{1}{y} + \frac{4}{5}}{\frac{-3}{20}} = \dfrac{\left(\frac{1}{y} + \frac{4}{5}\right) \cdot 20y}{\left(\frac{-3}{20}\right) \cdot 20y}$$
$$= \dfrac{20 + 16y}{-3y}$$
$$= -\dfrac{16y + 20}{3y}$$

90.
$$\dfrac{\frac{1}{y} + \frac{1}{x}}{\frac{1}{y} - \frac{1}{x}} = \dfrac{\left(\frac{1}{y} + \frac{1}{x}\right) \cdot xy}{\left(\frac{1}{y} - \frac{1}{x}\right) \cdot xy} = \dfrac{x + y}{x - y}$$

92. Answers may vary

94. $C(x) = 80\sqrt[3]{x} + 500$

$1620 = 80\sqrt[3]{x} + 500$

$1120 = 80\sqrt[3]{x}$

$14 = \sqrt[3]{x}$

$14^3 = \left(\sqrt[3]{x}\right)^3$

$2744 = x$

Thus, 2743 deliveries will keep overhead below $1620.

96. $3\sqrt{x^2 - 8x} = x^2 - 8x$

Let $t = x^2 - 8x$. Then

$3\sqrt{t} = t$

$\left(3\sqrt{t}\right)^2 = t^2$

$9t = t^2$

$0 = t^2 - 9t$

$0 = t(t - 9)$

$t = 0$ or $t = 9$

Replace t with $x^2 - 8x$.

$x^2 - 8x = 0$ or $x^2 - 8x = 9$

$x(x - 8) = 0$ $x^2 - 8x - 9 = 0$

$x = 0$ or $x = 8$ $(x - 9)(x + 1) = 0$

                            $x = 9$ or $x = -1$

The solutions are $-1, 0, 8,$ and 9.

98. $7 - (x^2 - 3x) = \sqrt{(x^2 - 3x) + 5}$

Let $t = x^2 - 3x$. Then

$7 - t = \sqrt{t + 5}$

$(7 - t)^2 = \left(\sqrt{t + 5}\right)^2$

$49 - 14t + t^2 = t + 5$

$t^2 - 15t + 44 = 0$

$(t - 11)(t - 4) = 0$

$t = 11$ or $t = 4$

Replace t with $x^2 - 3x$.

$x^2 - 3x = 11$ or $x^2 - 3x = 4$

$x^2 - 3x - 11 = 0$ $x^2 - 3x - 4 = 0$

Can't factor $(x - 4)(x + 1) = 0$

                      $x = 4$ or $x = -1$

The solutions are -1 and 4.

The Bigger Picture

1. $\dfrac{x}{4} + \dfrac{x + 18}{20} = \dfrac{x - 5}{5}$

$20\left(\dfrac{x}{4}\right) + 20\left(\dfrac{x + 18}{20}\right) = 20\left(\dfrac{x - 5}{5}\right)$

$5x + (x + 18) = 4(x - 5)$

$6x + 18 = 4x - 20$

$2x = -38$

$x = -19$

The solution set is $\{-19\}$.

2. $|3x - 5| = 10$

$3x - 5 = -10$ or $3x - 5 = 10$

$3x = -5$ $3x = 15$

$x = -\dfrac{5}{3}$ $x = 5$

The solution set is $\left\{-\dfrac{5}{3}, 5\right\}$.

3. $2x^2 - x = 45$

$2x^2 - x - 45 = 0$

$(2x + 9)(x - 5) = 0$

$2x + 9 = 0$ or $x - 5 = 0$

$x = -\dfrac{9}{2}$ $x = 5$

The solution set is $\left\{-\dfrac{9}{2}, 5\right\}$.

4. $-6 \le -5x - 1 \le 10$

$-5 \le -5x \le 11$

$1 \ge x \ge -\dfrac{11}{5}$

$-\dfrac{11}{5} \le x \le 1$

The solution is $\left[-\dfrac{11}{5}, 1\right]$.

5. $4(x - 1) + 3x > 1 + 2(x - 6)$

$4x - 4 + 3x > 1 + 2x - 12$

$7x - 4 > 2x - 11$

$5x > -7$

$x > -\dfrac{7}{5}$

The solution is $\left(-\dfrac{7}{5}, \infty\right)$.

6. $\sqrt{x}+14 = x-6$

$\sqrt{x} = x-20$

$\left(\sqrt{x}\right)^2 = (x-20)^2$

$x = x^2 - 40x + 400$

$0 = x^2 - 41x + 400$

$0 = (x-25)(x-16)$

$x-25 = 0$ or $x-16 = 0$

$x = 25$ $x = 16$

Discard 16 as an extraneous solution. The solution set is $\{25\}$.

7. $x \ge 10$ or $-x < 5$

$x \ge 10$ or $x > -5$

The solution is $(-5, \infty)$.

8. $\sqrt{3x-1}+4 = 1$

$\sqrt{3x-1} = -3$

There is no real number whose square root is negative. The solution set is $\varnothing$.

9. $|x-2| > 15$

$x-2 < -15$ or $x-2 > 15$

$x < -13$ or $x > 17$

The solution is $(-\infty, -13) \cup (17, \infty)$.

10. $5x - 4[x - 2(3x+1)] = 25$

$5x - 4(x - 6x - 2) = 25$

$5x - 4(-5x - 2) = 25$

$5x + 20x + 8 = 25$

$25x = 17$

$x = \dfrac{17}{25}$

The solution set is $\left\{\dfrac{17}{25}\right\}$.

Section 7.7

Practice Exercises

1. a. $\sqrt{-4} = \sqrt{-1 \cdot 4} = \sqrt{-1} \cdot \sqrt{4} = i \cdot 2$, or $2i$

b. $\sqrt{-7} = \sqrt{-1(7)} = \sqrt{-1} \cdot \sqrt{7} = i\sqrt{7}$

c. $-\sqrt{-18} = -\sqrt{-1 \cdot 18}$

$= -\sqrt{-1} \cdot \sqrt{9 \cdot 2}$

$= -i \cdot 3\sqrt{2}$

$= -3i\sqrt{2}$

2. a. $\sqrt{-5} \cdot \sqrt{-6} = i\sqrt{5}\left(i\sqrt{6}\right)$

$= i^2\sqrt{30}$

$= -1\sqrt{30}$

$= -\sqrt{30}$

b. $\sqrt{-9} \cdot \sqrt{-1} = 3i \cdot i = 3i^2 = 3(-1) = -3$

c. $\sqrt{125} \cdot \sqrt{-5} = 5\sqrt{5}\left(i\sqrt{5}\right)$

$= 5i\left(\sqrt{5}\sqrt{5}\right)$

$= 5i(5)$

$= 25i$

d. $\dfrac{\sqrt{-27}}{\sqrt{3}} = \dfrac{i\sqrt{27}}{\sqrt{3}} = i\sqrt{9} = 3i$

3. a. $(3-5i)+(-4+i) = (3-4)+(-5+1)i$

$= -1 - 4i$

b. $4i-(3-i) = 4i - 3 + i$

$= -3 + (4+1)i$

$= -3 + 5i$

c. $(-5-2i)-(-8) = -5 - 2i + 8$

$= (-5+8) - 2i$

$= 3 - 2i$

4. a. $-4i \cdot 5i = -20i^2 = -20(-1) = 20$

b. $5i(2+i) = 5i \cdot 2 + 5i \cdot i$

$= 10i + 5i^2$

$= 10i + 5(-1)$

$= 10i - 5$

$= -5 + 10i$

c. $(2+3i)(6-i) = 2(6) - 2(i) + 3i(6) - 3i(i)$

$= 12 - 2i + 18i - 3i^2$

$= 12 + 16i - 3(-1)$

$= 12 + 16i + 3$

$= 15 + 16i$

d. $(3-i)^2 = (3-i)(3-i)$

$= 3(3) - 3(i) - 3(i) + i^2$

$= 9 - 6i + (-1)$

$= 8 - 6i$

e. $(9+2i)(9-2i) = 9(9) - 9(2i) + 2i(9) - 2i(2i)$
$$= 81 - 18i + 18i - 4i^2$$
$$= 81 - 4(-1)$$
$$= 81 + 4$$
$$= 85$$

5. a. $\dfrac{4-i}{3+i} = \dfrac{(4-i)(3-i)}{(3+i)(3-i)}$

$$= \dfrac{4(3) - 4(i) - 3(i) + i^2}{3^2 - i^2}$$

$$= \dfrac{12 - 7i - 1}{9 + 1}$$

$$= \dfrac{11 - 7i}{10}$$

$$= \dfrac{11}{10} - \dfrac{7i}{10} \text{ or } \dfrac{11}{10} - \dfrac{7}{10}i$$

b. $\dfrac{5}{2i} = \dfrac{5(-2i)}{2i(-2i)}$

$$= \dfrac{-10i}{-4i^2}$$

$$= \dfrac{-10i}{-4(-1)}$$

$$= \dfrac{-10i}{4}$$

$$= \dfrac{-5i}{2}$$

$$= 0 - \dfrac{5i}{2} \text{ or } 0 - \dfrac{5}{2}i$$

6. a. $i^9 = i^4 \cdot i^4 \cdot i = 1 \cdot 1 \cdot i = i$

b. $i^{16} = (i^4)^4 = 1^4 = 1$

c. $i^{34} = i^{32} \cdot i^2 = (i^4)^8 \cdot i^2 = 1^8(-1) = -1$

d. $i^{-24} = \dfrac{1}{i^{24}} = \dfrac{1}{(i^4)^6} = \dfrac{1}{(1)^6} = \dfrac{1}{1} = 1$

Vocabulary and Readiness Check

1. A <u>complex</u> number is one that can be written in the form $a + bi$ where a and b are real numbers.

2. In the complex number system, i denotes the <u>imaginary unit</u>.

3. $i^2 = \underline{-1}$

4. $i = \sqrt{-1}$

5. A complex number, $a + bi$, is a <u>real</u> number if $b = 0$.

6. A complex number, $a + bi$, is a <u>pure imaginary</u> number if $a = 0$ and $b \neq 0$.

7. $\sqrt{-81} = 9i$

8. $\sqrt{-49} = 7i$

9. $\sqrt{-7} = i\sqrt{7}$

10. $\sqrt{-3} = i\sqrt{3}$

11. $-\sqrt{16} = -4$

12. $-\sqrt{4} = -2$

13. $\sqrt{-64} = 8i$

14. $\sqrt{-100} = 10i$

Exercise Set 7.7

2. $\sqrt{-32} = \sqrt{-1 \cdot 16 \cdot 2} = i \cdot 4\sqrt{2} = 4i\sqrt{2}$

4. $-\sqrt{-121} = -\sqrt{-1 \cdot 121} = -11i$

6. $4\sqrt{-20} = 4\sqrt{-1 \cdot 4 \cdot 5} = 4 \cdot i \cdot 2\sqrt{5} = 8i\sqrt{5}$

8. $\sqrt{-63} = \sqrt{-1 \cdot 9 \cdot 7} = 3i\sqrt{7}$

10. $\sqrt{-11} \cdot \sqrt{-3} = i\sqrt{11} \cdot i\sqrt{3} = i^2\sqrt{33} = -\sqrt{33}$

12. $\sqrt{-2} \cdot \sqrt{-6} = i\sqrt{2} \cdot i\sqrt{6} = i^2\sqrt{12} = -2\sqrt{3}$

14. $\sqrt{3} \cdot \sqrt{-27} = \sqrt{3} \cdot i\sqrt{27} = i\sqrt{81} = 9i$

16. $\dfrac{\sqrt{49}}{\sqrt{-10}} = \dfrac{7}{i\sqrt{10}}$

$= \dfrac{7\left(-i\sqrt{10}\right)}{i\sqrt{10}\left(-i\sqrt{10}\right)}$

$= \dfrac{-7i\sqrt{10}}{-i^2 \cdot 10}$

$= \dfrac{-7i\sqrt{10}}{-(-1) \cdot 10}$

$= -\dfrac{7i\sqrt{10}}{10}$

18. $\dfrac{\sqrt{-40}}{\sqrt{-8}} = \dfrac{i\sqrt{40}}{i\sqrt{8}} = \sqrt{\dfrac{40}{8}} = \sqrt{5}$

20. $(2-4i)-(2-i) = 2-4i-2+i$
$ = (2-2)+(-4i+i)$
$ = -3i$

22. $(8-3i)+(-8+3i) = 8-3i-8+3i$
$ = (8-8)+(-3i+3i)$
$ = 0$

24. $(9-4i)-9 = 9-4i-9$
$ = (9-9)-4i$
$ = -4i$

26. $-2i \cdot -11i = 22i^2 = 22(-1) = -22$

28. $5i(4-7i) = 20i-35i^2$
$ = 20i-35(-1)$
$ = 20i+35$
$ = 35+20i$

30. $\left(\sqrt{5}-5i\right)\left(\sqrt{5}+5i\right) = \left(\sqrt{5}\right)^2 - (5i)^2$
$\phantom{\left(\sqrt{5}-5i\right)\left(\sqrt{5}+5i\right)} = 5-25i^2$
$\phantom{\left(\sqrt{5}-5i\right)\left(\sqrt{5}+5i\right)} = 5+25$
$\phantom{\left(\sqrt{5}-5i\right)\left(\sqrt{5}+5i\right)} = 30$

32. $(6-3i)^2 = 36-2(6)(3i)+(3i)^2$
$ = 36-36i+9i^2$
$ = 36-36i-9$
$ = 27-36i$

34. $\dfrac{5}{6i} = \dfrac{5(-6i)}{6i(-6i)} = \dfrac{-30i}{-36i^2} = \dfrac{-30i}{36} = -\dfrac{5}{6}i$

36. $\dfrac{9}{1-2i} = \dfrac{9(1+2i)}{(1-2i)(1+2i)}$

$= \dfrac{9+18i}{1^2-4i^2}$

$= \dfrac{9+18i}{1+4}$

$= \dfrac{9+18i}{5}$

$= \dfrac{9}{5}+\dfrac{18}{5}i$

38. $\dfrac{6+2i}{4-3i} = \dfrac{(6+2i)(4+3i)}{(4-3i)(4+3i)}$

$= \dfrac{24+18i+8i+6i^2}{4^2-9i^2}$

$= \dfrac{24+26i-6}{16+9}$

$= \dfrac{18+26i}{25}$

$= \dfrac{18}{25}+\dfrac{26}{25}i$

40. $\dfrac{6-i}{2+i} = \dfrac{(6-i)(2-i)}{(2+i)(2-i)}$

$= \dfrac{12-6i-2i+i^2}{2^2-i^2}$

$= \dfrac{12-8i-1}{4+1}$

$= \dfrac{11-8i}{5}$

$= \dfrac{11}{5}-\dfrac{8}{5}i$

42. $(-6i)(-4i) = 24i^2 = 24(-1) = -24$

44. $(-2-4i)-(6-8i) = -2-4i-6+8i$
$ = -8+4i$

46. $-5i(-2+i) = 10i-5i^2 = 10i-5(-1) = 5+10i$

48. $\dfrac{6+8i}{3i} = \dfrac{6+8i}{3i} \cdot \dfrac{-3i}{-3i}$

$= \dfrac{-18i - 24i^2}{-9i^2}$

$= \dfrac{24 - 18i}{9}$

$= \dfrac{24}{9} - \dfrac{18}{9}i$

$= \dfrac{8}{3} - 2i$

50. $(3+i)(2+4i) = 6 + 12i + 2i + 4i^2$

$\qquad\qquad\qquad = 6 + 14i + 4(-1)$

$\qquad\qquad\qquad = 2 + 14i$

52. $(2-4i)(2-i) = 4 - 2i - 8i + 4i^2$

$\qquad\qquad\qquad = 4 - 10i - 4$

$\qquad\qquad\qquad = -10i$

54. $(7+4i) + (4-4i) = 7 + 4i + 4 - 4i = 11$

56. $(6+2i)(6-2i) = 6^2 - (2i)^2$

$\qquad\qquad\qquad = 36 - 4i^2$

$\qquad\qquad\qquad = 36 + 4$

$\qquad\qquad\qquad = 40$

58. $\dfrac{2-3i}{-7i} = \dfrac{(2-3i)(7i)}{-7i(7i)}$

$= \dfrac{14i - 21i^2}{-49i^2}$

$= \dfrac{14i + 21}{49}$

$= \dfrac{21}{49} + \dfrac{14}{49}i$

$= \dfrac{3}{7} + \dfrac{2}{7}i$

60. $(4-7i)^2 = 4^2 - 2(4)(7i) + (7i)^2$

$\qquad\qquad = 16 - 56i + 49i^2$

$\qquad\qquad = 16 - 56i - 49$

$\qquad\qquad = -33 - 56i$

62. $\dfrac{5}{3-2i} = \dfrac{5(3+2i)}{(3-2i)(3+2i)}$

$= \dfrac{15 + 10i}{3^2 - 4i^2}$

$= \dfrac{15 + 10i}{9 + 4}$

$= \dfrac{15 + 10i}{13}$

$= \dfrac{15}{13} + \dfrac{10}{13}i$

64. $(6-2i) + 7i = 6 - 2i + 7i = 6 + 5i$

66. $\dfrac{6+5i}{6-5i} = \dfrac{(6+5i)(6+5i)}{(6-5i)(6+5i)}$

$= \dfrac{36 + 30i + 30i + 25i^2}{6^2 - 25i^2}$

$= \dfrac{36 + 60i - 25}{36 + 25}$

$= \dfrac{11 + 60i}{61}$

$= \dfrac{11}{61} + \dfrac{60}{61}i$

68. $(5-3i) + (7-8i) = 5 - 3i + 7 - 8i$

$\qquad\qquad\qquad = 12 - 11i$

70. $\left(\sqrt{5} - 5i\right)\left(\sqrt{5} + 5i\right) = \left(\sqrt{5}\right)^2 - (5i)^2$

$\qquad\qquad\qquad\qquad = 5 - 25i^2$

$\qquad\qquad\qquad\qquad = 5 - 25(-1)$

$\qquad\qquad\qquad\qquad = 30$

72. $(6-3i)^2 = 6^2 - 2 \cdot 6 \cdot 3i + (3i)^2$

$\qquad\qquad = 36 - 36i + 9i^2$

$\qquad\qquad = 36 - 36i + 9(-1)$

$\qquad\qquad = 27 - 36i$

74. $i^{10} = (i^2)^5 = (-1)^5 = -1$

76. $i^{15} = i^{12} \cdot i^3 = (i^4)^3 \cdot (-i) = 1^4(-i) = -i$

78. $i^{40} = (i^4)^{10} = 1^{10} = 1$

80. $i^{-9} = \dfrac{1}{i^9} = \dfrac{1}{i^8 \cdot i} = \dfrac{1}{1 \cdot i} = \dfrac{1}{i} = \dfrac{1 \cdot i}{i \cdot i} = \dfrac{i}{i^2} = \dfrac{i}{-1} = -i$

82. $(5i)^4 = 5^4 i^4 = 625 \cdot 1 = 625$

84. $(-2i)^7 = (-2)^7 i^7$
$$= -128 i^4 \cdot i^3$$
$$= -128(1)(-i)$$
$$= 128i$$

86. $x + 57° + 90° = 180°$
$$x + 147° = 180°$$
$$x = 33°$$

88.

$$\underline{-2}\begin{array}{|rrrrr} 5 & 0 & -3 & 0 & 2 \\ & -10 & 20 & -34 & 68 \\ \hline 5 & -10 & 17 & -34 & 70 \end{array}$$

Answer: $5x^3 - 10x^2 + 17x - 34 + \dfrac{70}{x+2}$

90. 5 people

92. $6 + 2 + 3 = 11$ people

94. $\dfrac{5 \text{ people}}{30 \text{ people}} = \dfrac{1}{6} \approx 0.1666$

About 16.7% of the people reported an average checking balance of \$201 to \$300.

96. $i^8 - i^7 = (i^4)^2 - i^4 i^3 = 1^2 - 1(-i) = 1 + i$

98. $i^4 + i^{12} = i^4 + (i^4)^3 = 1 + 1^3 = 2$

100. $5 - \sqrt{-16} = 5 - i\sqrt{16} = 5 - 4i$

102. $\dfrac{4 - \sqrt{-8}}{2} = \dfrac{4 - i\sqrt{4 \cdot 2}}{2}$
$$= \dfrac{4 - 2i\sqrt{2}}{2}$$
$$= \dfrac{4}{2} - \dfrac{2i\sqrt{2}}{2}$$
$$= 2 - i\sqrt{2}$$

104. Answers may vary

106. $\left(8 - \sqrt{-3}\right) - \left(2 + \sqrt{-12}\right)$
$$= 8 - i\sqrt{3} - 2 - 2i\sqrt{3}$$
$$= 6 - 3i\sqrt{3}$$

108. $x^2 + 4 = 0$
$$(2i)^2 + 4 = 0$$
$$4i^2 + 4 = 0$$
$$4(-1) + 4 = 0$$
$$-4 + 4 = 0, \text{ which is true.}$$
Yes, $2i$ is a solution.

Chapter 7 Vocabulary Check

1. The <u>conjugate</u> of $\sqrt{3} + 2$ is $\sqrt{3} - 2$.

2. The <u>principal square root</u> of a nonnegative number a is written as $\sqrt{a}$.

3. The process of writing a radical expression as an equivalent expression but without a radical in the denominator is called <u>rationalizing</u> the denominator.

4. The <u>imaginary unit</u> written i, is the number whose square is -1.

5. The <u>cube root</u> of a number is written as $\sqrt[3]{a}$.

6. In the notation $\sqrt[n]{a}$, n is called the <u>index</u> and a is called the <u>radicand</u>.

7. Radicals with the same index and the same radicand are called <u>like radicals</u>.

8. A <u>complex number</u> is a number that can be written in the form $a + bi$, where a and b are real numbers.

9. The <u>distance</u> formula is
$d = \sqrt{(x_2 - x_1)^2 + (y_2 - y_1)^2}$.

10. The <u>midpoint</u> formula is $\left(\dfrac{x_1 + x_2}{2}, \dfrac{y_1 + y_2}{2} \right)$.

Chapter 7 Review

1. $\sqrt{81} = 9$ because $9^2 = 81$.

2. $\sqrt[4]{81} = 3$ because $3^4 = 81$.

3. $\sqrt[3]{-8} = -2$ because $(-2)^3 = -8$.

4. $\sqrt[4]{-16}$ is not a real number.

5. $-\sqrt{\dfrac{1}{49}} = -\dfrac{1}{7}$ because $\left(\dfrac{1}{7}\right)^2 = \dfrac{1}{49}$.

6. $\sqrt{x^{64}} = x^{32}$ because $(x^{32})^2 = x^{32\cdot2} = x^{64}$.

7. $-\sqrt{36} = -6$ because $6^2 = 36$.

8. $\sqrt[3]{64} = 4$ because $4^3 = 64$.

9. $\sqrt[3]{-a^6b^9} = \sqrt[3]{-1}\sqrt[3]{a^6}\sqrt[3]{b^9}$
$\phantom{\sqrt[3]{-a^6b^9}} = -1a^2b^3$
$\phantom{\sqrt[3]{-a^6b^9}} = -a^2b^3$

10. $\sqrt{16a^4b^{12}} = \sqrt{16}\sqrt{a^4}\sqrt{b^{12}} = 4a^2b^6$

11. $\sqrt[5]{32a^5b^{10}} = \sqrt[5]{32}\sqrt[5]{a^5}\sqrt[5]{b^{10}} = 2ab^2$

12. $\sqrt[5]{-32x^{15}y^{20}} = \sqrt[5]{-32}\sqrt[5]{x^{15}}\sqrt[5]{y^{20}} = -2x^3y^4$

13. $\sqrt{\dfrac{x^{12}}{36y^2}} = \dfrac{\sqrt{x^{12}}}{\sqrt{36y^2}} = \dfrac{x^6}{6y}$

14. $\sqrt[3]{\dfrac{27y^3}{z^{12}}} = \dfrac{\sqrt[3]{27y^3}}{\sqrt[3]{z^{12}}} = \dfrac{3y}{z^4}$

15. $\sqrt{(-x)^2} = |-x|$

16. $\sqrt[4]{(x^2-4)^4} = |x^2-4|$

17. $\sqrt[3]{(-27)^3} = -27$

18. $\sqrt[5]{(-5)^5} = -5$

19. $-\sqrt[5]{x^5} = -x$

20. $\sqrt[4]{16(2y+z)^{12}} = \sqrt[4]{16}\sqrt[4]{(2y+z)^{12}} = 2\left|(2y+z)^3\right|$

21. $\sqrt{25(x-y)^{10}} = \sqrt{25}\sqrt{(x-y)^{10}}$
$\phantom{\sqrt{25(x-y)^{10}}} = 5\left|(x-y)^5\right|$

22. $\sqrt[5]{-y^5} = \sqrt[5]{-1}\sqrt[5]{y^5} = -1y = -y$

23. $\sqrt[9]{-x^9} = \sqrt[9]{-1}\sqrt[9]{x^9} = -1x = -x$

24. $f(x) = \sqrt{x} + 3$
$x \geq 0$
Domain: $[0, \infty)$

x	0	1	4	9
$f(x)$	3	4	5	6

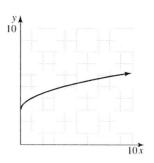

25. $g(x) = \sqrt[3]{x} - 3$
Domain: $(-\infty, \infty)$

x	-5	2	3	4	11
$g(x)$	-2	-1	0	1	2

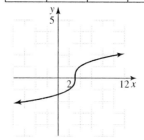

26. $\left(\dfrac{1}{81}\right)^{1/4} = \dfrac{1}{81^{1/4}} = \dfrac{1}{\sqrt[4]{81}} = \dfrac{1}{3}$

27. $\left(-\dfrac{1}{27}\right)^{1/3} = -\dfrac{1}{27^{1/3}} = -\dfrac{1}{\sqrt[3]{27}} = -\dfrac{1}{3}$

28. $(-27)^{-1/3} = \dfrac{1}{(-27)^{1/3}} = \dfrac{1}{\sqrt[3]{-27}} = \dfrac{1}{-3} = -\dfrac{1}{3}$

29. $(-64)^{-1/3} = \dfrac{1}{(-64)^{1/3}} = \dfrac{1}{\sqrt[3]{-64}} = \dfrac{1}{-4} = -\dfrac{1}{4}$

30. $-9^{3/2} = -\left(\sqrt{9}\right)^3 = -3^3 = -27$

31. $64^{-1/3} = \dfrac{1}{64^{1/3}} = \dfrac{1}{\sqrt[3]{64}} = \dfrac{1}{4}$

32. $(-25)^{5/2} = \left(\sqrt{-25}\right)^5$ is not a real number, since there is no real number whose square is -25.

33. $\left(\dfrac{25}{49}\right)^{-3/2} = \dfrac{1}{\left(\frac{25}{49}\right)^{3/2}}$

$= \dfrac{1}{\left(\sqrt{\frac{25}{49}}\right)^3}$

$= \dfrac{1}{\left(\frac{5}{7}\right)^3}$

$= \dfrac{1}{\frac{125}{343}}$

$= \dfrac{343}{125}$

34. $\left(\dfrac{8}{27}\right)^{-2/3} = \dfrac{1}{\left(\frac{8}{27}\right)^{2/3}} = \dfrac{1}{\left(\sqrt[3]{\frac{8}{27}}\right)^2} = \dfrac{1}{\left(\frac{2}{3}\right)^2} = \dfrac{1}{\frac{4}{9}} = \dfrac{9}{4}$

35. $\left(-\dfrac{1}{36}\right)^{-1/4} = \dfrac{1}{\left(-\frac{1}{36}\right)^{1/4}} = \dfrac{1}{\sqrt[4]{-\frac{1}{36}}}$ is not a real number, since there is no real number whose 4th power is $-\dfrac{1}{36}$.

36. $\sqrt[3]{x^2} = (x^2)^{1/3} = x^{2/3}$

37. $\sqrt[5]{5x^2 y^3} = (5x^2 y^3)^{1/5}$
$= 5^{1/5}(x^2)^{1/5}(y^3)^{1/5}$
$= 5^{1/5} x^{2/5} y^{3/5}$

38. $y^{4/5} = (y^4)^{1/5} = \sqrt[5]{y^4}$

39. $5(xy^2 z^5)^{1/3} = 5\sqrt[3]{xy^2 z^5}$

40. $(x+2y)^{-1/2} = \dfrac{1}{(x+2y)^{1/2}} = \dfrac{1}{\sqrt{x+2y}}$

41. $a^{1/3} a^{4/3} a^{1/2} = a^{\frac{1}{3}+\frac{4}{3}+\frac{1}{2}} = a^{\frac{2}{6}+\frac{8}{6}+\frac{3}{6}} = a^{13/6}$

42. $\dfrac{b^{1/3}}{b^{4/3}} = b^{1/3-4/3} = b^{-3/3} = b^{-1} = \dfrac{1}{b}$

43. $(a^{1/2} a^{-2})^3 = (a^{1/2-2})^3$
$= (a^{1/2-4/2})^3$
$= (a^{-3/2})^3$
$= a^{-9/2}$
$= \dfrac{1}{a^{9/2}}$

44. $(x^{-3} y^6)^{1/3} = (x^{-3})^{1/3}(y^6)^{1/3} = x^{-1} y^2 = \dfrac{y^2}{x}$

45. $\left(\dfrac{b^{3/4}}{a^{-1/2}}\right)^8 = (a^{1/2} b^{3/4})^8$
$= (a^{1/2})^8 (b^{3/4})^8$
$= a^4 b^6$

46. $\dfrac{x^{1/4} x^{-1/2}}{x^{2/3}} = x^{1/4+(-1/2)-2/3}$
$= x^{\frac{3}{12}-\frac{6}{12}-\frac{8}{12}}$
$= x^{-11/12}$
$= \dfrac{1}{x^{11/12}}$

47. $\left(\dfrac{49c^{5/3}}{a^{-1/4} b^{5/6}}\right)^{-1} = \dfrac{49^{-1} c^{-5/3}}{a^{1/4} b^{-5/6}} = \dfrac{b^{5/6}}{49a^{1/4} c^{5/3}}$

48. $a^{-1/4}(a^{5/4} - a^{9/4}) = a^{-1/4}(a^{5/4}) - a^{-1/4}(a^{9/4})$
$= a^{-1/4+5/4} - a^{-1/4+9/4}$
$= a^{4/4} - a^{8/4}$
$= a - a^2$

49. $\sqrt{20} \approx 4.472$

50. $\sqrt[3]{-39} \approx -3.391$

51. $\sqrt[4]{726} \approx 5.191$

52. $56^{1/3} \approx 3.826$

53. $-78^{3/4} \approx -26.246$

54. $105^{-2/3} \approx 0.045$

55. $\sqrt[3]{2} \cdot \sqrt{7} = 2^{1/3} \cdot 7^{1/2}$
$= 2^{2/6} \cdot 7^{3/6}$
$= (2^2 \cdot 7^3)^{1/6}$
$= \sqrt[6]{4 \cdot 343}$
$= \sqrt[6]{1372}$

56. $\sqrt[3]{3} \cdot \sqrt[4]{x} = 3^{1/3} \cdot x^{1/4}$
$= 3^{4/12} \cdot x^{3/12}$
$= (3^4 \cdot x^3)^{1/12}$
$= \sqrt[12]{81x^3}$

57. $\sqrt{3} \cdot \sqrt{8} = \sqrt{24} = \sqrt{4 \cdot 6} = 2\sqrt{6}$

58. $\sqrt[3]{7y} \cdot \sqrt[3]{x^2 z} = \sqrt[3]{7y \cdot x^2 z} = \sqrt[3]{7x^2 yz}$

59. $\dfrac{\sqrt{44x^3}}{\sqrt{11x}} = \sqrt{\dfrac{44x^3}{11x}} = \sqrt{4x^2} = 2x$

60. $\dfrac{\sqrt[4]{a^6 b^{13}}}{\sqrt[4]{a^2 b}} = \sqrt[4]{\dfrac{a^6 b^{13}}{a^2 b}} = \sqrt[4]{a^4 b^{12}} = ab^3$

61. $\sqrt{60} = \sqrt{4 \cdot 15} = 2\sqrt{15}$

62. $-\sqrt{75} = -\sqrt{25 \cdot 3} = -5\sqrt{3}$

63. $\sqrt[3]{162} = \sqrt[3]{27 \cdot 6} = 3\sqrt[3]{6}$

64. $\sqrt[3]{-32} = \sqrt[3]{-8 \cdot 4} = -2\sqrt[3]{4}$

65. $\sqrt{36x^7} = \sqrt{36x^6 \cdot x} = 6x^3 \sqrt{x}$

66. $\sqrt[3]{24a^5 b^7} = \sqrt[3]{8a^3 b^6 \cdot 3a^2 b} = 2ab^2 \sqrt[3]{3a^2 b}$

67. $\sqrt{\dfrac{p^{17}}{121}} = \dfrac{\sqrt{p^{17}}}{\sqrt{121}} = \dfrac{\sqrt{p^{16} \cdot p}}{11} = \dfrac{p^8 \sqrt{p}}{11}$

68. $\sqrt[3]{\dfrac{y^5}{27x^6}} = \dfrac{\sqrt[3]{y^5}}{\sqrt[3]{27x^6}} = \dfrac{\sqrt[3]{y^3 y^2}}{\sqrt[3]{27x^6}} = \dfrac{y\sqrt[3]{y^2}}{3x^2}$

69. $\sqrt[4]{\dfrac{xy^6}{81}} = \dfrac{\sqrt[4]{xy^6}}{\sqrt[4]{81}} = \dfrac{\sqrt[4]{y^4 \cdot xy^2}}{3} = \dfrac{y\sqrt[4]{xy^2}}{3}$

70. $\sqrt{\dfrac{2x^3}{49y^4}} = \dfrac{\sqrt{2x^3}}{\sqrt{49y^4}} = \dfrac{\sqrt{x^2 \cdot 2x}}{7y^2} = \dfrac{x\sqrt{2x}}{7y^2}$

71. $r = \sqrt{\dfrac{A}{\pi}}$

    a. $r = \sqrt{\dfrac{25}{\pi}} = \dfrac{\sqrt{25}}{\sqrt{\pi}} = \dfrac{5}{\sqrt{\pi}}$ meters, or

        $r = \dfrac{5}{\sqrt{\pi}} = \dfrac{5\sqrt{\pi}}{\sqrt{\pi}\sqrt{\pi}} = \dfrac{5\sqrt{\pi}}{\pi}$ meters

    b. $r = \sqrt{\dfrac{104}{\pi}} \approx 5.75$ inches

72. $(x_1, y_1) = (-6, 3),\ (x_2, y_2) = (8, 4)$
$d = \sqrt{(x_2 - x_1)^2 + (y_2 - y_1)^2}$
$= \sqrt{(8+6)^2 + (4-3)^2}$
$= \sqrt{196 + 1}$
$= \sqrt{197} \approx 14.036$ units

73. $(x_1, y_1) = (-4, -6),\ (x_2, y_2) = (-1, 5)$
$d = \sqrt{(x_2 - x_1)^2 + (y_2 - y_1)^2}$
$= \sqrt{(-1+4)^2 + (5+6)^2}$
$= \sqrt{9 + 121}$
$= \sqrt{130} \approx 11.402$ units

74. $(x_1, y_1) = (-1, 5),\ (x_2, y_2) = (2, -3)$
$d = \sqrt{(x_2 - x_1)^2 + (y_2 - y_1)^2}$
$= \sqrt{(2+1)^2 + (-3-5)^2}$
$= \sqrt{9 + 64}$
$= \sqrt{73} \approx 8.544$ units

75. $(x_1, y_1) = \left(-\sqrt{2}, 0\right),\ (x_2, y_2) = \left(0, -4\sqrt{6}\right)$
$d = \sqrt{(x_2 - x_1)^2 + (y_2 - y_1)^2}$
$= \sqrt{\left(0 + \sqrt{2}\right)^2 + \left(-4\sqrt{6} - 0\right)^2}$
$= \sqrt{2 + 96}$
$= \sqrt{98}$
$= 7\sqrt{2} \approx 9.899$ units

76. $(x_1, y_1) = \left(-\sqrt{5}, -\sqrt{11}\right),$

$(x_2, y_2) = \left(-\sqrt{5}, -3\sqrt{11}\right)$

$d = \sqrt{(x_2 - x_1)^2 + (y_2 - y_1)^2}$

$= \sqrt{\left(-\sqrt{5} + \sqrt{5}\right)^2 + \left(-3\sqrt{11} + \sqrt{11}\right)^2}$

$= \sqrt{0 + 44}$

$= \sqrt{44}$

$= 2\sqrt{11} \approx 6.633$ units

77. $(x_1, y_1) = (7.4, -8.6), (x_2, y_2) = (-1.2, 5.6)$

$d = \sqrt{(-1.2 - 7.4)^2 + (5.6 + 8.6)^2}$

$= \sqrt{(-8.6)^2 + (14.2)^2}$

$= \sqrt{73.96 + 201.64}$

$= \sqrt{275.6} \approx 16.601$ units

78. $(x_1, y_1) = (2, 6), (x_2, y_2) = (-12, 4)$

midpoint $= \left(\dfrac{x_1 + x_2}{2}, \dfrac{y_1 + y_2}{2}\right)$

$= \left(\dfrac{2 - 12}{2}, \dfrac{6 + 4}{2}\right)$

$= \left(\dfrac{-10}{2}, \dfrac{10}{2}\right)$

$= (-5, 5)$

79. $(x_1, y_1) = (-6, -5), (x_2, y_2) = (-9, 7)$

midpoint $= \left(\dfrac{x_1 + x_2}{2}, \dfrac{y_1 + y_2}{2}\right)$

$= \left(\dfrac{-6 - 9}{2}, \dfrac{-5 + 7}{2}\right)$

$= \left(\dfrac{-15}{2}, \dfrac{2}{2}\right)$

$= \left(-\dfrac{15}{2}, 1\right)$

80. $(x_1, y_1) = (4, -6), (x_2, y_2) = (-15, 2)$

midpoint $= \left(\dfrac{x_1 + x_2}{2}, \dfrac{y_1 + y_2}{2}\right)$

$= \left(\dfrac{4 - 15}{2}, \dfrac{-6 + 2}{2}\right)$

$= \left(\dfrac{-11}{2}, \dfrac{-4}{2}\right)$

$= \left(-\dfrac{11}{2}, -2\right)$

81. $(x_1, y_1) = \left(0, -\dfrac{3}{8}\right), (x_2, y_2) = \left(\dfrac{1}{10}, 0\right)$

midpoint $= \left(\dfrac{x_1 + x_2}{2}, \dfrac{y_1 + y_2}{2}\right)$

$= \left(\dfrac{0 + \frac{1}{10}}{2}, \dfrac{-\frac{3}{8} + 0}{2}\right)$

$= \left(\dfrac{1}{20}, -\dfrac{3}{16}\right)$

82. $(x_1, y_1) = \left(\dfrac{3}{4}, -\dfrac{1}{7}\right), (x_2, y_2) = \left(-\dfrac{1}{4}, -\dfrac{3}{7}\right)$

midpoint $= \left(\dfrac{x_1 + x_2}{2}, \dfrac{y_1 + y_2}{2}\right)$

$= \left(\dfrac{\frac{3}{4} - \frac{1}{4}}{2}, \dfrac{-\frac{1}{7} - \frac{3}{7}}{2}\right)$

$= \left(\dfrac{\frac{1}{2}}{2}, \dfrac{-\frac{4}{7}}{2}\right)$

$= \left(\dfrac{1}{4}, -\dfrac{2}{7}\right)$

83. $(x_1, y_1) = \left(\sqrt{3}, -2\sqrt{6}\right), (x_2, y_2) = \left(\sqrt{3}, -4\sqrt{6}\right)$

midpoint $= \left(\dfrac{x_1 + x_2}{2}, \dfrac{y_1 + y_2}{2}\right)$

$= \left(\dfrac{\sqrt{3} + \sqrt{3}}{2}, \dfrac{-2\sqrt{6} - 4\sqrt{6}}{2}\right)$

$= \left(\dfrac{2\sqrt{3}}{2}, \dfrac{-6\sqrt{6}}{2}\right)$

$= \left(\sqrt{3}, -3\sqrt{6}\right)$

84. $2\sqrt{50} - 3\sqrt{125} + \sqrt{98}$

$= 2\sqrt{25 \cdot 2} - 3\sqrt{25 \cdot 5} + \sqrt{49 \cdot 2}$

$= 2 \cdot 5\sqrt{2} - 3 \cdot 5\sqrt{5} + 7\sqrt{2}$

$= 10\sqrt{2} - 15\sqrt{5} + 7\sqrt{2}$

$= 17\sqrt{2} - 15\sqrt{5}$

85. $x\sqrt{75xy} - \sqrt{27x^3 y} = x\sqrt{25 \cdot 3xy} - \sqrt{9x^2 \cdot 3xy}$

$= x \cdot 5\sqrt{3xy} - 3x\sqrt{3xy}$

$= 2x\sqrt{3xy}$

86. $\sqrt[3]{128}+\sqrt[3]{250}=\sqrt[3]{64\cdot 2}+\sqrt[3]{125\cdot 2}$
$$=4\sqrt[3]{2}+5\sqrt[3]{2}$$
$$=9\sqrt[3]{2}$$

87. $3\sqrt[4]{32a^5}-a\sqrt[4]{162a}=3\sqrt[4]{16a^4\cdot 2a}-a\sqrt[4]{81\cdot 2a}$
$$=3\cdot 2a\sqrt[4]{2a}-3a\sqrt[4]{2a}$$
$$=6a\sqrt[4]{2a}-3a\sqrt[4]{2a}$$
$$=3a\sqrt[4]{2a}$$

88. $\dfrac{5}{\sqrt{4}}+\dfrac{\sqrt{3}}{3}=\dfrac{5}{2}+\dfrac{\sqrt{3}}{3}=\dfrac{5\cdot 3+2\sqrt{3}}{6}=\dfrac{15+2\sqrt{3}}{6}$

89. $\sqrt{\dfrac{8}{x^2}}-\sqrt{\dfrac{50}{16x^2}}=\dfrac{\sqrt{8}}{\sqrt{x^2}}-\dfrac{\sqrt{50}}{\sqrt{16x^2}}$
$$=\dfrac{\sqrt{4\cdot 2}}{x}-\dfrac{\sqrt{25\cdot 2}}{4x}$$
$$=\dfrac{2\sqrt{2}\cdot 4}{x\cdot 4}-\dfrac{5\sqrt{2}}{4x}$$
$$=\dfrac{8\sqrt{2}-5\sqrt{2}}{4x}$$
$$=\dfrac{3\sqrt{2}}{4x}$$

90. $2\sqrt{32x^2 y^3}-xy\sqrt{98y}$
$$=2\sqrt{16x^2 y^2\cdot 2y}-xy\sqrt{49\cdot 2y}$$
$$=2\cdot 4xy\sqrt{2y}-xy\cdot 7\sqrt{2y}$$
$$=8xy\sqrt{2y}-7xy\sqrt{2y}$$
$$=xy\sqrt{2y}$$

91. $2a\sqrt[4]{32b^5}-3b\sqrt[4]{162a^4 b}+\sqrt[4]{2a^4 b^5}$
$$=2a\sqrt[4]{16b^4\cdot 2b}-3b\sqrt[4]{81a^4\cdot 2b}+\sqrt[4]{a^4 b^4\cdot 2b}$$
$$=2a\cdot 2b\sqrt[4]{2b}-3b\cdot 3a\sqrt[4]{2b}+ab\sqrt[4]{2b}$$
$$=4ab\sqrt[4]{2b}-9ab\sqrt[4]{2b}+ab\sqrt[4]{2b}$$
$$=-4ab\sqrt[4]{2b}$$

92. $\sqrt{3}\left(\sqrt{27}-\sqrt{3}\right)=\sqrt{3}\left(\sqrt{9\cdot 3}-\sqrt{3}\right)$
$$=\sqrt{3}\left(3\sqrt{3}-\sqrt{3}\right)$$
$$=\sqrt{3}\left(2\sqrt{3}\right)$$
$$=2\sqrt{9}$$
$$=2(3)$$
$$=6$$

93. $\left(\sqrt{x}-3\right)^2=\left(\sqrt{x}\right)^2-2\cdot\sqrt{x}\cdot 3+3^2=x-6\sqrt{x}+9$

94. $\left(\sqrt{5}-5\right)\left(2\sqrt{5}+2\right)=2\sqrt{25}+2\sqrt{5}-10\sqrt{5}-10$
$$=2(5)-8\sqrt{5}-10$$
$$=10-8\sqrt{5}-10$$
$$=-8\sqrt{5}$$

95. $\left(2\sqrt{x}-3\sqrt{y}\right)\left(2\sqrt{x}+3\sqrt{y}\right)$
$$=\left(2\sqrt{x}\right)^2-\left(3\sqrt{y}\right)^2$$
$$=2^2\left(\sqrt{x}\right)^2-3^2\left(\sqrt{y}\right)^2$$
$$=4x-9y$$

96. $\left(\sqrt{a}+3\right)\left(\sqrt{a}-3\right)=\left(\sqrt{a}\right)^2-(3)^2=a-9$

97. $\left(\sqrt[3]{a}+2\right)^2=\left(\sqrt[3]{a}\right)^2+2\cdot\sqrt[3]{a}\cdot 2+2^2$
$$=\sqrt[3]{a^2}+4\sqrt[3]{a}+4$$

98. $\left(\sqrt[3]{5x}+9\right)\left(\sqrt[3]{5x}-9\right)=\left(\sqrt[3]{5x}\right)^2-9^2$
$$=\sqrt[3]{(5x)^2}-81$$
$$=\sqrt[3]{25x^2}-81$$

99. $\left(\sqrt[3]{a}+4\right)\left(\sqrt[3]{a^2}-4\sqrt[3]{a}+16\right)$
$$=\left(\sqrt[3]{a}\right)\left(\sqrt[3]{a^2}\right)-4\cdot\left(\sqrt[3]{a}\right)^2+16\sqrt[3]{a}+4\sqrt[3]{a^2}$$
$$\qquad -16\sqrt[3]{a}+64$$
$$=\sqrt[3]{a^3}-4\sqrt[3]{a^2}+4\sqrt[3]{a^2}+64$$
$$=a+64$$

100. $\dfrac{3}{\sqrt{7}}=\dfrac{3\cdot\sqrt{7}}{\sqrt{7}\cdot\sqrt{7}}=\dfrac{3\sqrt{7}}{7}$

101.
$$\sqrt{\frac{x}{12}} = \frac{\sqrt{x}}{\sqrt{12}}$$
$$= \frac{\sqrt{x}}{\sqrt{4 \cdot 3}}$$
$$= \frac{\sqrt{x}}{2\sqrt{3}}$$
$$= \frac{\sqrt{x} \cdot \sqrt{3}}{2\sqrt{3} \cdot \sqrt{3}}$$
$$= \frac{\sqrt{3x}}{2 \cdot 3}$$
$$= \frac{\sqrt{3x}}{6}$$

102.
$$\frac{5}{\sqrt[3]{4}} = \frac{5 \cdot \sqrt[3]{2}}{\sqrt[3]{4} \cdot \sqrt[3]{2}} = \frac{5\sqrt[3]{2}}{\sqrt[3]{8}} = \frac{5\sqrt[3]{2}}{2}$$

103.
$$\sqrt{\frac{24x^5}{3y^2}} = \sqrt{\frac{8x^5}{y^2}}$$
$$= \frac{\sqrt{8x^5}}{\sqrt{y^2}}$$
$$= \frac{\sqrt{4x^4 \cdot 2x}}{y}$$
$$= \frac{2x^2\sqrt{2x}}{y}$$

104.
$$\sqrt[3]{\frac{15x^6 y^7}{z^2}} = \frac{\sqrt[3]{15x^6 y^7}}{\sqrt[3]{z^2}}$$
$$= \frac{\sqrt[3]{15x^6 y^7} \cdot \sqrt[3]{z}}{\sqrt[3]{z^2} \cdot \sqrt[3]{z}}$$
$$= \frac{\sqrt[3]{15x^6 y^7 z}}{\sqrt[3]{z^3}}$$
$$= \frac{\sqrt[3]{15x^6 y^6 \cdot yz}}{z}$$
$$= \frac{x^2 y^2 \sqrt[3]{15yz}}{z}$$

105.
$$\frac{5}{2-\sqrt{7}} = \frac{5(2+\sqrt{7})}{(2-\sqrt{7})(2+\sqrt{7})}$$
$$= \frac{5(2+\sqrt{7})}{2^2 - (\sqrt{7})^2}$$
$$= \frac{10+5\sqrt{7}}{4-7}$$
$$= \frac{10+5\sqrt{7}}{-3}$$
$$= -\frac{10+5\sqrt{7}}{3}$$

106.
$$\frac{3}{\sqrt{y}-2} = \frac{3(\sqrt{y}+2)}{(\sqrt{y}-2)(\sqrt{y}+2)}$$
$$= \frac{3(\sqrt{y}+2)}{(\sqrt{y})^2 - 2^2}$$
$$= \frac{3\sqrt{y}+6}{y-4}$$

107.
$$\frac{\sqrt{2}-\sqrt{3}}{\sqrt{2}+\sqrt{3}} = \frac{(\sqrt{2}-\sqrt{3})(\sqrt{2}-\sqrt{3})}{(\sqrt{2}+\sqrt{3})(\sqrt{2}-\sqrt{3})}$$
$$= \frac{2-\sqrt{2}\sqrt{3}-\sqrt{3}\sqrt{2}+3}{(\sqrt{2})^2 - (\sqrt{3})^2}$$
$$= \frac{5-\sqrt{6}-\sqrt{6}}{2-3}$$
$$= \frac{5-2\sqrt{6}}{-1}$$
$$= -5+2\sqrt{6}$$

108.
$$\frac{\sqrt{11}}{3} = \frac{\sqrt{11} \cdot \sqrt{11}}{3 \cdot \sqrt{11}} = \frac{11}{3\sqrt{11}}$$

109.
$$\sqrt{\frac{18}{y}} = \frac{\sqrt{18}}{\sqrt{y}} = \frac{3\sqrt{2}}{\sqrt{y}} = \frac{3\sqrt{2} \cdot \sqrt{2}}{\sqrt{y} \cdot \sqrt{2}} = \frac{3 \cdot 2}{\sqrt{2y}} = \frac{6}{\sqrt{2y}}$$

110.
$$\frac{\sqrt[3]{9}}{7} = \frac{\sqrt[3]{9} \cdot \sqrt[3]{3}}{7 \cdot \sqrt[3]{3}} = \frac{\sqrt[3]{27}}{7\sqrt[3]{3}} = \frac{3}{7\sqrt[3]{3}}$$

111. $\sqrt{\dfrac{24x^5}{3y^2}} = \sqrt{\dfrac{8x^5}{y^2}}$

$\phantom{\sqrt{\dfrac{24x^5}{3y^2}}} = \dfrac{\sqrt{4x^4 \cdot 2x}}{\sqrt{y^2}}$

$\phantom{\sqrt{\dfrac{24x^5}{3y^2}}} = \dfrac{2x^2\sqrt{2x}}{y}$

$\phantom{\sqrt{\dfrac{24x^5}{3y^2}}} = \dfrac{2x^2\sqrt{2x} \cdot \sqrt{2x}}{y \cdot \sqrt{2x}}$

$\phantom{\sqrt{\dfrac{24x^5}{3y^2}}} = \dfrac{2x^2 \cdot 2x}{y\sqrt{2x}} = \dfrac{4x^3}{y\sqrt{2x}}$

112. $\sqrt[3]{\dfrac{xy^2}{10z}} = \dfrac{\sqrt[3]{xy^2}}{\sqrt[3]{10z}}$

$\phantom{\sqrt[3]{\dfrac{xy^2}{10z}}} = \dfrac{\sqrt[3]{xy^2} \cdot \sqrt[3]{x^2y}}{\sqrt[3]{10z} \cdot \sqrt[3]{x^2y}}$

$\phantom{\sqrt[3]{\dfrac{xy^2}{10z}}} = \dfrac{\sqrt[3]{x^3y^3}}{\sqrt[3]{10x^2yz}}$

$\phantom{\sqrt[3]{\dfrac{xy^2}{10z}}} = \dfrac{xy}{\sqrt[3]{10x^2yz}}$

113. $\dfrac{\sqrt{x}+5}{-3} = \dfrac{\left(\sqrt{x}+5\right)\left(\sqrt{x}-5\right)}{-3\left(\sqrt{x}-5\right)}$

$\phantom{\dfrac{\sqrt{x}+5}{-3}} = \dfrac{\left(\sqrt{x}\right)^2 - 5^2}{-3\sqrt{x}+15}$

$\phantom{\dfrac{\sqrt{x}+5}{-3}} = \dfrac{x-25}{-3\sqrt{x}+15}$

114. $\sqrt{y-7} = 5$

$\left(\sqrt{y-7}\right)^2 = 5^2$

$y - 7 = 25$

$y = 32$

The solution is 32.

115. $\sqrt{2x} + 10 = 4$

$\sqrt{2x} = -6$

No solution exists since the principle square root of a number is not negative.

116. $\sqrt[3]{2x-6} = 4$

$\left(\sqrt[3]{2x-6}\right)^3 = 4^3$

$2x - 6 = 64$

$2x = 70$

$x = 35$

The solution is 35.

117. $\sqrt{x+6} = \sqrt{x+2}$

$\left(\sqrt{x+6}\right)^2 = \left(\sqrt{x+2}\right)^2$

$x + 6 = x + 2$

$6 = 2,$ which is false.

There is no solution.

118. $2x - 5\sqrt{x} = 3$

$2x - 3 = 5\sqrt{x}$

$(2x-3)^2 = \left(5\sqrt{x}\right)^2$

$4x^2 - 12x + 9 = 25x$

$4x^2 - 37x + 9 = 0$

$(4x-1)(x-9) = 0$

$4x - 1 = 0 \ \text{ or } \ x - 9 = 0$

$4x = 1 \ \text{ or } \qquad x = 9$

$x = \dfrac{1}{4}$

Discard the solution $\dfrac{1}{4}$ as extraneous. The solution is 9.

119. $\sqrt{x+9} = 2 + \sqrt{x-7}$

$\left(\sqrt{x+9}\right)^2 = \left(2 + \sqrt{x-7}\right)^2$

$x + 9 = 4 + 4\sqrt{x-7} + (x-7)$

$x + 9 = x - 3 + 4\sqrt{x-7}$

$12 = 4\sqrt{x-7}$

$3 = \sqrt{x-7}$

$3^2 = \left(\sqrt{x-7}\right)^2$

$9 = x - 7$

$16 = x$

The solution is 16.

120. Let c = length of the hypotenuse.

$$3^2 + 3^2 = c^2$$
$$18 = c^2$$
$$\sqrt{18} = \sqrt{c^2}$$
$$3\sqrt{2} = c$$

The length is $3\sqrt{2}$ centimeters.

121. Let c = length of the hypotenuse.

$$7^2 + \left(8\sqrt{3}\right)^2 = c^2$$
$$49 + 64 \cdot 3 = c^2$$
$$241 = c^2$$
$$\sqrt{241} = \sqrt{c^2}$$
$$\sqrt{241} = c$$

The length is $\sqrt{241}$ feet.

122. Let b = width of the lake.

$$a^2 + b^2 = c^2$$
$$40^2 + b^2 = 65^2$$
$$1600 + b^2 = 4225$$
$$b^2 = 2625$$
$$\sqrt{b^2} = \sqrt{2625}$$
$$b = 51.23475$$

The width is about 51.2 feet.

123. Let c = length of the shortest pipe.

$$a^2 + b^2 = c^2$$
$$3^2 + 3^2 = c^2$$
$$18 = c^2$$
$$\sqrt{18} = \sqrt{c^2}$$
$$4.24264 = c$$

The shortest possible pipe is 4.24 feet.

124. $\sqrt{-8} = i\sqrt{4 \cdot 2} = 2i\sqrt{2}$

125. $-\sqrt{-6} = -i\sqrt{6}$

126. $\sqrt{-4} + \sqrt{-16} = 2i + 4i = 6i$

127. $\sqrt{-2} \cdot \sqrt{-5} = i\sqrt{2} \cdot i\sqrt{5}$
$$= i^2\sqrt{10}$$
$$= -1 \cdot \sqrt{10}$$
$$= -\sqrt{10}$$

128. $(12 - 6i) + (3 + 2i) = (12 + 3) + (-6 + 2)i$
$$= 15 + (-4)i$$
$$= 15 - 4i$$

129. $(-8 - 7i) - (5 - 4i) = -8 - 7i - 5 + 4i$
$$= -13 - 3i$$

130. $(2i)^6 = 2^6 i^6 = 64i^4 \cdot i^2 = 64(1)(-1) = -64$

131. $-3i(6 - 4i) = -18i + 12i^2$
$$= -18i + 12(-1)$$
$$= -12 - 18i$$

132. $(3 + 2i)(1 + i) = 3 + 3i + 2i + 2i^2$
$$= 3 + 5i + 2(-1)$$
$$= 1 + 5i$$

133. $(2 - 3i)^2 = 2^2 + 2 \cdot 2 \cdot (-3i) + (3i)^2$
$$= 4 - 12i + 9i^2$$
$$= 4 - 12i + 9(-1)$$
$$= -5 - 12i$$

134. $\left(\sqrt{6} - 9i\right)\left(\sqrt{6} + 9i\right) = \left(\sqrt{6}\right)^2 - (9i)^2$
$$= 6 - 81i^2$$
$$= 6 + 81$$
$$= 87$$

135. $\dfrac{2 + 3i}{2i} = \dfrac{(2 + 3i) \cdot (-2i)}{2i \cdot (-2i)}$
$$= \dfrac{-4i - 6i^2}{-4i^2}$$
$$= \dfrac{-4i + 6}{4}$$
$$= \dfrac{6}{4} - \dfrac{4}{4}i$$
$$= \dfrac{3}{2} - i$$

136. $\dfrac{1 + i}{-3i} = \dfrac{(1 + i) \cdot (3i)}{-3i \cdot (3i)}$
$$= \dfrac{3i + 3i^2}{-9i^2}$$
$$= \dfrac{3i - 3}{9}$$
$$= \dfrac{-3}{9} - \dfrac{3}{9}i$$
$$= -\dfrac{1}{3} + \dfrac{1}{3}i$$

137. $\sqrt[3]{x^3} = x$

138. $\sqrt{(x+2)^2} = |x+2|$

139. $-\sqrt{100} = -10$

140. $\sqrt[3]{-x^{12}y^3} = -x^4 y$

141. $\sqrt[4]{\dfrac{y^{20}}{16x^{12}}} = \dfrac{\sqrt[4]{y^{20}}}{\sqrt[4]{16x^{12}}} = \dfrac{y^5}{2x^3}$

142. $9^{1/2} = \sqrt{9} = 3$

143. $64^{-1/2} = \dfrac{1}{64^{1/2}} = \dfrac{1}{\sqrt{64}} = \dfrac{1}{8}$

144. $\left(\dfrac{27}{64}\right)^{-2/3} = \left(\dfrac{64}{27}\right)^{2/3}$

$\qquad = \left(\sqrt[3]{\dfrac{64}{27}}\right)^2$

$\qquad = \left(\dfrac{4}{3}\right)^2$

$\qquad = \dfrac{16}{9}$

145. $\dfrac{(x^{2/3}x^{-3})^3}{x^{-1/2}} = \dfrac{x^{6/3}x^{-9}}{x^{-1/2}}$

$\qquad = x^{2-9+\frac{1}{2}}$

$\qquad = x^{-13/2}$

$\qquad = \dfrac{1}{x^{13/2}}$

146. $\sqrt{200x^9} = \sqrt{100x^8 \cdot 2x} = 10x^4\sqrt{2x}$

147. $\sqrt{\dfrac{3n^3}{121m^{10}}} = \dfrac{\sqrt{3n^3}}{\sqrt{121m^{10}}} = \dfrac{\sqrt{n^2 \cdot 3n}}{\sqrt{121m^{10}}} = \dfrac{n\sqrt{3n}}{11m^5}$

148. $3\sqrt{20} - 7x\sqrt[3]{40} + 3\sqrt[3]{5x^3}$

$\qquad = 3\sqrt{4}\sqrt{5} - 7x\sqrt[3]{8}\sqrt[3]{5} + 3\sqrt[3]{x^3}\sqrt[3]{5}$

$\qquad = 6\sqrt{5} - 14x\sqrt[3]{5} + 3x\sqrt[3]{5}$

$\qquad = 6\sqrt{5} - 11x\sqrt[3]{5}$

149. $\left(2\sqrt{x} - 5\right)^2 = \left(2\sqrt{x}\right)^2 - 2(5)\left(2\sqrt{x}\right) + 5^2$

$\qquad = 4x - 20\sqrt{x} + 25$

150. $(x_1,\, y_1) = (-3,\, 5),\ (x_2,\, y_2) = (-8,\, 9)$

$d = \sqrt{(x_2 - x_1)^2 + (y_2 - y_1)^2}$

$\quad = \sqrt{(-8+3)^2 + (9-5)^2}$

$\quad = \sqrt{(-5)^2 + (4)^2}$

$\quad = \sqrt{25+16}$

$\quad = \sqrt{41}$

The distance is $\sqrt{41}$ units.

151. $(x_1,\, y_1) = (-3,\, 8),\ (x_2,\, y_2) = (11,\, 24)$

$\text{midpoint} = \left(\dfrac{x_1 + x_2}{2},\ \dfrac{y_1 + y_2}{2}\right)$

$\qquad = \left(\dfrac{-3+11}{2},\ \dfrac{8+24}{2}\right)$

$\qquad = \left(\dfrac{8}{2},\ \dfrac{32}{2}\right)$

$\qquad = (4,\, 16)$

152. $\dfrac{7}{\sqrt{13}} = \dfrac{7}{\sqrt{13}} \cdot \dfrac{\sqrt{13}}{\sqrt{13}} = \dfrac{7\sqrt{13}}{13}$

153. $\dfrac{2}{\sqrt{x}+3} = \dfrac{2}{\sqrt{x}+3} \cdot \dfrac{\sqrt{x}-3}{\sqrt{x}-3} = \dfrac{2\sqrt{x}-6}{x-9}$

154. $\sqrt{x} + 2 = x$

$\qquad \sqrt{x} = x - 2$

$\qquad \left(\sqrt{x}\right)^2 = (x-2)^2$

$\qquad\qquad x = x^2 - 4x + 4$

$\qquad\qquad 0 = x^2 - 5x + 4$

$\qquad\qquad 0 = (x-4)(x-1)$

$x - 4 = 0 \quad \text{or} \quad x - 1 = 0$

$\quad x = 4 \qquad\qquad x = 1$

Discard the extraneous solution 1. The solution set is $\{4\}$.

Chapter 7 Test

1. $\sqrt{216} = \sqrt{36 \cdot 6} = 6\sqrt{6}$

2. $-\sqrt[4]{x^{64}} = -x^{16}$

3. $\left(\dfrac{1}{125}\right)^{1/3} = \dfrac{1}{125^{1/3}} = \dfrac{1}{\sqrt[3]{125}} = \dfrac{1}{5}$

4. $\left(\dfrac{1}{125}\right)^{-1/3} = \dfrac{1}{\left(\frac{1}{125}\right)^{1/3}} = \dfrac{1}{\frac{1}{5}} = 5$

5. $\left(\dfrac{8x^3}{27}\right)^{2/3} = \dfrac{(8x^3)^{2/3}}{27^{2/3}}$

$= \dfrac{\left(\sqrt[3]{8x^3}\right)^2}{\left(\sqrt[3]{27}\right)^2}$

$= \dfrac{(2x)^2}{3^2}$

$= \dfrac{4x^2}{9}$

6. $\sqrt[3]{-a^{18}b^9} = \sqrt[3]{-1a^{18}b^9} = (-1)a^6b^3 = -a^6b^3$

7. $\left(\dfrac{64c^{4/3}}{a^{-2/3}b^{5/6}}\right)^{1/2} = \left(\dfrac{64a^{2/3}c^{4/3}}{b^{5/6}}\right)^{1/2}$

$= \dfrac{64^{1/2}(a^{2/3})^{1/2}(c^{4/3})^{1/2}}{(b^{5/6})^{1/2}}$

$= \dfrac{\sqrt{64}a^{1/3}c^{2/3}}{b^{5/12}}$

$= \dfrac{8a^{1/3}c^{2/3}}{b^{5/12}}$

8. $a^{-2/3}(a^{5/4} - a^3) = a^{-2/3}a^{5/4} - a^{-2/3}a^3$

$= a^{-\frac{2}{3}+\frac{5}{4}} - a^{-\frac{2}{3}+3}$

$= a^{-\frac{8}{12}+\frac{15}{12}} - a^{-\frac{2}{3}+\frac{9}{3}}$

$= a^{7/12} - a^{7/3}$

9. $\sqrt[4]{(4xy)^4} = |4xy| = 4|xy|$

10. $\sqrt[3]{(-27)^3} = -27$

11. $\sqrt{\dfrac{9}{y}} = \dfrac{\sqrt{9}}{\sqrt{y}} = \dfrac{3}{\sqrt{y}} = \dfrac{3\cdot\sqrt{y}}{\sqrt{y}\cdot\sqrt{y}} = \dfrac{3\sqrt{y}}{y}$

12. $\dfrac{4-\sqrt{x}}{4+2\sqrt{x}} = \dfrac{4-\sqrt{x}}{2\left(2+\sqrt{x}\right)}$

$= \dfrac{\left(4-\sqrt{x}\right)\left(2-\sqrt{x}\right)}{2\left(2+\sqrt{x}\right)\left(2-\sqrt{x}\right)}$

$= \dfrac{8-4\sqrt{x}-2\sqrt{x}+x}{2\left[2^2-\left(\sqrt{x}\right)^2\right]}$

$= \dfrac{8-6\sqrt{x}+x}{2(4-x)}$ or $\dfrac{8-6\sqrt{x}+x}{8-2x}$

13. $\dfrac{\sqrt[3]{ab}}{\sqrt[3]{ab^2}} = \sqrt[3]{\dfrac{ab}{ab^2}}$

$= \sqrt[3]{\dfrac{1}{b}}$

$= \dfrac{1}{\sqrt[3]{b}}$

$= \dfrac{1\cdot\sqrt[3]{b^2}}{\sqrt[3]{b}\cdot\sqrt[3]{b^2}}$

$= \dfrac{\sqrt[3]{b^2}}{b}$

14. $\dfrac{\sqrt{6}+x}{8} = \dfrac{\left(\sqrt{6}+x\right)\left(\sqrt{6}-x\right)}{8\left(\sqrt{6}-x\right)}$

$= \dfrac{\left(\sqrt{6}\right)^2 - x^2}{8\left(\sqrt{6}-x\right)}$

$= \dfrac{6-x^2}{8\left(\sqrt{6}-x\right)}$

15. $\sqrt{125x^3} - 3\sqrt{20x^3} = \sqrt{25x^2\cdot 5x} - 3\sqrt{4x^2\cdot 5x}$

$= 5x\sqrt{5x} - 3\cdot 2x\sqrt{5x}$

$= 5x\sqrt{5x} - 6x\sqrt{5x}$

$= -x\sqrt{5x}$

16. $\sqrt{3}\left(\sqrt{16}-\sqrt{2}\right) = \sqrt{3}\left(4-\sqrt{2}\right)$

$= 4\sqrt{3} - \sqrt{3}\sqrt{2}$

$= 4\sqrt{3} - \sqrt{6}$

17. $\left(\sqrt{x}+1\right)^2 = \left(\sqrt{x}\right)^2 + 2\sqrt{x} + 1^2$

$= x + 2\sqrt{x} + 1$

18. $\left(\sqrt{2}-4\right)\left(\sqrt{3}+1\right)=\sqrt{2}\sqrt{3}+1\cdot\sqrt{2}-4\sqrt{3}-4$
$$=\sqrt{6}+\sqrt{2}-4\sqrt{3}-4$$

19. $\left(\sqrt{5}+5\right)\left(\sqrt{5}-5\right)=\left(\sqrt{5}\right)^2-5^2$
$$=5-25$$
$$=-20$$

20. $\sqrt{561}\approx 23.685$

21. $386^{-2/3}\approx 0.019$

22.
$$x=\sqrt{x-2}+2$$
$$x-2=\sqrt{x-2}$$
$$(x-2)^2=\left(\sqrt{x-2}\right)^2$$
$$x^2-4x+4=x-2$$
$$x^2-5x+6=0$$
$$(x-2)(x-3)=0$$
$$x=2 \ \text{ or } \ x=3$$
The solutions are 2 and 3.

23. $\sqrt{x^2-7}+3=0$
$$\sqrt{x^2-7}=-3$$
No solution exists since the principle square root of a number is not negative.

24. $\sqrt[3]{x+5}=\sqrt[3]{2x-1}$
$$\left(\sqrt[3]{x+5}\right)^3=\left(\sqrt[3]{2x-1}\right)^3$$
$$x+5=2x-1$$
$$-x=-6$$
$$x=6$$
The solution is 6.

25. $\sqrt{-2}=i\sqrt{2}$

26. $-\sqrt{-8}=-i\sqrt{4\cdot 2}=-2i\sqrt{2}$

27. $(12-6i)-(12-3i)=12-6i-12+3i=-3i$

28. $(6-2i)(6+2i)=6^2-(2i)^2$
$$=36-4i^2$$
$$=36+4$$
$$=40$$

29. $(4+3i)^2=4^2+2\cdot 4\cdot 3i+(3i)^2$
$$=16+24i+9i^2$$
$$=16+24i-9$$
$$=7+24i$$

30. $\dfrac{1+4i}{1-i}=\dfrac{(1+4i)(1+i)}{(1-i)(1+i)}$
$$=\frac{1+i+4i+4i^2}{1^2-i^2}$$
$$=\frac{1+5i-4}{1-(-1)}$$
$$=\frac{-3+5i}{2}$$
$$=-\frac{3}{2}+\frac{5}{2}i$$

31. $x^2+x^2=5^2$
$$2x^2=25$$
$$x^2=\frac{25}{2}$$
$$\sqrt{x^2}=\sqrt{\frac{25}{2}}$$
$$x=\frac{5}{\sqrt{2}}=\frac{5\cdot\sqrt{2}}{\sqrt{2}\cdot\sqrt{2}}=\frac{5\sqrt{2}}{2}$$

32. $g(x)=\sqrt{x+2}$
$$x+2\geq 0$$
$$x\geq -2$$
Domain: $[-2, \infty)$

x	-2	-1	2	7
$g(x)$	0	1	2	3

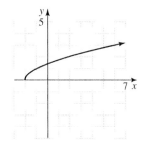

33. $(x_1, y_1) = (-6, 3), (x_2, y_2) = (-8, -7)$

$$d = \sqrt{(-8-(-6))^2 + (-7-3)^2}$$
$$= \sqrt{(-2)^2 + (-10)^2}$$
$$= \sqrt{4 + 100}$$
$$= \sqrt{104}$$
$$= \sqrt{4 \cdot 26}$$
$$= 2\sqrt{26}$$

The distance is $2\sqrt{26}$ units.

34. $(x_1, y_1) = \left(-2\sqrt{5}, \sqrt{10}\right),$
$(x_2, y_2) = \left(-\sqrt{5}, 4\sqrt{10}\right)$

$$d = \sqrt{(x_2 - x_1)^2 + (y_2 - y_1)^2}$$
$$= \sqrt{\left(-\sqrt{5} + 2\sqrt{5}\right)^2 + \left(4\sqrt{10} - \sqrt{10}\right)^2}$$
$$= \sqrt{\left(\sqrt{5}\right)^2 + \left(3\sqrt{10}\right)^2}$$
$$= \sqrt{5 + 90}$$
$$= \sqrt{95}$$

The distance is $\sqrt{95}$ units.

35. $(x_1, y_1) = (-2, -5), (x_2, y_2) = (-6, 12)$

$$\text{midpoint} = \left(\frac{x_1 + x_2}{2}, \frac{y_1 + y_2}{2}\right)$$
$$= \left(\frac{-2 - 6}{2}, \frac{-5 + 12}{2}\right)$$
$$= \left(-\frac{8}{2}, \frac{7}{2}\right)$$
$$= \left(-4, \frac{7}{2}\right)$$

36. $(x_1, y_1) = \left(-\frac{2}{3}, -\frac{1}{5}\right), (x_2, y_2) = \left(-\frac{1}{3}, \frac{4}{5}\right)$

$$\text{midpoint} = \left(\frac{x_1 + x_2}{2}, \frac{y_1 + y_2}{2}\right)$$
$$= \left(\frac{-\frac{2}{3} - \frac{1}{3}}{2}, \frac{-\frac{1}{5} + \frac{4}{5}}{2}\right)$$
$$= \left(\frac{-\frac{3}{3}}{2}, \frac{\frac{3}{5}}{2}\right)$$
$$= \left(-\frac{1}{2}, \frac{3}{10}\right)$$

37. $V(r) = \sqrt{2.5r}$
$$V(300) = \sqrt{2.5(300)} = \sqrt{750} \approx 27 \text{ mph}$$

38. $V(r) = \sqrt{2.5r}$
$$30 = \sqrt{2.5r}$$
$$30^2 = \left(\sqrt{2.5r}\right)^2$$
$$900 = 2.5r$$
$$r = \frac{900}{2.5} = 360 \text{ feet}$$

Chapter 7 Cumulative Review

1. a. $3xy - 2xy + 5 - 7 + xy = 2xy - 2$

   b. $7x^2 + 3 - 5(x^2 - 4) = 7x^2 + 3 - 5x^2 + 20$
$$= 2x^2 + 23$$

   c. $(2.1x - 5.6) - (-x - 5.3) = 2.1x - 5.6 + x + 5.3$
$$= 3.1x - 0.3$$

   d. $\frac{1}{2}(4a - 6b) - \frac{1}{3}(9a + 12b - 1) + \frac{1}{4}$
$$= 2a - 3b - 3a - 4b + \frac{1}{3} + \frac{1}{4}$$
$$= -a - 7b + \frac{4}{12} + \frac{3}{12}$$
$$= -a - 7b + \frac{7}{12}$$

2. a. $2(x - 3) + (5x + 3) = 2x - 6 + 5x + 3$
$$= 7x - 3$$

   b. $4(3x + 2) - 3(5x - 1) = 12x + 8 - 15x + 3$
$$= -3x + 11$$

   c. $7x + 2(x - 7) - 3x = 7x + 2x - 14 - 3x$
$$= 6x - 14$$

3. $\dfrac{x + 5}{2} + \dfrac{1}{2} = 2x - \dfrac{x - 3}{8}$
$$8\left(\frac{x + 5}{2} + \frac{1}{2}\right) = 8\left(2x - \frac{x - 3}{8}\right)$$
$$4(x + 5) + 4 = 16x - (x - 3)$$
$$4x + 20 + 4 = 16x - x + 3$$
$$4x + 24 = 15x + 3$$
$$-11x = -21$$
$$x = \frac{21}{11}$$

4.
$$\frac{a-1}{2} + a = 2 - \frac{2a+7}{8}$$
$$8\left(\frac{a-1}{2} + a\right) = 8\left(2 - \frac{2a+7}{8}\right)$$
$$4(a-1) + 8a = 16 - (2a+7)$$
$$4a - 4 + 8a = 16 - 2a - 7$$
$$12a - 4 = 9 - 2a$$
$$14a = 13$$
$$a = \frac{13}{14}$$

5. Let x = the sales needed.
$$600 + 0.20x > 1500$$
$$0.20x > 900$$
$$x > \frac{900}{0.20}$$
$$x > 4500$$
The salesperson needs sales of at least $4500.

6. Let r = their average speed.
$$t_{\text{going}} + t_{\text{returning}} = 4.5 \text{ hrs}$$
$$\frac{121.5}{r} + \frac{121.5}{r} = 4.5$$
$$\frac{243}{r} = 4.5$$
$$243 = 4.5r$$
$$r = \frac{243}{4.5} = 54$$
Their average speed was 54 mph.

7.
$$2|x| + 25 = 23$$
$$2|x| = -2$$
$$|x| = -1, \text{ which is impossible.}$$

There is no solution, or the solution set is $\varnothing$.

8.
$$|3x - 2| + 5 = 5$$
$$|3x - 2| = 0$$
$$3x - 2 = 0$$
$$3x = 2$$
$$x = \frac{2}{3}$$

9.
$$\left|\frac{x}{3} - 1\right| - 2 \geq 0$$
$$\left|\frac{x}{3} - 1\right| \geq 2$$
$$\frac{x}{3} - 1 \leq -2 \quad \text{or} \quad \frac{x}{3} - 1 \geq 2$$
$$\frac{x}{3} \leq -1 \quad \text{or} \quad \frac{x}{3} \geq 3$$
$$x \leq -3 \quad \text{or} \quad x \geq 9$$
$$(-\infty, -3] \cup [9, \infty)$$

10.
$$\left|\frac{x}{2} - 1\right| \leq 0$$
$$\frac{x}{2} - 1 = 0$$
$$\frac{x}{2} = 1$$
$$x = 2$$

11. $y = |x|$

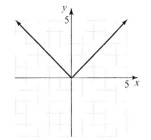

12. $y = |x - 2|$

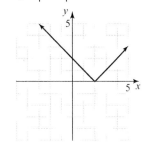

13. a. Domain: $\{2, 0, 3\}$
Range: $\{3, 4, -1\}$

b. Domain: $\{-4, -3, -2, -1, 0, 1, 2, 3\}$
Range: $\{1\}$

c. Domain: {Lubbock, Colorado Springs, Omaha, Yonkers, Sacramento}
Range: $\{307, 404, 445, 206, 197\}$

14. a. Domain: $(-\infty, 0]$, Range: $(-\infty, \infty)$

not a function

b. Domain: $(-\infty, \infty)$, Range: $(-\infty, \infty)$

function

c. Domain: $(-\infty, -2] \cup [2, \infty)$

Range: $(-\infty, \infty)$

not a function

15. $y = -3$

This is a horizontal line passing through $(0, -3)$.

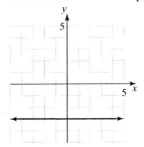

16. $f(x) = -2$

This is a horizontal line passing through $(0, -2)$.

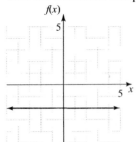

17. $x = -5$ is a vertical line. The slope is undefined.

18. $y = -3$ is a horizontal line. The slope is 0.

19. $\begin{cases} -\dfrac{x}{6} + \dfrac{y}{2} = \dfrac{1}{2} \\ \dfrac{x}{3} - \dfrac{y}{6} = -\dfrac{3}{4} \end{cases}$ or $\begin{cases} -x + 3y = 3 & (1) \\ 4x - 2y = -9 & (2) \end{cases}$

Solve equation (1) for x.

$-x + 3y = 3$

$3y - 3 = x$

Replace x with $3y - 3$ in equation (2).

$4(3y - 3) - 2y = -9$

$12y - 12 - 2y = -9$

$10y - 12 = -9$

$10y = 3$

$y = \dfrac{3}{10}$

Substitute $\dfrac{3}{10}$ for y in $x = 3y - 3$.

$x = 3\left(\dfrac{3}{10}\right) - 3 = \dfrac{9}{10} - \dfrac{30}{10} = -\dfrac{21}{10}$

The solution is $\left(-\dfrac{21}{10}, \dfrac{3}{10}\right)$.

20. $\begin{cases} \dfrac{x}{6} - \dfrac{y}{2} = 1 \\ \dfrac{x}{3} - \dfrac{y}{4} = 2 \end{cases}$ or $\begin{cases} x - 3y = 6 & (1) \\ 4x - 3y = 24 & (2) \end{cases}$

Solve equation (1) for x.

$x - 3y = 6$

$x = 3y + 6$

Replace x with $3y + 6$ in equation (2).

$4(3y + 6) - 3y = 24$

$12y + 24 - 3y = 24$

$9y + 24 = 24$

$9y = 0$

$y = 0$

Substitute 0 for y in $x = 3y + 6$.

$x = 3(0) + 6 = 0 + 6 = 6$

The solution is $(6, 0)$.

21. a. $2^2 \cdot 2^5 = 2^{2+5} = 2^7$

b. $x^7 x^3 = x^{7+3} = x^{10}$

c. $y \cdot y^2 \cdot y^4 = y^{1+2+4} = y^7$

22. Let $x = $ number of tee-shirts and
$y = $ number of shorts.

$\begin{cases} x + y = 9 & (1) \\ 3.50x + 4.25y = 33.75 & (2) \end{cases}$

Solve equation (1) for y.

$x + y = 9$

$y = 9 - x$

Substitute $9 - x$ for y in equation (2).

$3.50x + 4.25(9 - x) = 33.75$

$3.50x + 38.25 - 4.25x = 33.75$

$-0.75x + 38.25 = 33.75$

$-0.75x = -4.5$

$x = \dfrac{-4.5}{-0.75} = 6$

Replace x with 6 in $y = 9 - x$.

$y = 9 - 6 = 3$

Nana bought 6 shirts and 3 shorts.

23. $\dfrac{2000 \times 0.000021}{700} = \dfrac{(2 \times 10^3) \times (2.1 \times 10^{-5})}{7 \times 10^2}$

$\qquad\qquad\qquad = \dfrac{2(2.1)}{7} \times 10^{3+(-5)-2}$

$\qquad\qquad\qquad = 0.6 \times 10^{-4}$

$\qquad\qquad\qquad = (6 \times 10^{-1}) \times 10^{-4}$

$\qquad\qquad\qquad = 6 \times 10^{-5}$

24. $\dfrac{0.0000035 \times 4000}{0.28} = \dfrac{(3.5 \times 10^{-6}) \times (4 \times 10^3)}{2.8 \times 10^{-1}}$

$\qquad\qquad\qquad = \dfrac{3.5 \times 4}{2.8} \times 10^{-6+3-(-1)}$

$\qquad\qquad\qquad = 5 \times 10^{-2}$

25. $P(x) = 3x^2 - 2x - 5$

    a. $P(1) = 3(1)^2 - 2(1) - 5$

$\qquad\quad = 3(1) - 2(1) - 5$

$\qquad\quad = 3 - 2 - 5$

$\qquad\quad = -4$

    b. $P(-2) = 3(-2)^2 - 2(-2) - 5$

$\qquad\qquad = 3(4) - (-4) - 5$

$\qquad\qquad = 12 + 4 - 5$

$\qquad\qquad = 11$

26. $(5x^2 - 3x + 6) + (4x^2 + 5x - 3) - (2x - 5)$

$\quad = 5x^2 - 3x + 6 + 4x^2 + 5x - 3 - 2x + 5$

$\quad = 9x^2 + 8$

27. **a.** $(x+3)(2x+5) = 2x^2 + 5x + 6x + 15$

$\qquad\qquad\qquad\quad = 2x^2 + 11x + 15$

    b. $(2x-3)(5x^2 - 6x + 7)$

$\qquad = 10x^3 - 12x^2 + 14x - 15x^2 + 18x - 21$

$\qquad = 10x^3 - 27x^2 + 32x - 21$

28. **a.** $(y-2)(3y+4) = 3y^2 + 4y - 6y - 8$

$\qquad\qquad\qquad\quad = 3y^2 - 2y - 8$

    b. $(3y-1)(2y^2 + 3y - 1)$

$\qquad = 6y^3 + 9y^2 - 3y - 2y^2 - 3y + 1$

$\qquad = 6y^3 + 7y^2 - 6y + 1$

29. $20x^3 y = 2^2 \cdot 5x^3 y$

$\quad 10x^2 y^2 = 2 \cdot 5x^2 y^2$

$\quad 35x^3 = 5 \cdot 7x^3$

$\quad \text{GCF} = 5x^2$

30. $x^3 - x^2 + 4x - 4 = (x^3 - x^2) + (4x - 4)$

$\qquad\qquad\qquad\quad = x^2(x-1) + 4(x-1)$

$\qquad\qquad\qquad\quad = (x-1)(x^2 + 4)$

31. **a.** $\dfrac{x^3 + 8}{2 + x} = \dfrac{x^3 + 2^3}{x + 2}$

$\qquad\qquad = \dfrac{(x+2)(x^2 - 2x + 4)}{x + 2}$

$\qquad\qquad = x^2 - 2x + 4$

    b. $\dfrac{2y^2 + 2}{y^3 - 5y^2 + y - 5} = \dfrac{2(y^2 + 1)}{y^2(y-5) + 1(y-5)}$

$\qquad\qquad\qquad\qquad = \dfrac{2(y^2 + 1)}{(y-5)(y^2 + 1)}$

$\qquad\qquad\qquad\qquad = \dfrac{2}{y - 5}$

32. **a.** $\dfrac{a^3 - 8}{2 - a} = \dfrac{a^3 - 2^3}{2 - a}$

$\qquad\qquad = \dfrac{(a-2)(a^2 + 2a + 4)}{-1(a-2)}$

$\qquad\qquad = -1(a^2 + 2a + 4)$

$\qquad\qquad = -a^2 - 2a - 4$

    b. $\dfrac{3a^2 - 3}{a^3 + 5a^2 - a - 5} = \dfrac{3(a^2 - 1)}{a^2(a+5) - 1(a+5)}$

$\qquad\qquad\qquad\qquad = \dfrac{3(a^2 - 1)}{(a+5)(a^2 - 1)}$

$\qquad\qquad\qquad\qquad = \dfrac{3}{a + 5}$

33. **a.** $\dfrac{2}{x^2 y} + \dfrac{5}{3x^3 y} = \dfrac{2 \cdot 3x}{x^2 y \cdot 3x} + \dfrac{5}{3x^3 y}$

$\qquad\qquad\qquad = \dfrac{6x + 5}{3x^3 y}$

b. $\dfrac{3x}{x+2}+\dfrac{2x}{x-2}=\dfrac{3x(x-2)+2x(x+2)}{(x+2)(x-2)}$

$\qquad\qquad =\dfrac{3x^2-6x+2x^2+4x}{(x+2)(x-2)}$

$\qquad\qquad =\dfrac{5x^2-2x}{(x+2)(x-2)}$

c. $\dfrac{2x-6}{x-1}-\dfrac{4}{1-x}=\dfrac{2x-6}{x-1}+\dfrac{4}{x-1}$

$\qquad\qquad =\dfrac{2x-2}{x-1}$

$\qquad\qquad =\dfrac{2(x-1)}{x-1}$

$\qquad\qquad =2$

34. a. $\dfrac{3}{xy^2}-\dfrac{2}{3x^2y}=\dfrac{3\cdot 3x}{xy^2\cdot 3x}-\dfrac{2\cdot y}{3x^2y\cdot y}$

$\qquad\qquad =\dfrac{9x-2y}{3x^2y^2}$

b. $\dfrac{5x}{x+3}-\dfrac{2x}{x-3}=\dfrac{5x(x-3)-2x(x+3)}{(x+3)(x-3)}$

$\qquad\qquad =\dfrac{5x^2-15x-2x^2-6x}{(x+3)(x-3)}$

$\qquad\qquad =\dfrac{3x^2-21x}{(x+3)(x-3)}$

$\qquad\qquad$ or $\dfrac{3x(x-7)}{(x+3)(x-3)}$

c. $\dfrac{x}{x-2}-\dfrac{5}{2-x}=\dfrac{x}{x-2}+\dfrac{5}{x-2}=\dfrac{x+5}{x-2}$

35. a. $\dfrac{\frac{5x}{x+2}}{\frac{10}{x-2}}=\dfrac{5x}{x+2}\cdot\dfrac{x-2}{10}=\dfrac{x(x-2)}{2(x+2)}$

b. $\dfrac{\frac{x}{y^2}+\frac{1}{y}}{\frac{y}{x^2}+\frac{1}{x}}=\dfrac{\left(\frac{x}{y^2}+\frac{1}{y}\right)x^2y^2}{\left(\frac{y}{x^2}+\frac{1}{x}\right)x^2y^2}$

$\qquad\qquad =\dfrac{x^3+x^2y}{y^3+xy^2}$

$\qquad\qquad =\dfrac{x^2(x+y)}{y^2(y+x)}$

$\qquad\qquad =\dfrac{x^2}{y^2}$

36. a. $\dfrac{\frac{y-2}{16}}{\frac{2y+3}{12}}=\dfrac{y-2}{16}\cdot\dfrac{12}{2y+3}=\dfrac{3(y-2)}{4(2y+3)}$

b. $\dfrac{\frac{x}{16}-\frac{1}{x}}{1-\frac{4}{x}}=\dfrac{\left(\frac{x}{16}-\frac{1}{x}\right)16x}{\left(1-\frac{4}{x}\right)16x}$

$\qquad\qquad =\dfrac{x^2-16}{16x-64}$

$\qquad\qquad =\dfrac{(x+4)(x-4)}{16(x-4)}$

$\qquad\qquad =\dfrac{x+4}{16}$

37. $\dfrac{10x^3-5x^2+20x}{5x}=\dfrac{10x^3}{5x}-\dfrac{5x^2}{5x}+\dfrac{20x}{5x}$

$\qquad\qquad =2x^2-x+4$

38.

$$\begin{array}{r}
x^2+3 \\
x-2\overline{\smash{)}x^3-2x^2+3x-6} \\
\underline{x^3-2x^2} \\
3x-6 \\
\underline{3x-6} \\
0
\end{array}$$

Answer: x^2+3

39. $\begin{array}{r|rrrr} 3 & 2 & -1 & -13 & 1 \\ & & 6 & 15 & 6 \\ \hline & 2 & 5 & 2 & 7 \end{array}$

Answer: $2x^2+5x+2+\dfrac{7}{x-3}$

40. $\begin{array}{r|rrrr} 3 & 4 & -12 & -1 & 12 \\ & & 12 & 0 & -3 \\ \hline & 4 & 0 & -1 & 9 \end{array}$

Answer: $4y^2-1+\dfrac{9}{y-3}$

41. $\dfrac{x+6}{x-2}=\dfrac{2(x+2)}{x-2}$

$(x-2)\left(\dfrac{x+6}{x-2}\right)=(x-2)\left[\dfrac{2(x+2)}{x-2}\right]$

$\qquad x+6=2(x+2)$

$\qquad x+6=2x+4$

$\qquad\qquad -x=-2$

$\qquad\qquad\quad x=2$

which we discard as extraneous. There is no solution.

42.

$$\frac{28}{9-a^2} = \frac{2a}{a-3} + \frac{6}{a+3}$$

$$\frac{28}{-(a^2-9)} = \frac{2a}{a-3} + \frac{6}{a+3}$$

$$\frac{-28}{(a+3)(a-3)} = \frac{2a}{a-3} + \frac{6}{a+3}$$

$$(a+3)(a-3) \cdot \frac{-28}{(a+3)(a-3)} = (a+3)(a-3) \cdot \left(\frac{2a}{a-3} + \frac{6}{a+3}\right)$$

$$-28 = 2a(a+3) + 6(a-3)$$

$$-28 = 2a^2 + 6a + 6a - 18$$

$$0 = 2a^2 + 12a + 10$$

$$0 = 2(a^2 + 6a + 5)$$

$$0 = 2(a+5)(a+1)$$

$a = -5$ or $a = -1$

The solutions are -5 and -1.

43.

$$\frac{1}{x} + \frac{1}{y} = \frac{1}{z}$$

$$xyz\left(\frac{1}{x} + \frac{1}{y}\right) = xyz\left(\frac{1}{z}\right)$$

$$yz + xz = xy$$

$$yz = xy - xz$$

$$yz = x(y - z)$$

$$x = \frac{yz}{y - z}$$

44.

$$A = \frac{h(a+b)}{2}$$

$$2A = h(a+b)$$

$$2A = ah + bh$$

$$2A - bh = ah$$

$$\frac{2A - bh}{h} = a$$

45. $u = \dfrac{k}{w}$

$3 = \dfrac{k}{5}$

$k = 3(5) = 15$

$u = \dfrac{15}{w}$

46. $y = kx$

$0.51 = k(3)$

$k = \dfrac{0.51}{3} = 0.17$

$y = 0.17x$

47. a. $16^{-3/4} = \dfrac{1}{16^{3/4}} = \dfrac{1}{\left(\sqrt[4]{16}\right)^3} = \dfrac{1}{(2)^3} = \dfrac{1}{8}$

   b. $(-27)^{-2/3} = \dfrac{1}{(-27)^{2/3}}$

                     $= \dfrac{1}{\left(\sqrt[3]{-27}\right)^2}$

                     $= \dfrac{1}{(-3)^2}$

                     $= \dfrac{1}{9}$

48. a. $81^{-3/4} = \dfrac{1}{81^{3/4}} = \dfrac{1}{\left(\sqrt[4]{81}\right)^3} = \dfrac{1}{(3)^3} = \dfrac{1}{27}$

   b. $(-125)^{-2/3} = \dfrac{1}{(-125)^{2/3}}$

                     $= \dfrac{1}{\left(\sqrt[3]{-125}\right)^2}$

                     $= \dfrac{1}{(-5)^2}$

                     $= \dfrac{1}{25}$

49. $\dfrac{\sqrt{x}+2}{5} = \dfrac{\left(\sqrt{x}+2\right)\left(\sqrt{x}-2\right)}{5\left(\sqrt{x}-2\right)}$

           $= \dfrac{\left(\sqrt{x}\right)^2 - 2^2}{5\left(\sqrt{x}-2\right)}$

           $= \dfrac{x-4}{5\left(\sqrt{x}-2\right)}$

50. a. $\sqrt{36a^3} - \sqrt{144a^3} + \sqrt{4a^3}$

        $= \sqrt{36a^2 \cdot a} - \sqrt{144a^2 \cdot a} + \sqrt{4a^2 \cdot a}$

        $= 6a\sqrt{a} - 12a\sqrt{a} + 2a\sqrt{a}$

        $= -4a\sqrt{a}$

   b. $\sqrt[3]{128ab^3} - 3\sqrt[3]{2ab^3} + b\sqrt[3]{16a}$

        $= \sqrt[3]{64b^3 \cdot 2a} - 3\sqrt[3]{b^3 \cdot 2a} + b\sqrt[3]{8 \cdot 2a}$

        $= 4b\sqrt[3]{2a} - 3b\sqrt[3]{2a} + 2b\sqrt[3]{2a}$

        $= 3b\sqrt[3]{2a}$

   c. $\dfrac{\sqrt[3]{81}}{10} + \sqrt[3]{\dfrac{192}{125}} = \dfrac{\sqrt[3]{27 \cdot 3}}{10} + \dfrac{\sqrt[3]{192}}{\sqrt[3]{125}}$

                      $= \dfrac{3\sqrt[3]{3}}{10} + \dfrac{\sqrt[3]{64 \cdot 3}}{5}$

                      $= \dfrac{3\sqrt[3]{3}}{10} + \dfrac{4\sqrt[3]{3}}{5}$

                      $= \dfrac{3\sqrt[3]{3}}{10} + \dfrac{4\sqrt[3]{3} \cdot 2}{5 \cdot 2} = \dfrac{11\sqrt[3]{3}}{10}$

Chapter 8

Practice Exercises

1. $x^2 = 18$

   $x = \pm\sqrt{18}$

   $x = \pm 3\sqrt{2}$

   Check:

   Let $x = 3\sqrt{2}$.　　　Let $x = -3\sqrt{2}$.

   　$x^2 = 18$　　　　　$x^2 = 18$

   $\left(3\sqrt{2}\right)^2 \overset{?}{=} 18$　　$\left(-3\sqrt{2}\right)^2 \overset{?}{=} 18$

   　$9 \cdot 2 \overset{?}{=} 18$　　　$9 \cdot 2 \overset{?}{=} 18$

   　$18 = 18$　True　　$18 = 18$　True

   The solutions are $3\sqrt{2}$ and $-3\sqrt{2}$, or the

   solution set is $\left\{-3\sqrt{2},\, 3\sqrt{2}\right\}$.

2. First we get the squared variable alone on one side of the equation.

   $3x^2 - 30 = 0$

   　$3x^2 = 30$

   　　$x^2 = 10$

   　　$x = \pm\sqrt{10}$

   The solutions are $\sqrt{10}$ and $-\sqrt{10}$, or the

   solution set is $\left\{-\sqrt{10},\, \sqrt{10}\right\}$.

3. $(x+3)^2 = 20$

   $x + 3 = \pm\sqrt{20}$

   $x + 3 = \pm 2\sqrt{5}$

   　$x = -3 \pm 2\sqrt{5}$

   Check:

   　　　$(x+3)^2 = 20$

   $\left(-3 + 2\sqrt{5} + 3\right)^2 \overset{?}{=} 20$

   　　　$\left(2\sqrt{5}\right)^2 \overset{?}{=} 20$

   　　　　$4 \cdot 5 \overset{?}{=} 20$

   　　　　　$20 = 20$　True

   　　　$(x+3)^2 = 20$

   $\left(-3 - 2\sqrt{5} + 3\right)^2 \overset{?}{=} 20$

   　　　$\left(-2\sqrt{5}\right)^2 \overset{?}{=} 20$

   　　　　$4 \cdot 5 \overset{?}{=} 20$

   　　　　$20 = 20$　True

   The solutions are $-3 + 2\sqrt{5}$ and $-3 - 2\sqrt{5}$.

4. $(5x-2)^2 = -9$

   $5x - 2 = \pm\sqrt{-9}$

   $5x - 2 = \pm 3i$

   　$5x = 2 \pm 3i$

   　　$x = \dfrac{2 \pm 3i}{5}$

   The solutions are $\dfrac{2+3i}{5}$ and $\dfrac{2-3i}{5}$.

5. $b^2 + 4b = 3$

   Add the square of half the coefficient of b to both sides.

   $b^2 + 4b + \left(\dfrac{4}{2}\right)^2 = 3 + \left(\dfrac{4}{2}\right)^2$

   　　$b^2 + 4b + 4 = 7$

   　　　$(b+2)^2 = 7$

   　　　　$b + 2 = \pm\sqrt{7}$

   　　　　　$b = -2 \pm \sqrt{7}$

   The solutions are $-2 + \sqrt{7}$ and $-2 - \sqrt{7}$.

6. $p^2 - 3p + 1 = 0$

   Subtract 1 from both sides.

   $p^2 - 3p = -1$

   Add the square of half the coefficient of p to both sides.

$$p^2 - 3p + \left(\frac{-3}{2}\right)^2 = -1 + \left(\frac{-3}{2}\right)^2$$

$$p^2 - 3p + \frac{9}{4} = -1 + \frac{9}{4} = \frac{5}{4}$$

$$\left(p - \frac{3}{2}\right)^2 = \frac{5}{4}$$

$$p - \frac{3}{2} = \pm\frac{\sqrt{5}}{2}$$

$$p = \frac{3 \pm \sqrt{5}}{2}$$

The solutions are $\dfrac{3 + \sqrt{5}}{2}$ and $\dfrac{3 - \sqrt{5}}{2}$.

7. $3x^2 - 12x + 1 = 0$

Divide both sides by 3.

$$3x^2 - 12x + 1 = 0$$

$$x^2 - 4x + \frac{1}{3} = 0$$

$$x^2 - 4x = -\frac{1}{3}$$

Find the square of half of -4.

$$\left(\frac{-4}{2}\right)^2 = (-2)^2 = 4$$

Add 4 to both sides of the equation.

$$x^2 - 4x + 4 = -\frac{1}{3} + 4$$

$$(x - 2)^2 = -\frac{1}{3} + \frac{12}{3} = \frac{11}{3}$$

$$x - 2 = \pm\sqrt{\frac{11}{3}} = \pm\frac{\sqrt{33}}{3}$$

$$x = \frac{6}{3} \pm \frac{\sqrt{33}}{3} = \frac{6 \pm \sqrt{33}}{3}$$

The solutions are $\dfrac{6 + \sqrt{33}}{3}$ and $\dfrac{6 - \sqrt{33}}{3}$.

8. $2x^2 - 5x + 7 = 0$

$$2x^2 - 5x = -7$$

$$x^2 - \frac{5}{2}x = -\frac{7}{2}$$

Since $\dfrac{1}{2}\left(-\dfrac{5}{2}\right) = -\dfrac{5}{4}$ and $\left(-\dfrac{5}{4}\right)^2 = \dfrac{25}{16}$, we add

$\dfrac{25}{16}$ to both sides of the equation.

$$x^2 - \frac{5}{2}x + \frac{25}{16} = -\frac{7}{2} + \frac{25}{16}$$

$$\left(x - \frac{5}{4}\right)^2 = -\frac{56}{16} + \frac{25}{16} = -\frac{31}{16}$$

$$x - \frac{5}{4} = \pm\sqrt{-\frac{31}{16}}$$

$$x = \frac{5}{4} \pm \frac{i\sqrt{31}}{4} = \frac{5 \pm i\sqrt{31}}{4}$$

The solutions are $\dfrac{5 + i\sqrt{31}}{4}$ and $\dfrac{5 - i\sqrt{31}}{4}$.

9. $A = P(1 + r)^t$; $A = 5618$, $P = 5000$, $t = 2$

$$A = P(1 + r)^t$$

$$5618 = 5000(1 + r)^2$$

$$1.1236 = (1 + r)^2$$

$$\pm\sqrt{1.1236} = 1 + r$$

$$-1 \pm 1.06 = r$$

$$0.06 = r \text{ or } -2.06 = r$$

The rate cannot be negative, so we reject -2.06.

Check: $A = 5000(1 + 0.06)^2$

$$= 5000(1.06)^2$$

$$= 5000 \cdot 1.1236$$

$$= 5618$$

The interest rate is 6% compounded annually.

Exercise Set 8.1

2. $x^2 = 49$

$$x = \pm\sqrt{49}$$

$$x = \pm 7$$

4. $x^2 - 11 = 0$

$$x^2 = 11$$

$$x = \pm\sqrt{11}$$

6. $y^2 = 20$

$$y = \pm\sqrt{20}$$

$$y = \pm 2\sqrt{5}$$

8. $2x^2 - 4 = 0$

$$2x^2 = 4$$

$$x^2 = 2$$

$$x = \pm\sqrt{2}$$

10. $(y-3)^2 = 4$

$$y-3 = \pm\sqrt{4}$$
$$y-3 = \pm 2$$
$$y = 3 \pm 2$$
$$y = 1 \text{ or } y = 5$$

12. $(y+4)^2 = 27$

$$y+4 = \pm\sqrt{27}$$
$$y+4 = \pm 3\sqrt{3}$$
$$y = -4 \pm 3\sqrt{3}$$

14. $(4x+9)^2 = 6$

$$4x+9 = \pm\sqrt{6}$$
$$4x = -9 \pm \sqrt{6}$$
$$x = \frac{-9 \pm \sqrt{6}}{4}$$

16. $x^2 + 4 = 0$

$$x^2 = -4$$
$$x = \pm\sqrt{-4}$$
$$x = \pm 2i$$

18. $y^2 - 10 = 0$

$$y^2 = 10$$
$$y = \pm\sqrt{10}$$

20. $3p^2 + 36 = 0$

$$3p^2 = -36$$
$$p^2 = -12$$
$$p = \pm\sqrt{-12}$$
$$p = \pm 2i\sqrt{3}$$

22. $(y+2)^2 = -25$

$$y+2 = \pm\sqrt{-25}$$
$$y+2 = \pm 5i$$
$$y = -2 \pm 5i$$

24. $(x+10)^2 = 11$

$$x+10 = \pm\sqrt{11}$$
$$x = -10 \pm \sqrt{11}$$

26. $(y-4)^2 = -18$

$$y-4 = \pm\sqrt{-18}$$
$$y-4 = \pm 3i\sqrt{2}$$
$$y = 4 \pm 3i\sqrt{2}$$

28. $y^2 + 2y + \left(\dfrac{2}{2}\right)^2 = y^2 + 2y + 1$

$$= (y+1)^2$$

30. $x^2 - 8x + \left(\dfrac{-8}{2}\right)^2 = x^2 - 8x + 16$

$$= (x-4)^2$$

32. $n^2 + 5n + \left(\dfrac{5}{2}\right)^2 = n^2 + 5n + \dfrac{25}{4}$

$$= \left(n + \frac{5}{2}\right)^2$$

34. $y^2 - y + \left(\dfrac{-1}{2}\right)^2 = y^2 - y + \dfrac{1}{4}$

$$= \left(y - \frac{1}{2}\right)^2$$

36. $y^2 + 6y = -8$

$$y^2 + 6y + \left(\frac{6}{2}\right)^2 = -8 + 9$$
$$y^2 + 6y + 9 = 1$$
$$(y+3)^2 = 1$$
$$y+3 = \pm\sqrt{1}$$
$$y = -3 \pm 1$$
$$y = -4 \text{ or } y = -2$$

38. $x^2 - 2x - 2 = 0$

$$x^2 - 2x = 2$$
$$x^2 - 2x + \left(\frac{-2}{2}\right)^2 = 2 + 1$$
$$x^2 - 2x + 1 = 3$$
$$(x-1)^2 = 3$$
$$x-1 = \pm\sqrt{3}$$
$$x = 1 \pm \sqrt{3}$$

40.
$$x^2 + 3x - 2 = 0$$
$$x^2 + 3x = 2$$
$$x^2 + 3x + \left(\frac{3}{2}\right)^2 = 2 + \frac{9}{4}$$
$$x^2 + 3x + \frac{9}{4} = \frac{17}{4}$$
$$\left(x + \frac{3}{2}\right)^2 = \frac{17}{4}$$
$$x + \frac{3}{2} = \pm\sqrt{\frac{17}{4}}$$
$$x = -\frac{3}{2} \pm \frac{\sqrt{17}}{2} = \frac{-3 \pm \sqrt{17}}{2}$$

42.
$$y^2 + y - 7 = 0$$
$$y^2 + y = 7$$
$$y^2 + y + \left(\frac{1}{2}\right)^2 = 7 + \frac{1}{4}$$
$$y^2 + y + \frac{1}{4} = \frac{29}{4}$$
$$\left(y + \frac{1}{2}\right)^2 = \frac{29}{4}$$
$$y + \frac{1}{2} = \pm\sqrt{\frac{29}{4}}$$
$$y = -\frac{1}{2} \pm \frac{\sqrt{29}}{2} = \frac{-1 \pm \sqrt{29}}{2}$$

44.
$$2x^2 + 14x - 1 = 0$$
$$2x^2 + 14x = 1$$
$$x^2 + 7x = \frac{1}{2}$$
$$x^2 + 7x + \left(\frac{7}{2}\right)^2 = \frac{1}{2} + \frac{49}{4}$$
$$\left(x + \frac{7}{2}\right)^2 = \frac{51}{4}$$
$$x + \frac{7}{2} = \pm\sqrt{\frac{51}{4}}$$
$$x = -\frac{7}{2} \pm \frac{\sqrt{51}}{2} = \frac{-7 \pm \sqrt{51}}{2}$$

46.
$$6x^2 - 3 = 6x$$
$$6x^2 - 6x = 3$$
$$x^2 - x = \frac{1}{2}$$
$$x^2 - x + \left(\frac{-1}{2}\right)^2 = \frac{1}{2} + \frac{1}{4}$$
$$x^2 - x + \frac{1}{4} = \frac{3}{4}$$
$$\left(x - \frac{1}{2}\right)^2 = \frac{3}{4}$$
$$x - \frac{1}{2} = \pm\sqrt{\frac{3}{4}}$$
$$x = \frac{1}{2} \pm \frac{\sqrt{3}}{2} = \frac{1 \pm \sqrt{3}}{2}$$

48.
$$3x^2 - 4x = 4$$
$$x^2 - \frac{4}{3}x = \frac{4}{3}$$
$$x^2 - \frac{4}{3}x + \left(\frac{\frac{4}{3}}{2}\right)^2 = \frac{4}{3} + \frac{4}{9}$$
$$x^2 - \frac{4}{3}x + \frac{4}{9} = \frac{16}{9}$$
$$\left(x - \frac{2}{3}\right)^2 = \frac{16}{9}$$
$$x - \frac{2}{3} = \pm\sqrt{\frac{16}{9}}$$
$$x = \frac{2}{3} \pm \frac{4}{3}$$
$$x = -\frac{2}{3}, 2$$

50.
$$y^2 + 6y - 8 = 0$$
$$y^2 + 6y = 8$$
$$y^2 + 6y + \left(\frac{6}{2}\right)^2 = 8 + 9$$
$$y^2 + 6y + 9 = 17$$
$$(y + 3)^2 = 17$$
$$y + 3 = \pm\sqrt{17}$$
$$y = -3 \pm \sqrt{17}$$

52.
$$x^2 - 10x + 2 = 0$$
$$x^2 - 10x = -2$$
$$x^2 - 10 + \left(\frac{-10}{2}\right)^2 = -2 + 25$$
$$x^2 - 10x + 25 = 23$$
$$(x-5)^2 = 23$$
$$x - 5 = \pm\sqrt{23}$$
$$x = 5 \pm \sqrt{23}$$

54.
$$2y^2 + 12y + 3 = 0$$
$$2y^2 + 12y = -3$$
$$y^2 + 6y = -\frac{3}{2}$$
$$y^2 + 6y + \left(\frac{6}{2}\right)^2 = -\frac{3}{2} + 9$$
$$y^2 + 6y + 9 = \frac{15}{2}$$
$$(y+3)^2 = \frac{15}{2}$$
$$y + 3 = \pm\sqrt{\frac{15}{2}}$$
$$y + 3 = \pm\frac{\sqrt{15} \cdot \sqrt{2}}{\sqrt{2} \cdot \sqrt{2}}$$
$$y + 3 = \pm\frac{\sqrt{30}}{2}$$
$$y = -3 \pm \frac{\sqrt{30}}{2} = \frac{-6 \pm \sqrt{30}}{2}$$

56.
$$5x^2 + 3x - 2 = 0$$
$$5x^2 + 3x = 2$$
$$x^2 + \frac{3}{5}x = \frac{2}{5}$$
$$x^2 + \frac{3}{5}x + \left(\frac{\frac{3}{5}}{2}\right)^2 = \frac{2}{5} + \frac{9}{100}$$
$$x^2 + \frac{3}{5}x + \frac{9}{100} = \frac{49}{100}$$
$$\left(x + \frac{3}{10}\right)^2 = \frac{49}{100}$$
$$x + \frac{3}{10} = \pm\sqrt{\frac{49}{100}}$$
$$x = -\frac{3}{10} \pm \frac{7}{10}$$
$$x = \frac{-3 \pm 7}{10} = -1, \frac{2}{5}$$

58.
$$x^2 + 4x + 6 = 0$$
$$x^2 + 4x = -6$$
$$x^2 + 4x + \left(\frac{4}{2}\right)^2 = -6 + 4$$
$$x^2 + 4x + 4 = -2$$
$$(x+2)^2 = -2$$
$$x + 2 = \pm\sqrt{-2}$$
$$x = -2 \pm i\sqrt{2}$$

60.
$$x^2 - 7x - 1 = 0$$
$$x^2 - 7x = 1$$
$$x^2 - 7x + \left(\frac{-7}{2}\right)^2 = 1 + \frac{49}{4}$$
$$x^2 - 7x + \frac{49}{4} = \frac{53}{4}$$
$$\left(x - \frac{7}{2}\right)^2 = \frac{53}{4}$$
$$x - \frac{7}{2} = \pm\sqrt{\frac{53}{4}}$$
$$x = \frac{7}{2} \pm \frac{\sqrt{53}}{2} = \frac{7 \pm \sqrt{53}}{2}$$

62.
$$3x^2 + 12x = -14$$
$$x^2 + 4x = -\frac{14}{3}$$
$$x^2 + 4x + \left(\frac{4}{2}\right)^2 = -\frac{14}{3} + 4$$
$$x^2 + 4x + 4 = -\frac{2}{3}$$
$$(x+2)^2 = -\frac{2}{3}$$
$$x + 2 = \pm\sqrt{-\frac{2}{3}}$$
$$x + 2 = \pm\frac{i\sqrt{2}\cdot\sqrt{3}}{\sqrt{3}\cdot\sqrt{3}}$$
$$x = -2 \pm i\frac{\sqrt{6}}{3} = -\frac{6 \pm i\sqrt{6}}{3}$$

64.
$$y^2 + 8y + 18 = 0$$
$$y^2 + 8y = -18$$
$$y^2 + 8y + \left(\frac{8}{2}\right)^2 = -18 + 16$$
$$(y+4)^2 = -2$$
$$y + 4 = \pm\sqrt{-2}$$
$$y = -4 \pm i\sqrt{2}$$

66.
$$y^2 + y - 2 = 0$$
$$y^2 + y = 2$$
$$y^2 + y + \left(\frac{1}{2}\right)^2 = 2 + \frac{1}{4}$$
$$y^2 + y + \frac{1}{4} = \frac{9}{4}$$
$$\left(y + \frac{1}{2}\right)^2 = \frac{9}{4}$$
$$y + \frac{1}{2} = \pm\sqrt{\frac{9}{4}}$$
$$y = -\frac{1}{2} \pm \frac{3}{2}$$
$$y = -2, 1$$

68.
$$9x^2 - 36x = -40$$
$$x^2 - 4x = -\frac{40}{9}$$
$$x^2 - 4x + \left(\frac{-4}{2}\right)^2 = -\frac{40}{9} + 4$$
$$x^2 - 4x + 4 = -\frac{4}{9}$$
$$(x-2)^2 = -\frac{4}{9}$$
$$x - 2 = \pm\sqrt{-\frac{4}{9}}$$
$$x - 2 = \pm\frac{2}{3}i$$
$$x = 2 \pm \frac{2}{3}i = \frac{6 \pm 2i}{3}$$

70.
$$5y^2 - 15y = 1$$
$$y^2 - 3y = \frac{1}{5}$$
$$y^2 - 3y + \left(\frac{-3}{2}\right)^2 = \frac{1}{5} + \frac{9}{4}$$
$$y^2 - 3y + \frac{9}{4} = \frac{49}{20}$$
$$\left(y - \frac{3}{2}\right)^2 = \frac{49}{20}$$
$$y - \frac{3}{2} = \pm\sqrt{\frac{49}{20}}$$
$$y - \frac{3}{2} = \pm\frac{7}{2\sqrt{5}}$$
$$y - \frac{3}{2} = \pm\frac{7\cdot\sqrt{5}}{2\sqrt{5}\cdot\sqrt{5}}$$
$$y - \frac{3}{2} = \pm\frac{7\sqrt{5}}{10}$$
$$y = \frac{3}{2} \pm \frac{7\sqrt{5}}{10} = \frac{15 \pm 7\sqrt{5}}{10}$$

72. The graph has two *x*-intercepts. Thus, the equation has two real number solutions.

74. The graph has no *x*-intercepts. Thus, the equation has no real number solutions.

76.
$$A = P(1+r)^t$$
$$882 = 800(1+r)^2$$
$$\frac{882}{800} = (1+r)^2$$
$$1.1025 = (1+r)^2$$
$$\pm\sqrt{1.1025} = 1+r$$
$$\pm 1.05 = 1+r$$
$$-1 \pm 1.05 = r$$
$$-2.05 = r \text{ or } 0.05 = r$$
Rate cannot be negative, so the rate is 0.05 or 5%.

78.
$$A = P(1+r)^t$$
$$2880 = 2000(1+r)^2$$
$$\frac{2880}{2000} = (1+r)^2$$
$$1.44 = (1+r)^2$$
$$\pm\sqrt{1.44} = 1+r$$
$$-1 \pm 1.2 = r$$
$$-2.2 = r \text{ or } 0.2 = r$$
Rate cannot be negative, so the rate is 0.2 or 20%.

80. $s(t) = 16t^2$
$$1483 = 16t^2$$
$$t^2 = \frac{1483}{16}$$
$$t = \pm\sqrt{\frac{1483}{16}}$$
$$t \approx 9.63 \text{ or } -9.63 \text{ (disregard)}$$
It would take 9.63 seconds.

82. $s(t) = 16t^2$
$$984 = 16t^2$$
$$t^2 = \frac{984}{16}$$
$$t = \pm\sqrt{\frac{984}{16}}$$
$$t \approx 7.84 \text{ or } -7.84 \text{ (disregard)}$$
It would take 7.84 seconds.

84. Compound; answers may vary.

86. $\dfrac{3}{4} - \sqrt{\dfrac{25}{16}} = \dfrac{3}{4} - \dfrac{5}{4} = -\dfrac{2}{4} = -\dfrac{1}{2}$

88. $\dfrac{1}{2} - \sqrt{\dfrac{9}{4}} = \dfrac{1}{2} - \dfrac{3}{2} = -\dfrac{2}{2} = -1$

90. $\dfrac{6+4\sqrt{5}}{2} = \dfrac{6}{2} + \dfrac{4\sqrt{5}}{2} = 3 + 2\sqrt{5}$

92. $\dfrac{3-9\sqrt{2}}{6} = \dfrac{3}{6} - \dfrac{9\sqrt{2}}{6} = \dfrac{1}{2} - \dfrac{3\sqrt{2}}{2} = \dfrac{1-3\sqrt{2}}{2}$

94.
$$\sqrt{b^2 - 4ac} = \sqrt{(4)^2 - 4(2)(-1)}$$
$$= \sqrt{16+8}$$
$$= \sqrt{24}$$
$$= 2\sqrt{6}$$

96.
$$\sqrt{b^2 - 4ac} = \sqrt{(-1)^2 - 4(3)(-2)}$$
$$= \sqrt{1+24}$$
$$= \sqrt{25}$$
$$= 5$$

98. The solutions of $(x+1)^2 = -1$ are complex, but not real numbers; answers may vary.

100. The solutions of $3z^2 = 10$ are real; answers may vary.

102. The solutions of $(2y-5)^2 + 7 = 3$ are complex, but not real numbers; answers may vary.

104. $x^2 + \underline{} + 16$
$$\left(\frac{b}{2}\right)^2 = 16$$
$$\frac{b}{2} = \pm\sqrt{16}$$
$$\frac{b}{2} = \pm 4$$
$$b = \pm 8$$
Answer: $\pm 8x$

106. $z^2 + \underline{} + \dfrac{25}{4}$
$$\left(\frac{b}{2}\right)^2 = \frac{25}{4}$$
$$\frac{b}{2} = \pm\sqrt{\frac{25}{4}}$$
$$\frac{b}{2} = \pm\frac{5}{2}$$
$$b = \pm 5$$
Answer: $\pm 5z$

108.
$$A = s^2$$
$$225 = s^2$$
$$\pm\sqrt{225} = s^2$$
$$s = 15 \text{ or } -15 \text{ (disregard)}$$
The dimensions are 15 ft by 15 ft.

110. $a^2 + b^2 = c^2$
$$x^2 + x^2 = 20^2$$
$$2x^2 = 400$$
$$x^2 = 200$$
$$x = \pm\sqrt{200}$$
$$x = \pm 10\sqrt{2}$$
$$x = 10\sqrt{2} \text{ or } -10\sqrt{2} \text{ (disregard)}$$
The side of each leg is $10\sqrt{2}$ cm.

112. $p = -x^2 + 47$
$$11 = -x^2 + 47$$
$$x^2 = 36$$
$$x = \pm\sqrt{36}$$
$$x = \pm 6$$
Demand cannot be negative. Therefore, the demand is 6 thousand scissors.

Section 8.2

Practice Exercises

1. $3x^2 - 5x - 2 = 0$
$$a = 3, b = -5, c = -2$$
$$x = \frac{-b \pm \sqrt{b^2 - 4ac}}{2a}$$
$$= \frac{-(-5) \pm \sqrt{(-5)^2 - 4(3)(-2)}}{2(3)}$$
$$= \frac{5 \pm \sqrt{25 + 24}}{6}$$
$$= \frac{5 \pm \sqrt{49}}{6}$$
$$= \frac{5 \pm 7}{6}$$
$$x = \frac{5+7}{6} = \frac{12}{6} = 2 \text{ or } x = \frac{5-7}{6} = \frac{-2}{6} = -\frac{1}{3}$$

The solutions are $-\frac{1}{3}$ and 2, or the solution set is $\left\{-\frac{1}{3}, 2\right\}$.

2. $3x^2 - 8x = 2$
Write in standard form.
$$3x^2 - 8x - 2 = 0$$
$$a = 3, b = -8, c = -2$$
$$x = \frac{-b \pm \sqrt{b^2 - 4ac}}{2a}$$
$$= \frac{-(-8) \pm \sqrt{(-8)^2 - 4(3)(-2)}}{2(3)}$$
$$= \frac{8 \pm \sqrt{64 + 24}}{6}$$
$$= \frac{8 \pm \sqrt{88}}{6}$$
$$= \frac{8 \pm 2\sqrt{22}}{6}$$
$$= \frac{4 \pm \sqrt{22}}{3}$$

The solutions are $\frac{4 + \sqrt{22}}{3}$ and $\frac{4 - \sqrt{22}}{3}$, or the solution set is $\left\{\frac{4 + \sqrt{22}}{3}, \frac{4 - \sqrt{22}}{3}\right\}$.

3. $\frac{1}{8}x^2 - \frac{1}{4}x - 2 = 0$
Multiply both sides of the equation by 8.
$$8\left(\frac{1}{8}x^2 - \frac{1}{4}x - 2\right) = 8 \cdot 0$$
$$x^2 - 2x - 16 = 0$$
Substitute $a = 1$, $b = -2$, and $c = -16$ into the quadratic formula and simplify.
$$x = \frac{-(-2) \pm \sqrt{(-2)^2 - 4(1)(-16)}}{2(1)}$$
$$= \frac{2 \pm \sqrt{4 + 64}}{2}$$
$$= \frac{2 \pm \sqrt{68}}{2}$$
$$= \frac{2 \pm 2\sqrt{17}}{2}$$
$$= 1 \pm \sqrt{17}$$
The solutions are $1 + \sqrt{17}$ or $1 - \sqrt{17}$.

4. $x = -2x^2 - 2$

The equation in standard form is

$2x^2 + x + 2 = 0$. Thus, let $a = 2$, $b = 1$, and $c = 2$ in the quadratic formula.

$x = \dfrac{-1 \pm \sqrt{1^2 - 4(2)(2)}}{2(2)}$

$= \dfrac{-1 \pm \sqrt{1 - 16}}{4}$

$= \dfrac{-1 \pm \sqrt{-15}}{4}$

$= \dfrac{-1 \pm i\sqrt{15}}{4}$

The solutions are $\dfrac{-1 + i\sqrt{15}}{4}$ and $\dfrac{-1 - i\sqrt{15}}{4}$.

5. a. $x^2 - 6x + 9 = 0$

In $x^2 - 6x + 9$, $a = 1$, $b = -6$, and $c = 9$. Thus,

$b^2 - 4ac = (-6)^2 - 4(1)(9) = 36 - 36 = 0$

Since $b^2 - 4ac = 0$, this equation has one real solution.

b. $x^2 - 3x - 1 = 0$

In this equation, $a = 1$, $b = -3$, and $c = -1$.

$b^2 - 4ac = (-3)^2 - 4(1)(-1) = 9 + 4 = 13 > 0$

Since $b^2 - 4ac$ is positive, this equation has two real solutions.

c. $7x^2 + 11 = 0$

In this equation, $a = 7$, $b = 0$, and $c = 11$.

$b^2 - 4ac = 0^2 - 4(7)(11) = -308 < 0$

Since $b^2 - 4ac$ is negative, this equation has two complex but not real solutions.

6. By the Pythagorean theorem, we have

$x^2 + (x + 3)^2 = 15^2$

$x^2 + x^2 + 6x + 9 = 225$

$2x^2 + 6x - 216 = 0$

$x^2 + 3x - 108 = 0$

Here, $a = 1$, $b = 3$, and $c = -108$. By the quadratic formula,

$x = \dfrac{-3 \pm \sqrt{3^2 - 4(1)(-108)}}{2(1)}$

$= \dfrac{-3 \pm \sqrt{9 + 432}}{2}$

$= \dfrac{-3 \pm \sqrt{441}}{2}$

$= \dfrac{-3 \pm 21}{2}$

$x = \dfrac{-3 + 21}{2} = \dfrac{18}{2} = 9$ or

$x = \dfrac{-3 - 21}{2} = \dfrac{-24}{2} = -12$

The length can't be negative, so reject -12. The distance along the sidewalk is

$x + (x + 3) = 2x + 3 = 2(9) + 3 = 18 + 3 = 21$ feet

A person can save $21 - 15 = 6$ feet by cutting across the lawn.

7. $h = -16t^2 + 20t + 45$

At the ground, $h = 0$.

$0 = -16t^2 + 20t + 45$

Here, $a = -16$, $b = 20$, and $c = 45$. By the quadratic formula,

$t = \dfrac{-20 \pm \sqrt{20^2 - 4(-16)(45)}}{2(-16)}$

$= \dfrac{-20 \pm \sqrt{400 + 2880}}{-32}$

$= \dfrac{-20 \pm \sqrt{3280}}{-32}$

$= \dfrac{20 \pm \sqrt{16 \cdot 205}}{32}$

$= \dfrac{20 \pm 4\sqrt{205}}{32}$

$= \dfrac{5 \pm \sqrt{205}}{8}$

$t = \dfrac{5 + \sqrt{205}}{8} \approx 2.4$ or $t = \dfrac{5 - \sqrt{205}}{8} \approx -1.2$

Since the time won't be negative, we reject -1.2. The rocket will strike the ground 2.4 seconds after launch.

Vocabulary and Readiness Check

1. The quadratic formula is $x = \dfrac{-b \pm \sqrt{b^2 - 4ac}}{2a}$.

2. For $2x^2 + x + 1 = 0$, if $a = 2$, then $b = \underline{1}$ and $c = \underline{1}$.

3. For $5x^2 - 5x - 7 = 0$, if $a = 5$, then $b = \underline{-5}$ and $c = \underline{-7}$.

4. For $7x^2 - 4 = 0$, if $a = 7$, then $b = \underline{0}$ and $c = \underline{-4}$.

5. For $x^2 + 9 = 0$, if $c = 9$, then $a = \underline{1}$ and $b = \underline{0}$.

6. The correct simplified form of $\dfrac{5 \pm 10\sqrt{2}}{5}$ is $1 \pm 2\sqrt{2}$. The answer is **c.**

Exercise Set 8.2

2. $p^2 + 11p - 12 = 0$
$a = 1, b = 11, c = -12$

$$p = \frac{-11 \pm \sqrt{(11)^2 - 4(1)(-12)}}{2(1)}$$
$$= \frac{-11 \pm \sqrt{169}}{2}$$
$$= \frac{-11 \pm 13}{2} = -12 \text{ or } 1$$

The solutions are -12 and 1.

4. $5x^2 - 3 = 14x$
$5x^2 - 14x - 3 = 0$
$a = 5, b = -14, c = -3$

$$x = \frac{14 \pm \sqrt{(-14)^2 - 4(5)(-3)}}{2(5)}$$
$$= \frac{14 \pm \sqrt{256}}{10}$$
$$= \frac{14 \pm 16}{10} = -\frac{1}{5} \text{ or } 3$$

The solutions are $-\dfrac{1}{5}$ and 3.

6. $y^2 + 10y + 25 = 0$
$a = 1, b = 10, c = 25$

$$y = \frac{-10 \pm \sqrt{(10)^2 - 4(1)(25)}}{2(1)}$$
$$= \frac{-10 \pm \sqrt{0}}{2}$$
$$= \frac{-10}{2} = -5$$

The solution is -5.

8. $y^2 + 5y + 3 = 0$
$a = 1, b = 5, c = 3$

$$y = \frac{-5 \pm \sqrt{(5)^2 - 4(1)(3)}}{2(1)} = \frac{-5 \pm \sqrt{13}}{2}$$

The solutions are $\dfrac{-5 + \sqrt{13}}{2}$ and $\dfrac{-5 - \sqrt{13}}{2}$.

10. $11n^2 - 9n = 1$
$11n^2 - 9n - 1 = 0$
$a = 11, b = -9, c = -1$

$$n = \frac{9 \pm \sqrt{(-9)^2 - 4(11)(-1)}}{2(11)}$$
$$= \frac{9 \pm \sqrt{125}}{22}$$
$$= \frac{9 \pm 5\sqrt{5}}{22}$$

The solutions are $\dfrac{9 + 5\sqrt{5}}{22}$ and $\dfrac{9 - 5\sqrt{5}}{22}$.

12. $x^2 - 13 = 5x$
$x^2 - 5x - 13 = 0$
$a = 1, b = -5, c = -13$

$$x = \frac{5 \pm \sqrt{(-5)^2 - 4(1)(-13)}}{2(1)}$$
$$= \frac{5 \pm \sqrt{77}}{2}$$

The solutions are $\dfrac{5 + \sqrt{77}}{2}$ and $\dfrac{5 - \sqrt{77}}{2}$.

14. $\dfrac{1}{6}x^2 + x + \dfrac{1}{3} = 0$

$x^2 + 6x + 2 = 0$

$a = 1, b = 6, c = 2$

$x = \dfrac{-6 \pm \sqrt{(6)^2 - 4(1)(2)}}{2(1)}$

$= \dfrac{-6 \pm \sqrt{28}}{2}$

$= \dfrac{-6 \pm 2\sqrt{7}}{2}$

$= -3 \pm \sqrt{7}$

The solutions are $-3 + \sqrt{7}$ and $-3 - \sqrt{7}$.

16. $\dfrac{1}{8}x^2 + x = \dfrac{5}{2}$

$x^2 + 8x - 20 = 0$

$a = 1, b = 8, c = -20$

$x = \dfrac{-8 \pm \sqrt{(-8)^2 - 4(1)(-20)}}{2(1)}$

$= \dfrac{-8 \pm \sqrt{144}}{2}$

$= \dfrac{-8 \pm 12}{2} = -10$ or 2

The solutions are -10 and 2.

18. $\dfrac{1}{2}y^2 = y + \dfrac{1}{2}$

$y^2 - 2y - 1 = 0$

$a = 1, b = -2, c = -1$

$y = \dfrac{2 \pm \sqrt{(-2)^2 - 4(1)(-1)}}{2(1)}$

$= \dfrac{2 \pm \sqrt{8}}{2}$

$= \dfrac{2 \pm 2\sqrt{2}}{2} = 1 \pm \sqrt{2}$

The solutions are $1 + \sqrt{2}$ and $1 - \sqrt{2}$.

20. $y^2 - 8 = 4y$

$y^2 - 4y - 8 = 0$

$a = 1, b = -4, c = -8$

$y = \dfrac{4 \pm \sqrt{(-4)^2 - 4(1)(-8)}}{2(1)}$

$= \dfrac{4 \pm \sqrt{48}}{2}$

$= \dfrac{4 \pm 4\sqrt{3}}{2} = 2 \pm 2\sqrt{3}$

The solutions are $2 + 2\sqrt{3}$ and $2 - 2\sqrt{3}$.

22. $7p(p - 2) + 2(p + 4) = 3$

$7p^2 - 14p + 2p + 8 = 3$

$7p^2 - 12p + 5 = 0$

$a = 7, b = -12, c = 5$

$p = \dfrac{12 \pm \sqrt{(-12)^2 - 4(7)(5)}}{2(7)}$

$= \dfrac{12 \pm \sqrt{4}}{14}$

$= \dfrac{12 \pm 2}{14} = \dfrac{5}{7}$ or 1

The solutions are $\dfrac{5}{7}$ and 1.

24. $x^2 + 2x + 2 = 0$

$a = 1, b = 2, c = 2$

$x = \dfrac{-2 \pm \sqrt{(2)^2 - 4(1)(2)}}{2(1)}$

$= \dfrac{-2 \pm \sqrt{-4}}{2}$

$= \dfrac{-2 \pm 2i}{2} = -1 \pm i$

The solutions are $-1 + i$ and $-1 - i$.

26. $x(x + 6) = 2$

$x^2 + 6x - 2 = 0$

$a = 1, b = 6, c = -2$

$x = \dfrac{-6 \pm \sqrt{(6)^2 - 4(1)(-2)}}{2(1)}$

$= \dfrac{-6 \pm \sqrt{44}}{2}$

$= \dfrac{-6 \pm 2\sqrt{11}}{2} = -3 \pm \sqrt{11}$

The solutions are $-3 + \sqrt{11}$ and $-3 - \sqrt{11}$.

28.
$$2 = -9x^2 - x$$
$$9x^2 + x + 2 = 0$$
$$a = 9, b = 1, c = 2$$
$$x = \frac{-1 \pm \sqrt{(1)^2 - 4(9)(2)}}{2(9)}$$
$$= \frac{-1 \pm \sqrt{-71}}{18}$$
$$= \frac{-1 \pm i\sqrt{71}}{18}$$
The solutions are $\dfrac{-1 + i\sqrt{71}}{18}$ and $\dfrac{-1 - i\sqrt{71}}{18}$.

30.
$$\frac{x^2}{2} - 3 = -\frac{9}{2}x$$
$$x^2 + 9x - 6 = 0$$
$$a = 1, b = 9, c = -6$$
$$x = \frac{-9 \pm \sqrt{(9)^2 - 4(1)(-6)}}{2(1)}$$
$$= \frac{-9 \pm \sqrt{105}}{2}$$
The solutions are $\dfrac{-9 + \sqrt{105}}{2}$ and $\dfrac{-9 - \sqrt{105}}{2}$.

32. $3y^2 + 6y + 5 = 0$
$$a = 3, b = 6, c = 5$$
$$y = \frac{-6 \pm \sqrt{(6)^2 - 4(3)(5)}}{2(3)}$$
$$= \frac{-6 \pm \sqrt{-24}}{6}$$
$$= \frac{-6 \pm 2i\sqrt{6}}{6}$$
$$= \frac{-3 \pm i\sqrt{6}}{3}$$
The solutions are $\dfrac{-3 + i\sqrt{6}}{3}$ and $\dfrac{-3 - i\sqrt{6}}{3}$.

34. $x(7x + 1) = 2$
$$7x^2 + x - 2 = 0$$
$$a = 7, b = 1, c = -2$$
$$x = \frac{-1 \pm \sqrt{(1)^2 - 4(7)(-2)}}{2(7)}$$
$$= \frac{-1 \pm \sqrt{57}}{14}$$
The solutions are $\dfrac{-1 + \sqrt{57}}{14}$ and $\dfrac{-1 - \sqrt{57}}{14}$.

36.
$$\frac{1}{8}x^2 + x + \frac{5}{2} = 0$$
$$x^2 + 8x + 20 = 0$$
$$a = 1, b = 8, c = 20$$
$$x = \frac{-8 \pm \sqrt{(8)^2 - 4(1)(20)}}{2(1)}$$
$$= \frac{-8 \pm \sqrt{-16}}{2}$$
$$= \frac{-8 \pm 4i}{2} = -4 \pm 2i$$
The solutions are $-4 + 2i$ and $-4 - 2i$.

38.
$$\frac{2}{3}x^2 - \frac{20}{3}x = -\frac{100}{6}$$
$$4x^2 - 40x + 100 = 0$$
$$x^2 - 10x + 25 = 0$$
$$a = 1, b = -10, c = 25$$
$$x = \frac{10 \pm \sqrt{(-10)^2 - 4(1)(25)}}{2(1)}$$
$$= \frac{10 \pm \sqrt{0}}{2} = \frac{10}{2} = 5$$
The solution is 5.

40.
$$\left(p - \frac{1}{2}\right)^2 = \frac{p}{2}$$
$$p^2 - p + \frac{1}{4} = \frac{p}{2}$$
$$4p^2 - 4p + 1 = 2p$$
$$4p^2 - 6p + 1 = 0$$
$$a = 4, b = -6, c = 1$$

$$p = \frac{6 \pm \sqrt{(-6)^2 - 4(4)(1)}}{2(4)}$$

$$= \frac{6 \pm \sqrt{20}}{8}$$

$$= \frac{6 \pm 2\sqrt{5}}{8} = \frac{3 \pm \sqrt{5}}{4}$$

The solutions are $\dfrac{3 + \sqrt{5}}{4}$ and $\dfrac{3 - \sqrt{5}}{4}$.

42. $x^2 - 7 = 0$

$a = 1, b = 0, c = -7$

$b^2 - 4ac = 0^2 - 4(1)(-7) = 0 + 28 = 28 > 0$

Therefore, there are two real solutions.

44. $\qquad 9x^2 + 1 = 6x$

$9x^2 - 6x + 1 = 0$

$a = 9, b = -6, c = 1$

$b^2 - 4ac = (-6)^2 - 4(9)(1)$

$\qquad\qquad = 36 - 36$

$\qquad\qquad = 0$

Therefore, there is one real solution.

46. $\qquad\qquad 3x^2 = 5 - 7x$

$3x^2 + 7x - 5 = 0$

$a = 3, b = 7, c = -5$

$b^2 - 4ac = 7^2 - 4(3)(-5)$

$\qquad\qquad = 49 + 60$

$\qquad\qquad = 109 > 0$

Therefore, there are two real solutions.

48. $\quad 5 - 4x + 12x^2 = 0$

$12x^2 - 4x + 5 = 0$

$a = 12, b = -4, c = 5$

$b^2 - 4ac = (-4)^2 - 4(12)(5)$

$\qquad\qquad = 16 - 240$

$\qquad\qquad = -224 < 0$

Therefore, there are two complex but not real solutions.

50. a. The graph has no x-intercepts. Thus, the related equation has no real number solutions.

    b. The graph has two x-intercepts. Thus the related equation has two real number solutions.

52. $\qquad\qquad (x + 10)^2 + x^2 = 40^2$

$(x^2 + 20x + 100) + x^2 = 1600$

$\qquad 2x^2 + 20x - 1500 = 0$

$\qquad\quad x^2 + 10x - 750 = 0$

$a = 1, b = 10, c = -750$

$$x = \frac{-10 \pm \sqrt{(10)^2 - 4(1)(-750)}}{2(1)}$$

$$= \frac{-10 \pm \sqrt{3100}}{2}$$

$x \approx 23$ or $x \approx -33$ (disregard)

$x + (x + 10) = 23 + 23 + 10 = 56$

$56 - 40 = 16$

They saved about 16 feet of walking distance.

54. Let x = length of leg. Then $x + 1$ = length of hypotenuse.

$\qquad x^2 + x^2 = (x + 1)^2$

$\qquad\quad 2x^2 = x^2 + 2x + 1$

$x^2 - 2x - 1 = 0$

$a = 1, b = -2, c = -1$

$$x = \frac{2 \pm \sqrt{(-2)^2 - 4(1)(-1)}}{2(1)}$$

$$= \frac{2 \pm \sqrt{8}}{2}$$

$$= \frac{2 \pm 2\sqrt{2}}{2}$$

$= 1 \pm \sqrt{2}$ (disregard the negative)

$= 1 + \sqrt{2}$

The sides measure $1 + \sqrt{2}$ m, $1 + \sqrt{2}$ m, and $2 + \sqrt{2}$ m.

56. Let x = width; then $x + 20$ = length.

Area = length · width

$1200 = (x + 20)x$

$\quad 0 = x^2 + 20x - 1200$

$a = 1, b = 20, c = -1200$

$$x = \frac{-20 \pm \sqrt{(20)^2 - 4(1)(-1200)}}{2(1)}$$

$$= \frac{-20 \pm \sqrt{5200}}{2}$$

$$= \frac{-20 \pm 20\sqrt{13}}{2}$$

$= -10 \pm 10\sqrt{13}$

Disregard the negative length. The width is $-10 + 10\sqrt{13}$ in. and the length is $10 + 10\sqrt{13}$ in.

58. a. Let $x =$ width. Then $3x =$ length.

$$x^2 + (3x)^2 = 50^2$$
$$x^2 + 9x^2 = 2500$$
$$10x^2 - 2500 = 0$$
$$x^2 - 250 = 0$$
$$a = 1, b = 0, c = -250$$

$$x = \frac{0 \pm \sqrt{(0)^2 - 4(1)(-250)}}{2(1)}$$

$$= \frac{\pm\sqrt{1000}}{2}$$

$$= \frac{\pm 10\sqrt{10}}{2} = \pm 5\sqrt{10}$$

Disregard the negative width. The width is $5\sqrt{10}$ cm and the length is $15\sqrt{10}$ cm.

b. Perimeter $= 2l + 2w$

$$= 2\left(15\sqrt{10}\right) + 2\left(5\sqrt{10}\right)$$
$$= 40\sqrt{10} \text{ cm}$$

60. Let $w =$ width; then $w + 7.3 =$ length.

Area $=$ length $\cdot$ width

$$569.9 = (w + 7.3)w$$
$$0 = w^2 + 7.3w - 569.9$$
$$a = 1, b = 7.3, c = -569.9$$

$$w = \frac{-7.3 \pm \sqrt{(7.3)^2 - 4(1)(-569.9)}}{2(1)}$$

$$= \frac{-7.3 \pm \sqrt{2332.89}}{2}$$

$$= 20.5 \text{ or } -27.8 \text{ (disregard)}$$

Its width is 20.5 inches and its height is 27.8 inches.

62.

$$\frac{x-1}{1} = \frac{1}{x}$$
$$x(x-1) = 1$$
$$x^2 - x - 1 = 0$$
$$a = 1, b = -1, c = -1$$

$$x = \frac{1 \pm \sqrt{(-1)^2 - 4(1)(-1)}}{2(1)}$$

$$= \frac{1 \pm \sqrt{5}}{2} \text{ (disregard the negative)}$$

The value is $\dfrac{1+\sqrt{5}}{2}$.

64.

$$h = -16t^2 + 20t + 1100$$
$$550 = -16t^2 + 20t + 1100$$
$$0 = -16t^2 + 20t + 550$$
$$a = -16, b = 20, c = 550$$

$$t = \frac{-20 \pm \sqrt{(20)^2 - 4(-16)(550)}}{2(-16)}$$

$$= \frac{-20 \pm \sqrt{35,600}}{-32}$$

$$\approx 6.5 \text{ or } -5.3 \text{ (disregard)}$$

It will take about 6.5 seconds.

66.

$$h = -16t^2 - 20t + 180$$
$$50 = -16t^2 - 20t + 180$$
$$0 = -16t^2 - 20t + 130$$
$$a = -16, b = -20, c = 130$$

$$t = \frac{20 \pm \sqrt{(-20)^2 - 4(-16)(130)}}{2(-16)}$$

$$= \frac{20 \pm \sqrt{8720}}{-32}$$

$$\approx 2.3 \text{ or } -3.5 \text{ (disregard)}$$

It will take about 2.3 seconds.

68.

$$\sqrt{y+2} + 7 = 12$$
$$\sqrt{y+2} = 5$$
$$y + 2 = 5^2$$
$$y + 2 = 25$$
$$y = 23$$

70.

$$\frac{10}{z} = \frac{5}{z} - \frac{1}{3}$$
$$3z\left(\frac{10}{z}\right) = 3z\left(\frac{5}{z} - \frac{1}{3}\right)$$
$$30 = 15 - z$$
$$z = -15$$

72. $2y^4 + 11y^2 - 6 = (2y^2 - 1)(y^2 + 6)$

74. $x^4 - 1 = (x^2 + 1)(x^2 - 1)$
$$= (x^2 + 1)(x + 1)(x - 1)$$

76.

$$x^2 + 5 = -x$$
$$x^2 + x + 5 = 0$$
$$a = 1, b = 1, c = 5$$

The correct substitution is **d**.

78. $p^2 + 11p - 12 = 0$
$(p + 12)(p - 1) = 0$
$p + 12 = 0$ or $p - 1 = 0$
$p = -12$ or $p = 1$
The results are the same. Answers may vary.

80. $3.6x^2 + 1.8x - 4.3 = 0$
$a = 3.6, b = 1.8, c = -4.3$
$x = \dfrac{-1.8 \pm \sqrt{(1.8)^2 - 4(3.6)(-4.3)}}{2(3.6)}$
$= \dfrac{-1.8 \pm \sqrt{65.16}}{7.2}$
≈ -1.4 or 0.9

82.   From Friday to Saturday

84. $33°F$

86. $f(x) = 3x^2 - 18x + 56$
$35 = 3x^2 - 18x + 56$
$0 = 3x^2 - 18x + 21$
$0 = x^2 - 6x + 7$
$a = 1, b = -6, c = 7$
$x = \dfrac{6 \pm \sqrt{(-6)^2 - 4(1)(7)}}{2(1)}$
$= \dfrac{6 \pm \sqrt{8}}{2} \approx 4.4$ or 1.6

This means the temperature was $35°$ on Monday and Thursday. This agrees with the graph.

88. $v(x) = 0.25x^2 + 2.6x + 315.6$

   a. $x = 2005 - 2000 = 5$
$v(5) = 0.25(5)^2 + 2.6(5) + 315.6$
$= 334.85 \approx 335$
There were approximately 335 million visitors.

   b. $x = 2010 - 2000 = 10$
$v(10) = 0.25(10)^2 + 2.6(10) + 315.6$
$= 366.6 \approx 367$
There will be approximately 367 million visitors.

90. $\dfrac{-b + \sqrt{b^2 - 4ac}}{2a} \cdot \dfrac{-b - \sqrt{b^2 - 4ac}}{2a}$
$= \dfrac{\left(-b + \sqrt{b^2 - 4ac}\right)\left(-b - \sqrt{b^2 - 4ac}\right)}{4a^2}$
$= \dfrac{b^2 - (b^2 - 4ac)}{4a^2}$
$= \dfrac{4ac}{4a^2}$
$= \dfrac{c}{a}$

92. $5x^2 + \sqrt{20}x + 1 = 0$
$a = 5, b = \sqrt{20}, c = 1$
$x = \dfrac{-\sqrt{20} \pm \sqrt{\left(\sqrt{20}\right)^2 - 4(5)(1)}}{2(5)}$
$= \dfrac{-\sqrt{20} \pm \sqrt{0}}{10}$
$= \dfrac{-2\sqrt{5}}{10} = -\dfrac{\sqrt{5}}{5}$
The solution is $-\dfrac{\sqrt{5}}{5}$.

94. $x^2 - \sqrt{2}x + 1 = 0$
$a = 1, b = -\sqrt{2}, c = 1$
$x = \dfrac{\sqrt{2} \pm \sqrt{\left(-\sqrt{2}\right)^2 - 4(1)(1)}}{2(1)}$
$= \dfrac{\sqrt{2} \pm \sqrt{-2}}{2}$
$= \dfrac{\sqrt{2} \pm i\sqrt{2}}{2}$
The solutions are $\dfrac{\sqrt{2} + i\sqrt{2}}{2}$ and $\dfrac{\sqrt{2} - i\sqrt{2}}{2}$.

96. $7x^2 + \sqrt{7}x - 2 = 0$

$a = 7, b = \sqrt{7}, c = -2$

$$x = \frac{-\sqrt{7} \pm \sqrt{\left(\sqrt{7}\right)^2 - 4(7)(-2)}}{2(7)}$$

$$= \frac{-\sqrt{7} \pm \sqrt{63}}{14}$$

$$= \frac{-\sqrt{7} \pm 3\sqrt{7}}{14} = \frac{\sqrt{7}}{7} \text{ or } -\frac{2\sqrt{7}}{7}$$

The solutions are $\dfrac{\sqrt{7}}{7}$ and $-\dfrac{2\sqrt{7}}{7}$.

Section 8.3

Practice Exercises

1. $x - \sqrt{x+1} - 5 = 0$

Get the radical alone on one side of the equation. Then square both sides.

$$x - \sqrt{x+1} - 5 = 0$$

$$x - 5 = \sqrt{x+1}$$

$$(x-5)^2 = x+1$$

$$x^2 - 10x + 25 = x+1$$

$$x^2 - 11x + 24 = 0$$

$$(x-8)(x-3) = 0$$

$$x - 8 = 0 \quad \text{or} \quad x - 3 = 0$$

$$x = 8 \quad \text{or} \quad x = 3$$

Check:

Let $x = 3$.

$$x - \sqrt{x+1} - 5 = 0$$

$$3 - \sqrt{3+1} - 5 \stackrel{?}{=} 0$$

$$-2 - \sqrt{4} \stackrel{?}{=} 0$$

$$-2 - 2 \stackrel{?}{=} 0$$

$$-4 = 0 \quad \text{False}$$

Let $x = 8$.

$$x - \sqrt{x+1} - 5 = 0$$

$$8 - \sqrt{8+1} - 5 \stackrel{?}{=} 0$$

$$3 - \sqrt{9} \stackrel{?}{=} 0$$

$$3 - 3 \stackrel{?}{=} 0$$

$$0 = 0 \quad \text{True}$$

The solution is 8 or the solution set is $\{8\}$.

2. $\dfrac{5x}{x+1} - \dfrac{x+4}{x} = \dfrac{3}{x(x+1)}$

x cannot be either -1 or 0, because these values cause denominators to equal zero. Multiply both sides of the equation by $x(x + 1)$.

$$x(x+1)\left(\frac{5x}{x+1}\right) - x(x+1)\left(\frac{x+4}{x}\right) = x(x+1)\left[\frac{3}{x(x+1)}\right]$$

$$5x^2 - (x+1)(x+4) = 3$$

$$5x^2 - x^2 - 5x - 4 = 3$$

$$4x^2 - 5x - 7 = 0$$

Use the quadratic formula with $a = 4$, $b = -5$, and $c = -7$.

$$x = \frac{-(-5) \pm \sqrt{(-5)^2 - 4(4)(-7)}}{2(4)} = \frac{5 \pm \sqrt{25 + 112}}{8} = \frac{5 \pm \sqrt{137}}{8}$$

Neither proposed solution will make denominators 0. The solutions are $\dfrac{5 + \sqrt{137}}{8}$ and $\dfrac{5 - \sqrt{137}}{8}$ or the solution

set is $\left\{\dfrac{5 + \sqrt{137}}{8}, \dfrac{5 - \sqrt{137}}{8}\right\}$.

3.
$$p^4 - 7p^2 - 144 = 0$$

$$(p^2 + 9)(p^2 - 16) = 0$$

$$(p^2 + 9)(p + 4)(p - 4) = 0$$

$$p^2 + 9 = 0 \quad \text{or} \quad p + 4 = 0 \quad \text{or} \quad p - 4 = 0$$

$$p^2 = -9 \qquad\qquad p = -4 \qquad\quad p = 4$$

$$p = \pm\sqrt{-9}$$

$$p = \pm 3i$$

The solutions are 4, -4, $3i$, and $-3i$.

4. $(x+2)^2 - 2(x+2) - 3 = 0$

Let $y = x + 2$.

$$y^2 - 2y - 3 = 0$$

$$(y - 3)(y + 1) = 0$$

$$y - 3 = 0 \quad \text{or} \quad y + 1 = 0$$

$$y = 3 \qquad\qquad y = -1$$

Substitute $x + 2$ for y.

$$x + 2 = 3 \quad \text{or} \quad x + 2 = -1$$

$$x = 1 \qquad\qquad x = -3$$

Both 1 and -3 check. The solutions are 1 and -3.

5. $x^{2/3} - 5x^{1/3} + 4 = 0$

Let $m = x^{1/3}$.

$$m^2 - 5m + 4 = 0$$

$$(m - 4)(m - 1) = 0$$

$$m - 4 = 0 \quad \text{or} \quad m - 1 = 0$$

$$m = 4 \qquad\qquad m = 1$$

Since $m = x^{1/3}$, we have

$$x^{1/3} = 4 \qquad\qquad \text{or} \quad x^{1/3} = 1$$

$$x = 4^3 = 64 \qquad\qquad x = 1^3 = 1$$

Both 64 and 1 check. The solutions are 64 and 1.

6. Let $x =$ the time in hours it takes Steve to groom all the dogs. Then,
$x - 1 =$ the time it takes Katy to groom all the dogs.

The part of the job completed in one hour by Steve is $\dfrac{1}{x}$, and the part completed by Katy in one hour is $\dfrac{1}{x-1}$. In

one hour, $\dfrac{1}{4}$ of the job is completed. We have,

$$\frac{1}{x} + \frac{1}{x-1} = \frac{1}{4}$$

$$4x(x-1)\left(\frac{1}{x}\right) + 4x(x-1)\left(\frac{1}{x-1}\right) = 4x(x-1)\left(\frac{1}{4}\right)$$

$$4(x-1) + 4x = x(x-1)$$

$$4x - 4 + 4x = x^2 - x$$

$$0 = x^2 - 9x + 4$$

Use the quadratic formula with $a = 1$, $b = -9$, and $c = 4$.

$$x = \frac{-(-9) \pm \sqrt{(-9)^2 - 4(1)(4)}}{2(1)}$$

$$x = \frac{9 \pm \sqrt{81 - 16}}{2} = \frac{9 \pm \sqrt{65}}{2}$$

$x \approx 8.53$ or $x \approx 0.47$

Since $x - 1 = 0.47 - 1 = -0.53 < 0$, representing negative time worked, we reject 0.47. It takes Steve

$\dfrac{9 + \sqrt{65}}{2} \approx 8.5$ hours and Katy $\dfrac{9 + \sqrt{65}}{2} - 1 = \dfrac{7 + \sqrt{65}}{2} \approx 7.5$ hours to groom all the dogs when working alone.

7. Let $x =$ the speed driven to Shanghai. Then
$x + 50 =$ the speed driven to Ningbo.

	distance =	rate	·	time
To Shanghai	36	x		$\dfrac{36}{x}$
To Ningbo	36	$x + 50$		$\dfrac{36}{x+50}$

The total travel time was 1.3 hours, so

$$\frac{36}{x} + \frac{36}{x+50} = 1.3$$

$$x(x+50)\left(\frac{36}{x}\right) + x(x+50)\left(\frac{36}{x+50}\right) = 1.3x(x+50)$$

$$36(x+50) + 36x = 1.3x^2 + 65x$$

$$36x + 1800 + 36x = 1.3x^2 + 65x$$

$$0 = 1.3x^2 - 7x - 1800$$

Use the quadratic formula with $a = 1.3$, $b = -7$, and $c = -1800$.

$$x = \frac{-(-7) \pm \sqrt{(-7)^2 - 4(1.3)(-1800)}}{2(1.3)} = \frac{7 \pm \sqrt{9409}}{2.6}$$

$$x = \frac{7 + \sqrt{9409}}{2.6} = 40 \quad \text{or} \quad x = \frac{7 - \sqrt{9409}}{2.6} \approx -34.6$$

The speed is not negative, so reject -34.6. The speed to Shanghai was 40 km/hr and to Ningbo it was
$40 + 50 = 90$ km/hr.

Exercise Set 8.3

2.
$$3x = \sqrt{8x+1}$$
$$9x^2 = 8x+1$$
$$9x^2 - 8x - 1 = 0$$
$$(9x+1)(x-1) = 0$$
$$9x+1 = 0 \quad \text{or} \quad x-1 = 0$$
$$x = -\frac{1}{9} \quad \text{or} \quad x = 1$$
Discard $-\frac{1}{9}$. The solution is 1.

4.
$$x - \sqrt{2x} = 4$$
$$x - 4 = \sqrt{2x}$$
$$(x-4)^2 = 2x$$
$$x^2 - 8x + 16 = 2x$$
$$x^2 - 10x + 16 = 0$$
$$(x-8)(x-2) = 0$$
$$x - 8 = 0 \quad \text{or} \quad x - 2 = 0$$
$$x = 8 \quad \text{or} \quad x = 2 \text{ (discard)}$$
The solution is 8.

6.
$$\sqrt{16x} = x+3$$
$$16x = (x+3)^2$$
$$16x = x^2 + 6x + 9$$
$$0 = x^2 - 10x + 9$$
$$0 = (x-9)(x-1)$$
$$x - 9 = 0 \text{ or } x - 1 = 0$$
$$x = 9 \quad \text{or} \quad x = 1$$
The solutions are 1 and 9.

8.
$$\frac{6}{x^2} = \frac{3}{x+1}$$
$$3x^2 = 6(x+1)$$
$$3x^2 - 6x - 6 = 0$$
$$x^2 - 2x - 2 = 0$$
$$x = \frac{2 \pm \sqrt{(-2)^2 - 4(1)(-2)}}{2(1)}$$
$$= \frac{2 \pm \sqrt{12}}{2}$$
$$= \frac{2 \pm 2\sqrt{3}}{2} = 1 \pm \sqrt{3}$$
The solutions are $1 + \sqrt{3}$ and $1 - \sqrt{3}$.

10.
$$\frac{5}{x-2} + \frac{4}{x-2} = 1$$
$$5(x+2) + 4(x-2) = 1(x+2)(x-2)$$
$$5x + 10 + 4x - 8 = x^2 - 4$$
$$0 = x^2 - 9x - 6$$
$$x = \frac{9 \pm \sqrt{(-9)^2 - 4(1)(-6)}}{2(1)} = \frac{9 \pm \sqrt{105}}{2}$$
The solutions are $\dfrac{9 + \sqrt{105}}{2}$ and $\dfrac{9 - \sqrt{105}}{2}$.

12.
$$\frac{11}{2x^2 + x - 15} = \frac{5}{2x-5} - \frac{x}{x+3}$$
$$\frac{11}{(2x-5)(x+3)} = \frac{5}{2x-5} - \frac{x}{x+3}$$
$$11 = 5(x+3) - x(2x-5)$$
$$11 = -2x^2 + 10x + 15$$
$$2x^2 - 10x - 4 = 0$$
$$x^2 - 5x - 2 = 0$$
$$x = \frac{5 \pm \sqrt{(-5)^2 - 4(1)(-2)}}{2(1)} = \frac{5 \pm \sqrt{33}}{2}$$
The solutions are $\dfrac{5 + \sqrt{33}}{2}$ and $\dfrac{5 - \sqrt{33}}{2}$.

14.
$$x^4 + 2x^2 - 3 = 0$$
$$(x^2 - 1)(x^2 + 3) = 0$$
$$(x+1)(x-1)(x^2 + 3) = 0$$
$$x + 1 = 0 \quad \text{or} \quad x - 1 = 0 \text{ or } x^2 + 3 = 0$$
$$x = -1 \text{ or} \quad x = 1 \text{ or} \quad x^2 = -3$$
$$x = \pm i\sqrt{3}$$
The solutions are -1, 1, $-i\sqrt{3}$, and $i\sqrt{3}$.

16.
$$z^4 = 81$$
$$z^4 - 81 = 0$$
$$(z^2 - 9)(z^2 + 9) = 0$$
$$(z+3)(z-3)(z^2 + 9) = 0$$
$$z + 3 = 0 \quad \text{or } z - 3 = 0 \text{ or } z^2 + 9 = 0$$
$$z = -3 \text{ or} \quad z = 3 \text{ or} \quad z^2 = -9$$
$$z = \pm 3i$$
The solutions are -3, 3, $-3i$, and $3i$.

18.
$$9x^4 + 5x^2 - 4 = 0$$
$$(9x^2 - 4)(x^2 + 1) = 0$$
$$(3x + 2)(3x - 2)(x^2 + 1) = 0$$
$$3x + 2 = 0 \quad \text{or} \quad 3x - 2 = 0 \quad \text{or} \quad x^2 + 1 = 0$$
$$x = -\frac{2}{3} \quad \text{or} \quad x = \frac{2}{3} \quad \text{or} \quad x^2 = -1$$
$$x = \pm i$$

The solutions are $-\dfrac{2}{3}, \dfrac{2}{3}, -i$, and i.

20. $x^{2/3} + 2x^{1/3} + 1 = 0$

Let $y = x^{1/3}$. Then $y^2 = x^{2/3}$ and

$$y^2 + 2y + 1 = 0$$
$$(y + 1)^2 = 0$$
$$y + 1 = 0$$
$$y = -1$$
$$x^{1/3} = -1$$
$$x = (-1)^3 = -1$$

The solution is -1.

22. $(m - 6)^2 + 5(m - 6) + 4 = 0$

Let $y = m - 6$. Then $y^2 = (m - 6)^2$ and

$$y^2 + 5y + 4 = 0$$
$$(y + 4)(y + 1) = 0$$
$$y + 4 = 0 \quad \text{or} \quad y + 1 = 0$$
$$y = -4 \quad \text{or} \quad y = -1$$
$$m - 6 = -4 \quad \text{or} \quad m - 6 = -1$$
$$m = 2 \quad \text{or} \quad m = 5$$

The solutions are 2 and 5.

24. $3x^{2/3} + 11x^{1/3} = 4$

Let $y = x^{1/3}$. Then $y^2 = x^{2/3}$ and

$$3y^2 + 11y = 4$$
$$3y^2 + 11y - 4 = 0$$
$$(3y - 1)(y + 4) = 0$$
$$3y - 1 = 0 \quad \text{or} \quad y + 4 = 0$$
$$y = \frac{1}{3} \quad \text{or} \quad y = -4$$
$$x^{1/3} = \frac{1}{3} \quad \text{or} \quad x^{1/3} = -4$$
$$x = \frac{1}{27} \quad \text{or} \quad x = -64$$

The solutions are -64 and $\dfrac{1}{27}$.

26.
$$2 - \frac{7}{x + 6} = \frac{15}{(x + 6)^2}$$
$$2(x + 6)^2 - 7(x + 6) - 15 = 0$$

Let $y = x + 6$. Then $y^2 = (x + 6)^2$ and

$$2y^2 - 7y - 15 = 0$$
$$(2y + 3)(y - 5) = 0$$
$$2y + 3 = 0 \quad \text{or} \quad y - 5 = 0$$
$$y = -\frac{3}{2} \quad \text{or} \quad y = 5$$
$$x + 6 = -\frac{3}{2} \quad \text{or} \quad x + 6 = 5$$
$$x = -\frac{15}{2} \quad \text{or} \quad x = -1$$

The solutions are $-\dfrac{15}{2}$ and -1.

28.
$$4x^{2/3} + 16x^{1/3} = -15$$
$$4x^{2/3} + 16x^{1/3} + 15 = 0$$

Let $y = x^{1/3}$. Then $y^2 = x^{2/3}$ and

$$4y^2 + 16y + 15 = 0$$
$$(2y + 5)(2y + 3) = 0$$
$$2y + 5 = 0 \quad \text{or} \quad 2y + 3 = 0$$
$$y = -\frac{5}{2} \quad \text{or} \quad y = -\frac{3}{2}$$
$$x^{1/3} = -\frac{5}{2} \quad \text{or} \quad x^{1/3} = -\frac{3}{2}$$
$$x = -\frac{125}{8} \quad \text{or} \quad x = -\frac{27}{8}$$

The solutions are $-\dfrac{125}{8}$ and $-\dfrac{27}{8}$.

30.
$$x^4 - 12x^2 + 11 = 0$$
$$(x^2 - 11)(x^2 - 1) = 0$$
$$x^2 - 11 = 0 \quad \text{or} \quad x^2 - 1 = 0$$
$$x^2 = 11 \quad \text{or} \quad x^2 = 1$$
$$x = \pm\sqrt{11} \quad \text{or} \quad x = \pm 1$$

The solutions are $-\sqrt{11}, \sqrt{11}, -1$, and 1.

32.
$$\frac{5}{x - 3} + \frac{x}{x + 3} = \frac{19}{x^2 - 9}$$
$$\frac{5}{x - 3} + \frac{x}{x + 3} = \frac{19}{(x + 3)(x - 3)}$$
$$5(x + 3) + x(x - 3) = 19$$
$$x^2 + 2x - 4 = 0$$

$$x = \frac{-2 \pm \sqrt{(2)^2 - 4(1)(-4)}}{2(1)}$$

$$= \frac{-2 \pm \sqrt{20}}{2}$$

$$= \frac{-2 \pm 2\sqrt{5}}{2}$$

$$= -1 \pm \sqrt{5}$$

The solutions are $-1 + \sqrt{5}$ and $-1 - \sqrt{5}$.

34. $2(4m - 3)^2 - 9(4m - 3) = 5$

Let $x = 4m - 3$. Then $x^2 = (4m - 3)^2$ and

$$2x^2 - 9x - 5 = 0$$
$$(2x + 1)(x - 5) = 0$$
$$2x + 1 = 0 \quad \text{or} \quad x - 5 = 0$$
$$x = -\frac{1}{2} \quad \text{or} \quad x = 5$$
$$4m - 3 = -\frac{1}{2} \quad \text{or} \quad 4m - 3 = 5$$
$$4m = \frac{5}{2} \quad \text{or} \quad 4m = 8$$
$$m = \frac{5}{8} \quad \text{or} \quad m = 2$$

The solutions are $\frac{5}{8}$ and 2.

36. $\qquad 4x = \sqrt{2x + 3}$

$$16x^2 - 2x - 3 = 0$$
$$(8x + 3)(2x - 1) = 0$$
$$x = -\frac{3}{8} \text{ (discard) or } x = \frac{1}{2}$$

The solution is $\frac{1}{2}$.

38. $x^{2/3} - 2x^{1/3} - 8 = 0$

Let $y = x^{1/3}$. Then $y^2 = x^{2/3}$ and

$$y^2 - 2y - 8 = 0$$
$$(y - 4)(y + 2) = 0$$
$$y = 4 \quad \text{or} \quad y = -2$$
$$x^{1/3} = 4 \quad \text{or} \quad x^{1/3} = -2$$
$$x = 64 \quad \text{or} \quad x = -8$$

The solutions are -8 and 64.

40. $\qquad x^3 + x - 3x^2 - 3 = 0$

$$x(x^2 + 1) - 3(x^2 + 1) = 0$$
$$(x^2 + 1)(x - 3) = 0$$
$$x^2 + 1 = 0 \qquad \text{or} \quad x - 3 = 0$$
$$x^2 = -1 \qquad \text{or} \qquad x = 3$$
$$x = \pm i$$

The solutions are 3, $-i$, and i.

42. $6x^{2/3} - 25x^{1/3} - 25 = 0$

Let $y = x^{1/3}$. Then $y^2 = x^{2/3}$ and

$$6y^2 - 25y - 25 = 0$$
$$(6y + 5)(y - 5) = 0$$
$$y = -\frac{5}{6} \quad \text{or} \quad y = 5$$
$$x^{1/3} = -\frac{5}{6} \quad \text{or} \quad x^{1/3} = 5$$
$$x = -\frac{125}{216} \quad \text{or} \quad x = 125$$

The solutions are $-\frac{125}{216}$ and 125.

44. $y^{-2} - 8y^{-1} + 7 = 0$

Let $x = y^{-1}$. Then $x^2 = y^{-2}$ and

$$x^2 - 8x + 7 = 0$$
$$(x - 7)(x - 1) = 0$$
$$x = 7 \text{ or } x = 1$$
$$y^{-1} = 7 \text{ or } y^{-1} = 1$$
$$\frac{1}{y} = 7 \text{ or } \frac{1}{y} = 1$$
$$y = \frac{1}{7} \text{ or } y = 1$$

The solutions are $\frac{1}{7}$ and 1.

46. $\qquad x - \sqrt{3x} = 6$

$$x - 6 = \sqrt{3x}$$
$$(x - 6)^2 = 3x$$
$$x^2 - 12x + 36 = 3x$$
$$x^2 - 15x + 36 = 0$$
$$(x - 12)(x - 3) = 0$$
$$x = 12 \text{ or } x = 3 \text{ (discard)}$$

The solution is 12.

48.
$$\frac{x}{x-5}+\frac{5}{x+5}=-\frac{1}{x^2-25}$$
$$\frac{x}{x-5}+\frac{5}{x+5}=-\frac{1}{(x+5)(x-5)}$$
$$x(x+5)+5(x-5)=-1$$
$$x^2+10x-24=0$$
$$(x+12)(x-2)=0$$
$$x=-12 \text{ or } x=2$$
The solutions are –12 and 2.

50.
$$x^4-10x^2+9=0$$
$$(x^2-9)(x^2-1)=0$$
$$(x+3)(x-3)(x+1)(x-1)=0$$
$$x=-3 \text{ or } x=3 \text{ or } x=-1 \text{ or } x=1$$
The solutions are –3, 3, –1, 1.

52. $(x-6)(x^2+6x+36)=0$
$$x-6=0 \text{ or } x^2+6x+36=0$$
$$x=6 \text{ or } x=\frac{-6\pm\sqrt{(6)^2-4(1)(36)}}{2(1)}$$
$$=\frac{-6\pm\sqrt{-108}}{2}$$
$$=\frac{-6\pm6i\sqrt{3}}{2}$$
$$=-3\pm3i\sqrt{3}$$
The solutions are 6, $-3+3i\sqrt{3}$, and $-3-3i\sqrt{3}$.

54.
$$3+\frac{1}{2p+4}=\frac{10}{(2p+4)^2}$$
$$3(2p+4)^2+(2p+4)-10=0$$
Let $y=2p+4$. Then $y^2=(2p+4)^2$ and
$$3y^2+y-10=0$$
$$(3y-5)(y+2)=0$$
$$y=\frac{5}{3} \text{ or } y=-2$$
$$2p+4=\frac{5}{3} \text{ or } 2p+4=-2$$
$$2p=-\frac{7}{3} \text{ or } 2p=-6$$
$$p=-\frac{7}{6} \text{ or } p=-3$$
The solutions are $-\frac{7}{6}$ and –3.

56.
$$8z^4+14z^2=-5$$
$$8z^4+14z^2+5=0$$
$$(4z^2+5)(2z^2+1)=0$$
$$z^2=-\frac{5}{4} \text{ or } z^2=-\frac{1}{2}$$
$$z=\pm\frac{i\sqrt{5}}{2} \text{ or } z=\pm\frac{i}{\sqrt{2}}=\pm\frac{i\sqrt{2}}{2}$$
The solutions are $-\frac{i\sqrt{5}}{2},\frac{i\sqrt{5}}{2},-\frac{i\sqrt{2}}{2},$ and $\frac{i\sqrt{2}}{2}$.

58. Let x = his jogging speed. Then $x+4$ = his biking speed.
$$d=rt \Rightarrow t=\frac{d}{r}$$
$$t_{jogging}+t_{biking}=1$$
$$\frac{3}{x}+\frac{5}{x+4}=1$$
$$3(x+4)+5x=x(x+4)$$
$$3x+12+5x=x^2+4x$$
$$0=x^2-4x-12$$
$$0=(x-6)(x+2)$$
$$x=6 \text{ or } x=-2$$
Discard –2. His jogging speed is 6 mph and his biking speed is 10 mph.

60. Let x = time for the small pipe. Then $x-2$ = time for the large pipe.
$$\frac{1}{x}+\frac{1}{x-2}=\frac{1}{3}$$
$$3(x-2)+3x=x(x-2)$$
$$3x-6+3x=x^2-2x$$
$$0=x^2-8x+6$$
$$x=\frac{8\pm\sqrt{(-8)^2-4(1)(6)}}{2(1)}$$
$$=\frac{8\pm\sqrt{40}}{2}$$
$$x\approx 0.8 \text{ (discard) or } x\approx 7.2$$
$$x-2\approx 5.2$$
Large pipe: 5.2 hrs; small pipe: 7.2 hrs

62. Let x = original speed. Then
$x - 15$ = rainfall speed.

$$d = rt \implies t = \frac{d}{r}$$

$$t_{\text{before rain}} + t_{\text{after rain}} = 6$$

$$\frac{220}{x} + \frac{80}{x-15} = 6$$

$$220(x-15) + 80(x) = 6x(x-15)$$

$$220x - 3300 + 80x = 6x^2 - 90x$$

$$0 = 6x^2 - 390x + 3300$$

$$0 = x^2 - 65x + 550$$

$$0 = (x-55)(x-10)$$

$$x = 55 \quad \text{or} \quad x = 10 \text{ (discard)}$$

$$x - 15 = 55 - 15 = 40$$

Original speed: 55 mph
Rainfall speed: 40 mph

64. Let x = days for Freckels to eat the food
$x - 14$ = days for Noodles to eat the food.

$$\frac{1}{x} + \frac{1}{x-14} = \frac{1}{30}$$

$$30(x-14) + 30x = x(x-14)$$

$$30x - 420 + 30x = x^2 - 14x$$

$$0 = x^2 - 74x + 420$$

$$x = \frac{74 \pm \sqrt{(-74)^2 - 4(1)(420)}}{2(1)}$$

$$= \frac{74 \pm \sqrt{3796}}{2}$$

$$\approx 6 \text{ (discard)} \quad \text{or} \quad 68$$

It would take Freckels about 68 days to eat the dog food.

66. Let x = the number.

$$x + x^2 = 2x + 2$$

$$x^2 - x - 2 = 0$$

$$(x-2)(x+1) = 0$$

$$x = 2 \quad \text{or} \quad x = -1 \text{ (discard)}$$

The number is 2.

68. a. length = $x - 4$

b. $V = lwh$
$$128 = (x-4)(x-4) \cdot 2$$

c. $128 = 2(x-4)^2$

$$64 = x^2 - 8x + 16$$

$$0 = x^2 - 8x - 48$$

$$0 = (x-12)(x+4)$$

$$x = 12 \quad \text{or} \quad x = -4 \text{ (discard)}$$

The sheet is 12 in. by 12 in.

70. Let x = length of the side of the square.

$$\text{Area} = x^2$$

$$6270 = x^2$$

$$\sqrt{6270} = x$$

Adding another radial line to a different corner would yield a right triangle with legs r and hypotenuse x.

$$r^2 + r^2 = x^2$$

$$2r^2 = \left(\sqrt{6270}\right)^2$$

$$2r^2 = 6270$$

$$r^2 = 3135$$

$$r = \pm\sqrt{3135} = \pm 55.99107$$

Disregard the negative. The smallest radius would be 56 feet.

72.

$$\frac{2x}{3} + \frac{1}{6} \geq 2$$

$$6\left(\frac{2x}{3} + \frac{1}{6}\right) \geq 6(2)$$

$$4x + 1 \geq 12$$

$$4x \geq 11$$

$$x \geq \frac{11}{4}$$

$$\left[\frac{11}{4}, \infty\right)$$

74.

$$\frac{z-2}{12} < \frac{1}{4}$$

$$z - 2 < 3$$

$$z < 5$$

$$(-\infty, 5)$$

76. Domain: $\{x \mid -3 \leq x \leq 3\}$ or $[-3, 3]$
Range: $\{y \mid -2 \leq y \leq 2\}$ or $[-2, 2]$
It is not a function.

78. Domain: $\{x \mid x \leq -1\}$ or $(-\infty, -1]$
Range: $\{y \mid y \leq 2\}$ or $(-\infty, 2]$
It is a function.

80. $x^3 + x - 3x^2 - 3 = 0$

$x(x^2 + 1) - 3(x^2 + 1) = 0$

$(x - 3)(x^2 + 1) = 0$

$x - 3 = 0$ or $x^2 + 1 = 0$

$x = 3$ $x^2 = -1$

$x = \pm\sqrt{-1} = \pm i$

The solutions are 3, $-i$, and i.

82. $y^{-2} - 8y^{-1} + 7 = 0$

$1 - 8y + 7y^2 = 0$

$(1 - y)(1 - 7y) = 0$

$1 - y = 0$ or $1 - 7y = 0$

$1 = y$ $1 = 7y$

$\dfrac{1}{7} = y$

The solutions are 1 and $\dfrac{1}{7}$.

84. $y^3 - 216 = 0$

$(y - 6)(y^2 + 6y + 36) = 0$

$y - 6 = 0$ or $y^2 + 6y + 36 = 0$

$y = 6$ or $y = \dfrac{-6 \pm \sqrt{(6)^2 - 4(1)(36)}}{2(1)}$

$= \dfrac{-6 \pm \sqrt{-108}}{2}$

$= \dfrac{-6 \pm 6i\sqrt{3}}{2}$

$= -3 \pm 3i\sqrt{3}$

The solutions are 6, $-3 + 3i\sqrt{3}$, and $-3 - 3i\sqrt{3}$.

86. Answers may vary

88. Answers may vary

Integrated Review

1. $x^2 - 10 = 0$

$x^2 = 10$

$x = \pm\sqrt{10}$

2. $x^2 - 14 = 0$

$x^2 = 14$

$x = \pm\sqrt{14}$

3. $(x - 1)^2 = 8$

$x - 1 = \pm\sqrt{8}$

$x - 1 = \pm 2\sqrt{2}$

$x = 1 \pm 2\sqrt{2}$

4. $(x + 5)^2 = 12$

$x + 5 = \pm\sqrt{12}$

$x + 5 = \pm 2\sqrt{3}$

$x = -5 \pm 2\sqrt{3}$

5. $x^2 + 2x - 12 = 0$

$x^2 + 2x + \left(\dfrac{2}{2}\right)^2 = 12 + 1$

$x^2 + 2x + 1 = 13$

$(x + 1)^2 = 13$

$x + 1 = \pm\sqrt{13}$

$x = -1 \pm \sqrt{13}$

6. $x^2 - 12x + 11 = 0$

$x^2 - 12x + \left(\dfrac{-12}{2}\right)^2 = -11 + 36$

$x^2 - 12x + 36 = 25$

$(x - 6)^2 = \pm\sqrt{25}$

$x - 6 = \pm 5$

$x = 6 \pm 5$

$x = 1$ or $x = 11$

7.
$$3x^2 + 3x = 5$$
$$x^2 + x = \frac{5}{3}$$
$$x^2 + x + \left(\frac{1}{2}\right)^2 = \frac{5}{3} + \frac{1}{4}$$
$$x^2 + x + \frac{1}{4} = \frac{23}{12}$$
$$\left(x + \frac{1}{2}\right)^2 = \frac{23}{12}$$
$$x + \frac{1}{2} = \pm\sqrt{\frac{23}{12}}$$
$$x + \frac{1}{2} = \pm\frac{\sqrt{23}}{2\sqrt{3}}$$
$$x + \frac{1}{2} = \pm\frac{\sqrt{23} \cdot \sqrt{3}}{2\sqrt{3} \cdot \sqrt{3}}$$
$$x + \frac{1}{2} = \pm\frac{\sqrt{69}}{6}$$
$$x = -\frac{1}{2} \pm \frac{\sqrt{69}}{6} = \frac{-3 \pm \sqrt{69}}{6}$$

8.
$$16y^2 + 16y = 1$$
$$y^2 + y = \frac{1}{16}$$
$$y^2 + y + \left(\frac{1}{2}\right)^2 = \frac{1}{16} + \frac{1}{4}$$
$$y^2 + y + \frac{1}{4} = \frac{5}{16}$$
$$\left(y + \frac{1}{2}\right)^2 = \frac{5}{16}$$
$$y + \frac{1}{2} = \pm\sqrt{\frac{5}{16}}$$
$$y + \frac{1}{2} = \pm\frac{\sqrt{5}}{4}$$
$$y = -\frac{1}{2} \pm \frac{\sqrt{5}}{4} = \frac{-2 \pm \sqrt{5}}{4}$$

9. $2x^2 - 4x + 1 = 0$
$$a = 2, b = -4, c = 1$$
$$x = \frac{4 \pm \sqrt{(-4)^2 - 4(2)(1)}}{2(2)}$$
$$= \frac{4 \pm \sqrt{8}}{4}$$
$$= \frac{4 \pm 2\sqrt{2}}{4} = \frac{2 \pm \sqrt{2}}{2}$$

10. $\frac{1}{2}x^2 + 3x + 2 = 0$
$$x^2 + 6x + 4 = 0$$
$$a = 1, b = 6, c = 4$$
$$x = \frac{-6 \pm \sqrt{(6)^2 - 4(1)(4)}}{2(1)}$$
$$= \frac{-6 \pm \sqrt{20}}{2}$$
$$= \frac{-6 \pm 2\sqrt{5}}{2} = -3 \pm \sqrt{5}$$

11.
$$x^2 + 4x = -7$$
$$x^2 + 4x + 7 = 0$$
$$a = 1, b = 4, c = 7$$
$$x = \frac{-4 \pm \sqrt{(4)^2 - 4(1)(7)}}{2(1)}$$
$$= \frac{-4 \pm \sqrt{-12}}{2}$$
$$= \frac{-4 \pm i\sqrt{4 \cdot 3}}{2}$$
$$= \frac{-4 \pm 2i\sqrt{3}}{2} = -2 \pm i\sqrt{3}$$

12.
$$x^2 + x = -3$$
$$x^2 + x + 3 = 0$$
$$a = 1, b = 1, c = 3$$
$$x = \frac{-1 \pm \sqrt{(1)^2 - 4(1)(3)}}{2(1)}$$
$$= \frac{-1 \pm \sqrt{-11}}{2}$$
$$= \frac{-1 \pm i\sqrt{11}}{2}$$

13. $x^2 + 3x + 6 = 0$
$$a = 1, b = 3, c = 6$$
$$x = \frac{-3 \pm \sqrt{(3)^2 - 4(1)(6)}}{2(1)}$$
$$= \frac{-3 \pm \sqrt{-15}}{2}$$
$$= \frac{-3 \pm i\sqrt{15}}{2}$$

14. $2x^2 + 18 = 0$

$2x^2 = -18$

$x^2 = -9$

$x = \pm\sqrt{-9}$

$x = \pm 3i$

15. $x^2 + 17x = 0$

$x(x + 17) = 0$

$x = 0$ or $x + 17 = 0$

$\qquad\qquad\qquad x = -17$

$x = 0, -17$

16. $4x^2 - 2x - 3 = 0$

$a = 4, b = -2, c = -3$

$x = \dfrac{2 \pm \sqrt{(-2)^2 - 4(4)(-3)}}{2(4)}$

$= \dfrac{2 \pm \sqrt{52}}{8}$

$= \dfrac{2 \pm 2\sqrt{13}}{8}$

$= \dfrac{1 \pm \sqrt{13}}{4}$

17. $(x - 2)^2 = 27$

$x - 2 = \pm\sqrt{27}$

$x - 2 = \pm 3\sqrt{3}$

$x = 2 \pm 3\sqrt{3}$

18. $\dfrac{1}{2}x^2 - 2x + \dfrac{1}{2} = 0$

$x^2 - 4x + 1 = 0$

$x^2 - 4x + \left(\dfrac{-4}{2}\right)^2 = -1 + 4$

$x^2 - 4x + 4 = 3$

$(x - 2)^2 = 3$

$x - 2 = \pm\sqrt{3}$

$x = 2 \pm \sqrt{3}$

19. $3x^2 + 2x = 8$

$3x^2 + 2x - 8 = 0$

$(3x - 4)(x + 2) = 0$

$3x - 4 = 0$ or $x + 2 = 0$

$x = \dfrac{4}{3}$ or $\quad x = -2$

20. $2x^2 = -5x - 1$

$2x^2 + 5x + 1 = 0$

$a = 2, b = 5, c = 1$

$x = \dfrac{-5 \pm \sqrt{(5)^2 - 4(2)(1)}}{2(2)}$

$= \dfrac{-5 \pm \sqrt{17}}{4}$

21. $x(x - 2) = 5$

$x^2 - 2x = 5$

$x^2 - 2x + \left(\dfrac{-2}{2}\right)^2 = 5 + 1$

$x^2 - 2x + 1 = 6$

$(x - 1)^2 = 6$

$x - 1 = \pm\sqrt{6}$

$x = 1 \pm \sqrt{6}$

22. $x^2 - 31 = 0$

$x^2 = 31$

$x = \pm\sqrt{31}$

23. $5x^2 - 55 = 0$

$5x^2 = 55$

$x^2 = 11$

$x = \pm\sqrt{11}$

24. $5x^2 + 55 = 0$

$5x^2 = -55$

$x^2 = -11$

$x = \pm\sqrt{-11}$

$x = \pm i\sqrt{11}$

25. $x(x + 5) = 66$

$x^2 + 5x = 66$

$x^2 + 5x - 66 = 0$

$(x + 11)(x - 6) = 0$

$x + 11 = 0$ or $x - 6 = 0$

$x = -11$ or $\quad x = 6$

26. $5x^2 + 6x - 2 = 0$

$a = 5, b = 6, c = -2$

$x = \dfrac{-6 \pm \sqrt{(6)^2 - 4(5)(-2)}}{2(5)}$

$= \dfrac{-6 \pm \sqrt{76}}{10}$

$= \dfrac{-6 \pm \sqrt{4 \cdot 19}}{10}$

$= \dfrac{-6 \pm 2\sqrt{19}}{10}$

$= \dfrac{-3 \pm \sqrt{19}}{5}$

27. $2x^2 + 3x = 1$

$2x^2 + 3x - 1 = 0$

$a = 2, b = 3, c = -1$

$x = \dfrac{-3 \pm \sqrt{(3)^2 - 4(2)(-1)}}{2(2)}$

$= \dfrac{-3 \pm \sqrt{17}}{4}$

28. $a^2 + b^2 = c^2$

$x^2 + x^2 = 20^2$

$2x^2 = 400$

$x^2 = 200$

$x = \pm\sqrt{200}$

$= \pm 10\sqrt{2} \approx 14.1421$

Disregard the negative. A side of the room is $10\sqrt{2}$ feet ≈ 14.1 feet.

29. Let $x =$ time for Jack alone. Then $x - 2 =$ time for Lucy alone.

$\dfrac{1}{x} + \dfrac{1}{x-2} = \dfrac{1}{4}$

$4(x-2) + 4x = x(x-2)$

$4x - 8 + 4x = x^2 - 2x$

$0 = x^2 - 10x + 8$

$x = \dfrac{10 \pm \sqrt{(-10)^2 - 4(1)(8)}}{2(1)}$

$= \dfrac{10 \pm \sqrt{68}}{2}$

≈ 9.1 or 0.9 (disregard)

$x - 2 = 9.1 - 2 = 7.1$

It would take Jack 9.1 hours and Lucy 7.1 hours.

30. Let $x =$ initial speed on treadmill. Then $x + 1 =$ speed increased.

$t_{\text{initial}} + t_{\text{increased}} = \dfrac{4}{3}$

$\dfrac{5}{x} + \dfrac{2}{x+1} = \dfrac{4}{3}$

$5 \cdot 3(x+1) + 2 \cdot 3x = 4x(x+1)$

$15x + 15 + 6x = 4x^2 + 4x$

$0 = 4x^2 - 17x - 15$

$0 = (4x + 3)(x - 5)$

$x = -\dfrac{4}{3}$ (disregard) or $x = 5$

$x + 1 = 5 + 1 = 6$

Initial speed: 5 mph

Increased speed: 6 mph

Section 8.4

Practice Exercises

1. $(x - 4)(x + 3) > 0$

Solve the related equation, $(x - 4)(x + 3) = 0$.

$(x - 4)(x + 3) = 0$

$x - 4 = 0 \quad$ or $\quad x + 3 = 0$

$x = 4 \qquad\qquad x = -3$

Test points in the three regions separated by $x = 4$ and $x = -3$.

Region	Test Point	$(x-4)(x+3) > 0$ Result
A: $(-\infty, -3)$	-4	$(-8)(-1) > 0$ True
B: $(-3, 4)$	0	$(-4)(3) > 0$ False
C: $(4, \infty)$	5	$(1)(8) > 0$ True

The points in regions A and C satisfy the inequality. The numbers 4 and -3 are not included in the solution since the inequality symbol is >. The solution set is $(-\infty, -3) \cup (4, \infty)$.

2. $x^2 - 8x \leq 0$

Solve the related equation, $x^2 - 8x = 0$.

$x^2 - 8x = 0$

$x(x - 8) = 0$

$x = 0 \quad$ or $\quad x - 8 = 0$

$x = 8$

The numbers 0 and 8 separate the number line

into three regions, A, B, and C. Test a point in each region.

Region	Test Point	$x^2 - 8x \le 0$ Result
A: $(-\infty, 0]$	-1	$1 + 8 \le 0$ False
B: $[0, 8]$	1	$1 - 8 \le 0$ True
C: $[8, \infty)$	9	$81 - 72 \le 0$ False

Values in region B satisfy the inequality. The numbers 0 and 8 are included in the solution since the inequality symbol is $\le$. The solution set is $[0, 8]$.

3. The solutions of $x^2 - 8x \ge 0$ are where the graph is on or above the x-axis.

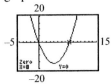

The solution set is $(-\infty, 0] \cup [8, \infty)$.

4. The solutions of $(x + 3)(x - 2)(x + 1) \le 0$ are where the graph is on or below the x-axis.

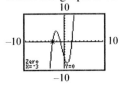

The solution set is $(-\infty, -3] \cup [-1, 2]$.

5. In standard form, the inequality is
$$x^2 + 3x + 7 < 0.$$

Since the entire graph lies above the x-axis, the inequality has no solution or $\varnothing$.

6. $\dfrac{x-5}{x+4} \le 0$
$x + 4 = 0$
$\quad x = -4$
$x = -4$ makes the denominator zero. Solve the

related equation $\dfrac{x-5}{x+4} = 0$.

$\dfrac{x-5}{x+4} = 0$
$x - 5 = 0$
$\quad x = 5$

Test points in the three regions separated by $x = -4$ and $x = 5$.

Region	Test Point	$\dfrac{x-5}{x+4} \le 0$ Result
A: $(-\infty, -4)$	-5	$\dfrac{-10}{-1} \le 0$ False
B: $(-4, 5]$	0	$\dfrac{-5}{4} \le 0$ True
C: $[5, \infty)$	6	$\dfrac{1}{10} \le 0$ False

The solution set is $(-4, 5]$. The interval includes 5 because 5 satisfies the original inequality. This interval does not include -4, because -4 would make the denominator zero.

7. $\dfrac{7}{x+3} < 5$
$x + 3 = 0$
$\quad x = -3$
$x = -3$ makes the denominator zero.

Solve $\dfrac{7}{x+3} = 5$.

$(x+3)\left(\dfrac{7}{x+3}\right) = 5(x+3)$
$\qquad\qquad 7 = 5x + 15$
$\qquad\quad -8 = 5x$
$\qquad -\dfrac{8}{5} = x$

We use these two solutions to divide the number line into three regions and choose test points.

Region	Test Point	$\dfrac{7}{x+3} < 5$ Result
$A: (-\infty, -3)$	-4	$\dfrac{7}{-1} < 5$ True
$B: \left(-3, -\dfrac{8}{5}\right)$	-2	$\dfrac{7}{1} < 5$ False
$C: \left(-\dfrac{8}{5}, \infty\right)$	0	$\dfrac{7}{3} < 5$ True

The solution set is $(-\infty, -3) \cup \left(-\dfrac{8}{5}, \infty\right)$.

Vocabulary and Readiness Check

1. $[-7, 3)$

2. $(-1, 5]$

3. $(-\infty, 0]$

4. $(-\infty, -8]$

5. $(-\infty, -12) \cup [-10, \infty)$

6. $(-\infty, -3] \cup (4, \infty)$

Exercise Set 8.4

2. $(x+1)(x+5) \le 0$
   $x = -1$ or $x = -5$

Region	Test Point	$(x+1)(x+5) \le 0$ Result
$A: (-\infty, -5]$	-6	$(-5)(-1) \le 0$ False
$B: [-5, -1]$	-2	$(-1)(3) \le 0$ True
$C: [-1, \infty)$	0	$(1)(5) \le 0$ False

Solution: $[-5, -1]$

4. $(x+4)(x-1) > 0$
   $x = -4$ or $x = 1$

Region	Test Point	$(x+4)(x-1) > 0$ Result
$A: (-\infty, -4)$	-5	$(-1)(-6) > 0$ True
$B: (-4, 1)$	0	$(4)(-1) > 0$ False
$C: (1, \infty)$	2	$(6)(1) > 0$ True

Solution: $(-\infty, -4) \cup (1, \infty)$

6. $x^2 + 8x + 15 \ge 0$
   $(x+5)(x+3) \ge 0$
   $x = -5$ or $x = -3$

Region	Test Point	$(x+5)(x+3) \ge 0$ Result
$A: (-\infty, -5]$	-6	$(-1)(-3) \ge 0$ True
$B: [-5, -3]$	-4	$(1)(-1) \ge 0$ False
$C: [-3, \infty)$	0	$(5)(3) \ge 0$ True

Solution: $(-\infty, -5] \cup [-3, \infty)$

8. $2x^2 - 5x < 7$
   $2x^2 - 5x - 7 < 0$
   $(2x-7)(x+1) < 0$
   $x = \dfrac{7}{2}$ or $x = -1$

Region	Test Point	$(2x-7)(x+1) < 0$ Result
$A: (-\infty, -1)$	-2	$(-11)(-1) < 0$ False
$B: \left(-1, \dfrac{7}{2}\right)$	0	$(-7)(1) < 0$ True
$C: \left(\dfrac{7}{2}, \infty\right)$	4	$(1)(5) < 0$ False

Solution: $\left(-1, \dfrac{7}{2}\right)$

10. $(x-6)(x-4)(x-2) \le 0$
$x = 6$ or $x = 4$ or $x = 2$

Region	Test Point	$(x-6)(x-4)(x-2) \le 0$ Result
$A: (-\infty, 2]$	0	$(-6)(-4)(-2) \le 0$ True
$B: [2, 4]$	3	$(-3)(-1)(1) \le 0$ False
$C: [4, 6]$	5	$(-1)(1)(3) \le 0$ True
$D: [6, \infty)$	7	$(1)(3)(5) \le 0$ False

Solution: $(-\infty, 2] \cup [4, 6]$

12. $x(x-6)(x+2) > 0$
$x = 0$ or $x = 6$ or $x = -2$

Region	Test Point	$x(x-6)(x+2) > 0$ Result
$A: (-\infty, -2)$	-5	$-5(-11)(-3) > 0$ False
$B: (-2, 0)$	-1	$-1(-7)(1) > 0$ True
$C: (0, 6)$	1	$1(-5)(3) > 0$ False
$D: (6, \infty)$	7	$7(1)(9) > 0$ True

Solution: $(-2, 0) \cup (6, \infty)$

14. The solutions are where the graph is on or below the x-axis. The solution set is $[-4, -1] \cup [1, 4]$.

16. $\dfrac{x-5}{x-6} > 0$
$x = 5$ or $x = 6$

Region	Test Point	$\dfrac{x-5}{x-6} > 0$; Result
$A: (-\infty, 5)$	0	$\dfrac{-5}{-6} > 0$; True
$B: (5, 6)$	5.5	$\dfrac{0.5}{-0.5} > 0$; False
$C: (6, \infty)$	7	$\dfrac{2}{1} > 0$; True

Solution: $(-\infty, 5) \cup (6, \infty)$

18. $\dfrac{3}{y-5} < 0$
$y = 5$

Region	Test Point	$\dfrac{3}{y-5} < 0$; Result
$A: (-\infty, 5)$	0	$\dfrac{3}{-5} < 0$; True
$B: (5, \infty)$	6	$\dfrac{3}{1} < 0$; False

Solution: $(-\infty, 5)$

20. From the graph, the solution set is $[-1, 4)$.

22. $\dfrac{-2}{y+3} > 2$

The denominator is equal to 0 when
$y + 3 = 0$, or $y = -3$.
$$\dfrac{-2}{y+3} = 2$$
$$-2 = 2y + 6$$
$$-8 = 2y$$
$$-4 = y$$

Region	Test Point	$\dfrac{-2}{y+3} > 2$; Result
A: $(-\infty, -4)$	-5	$\dfrac{-2}{-2} > 2$; False
B: $(-4, -3)$	-3.5	$\dfrac{-2}{-0.5} = 4 > 2$; True
C: $(-3, \infty)$	4	$\dfrac{-2}{7} > 2$; False

Solution: $(-4, -3)$

24. $\dfrac{y^2 + 15}{8y} \le 1$

The denominator is equal to 0 when $8y = 0$, or $y = 0$.

$$\frac{y^2 + 15}{8y} = 1$$
$$y^2 + 15 = 8y$$
$$y^2 - 8y + 15 = 0$$
$$(y - 5)(y - 3) = 0$$
$$y = 5 \text{ or } y = 3$$

Region	Test Point	$\dfrac{y^2 + 15}{8y} \le 1$; Result
A: $(-\infty, 0)$	-1	$\dfrac{16}{-8} \le 1$; True
B: $(0, 3]$	1	$\dfrac{16}{8} \le 1$; False
C: $[3, 5]$	4	$\dfrac{31}{32} \le 1$; True
D: $[5, \infty)$	6	$\dfrac{51}{48} \le 1$; False

Solution: $(-\infty, 0) \cup [3, 5]$

26. $(x-5)(x+1) < 0$

$x = 5$ or $x = -1$

Region	Test Point	$(x-5)(x+1) < 0$ Result
$A: (-\infty, -1)$	-2	$(-7)(-1) < 0$ False
$B: (-1, 5)$	0	$(-5)(1) < 0$ True
$C: (5, \infty)$	6	$(1)(7) < 0$ False

Solution: $(-1, 5)$

28. $(6x+7)(7x-12) > 0$

$6x+7 = 0$ or $7x-12 = 0$

$x = -\dfrac{7}{6}$ or $x = \dfrac{12}{7}$

Region	Test Point	$(6x+7)(7x-12) > 0$ Result
$A: \left(-\infty, -\dfrac{7}{6}\right)$	-2	$(-5)(-26) > 0$ True
$B: \left(-\dfrac{7}{6}, \dfrac{12}{7}\right)$	0	$(7)(-12) > 0$ False
$C: \left(\dfrac{12}{7}, \infty\right)$	2	$(19)(2) > 0$ True

Solution: $\left(-\infty, -\dfrac{7}{6}\right) \cup \left(\dfrac{12}{7}, \infty\right)$

30. $x^2 < 25$

$x^2 - 25 < 0$

$(x+5)(x-5) < 0$

$x = -5$ or $x = 5$

Region	Test Point	$(x+5)(x-5) < 0$ Result
$A: (-\infty, -5)$	-6	$(-1)(-11) < 0$ False
$B: (-5, 5)$	0	$(5)(-5) < 0$ True
$C: (5, \infty)$	6	$(11)(1) < 0$ False

Solution: $(-5, 5)$

32. $(3x - 12)(x + 5)(2x - 3) \geq 0$

$3x - 12 = 0$ or $x + 5 = 0$ or $2x - 3 = 0$

$x = 4$ $x = -5$ or $x = \dfrac{3}{2}$

Region	Test Point	$(3x - 12)(x + 5)(2x - 3) \geq 0$ Result
$A: (-\infty, -5]$	-6	$(-30)(-1)(-15) \geq 0$ False
$B: \left[-5, \dfrac{3}{2}\right]$	0	$(-12)(5)(-3) \geq 0$ True
$C: \left[\dfrac{3}{2}, 4\right]$	2	$(-6)(7)(1) \geq 0$ False
$D: [4, \infty)$	5	$(3)(10)(7) \geq 0$ True

Solution: $\left[-5, \dfrac{3}{2}\right] \cup [4, \infty)$

34. $\qquad 12x^2 + 11x \leq 15$

$\qquad 12x^2 + 11x - 15 \leq 0$

$\qquad (3x + 5)(4x - 3) \leq 0$

$x = -\dfrac{5}{3}$ or $x = \dfrac{3}{4}$

Region	Test Point	$(3x + 5)(4x - 3) \leq 0$ Result
$A: \left(-\infty, -\dfrac{5}{3}\right]$	-2	$(-1)(-11) \leq 0$ False
$B: \left[-\dfrac{5}{3}, \dfrac{3}{4}\right]$	0	$(5)(-3) \leq 0$ True
$C: \left[\dfrac{3}{4}, \infty\right)$	1	$(8)(1) \leq 0$ False

Solution: $\left[-\dfrac{5}{3}, \dfrac{3}{4}\right]$

36. $x^3 + 2x^2 - 4x - 8 < 0$

$x^2(x+2) - 4(x+2) < 0$

$(x+2)(x^2-4) < 0$

$(x+2)^2(x-2) < 0$

$x = -2$ or $x = 2$

Region	Test Point	$(x+2)^2(x-2) < 0$ Result
A: $(-\infty, -2)$	-3	$(1)(-5) < 0$ True
B: $(-2, 2)$	0	$(4)(-2) < 0$ True
C: $(2, \infty)$	3	$(25)(1) < 0$ False

Solution: $(-\infty, -2) \cup (-2, 2)$

38. $16x^4 - 40x^2 + 9 \le 0$

$(4x^2 - 9)(4x^2 - 1) \le 0$

$(2x+3)(2x-3)(2x+1)(2x-1) \le 0$

$x = -\dfrac{3}{2}$ or $x = \dfrac{3}{2}$ or $x = -\dfrac{1}{2}$ or $x = \dfrac{1}{2}$

Region	Test Point	$(2x+3)(2x-3)(2x+1)(2x-1) \le 0$ Result
A: $\left(-\infty, -\dfrac{3}{2}\right]$	-2	$(-1)(-7)(-3)(-5) \le 0$ False
B: $\left[-\dfrac{3}{2}, -\dfrac{1}{2}\right]$	-1	$(1)(-5)(-1)(-3) \le 0$ True
C: $\left[-\dfrac{1}{2}, \dfrac{1}{2}\right]$	0	$(3)(-3)(1)(-1) \le 0$ False
D: $\left[\dfrac{1}{2}, \dfrac{3}{2}\right]$	1	$(5)(-1)(3)(1) \le 0$ True
E: $\left[\dfrac{3}{2}, \infty\right)$	2	$(7)(1)(5)(3) \le 0$ False

Solution: $\left[-\dfrac{3}{2}, -\dfrac{1}{2}\right] \cup \left[\dfrac{1}{2}, \dfrac{3}{2}\right]$

40. $(4x-9)(2x+5)<0$

$x=\dfrac{9}{4}$ or $x=-\dfrac{5}{2}$

Region	Test Point	$(4x-9)(2x+5)<0$ Result
$A:\left(-\infty,-\dfrac{5}{2}\right)$	-3	$(-21)(-1)<0$ False
$B:\left(-\dfrac{5}{2},\dfrac{9}{4}\right)$	0	$(-9)(5)<0$ True
$C:\left(\dfrac{9}{4},\infty\right)$	3	$(3)(11)<0$ False

Solution: $\left(-\dfrac{5}{2},\dfrac{9}{4}\right)$

42. $\dfrac{x+10}{x-10}>0$

$x=-10$ or $x=10$

Region	Test Point	$\dfrac{x+10}{x-10}>0$ Result
$A:(-\infty,-10)$	-11	$\dfrac{-1}{-21}>0$ True
$B:(-10,10)$	0	$\dfrac{10}{-10}>0$ False
$C:(10,\infty)$	11	$\dfrac{21}{1}>0$ True

Solution: $(-\infty,-10)\cup(10,\infty)$

44. $\dfrac{x-3}{x+2}\le0$

$x=3$ or $x=-2$

Region	Test Point	$\dfrac{x-3}{x+2}\le0$ Result
$A:(-\infty,-2)$	-3	$\dfrac{-6}{-1}\le0$ False
$B:(-2,3]$	0	$\dfrac{-3}{2}\le0$ True
$C:[3,\infty)$	4	$\dfrac{1}{6}\le0$ False

Solution: $(-2,3]$

46. $\dfrac{(x-2)(x+2)}{(x+1)(x-4)}\le0$

$x=2$ or $x=-2$ or $x=-1$ or $x=4$

Region	Test Point	$\dfrac{(x-2)(x+2)}{(x+1)(x-4)}\le0$ Result
$A:(-\infty,-2]$	-3	$\dfrac{(-5)(-1)}{(-2)(-7)}\le0$ False
$B:[-2,-1)$	-1.5	$\dfrac{(-3.5)(0.5)}{(-0.5)(-5.5)}\le0$ True
$C:(-1,2]$	0	$\dfrac{(-2)(2)}{(1)(-4)}\le0$ False
$D:[2,4)$	3	$\dfrac{(1)(5)}{(4)(-1)}\le0$ True
$E:(4,\infty)$	5	$\dfrac{(3)(7)}{(6)(1)}\le0$ False

Solution: $[-2,-1)\cup[2,4)$

48. $\dfrac{4}{y+2} < -2$

The denominator is equal to 0 when $y + 2 = 0$, or $y = -2$.

$$\dfrac{4}{y+2} = -2$$
$$4 = -2y - 4$$
$$2y = -8$$
$$y = -4$$

Region	Test Point	$\dfrac{4}{y+2} < -2$ Result
A: $(-\infty, -4)$	-5	$\dfrac{4}{-3} < -2$ False
B: $(-4, -2)$	-3	$\dfrac{4}{-1} < -2$ True
C: $(-2, \infty)$	0	$\dfrac{4}{2} < -2$ False

Solution: $(-4, -2)$

50. $\dfrac{4x}{x-3} \geq 5$

The denominator is equal to 0 when $x - 3 = 0$, or $x = 3$.

$$\dfrac{4x}{x-3} = 5$$
$$4x = 5x - 15$$
$$x = 15$$

Region	Test Point	$\dfrac{4x}{x-3} \geq 5$ Result
A: $(-\infty, 3)$	0	$\dfrac{4(0)}{-3} \geq 5$ False
B: $(3, 15]$	4	$\dfrac{4(4)}{1} \geq 5$ True
C: $[15, \infty)$	16	$\dfrac{4(16)}{13} \geq 5$ False

Solution: $(3, 15]$

52. $\dfrac{p}{p+4} \leq 3p$

The denominator is equal to 0 when $p + 4 = 0$, or $p = -4$.

$$\dfrac{p}{p+4} = 3p$$
$$p = 3p^2 + 12p$$
$$0 = 3p^2 + 11p$$
$$0 = p(3p + 11)$$
$$p = 0 \quad \text{or} \quad p = -\dfrac{11}{3}$$

Region	Test Point	$\dfrac{p}{p+4} \leq 3p$ Result
A: $(-\infty, -4)$	-5	$\dfrac{-5}{-1} \leq 3(-5)$ False
B: $\left(-4, -\dfrac{11}{3}\right]$	-3.9	$\dfrac{-3.9}{0.1} \leq 3(-3.9)$ True
C: $\left[-\dfrac{11}{3}, 0\right]$	-1	$\dfrac{-1}{3} \leq 3(-1)$ False
D: $[0, \infty)$	1	$\dfrac{1}{5} \leq 3(1)$ True

Solution: $\left(-4, -\dfrac{11}{3}\right] \cup [0, \infty)$

54. $\dfrac{(2x-3)^2}{x} < 0$

$$x = \dfrac{3}{2} \quad \text{or} \quad x = 0$$

Region	Test Point	$\dfrac{(2x-3)^2}{x} < 0$ Result
$A: (-\infty, 0)$	-1	$\dfrac{25}{-1} < 0$ True
$B: \left(0, \dfrac{3}{2}\right)$	1	$\dfrac{1}{1} < 0$ False
$C: \left(\dfrac{3}{2}, \infty\right)$	2	$\dfrac{1}{2} < 0$ False

Solution: $(-\infty, 0)$

56. $H(x) = |x| - 2$

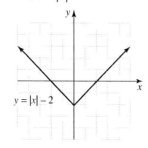

$y = |x| - 2$

58. $h(x) = |x| + 5$

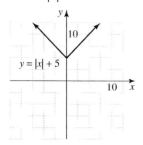

$y = |x| + 5$

60. $h(x) = x^2 - 4$

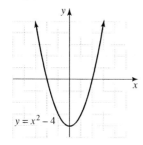

$y = x^2 - 4$

62. $g(x) = x^2 + 3$

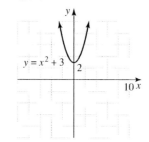

$y = x^2 + 3$

64. Answers may vary

66. Let $x =$ the number. Then

$\dfrac{1}{x}$ = the reciprocal of the number.

$2x + \dfrac{1}{x} \geq 0$

$\dfrac{2x^2 + 1}{x} \geq 0$

$x = 0$

Region	Test Point	$\dfrac{2x^2 + 1}{x} \geq 0$ Result
$A: (-\infty, 0)$	-1	$\dfrac{3}{-1} \geq 0$ False
$B: (0, \infty)$	1	$\dfrac{3}{1} \geq 0$ True

Any number greater than 0 and its reciprocal satisfy the conditions.

68. $s(t) = -16t^2 + 80t$

$-16t^2 + 80t > 96$

$-16(t^2 - 5t + 6) > 0$

$-16(t - 2)(t - 3) > 0$

$t = 2 \text{ or } t = 3$

Region	Test Point	$-16(t-2)(t-3) > 0$ Result
A: (0, 2)	1	$-16(-1)(-2) > 0$ False
B: (2, 3)	2.5	$-16(0.5)(-0.5) > 0$ True
C: (3, ∞)	4	$-16(2)(1) > 0$ False

The height of the projectile is greater than 96 feet between 2 and 3 seconds.

70.

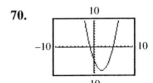

72.

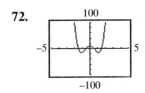

The Bigger Picture

1. $|x-8| = |2x+1|$

$x-8 = 2x+1$ or $x-8 = -(2x+1)$

$-9 = x$ $\qquad$ $x-8 = -2x-1$

$\qquad\qquad\qquad$ $3x = 7$

$\qquad\qquad\qquad$ $x = \dfrac{7}{3}$

2. $0 < -x+7 < 3$

$-7 < -x < -4$

$7 > x > 4$

$4 < x < 7$

Solution: (4, 7)

3. $\sqrt{3x-11} + 3 = x$

$\sqrt{3x-11} = x-3$

$3x-11 = (x-3)^2$

$3x-11 = x^2 - 6x + 9$

$0 = x^2 - 9x + 20$

$0 = (x-4)(x-5)$

$x-4 = 0$ or $x-5 = 0$

$x = 4$ $\qquad$ $x = 5$

The solutions are 4 and 5.

4. $x(3x+1) = 1$

$3x^2 + x - 1 = 0$

$a = 3, b = 1, c = -1$

$x = \dfrac{-1 \pm \sqrt{1^2 - 4(3)(-1)}}{2(3)}$

$= \dfrac{-1 \pm \sqrt{1+12}}{6}$

$= \dfrac{-1 \pm \sqrt{13}}{6}$

The solutions are $\dfrac{-1+\sqrt{13}}{6}$ and $\dfrac{-1-\sqrt{13}}{6}$.

5. $\dfrac{x+2}{x-7} \le 0$

$x - 7 = 0$, so $x = 7$ makes the denominator 0.

$\dfrac{x+2}{x-7} = 0$

$x + 2 = 0$

$x = -2$

Region	Test Point	$\dfrac{x+2}{x-7} \le 0$ Result
A: (−∞, −2]	−3	$\dfrac{-1}{-10} \le 0$ False
B: [−2, 7)	0	$\dfrac{2}{-7} \le 0$
C: (7, ∞)	8	$\dfrac{10}{1} \le 0$ False

Solution: [−2, 7)

6. $x(x-6) + 4 = x^2 - 2(3-x)$

$x^2 - 6x + 4 = x^2 - 6 + 2x$

$-6x + 4 = -6 + 2x$

$10 = 8x$

$\dfrac{5}{4} = x$

The solution is $\dfrac{5}{4}$.

7. $x(5x - 36) = -7$

$5x^2 - 36x + 7 = 0$

$a = 5, \; b = -36, \; c = 7$

$$x = \frac{-(-36) \pm \sqrt{(-36)^2 - 4(5)(7)}}{2(5)}$$

$$= \frac{36 \pm \sqrt{1156}}{10}$$

$$= \frac{36 \pm 34}{10}$$

$x = \dfrac{36 + 34}{10} = \dfrac{70}{10} = 7$ or $x = \dfrac{36 - 34}{10} = \dfrac{2}{10} = \dfrac{1}{5}$

The solutions are 7 and $\dfrac{1}{5}$.

8. $2x^2 - 4 \geq 7x$

Solve $2x^2 - 4 = 7x$.

$2x^2 - 7x - 4 = 0$

$(2x + 1)(x - 4) = 0$

$2x + 1 = 0$ or $x - 4 = 0$

$2x = -1$ $x = 4$

$x = -\dfrac{1}{2}$

Region	Test Point	$2x^2 - 4 \geq 7x$ Result
$A: \left(-\infty, -\dfrac{1}{2}\right]$	-1	$2 - 4 \geq -7$ True
$B: \left[-\dfrac{1}{2}, 4\right]$	0	$-4 \geq 0$ False
$C: [4, \infty)$	5	$50 - 4 \geq 35$ True

Solution: $\left(-\infty, -\dfrac{1}{2}\right] \cup [4, \infty)$

9. $\left|\dfrac{x-7}{3}\right| > 5$

$\dfrac{x-7}{3} > 5$ or $\dfrac{x-7}{3} < -5$

$x - 7 > 15$ or $x - 7 < -15$

$x > 22$ or $x < -8$

Solution: $(-\infty, -8) \cup (22, \infty)$

10. $2(x - 5) + 4 < 1 + 7(x - 5) - x$

$2x - 10 + 4 < 1 + 7x - 35 - x$

$2x - 6 < 6x - 34$

$28 < 4x$

$7 < x$

Solution: $(7, \infty)$

Section 8.5

Practice Exercises

1.   **a.** $f(x) = x^2 - 5$

The graph of $f(x)$ is obtained by shifting the graph of $y = x^2$ downward 5 units.

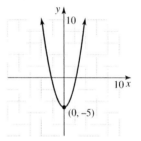

b. $g(x) = x^2 + 3$

The graph of $g(x)$ is obtained by shifting the graph of $y = x^2$ upward 3 units.

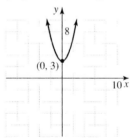

2.   **a.** $G(x) = (x + 4)^2$

The graph of $G(x)$ is obtained by shifting the graph of $y = x^2$ to the left 4 units.

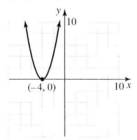

b. $H(x) = (x-7)^2$

The graph of $H(x)$ is obtained by shifting the graph of $y = x^2$ to the right 7 units.

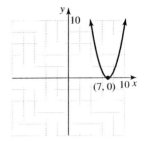

(7, 0) 10 x

3. $f(x) = (x+2)^2 + 2$

The graph of $f(x)$ is the graph of $y = x^2$ shifted 2 units to the left and 2 units upward. The vertex is then $(-2, 2)$, and the axis of symmetry is $x = -2$.

x	$f(x) = (x+2)^2 + 2$
-4	6
-3	3
-1	3
0	6

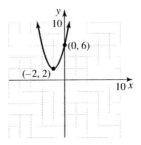

(0, 6)

(−2, 2)

10 x

4. $f(x) = -\frac{1}{2}x^2$

Because $a = -\frac{1}{2}$, a negative value, this parabola opens downward. Since $\left|-\frac{1}{2}\right| = \frac{1}{2} < 1$, the parabola is wider than the graph of $y = x^2$. The vertex is $(0, 0)$, and the axis of symmetry is the y-axis.

x	$f(x) = -\frac{1}{2}x^2$
-2	-2
-1	$-\frac{1}{2}$
0	0
1	$-\frac{1}{2}$
2	-2

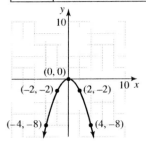

(0, 0)

(−2, −2)   (2, −2)   10 x

(−4, −8)   (4, −8)

5. $h(x) = \frac{1}{3}(x-4)^2 - 3$

This graph is the same as $y = x^2$ shifted 4 units to the right and 3 units downward, and it is wider because a is $\frac{1}{3}$. The vertex is $(4, -3)$, and the axis of symmetry is $x = 4$.

x	$h(x) = \frac{1}{3}(x-4)^2 - 3$
2	$-\frac{5}{3}$
3	$-\frac{8}{3}$
4	-3
5	$-\frac{8}{3}$
6	$-\frac{5}{3}$

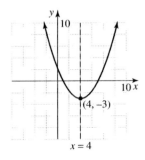

(4, −3)   10 x

$x = 4$

Vocabulary and Readiness Check

1. A <u>quadratic</u> function is one that can be written in the form $f(x) = ax^2 + bx + c$, $a \neq 0$.

2. The graph of a quadratic function is a <u>parabola</u> opening <u>upward</u> or <u>downward</u>.

3. If $a > 0$, the graph of the quadratic function opens <u>upward</u>.

4. If $a < 0$, the graph of the quadratic function opens <u>downward</u>.

5. The vertex of a parabola is the <u>lowest</u> point if $a > 0$.

6. The vertex of a parabola is the <u>highest</u> point if $a < 0$.

7. $f(x) = x^2$; vertex: $(0, 0)$

8. $f(x) = -5x^2$; vertex: $(0, 0)$

9. $g(x) = (x-2)^2$; vertex: $(2, 0)$

10. $g(x) = (x+5)^2$; vertex: $(-5, 0)$

11. $f(x) = 2x^2 + 3$; vertex: $(0, 3)$

12. $h(x) = x^2 - 1$; vertex: $(0, -1)$

13. $g(x) = (x+1)^2 + 5$; vertex: $(-1, 5)$

14. $h(x) = (x-10)^2 - 7$; vertex: $(10, -7)$

Exercise Set 8.5

2. The graph of $g(x) = x^2 + 3$ is the graph of $y = x^2$ shifted up 3 units. The vertex is then $(0, 3)$, and the axis of symmetry is $x = 0$.

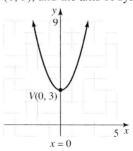

4. The graph of $h(x) = x^2 - 4$ is the graph of $y = x^2$ shifted down 4 units. The vertex is then $(0, -4)$, and the axis of symmetry is $x = 0$.

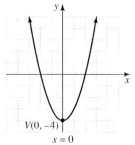

6. The graph of $f(x) = x^2 - 2$ is the graph of $y = x^2$ shifted down 2 units. The vertex is then $(0, -2)$, and the axis of symmetry is $x = 0$.

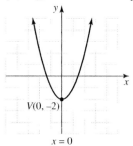

8. The graph of $g(x) = (x+5)^2$ is the graph of $y = x^2$ shifted left 5 units. The vertex is then $(-5, 0)$, and the axis of symmetry is $x = -5$.

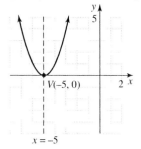

10. The graph of $H(x) = (x-1)^2$ is the graph of $y = x^2$ shifted right 1 unit. The vertex is then $(1, 0)$, and the axis of symmetry is $x = 1$.

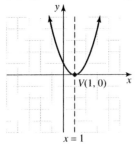

12. The graph of $f(x) = (x-6)^2$ is the graph of $y = x^2$ shifted right 6 units. The vertex is then $(6, 0)$, and the axis of symmetry is $x = 6$.

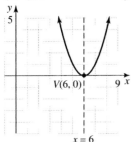

14. The graph of $g(x) = (x-6)^2 + 1$ is the graph of $y = x^2$ shifted right 6 units and up 1 unit. The vertex is then $(6, 1)$, and the axis of symmetry is $x = 6$.

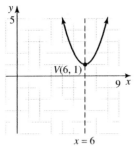

16. The graph of $G(x) = (x+3)^2 + 3$ is the graph of $y = x^2$ shifted left 3 units and up 3 units. The vertex is then $(-3, 3)$, and the axis of symmetry is $x = -3$.

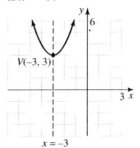

18. The graph of $h(x) = (x+4)^2 - 6$ is the graph of $y = x^2$ shifted left 4 units and down 6 units. The vertex is then $(-4, -6)$, and the axis of symmetry is $x = -4$.

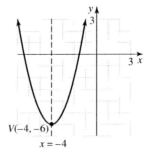

20. The graph of $f(x) = 5x^2$ is the graph of $y = x^2$ but made narrower. The vertex is then $(0, 0)$, and the axis of symmetry is $x = 0$.

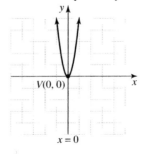

22. The graph of $f(x) = -\dfrac{1}{4}x^2$ is the graph of

$y = x^2$ but opening down and made wider. The vertex is then $(0, 0)$, and the axis of symmetry is $x = 0$.

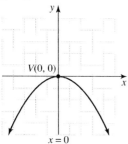

24. The graph of $g(x) = -3x^2$ is the graph of

$y = x^2$ but opening down and made narrower. The vertex is then $(0, 0)$, and the axis of symmetry is $x = 0$.

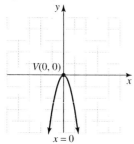

26. The graph of $g(x) = 4(x-4)^2 + 2$ is the graph of

$y = x^2$ shifted right 4 units, made narrower, and shifted up 2 units. The vertex is then $(4, 2)$, and the axis of symmetry is $x = 4$.

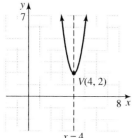

28. The graph of $f(x) = -(x-2)^2 - 6$ is the graph

of $y = x^2$ shifted right 2 units, opening down, and shifted down 6 units. The vertex is then $(2, -6)$, and the axis of symmetry is $x = 2$.

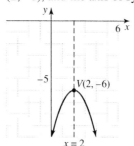

30. The graph of $G(x) = \dfrac{1}{5}(x+4)^2 + 3$ is the graph

of $y = x^2$ shifted left 4 units, made wider, and shifted up 3 units. The vertex is then $(-4, 3)$, and the axis of symmetry is $x = -4$.

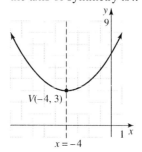

32. The graph of $g(x) = -(x+6)^2$ is the graph of

$y = x^2$ shifted left 6 units and opening down. The vertex is then $(-6, 0)$, and the axis of symmetry is $x = -6$.

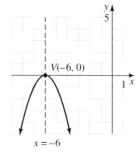

34. The graph of $H(x) = -x^2 + 10$ is the graph of

$y = x^2$ opening down and then shifted up

10 units. The vertex is then (0, 10), and the axis

of symmetry is $x = 0$.

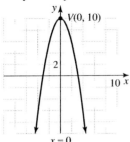

36. The graph of $g(x) = \frac{1}{2}x^2 - 2$ is the graph of

$y = x^2$ made wider and then shifted down

2 units. The vertex is then (0, −2), and the axis of

symmetry is $x = 0$.

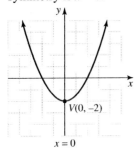

38. The graph of $f(x) = (x-5)^2 + 2$ is the graph of

$y = x^2$ shifted right 5 units and up 2 units. The

vertex is then (5, 2), and the axis of symmetry is

$x = 5$.

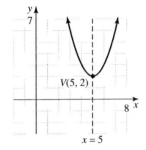

40. The graph of $H(x) = \left(x + \frac{1}{2}\right)^2 - 3$ is the graph

of $y = x^2$ shifted left $\frac{1}{2}$ unit and down 3 units.

The vertex is then $\left(-\frac{1}{2}, -3\right)$, and the axis of

symmetry is $x = -\frac{1}{2}$.

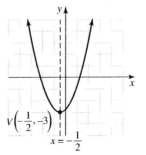

42. The graph of $g(x) = -\frac{3}{2}(x-1)^2 - 5$ is the graph

of $y = x^2$ shifted right 1 unit, made narrower,

opening down, and shifted down 5 units. The

vertex is then (1, −5), and the axis of symmetry

is $x = 1$.

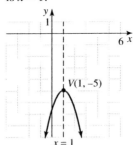

44. The graph of $H(x) = \frac{3}{4}x^2 - 2$ is the graph of

$y = x^2$ made wider and shifted down 2 units.

The vertex is then (0, −2), and the axis of

symmetry is $x = 0$.

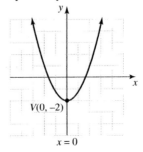

46. The graph of $F(x) = 3\left(x - \dfrac{3}{2}\right)^2$ is the graph of

$y = x^2$ shifted right $\dfrac{3}{2}$ units and made narrower.

The vertex is then $\left(\dfrac{3}{2}, 0\right)$, and the axis of

symmetry is $x = \dfrac{3}{2}$.

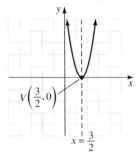

48. The graph of $f(x) = -3(x+2)^2 + 2$ is the graph

of $y = x^2$ shifted left 2 units, made narrower,
opening down, and shifted up 2 units. The vertex
is then $(-2, 2)$, and the axis of symmetry is
$x = -2$.

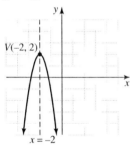

50. The graph of $G(x) = \sqrt{5}(x-7)^2 - \dfrac{1}{2}$ is the graph

of $y = x^2$ shifted right 7 units, made narrower,

and shifted down $\dfrac{1}{2}$ unit. The vertex is then

$\left(7, -\dfrac{1}{2}\right)$, and the axis of symmetry is $x = 7$.

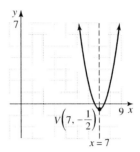

52. The graph of $h(x) = 8(x+1)^2 + 9$ is the graph of

$y = x^2$ shifted left 1 unit, made narrower, and
shifted up 9 units. The vertex is then $(-1, 9)$, and
the axis of symmetry is $x = -1$.

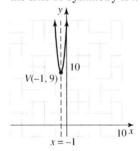

54. The graph of $G(x) = -4(x+9)^2 - 1$ is the graph

of $y = x^2$ shifted left 9 units, made narrower,
opening down, and shifted down 1 unit. The
vertex is then $(-9, -1)$, and the axis of symmetry
is $x = -9$.

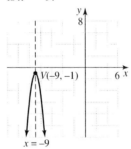

56. $y^2 + 4y$

$$\left[\dfrac{1}{2}(4)\right]^2 = (2)^2 = 4$$

$y^2 + 4y + 4$

58. $x^2 - 10x$

$$\left[\dfrac{1}{2}(-10)\right]^2 = (-5)^2 = 25$$

$x^2 - 10x + 25$

60. $z^2 - 3z$

$$\left[\frac{1}{2}(-3)\right]^2 = \left(-\frac{3}{2}\right)^2 = \frac{9}{4}$$

$$z^2 - 3z + \frac{9}{4}$$

62. $\qquad y^2 + 6y = -5$

$$y^2 + 6y + \left(\frac{6}{2}\right)^2 = -5 + 9$$

$$(y+3)^2 = 4$$

$$y + 3 = \pm 2$$

$$y = -3 \pm 2$$

$$y = -5 \text{ or } -1$$

The solutions are −5 and −1.

64. $\qquad x^2 + 14x + 20 = 0$

$$x^2 + 14x = -20$$

$$x^2 + 14x + \left(\frac{14}{2}\right)^2 = -20 + 49$$

$$(x+7)^2 = 29$$

$$x + 7 = \pm\sqrt{29}$$

$$x = -7 \pm \sqrt{29}$$

The solutions are $-7 + \sqrt{29}$ and $-7 - \sqrt{29}$.

66. $\qquad y^2 - 10y = 3$

$$y^2 - 10y + \left(\frac{-10}{2}\right)^2 = 3 + 25$$

$$(y-5)^2 = 28$$

$$y - 5 = \pm 2\sqrt{7}$$

$$y = 5 \pm 2\sqrt{7}$$

The solutions are $5 + 2\sqrt{7}$ and $5 - 2\sqrt{7}$.

68. $f(x) = 5\left(x + \frac{1}{2}\right)^2 + \frac{1}{2}$

Since 5 > 0, the graph opens upward.

$x - h = x + \frac{1}{2}$, so $h = -\frac{1}{2}$, and $k = \frac{1}{2}$.

$(h, k) = \left(-\frac{1}{2}, \frac{1}{2}\right)$

The correct description is **b**.

70. We need a function with the form:

$$f(x) = 5(x - h)^2 + k$$

Since the vertex is $(h, k) = (1, 6)$, we get:

$$f(x) = 5(x - 1)^2 + 6$$

72. We need a function with the form:

$$f(x) = 5(x - h)^2 + k$$

Since the vertex is $(h, k) = (4, -1)$, we get:

$$f(x) = 5(x - 4)^2 + (-1)$$

$$= 5(x - 4)^2 - 1$$

74. $y = f(x) - 2$

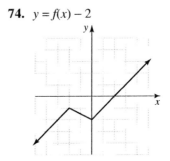

76. $h = f(x + 3)$

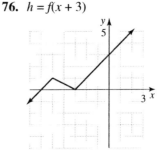

78. $y = f(x - 1) + 1$

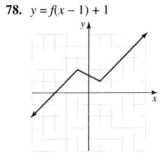

80. $f(x) = 668.8x^2 - 2990.1x + 939$

a. $x = 2012 - 1985 = 27$

$$f(27) = 668.8(27)^2 - 2990.1(27) + 939$$

$$= 407{,}761.5$$

There will be 407,762 thousand subscribers.

b. Answers may vary—around 300,000,000.

c. Answers may vary

Section 8.6

Practice Exercises

1. $g(x) = x^2 - 2x - 3$

Write in the form $y = (x-h)^2 + k$ by completing the square.
$$y = x^2 - 2x - 3$$
$$y + 3 = x^2 - 2x$$
$$y + 3 + \left(\frac{-2}{2}\right)^2 = x^2 - 2x + \left(\frac{-2}{2}\right)^2$$
$$y + 4 = x^2 - 2x + 1$$
$$y = (x-1)^2 - 4$$
The vertex is at (1, –4).
Let $g(x) = 0$.
$$0 = x^2 - 2x - 3$$
$$0 = (x-3)(x+1)$$
$$x - 3 = 0 \quad \text{or} \quad x + 1 = 0$$
$$x = 3 \qquad\qquad x = -1$$
The *x*-intercepts are (3, 0) and (–1, 0).
Let $x = 0$.
$$g(0) = 0^2 - 2(0) - 3 = -3$$
The *y*-intercept is (0, –3).

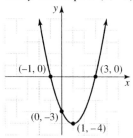

2. Graph $y_1 = x^2 - x - 6$ in a standard window.

Since the parabola opens upward, use the minimum feature.

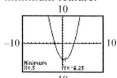

The vertex is (0.5, –6.25) and the axis of symmetry is the line $x = 0.5$.

3. $g(x) = 4x^2 + 4x + 3$

Replace $g(x)$ with y and complete the square to write the equation in the form $y = a(x-h)^2 + k$.
$$y = 4x^2 + 4x + 3$$
$$y - 3 = 4x^2 + 4x = 4(x^2 + x)$$
$$y - 3 + 4\left(\frac{1}{2}\right)^2 = 4\left[x^2 + x + \left(\frac{1}{2}\right)^2\right]$$
$$y - 3 + 1 = 4\left(x^2 + x + \frac{1}{4}\right)$$
$$y = 4\left(x + \frac{1}{2}\right)^2 + 2$$

$a = 4$, $h = -\frac{1}{2}$, and $k = 2$.
The parabola opens upward with vertex $\left(-\frac{1}{2}, 2\right)$, and has an axis of symmetry $x = -\frac{1}{2}$.
Let $x = 0$.
$$g(0) = 4(0)^2 + 4(0) + 3 = 3$$
The *y*-intercept is (0, 3). There are no *x*-intercepts.

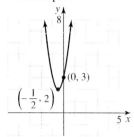

4. $g(x) = x^2 - 2x - 3$

$a = 1$, $b = -2$, and $c = -3$
$$\frac{-b}{2a} = \frac{-(-2)}{2(1)} = \frac{2}{2} = 1$$
The *x*-value of the vertex is 1.
$$g(1) = 1^2 - 2(1) - 3 = 1 - 2 - 3 = -4$$
The vertex is (1, –4).

5.

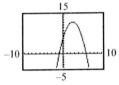

For $g(x) = -x^2 + 5x + 6$, $a = -1$, $b = 5$, and $c = 6$.

$$x = \frac{-b}{2a} = \frac{-5}{2(-1)} = \frac{5}{2}$$

$$g\left(\frac{5}{2}\right) = \frac{49}{4}$$

The vertex is $\left(\frac{5}{2}, \frac{49}{4}\right)$.

$g(0) = 6$, so the y-intercept is $(0, 6)$.
Let y or $g(x) = 0$.

$$g(x) = -x^2 + 5x + 6$$
$$0 = -x^2 + 5x + 6$$
$$0 = -(x^2 - 5x - 6)$$
$$0 = -(x+1)(x-6)$$
$$x+1 = 0 \quad \text{or} \quad x-6 = 0$$
$$x = -1 \quad \text{or} \quad x = 6$$

The x-intercepts are $(-1, 0)$ and $(6, 0)$.

6. $h(t) = -16t^2 + 24t$

Find the vertex of $h(t)$ to find its maximum value.
$a = -16$, $b = 24$, and $c = 0$

$$\frac{-b}{2a} = \frac{-24}{2(-16)} = \frac{3}{4}$$

The t-value of the vertex is $\frac{3}{4}$.

$$h\left(\frac{3}{4}\right) = -16\left(\frac{3}{4}\right)^2 + 24\left(\frac{3}{4}\right)$$
$$= -16\left(\frac{9}{16}\right) + 18$$
$$= -9 + 18$$
$$= 9$$

The vertex is $\left(\frac{3}{4}, 9\right)$. Thus, the ball reaches its maximum height of 9 feet in $\frac{3}{4}$ second.

Vocabulary and Readiness Check

1. If a quadratic function is in the form $f(x) = a(x-h)^2 + k$, the vertex of its graph is (h, k).

2. The graph of $f(x) = ax^2 + bx + c$, $a \neq 0$ is a parabola whose vertex has x-value of $\underline{\frac{-b}{2a}}$.

	Parabola Opens	Vertex Location	Number of x-intercept(s)	Number of y-intercept(s)
3.	up	Q I	0	1
4.	up	Q III	2	1
5.	down	Q II	2	1
6.	down	Q IV	0	1
7.	up	x-axis	1	1
8.	down	x-axis	1	1
9.	down	Q III	0	
10.	down	Q I	2	
11.	up	Q IV	2	
12.	up	Q II	0	

Exercise Set 8.6

2. $f(x) = x^2 + 6x + 5$

$-\dfrac{b}{2a} = \dfrac{-6}{2(1)} = -3$ and

$f(-3) = (-3)^2 + 6(-3) + 5 = -4$

Thus, the vertex is $(-3, -4)$.

4. $f(x) = -x^2 - 8x + 2$

$-\dfrac{b}{2a} = \dfrac{-(-8)}{2(-1)} = -4$ and

$f(-4) = -(-4)^2 - 8(-4) + 2 = 18$

Thus, the vertex is $(-4, 18)$.

6. $f(x) = -3x^2 + 6x + 4$

$-\dfrac{b}{2a} = \dfrac{-6}{2(-3)} = 1$ and

$f(1) = -3(1)^2 + 6(1) + 4 = 7$

Thus, the vertex is $(1, 7)$.

8. $f(x) = x^2 - 9x + 8$

$-\dfrac{b}{2a} = \dfrac{-(-9)}{2(1)} = \dfrac{9}{2}$ and

$f\left(\dfrac{9}{2}\right) = \left(\dfrac{9}{2}\right)^2 - 9\left(\dfrac{9}{2}\right) + 8 = -\dfrac{49}{4}$

Thus, the vertex is $\left(\dfrac{9}{2}, -\dfrac{49}{4}\right)$.

10. $f(x) = x^2 + 2x - 3$

$-\dfrac{b}{2a} = \dfrac{-2}{2(1)} = -1$ and

$f(-1) = (-1)^2 + 2(-1) - 3 = -4$

The vertex is $(-1, -4)$, so the graph is A.

12. $f(x) = x^2 + 4x + 3$

$-\dfrac{b}{2a} = \dfrac{-4}{2(1)} = -2$ and

$f(-2) = (-2)^2 + 4(-2) + 3 = -1$

The vertex is $(-2, -1)$, so the graph is C.

14. $f(x) = x^2 + 2x - 3$

$-\dfrac{b}{2a} = \dfrac{-2}{2(1)} = -1$ and

$f(-1) = (-1)^2 + 2(-1) - 3 = -4$

Thus, the vertex is $(-1, -4)$.

The graph opens upward $(a = 1 > 0)$.

$x^2 + 2x - 3 = 0$

$(x+3)(x-1) = 0$

$x = -3$ or $x = 1$

x-intercepts: $(-3, 0)$ and $(1, 0)$.

$f(0) = -3$; y-intercept is $(0, -3)$.

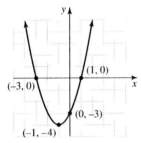

16. $f(x) = -x^2 + 4x - 4$

$-\dfrac{b}{2a} = \dfrac{-4}{2(-1)} = 2$ and

$f(2) = -(2)^2 + 4(2) - 4 = 0$

Thus, the vertex is $(2, 0)$.

The graph opens downward $(a = -1 < 0)$.

$-x^2 + 4x - 4 = 0$

$x^2 - 4x + 4 = 0$

$(x-2)^2 = 0$

$x = 2$

x-intercept: $(2, 0)$.

$f(0) = -4$; y-intercept is $(0, -4)$.

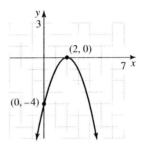

18. $f(x) = x^2 - 1$

$-\dfrac{b}{2a} = \dfrac{-0}{2(1)} = 0$ and

$f(0) = (0)^2 - 1 = -1$

Thus, the vertex is $(0, -1)$.

The graph opens upward $(a = 1 > 0)$.

$x^2 - 1 = 0$

$(x+1)(x-1) = 0$

$x = -1$ or $x = 1$

x-intercepts: $(-1, 0)$ and $(1, 0)$.

$f(0) = -1$; y-intercept is $(0, -1)$.

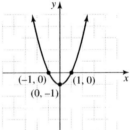

20. $f(x) = 2x^2 - x - 3$

$-\dfrac{b}{2a} = \dfrac{-(-1)}{2(2)} = \dfrac{1}{4}$ and

$f\left(\dfrac{1}{4}\right) = 2\left(\dfrac{1}{4}\right)^2 - \left(\dfrac{1}{4}\right) - 3 = -\dfrac{25}{8}$

Thus, the vertex is $\left(\dfrac{1}{4}, -\dfrac{25}{8}\right)$.

The graph opens upward $(a = 2 > 0)$.

$2x^2 - x - 3 = 0$

$(2x-3)(x+1) = 0$

$x = \dfrac{3}{2}$ or $x = -1$

x-intercepts: $\left(\dfrac{3}{2}, 0\right)$ and $(-1, 0)$.

$f(0) = -3$, so the y-intercept is $(0, -3)$.

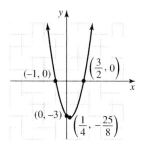

22.
$$f(x) = x^2 + 10x + 9$$
$$y = x^2 + 10x + 9$$
$$y - 9 = x^2 + 10x$$
$$y - 9 + 25 = x^2 + 10x + 25$$
$$y + 16 = (x + 5)^2$$
$$f(x) = (x + 5)^2 - 16$$

Thus, the vertex is $(-5, -16)$.
The graph opens upward ($a = 1 > 0$).
$$x^2 + 10x + 9 = 0$$
$$(x + 9)(x + 1) = 0$$
$$x = -9 \text{ or } x = -1$$
x-intercepts: $(-9, 0)$ and $(-1, 0)$.
$f(0) = 9$; y-intercept is $(0, 9)$.

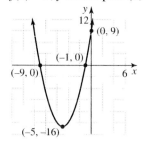

24.
$$f(x) = x^2 - 4x + 3$$
$$y - 3 = x^2 - 4x$$
$$y - 3 + 4 = x^2 - 4x + 4$$
$$y + 1 = (x - 2)^2$$
$$f(x) = (x - 2)^2 - 1$$

Thus, the vertex is $(2, -1)$.
The graph opens upward ($a = 1 > 0$).
$$x^2 - 4x + 3 = 0$$
$$(x - 3)(x - 1) = 0$$
$$x = 3 \text{ or } x = 1$$
x-intercepts: $(3, 0)$ and $(1, 0)$.
$f(0) = 3$; y-intercept is $(0, 3)$.

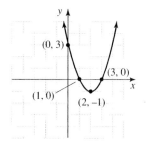

26.
$$f(x) = x^2 - 6x + 11$$
$$y - 11 = x^2 - 6x$$
$$y - 11 + 9 = x^2 - 6x + 9$$
$$y - 2 = (x - 3)^2$$
$$f(x) = (x - 3)^2 + 2$$

Thus, the vertex is $(3, 2)$.
The graph opens upward ($a = 1 > 0$).
$$x^2 - 6x + 11 = 0$$
$$x = \frac{6 \pm \sqrt{(-6)^2 - 4(1)(11)}}{2(1)} = \frac{6 \pm \sqrt{-8}}{2}$$
which give non-real solutions.
Hence, there are no x-intercepts.
$f(0) = 11$; y-intercept is $(0, 11)$.

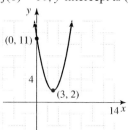

28.
$$f(x) = 3x^2 + 12x + 16$$
$$y - 16 = 3(x^2 + 4x)$$
$$y - 16 + 3(4) = 3(x^2 + 4x + 4)$$
$$y - 4 = 3(x + 2)^2$$
$$f(x) = 3(x + 2)^2 + 4$$

Thus, the vertex is $(-2, 4)$.
The graph opens upward ($a = 3 > 0$).
$$3x^2 + 12x + 16 = 0$$
$$x = \frac{-12 \pm \sqrt{(12)^2 - 4(3)(16)}}{2(3)}$$
$$= \frac{-12 \pm \sqrt{-48}}{6}$$
which give non-real solutions.
Hence, there are no x-intercepts.
$f(0) = 16$; y-intercept is $(0, 16)$.

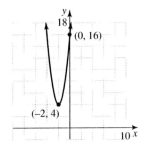

30.
$$f(x) = -4x^2 + 8x$$
$$y = -4(x^2 - 2x)$$
$$y + [-4(1)] = -4(x^2 - 2x + 1)$$
$$y - 4 = -4(x-1)^2$$
$$f(x) = -4(x-1)^2 + 4$$

Thus, the vertex is (1, 4).
The graph opens downward ($a = -4 < 0$).
$$-4x^2 + 8x = 0$$
$$-4x(x-2) = 0$$
$$x = 0 \text{ or } x = 2$$
x-intercepts: (0, 0) and (2, 0)
$f(0) = 0$; *y*-intercept is (0, 0).

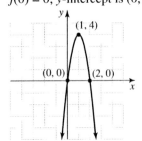

32. $f(x) = x^2 + 4$
$$x = -\frac{b}{2a} = -\frac{0}{2(1)} = 0$$
$$f(0) = (0)^2 + 4 = 4$$
Thus, the vertex is (0, 4).
The graph opens upward ($a = 1 > 0$).
$$x^2 + 4 = 0$$
$$x^2 = -4$$
which give non-real solutions.
Hence, there are no *x*-intercepts.
$f(0) = 4$ so the *y*-intercept is (0, 4).

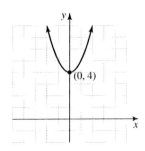

34.
$$f(x) = x^2 - x - 12$$
$$y + 12 = x^2 - x$$
$$y + 12 + \frac{1}{4} = x^2 - x + \frac{1}{4}$$
$$y + \frac{49}{4} = \left(x - \frac{1}{2}\right)^2$$
$$f(x) = \left(x - \frac{1}{2}\right)^2 - \frac{49}{4}$$

Thus, the vertex is $\left(\frac{1}{2}, -\frac{49}{4}\right)$. The graph opens
upward ($a = 1 > 0$).
$$x^2 - x - 12 = 0$$
$$(x-4)(x+3) = 0$$
$$x = 4 \text{ or } x = -3$$
x-intercepts: (4, 0) and (−3, 0).
$f(0) = -12$, so the *y*-intercept is (0, −12)

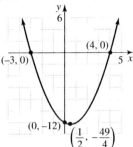

36. $f(x) = 3x^2 - 12x$
$$x = -\frac{b}{2a} = \frac{-(-12)}{2(3)} = 2 \text{ and}$$
$$f(2) = 3(2)^2 - 12(2) = -12$$
Thus, the vertex is (2, −12).
The graph opens upward ($a = 3 > 0$).
$$3x^2 - 12x = 0$$
$$3x(x-4) = 0$$
$$x = 0 \text{ or } x = 4$$
x-intercepts: (0, 0) and (4, 0)
$f(0) = 0$; *y*-intercept is (0, 0).

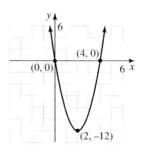

38. $f(x) = -x^2 + 8x - 17$

$x = -\dfrac{b}{2a} = \dfrac{-8}{2(-1)} = 4$ and

$f(4) = -(4)^2 + 8(4) - 17 = -1$

Thus, the vertex is $(4, -1)$.

The graph opens downward ($a = -1 < 0$).

$-x^2 + 8x - 17 = 0$

$x^2 - 8x + 17 = 0$

$x = \dfrac{8 \pm \sqrt{(-8)^2 - 4(1)(17)}}{2(1)} = \dfrac{8 \pm \sqrt{-4}}{2}$

which yields non-real solutions.

Hence, there are no x-intercepts.

$f(0) = -17$; y-intercept is $(0, -17)$.

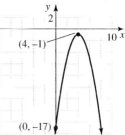

40. $f(x) = 2x^2 - 8x + 11$

$x = -\dfrac{b}{2a} = \dfrac{-(-8)}{2(2)} = 2$ and

$f(2) = 2(2)^2 - 8(2) + 11 = 3$

Thus, the vertex is $(2, 3)$.

The graph opens upward ($a = 2 > 0$).

$2x^2 - 8x + 11 = 0$

$x = \dfrac{8 \pm \sqrt{(-8)^2 - 4(2)(11)}}{2(2)} = \dfrac{8 \pm \sqrt{-24}}{4}$

which yields non-real solutions.

Hence, there are no x-intercepts.

$f(0) = 11$; so the y-intercept is $(0, 11)$.

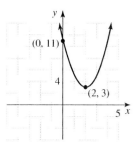

42. $f(x) = x^2 + 3x - 18$

$x = -\dfrac{b}{2a} = \dfrac{-3}{2(1)} = -\dfrac{3}{2}$ and

$f\left(-\dfrac{3}{2}\right) = \left(-\dfrac{3}{2}\right)^2 + 3\left(-\dfrac{3}{2}\right) - 18 = -\dfrac{81}{4}$

Thus, the vertex is $\left(-\dfrac{3}{2}, -\dfrac{81}{4}\right)$.

The graph opens upward ($a = 1 > 0$).

$x^2 + 3x - 18 = 0$

$(x + 6)(x - 3) = 0$

$x = -6$ or $x = 3$

x-intercepts: $(-6, 0)$ and $(3, 0)$.

$f(0) = -18$; y-intercept is $(0, -18)$.

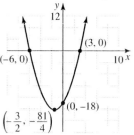

44. $f(x) = 3x^2 - 13x - 10$

$x = -\dfrac{b}{2a} = \dfrac{-(-13)}{2(3)} = \dfrac{13}{6}$ and

$f\left(\dfrac{13}{6}\right) = 3\left(\dfrac{13}{6}\right)^2 - 13\left(\dfrac{13}{6}\right) - 10 = -\dfrac{289}{12}$

Thus, the vertex is $\left(\dfrac{13}{6}, -\dfrac{289}{12}\right)$.

The graph opens upward ($a = 3 > 0$).

$3x^2 - 13x - 10 = 0$

$(3x + 2)(x - 5) = 0$

$x = -\dfrac{2}{3}$ or $x = 5$

x-intercepts: $(5, 0)$ and $\left(-\dfrac{2}{3}, 0\right)$.

$f(0) = -10$; y-intercept is $(0, -10)$.

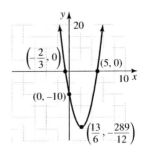

46. $h(t) = -16t^2 + 32t$

$t = -\dfrac{b}{2a} = \dfrac{-32}{2(-16)} = \dfrac{32}{32} = 1$ and

$h(1) = -16(1)^2 + 32(1)$
$= -16 + 32$
$= 16$

The maximum height is 16 feet.

48. $P(x) = 360x - x^2$

a. $x = -\dfrac{b}{2a} = \dfrac{-360}{2(-1)} = 180$

180 calendars are needed to maximize profit.

b. $P(180) = 360(180) - (180)^2 = 32,400$

The maximum profit is $32,400.

50. Let x = one number. Then
$11 - x$ = the other number.

$f(x) = x(11-x) = -x^2 + 11x$

The maximum will occur at the vertex.

$x = -\dfrac{b}{2a} = \dfrac{-11}{2(-1)} = 5.5$

$11 - x = 11 - 5.5 = 5.5$

The two numbers are 5.5 and 5.5.

52. Let x = one number. Then
$8 + x$ = the other number.

$f(x) = x(8+x) = x^2 + 8x$

The minimum will occur at the vertex.

$x = -\dfrac{b}{2a} = \dfrac{-8}{2(1)} = -4$

$8 + x = 8 + (-4) = 4$

The numbers are –4 and 4.

54. Let x = width. Then
$50 - x$ = the length.
Area = length · width

$A(x) = (50-x)x = -x^2 + 50x$

The maximum will occur at the vertex.

$x = -\dfrac{b}{2a} = \dfrac{-50}{2(-1)} = 25$

$50 - x = 50 - 25 = 25$

The maximum area will occur when the length and width are 25 units each.

56. The graph of $f(x) = (x-3)^2$ is the graph of $y = x^2$ shifted right 3 units. The vertex is then (3, 0), and the axis of symmetry is $x = 3$.

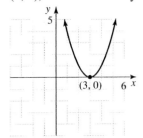

58. The graph of $h(x) = x - 3$ is the graph of $y = x$ shifted down 3 units.

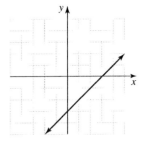

60. The graph of $f(x) = 2(x-3)^2 + 2$ is the graph of $y = x^2$ shifted right 3 units, made narrower, and shifted up 2 units. The vertex is then (3, 2), and the axis of symmetry is $x = 3$.

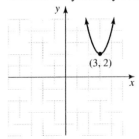

62. The graph of $f(x) = (x+1)^2 + 4$ is the graph of

$y = x^2$ shifted left 1 unit and shifted up

4 units. The vertex is then $(-1, 4)$, and the axis of

symmetry is $x = -1$.

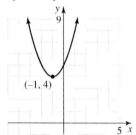

64. The graph of $f(x) = -2(x+7)^2 + \dfrac{1}{2}$ is the graph

of $y = x^2$ shifted left 7 units, made narrower,

opening down, and shifted up $\dfrac{1}{2}$ unit. The vertex

is then $\left(-7, \dfrac{1}{2}\right)$, and the axis of symmetry is $x =$

-7.

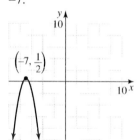

66. $g(x) = -7x^2 + x + 1$

Since $a = -7 < 0$, the graph opens downward;

thus, $g(x)$ has a maximum value.

68. $G(x) = 3 - \dfrac{1}{2}x + 0.8x^2$

Since $a = 0.8 > 0$, the graph opens upward; thus,

$G(x)$ has a minimum value.

70. $f(x) = x^2 - 6x + 4$

$x = -\dfrac{b}{2a} = \dfrac{-(-6)}{2(1)} = 3$ and

$f(3) = (3)^2 - 6(3) + 4 = -5$

Thus, the vertex is $(3, -5)$.

The graph opens upward $(a = 1 > 0)$.

$f(0) = 4$; y-intercept is $(0, 4)$.

$x^2 - 6x + 4 = 0$

$x = \dfrac{6 \pm \sqrt{(-6)^2 - 4(1)(4)}}{2(1)}$

$= \dfrac{6 \pm \sqrt{20}}{2} \approx 5.2 \text{ or } 0.8$

The x-intercepts are approximately $(0.8, 0)$ and

$(5.2, 0)$.

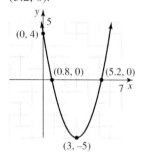

72. $f(x) = 2x^2 + 4x - 1$

$x = -\dfrac{b}{2a} = \dfrac{-4}{2(2)} = -1$ and

$f(-1) = 2(-1)^2 + 4(-1) - 1 = -3$

Thus, the vertex is $(-1, -3)$.

The graph opens upward $(a = 2 > 0)$.

$f(0) = -1$; y-intercept is $(0, -1)$.

$2x^2 + 4x - 1 = 0$

$x = \dfrac{-4 \pm \sqrt{(4)^2 - 4(2)(-1)}}{2(2)}$

$= \dfrac{-4 \pm \sqrt{24}}{4} \approx -2.2 \text{ or } 0.2$

The x-intercepts are approximately $(-2.2, 0)$ and

$(0.2, 0)$.

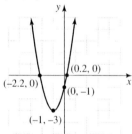

74. $f(x) = 7.6x^2 + 9.8x - 2.1$

$x = \dfrac{-9.8}{2(7.6)} \approx -0.64$

$f(-0.64) \approx -5.26$

minimum ≈ -5.26

Alternative solution:

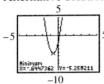

76. $f(x) = -5.2x^2 - 3.8x + 5.1$

$$x = \frac{-(-3.8)}{2(-5.2)} \approx -0.37$$

$f(-0.37) \approx 5.79$

maximum ≈ 5.79

Alternative solution:

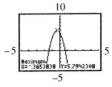

78. $f(x) = -0.072x^2 + 1.93x + 173.9$

a. $x = 2009 - 2000 = 9$

$$f(9) = -0.072(9)^2 + 1.93(9) + 173.9$$
$$= 185.438$$

According to the model, there will be about 185.44 million metric tons of methane emissions produced in the U.S. during 2009.

b. Since the coefficient of x^2 is negative, the graph will open down. Therefore, it will have a maximum.

c. $x = -\dfrac{b}{2a} = \dfrac{-1.93}{2(-0.072)} \approx 13.4$

$2000 + 13.4 = 2013.4$

According to the model, the methane emissions in the U.S. will reach a maximum in the year 2013.

d. $f(13) = -0.072(13)^2 + 1.93(13) + 173.9$
$$= 186.822$$

According to the model, the maximum methane emissions in the U.S. will be about 186.82 million metric tons.

Section 8.7

Practice Exercises

1. a.

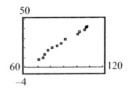

b.

The linear regression equation is $y = 0.869x - 52.044$. Store this in Y_1.

c.

The quadratic regression equation is

$y = -0.006x^2 + 2.033x - 103.516$. Store this in Y_2.

d. From the R^2 values, the quadratic equation is the better fit, although the R^2-values are both close to 1, as seen in the graphs.

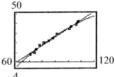

The cost of a first-class stamp is predicted to be 48¢ in 2020.

2. a.

The linear regression equation is $y = 0.064x + 22.933$.

b.

The quadratic regression equation is

$y = -9.967x^2 + 0.071x + 22.926.$

c.

The linear model predicts 23.8 MPG in 2013, while the quadratic model predicts 23.7 MPG.

d. Answers may vary

3. a.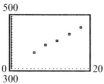

From the graph, a linear model appears to fit the data.

b.

The linear regression equation is $y = 7.767x + 316.6.$

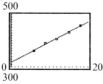

c.

Truck sales of 511 are predicted for 2015.

4. a.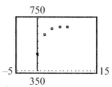

A quadratic model appears to fit the data.

b.

The quadratic regression equation is

$y = -5.214x^2 + 62.314x + 471.286.$

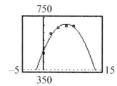

c.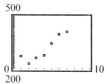

The expected funding in 2012 is $468.2 million.

5. a.

A quadratic model appears to fit the data.

The quadratic regression equation is

$y = 5.893x^2 - 17.679x + 266.429.$

b.

785 films are predicted to be released in 2011.

Exercise Set 8.7

2. The data appears to be linear.

4. The data appears to be neither linear nor quadratic.

6. The data appears to be quadratic.

8. The data appears to be quadratic.

10.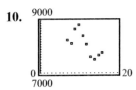

The data do not appear to be either linear or quadratic.

12.

The data appear to be quadratic.

The regression equation is

$$y = 0.719x^2 + 14.025x + 646.945.$$

Earnings in 2012 are predicted to be $1303.31.

14.

The quadratic regression equation is

$$y = 1.916x^2 + 2.528x + 3.582.$$

The number of households using personal rich media are predicted to be 310 million in 2012.

16. Answers may vary

18. a.

The linear regression model is
$$y = 15.357x + 13.929.$$

b.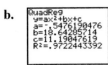

The quadratic regression model is

$$y = -0.548x^2 + 18.643x + 11.190.$$

c.

The linear model predicts 214 million North American broadband access lines in 2013; the quadratic model predicts 161 million.

20. a.

Based on the graph, it appears that a quadratic model would best fit the data.

b.

The quadratic model is

$$y = -4.990x^2 + 292.99x + 1844.291.$$

e.

The flip flops should be sold for about $29 to achieve the maximum profit.

22.

The data appears to be linear so we will fit a linear model.

The linear model is $y = 114.453x - 81,378.675$ where x is the number of square feet and y is the selling price in dollars.

24. The model from Exercise 22 is
$$y = 114.453x - 81,378.675.$$
Evaluate this model when $x = 2200$.
$$y = 114.453(2200) - 81,378.675$$
$$= 251,796.6 - 81,378.675$$
$$= 170,417.925$$

According to the model, a house with 2200 square feet will sell for about $170,418.

26.

The linear model for the data is
$y = -29.3x + 60{,}248.2$.
Use a table of values to get the predicted
consumption per person.

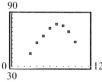

x (year)	Actual (per person)	Predicted (per person)	Difference
2000	1637	1648.2	-11.2
2001	1626	1618.9	7.1
2002	1609	1589.6	19.4
2003	1545	1560.3	-15.3

28.

Based on the graph, it appears that a quadratic
model would best fit the data.

The quadratic model of best fit is
$y = -1.994x^2 + 28.220x - 23.339$.
Answers may vary

30. Since the commission is given as a constant rate,
a linear model would best fit the relationship.

32. Since computing the area of a circle involves
squaring the radius, the relationship would best
be described with a quadratic model.

34. The temperatures will decline more quickly at
first and then decrease more slowly as the oven
temperature approaches the room temperature.
This implies that the data will have some
curvature, so the relationship would be described
better by a quadratic model.

36. The distance-traveled formula indicates that
distance is directly related to time ($d = r \cdot t$).
Therefore, assuming a constant rate of travel, the
relationship would best be described by a linear
model.

38. $(x-1)(x+19) = 0$
$x - 1 = 0$　or　$x + 19 = 0$
　　$x = 1$　or　$x = -19$
The solution set is $\{-19, 1\}$.

40. $6x^2 + 13x - 5 = 0$
$a = 6, b = 13, c = -5$
$$x = \frac{-13 \pm \sqrt{13^2 - 4(6)(-5)}}{2(6)}$$
$$= \frac{-13 \pm \sqrt{169 + 120}}{12}$$
$$= \frac{-13 \pm \sqrt{289}}{12}$$
$$= \frac{-13 \pm 17}{12}$$
$$x = -\frac{30}{12} = -\frac{5}{2} \quad \text{or} \quad x = \frac{4}{12} = \frac{1}{3}$$
The solution set is $\left\{ -\dfrac{5}{2}, \dfrac{1}{3} \right\}$.

42. $4(2x+7) = 2(x-4)$
$8x + 28 = 2x - 8$
$6x + 28 = -8$
$6x = -36$
$x = -6$
The solution set is $\{-6\}$.

44. $f(x) = 2x^3 + x^2 - 7x + 12$
To find the y-intercept, we evaluate the function
when $x = 0$.
$f(0) = 2(0)^3 + (0)^2 - 7(0) + 12 = 12$
The y-intercept is $(0, 12)$.

46. $g(x) = 3x^2 - 5x - 10$
To find the y-intercept, we evaluate the function
when $x = 0$.
$g(0) = 3(0)^2 - 5(0) - 10 = -10$
The y-intercept is $(0, -10)$.

Chapter 8 Vocabulary Check

1. The <u>discriminant</u> helps us find the number and type of solutions of a quadratic equation.

2. If $a^2 = b$, then $a = \underline{\pm\sqrt{b}}$.

3. The graph of $f(x) = ax^2 + bx + c$ where a is not 0 is a parabola whose vertex has x-value of $\underline{\dfrac{-b}{2a}}$.

4. A <u>quadratic inequality</u> is an inequality that can be written so that one side is a quadratic expression and the other side is 0.

5. The process of writing a quadratic equation so that one side is a perfect square trinomial is called <u>completing the square</u>.

6. The graph of $f(x) = x^2 + k$ has vertex <u>(0, k)</u>.

7. The graph of $f(x) = (x-h)^2$ has vertex <u>(h, 0)</u>.

8. The graph of $f(x) = (x-h)^2 + k$ has vertex <u>(h, k)</u>.

9. The formula $x = \dfrac{-b \pm \sqrt{b^2 - 4ac}}{2a}$ is called the <u>quadratic formula</u>.

10. A <u>quadratic</u> equation is one that can be written in the form $ax^2 + bx + c = 0$ where a, b, and c are real numbers and a is not 0.

Chapter 8 Review

1. $x^2 - 15x + 14 = 0$
$(x-14)(x-1) = 0$
$x - 14 = 0 \quad \text{or} \quad x - 1 = 0$
$\quad x = 14 \quad \text{or} \quad x = 1$
The solutions are 1 and 14.

2. $\quad 7a^2 = 29a + 30$
$7a^2 - 29a - 30 = 0$
$(7a+6)(a-5) = 0$
$7a + 6 = 0 \quad \text{or} \quad a - 5 = 0$
$\quad 7a = -6 \quad \text{or} \quad \quad a = 5$
$\quad a = -\dfrac{6}{7}$
The solutions are $-\dfrac{6}{7}$ and 5.

3. $4m^2 = 196$
$\quad m^2 = 49$
$\quad m = \pm\sqrt{49}$
$\quad m = \pm 7$
The solutions are -7 and 7.

4. $(5x-2)^2 = 2$
$\quad 5x - 2 = \pm\sqrt{2}$
$\quad\quad 5x = 2 \pm \sqrt{2}$
$\quad\quad\quad x = \dfrac{2 \pm \sqrt{2}}{5}$
The solutions are $\dfrac{2+\sqrt{2}}{5}$ and $\dfrac{2-\sqrt{2}}{5}$.

5. $\quad z^2 + 3z + 1 = 0$
$\quad z^2 + 3z = -1$
$z^2 + 3z + \left(\dfrac{3}{2}\right)^2 = -1 + \dfrac{9}{4}$
$\quad\quad \left(z + \dfrac{3}{2}\right)^2 = \dfrac{5}{4}$
$\quad\quad\quad z + \dfrac{3}{2} = \pm\sqrt{\dfrac{5}{4}}$
$\quad\quad\quad z + \dfrac{3}{2} = \pm\dfrac{\sqrt{5}}{2}$
$\quad\quad\quad\quad z = -\dfrac{3}{2} \pm \dfrac{\sqrt{5}}{2} = \dfrac{-3 \pm \sqrt{5}}{2}$
The solutions are $\dfrac{-3+\sqrt{5}}{2}$ and $\dfrac{-3-\sqrt{5}}{2}$.

6.
$$(2x+1)^2 = x$$
$$4x^2 + 4x + 1 = x$$
$$4x^2 + 3x = -1$$
$$x^2 + \frac{3}{4}x = -\frac{1}{4}$$
$$x^2 + \frac{3}{4}x + \left(\frac{\frac{3}{4}}{2}\right)^2 = -\frac{1}{4} + \frac{9}{64}$$
$$\left(x + \frac{3}{8}\right)^2 = -\frac{7}{64}$$
$$x + \frac{3}{8} = \pm\sqrt{-\frac{7}{64}}$$
$$x + \frac{3}{8} = \pm\frac{i\sqrt{7}}{8}$$
$$x = -\frac{3}{8} \pm \frac{i\sqrt{7}}{8} = \frac{-3 \pm i\sqrt{7}}{8}$$

The solutions are $\dfrac{-3+i\sqrt{7}}{8}$ and $\dfrac{-3-i\sqrt{7}}{8}$.

7.
$$A = P(1+r)^2$$
$$2717 = 2500(1+r)^2$$
$$\frac{2717}{2500} = (1+r)^2$$
$$(1+r)^2 = 1.0868$$
$$1 + r = \pm\sqrt{1.0868}$$
$$1 + r = \pm 1.0425$$
$$r = -1 \pm 1.0425$$
$$= 0.0425 \text{ or } -2.0425 \text{ (disregard)}$$

The interest rate is 4.25%.

8. Let x = distance traveled.
$$a^2 + b^2 = c^2$$
$$x^2 + x^2 = (150)^2$$
$$2x^2 = 22,500$$
$$x^2 = 11,250$$
$$x = \pm 75\sqrt{2} \approx \pm 106.1$$

Disregard the negative. The ships each traveled $75\sqrt{2} \approx 106.1$ miles.

9. Two complex but not real solutions exist.

10. Two real solutions exist.

11. Two real solutions exist.

12. One real solution exists.

13. $x^2 - 16x + 64 = 0$
$$a = 1,\, b = -16,\, c = 64$$
$$x = \frac{16 \pm \sqrt{(-16)^2 - 4(1)(64)}}{2(1)}$$
$$= \frac{16 \pm \sqrt{256 - 256}}{2}$$
$$= \frac{16 \pm \sqrt{0}}{2}$$
$$= 8$$

The solution is 8.

14. $x^2 + 5x = 0$
$$a = 1,\, b = 5,\, c = 0$$
$$x = \frac{-5 \pm \sqrt{(5)^2 - 4(1)(0)}}{2(1)}$$
$$= \frac{-5 \pm \sqrt{25}}{2}$$
$$= \frac{-5 \pm 5}{2}$$
$$= 0 \text{ or } -5$$

The solutions are –5 and 0.

15.
$$2x^2 + 3x = 5$$
$$2x^2 + 3x - 5 = 0$$
$$a = 2,\, b = 3,\, c = -5$$
$$x = \frac{-3 \pm \sqrt{(3)^2 - 4(2)(-5)}}{2(2)}$$
$$= \frac{-3 \pm \sqrt{49}}{4}$$
$$= \frac{-3 \pm 7}{4}$$
$$= 1 \text{ or } -\frac{5}{2}$$

The solutions are $-\dfrac{5}{2}$ and 1.

16.
$$9a^2 + 4 = 2a$$
$$9a^2 - 2a + 4 = 0$$
$$a = \frac{2 \pm \sqrt{(-2)^2 - 4(9)(4)}}{2(9)}$$
$$= \frac{2 \pm \sqrt{-140}}{18}$$
$$= \frac{2 \pm i\sqrt{4 \cdot 35}}{18}$$
$$= \frac{2 \pm 2i\sqrt{35}}{18}$$
$$= \frac{1 \pm i\sqrt{35}}{9}$$

The solutions are $\dfrac{1 + i\sqrt{35}}{9}$ and $\dfrac{1 - i\sqrt{35}}{9}$.

17.
$$6x^2 + 7 = 5x$$
$$6x^2 - 5x + 7 = 0$$
$$a = 6, b = -5, c = 7$$
$$x = \frac{5 \pm \sqrt{(-5)^2 - 4(6)(7)}}{2(6)}$$
$$= \frac{5 \pm \sqrt{25 - 168}}{12}$$
$$= \frac{5 \pm \sqrt{-143}}{12}$$
$$= \frac{5 \pm i\sqrt{143}}{12}$$

The solutions are $\dfrac{5 + i\sqrt{143}}{12}$ and $\dfrac{5 - i\sqrt{143}}{12}$.

18.
$$(2x - 3)^2 = x$$
$$4x^2 - 12x + 9 - x = 0$$
$$4x^2 - 13x + 9 = 0$$
$$a = 4, b = -13, c = 9$$
$$x = \frac{13 \pm \sqrt{(-13)^2 - 4(4)(9)}}{2(4)}$$
$$= \frac{13 \pm \sqrt{169 - 144}}{8}$$
$$= \frac{13 \pm \sqrt{25}}{8}$$
$$= \frac{13 \pm 5}{8}$$
$$= \frac{9}{4} \text{ or } 1$$

The solutions are 1 and $\dfrac{9}{4}$.

19. $d(t) = -16t^2 + 30t + 6$

a.
$$d(1) = -16(1)^2 + 30(1) + 6$$
$$= -16 + 30 + 6$$
$$= 20 \text{ feet}$$

b.
$$-16t^2 + 30t + 6 = 0$$
$$8t^2 - 15t - 3 = 0$$
$$a = 8, b = -15, c = -3$$
$$t = \frac{15 \pm \sqrt{(-15)^2 - 4(8)(-3)}}{2(8)}$$
$$= \frac{15 \pm \sqrt{225 + 96}}{16}$$
$$= \frac{15 \pm \sqrt{321}}{16}$$
Disregarding the negative, we have
$$t = \frac{15 + \sqrt{321}}{16} \text{ seconds}$$
$$\approx 2.1 \text{ seconds.}$$

20. Let x = length of the legs. Then
$x + 6$ = length of the hypotenuse.
$$x^2 + x^2 = (x + 6)^2$$
$$2x^2 = x^2 + 12x + 36$$
$$x^2 - 12x - 36 = 0$$
$$a = 1, b = -12, c = -36$$

$$x = \frac{12 \pm \sqrt{(-12)^2 - 4(1)(-36)}}{2(1)}$$

$$= \frac{12 \pm \sqrt{144 + 144}}{2}$$

$$= \frac{12 \pm \sqrt{144 \cdot 2}}{2}$$

$$= \frac{12 \pm 12\sqrt{2}}{2}$$

$$= 6 \pm 6\sqrt{2}$$

Disregard the negative. The length of each leg is $\left(6 + 6\sqrt{2}\right)$ cm.

21.

$$x^3 = 27$$

$$x^3 - 27 = 0$$

$$(x-3)(x^2 + 3x + 9) = 0$$

$$x - 3 = 0 \text{ or } x^2 + 3x + 9 = 0$$

$$x = 3 \quad\quad a = 1, b = 3, c = 9$$

$$x = \frac{-3 \pm \sqrt{(3)^2 - 4(1)(9)}}{2(1)}$$

$$= \frac{-3 \pm \sqrt{9 - 36}}{2}$$

$$= \frac{-3 \pm \sqrt{-27}}{2}$$

$$= \frac{-3 \pm 3i\sqrt{3}}{2}$$

The solutions are 3, $\dfrac{-3 + 3i\sqrt{3}}{2}$, and $\dfrac{-3 - 3i\sqrt{3}}{2}$.

22.

$$y^3 = -64$$

$$y^3 + 64 = 0$$

$$(y+4)(y^2 - 4y + 16) = 0$$

$$y + 4 = 0 \text{ or } y^2 - 4y + 16 = 0$$

$$y = -4 \quad\quad a = 1, b = -4, c = 16$$

$$y = \frac{4 \pm \sqrt{(-4)^2 - 4(1)(16)}}{2(1)}$$

$$= \frac{4 \pm \sqrt{16 - 64}}{2}$$

$$= \frac{4 \pm \sqrt{-48}}{2}$$

$$= \frac{4 \pm 4i\sqrt{3}}{2}$$

$$= 2 \pm 2i\sqrt{3}$$

The solutions are -4, $2 + 2i\sqrt{3}$, and $2 - 2i\sqrt{3}$.

23.

$$\frac{5}{x} + \frac{6}{x-2} = 3$$

$$x(x-2)\left(\frac{5}{x} + \frac{6}{x-2}\right) = 3x(x-2)$$

$$5(x-2) + 6x = 3x^2 - 6x$$

$$5x - 10 + 6x = 3x^2 - 6x$$

$$0 = 3x^2 - 17x + 10$$

$$0 = (3x - 2)(x - 5)$$

$$3x - 2 = 0 \text{ or } x - 5 = 0$$

$$x = \frac{2}{3} \text{ or } \quad x = 5$$

The solutions are $\dfrac{2}{3}$ and 5.

24.

$$x^4 - 21x^2 - 100 = 0$$

$$(x^2 - 25)(x^2 + 4) = 0$$

$$(x + 5)(x - 5)(x^2 + 4) = 0$$

$$x + 5 = 0 \quad \text{or} \quad x - 5 = 0 \text{ or } x^2 + 4 = 0$$

$$x = -5 \text{ or} \quad\quad x = 5 \text{ or} \quad\quad x^2 = -4$$

$$x = \pm 2i$$

The solutions are -5, 5, $-2i$, and $2i$.

25. $x^{2/3} - 6x^{1/3} + 5 = 0$

Let $y = x^{1/3}$. Then $y^2 = x^{2/3}$ and

$$y^2 - 6y + 5 = 0$$

$$(y - 5)(y - 1) = 0$$

$$y - 5 = 0 \quad \text{or} \quad y - 1 = 0$$

$$y = 5 \quad \text{or} \quad\quad y = 1$$

$$x^{1/3} = 5 \quad \text{or} \quad x^{1/3} = 1$$

$$x = 125 \text{ or} \quad\quad x = 1$$

The solutions are 1 and 125.

26.

$$5(x+3)^2 - 19(x+3) = 4$$

$$5(x+3)^2 - 19(x+3) - 4 = 0$$

Let $y = x + 3$. Then $y^2 = (x+3)^2$ and

$5y^2 - 19y - 4 = 0$

$(5y+1)(y-4) = 0$

$5y + 1 = 0$ or $y - 4 = 0$

$y = -\dfrac{1}{5}$ or $y = 4$

$x + 3 = -\dfrac{1}{5}$ or $x + 3 = 4$

$x = -\dfrac{16}{5}$ or $x = 1$

The solutions are $-\dfrac{16}{5}$ and 1.

27.
$$a^6 - a^2 = a^4 - 1$$
$$a^6 - a^4 - a^2 + 1 = 0$$
$$a^4(a^2 - 1) - 1(a^2 - 1) = 0$$
$$(a^2 - 1)(a^4 - 1) = 0$$
$$(a+1)(a-1)(a^2 + 1)(a^2 - 1) = 0$$
$$(a+1)(a-1)(a^2 + 1)(a+1)(a-1) = 0$$
$$(a+1)^2(a-1)^2(a^2 + 1) = 0$$
$$(a+1)^2 = 0 \text{ or } (a-1)^2 = 0 \text{ or } a^2 + 1 = 0$$
$$a+1 = 0 \text{ or } \quad a - 1 = 0 \text{ or } \quad a^2 = -1$$
$$a = -1 \text{ or } \quad\quad a = 1 \text{ or } \quad\quad a = \pm i$$
The solutions are -1, 1, $-i$, and i.

28. $y^{-2} + y^{-1} = 20$

$\dfrac{1}{y^2} + \dfrac{1}{y} = 20$

$1 + y = 20y^2$

$0 = 20y^2 - y - 1$

$0 = (5y + 1)(4y - 1)$

$5y + 1 = 0$ or $4y - 1 = 0$

$y = -\dfrac{1}{5}$ or $y = \dfrac{1}{4}$

The solutions are $-\dfrac{1}{5}$ and $\dfrac{1}{4}$.

29. Let $x =$ time for Jerome alone. Then $x - 1 =$ time for Tim alone.

$\dfrac{1}{x} + \dfrac{1}{x-1} = \dfrac{1}{5}$

$5(x-1) + 5x = x(x-1)$

$5x - 5 + 5x = x^2 - x$

$0 = x^2 - 11x + 5$

$a = 1, b = -11, c = 5$

$x = \dfrac{11 \pm \sqrt{(-11)^2 - 4(1)(5)}}{2(1)}$

$= \dfrac{11 \pm \sqrt{101}}{2}$

≈ 0.475 (disregard) or 10.525

Jerome: 10.5 hours
Tim: 9.5 hours

30. Let $x =$ the number; then

$\dfrac{1}{x} =$ the reciprocal of the number.

$x - \dfrac{1}{x} = -\dfrac{24}{5}$

$5x\left(x - \dfrac{1}{x}\right) = 5x\left(-\dfrac{24}{5}\right)$

$5x^2 - 5 = -24x$

$5x^2 + 24x - 5 = 0$

$(5x - 1)(x + 5) = 0$

$5x - 1 = 0$ or $x + 5 = 0$

$x = \dfrac{1}{5}$ or $x = -5$

Disregard the positive value as extraneous. The number is -5.

31. $2x^2 - 50 \le 0$

$2(x^2 - 25) \le 0$

$2(x + 5)(x - 5) \le 0$

$x + 5 = 0$ or $x - 5 = 0$

$x = -5$ or $x = 5$

Region	Test Point	$2(x+5)(x-5) \le 0$ Result
A: $(-\infty, -5]$	-6	$2(-1)(-11) \le 0$ False
B: $[-5, 5]$	0	$2(5)(-5) \le 0$ True
C: $[5, \infty)$	6	$2(11)(1) \le 0$ False

Solution: $[-5, 5]$

32.

$$\frac{1}{4}x^2 < \frac{1}{16}$$

$$x^2 < \frac{1}{4}$$

$$x^2 - \frac{1}{4} < 0$$

$$\left(x + \frac{1}{2}\right)\left(x - \frac{1}{2}\right) < 0$$

$$x + \frac{1}{2} = 0 \quad \text{or} \quad x - \frac{1}{2} = 0$$

$$x = -\frac{1}{2} \quad \text{or} \quad x = \frac{1}{2}$$

Region	Test Point	$\left(x + \frac{1}{2}\right)\left(x - \frac{1}{2}\right) < 0$ Result
$A: \left(-\infty, -\frac{1}{2}\right)$	-1	$\left(-\frac{1}{2}\right)\left(-\frac{3}{2}\right) < 0$ False
$B: \left(-\frac{1}{2}, \frac{1}{2}\right)$	0	$\left(\frac{1}{2}\right)\left(-\frac{1}{2}\right) < 0$ True
$C: \left(\frac{1}{2}, \infty\right)$	1	$\left(\frac{3}{2}\right)\left(\frac{1}{2}\right) < 0$ False

Solution: $\left(-\frac{1}{2}, \frac{1}{2}\right)$

33. $\dfrac{x-5}{x-6} < 0$

$x - 5 = 0$ or $x - 6 = 0$

$x = 5$ or $\quad x = 6$

Region	Test Point	$\dfrac{x-5}{x-6} < 0$ Result
$A: (-\infty, 5)$	0	$\dfrac{-5}{-6} < 0$ False
$B: (5, 6)$	$\dfrac{11}{2}$	$\dfrac{\frac{1}{2}}{-\frac{1}{2}} < 0$ True
$C: (6, \infty)$	7	$\dfrac{2}{1} < 0$ False

Solution: $(5, 6)$

34. $\quad (x^2 - 16)(x^2 - 1) > 0$

$(x+4)(x-4)(x+1)(x-1) > 0$

$x + 4 = 0$ or $x - 4 = 0$ or $x + 1 = 0$ or $x - 1 = 0$

$x = -4$ or $\quad x = 4$ or $\quad x = -1$ or $\quad x = 1$

Region	Test Point	$(x+4)(x-4)(x+1)(x-1) > 0$ Result
$A: (-\infty, -4)$	-5	$(-1)(-9)(-4)(-6) > 0$ True
$B: (-4, -1)$	-2	$(2)(-6)(-1)(-3) > 0$ False
$C: (-1, 1)$	0	$(4)(-4)(1)(-1) > 0$ True
$D: (1, 4)$	2	$(6)(-2)(3)(1) > 0$ False
$E: (4, \infty)$	5	$(9)(1)(6)(4) > 0$ True

Solution: $(-\infty, -4) \cup (-1, 1) \cup (4, \infty)$

35. $\dfrac{(4x+3)(x-5)}{x(x+6)} > 0$

$4x+3=0,\ x-5=0,\ x=0,\ \text{or}\ x+6=0$

$x=-\dfrac{3}{4},\ x=5,\ x=0,\ \text{or}\ x=-6$

Region	Test Point	$\dfrac{(4x+3)(x-5)}{x(x+6)} > 0$ Result
A: $(-\infty, -6)$	-7	$\dfrac{(-25)(-12)}{-7(-1)} > 0$ True
B: $\left(-6, -\dfrac{3}{4}\right)$	-3	$\dfrac{(-9)(-8)}{-3(3)} > 0$ False
C: $\left(-\dfrac{3}{4}, 0\right)$	$-\dfrac{1}{2}$	$\dfrac{(1)\left(-\frac{11}{2}\right)}{-\frac{1}{2}\left(\frac{11}{2}\right)} > 0$ True
D: $(0, 5)$	1	$\dfrac{(7)(-4)}{1(7)} > 0$ False
E: $(5, \infty)$	6	$\dfrac{(27)(1)}{6(12)} > 0$ True

Solution: $(-\infty, -6) \cup \left(-\dfrac{3}{4}, 0\right) \cup (5, \infty)$

36. $(x+5)(x-6)(x+2) \le 0$

$x+5=0\quad \text{or}\ x-6=0\ \text{or}\ x+2=0$

$x=-5\quad \text{or}\quad x=6\ \text{or}\quad x=-2$

Region	Test Point	$(x+5)(x-6)(x+2) \le 0$ Result
A: $(-\infty, -5]$	-6	$(-1)(-12)(-4) \le 0$ True
B: $[-5, -2]$	-3	$(2)(-9)(-1) \le 0$ False
C: $[-2, 6]$	0	$(5)(-6)(2) \le 0$ True
D: $[6, \infty)$	7	$(12)(1)(9) \le 0$ False

Solution: $(-\infty, -5] \cup [-2, 6]$

37. $x^3 + 3x^2 - 25x - 75 > 0$

$x^2(x+3) - 25(x+3) > 0$

$(x+3)(x^2 - 25) > 0$

$(x+3)(x+5)(x-5) > 0$

$x+3=0\quad \text{or}\ x+5=0\quad \text{or}\ x-5=0$

$x=-3\ \text{or}\qquad x=-5\ \text{or}\qquad x=5$

Region	Test Point	$(x+3)(x+5)(x-5) > 0$ Result
A: $(-\infty, -5)$	-6	$(-3)(-1)(-11) > 0$ False
B: $(-5, -3)$	-4	$(-1)(1)(-9) > 0$ True
C: $(-3, 5)$	0	$(3)(5)(-5) > 0$ False
D: $(5, \infty)$	6	$(9)(11)(1) > 0$ True

Solution: $(-5, -3) \cup (5, \infty)$

38. $\dfrac{x^2 + 4}{3x} \le 1$

The denominator equals 0 when $3x = 0$, or $x = 0$.

$$\dfrac{x^2 + 4}{3x} = 1$$

$$x^2 + 4 = 3x$$

$$x^2 - 3x + 4 = 0$$

$$x = \dfrac{3 \pm \sqrt{(-3)^2 - 4(1)(4)}}{2(1)} = \dfrac{3 \pm \sqrt{-7}}{2}$$

which yields non-real solutions.

Region	Test Point	$\dfrac{x^2+4}{3x} \le 1$ Result
$A: (-\infty, 0)$	-1	$\dfrac{5}{-3} \le 1$ True
$B: (0, \infty)$	1	$\dfrac{5}{3} \le 1$ False

Solution: $(\infty, 0)$

39. $\dfrac{(5x+6)(x-3)}{x(6x-5)} < 0$

$x = -\dfrac{6}{5}$ or $x = 3$ or $x = 0$ or $x = \dfrac{5}{6}$

Region	Test Point	$\dfrac{(5x+6)(x-3)}{x(6x-5)} < 0$ Result
$A: \left(-\infty, -\dfrac{6}{5}\right)$	-2	$\dfrac{(-4)(-5)}{-2(-17)} < 0$ False
$B: \left(-\dfrac{6}{5}, 0\right)$	-1	$\dfrac{(1)(-4)}{-1(-11)} < 0$ True
$C: \left(0, \dfrac{5}{6}\right)$	$\dfrac{1}{2}$	$\dfrac{\left(\frac{17}{2}\right)\left(-\frac{5}{2}\right)}{\frac{1}{2}(-2)} < 0$ False
$D: \left(\dfrac{5}{6}, 3\right)$	2	$\dfrac{(16)(-1)}{2(7)} < 0$ True
$E: (3, \infty)$	4	$\dfrac{(26)(1)}{4(19)} < 0$ False

Solution: $\left(-\dfrac{6}{5}, 0\right) \cup \left(\dfrac{5}{6}, 3\right)$

40. $\dfrac{3}{x-2} > 2$

The denominator is equal to 0 when $x - 2 = 0$, or $x = 2$.

$$\dfrac{3}{x-2} = 2$$
$$3 = 2(x-2)$$
$$3 = 2x - 4$$
$$7 = 2x$$
$$\dfrac{7}{2} = x$$

Region	Test Point	$\dfrac{3}{x-2} > 2$ Result
$A: (-\infty, 2)$	0	$\dfrac{3}{-2} > 2$ False
$B: \left(2, \dfrac{7}{2}\right)$	3	$\dfrac{3}{1} > 2$ True
$C: \left(\dfrac{7}{2}, \infty\right)$	5	$\dfrac{3}{3} > 2$ False

Solution: $\left(2, \dfrac{7}{2}\right)$

41. $f(x) = x^2 - 4$

Vertex: $(0, -4)$

Axis of symmetry: $x = 0$

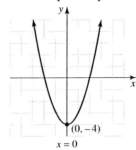

$x = 0$

42. $g(x) = x^2 + 7$

Vertex: (0, 7)

Axis of symmetry: $x = 0$

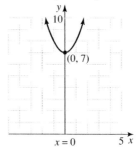

43. $H(x) = 2x^2$

Vertex: (0, 0)

Axis of symmetry: $x = 0$

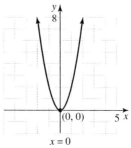

44. $h(x) = -\dfrac{1}{3}x^2$

Vertex: (0, 0)

Axis of symmetry: $x = 0$

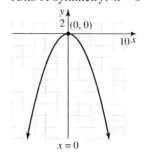

45. $F(x) = (x-1)^2$

Vertex: (1, 0)

Axis of symmetry: $x = 1$

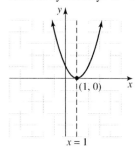

46. $G(x) = (x+5)^2$

Vertex: (−5, 0)

Axis of symmetry: $x = -5$

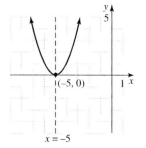

47. $f(x) = (x-4)^2 - 2$

Vertex: (4, −2)

Axis of symmetry: $x = 4$

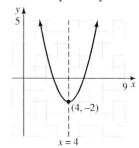

48. $f(x) = -3(x-1)^2 + 1$

Vertex: (1, 1)

Axis of symmetry: $x = 1$

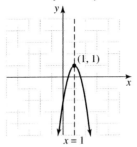

49. $f(x) = x^2 + 10x + 25$

$x = -\dfrac{b}{2a} = \dfrac{-10}{2(1)} = -5$

$f(-5) = (-5)^2 + 10(-5) + 25 = 0$

Vertex: (-5, 0)

$x^2 + 10x + 25 = 0$

$(x+5)^2 = 0$

$x + 5 = 0$

$x = -5$

x-intercept: (-5, 0)

$f(0) = 25$ so the y-intercept is (0, 25).

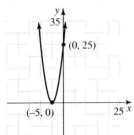

50. $f(x) = -x^2 + 6x - 9$

$x = -\dfrac{b}{2a} = \dfrac{-6}{2(-1)} = 3$

$f(3) = -(3)^2 + 6(3) - 9 = 0$

Vertex: (3, 0)

x-intercept: (3, 0)

$f(0) = -9$

y-intercept: (0, -9)

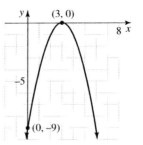

51. $f(x) = 4x^2 - 1$

$x = -\dfrac{b}{2a} = \dfrac{-0}{2(4)} = 0$

$f(0) = 4(0)^2 - 1 = -1$

Vertex: (0, -1)

$4x^2 - 1 = 0$

$(2x+1)(2x-1) = 0$

$x = -\dfrac{1}{2}$ or $x = \dfrac{1}{2}$

x-intercepts: $\left(-\dfrac{1}{2}, 0\right), \left(\dfrac{1}{2}, 0\right)$

$f(0) = -1$

y-intercept: (0, -1)

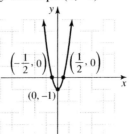

52. $f(x) = -5x^2 + 5$

$x = -\dfrac{b}{2a} = \dfrac{-0}{2(-5)} = 0$

$f(0) = -5(0)^2 + 5 = 5$

Vertex: (0, 5)

$-5x^2 + 5 = 0$

$-5x^2 = -5$

$x^2 = 1$

$x = \pm 1$

x-intercepts: (-1, 0), (1, 0)

$f(0) = 5$

y-intercept: (0, 5)

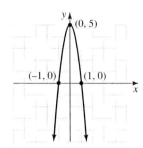

53. $f(x) = -3x^2 - 5x + 4$

$$x = -\frac{b}{2a} = \frac{-(-5)}{2(-3)} = -\frac{5}{6}$$

$$f\left(-\frac{5}{6}\right) = -3\left(-\frac{5}{6}\right)^2 - 5\left(-\frac{5}{6}\right) + 4 = \frac{73}{12}$$

Vertex: $\left(-\frac{5}{6}, \frac{73}{12}\right)$

The graph opens downward $(a = -3 < 0)$.

$f(0) = 4 \Rightarrow$ *y*-intercept: $(0, 4)$

$$-3x^2 - 5x + 4 = 0$$

$$x = \frac{5 \pm \sqrt{(-5)^2 - 4(-3)(4)}}{2(-3)}$$

$$= \frac{5 \pm \sqrt{73}}{-6}$$

$$\approx -2.2573 \text{ or } 0.5907$$

x-intercepts: $(-2.3, 0), (0.6, 0)$

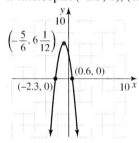

54. $h(t) = -16t^2 + 120t + 300$

   a. $\qquad\qquad 350 = -16t^2 + 120t + 300$

$$16t^2 - 120t + 50 = 0$$

$$8t^2 - 60t + 25 = 0$$

$$a = 8, b = -60, c = 25$$

$$t = \frac{60 \pm \sqrt{(-60)^2 - 4(8)(25)}}{2(8)}$$

$$= \frac{60 \pm \sqrt{2800}}{16}$$

$$\approx 0.4 \text{ second and } 7.1 \text{ seconds}$$

   b. The object will be at 350 feet on the way up and on the way down.

55. Let $x =$ one number; then
$420 - x =$ the other number.
Let $f(x)$ represent their product.

$$f(x) = x(420 - x)$$

$$= 420x - x^2$$

$$= -x^2 + 420x$$

$$x = -\frac{b}{2a} = \frac{-420}{2(-1)} = 210;$$

$$420 - x = 420 - 210 = 210$$

Therefore, the numbers are both 210.

56. $y = a(x - h)^2 + k$

vertex $(-3, 7)$ gives $y = a(x + 3)^2 + 7$.

Passing through the origin gives

$$0 = a(0 + 3)^2 + 7$$

$$-7 = 9a$$

$$-\frac{7}{9} = a$$

Thus, $y = -\frac{7}{9}(x + 3)^2 + 7$.

57. a.

The linear regression equation is
$y = 2.575x + 200.939$.

The linear model predicts a U.S. population of 317 million in 2015.

   b.

The quadratic regression equation is

$y = 0.017x^2 + 1.919x + 203.991$.

The quadratic model predicts a U.S. population of 325 million in 2015.

58. a.

The linear regression equation is
$y = 0.85x - 3.05$.

The linear model predicts sales of
$7.15 billion in 2012.

b.

The quadratic regression equation is
$y = 0.025x^2 + 0.575x - 2.325$.

The quadratic model predicts sales of
$8.175 billion in 2012.

59. $x^2 - x - 30 = 0$

$(x + 5)(x - 6) = 0$

$x + 5 = 0$ or $x - 6 = 0$

$x = -5$ or $x = 6$

The solutions are –5 and 6.

60. $(9n + 1)^2 = 9$

$9n + 1 = \pm\sqrt{9}$

$9n + 1 = \pm 3$

$9n = -1 \pm 3$

$n = \dfrac{-1 \pm 3}{9} = \dfrac{2}{9}, -\dfrac{4}{9}$

The solutions are $-\dfrac{4}{9}$ and $\dfrac{2}{9}$.

61. $x^2 + x + 7 = 0$

$x^2 + x = -7$

$x^2 + x + \left(\dfrac{1}{2}\right)^2 = -7 + \dfrac{1}{4}$

$\left(x + \dfrac{1}{2}\right)^2 = -\dfrac{27}{4}$

$x + \dfrac{1}{2} = \pm\sqrt{-\dfrac{27}{4}}$

$x + \dfrac{1}{2} = \pm\dfrac{i\sqrt{9 \cdot 3}}{2}$

$x + \dfrac{1}{2} = \pm\dfrac{3i\sqrt{3}}{2}$

$x = -\dfrac{1}{2} \pm \dfrac{3i\sqrt{3}}{2} = \dfrac{-1 \pm 3i\sqrt{3}}{2}$

The solutions are $\dfrac{-1 + 3i\sqrt{3}}{2}$ and $\dfrac{-1 - 3i\sqrt{3}}{2}$.

62. $(3x - 4)^2 = 10x$

$9x^2 - 24x + 16 = 10x$

$9x^2 - 34x = -16$

$x^2 - \dfrac{34}{9}x = -\dfrac{16}{9}$

$x^2 - \dfrac{34}{9}x + \left(\dfrac{-\dfrac{34}{9}}{2}\right)^2 = -\dfrac{16}{9} + \dfrac{289}{81}$

$\left(x - \dfrac{17}{9}\right)^2 = \dfrac{145}{81}$

$x - \dfrac{17}{9} = \pm\sqrt{\dfrac{145}{81}}$

$x - \dfrac{17}{9} = \pm\dfrac{\sqrt{145}}{9}$

$x = \dfrac{17 \pm \sqrt{145}}{9}$

The solutions are $\dfrac{17 + \sqrt{145}}{9}$ and $\dfrac{17 - \sqrt{145}}{9}$.

63. $x^2 + 11 = 0$

$a = 1, b = 0, c = 11$

$x = \dfrac{0 \pm \sqrt{(0)^2 - 4(1)(11)}}{2(1)}$

$= \dfrac{\pm\sqrt{-44}}{2}$

$= \dfrac{\pm 2i\sqrt{11}}{2}$

$= \pm i\sqrt{11}$

The solutions are $-i\sqrt{11}$ and $i\sqrt{11}$.

64. $(5a - 2)^2 - a = 0$

$25a^2 - 20a + 4 - a = 0$

$25a^2 - 21a + 4 = 0$

$a = \dfrac{21 \pm \sqrt{(-21)^2 - 4(25)(4)}}{2(25)}$

$= \dfrac{21 \pm \sqrt{441 - 400}}{50}$

$= \dfrac{21 \pm \sqrt{41}}{50}$

The solutions are $\dfrac{21 + \sqrt{41}}{50}$ and $\dfrac{21 - \sqrt{41}}{50}$.

65. $\dfrac{7}{8} = \dfrac{8}{x^2}$

$7x^2 = 64$

$x^2 = \dfrac{64}{7}$

$x = \pm\sqrt{\dfrac{64}{7}}$

$x = \pm\dfrac{8}{\sqrt{7}} = \pm\dfrac{8 \cdot \sqrt{7}}{\sqrt{7} \cdot \sqrt{7}} = \pm\dfrac{8\sqrt{7}}{7}$

The solutions are $-\dfrac{8\sqrt{7}}{7}$ and $\dfrac{8\sqrt{7}}{7}$.

66. $x^{2/3} - 6x^{1/3} = -8$

$x^{2/3} - 6x^{1/3} + 8 = 0$

Let $y = x^{1/3}$. Then $y^2 = x^{2/3}$ and

$y^2 - 6y + 8 = 0$

$(y - 4)(y - 2) = 0$

$y - 4 = 0$ or $y - 2 = 0$

$y = 4$ or $y = 2$

$x^{1/3} = 4$ or $x^{1/3} = 2$

$x = 64$ or $x = 8$

The solutions are 8 and 64.

67. $(2x - 3)(4x + 5) \geq 0$

$2x - 3 = 0$ or $4x + 5 = 0$

$x = \dfrac{3}{2}$ or $x = -\dfrac{5}{4}$

Region	Test Point	$(2x - 3)(4x + 5) \geq 0$ Result
$A: \left(-\infty, -\dfrac{5}{4}\right]$	-2	$(-7)(-3) \geq 0$ True
$B: \left[-\dfrac{5}{4}, \dfrac{3}{2}\right]$	0	$(-3)(5) \geq 0$ False
$C: \left[\dfrac{3}{2}, \infty\right)$	3	$(3)(17) \geq 0$ True

Solution: $\left(-\infty, -\dfrac{5}{4}\right] \cup \left[\dfrac{3}{2}, \infty\right)$

68. $\dfrac{x(x + 5)}{4x - 3} \geq 0$

$x = 0$ or $x + 5 = 0$ or $4x - 3 = 0$

           $x = -5$ or $x = \dfrac{3}{4}$

Region	Test Point	$\dfrac{x(x+5)}{4x-3} \geq 0$ Result
$A: (-\infty, -5]$	-6	$\dfrac{-6(-1)}{-27} \geq 0$ False
$B: [-5, 0]$	-1	$\dfrac{-1(4)}{-7} \geq 0$ True
$C: \left[0, \dfrac{3}{4}\right)$	$\dfrac{1}{2}$	$\dfrac{\frac{1}{2}\left(\frac{11}{2}\right)}{-1} \geq 0$ False
$D: \left(\dfrac{3}{4}, \infty\right)$	1	$\dfrac{1(6)}{1} \geq 0$ True

Solution: $[-5, 0] \cup \left(\dfrac{3}{4}, \infty\right)$

69. $\dfrac{3}{x-2} > 2$

The denominator is equal to 0 when $x - 2 = 0$, or $x = 2$.
$$\frac{3}{x-2} = 2$$
$$3 = 2(x-2)$$
$$3 = 2x - 4$$
$$7 = 2x$$
$$\frac{7}{2} = x$$

Region	Test Point	$\dfrac{3}{x-2} > 2$ Result
$A: (-\infty, 2)$	0	$\dfrac{3}{-2} > 2$ False
$B: \left(2, \dfrac{7}{2}\right)$	3	$\dfrac{3}{1} > 2$ True
$C: \left(\dfrac{7}{2}, \infty\right)$	5	$\dfrac{3}{3} > 2$ False

Solution: $\left(2, \dfrac{7}{2}\right)$

70. $y = 6.46x^2 + 1236.5x + 7289$

a. $x = 2000 - 1980 = 20$
$$y = 6.46(20)^2 + 1236.5(20) + 7289$$
$$= 34,603 \text{ thousand}$$
The passenger traffic was approximately 34,603,000.

b. Let $y = 60,000$.
$$60,000 = 6.46x^2 + 1236.5x + 7289$$
$$0 = 6.46x^2 + 1236.5x - 52,711$$
$$x = \frac{-1236.5 \pm \sqrt{1236.5^2 - 4(6.46)(-52,711)}}{2(6.46)}$$

Choosing the positive root, $x \approx 36$, we see that there will be 60,000,000 passengers in $1980 + 36 = 2016$.

Chapter 8 Test

1. $5x^2 - 2x = 7$
$$5x^2 - 2x - 7 = 0$$
$$(5x-7)(x+1) = 0$$
$$5x - 7 = 0 \quad \text{or} \quad x + 1 = 0$$
$$x = \frac{7}{5} \quad \text{or} \quad x = -1$$

The solutions are -1 and $\dfrac{7}{5}$.

2. $(x+1)^2 = 10$
$$x + 1 = \pm\sqrt{10}$$
$$x = -1 \pm \sqrt{10}$$
The solutions are $-1 + \sqrt{10}$ and $-1 - \sqrt{10}$.

3. $m^2 - m + 8 = 0$
$a = 1, b = -1, c = 8$
$$m = \frac{1 \pm \sqrt{(-1)^2 - 4(1)(8)}}{2(1)}$$
$$= \frac{1 \pm \sqrt{1 - 32}}{2}$$
$$= \frac{1 \pm \sqrt{-31}}{2}$$
$$= \frac{1 \pm i\sqrt{31}}{2}$$

The solutions are $\dfrac{1 + i\sqrt{31}}{2}$ and $\dfrac{1 - i\sqrt{31}}{2}$.

4. $u^2 - 6u + 2 = 0$

$a = 1, b = -6, c = 2$

$u = \dfrac{-(-6) \pm \sqrt{(-6)^2 - 4(1)(2)}}{2(1)}$

$= \dfrac{6 \pm \sqrt{36 - 8}}{2}$

$= \dfrac{6 \pm \sqrt{28}}{2}$

$= \dfrac{6 \pm 2\sqrt{7}}{2}$

$= 3 \pm \sqrt{7}$

The solutions are $3 + \sqrt{7}$ and $3 - \sqrt{7}$.

5. $7x^2 + 8x + 1 = 0$

$(7x + 1)(x + 1) = 0$

$7x + 1 = 0 \quad$ or $\quad x + 1 = 0$

$\quad 7x = -1 \qquad\qquad x = -1$

$\quad\ x = -\dfrac{1}{7}$

The solutions are $-\dfrac{1}{7}$ and -1.

6. $y^2 - 3y = 5$

$y^2 - 3y - 5 = 0$

$a = 1, b = -3, c = -5$

$y = \dfrac{3 \pm \sqrt{(-3)^2 - 4(1)(-5)}}{2(1)}$

$= \dfrac{3 \pm \sqrt{9 + 20}}{2}$

$= \dfrac{3 \pm \sqrt{29}}{2}$

The solutions are $\dfrac{3 + \sqrt{29}}{2}$ and $\dfrac{3 - \sqrt{29}}{2}$.

7. $\dfrac{4}{x + 2} + \dfrac{2x}{x - 2} = \dfrac{6}{x^2 - 4}$

$\dfrac{4}{x + 2} + \dfrac{2x}{x - 2} = \dfrac{6}{(x + 2)(x - 2)}$

$4(x - 2) + 2x(x + 2) = 6$

$4x - 8 + 2x^2 + 4x = 6$

$2x^2 + 8x - 14 = 0$

$x^2 + 4x - 7 = 0$

$a = 1, b = 4, c = -7$

$x = \dfrac{-4 \pm \sqrt{(4)^2 - 4(1)(-7)}}{2(1)}$

$= \dfrac{-4 \pm \sqrt{16 + 28}}{2}$

$= \dfrac{-4 \pm \sqrt{44}}{2}$

$= \dfrac{-4 \pm 2\sqrt{11}}{2}$

$= -2 \pm \sqrt{11}$

The solutions are $-2 + \sqrt{11}$ and $-2 - \sqrt{11}$.

8. $\qquad\qquad x^5 + 3x^4 = x + 3$

$\qquad\qquad x^5 + 3x^4 - x - 3 = 0$

$\qquad\qquad x^4(x + 3) - 1(x + 3) = 0$

$\qquad\qquad (x + 3)(x^4 - 1) = 0$

$(x + 3)(x^2 + 1)(x^2 - 1) = 0$

$x + 3 = 0 \quad$ or $\ x^2 + 1 = 0 \ $ or $\ x^2 - 1 = 0$

$\quad x = -3 \ $ or $\quad x^2 = -1 \ $ or $\quad x^2 = 1$

$\qquad\qquad\qquad\qquad x = \pm i \ $ or $\quad x = \pm 1$

The solutions are $-3, -1, 1, -i,$ and i.

9. $\qquad\qquad\qquad x^6 + 1 = x^4 + x^2$

$\qquad\qquad\qquad x^6 - x^4 - x^2 + 1 = 0$

$\qquad\qquad x^4(x^2 - 1) - (x^2 - 1) = 0$

$\qquad\qquad\qquad (x^4 - 1)(x^2 - 1) = 0$

$\ (x^2 + 1)(x^2 - 1)(x + 1)(x - 1) = 0$

$\quad (x^2 + 1)(x + 1)^2(x - 1)^2 = 0$

$x^2 + 1 = 0 \quad$ or $\ x + 1 = 0 \ $ or $\ x - 1 = 0$

$\quad x^2 = -1 \qquad\qquad x = -1 \qquad\quad x = 1$

$\quad\ x = \pm i$

The solutions are $-i, i, -1,$ and 1.

10. $(x + 1)^2 - 15(x + 1) + 56 = 0$

Let $y = x + 1$. Then $y^2 = (x + 1)^2$ and

$y^2 - 15y + 56 = 0$

$(y - 8)(y - 7) = 0$

$\quad y = 8 \quad$ or $\quad y = 7$

$x + 1 = 8 \ $ or $\ x + 1 = 7$

$\quad x = 7 \quad$ or $\quad x = 6$

The solutions are 6 and 7.

11.
$$x^2 - 6x = -2$$
$$x^2 - 6x + \left(\frac{-6}{2}\right)^2 = -2 + 9$$
$$x^2 - 6x + 9 = 7$$
$$(x-3)^2 = 7$$
$$x - 3 = \pm\sqrt{7}$$
$$x = 3 \pm \sqrt{7}$$

The solutions are $3 + \sqrt{7}$ and $3 - \sqrt{7}$.

12.
$$2a^2 + 5 = 4a$$
$$2a^2 - 4a = -5$$
$$a^2 - 2a = -\frac{5}{2}$$
$$a^2 - 2a + \left(\frac{-2}{2}\right)^2 = -\frac{5}{2} + 1$$
$$a^2 - 2a + 1 = -\frac{3}{2}$$
$$(a-1)^2 = -\frac{3}{2}$$
$$a - 1 = \pm\sqrt{-\frac{3}{2}} = \pm\frac{i\sqrt{3}}{\sqrt{2}}$$
$$a - 1 = \pm\frac{i\sqrt{6}}{2}$$
$$a = 1 \pm \frac{i\sqrt{6}}{2} \quad \text{or} \quad \frac{2 \pm i\sqrt{6}}{2}$$

The solutions are $\dfrac{2 + i\sqrt{6}}{2}$ and $\dfrac{2 - i\sqrt{6}}{2}$.

13.
$$2x^2 - 7x > 15$$
$$2x^2 - 7x - 15 > 0$$
$$(2x + 3)(x - 5) > 0$$
$$2x + 3 = 0 \quad \text{or} \quad x - 5 = 0$$
$$x = -\frac{3}{2} \quad \text{or} \quad x = 5$$

Region	Test Point	$(2x + 3)(x - 5) > 0$ Result
A: $\left(-\infty, -\dfrac{3}{2}\right)$	-2	$(-1)(-7) > 0$ True
B: $\left(-\dfrac{3}{2}, 5\right)$	0	$(3)(-5) > 0$ False
C: $(5, \infty)$	6	$(15)(1) > 0$ True

Solution: $\left(-\infty, -\dfrac{3}{2}\right) \cup (5, \infty)$

14.
$$(x^2 - 16)(x^2 - 25) \geq 0$$
$$(x+4)(x-4)(x+5)(x-5) \geq 0$$
$$x+4 = 0 \quad \text{or} \quad x-4 = 0 \quad \text{or} \quad x+5 = 0 \quad \text{or} \quad x-5 = 0$$
$$x = -4 \quad \text{or} \quad x = 4 \quad \text{or} \quad x = -5 \quad \text{or} \quad x = 5$$

Region	Test Point	$(x+4)(x-4)(x+5)(x-5) \geq 0$ Result
A: $(-\infty, -5]$	-6	$(-2)(-10)(-1)(-11) \geq 0$ True
B: $[-5, -4]$	$-\dfrac{9}{2}$	$\left(-\dfrac{1}{2}\right)\left(-\dfrac{17}{2}\right)\left(\dfrac{1}{2}\right)\left(-\dfrac{19}{2}\right) \geq 0$ False
C: $[-4, 4]$	0	$(4)(-4)(5)(-5) \geq 0$ True
D: $[4, 5]$	$\dfrac{9}{2}$	$\left(\dfrac{17}{2}\right)\left(\dfrac{1}{2}\right)\left(\dfrac{19}{2}\right)\left(-\dfrac{1}{2}\right) \geq 0$ False
E: $[5, \infty)$	6	$(10)(2)(11)(1) \geq 0$ True

Solution: $(-\infty, -5] \cup [-4, 4] \cup [5, \infty)$

15. $\dfrac{5}{x+3} < 1$

The denominator is equal to 0 when $x + 3 = 0$, or $x = -3$.

$$\dfrac{5}{x+3} = 1$$
$$5 = x+3 \quad \text{so} \quad x = 2$$

Region	Test Point	$\dfrac{5}{x+3} < 1$ Result
A: $(-\infty, -3)$	-4	$\dfrac{5}{-1} < 1$ True
B: $(-3, 2)$	0	$\dfrac{5}{3} < 1$ False
C: $(2, \infty)$	3	$\dfrac{5}{6} < 1$ True

Solution: $(-\infty, -3) \cup (2, \infty)$

16.

$$\frac{7x-14}{x^2-9} \le 0$$

$$\frac{7(x-2)}{(x+3)(x-3)} \le 0$$

$x-2=0$ or $x+3=0$ or $x-3=0$

$\quad x=2$ or $\quad x=-3$ or $\quad x=3$

Region	Test Point	$\dfrac{7(x-2)}{(x+3)(x-3)} \le 0$ Result
$A: (-\infty, -3)$	-4	$\dfrac{7(-6)}{(-1)(-7)} \le 0$ True
$B: (-3, 2]$	0	$\dfrac{7(-2)}{(3)(-3)} \le 0$ False
$C: [2, 3)$	$\dfrac{5}{2}$	$\dfrac{7\left(\frac{1}{2}\right)}{\left(\frac{11}{2}\right)\left(-\frac{1}{2}\right)} \le 0$ True
$D: (3, \infty)$	4	$\dfrac{7(2)}{(7)(1)} \le 0$ False

Solution: $(-\infty, -3) \cup [2, 3)$

17. $f(x) = 3x^2$

Vertex: $(0, 0)$

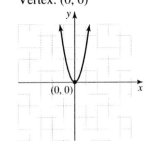

18. $G(x) = -2(x-1)^2 + 5$

Vertex: $(1, 5)$

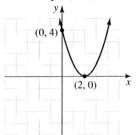

19. $h(x) = x^2 - 4x + 4$

$$x = -\frac{b}{2a} = \frac{-(-4)}{2(1)} = 2$$

$$h(2) = (2)^2 - 4(2) + 4 = 0$$

Vertex: $(2, 0)$

$h(0) = 4 \Rightarrow$ *y*-intercept: $(0, 4)$

x-intercept: $(2, 0)$

20. $F(x) = 2x^2 - 8x + 9$

$$x = -\frac{b}{2a} = \frac{-(-8)}{2(2)} = 2$$

$$F(2) = 2(2)^2 - 8(2) + 9 = 1$$

Vertex: $(2, 1)$

$F(0) = 9 \Rightarrow$ *y*-intercept: $(0, 9)$

$2x^2 - 8x + 9 = 0$

$a = 2, b = -8, c = 9$

$$x = \frac{8 \pm \sqrt{(-8)^2 - 4(2)(9)}}{2(2)}$$

$$= \frac{8 \pm \sqrt{-8}}{4}$$

which yields non-real solutons.

Therefore, there are no *x*-intercepts.

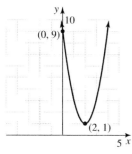

21. Let t = time for Sandy alone. Then $t - 2$ = time for Dave alone.

$$\frac{1}{t} + \frac{1}{t-2} = \frac{1}{4}$$
$$4(t-2) + 4t = t(t-2)$$
$$4t - 8 + 4t = t^2 - 2t$$
$$0 = t^2 - 10t + 8$$
$$a = 1, b = -10, c = 8$$
$$t = \frac{10 \pm \sqrt{(-10)^2 - 4(1)(8)}}{2(1)}$$
$$= \frac{10 \pm \sqrt{68}}{2}$$
$$= \frac{10 \pm 2\sqrt{17}}{2}$$
$$= 5 \pm \sqrt{17}$$
$$\approx 9.12 \text{ or } 0.88 \text{ (discard)}$$

It takes her about 9.12 hours.

22. $s(t) = -16t^2 + 32t + 256$

a. $t = -\frac{b}{2a} = \frac{-32}{2(-16)} = 1$

$s(1) = -16(1)^2 + 32(1) + 256 = 272$

Vertex: $(1, 272)$

The maximum height is 272 feet.

b. $-16t^2 + 32t + 256 = 0$
$$t^2 - 2t - 16 = 0$$
$$a = 1, b = -2, c = -16$$
$$t = \frac{2 \pm \sqrt{(-2)^2 - 4(1)(-16)}}{2(1)}$$
$$= \frac{2 \pm \sqrt{68}}{2}$$
$$= \frac{2 \pm 2\sqrt{17}}{2}$$
$$= 1 \pm \sqrt{17}$$
$$\approx -3.12 \text{ and } 5.12$$

Disregard the negative. The stone will hit the water in about 5.12 seconds.

23.
$$a^2 + b^2 = c^2$$
$$x^2 + (x+8)^2 = (20)^2$$
$$x^2 + (x^2 + 16x + 64) = 400$$
$$2x^2 + 16x - 336 = 0$$
$$x^2 + 8x - 168 = 0$$
$$a = 1, b = 8, c = -168$$
$$x = \frac{-8 \pm \sqrt{(8)^2 - 4(1)(-168)}}{2(1)}$$
$$= \frac{-8 \pm \sqrt{736}}{2}$$
$$\approx -17.565 \text{ or } 9.565$$

Disregard the negative.
$$x \approx 9.6$$
$$x + 8 \approx 9.6 + 8 = 17.6$$
$$17.6 + 9.6 = 27.2$$
$$27.2 - 20 = 7.2$$

They would save about 7 feet.

24. a. Let x = the number of years after 1990.

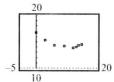

From the graph, the data appears quadratic.

b.

The quadratic regression equation is

$y = 0.025x^2 - 0.520x + 16.708$.

The model predicts a birth rate of 17.30 births per 1000 people in 2012.

Chapter 8 Cumulative Review

1. a. $5 + y \geq 7$

b. $11 \neq z$

c. $20 < 5 - 2x$

2. $|3x - 2| = -5$ which is impossible. Thus, there is no solution, or $\varnothing$.

3. $m = \dfrac{5-3}{2-0} = \dfrac{2}{2} = 1$

Plot the given points and draw a line through them.

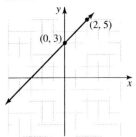

4. $\begin{cases} -6x + y = 5 \ \ (1) \\ 4x - 2y = 6 \ \ (2) \end{cases}$

Multiply E1 by 2 and add to E2.

$-12x + 2y = 10$

$\underline{4x - 2y = 6}$

$-8x = 16$

$x = -2$

Replace x with –2 in E1.

$-6(-2) + y = 5$

$12 + y = 5$

$y = -7$

The solution is $(-2, -7)$.

5. $\begin{cases} x - 5y = -12 \ \ (1) \\ -x + y = 4 \ (2) \end{cases}$

Add E1 and E2.

$-4y = -8$

$y = 2$

Replace y with 2 in E1.

$x - 5(2) = -12$

$x - 10 = -12$

$x = -2$

The solution is $(-2, 2)$.

6. a. $(a^{-2}bc^3)^{-3} = (a^{-2})^{-3}b^{-3}(c^3)^{-3}$

$\phantom{(a^{-2}bc^3)^{-3}} = a^6 b^{-3} c^{-9}$

$\phantom{(a^{-2}bc^3)^{-3}} = \dfrac{a^6}{b^3 c^9}$

b. $\left(\dfrac{a^{-4}b^2}{c^3}\right)^{-2} = \dfrac{(a^{-4})^{-2}(b^2)^{-2}}{(c^3)^{-2}}$

$\phantom{\left(\dfrac{a^{-4}b^2}{c^3}\right)^{-2}} = \dfrac{a^8 b^{-4}}{c^{-6}}$

$\phantom{\left(\dfrac{a^{-4}b^2}{c^3}\right)^{-2}} = \dfrac{a^8 c^6}{b^4}$

c. $\left(\dfrac{3a^8 b^2}{12a^5 b^5}\right)^{-2} = \left(\dfrac{a^3}{4b^3}\right)^{-2}$

$\phantom{\left(\dfrac{3a^8 b^2}{12a^5 b^5}\right)^{-2}} = \dfrac{(a^3)^{-2}}{4^{-2}(b^3)^{-2}}$

$\phantom{\left(\dfrac{3a^8 b^2}{12a^5 b^5}\right)^{-2}} = \dfrac{4^2 a^{-6}}{b^{-6}}$

$\phantom{\left(\dfrac{3a^8 b^2}{12a^5 b^5}\right)^{-2}} = \dfrac{16b^6}{a^6}$

7. a. $(2x - 7)(3x - 4) = 6x^2 - 8x - 21x + 28$

$ = 6x^2 - 29x + 28$

b. $(3x^2 + y)(5x^2 - 2y)$

$ = 15x^4 - 6x^2 y + 5x^2 y - 2y^2$

$ = 15x^4 - x^2 y - 2y^2$

8. a. $(4a - 3)(7a - 2) = 28a^2 - 8a - 21a + 6$

$ = 28a^2 - 29a + 6$

b. $(2a + b)(3a - 5b)$

$ = 6a^2 - 10ab + 3ab - 5b^2$

$ = 6a^2 - 7ab - 5b^2$

9. a. $8x^2 + 4 = 4(2x^2 + 1)$

b. $5y - 2z^4$ is a prime polynomial.

c. $6x^2 - 3x^3 + 12x^4 = 3x^2(2 - x + 4x^2)$

10. a. $9x^3 + 27x^2 - 15x = 3x(3x^2 + 9x - 5)$

b. $2x(3y - 2) - 5(3y - 2)$

$ = (3y - 2)(2x - 5)$

c. $2xy + 6x - y - 3 = 2x(y + 3) - 1(y + 3)$

$ = (y + 3)(2x - 1)$

11. $x^2 - 12x + 35 = (x - 5)(x - 7)$

12. $x^2 - 2x - 48 = (x + 6)(x - 8)$

13. $3a^2x - 12abx + 12b^2x = 3x(a^2 - 4ab + 4b^2)$
$$= 3x(a - 2b)(a - 2b)$$
$$= 3x(a - 2b)^2$$

14. $2ax^2 - 12axy + 18ay^2 = 2a(x^2 - 6xy + 9y^2)$
$$= 2a(x - 3y)(x - 3y)$$
$$= 2a(x - 3y)^2$$

15. $3(x^2 + 4) + 5 = -6(x^2 + 2x) + 13$
$$3x^2 + 12 + 5 = -6x^2 - 12x + 13$$
$$9x^2 + 12x + 4 = 0$$
$$(3x + 2)^2 = 0$$
$$3x + 2 = 0$$
$$3x = -2$$
$$x = -\frac{2}{3}$$

The solutions is $-\frac{2}{3}$.

16. $2(a^2 + 2) - 8 = -2a(a - 2) - 5$
$$2a^2 + 4 - 8 = -2a^2 + 4a - 5$$
$$4a^2 - 4a + 1 = 0$$
$$(2a - 1)^2 = 0$$
$$2a - 1 = 0$$
$$2a = 1$$
$$a = \frac{1}{2}$$

The solution is $\frac{1}{2}$.

17. $x^3 = 4x$
$$x^3 - 4x = 0$$
$$x(x^2 - 4) = 0$$
$$x(x + 2)(x - 2) = 0$$
$$x = 0 \quad \text{or} \quad x + 2 = 0 \quad \text{or} \quad x - 2 = 0$$
$$x = -2 \quad \text{or} \quad x = 2$$

The solutions are –2, 0, and 2.

18. $f(x) = x^2 + x - 12$
$$x = -\frac{b}{2a} = \frac{-1}{2(1)} = -\frac{1}{2}$$
$$f\left(-\frac{1}{2}\right) = \left(-\frac{1}{2}\right)^2 + \left(-\frac{1}{2}\right) - 12$$
$$= \frac{1}{4} - \frac{1}{2} - 12$$
$$= -\frac{49}{4}$$

Vertex: $\left(-\frac{1}{2}, -\frac{49}{4}\right)$

$$x^2 + x - 12 = 0$$
$$(x + 4)(x - 3) = 0$$
$$x + 4 = 0 \quad \text{or} \quad x - 3 = 0$$
$$x = -4 \quad\quad\quad x = 3$$

x-intercepts: $(-4, 0), (3, 0)$

$$f(0) = 0^2 + 0 - 12 = -12$$

y-intercept: $(0, -12)$

19. $\dfrac{2x^2}{10x^3 - 2x^2} = \dfrac{2x^2}{2x^2(5x - 1)} = \dfrac{1}{5x - 1}$

20. $\dfrac{x^2 - 4x + 4}{2 - x} = \dfrac{(x - 2)^2}{-(x - 2)} = \dfrac{x - 2}{-1} = 2 - x$

21. $\dfrac{2x - 1}{2x^2 - 9x - 5} + \dfrac{x + 3}{6x^2 - x - 2}$

$$= \frac{2x - 1}{(2x + 1)(x - 5)} + \frac{x + 3}{(2x + 1)(3x - 2)}$$

$$= \frac{(2x - 1)(3x - 2) + (x + 3)(x - 5)}{(2x + 1)(x - 5)(3x - 2)}$$

$$= \frac{(6x^2 - 4x - 3x + 2) + (x^2 - 5x + 3x - 15)}{(2x + 1)(x - 5)(3x - 2)}$$

$$= \frac{7x^2 - 9x - 13}{(2x + 1)(x - 5)(3x - 2)}$$

22. $\dfrac{a+1}{a^2-6a+8}-\dfrac{3}{16-a^2}$

$=\dfrac{a+1}{(a-4)(a-2)}-\dfrac{3}{(4+a)(4-a)}$

$=\dfrac{a+1}{(a-4)(a-2)}+\dfrac{3}{(4+a)(a-4)}$

$=\dfrac{(a+1)(a+4)+3(a-2)}{(a-4)(a-2)(a+4)}$

$=\dfrac{(a^2+4a+a+4)+3a-6}{(a-4)(a-2)(a+4)}$

$=\dfrac{a^2+8a-2}{(a-4)(a-2)(a+4)}$

23. $\dfrac{x^{-1}+2xy^{-1}}{x^{-2}-x^{-2}y^{-1}}=\dfrac{\dfrac{1}{x}+\dfrac{2x}{y}}{\dfrac{1}{x^2}-\dfrac{1}{x^2y}}$

$=\dfrac{\left(\dfrac{1}{x}+\dfrac{2x}{y}\right)x^2y}{\left(\dfrac{1}{x^2}-\dfrac{1}{x^2y}\right)x^2y}$

$=\dfrac{xy+2x^3}{y-1}$

24. $\dfrac{(2a)^{-1}+b^{-1}}{a^{-1}+(2b)^{-1}}=\dfrac{\dfrac{1}{2a}+\dfrac{1}{b}}{\dfrac{1}{a}+\dfrac{1}{2b}}$

$=\dfrac{\left(\dfrac{1}{2a}+\dfrac{1}{b}\right)2ab}{\left(\dfrac{1}{a}+\dfrac{1}{2b}\right)2ab}$

$=\dfrac{b+2a}{2b+a}$

$=\dfrac{2a+b}{a+2b}$

25. $\dfrac{3x^5y^2-15x^3y-x^2y-6x}{x^2y}$

$=\dfrac{3x^5y^2}{x^2y}-\dfrac{15x^3y}{x^2y}-\dfrac{x^2y}{x^2y}-\dfrac{6x}{x^2y}$

$=3x^3y-15x-1-\dfrac{6}{xy}$

26.
$$\begin{array}{r} x^2-6x+8 \\ x+3\overline{)x^3-3x^2-10x+24} \\ \underline{x^3+3x^2} \\ -6x^2-10x \\ \underline{-6x^2-18x} \\ 8x+24 \\ \underline{8x+24} \\ 0 \end{array}$$

Answer: x^2-6x+8

27. $P(x)=2x^3-4x^2+5$

a. $P(2)=2(2)^3-4(2)^2+5$
  $=2(8)-4(4)+5$
  $=16-16+5$
  $=5$

b.
$$\begin{array}{r|rrrr} 2 & 2 & -4 & 0 & 5 \\ & & 4 & 0 & 0 \\ \hline & 2 & 0 & 0 & 5 \end{array}$$
  Thus, $P(2)=5$.

28. $P(x)=4x^3-2x^2+3$

a. $P(-2)=4(-2)^3-2(-2)^2+3$
  $=4(-8)-2(4)+3$
  $=-32-8+3$
  $=-37$

b.
$$\begin{array}{r|rrrr} -2 & 4 & -2 & 0 & 3 \\ & & -8 & 20 & -40 \\ \hline & 4 & -10 & 20 & -37 \end{array}$$
  Thus, $P(-2)=-37$.

29.
  $\dfrac{4x}{5}+\dfrac{3}{2}=\dfrac{3x}{10}$
  $10\left(\dfrac{4x}{5}+\dfrac{3}{2}\right)=10\left(\dfrac{3x}{10}\right)$
  $2(4x)+5(3)=3x$
  $8x+15=3x$
  $5x=-15$
  $x=-3$
  The solution is -3.

30. $\dfrac{x+3}{x^2+5x+6}=\dfrac{3}{2x+4}-\dfrac{1}{x+3}$

$\dfrac{x+3}{(x+3)(x+2)}=\dfrac{3}{2(x+2)}-\dfrac{1}{x+3}$

$2(x+3)=3(x+3)-2(x+2)$

$2x+6=3x+9-2x-4$

$2x+6=x+5$

$x=-1$

31. Let $x=$ the number.

$\dfrac{9-x}{19+x}=\dfrac{1}{3}$

$3(9-x)=1(19+x)$

$27-3x=19+x$

$-4x=-8$

$x=2$

The number is 2.

32. Let $t=$ time to roof the house together.

$\dfrac{1}{24}+\dfrac{1}{40}=\dfrac{1}{t}$

$120t\left(\dfrac{1}{24}+\dfrac{1}{40}\right)=120t\left(\dfrac{1}{t}\right)$

$5t+3t=120$

$8t=120$

$t=\dfrac{120}{8}=15$

It would take them 15 hours to roof the house working together.

33. $y=kx$

$5=k(30)$

$k=\dfrac{5}{30}=\dfrac{1}{6}$ and $y=\dfrac{1}{6}x$

34. $y=\dfrac{k}{x}$

$8=\dfrac{k}{14}$

$k=8(14)=112$ and $y=\dfrac{112}{x}$

35. a. $\sqrt{(-3)^2}=|-3|=3$

    b. $\sqrt{x^2}=|x|$

    c. $\sqrt[4]{(x-2)^4}=|x-2|$

    d. $\sqrt[3]{(-5)^3}=-5$

    e. $\sqrt[5]{(2x-7)^5}=2x-7$

    f. $\sqrt{25x^2}=\sqrt{25}\cdot\sqrt{x^2}=5|x|$

    g. $\sqrt{x^2+2x+1}=\sqrt{(x+1)^2}=|x+1|$

36. a. $\sqrt{(-2)^2}=|-2|=2$

    b. $\sqrt{y^2}=|y|$

    c. $\sqrt[4]{(a-3)^4}=|a-3|$

    d. $\sqrt[3]{(-6)^3}=-6$

    e. $\sqrt[5]{(3x-1)^5}=3x-1$

37. a. $\sqrt[8]{x^4}=x^{4/8}=x^{1/2}=\sqrt{x}$

    b. $\sqrt[6]{25}=(25)^{1/6}$

         $=(5^2)^{1/6}=5^{2/6}=5^{1/3}=\sqrt[3]{5}$

    c. $\sqrt[4]{r^2s^6}=(r^2s^6)^{1/4}$

         $=r^{2/4}s^{6/4}$

         $=r^{1/2}s^{3/2}$

         $=(rs^3)^{1/2}=\sqrt{rs^3}$

38. a. $\sqrt[4]{5^2}=5^{2/4}=5^{1/2}=\sqrt{5}$

    b. $\sqrt[12]{x^3}=x^{3/12}=x^{1/4}=\sqrt[4]{x}$

    c. $\sqrt[6]{x^2y^4}=(x^2y^4)^{1/6}$

         $=x^{2/6}y^{4/6}$

         $=x^{1/3}y^{2/3}$

         $=(xy^2)^{1/3}=\sqrt[3]{xy^2}$

39. a. $\sqrt{25x^3}=\sqrt{25x^2\cdot x}=5x\sqrt{x}$

    b. $\sqrt[3]{54x^6y^8}=\sqrt[3]{27x^6y^6\cdot 2y^2}$

         $=3x^2y^2\sqrt[3]{2y^2}$

    c. $\sqrt[4]{81z^{11}}=\sqrt[4]{81z^8\cdot z^3}=3z^2\sqrt[4]{z^3}$

40. a. $\sqrt{64a^5} = \sqrt{64a^4 \cdot a} = 8a^2\sqrt{a}$

b. $\sqrt[3]{24a^7b^9} = \sqrt[3]{8a^6b^9 \cdot 3a} = 2a^2b^3\sqrt[3]{3a}$

c. $\sqrt[4]{48x^9} = \sqrt[4]{16x^8 \cdot 3x} = 2x^2\sqrt[4]{3x}$

41. a. $\dfrac{2}{\sqrt{5}} = \dfrac{2 \cdot \sqrt{5}}{\sqrt{5} \cdot \sqrt{5}} = \dfrac{2\sqrt{5}}{5}$

b. $\dfrac{2\sqrt{16}}{\sqrt{9x}} = \dfrac{2 \cdot 4}{3\sqrt{x}} = \dfrac{8 \cdot \sqrt{x}}{3\sqrt{x} \cdot \sqrt{x}} = \dfrac{8\sqrt{x}}{3x}$

c. $\sqrt[3]{\dfrac{1}{2}} = \dfrac{\sqrt[3]{1}}{\sqrt[3]{2}} = \dfrac{1}{\sqrt[3]{2}} = \dfrac{1 \cdot \sqrt[3]{2^2}}{\sqrt[3]{2} \cdot \sqrt[3]{2^2}} = \dfrac{\sqrt[3]{4}}{2}$

42. a. $\left(\sqrt{3}-4\right)\left(2\sqrt{3}+2\right)$
$= \sqrt{3} \cdot 2\sqrt{3} + 2\sqrt{3} - 4 \cdot 2\sqrt{3} - 4 \cdot 2$
$= 2(3) + 2\sqrt{3} - 8\sqrt{3} - 8$
$= 6 - 6\sqrt{3} - 8$
$= -2 - 6\sqrt{3}$

b. $\left(\sqrt{5}-x\right)^2 = \left(\sqrt{5}\right)^2 - 2 \cdot \sqrt{5} \cdot x + x^2$
$= 5 - 2x\sqrt{5} + x^2$

c. $\left(\sqrt{a}+b\right)\left(\sqrt{a}-b\right) = \left(\sqrt{a}\right)^2 - b^2$
$= a - b^2$

43. $\sqrt{2x+5} + \sqrt{2x} = 3$
$\sqrt{2x+5} = 3 - \sqrt{2x}$
$\left(\sqrt{2x+5}\right)^2 = \left(3 - \sqrt{2x}\right)^2$
$2x+5 = 9 - 6\sqrt{2x} + 2x$
$-4 = -6\sqrt{2x}$
$(-4)^2 = \left(-6\sqrt{2x}\right)^2$
$16 = 36(2x)$
$16 = 72x$
$x = \dfrac{16}{72} = \dfrac{2}{9}$

The solution is $\dfrac{2}{9}$.

44. $\sqrt{x-2} = \sqrt{4x+1} - 3$
$\left(\sqrt{x-2}\right)^2 = \left(\sqrt{4x+1}-3\right)^2$
$x-2 = (4x+1) - 6\sqrt{4x+1} + 9$
$6\sqrt{4x+1} = 3x+12$
$2\sqrt{4x+1} = x+4$
$\left(2\sqrt{4x+1}\right)^2 = (x+4)^2$
$4(4x+1) = x^2 + 8x + 16$
$16x+4 = x^2 + 8x + 16$
$0 = x^2 - 8x + 12$
$0 = (x-6)(x-2)$
$x-6=0 \ \text{ or } \ x-2=0$
$x=6 \ \text{ or } \qquad x=2$
The solutions are 2 and 6.

45. a. $\dfrac{2+i}{1-i} = \dfrac{(2+i) \cdot (1+i)}{(1-i) \cdot (1+i)}$
$= \dfrac{2 + 2i + 1i + i^2}{1^2 - i^2}$
$= \dfrac{2 + 3i - 1}{1+1}$
$= \dfrac{1+3i}{2} \ \text{ or } \ \dfrac{1}{2} + \dfrac{3}{2}i$

b. $\dfrac{7}{3i} = \dfrac{7 \cdot (-3i)}{3i \cdot (-3i)} = \dfrac{-21i}{-9i^2} = \dfrac{-21i}{9} = -\dfrac{7}{3}i$

46. a. $3i(5-2i) = 15i - 6i^2$
$= 15i + 6$
$= 6 + 15i$

b. $(6-5i)^2 = 6^2 - 2(6)(5i) + (5i)^2$
$= 36 - 60i + 25i^2$
$= 36 - 60i - 25$
$= 11 - 60i$

c. $\left(\sqrt{3}+2i\right)\left(\sqrt{3}-2i\right) = \left(\sqrt{3}\right)^2 - (2i)^2$
$= 3 - 4i^2$
$= 3 + 4$
$= 7$

47. $(x+1)^2 = 12$

$\quad x+1 = \pm\sqrt{12}$

$\quad x+1 = \pm 2\sqrt{3}$

$\quad\quad x = -1 \pm 2\sqrt{3}$

The solutions are $-1+2\sqrt{3}$ and $-1-2\sqrt{3}$.

48. $(y-1)^2 = 24$

$\quad y-1 = \pm\sqrt{24}$

$\quad y-1 = \pm 2\sqrt{6}$

$\quad\quad y = 1 \pm 2\sqrt{6}$

The solutions are $1+2\sqrt{6}$ and $1-2\sqrt{6}$.

49. $x - \sqrt{x} - 6 = 0$

Let $y = \sqrt{x}$. Then $y^2 = x$ and $\begin{array}{l} y^2 - y - 6 = 0 \\ (y-3)(y+2) = 0 \end{array}$

$y - 3 = 0$ or $y + 2 = 0$

$\quad y = 3$ or $\quad y = -2$

$\quad \sqrt{x} = 3$ or $\sqrt{x} = -2$ (can't happen)

$\quad\quad x = 9$

The solution is 9.

50. $\quad\quad m^2 = 4m + 8$

$\quad m^2 - 4m - 8 = 0$

$a = 1, b = -4, c = -8$

$x = \dfrac{4 \pm \sqrt{(-4)^2 - 4(1)(-8)}}{2(1)}$

$\quad = \dfrac{4 \pm \sqrt{16 + 32}}{2}$

$\quad = \dfrac{4 \pm \sqrt{48}}{2}$

$\quad = \dfrac{4 \pm 4\sqrt{3}}{2}$

$\quad = 2 \pm 2\sqrt{3}$

The solutions are $2+2\sqrt{3}$ and $2-2\sqrt{3}$.

Chapter 9

Section 9.1

Practice Exercises

1. $f(x) = x + 2; \; g(x) = 3x + 5$

   a. $(f + g)(x) = f(x) + g(x)$
$$= (x + 2) + (3x + 5)$$
$$= 4x + 7$$

   b. $(f - g)(x) = f(x) - g(x)$
$$= (x + 2) - (3x + 5)$$
$$= x + 2 - 3x - 5$$
$$= -2x - 3$$

   c. $(f \cdot g)(x) = f(x) \cdot g(x)$
$$= (x + 2)(3x + 5)$$
$$= 3x^2 + 6x + 5x + 10$$
$$= 3x^2 + 11x + 10$$

   d. $\left(\dfrac{f}{g}\right)(x) = \dfrac{f(x)}{g(x)} = \dfrac{x + 2}{3x + 5}$, where $x \neq -\dfrac{5}{3}$.

2. $f(x) = x^2 + 1; \; g(x) = 3x - 5$

   a. $(f \circ g)(4) = f(g(4)) = f(7) = 50$
$$(g \circ f)(4) = g(f(4)) = g(17) = 46$$

   b. $(f \circ g)(x) = f(g(x))$
$$= f(3x - 5)$$
$$= (3x - 5)^2 + 1$$
$$= 9x^2 - 30x + 26$$
$$(g \circ f)(x) = g(f(x))$$
$$= g(x^2 + 1)$$
$$= 3(x^2 + 1) - 5$$
$$= 3x^2 - 2$$

3. $f(x) = x^2 + 5; \; g(x) = x + 3$

   a. $(f \circ g)(x) = f(g(x))$
$$= f(x + 3)$$
$$= (x + 3)^2 + 5$$
$$= x^2 + 6x + 14$$

   b. $(g \circ f)(x) = g(f(x))$
$$= g(x^2 + 5)$$
$$= (x^2 + 5) + 3$$
$$= x^2 + 8$$

4. $f(x) = 3x; \; g(x) = x - 4; \; h(x) = |x|$

   a. $F(x) = |x - 4|$
$$F(x) = (h \circ g)(x)$$
$$= h(g(x))$$
$$= h(x - 4)$$
$$= |x - 4|$$

   b. $G(x) = 3x - 4$
$$G(x) = (g \circ f)(x)$$
$$= g(f(x))$$
$$= g(3x)$$
$$= 3x - 4$$

Vocabulary and Readiness Check

1. C

2. E

3. F

4. A

5. D

6. B

Exercise Set 9.1

   2. a. $(f + g)(x) = (x + 4) + (5x - 2)$
$$= 6x + 2$$

      b. $(f - g)(x) = (x + 4) - (5x - 2)$
$$= x + 4 - 5x + 2$$
$$= -4x + 6$$

      c. $(f \cdot g)(x) = (x + 4)(5x - 2)$
$$= 5x^2 + 18x - 8$$

      d. $\left(\dfrac{f}{g}\right)(x) = \dfrac{x + 4}{5x - 2}$, where $x \neq \dfrac{2}{5}$

4. a. $(f+g)(x) = (x^2-2)+(3x)$
$$= x^2+3x-2$$

b. $(f-g)(x) = (x^2-2)-(3x)$
$$= x^2-3x-2$$

c. $(f \cdot g)(x) = (x^2-2)(3x) = 3x^3-6x$

d. $\left(\dfrac{f}{g}\right)(x) = \dfrac{x^2-2}{3x}$, where $x \neq 0$

6. a. $(f+g)(x) = \sqrt[3]{x} + x - 3$

b. $(f-g)(x) = \sqrt[3]{x} - (x-3) = \sqrt[3]{x} - x + 3$

c. $(f \cdot g)(x) = \sqrt[3]{x} \cdot (x-3) = x\sqrt[3]{x} - 3\sqrt[3]{x}$

d. $\left(\dfrac{f}{g}\right)(x) = \dfrac{\sqrt[3]{x}}{x-3}$, where $x \neq 3$

8. a. $(f+g)(x) = 4x^3 + (-6x) = 4x^3 - 6x$

b. $(f-g)(x) = 4x^3 - (-6x) = 4x^3 + 6x$

c. $(f \cdot g)(x) = 4x^3(-6x) = -24x^4$

d. $\left(\dfrac{f}{g}\right)(x) = \dfrac{4x^3}{-6x} = -\dfrac{2x^2}{3}$, where $x \neq 0$

10. $(h \circ f)(-2) = h(f(-2))$
$$= h\left((-2)^2 - 6(-2) + 2\right)$$
$$= h(18)$$
$$= \sqrt{18}$$
$$= 3\sqrt{2}$$

12. $(f \circ h)(1) = f(h(1))$
$$= f\left(\sqrt{1}\right)$$
$$= f(1)$$
$$= (1)^2 - 6(1) + 2$$
$$= -3$$

14. $(h \circ g)(0) = h(g(0))$
$$= h(-2(0))$$
$$= h(0)$$
$$= \sqrt{0}$$
$$= 0$$

16. $(f \circ g)(x) = f(g(x))$
$$= f\left(x^2\right)$$
$$= x^2 - 3$$
$(g \circ f)(x) = g(f(x))$
$$= g(x-3)$$
$$= (x-3)^2$$
$$= x^2 - 6x + 9$$

18. $(f \circ g)(x) = f(g(x))$
$$= f(3x+1)$$
$$= (3x+1)+10 = 3x+11$$
$(g \circ f)(x) = g(f(x))$
$$= g(x+10)$$
$$= 3(x+10)+1 = 3x+31$$

20. $(f \circ g)(x) = f(g(x))$
$$= f\left(x^3 + x^2 - 6\right)$$
$$= -4(x^3 + x^2 - 6)$$
$$= -4x^3 - 4x^2 + 24$$
$(g \circ f)(x) = g(f(x))$
$$= g(-4x)$$
$$= (-4x)^3 + (-4x)^2 - 6$$
$$= -64x^3 + 16x^2 - 6$$

22. $(f \circ g)(x) = f(g(x)) = f(14x-8) = |14x-8|$
$(g \circ f)(x) = g(f(x)) = g(|x|) = 14|x| - 8$

24. $(f \circ g)(x) = f(g(x))$
$$= f\left(\sqrt[3]{x}\right)$$
$$= 7\sqrt[3]{x} - 1$$
$(g \circ f)(x) = g(f(x))$
$$= g(7x-1)$$
$$= \sqrt[3]{7x-1}$$

26. $G(x) = (g \circ f)(x)$
$$= g(f(x))$$
$$= g(3x)$$
$$= \sqrt{3x}$$

28. $H(x) = (f \circ h)(x)$
$= f(h(x))$
$= f(x^2 + 2)$
$= 3(x^2 + 2)$
$= 3x^2 + 6$

30. $F(x) = (h \circ g)(x)$
$= h(g(x))$
$= h(\sqrt{x})$
$= (\sqrt{x})^2 + 2$
$= x + 2$

32. Answers may vary; for example, $g(x) = x - 1$ and $f(x) = |x|$.

34. Answers may vary; for example, $g(x) = 3x + 4$ and $f(x) = x^2 + 3$.

36. Answers may vary; for example, $g(x) = x + 10$ and $f(x) = \dfrac{1}{x}$.

38. $x = y - 5$
$x + 5 = y$
$y = x + 5$

40. $x = -6y$
$\dfrac{x}{-6} = y$
$y = -\dfrac{x}{6}$

42. $x = 4y + 7$
$x - 7 = 4y$
$\dfrac{x - 7}{4} = y$
$y = \dfrac{x - 7}{4}$

44. $(f - g)(7) = f(7) - g(7) = 1 - 4 = -3$

46. $(g \circ f)(2) = g(f(2)) = g(7) = 4$

48. $(f \cdot g)(0) = f(0) \cdot g(0) = 5(-3) = -15$

50. $\left(\dfrac{g}{f}\right)(-1) = \dfrac{g(-1)}{f(-1)} = \dfrac{-4}{4} = -1$

52. Answers may vary

54. $P(x) = R(x) - C(x)$

$\qquad = 25x - (50 + x^2 + 4x)$

$\qquad = -x^2 + 21x - 50$

Section 9.2

Practice Exercises

1. a. $f = \{(4, -3), (3, -4), (2, 7), (5, 0)\}$

      f is one-to-one since each y-value corresponds to only one x-value.

b. $g = \{(8, 4), (-2, 0), (6, 4), (2, 6)\}$

      g is not one-to-one because the y-value 4 in (8, 4) and (6, 4) corresponds to two different x-values.

c. $h = \{(2, 4), (1, 3), (4, 6), (-2, 4)\}$

      h is not one-to-one because the y-value 4 in (2, 4) and (−2, 4) corresponds to two different x-values.

d.

Year	1950	1963	1968	1975	1997	2002
Federal Minimum Wage	$0.75	$1.25	$1.60	$2.10	$5.15	$5.15

      This function is not one-to-one because the wage $5.15 corresponds to two different years.

e. The function represented by the graph is not one-to-one because the y-value 2 in (2, 2) and (3, 2) corresponds to two different x-values.

f. The function represented by the diagram is not one-to-one because the score 509 corresponds to two different states.

2. Graphs **a**, **b**, and **c** all pass the vertical line test, so only these graphs are functions. But, of these, only **b** and **c** pass the horizontal line test, so only **b** and **c** are graphs of one-to-one functions.

3. $f(x) = \{(3, 4), (-2, 0), (2, 8), (6, 6)\}$

Switching the coordinates of each ordered pair gives $f^{-1}(x) = \{(4, 3), (0, -2), (8, 2), (6, 6)\}$

4. $f(x) = 6 - x$

Replace $f(x)$ with y.

$y = 6 - x$

Interchange x and y.

$x = 6 - y$

Solve for y.

$x = 6 - y$

$y = 6 - x$

Replace y with $f^{-1}(x)$.

$f^{-1}(x) = 6 - x$

5. $f(x) = 5x + 2$

Replace $f(x)$ with y.

$y = 5x + 2$

Interchange x and y.

$x = 5y + 2$

Solve for y.

$x = 5y + 2$

$x - 2 = 5y$

$\dfrac{x-2}{5} = y$

Replace y with $f^{-1}(x)$.

$f^{-1}(x) = \dfrac{x-2}{5}$

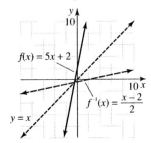

6. a. $f(x) = 2x - 3$

$y = 2x - 3$

$x = 2y - 3$

$x + 3 = 2y$

$\dfrac{x+3}{2} = y$

$f^{-1}(x) = \dfrac{x+3}{2}$

b. $f(x) = x^3$

$y = x^3$

$x = y^3$

$\sqrt[3]{x} = y$

$f^{-1}(x) = \sqrt[3]{x}$

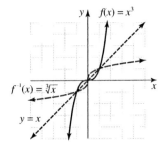

7. $f(x) = 4x - 1; \ f^{-1}(x) = \dfrac{x+1}{4}$

$(f \circ f^{-1})(x) = f(f^{-1}(x))$

$\qquad = f\left(\dfrac{x+1}{4}\right)$

$\qquad = 4\left(\dfrac{x+1}{4}\right) - 1$

$\qquad = x + 1 - 1$

$\qquad = x$

$(f^{-1} \circ f)(x) = f^{-1}(f(x))$

$\qquad = f^{-1}(4x - 1)$

$\qquad = \dfrac{(4x-1)+1}{4}$

$\qquad = \dfrac{4x-1+1}{4}$

$\qquad = \dfrac{4x}{4}$

$\qquad = x$

Since $f \circ f^{-1} = x$ and $f^{-1} \circ f = x$, if

$f(x) = 4x - 1, \ f^{-1}(x) = \dfrac{x+1}{4}$.

Vocabulary and Readiness Check

1. If $f(2) = 11$, the corresponding ordered pair is (2, 11).

2. The symbol f^{-1} means the inverse of f.

3. If (7, 3) is an ordered pair solution of $f(x)$, and $f(x)$ has an inverse, then an ordered pair solution of $f^{-1}(x)$ is (3, 7).

4. To tell whether a graph is the graph of a function, use the <u>vertical</u> line test.

5. To tell whether the graph of a function is also a one-to-one function, use the <u>horizontal</u> line test.

6. The graphs of f and f^{-1} are symmetric about the <u>$y = x$</u> line.

7. Two functions are inverse of each other if $(f \circ f^{-1})(x) = \underline{x}$ and $(f^{-1} \circ f)(x) = \underline{x}$.

Exercise Set 9.2

2. $g = \{(8, 6), (9, 6), (3, 4), (-4, 4)\}$ is not a one-to-one function. The y-values 6 and 4 are each assigned two different x-values.

4. $r = \{(1, 2), (3, 4), (5, 6), (6, 7)\}$ is a one-to-one function.
   $r^{-1} = \{(2, 1), (4, 3), (6, 5), (7, 6)\}$

6. $g = \{(0, 3), (3, 7), (6, 7), (-2, -2)\}$ is not a one-to-one function. The y-value 7 is assigned two different x-values.

8. This function is not one-to-one because the states Wisconsin and Arizona have the same output, 10.

10. This function is one-to-one.

No. of Sides (Input)	3	5	4	6	10
Shape (Output)	Triangle	Pentagon	Quadrilateral	Hexagon	Decagon

12. $f(x) = x^3 + 2$

   a. $f(0) = (0)^3 + 2 = 2$

   b. $f^{-1}(2) = 0$

14. $f(x) = x^3 + 2$

   a. $f(-2) = (-2)^3 + 2 = -6$

   b. $f^{-1}(-6) = -2$

16. The graph does not represent a one-to-one function because it does not pass the horizontal line test.

18. The graph does not represent a one-to-one function because it does not pass the horizontal line test.

20. The graph does not represent a one-to-one function because it does not pass the horizontal line test.

22. The graph represents a one-to-one function because it passes the horizontal line test.

24. $f(x) = x - 5$
$y = x - 5$
$x = y - 5$
$x + 5 = y$
$f^{-1}(x) = x + 5$

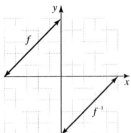

26. $f(x) = 4x + 9$
$y = 4x + 9$
$x = 4y + 9$
$x - 9 = 4y$
$\dfrac{x-9}{4} = y$
$f^{-1}(x) = \dfrac{x-9}{4}$

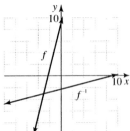

28. $f(x) = -\dfrac{1}{2}x + 2$
$y = -\dfrac{1}{2}x + 2$
$x = -\dfrac{1}{2}y + 2$
$x - 2 = -\dfrac{1}{2}y$
$-2x + 4 = y$
$f^{-1}(x) = -2x + 4$

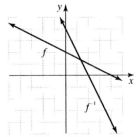

30. $f(x) = x^3 - 1$
$y = x^3 - 1$
$x = y^3 - 1$
$x + 1 = y^3$
$\sqrt[3]{x+1} = y$
$f^{-1}(x) = \sqrt[3]{x+1}$

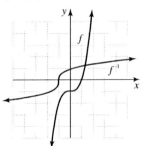

32. $f(x) = 6x - 1$
$y = 6x - 1$
$x = 6y - 1$
$x + 1 = 6y$
$\dfrac{x+1}{6} = y$
$f^{-1}(x) = \dfrac{x+1}{6}$

34. $f(x) = \dfrac{4x-3}{2}$
$y = \dfrac{4x-3}{2}$
$x = \dfrac{4y-3}{2}$
$2x = 4y - 3$
$2x + 3 = 4y$
$\dfrac{2x+3}{4} = y$
$f^{-1}(x) = \dfrac{2x+3}{4}$

36. $f(x) = \sqrt[3]{x+1}$
$y = \sqrt[3]{x+1}$
$x = \sqrt[3]{y+1}$
$x^3 = y + 1$
$x^3 - 1 = y$
$f^{-1}(x) = x^3 - 1$

38.
$$f(x) = \frac{7}{2x+4}$$
$$y = \frac{7}{2x+4}$$
$$x = \frac{7}{2y+4}$$
$$x(2y+4) = 7$$
$$2xy + 4x = 7$$
$$2xy = 7 - 4x$$
$$y = \frac{7-4x}{2x}$$
$$f^{-1}(x) = \frac{7-4x}{2x}$$

40.
$$f(x) = (x-5)^3$$
$$y = (x-5)^3$$
$$x = (y-5)^3$$
$$\sqrt[3]{x} = y-5$$
$$\sqrt[3]{x} + 5 = y$$
$$f^{-1}(x) = \sqrt[3]{x} + 5$$

42.

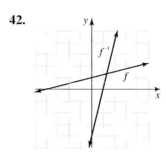

44.

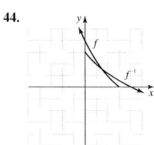

46.

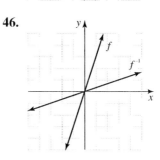

48.
$$(f^{-1} \circ f)(x) = f^{-1}(f(x))$$
$$= f^{-1}(3x-10)$$
$$= \frac{(3x-10)+10}{3}$$
$$= \frac{3x}{3}$$
$$= x$$
$$(f \circ f^{-1})(x) = f(f^{-1}(x))$$
$$= f\left(\frac{x+10}{3}\right)$$
$$= 3\left(\frac{x+10}{3}\right) - 10$$
$$= x + 10 - 10$$
$$= x$$

50.
$$(f^{-1} \circ f)(x) = f^{-1}(f(x))$$
$$= f^{-1}(x^3 - 5)$$
$$= \sqrt[3]{(x^3-5)+5}$$
$$= x$$
$$(f \circ f^{-1})(x) = f(f^{-1}(x))$$
$$= f\left(\sqrt[3]{x+5}\right)$$
$$= \left(\sqrt[3]{x+5}\right)^3 - 5$$
$$= x + 5 - 5$$
$$= x$$

52. $49^{1/2} = \sqrt{49} = 7$

54. $27^{2/3} = \left(\sqrt[3]{27}\right)^2 = 3^2 = 9$

56. $81^{-3/4} = \dfrac{1}{81^{3/4}} = \dfrac{1}{\left(\sqrt[4]{81}\right)^3} = \dfrac{1}{3^3} = \dfrac{1}{27}$

58.
$$f(x) = 3^x$$
$$f(0) = 3^0 = 1$$

60.
$$f(x) = 3^x$$
$$f\left(\frac{2}{3}\right) = 3^{2/3} \approx 2.08$$

62. $F\left(\dfrac{1}{2}\right) = -0.7$

    a. $F(x) = y$, so $(x, y) = \left(\dfrac{1}{2}, -0.7\right)$.

b. One ordered pair is (y, x), or $\left(-0.7, \dfrac{1}{2}\right)$.

64. a. $(-2, -9), (-1, -2), (0, -1), (1, 0), (2, 7)$

b. $(-9, -2), (-2, -1), (-1, 0), (0, 1), (7, 2)$

c, d.

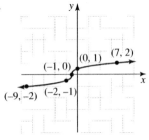

66. Answers may vary.

68.
$$f(x) = -2x - 6$$
$$y = -2x - 6$$
$$x = -2y - 6$$
$$2y = -x - 6$$
$$y = \frac{-x - 6}{2}$$
$$f^{-1}(x) = \frac{-x - 6}{2}$$

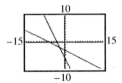

70.
$$f(x) = x^3 - 3$$
$$y = x^3 - 3$$
$$x = y^3 - 3$$
$$x + 3 = y^3$$
$$\sqrt[3]{x + 3} = y$$
$$f^{-1}(x) = \sqrt[3]{x + 3}$$

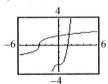

Section 9.3

Practice Exercises

1.

$f(x) = 2^x$	x	0	1	2	3	-1	-2
	$f(x)$	1	2	4	8	$\frac{1}{2}$	$\frac{1}{4}$

$g(x) = 7^x$	x	0	1	2	3	-1	-2
	$g(x)$	1	7	49	343	$\frac{1}{7}$	$\frac{1}{49}$

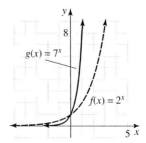

2.

$f(x) = \left(\frac{1}{3}\right)^x$	x	0	1	2	3	-1	-2
	$f(x)$	1	$\frac{1}{3}$	$\frac{1}{9}$	$\frac{1}{27}$	3	9

$g(x) = \left(\frac{1}{5}\right)^x$	x	0	1	2	3	-1	-2
	$g(x)$	1	$\frac{1}{5}$	$\frac{1}{25}$	$\frac{1}{125}$	5	25

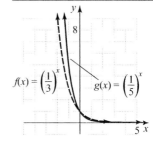

3. $f(x) = 2^{x+3}$

$y = 2^{x+3}$	x	0	-1	-2	-3	-4	-5
	y	8	4	2	1	$\frac{1}{2}$	$\frac{1}{4}$

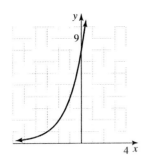

4. a. $3^x = 9$

Write 9 as a power of 3, $9 = 3^2$.

$3^x = 3^2$, thus, $x = 2$.

b. $8^x = 16$

Write 8 and 16 as powers of 2.

$8 = 2^3$ and $16 = 2^4$.

$$8^x = 16$$
$$(2^3)^x = 2^4$$
$$2^{3x} = 2^4$$
$$3x = 4$$
$$x = \frac{4}{3}$$

c. $125^x = 25^{x-2}$

Write 125 and 25 as powers of 5.

$125 = 5^3$ and $25 = 5^2$.

$$125^x = 25^{x-2}$$
$$(5^3)^x = (5^2)^{x-2}$$
$$5^{3x} = 5^{2x-4}$$
$$3x = 2x - 4$$
$$x = -4$$

d. Graph $y_1 = 7^x$ and $y_2 = 21$.

25

−5 | Intersection | 5
X=1.564575 Y=21

−5

The solution is ≈ 1.565.

5. $P = \$3000$, $r = 7\% = 0.07$, $n = 2$, and $t = 4$.

$$A = P\left(1 + \frac{r}{n}\right)^{nt}$$
$$A = 3000\left(1 + \frac{0.07}{2}\right)^{2(4)}$$
$$= 3000(1.035)^8$$
$$\approx 3950.43$$

Thus, the amount A owed is approximately $\$3950.43$.

6. $p(n) = 100(2.7)^{-0.05n}$, $n = 10$ sheets of glass.

$p(10) = 100(2.7)^{-0.05(10)} = 100(2.7)^{-0.5} \approx 60.86$

Thus, approximately 60.86% of the light passes through.

7.

X	Y1
4	67.213
35	3.0919

Y1■100*2.7^(-0....

a. The expected percent after 4 days is 67.21%.

b. The expected percent after 35 days is 3.09%.

Vocabulary and Readiness Check

1. A function such as $f(x) = 2^x$ is an <u>exponential</u> function; **C**.

2. If $7^x = 7^y$, then <u>$x = y$</u>; **B**.

3. Yes, the function passes both the vertical- and horizontal-line tests.

4. The function has no x-intercept.

5. The function has a y-intercept of <u>(0, 1)</u>.

6. The domain of this function, in interval notation, is <u>$(-\infty, \infty)$</u>.

7. The range of this function, in interval notation, is <u>$(0, \infty)$</u>.

Exercise Set 9.3

2. $y = 5^x$

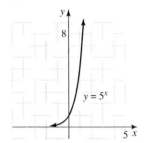

4. $y = 3^x - 1$

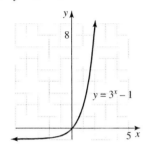

6. $y = \left(\dfrac{1}{5}\right)^x$

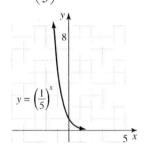

8. $y = \left(\dfrac{1}{3}\right)^x + 2$

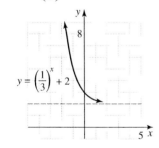

10. $y = -3^x$

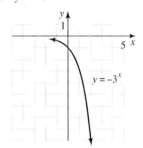

12. $y = -\left(\dfrac{1}{5}\right)^x$

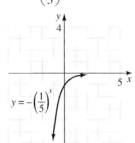

14. $f(x) = 3^{x-1}$

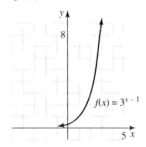

16. $f(x) = 2^{x+3}$

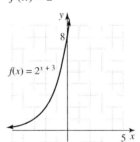

18. D

20. A

22. $6^x = 36$
$6^x = 6^2$
$x = 2$
The solution is 2.

24. $64^x = 16$
$(4^3)^x = 4^2$
$4^{3x} = 4^2$
$3x = 2$
$x = \dfrac{2}{3}$
The solution is $\dfrac{2}{3}$.

26. $9^{2x+1} = 81$
$9^{2x+1} = 9^2$
$2x + 1 = 2$
$2x = 1$
$x = \dfrac{1}{2}$
The solution is $\dfrac{1}{2}$.

28. $\dfrac{1}{27} = 3^{2x}$
$3^{-3} = 3^{2x}$
$-3 = 2x$
$-\dfrac{3}{2} = x$
The solution is $-\dfrac{3}{2}$.

30. $2^x = 64$
$2^x = 2^6$
$x = 6$
The solution is 6.

32. $32^x = 4$
$(2^5)^x = 2^2$
$2^{5x} = 2^2$
$5x = 2$
$x = \dfrac{2}{5}$
The solution is $\dfrac{2}{5}$.

34. $125^{x-2} = 25$
$(5^3)^{x-2} = 5^2$
$5^{3x-6} = 5^2$
$3x - 6 = 2$
$3x = 8$
$x = \dfrac{8}{3}$
The solution is $\dfrac{8}{3}$.

36. $4^{3x-7} = 32^{2x}$
$(2^2)^{3x-7} = (2^5)^{2x}$
$2^{6x-14} = 2^{10x}$
$6x - 14 = 10x$
$-14 = 4x$
$-\dfrac{7}{2} = x$
The solution is $-\dfrac{7}{2}$.

38. $y = 150(2.7)^{-0.03t}, t = 10$
$y = 150(2.7)^{-0.03(10)}$
$= 150(2.7)^{-0.3}$
≈ 111.3
Approximately 111.3 pounds of nuclear waste will be left after 10 centuries.

40. $y = 200(2.7)^{0.08t}, t = 12$
$y = 200(2.7)^{0.08(12)}$
$= 200(2.7)^{0.96}$
≈ 519
519 rats are expected by next January.

42. $y = 75(2.7)^{-0.04t}, t = 14$
$y = 75(2.7)^{-0.04(14)}$
$= 75(2.7)^{-0.56}$
≈ 43.0
After 14 days, 43 grams of debris remain.

44. $y = 200,000(2.7)^{0.08t}, t = 13$
$y = 200,000(2.7)^{0.08(13)}$
$= 200,000(2.7)^{1.04}$
$\approx 562,000$
There will be approximately 562,000 mosquitoes on May 25.

46. $y = 369.4(1.004)^t$

   a. $t = 2015 - 2000 = 15$

      $y = 369.4(1.004)^{15} \approx 392.2$

      In 2015, the CO_2 concentration is predicted to be 392.2 parts per million.

   b. $t = 2030 - 2000 = 30$

      $y = 369.4(1.004)^{30} \approx 416.4$

      In 2030, the CO_2 concentration is predicted to be 416.4 parts per million.

48. $A = P\left(1 + \dfrac{r}{n}\right)^{nt}$

$t = 5$, $P = 6000$, $r = 0.10$, and $n = 4$

$A = 3000\left(1 + \dfrac{0.10}{4}\right)^{4(5)}$

$\quad = 3000(1.025)^{20}$

$\quad \approx 4915.85$

$4915.85 would be owed after 5 years.

50. $A = P\left(1 + \dfrac{r}{n}\right)^{nt}$

$P = 500$, $r = 0.07$, $n = 4$, and $t = 4$

$A = 500\left(1 + \dfrac{0.07}{12}\right)^{12(4)}$

$\quad = 500\left(1 + \dfrac{0.07}{12}\right)^{48}$

$\quad \approx 661.03$

$661.03 accrues after 4 years.

52. $y = 18(1.24)^x$

$x = 2014 - 1994 = 20$

$y = 18(1.24)^{20}$

$\quad \approx 1330$

There will be approximately 1330 million cellular phone users in 2014.

54. $3x - 7 = 11$

$\quad 3x = 18$

$\quad\quad x = 6$

The solution is 6.

56. $2 - 6x = 6(1 - x)$

$\quad 2 - 6x = 6 - 6x$

$\quad\quad\quad 2 = 6$

This is a false statement. The solution set is $\varnothing$.

58. $\quad\quad 18 = 11x - x^2$

$\quad x^2 - 11x + 18 = 0$

$\quad (x - 9)(x - 2) = 0$

$\quad x = 9 \;\; \text{or} \;\; x = 2$

The solutions are 2 and 9.

60. $3^x = 9$

$\quad 3^2 = 9$

$\quad\; x = 2$

62. $4^x = 1$

$\quad 4^0 = 1$

$\quad\; x = 0$

64. Answers may vary

66. $y = \left|\left(\dfrac{1}{3}\right)^x\right|$

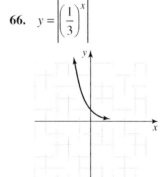

68. $y = \left(\dfrac{1}{3}\right)^{|x|}$

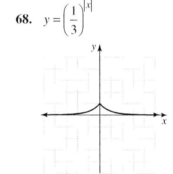

70. Answers may vary

72. $y = 30(2.7)^{-0.004x}$

20.16 pounds will be available after 100 days.

74. $y = 75(2.7)^{-0.04x}$

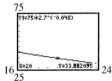

33.88 grams remain after 20 days.

Section 9.4

Practice Exercises

1. a. $\log_3 81 = 4$ means $3^4 = 81$.

   b. $\log_5 \dfrac{1}{5} = -1$ means $5^{-1} = \dfrac{1}{5}$.

   c. $\log_7 \sqrt{7} = \dfrac{1}{2}$ means $7^{1/2} = \sqrt{7}$.

   d. $\log_{13} y = 4$ means $13^4 = y$.

2. a. $4^3 = 64$ means $\log_4 64 = 3$.

   b. $6^{1/3} = \sqrt[3]{6}$ means $\log_6 \sqrt[3]{6} = \dfrac{1}{3}$.

   c. $5^{-3} = \dfrac{1}{125}$ means $\log_5 \dfrac{1}{125} = -3$.

   d. $\pi^7 = z$ means $\log_\pi z = 7$.

3. a. $\log_3 9 = 2$ because $3^2 = 9$.

   b. $\log_2 \dfrac{1}{8} = -3$ because $2^{-3} = \dfrac{1}{8}$.

   c. $\log_{49} 7 = \dfrac{1}{2}$ because $49^{1/2} = 7$.

4. a. $\log_5 \dfrac{1}{25} = x$

   $\log_5 \dfrac{1}{25} = x$ means $5^x = \dfrac{1}{25}$. Solve

   $5^x = \dfrac{1}{25}$.

$$5^x = \dfrac{1}{25}$$
$$5^x = 5^{-2}$$

Since the bases are the same, by the uniqueness of b^x, we have that $x = -2$. The solution is -2 or the solution set is $\{-2\}$.

   b. $\log_x 8 = 3$
$$x^3 = 8$$
$$x^3 = 2^3$$
$$x = 2$$

   c. $\log_6 x = 2$
$$6^2 = x$$
$$36 = x$$

   d. $\log_{13} 1 = x$
$$13^x = 1$$
$$13^x = 13^0$$
$$x = 0$$

   e. $\log_h 1 = x$
$$h^x = 1$$
$$h^x = h^0$$
$$x = 0$$

5. a. From Property 2, $\log_5 5^4 = 4$.

   b. From Property 2, $\log_9 9^{-2} = -2$.

   c. From Property 3, $6^{\log_6 5} = 5$.

   d. From Property 3, $7^{\log_7 4} = 4$.

6. $y = \log_7 x$ means that $7^y = x$. Find some ordered pair solutions that satisfy $7^y = x$.

$x = 7^y$	y
1	0
7	1
$\dfrac{1}{7}$	-1
$\dfrac{1}{49}$	-2

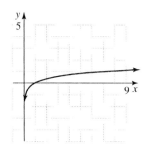

7. $y = \log_{1/4} x$ means that $\left(\dfrac{1}{4}\right)^y = x$. Find some

ordered-pair solutions that satisfy $\left(\dfrac{1}{4}\right)^y = x$.

$x = \left(\dfrac{1}{4}\right)^y$	y
1	0
$\dfrac{1}{4}$	1
4	-1
16	-2

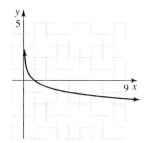

Vocabulary and Readiness Check

1. A function, such as $y = \log_2 x$ is a <u>logarithmic</u> function; **B**.

2. If $y = \log_2 x$, then $\underline{2^y = x}$; **C**.

3. Yes, the function passes both the horizontal- and vertical-line tests.

4. The function has an *x*-intercept of <u>(1, 0)</u>.

5. The function has no *y*-intercept.

6. The domain of this function, in interval notation, is <u>(0, ∞)</u>.

7. The range of this function, in interval notation, is <u>(−∞, ∞)</u>.

Exercise Set 9.4

2. $\log_2 32 = 5$
    $2^5 = 32$

4. $\log_5 \dfrac{1}{25} = -2$
    $5^{-2} = \dfrac{1}{25}$

6. $\log_{10} 10 = 1$
    $10^1 = 10$

8. $\log_8 y = 7$
    $8^7 = y$

10. $\log_e \dfrac{1}{e} = -1$
    $e^{-1} = \dfrac{1}{e}$

12. $\log_{11} \sqrt[4]{11} = \dfrac{1}{4}$
    $11^{1/4} = \sqrt[4]{11}$

14. $\log_{1.2} 1.44 = 2$
    $1.2^2 = 1.44$

16. $\log_{1/4} 16 = -2$
    $\left(\dfrac{1}{4}\right)^{-2} = 16$

18. $\quad 5^3 = 125$
    $\log_5 125 = 3$

20. $\quad\quad 10^4 = 10,000$
    $\log_{10} 10,000 = 4$

22. $\quad \pi^5 = y$
    $\log_\pi y = 5$

24. $\quad\quad 10^{-2} = \dfrac{1}{100}$
    $\log_{10} \dfrac{1}{100} = -2$

26. $3^{-4} = \dfrac{1}{81}$

$\log_3 \dfrac{1}{81} = -4$

28. $4^{1/3} = \sqrt[3]{4}$

$\log_4 \sqrt[3]{4} = \dfrac{1}{3}$

30. $\log_3 9 = 2$ since $3^2 = 9$.

32. $\log_2 \dfrac{1}{32} = -5$ since $2^{-5} = \dfrac{1}{32}$.

34. $\log_8 \dfrac{1}{2} = -\dfrac{1}{3}$ since $8^{-1/3} = \dfrac{1}{2}$.

36. $\log_{2/3} \dfrac{4}{9} = 2$ since $\left(\dfrac{2}{3}\right)^2 = \dfrac{4}{9}$.

38. $\log_9 9 = 1$ since $9^1 = 9$.

40. $\log_{10} \dfrac{1}{10} = \log_{10} 10^{-1} = -1$

42. $\log_2 16 = \log_2 2^4 = 4$

44. $\log_3 \dfrac{1}{9} = \log_3 3^{-2} = -2$

46. $\log_2 8 = x$

$2^x = 8$

$2^x = 2^3$

$x = 3$

48. $\log_2 x = 3$

$2^3 = x$

$x = 8$

50. $\log_x 8 = 3$

$x^3 = 8$

$x^3 = 2^3$

$x = 2$

52. $\log_3 \dfrac{1}{81} = x$

$3^x = \dfrac{1}{81}$

$3^x = 3^{-4}$

$x = -4$

54. $\log_5 \dfrac{1}{125} = x$

$5^x = \dfrac{1}{125}$

$5^x = 5^{-3}$

$x = -3$

56. $\log_9 x = \dfrac{1}{2}$

$9^{1/2} = x$

$x = \sqrt{9}$

$x = 3$

58. $\log_2 16 = x$

$2^x = 16$

$2^x = 2^4$

$x = 4$

60. $\log_{2/3} x = 2$

$\left(\dfrac{2}{3}\right)^2 = x$

$x = \dfrac{4}{9}$

62. $\log_x 27 = 3$

$x^3 = 27$

$x^3 = 3^3$

$x = 3$

64. $\log_6 6^{-2} = x$

$6^x = 6^{-2}$

$x = -2$

66. $5^{\log_5 7} = x$

$7 = x$

68. $\log_x 2 = -\dfrac{1}{3}$

$x^{-1/3} = 2$

$x = 2^{-3}$

$x = \dfrac{1}{8}$

70. $\log_6 6^2 = 2$

72. $7^{\log_7 4} = 4$

74. $\log_8 (8)^{-1} = -1$

76. $y = \log_8 x$

$y = 0:\ \log_8 x = 0$

$\qquad x = 8^0 = 1$

$(1, 0)$ is the only x-intercept.
No y-intercept exists.

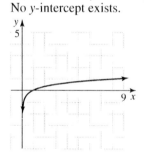

78. $f(x) = \log_{1/2} x$

$y = 0:\ \log_{1/2} x = 0$

$\qquad x = \left(\dfrac{1}{2}\right)^0 = 1$

$(1, 0)$ is the only x-intercept.
No y-intercept exists.

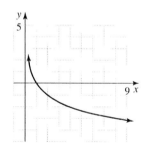

80. $f(x) = \log_6 x$

$y = 0:\ \log_6 x = 0$

$\qquad x = 6^0 = 1$

$(1, 0)$ is the only x-intercept.
No y-intercept exists.

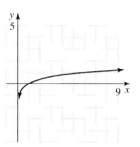

82. $f(x) = \log_{1/5} x$

$y = 0:\ \log_{1/5} x = 0$

$\qquad x = \left(\dfrac{1}{5}\right)^0 = 1$

$(1, 0)$ is the only x-intercept.
No y-intercept exists.

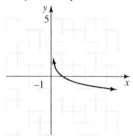

84. $\dfrac{x-5}{5-x} = \dfrac{x-5}{-1(x-5)} = -1$

86. $\dfrac{x^2 - 3x - 10}{2 + x} = \dfrac{(x-5)(x+2)}{2+x} = x - 5$

88. $\dfrac{3x}{x+3} + \dfrac{9}{x+3} = \dfrac{3x+9}{x+3} = \dfrac{3(x+3)}{x+3} = 3$

90. $\dfrac{5}{y+1} - \dfrac{4}{y-1} = \dfrac{5(y-1) - 4(y+1)}{(y+1)(y-1)}$

$\qquad = \dfrac{5y - 5 - 4y - 4}{(y+1)(y-1)}$

$\qquad = \dfrac{y - 9}{(y+1)(y-1)}$

$\qquad = \dfrac{y - 9}{y^2 - 1}$

92. $f(x) = \log_{0.3} x;\ g(x) = 0.3^x = f^{-1}(x)$

   a. $(3, 0.027)$ implies $g(3) = 0.027$.

   b. Since $f^{-1}(x) = g(x)$, $(0.027, 3)$ is a solution of $f(x)$.

c. $(0.027, 3)$ implies $f(0.027) = 3$.

94.   Answers may vary

96. $\log_3(2x+4) = 2$
$$3^2 = 2x+4$$
$$9 = 2x+4$$
$$5 = 2x$$
$$x = \frac{5}{2}$$

98. $\log_7(\log_4(\log_2 16)) = \log_7(\log_4(4))$
$$= \log(1)$$
$$= 0$$

100. $y = 3^x$; $y = \log_3 x$

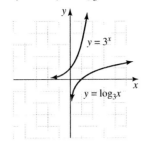

102. $y = \left(\frac{1}{2}\right)^x$; $y = \log_{1/2} x$

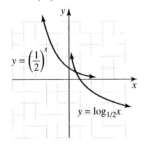

104. $\log_3 10 = x$ implies $3^x = 10$. $3^2 = 9$ and
$3^3 = 27$.
Since $9 < 10 < 27$, $\log_3 10$ is between 2 and 3.

106. $pH = -\log_{10}(H^+)$; $H^+ = 0.0050$
$pH = -\log_{10} 0.0050 \approx 2.3$
The pH of lemonade is 2.3.

Section 9.5

Practice Exercises

1. a. $\log_8 5 + \log_8 3 = \log_8(5 \cdot 3) = \log_8 15$

b. $\log_2 \frac{1}{3} + \log_2 18 = \log_2\left(\frac{1}{3} \cdot 18\right) = \log_2 6$

c. $\log_5(x-1) + \log_5(x+1) = \log_5[(x+1)(x+1)]$
$$= \log_5(x^2 - 1)$$

2. a. $\log_5 18 - \log_5 6 = \log_5 \frac{18}{6} = \log_5 3$

b. $\log_6 x - \log_6 3 = \log_6 \frac{x}{3}$

c. $\log_4(x^2+1) - \log_4(x^2+3) = \log_4 \frac{x^2+1}{x^2+3}$

3. a. $\log_7 x^8 = 8\log_7 x$

b. $\log_5 \sqrt[4]{7} = \log_5 7^{1/4} = \frac{1}{4}\log_5 7$

4. a. $2\log_5 4 + 5\log_5 2 = \log_5 4^2 + \log_5 2^5$
$$= \log_5 16 + \log_5 32$$
$$= \log_5(16 \cdot 32)$$
$$= \log_5 512$$

b. $2\log_8 x - \log_8(x+3) = \log_8 x^2 - \log_8(x+3)$
$$= \log_8 \frac{x^2}{x+3}$$

c. $\log_7 12 + \log_7 5 - \log_7 4$
$$= \log_7(12 \cdot 5) - \log_7 4$$
$$= \log_7 60 - \log_7 4$$
$$= \log_7 \frac{60}{4}$$
$$= \log_7 15$$

5. a. $\log_5 \frac{4 \cdot 3}{7} = \log_5(4 \cdot 3) - \log_5 7$
$$= \log_5 4 + \log_5 3 - \log_5 7$$

b. $\log_4 \dfrac{a^2}{b^5} = \log_4 a^2 - \log_4 b^5$

$\qquad\qquad = 2\log_4 a - 5\log_4 b$

6. $\log_b 5 = 0.83$ and $\log_b 3 = 0.56$

     a. $\log_b 15 = \log_b (3 \cdot 5)$

$\qquad\qquad = \log_b 3 + \log_b 5$

$\qquad\qquad = 0.56 + 0.83$

$\qquad\qquad = 1.39$

     b. $\log_b 25 = \log_b 5^2 = 2\log_b 5 = 2(0.83) = 1.66$

     c. $\log_b \sqrt{3} = \log_b 3^{1/2}$

$\qquad\qquad = \dfrac{1}{2}\log_b 3$

$\qquad\qquad = \dfrac{1}{2}(0.56)$

$\qquad\qquad = 0.28$

Vocabulary and Readiness Check

1. $\log_b 12 + \log_b 3 = \log_b (12 \cdot 3) = \log_b \underline{36}$; **a.**

2. $\log_b 12 - \log_b 3 = \log_b \dfrac{12}{3} = \log_b \underline{4}$; **c.**

3. $7\log_b 2 = \underline{\log_b 2^7}$; **b.**

4. $\log_b 1 = \underline{0}$; **c.**

5. $b^{\log_b x} = \underline{x}$; **a.**

6. $\log_5 5^2 = \underline{2}$; **b.**

Exercise Set 9.5

2. $\log_3 8 + \log_3 4 = \log_3 (8 \cdot 4) = \log_3 32$

4. $\log_2 x + \log_2 y = \log_2 (x \cdot y) = \log_2 xy$

6. $\log_5 y^3 + \log_5 (y - 7) = \log_5 [y^3 (y - 7)]$

$\qquad\qquad\qquad\qquad\quad = \log_5 (y^4 - 7y^3)$

8. $\log_6 3 + \log_6 (x + 4) + \log_6 5$

$\quad = \log_6 [3 \cdot 5(x + 4)]$

$\quad = \log_6 (15x + 60)$

10. $\log_7 20 - \log_7 4 = \log_7 \dfrac{20}{4} = \log_7 5$

12. $\log_5 12 - \log_5 3 = \log_5 \dfrac{12}{3} = \log_5 4$

14. $\log_3 12 - \log_3 z = \log_3 \dfrac{12}{z}$

16. $\log_7 (x + 9) - \log_7 (x^2 + 10) = \log_7 \dfrac{x + 9}{x^2 + 10}$

18. $\log_2 x^5 = 5\log_2 x$

20. $\log_6 7^{-2} = -2\log_6 7$

22. $\log_5 \sqrt[3]{x} = \log_5 x^{1/3} = \dfrac{1}{3}\log_5 x$

24. $\log_5 2 + \log_5 y^2 = \log_5 2y^2$

26. $2\log_3 5 + \log_3 2 = \log_3 5^2 + \log_3 2$

$\qquad\qquad\qquad\quad = \log_3 25 + \log_3 2$

$\qquad\qquad\qquad\quad = \log_3 (25 \cdot 2)$

$\qquad\qquad\qquad\quad = \log_3 50$

28. $2\log_7 y + 6\log_7 z = \log_7 y^2 + \log_7 z^6$

$\qquad\qquad\qquad\qquad = \log_7 y^2 z^6$

30. $\log_6 18 + \log_6 2 - \log_6 9 = \log_6 (18 \cdot 2) - \log_6 9$

$\qquad\qquad\qquad\qquad\qquad = \log_6 \dfrac{36}{9}$

$\qquad\qquad\qquad\qquad\qquad = \log_6 4$

32. $\log_8 5 + \log_8 15 - \log_8 20$

$\quad = \log_8 (5 \cdot 15) - \log_8 20$

$\quad = \log_8 \dfrac{75}{20}$

$\quad = \log_8 \dfrac{15}{4}$

34. $\log_9(4x) - \log_9(x-3) + \log_9(x^3+1)$

$\quad = \log_9 \dfrac{4x}{x-3} + \log_9(x^3+1)$

$\quad = \log_9 \dfrac{4x(x^3+1)}{x-3}$

$\quad = \log_9 \dfrac{4x^4+4x}{x-3}$

36. $2\log_5 x + \dfrac{1}{3}\log_5 x - 3\log_5(x+5)$

$\quad = \log_5 x^2 + \log_5 x^{1/3} - \log_5(x+5)^3$

$\quad = \log_5(x^2 \cdot x^{1/3}) - \log_5(x+5)^3$

$\quad = \log_5 x^{7/3} - \log_5(x+5)^3$

$\quad = \log_5 \dfrac{x^{7/3}}{(x+5)^3}$

38. $5\log_6 x - \dfrac{3}{4}\log_6 x + 3\log_6 x = \left(5 - \dfrac{3}{4} + 3\right)\log_6 x$

$\qquad\qquad = \dfrac{29}{4}\log_6 x$

$\qquad\qquad = \log_6 x^{29/4}$

40. $\log_7 \dfrac{5x}{4} = \log_7 5x - \log_7 4$

$\qquad\quad = \log_7 5 + \log_7 x - \log_7 4$

42. $\log_9 \dfrac{7}{8y} = \log_9 7 - \log_9 8y$

$\qquad\quad = \log_9 7 - (\log_9 8 + \log_9 y)$

$\qquad\quad = \log_9 7 - \log_9 8 - \log_9 y$

44. $\log_5 \dfrac{x}{y^4} = \log_5 x - \log_5 y^4$

$\qquad\quad = \log_5 x - 4\log_5 y$

46. $\log_b \sqrt{\dfrac{3}{y}} = \log_b \left(\dfrac{3}{y}\right)^{1/2}$

$\qquad\quad = \log_b \dfrac{3^{1/2}}{y^{1/2}}$

$\qquad\quad = \log_b 3^{1/2} - \log_b y^{1/2}$

$\qquad\quad = \dfrac{1}{2}\log_b 3 - \dfrac{1}{2}\log_b y$

48. $\log_2 y^3 z = \log_2 y^3 + \log_2 z$

$\qquad\quad = 3\log_2 y + \log_2 z$

50. $\log_3 x^2(x-9) = \log_3 x^2 + \log_3(x-9)$

$\qquad\qquad\quad = 2\log_3 x + \log_3(x-9)$

52. $\log_3 \dfrac{(x+5)^2}{x} = \log_3(x+5)^2 - \log_3 x$

$\qquad\qquad\quad = 2\log_3(x+5) - \log_3 x$

54. $\log_b 25 = \log_b 5^2 = 2\log_b 5 = 2(0.7) = 1.4$

56. $\log_b \dfrac{3}{5} = \log_b 3 - \log_b 5 = 0.5 - 0.7 = -0.2$

58. $\log_b \sqrt[4]{3} = \log_b 3^{1/4} = \dfrac{1}{4}\log_b 3 = \dfrac{1}{4}(0.5) = 0.125$

60. $\log_b 81 = \log_b 3^4 = 4\log_b 3 = 4(0.68) = 2.72$

62. $\log_b \dfrac{4}{32} = \log_b 4 - \log_b 32$

$\qquad\quad = \log_b 2^2 - \log_b 2^5$

$\qquad\quad = 2\log_b 2 - 5\log_b 2$

$\qquad\quad = -3\log_b 2$

$\qquad\quad = -3(0.43)$

$\qquad\quad = -1.29$

64. $\log_b \sqrt{\dfrac{3}{2}} = \log_b \dfrac{3^{1/2}}{2^{1/2}}$

$\qquad\quad = \log_b 3^{1/2} - \log_b 2^{1/2}$

$\qquad\quad = \dfrac{1}{2}\log_b 3 - \dfrac{1}{2}\log_b 3$

$\qquad\quad = \dfrac{1}{2}(0.68) - \dfrac{1}{2}(0.43)$

$\qquad\quad = 0.34 - 0.215$

$\qquad\quad = 0.125$

66. $\log_{10} 100 = \log_{10} 10^2 = 2$

68. $\log_7 7^2 = 2$

70. $\log_3 \dfrac{14}{11} = \log_3 14 - \log_3 11;$ **b**

72. $\log_2 x^3 = 3\log_2 x$ is true.

74. $\dfrac{\log_7 10}{\log_7 5} = \log_7 2$ is false.

76. $\dfrac{\log_7 x}{\log_7 y} = (\log_7 x) - (\log_7 y)$ is false.

78. Yes, this is true, since $\log 1 = 0$.

Integrated Review

1. $(f+g)(x) = x - 6 + x^2 + 1 = x^2 + x - 5$

2. $(f-g)(x) = x - 6 - (x^2 + 1) = -x^2 + x - 7$

3. $(f \cdot g)(x) = (x-6)(x^2+1) = x^3 - 6x^2 + x - 6$

4. $\left(\dfrac{f}{g}\right)(x) = \dfrac{x-6}{x^2+1}$

5. $(f \circ g)(x) = f(g(x)) = f(3x-1) = \sqrt{3x-1}$

6. $(g \circ f)(x) = g(f(x)) = g\left(\sqrt{x}\right) = 3\sqrt{x} - 1$

7. one-to-one; inverse:
$$\{(6,-2),(8,4),(-6,2),(3,3)\}$$

8. not one-to-one

9. not one-to-one

10. one-to-one

11. not one-to-one

12. $f(x) = 3x$
$\quad\quad y = 3x$

$\quad\quad x = 3y$
$\quad\quad y = \dfrac{x}{3}$
$\quad f^{-1}(x) = \dfrac{x}{3}$

13. $f(x) = x + 4$
$\quad\quad y = x + 4$

$\quad\quad x = y + 4$
$\quad\quad y = x - 4$
$\quad f^{-1}(x) = x - 4$

14. $f(x) = 5x - 1$
$\quad\quad y = 5x - 1$

$\quad\quad x = 5y - 1$
$\quad\quad 5y = x + 1$
$\quad\quad y = \dfrac{x+1}{5}$
$\quad f^{-1}(x) = \dfrac{x+1}{5}$

15. $f(x) = 3x + 2$
$\quad\quad y = 3x + 2$

$\quad\quad x = 3y + 2$
$\quad\quad 3y = x - 2$
$\quad\quad y = \dfrac{x-2}{3}$
$\quad f^{-1}(x) = \dfrac{x-2}{3}$

16. $y = \left(\dfrac{1}{2}\right)^x$

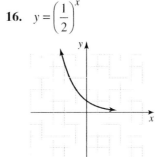

17. $y = 2^x + 1$

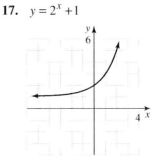

18. $y = \log_3 x$

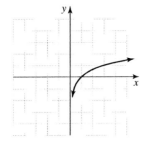

19. $y = \log_{1/3} x$

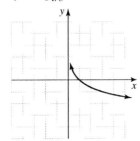

20. $2^x = 8$

$2^x = 2^3$

$x = 3$

The solution is 3.

21. $9 = 3^{x-5}$

$3^2 = 3^{x-5}$

$2 = x - 5$

$7 = x$

The solution is 7.

22. $4^{x-1} = 8^{x+2}$

$(2^2)^{x-1} = (2^3)^{x+2}$

$2^{2x-2} = 2^{3x+6}$

$2x - 2 = 3x + 6$

$-8 = x$

The solution is -8.

23. $25^x = 125^{x-1}$

$(5^2)^x = (5^3)^{x-1}$

$5^{2x} = 5^{3x-3}$

$2x = 3x - 3$

$3 = x$

The solution is 3.

24. $\log_4 16 = x$

$4^x = 16$

$4^x = 4^2$

$x = 2$

The solution is 2.

25. $\log_{49} 7 = x$

$49^x = 7$

$(7^2)^x = 7$

$7^{2x} = 7$

$2x = 1$

$x = \dfrac{1}{2}$

The solution is $\dfrac{1}{2}$.

26. $\log_2 x = 5$

$2^5 = x$

$32 = x$

The solution is 32.

27. $\log_x 64 = 3$

$x^3 = 64$

$x^3 = 4^3$

$x = 4$

The solution is 4.

28. $\log_x \dfrac{1}{125} = -3$

$x^{-3} = \dfrac{1}{125}$

$x^{-3} = 5^{-3}$

$x = 5$

The solution is 5.

29. $\log_3 x = -2$

$3^{-2} = x$

$x = \dfrac{1}{3^2} = \dfrac{1}{9}$

The solution is $\dfrac{1}{9}$.

30. $5 \log_2 x = \log_2 x^5$

31. $x \log_2 5 = \log_2 5^x$

32. $3\log_5 x - 5\log_5 y = \log_5 x^3 - \log_5 y^5 = \log_5 \dfrac{x^3}{y^5}$

33. $9\log_5 x + 3\log_5 y = \log_5 x^9 + \log_5 y^3$
$$= \log_5 x^9 y^3$$

34. $\log_2 x + \log_2(x-3) - \log_2(x^2+4)$
$$= \log_2[x(x-3)] - \log_2(x^2+4)$$
$$= \log_2(x^2-3x) - \log_2(x^2+4)$$
$$= \log_2 \frac{x^2-3x}{x^2+4}$$

35. $\log_3 y - \log_3(y+2) + \log_3(y^3+11)$
$$= \log_3 \frac{y}{y+2} + \log_3(y^3+11)$$
$$= \log_3 \frac{y(y^3+11)}{y+2}$$
$$= \log_3 \frac{y^4+11y}{y+2}$$

36. $\log_7 \dfrac{9x^2}{y} = \log_7 9x^2 - \log_7 y$
$$= \log_7 9 + \log_7 x^2 - \log_7 y$$
$$= \log_7 9 + 2\log_7 x - \log_7 y$$

37. $\log_6 \dfrac{5y}{z^2} = \log_6 5y - \log_6 z^2$
$$= \log_6 5 + \log_6 y - 2\log_6 z$$

Section 9.6

Practice Exercises

1. To four decimal places, $\log 15 \approx 1.1761$.

2. a. $\log \dfrac{1}{100} = \log 10^{-2} = 2$

b. $\log 100,000 = \log 10^5 = 5$

c. $\log \sqrt[5]{10} = \log 10^{1/5} = \dfrac{1}{5}$

d. $\log 0.001 = \log 10^{-3} = -3$

3. $\log x = 3.4$
$$x = 10^{3.4}$$
$$x \approx 2511.8864$$

4. $a = 450$ micrometers
$T = 4.2$ seconds
$B = 3.6$
$$R = \log\left(\frac{a}{T}\right) + B$$
$$= \log\left(\frac{450}{4.2}\right) + 3.6$$
$$\approx 2.0 + 3.6$$
$$= 5.6$$
The earthquake had a magnitude of 5.6 on the Richter scale.

5. To four decimal places, $\ln 13 \approx 2.5649$.

6. a. $\ln e^4 = 4$

b. $\ln \sqrt[3]{e} = \ln e^{1/3} = \dfrac{1}{3}$

7. $\ln 5x = 8$
$$e^8 = 5x$$
$$\frac{e^8}{5} = x$$
$$x = \frac{1}{5}e^8 \approx 596.1916$$

8. $P = \$2400$
$r = 6\% = 0.06$
$t = 4$ years
$$A = Pe^{rt} = 2400e^{0.06(4)} = 2400e^{0.24} \approx 3051.00$$
The total amount of money owed is \$3051.00.

9. $\log_8 5 = \dfrac{\log 5}{\log 8} \approx \dfrac{0.6989700043}{0.903089987} \approx 0.773976$

To four decimal places, $\log_8 5 \approx 0.7740$.

Vocabulary and Readiness Check

1. The base of $\log 7$ is <u>10</u>; **c.**

2. The base of $\ln 7$ is <u>e</u>; **a.**

3. $\log_{10} 10^7 = \underline{7}$; **b.**

4. $\log_7 1 = \underline{0}$; **d.**

5. $\log_e e^5 = \underline{5}$; **b.**

6. $\ln e^5 = \underline{5}$; **b.**

7. $\log_2 7 = \dfrac{\log 7}{\log 2} = \dfrac{\ln 7}{\ln 2}$; **a** and **b.**

Exercise Set 9.6

2. $\log 6 \approx 0.7782$

4. $\log 4.86 \approx 0.6866$

6. $\ln 3 \approx 1.0986$

8. $\ln 0.0032 \approx -5.7446$

10. $\log 25.9 \approx 1.4133$

12. $\ln 7 \approx 1.9459$

14. $\ln 41.5 \approx 3.7257$

16. Answers may vary

18. $\log 10,000 = \log 10^4 = 4$

20. $\log\left(\dfrac{1}{100}\right) = \log 10^{-2} = -2$

22. $\ln e^4 = 4$

24. $\ln \sqrt[5]{e} = \ln e^{1/5} = \dfrac{1}{5}$

26. $\log 10^7 = 7$

28. $\ln e^{-5} = -5$

30. $\log 0.001 = \log 10^{-3} = -3$

32. $\log \sqrt{10} = \log 10^{1/2} = \dfrac{1}{2}$

34. $\ln 5x = 9$
$$5x = e^9$$
$$x = \dfrac{e^9}{5} \approx 1620.6168$$

36. $\log x = 2.1$
$$x = 10^{2.1} \approx 125.8925$$

38. $\log 3x = 1.3$
$$3x = 10^{1.3}$$
$$x = \dfrac{10^{1.3}}{3} \approx 6.6509$$

40. $\ln x = 2.1$
$$x = e^{2.1} \approx 8.1662$$

42. $\ln(2x+5) = 3.4$
$$2x + 5 = e^{3.4}$$
$$2x = e^{3.4} - 5$$
$$x = \dfrac{e^{3.4} - 5}{2} \approx 12.4821$$

44. $\log x = 3.1$
$$x = 10^{3.1} \approx 1258.9254$$

46. $\ln x = -3.7$
$$x = e^{-3.7} \approx 0.0247$$

48. $\log(3x-2) = -0.8$
$$3x - 2 = 10^{-0.8}$$
$$3x = 2 + 10^{-0.8}$$
$$x = \dfrac{2 + 10^{-0.8}}{3} \approx 0.7195$$

50. $\ln 3x = 0.76$
$$3x = e^{0.76}$$
$$x = \dfrac{e^{0.76}}{3} \approx 0.7128$$

52. $\log_3 2 = \dfrac{\log 2}{\log 3} \approx 0.6309$

54. $\log_{1/3} 2 = \dfrac{\log 2}{\log\left(\frac{1}{3}\right)} \approx -0.6309$

56. $\log_9 4 = \dfrac{\log 4}{\log 9} \approx 0.6309$

58. $\log_6 \dfrac{2}{3} = \dfrac{\log \frac{2}{3}}{\log 6} \approx -0.2263$

60. $\log_6 8 = \dfrac{\log 8}{\log 6} \approx 1.1606$

62. $R = \log\left(\dfrac{a}{T}\right) + B = \log\left(\dfrac{150}{3.6}\right) + 1.9 \approx 3.5$

The earthquake measures 3.5 on the Richter scale.

64. $R = \log\left(\dfrac{a}{T}\right) + B = \log\left(\dfrac{450}{4.2}\right) + 2.7 \approx 4.7$

The earthquake measures 4.7 on the Richter scale.

66. $A = Pe^{rt} = 3500e^{0.06(1)} \approx 3716.43$

The account contains \$3716.43.

68. $A = Pe^{rt} = 2500e^{(0.10)(3)} \approx 3374.65$

The certificate of deposit is worth \$3374.65.

70. $2x + 3 = 5 - 2(3x - 1)$

$2x + 3 = 5 - 6x + 2$

$2x + 3 = 7 - 6x$

$8x = 4$

$x = \dfrac{4}{8} = \dfrac{1}{2}$

The solution is $\dfrac{1}{2}$.

72. $4x - 8y = 10x$

$-8y = 6x$

$\dfrac{-8y}{6} = x$

$-\dfrac{4y}{3} = x$

74. $x^2 + 4x = 12$

$x^2 + 4x - 12 = 0$

$(x + 6)(x - 2) = 0$

$x + 6 = 0 \quad$ or $\quad x - 2 = 0$

$x = -6 \quad$ or $\quad x = 2$

The solutions are –6 and 2.

76. $\begin{cases} 5x + y = 5 \\ -3x - 2y = -10 \end{cases}$

Multiply the first equation by 2, then add.

$10x + 2y = 10$

$\underline{-3x - 2y = -10}$

$7x \quad\quad = 0$

$x = 0$

Replace x with 0 in the first equation.

$5(0) + y = 5$

$y = 5$

The solution is (0, 5).

78. $\log 50^{-1}$ must be larger. Answers may vary

80. $f(x) = e^{2x}$

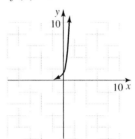

82. $f(x) = e^{-x}$

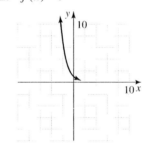

84. $f(x) = e^{x} - 3$

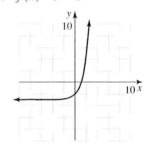

86. $f(x) = e^{x+4}$

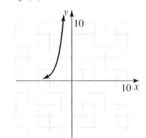

88. $f(x) = -2e^x$

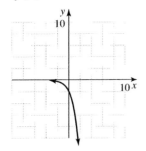

90. $f(x) = \log x$

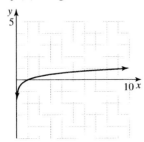

92. $f(x) = 3 \ln x$

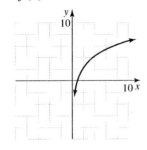

94. $f(x) = \log (x - 2)$

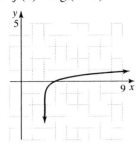

96. $f(x) = \ln x + 3$

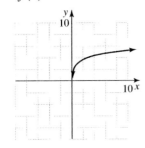

98. $f(x) = \ln x$
$f(x) = \ln x - 3$
$f(x) = \ln x + 3$

Answers may vary

Section 9.7

Practice Exercises

1. $5^x = 9$

$\log 5^x = \log 9$

$x \log 5 = \log 9$

$x = \dfrac{\log 9}{\log 5} \approx 1.3652$

The solution is $\dfrac{\log 9}{\log 5}$, or approximately 1.3652.

2. $\log_2 (x - 1) = 5$

$2^5 = x - 1$

$32 = x - 1$

$33 = x$

Check: $\log_2 (x - 1) = 5$

$\log_2 (33 - 1) \stackrel{?}{=} 5$

$\log_2 32 \stackrel{?}{=} 5$

$2^5 = 32$ True

The solution is 33.

3. $\log_5 x + \log_5 (x + 4) = 1$

$\log_5 x(x + 4) = 1$

$\log_5 (x^2 + 4x) = 1$

$5^1 = x^2 + 4x$

$0 = x^2 + 4x - 5$

$0 = (x + 5)(x - 1)$

$x + 5 = 0$ or $x - 1 = 0$

$x = -5$ $x = 1$

Since $\log_5 (-5)$ is undefined, -5 is rejected. The solution is 1.

4. $\log(x+3) - \log x = 1$

$$\log\frac{x+3}{x} = 1$$

$$10^1 = \frac{x+3}{x}$$

$$10x = x+3$$

$$9x = 3$$

$$x = \frac{1}{3}$$

The solution is $\frac{1}{3}$.

5. $y_0 = 60;\ t = 3$

$y = y_0 e^{0.916t}$

$y = 60e^{0.916(3)} = 60e^{2.748} \approx 937$

The population will be approximately 937 rabbits.

6. $P = \$3000;\ r = 7\% = 0.07;\ n = 12;$
$A = 2P = \$6000$

$$A = P\left(1+\frac{r}{n}\right)^{nt}$$

$$6000 = 3000\left(1+\frac{0.07}{12}\right)^{12t}$$

$$2 = \left(1+\frac{0.07}{12}\right)^{12t}$$

$$\log 2 = \log\left(1+\frac{0.07}{12}\right)^{12t}$$

$$\log 2 = 12t\log\left(1+\frac{0.07}{12}\right)$$

$$\frac{\log 2}{12\log\left(1+\frac{0.07}{12}\right)} = t$$

$$9.9 \approx t$$

It takes nearly 10 years to double.

7. $y_1 = 5000\left(1+\frac{0.05}{4}\right)^{4x},\ y_2 = 6000$

It takes 3.67 years, or 3 years and 8 months.

2. $4^x = 7$

$\log 4^x = \log 7$

$x\log 7 = \log 7$

$$x = \frac{\log 7}{\log 4} \approx 1.4037$$

4. $5^{3x} = 5.6$

$\log 5^{3x} = \log 5.6$

$3x\log 5 = \log 5.6$

$$x = \frac{\log 5.6}{3\log 5} \approx 0.3568$$

6. $8^{x-2} = 12$

$\log 8^{x-2} = \log 12$

$(x-2)\log 8 = \log 12$

$$x-2 = \frac{\log 12}{\log 8}$$

$$x = 2 + \frac{\log 12}{\log 8} \approx 3.1950$$

8. $3^x = 11$

$\log 3^x = \log 11$

$x\log 3 = \log 11$

$$x = \frac{\log 11}{\log 3} \approx 2.1827$$

10. $6^{x+3} = 2$

$\log 6^{x+3} = \log 2$

$(x+3)\log 6 = \log 2$

$$x+3 = \frac{\log 2}{\log 6}$$

$$x = -3 + \frac{\log 2}{\log 6} \approx -2.6131$$

12. $5^{2x-6} = 12$

$\log 5^{2x-6} = \log 12$

$(2x-6)\log 5 = \log 12$

$$2x-6 = \frac{\log 12}{\log 5}$$

$$2x = 6 + \frac{\log 12}{\log 5}$$

$$x = \frac{1}{2}\left(6 + \frac{\log 12}{\log 5}\right) \approx 3.7720$$

14. $e^{2x} = 8$

$\ln e^{2x} = \ln 8$

$2x = \ln 8$

$x = \dfrac{\ln 8}{2} \approx 1.0397$

16. $\log_6(x^2 - x) = 1$

$6^1 = x^2 - x$

$0 = x^2 - x - 6$

$0 = (x-3)(x+2)$

$x = 3$ or $x = -2$

18. $\log_2 x^2 = 6$

$2^6 = x^2$

$64 = x^2$

$\pm 8 = x$

20. $\log_3 5 + \log_3 x = 1$

$\log_3 5x = 1$

$3^1 = 5x$

$\dfrac{3}{5} = x$

22. $\log_4 10 - \log_4 x = 2$

$\log_4 \dfrac{10}{x} = 2$

$4^2 = \dfrac{10}{x}$

$16x = 10$

$x = \dfrac{5}{8}$

24. $\log_3 x + \log_3(x+6) = 3$

$\log_3[x(x+6)] = 3$

$3^3 = x^2 + 6x$

$0 = x^2 + 6x - 27$

$0 = (x+9)(x-3)$

$x = -9$ or $x = 3$

We discard -9 as extraneous, the solution is 3.

26. $\log_6(x+2) - \log_6 x = 2$

$\log_6 \dfrac{x+2}{x} = 2$

$6^2 = \dfrac{x+2}{x}$

$36x = x + 2$

$35x = 2$

$x = \dfrac{2}{35}$

28. $\log_2(x-5) = 3$

$2^3 = x - 5$

$8 = x - 5$

$13 = x$

30. $\log_8(x^2 - 2x) = 1$

$8^1 = x^2 - 2x$

$0 = x^2 - 2x - 8$

$0 = (x-4)(x+2)$

$x = 4$ or $x = -2$

32. $\ln 3 + \ln(x-1) = 0$

$\ln[3(x-1)] = 0$

$e^0 = 3x - 3$

$1 = 3x - 3$

$4 = 3x$

$\dfrac{4}{3} = x$

34. $2\log x - \log x = 3$

$\log x = 3$

$x = 10^3 = 1000$

36. $\log_4 x + \log_4(x+7) = 1$

$\log_4[x(x+7)] = 1$

$4^1 = x^2 + 7x$

$0 = x^2 + 7x - 4$

$x = \dfrac{-7 \pm \sqrt{7^2 - 4(1)(-4)}}{2(1)}$

$= \dfrac{-7 \pm \sqrt{65}}{2}$

Discard $\dfrac{-7 - \sqrt{65}}{2}$, the solution is

$x = \dfrac{-7 + \sqrt{65}}{2}$.

38. $\log_2 x - \log_2 (3x+5) = 4$

$$\log_2 \frac{x}{3x+5} = 4$$

$$2^4 = \frac{x}{3x+5}$$

$$16(3x+5) = x$$

$$48x + 80 = x$$

$$47x = -80$$

$$x = -\frac{80}{47} \text{ (extraneous)}$$

No solution, or $\varnothing$

40. $\log_3 x + \log_3 (x-8) = 2$

$$\log_3 [x(x-8)] = 2$$

$$3^2 = x^2 - 8x$$

$$0 = x^2 - 8x - 9$$

$$0 = (x-9)(x+1)$$

$x = 9$ or $x = -1$

We discard -1 as extraneous, the solution is 9.

42. $y = y_0 e^{0.075t}$

$$45,000 = 20,000 e^{0.075t}$$

$$\frac{45,000}{20,000} = e^{0.075t}$$

$$\frac{9}{4} = e^{0.075t}$$

$$\ln \frac{9}{4} = \ln e^{0.075t}$$

$$\ln \frac{9}{4} = 0.075t$$

$$t = \frac{\ln\left(\frac{9}{4}\right)}{0.075} \approx 10.81$$

45,000 people will have the flu in 10.81 weeks or $10.81 \cdot 7 \approx 76$ days.

44. $y = y_0 e^{0.016t}$

$$2000 = 1730 e^{0.016t}$$

$$\frac{2000}{1730} = e^{0.016t}$$

$$\ln \frac{200}{173} = \ln e^{0.016t}$$

$$\ln \frac{200}{173} = 0.016t$$

$$t = \frac{\ln \frac{200}{173}}{0.016} \approx 9.1$$

The population will be 2 billion in 9.1 years.

46. $y = y_0 e^{0.00894t}$, $t = 2020 - 2007 = 13$,

$y_0 = 301,140,000$

$$y = 301,140,000 e^{0.00894(13)}$$

$$\approx 338,250,000$$

There will be 338,250,000 inhabitants in 2020.

48. $A = P\left(1 + \dfrac{r}{n}\right)^{nt}$

$$1200 = 600\left(1 + \frac{0.12}{12}\right)^{12t}$$

$$2 = (1.01)^{12t}$$

$$\log 2 = \log (1.01)^{12t}$$

$$\log 2 = 12t \log 1.01$$

$$t = \frac{\log 2}{12 \log 1.01} \approx 5.8$$

It takes 5.8 years for the \$600 to double.

50. $A = P\left(1 + \dfrac{r}{n}\right)^{nt}$; $P = 1500$,

$A = 1500 + 200 = 1700$, $r = 0.10$, $n = 2$

$$1700 = 1500\left(1 + \frac{0.10}{2}\right)^{2t}$$

$$\frac{17}{15} = (1.05)^{2t}$$

$$\log \frac{17}{15} = \log (1.05)^{2t}$$

$$\log \frac{17}{15} = 2t \log 1.05$$

$$t = \frac{\log\left(\frac{17}{15}\right)}{2 \log 1.05} \approx 1.3$$

It takes 1.3 years to earn \$200.

52.
$$A = P\left(1+\frac{r}{n}\right)^{nt}$$
$$2000 = 1000\left(1+\frac{0.08}{12}\right)^{12t}$$
$$2 = \left(1+\frac{0.08}{12}\right)^{12t}$$
$$\log 2 = \log\left(1+\frac{0.08}{12}\right)^{12t}$$
$$\log 2 = 12t\log\left(1+\frac{0.08}{12}\right)$$
$$t = \frac{\log 2}{12\log\left(1+\frac{0.08}{12}\right)}$$
$$t \approx 8.7$$
It takes 8.7 years to double.

54. $w = 0.00185h^{2.67}$

$w = 0.00185(43)^{2.67} \approx 42.5$

The expected weight of a boy 43 inches tall is 42.5 pounds.

56.
$$w = 0.00185h^{2.67}$$
$$140 = 0.00185h^{2.67}$$
$$\frac{140}{0.00185} = h^{2.67}$$
$$\sqrt[2.67]{\frac{140}{0.00185}} = \sqrt[2.67]{h^{2.67}}$$
$$h \approx 67.2$$
The expected height of the boy is 67.2 inches.

58. $P = 14.7e^{-0.21x}$, $x = 2.7$

$P = 14.7e^{-0.21(2.7)} \approx 8.3$

The average atmospheric pressure at Pikes Peak is 8.3 pounds per square inch.

60.
$$P = 14.7e^{-0.21x}$$
$$6.5 = 14.7e^{-0.21x}$$
$$\frac{6.5}{14.7} = e^{-0.21x}$$
$$\ln\frac{6.5}{14.7} = \ln e^{-0.21x}$$
$$\ln\frac{6.5}{14.7} = -0.21x$$
$$x = \frac{\ln\left(\frac{6.5}{14.7}\right)}{-0.21} \approx 3.9$$
The elevation is about 3.9 miles.

62.
$$t = \frac{1}{c}\ln\left(\frac{A}{A-N}\right)$$
$$t = \frac{1}{0.03}\ln\left(\frac{65}{65-30}\right) \approx 20.63$$
It will take 21 weeks.

64.
$$t = \frac{1}{c}\ln\left(\frac{A}{A-N}\right)$$
$$t = \frac{1}{0.17}\ln\left(\frac{24}{24-15}\right) \approx 5.77$$
It will take 6 weeks.

66. $\dfrac{x^3 - 2y + z}{2z} = \dfrac{(-2)^3 - 2(0) + 3}{2(3)} = \dfrac{-5}{6} = -\dfrac{5}{6}$

68. $\dfrac{4y - 3x + z}{2x + y} = \dfrac{4(0) - 3(-2) + 3}{2(-2) + 0} = \dfrac{9}{-4} = -\dfrac{9}{4}$

70.
$$f(x) = \frac{x-3}{4}$$
$$y = \frac{x-3}{4}$$
$$x = \frac{y-3}{4}$$
$$4x = y - 3$$
$$4x + 3 = y$$
$$f^{-1}(x) = 4x + 3$$

72. $y = 2{,}495{,}529$, $y_0 = 2{,}018{,}456$, and $t = 6$
$$y = y_0 e^{kt}$$
$$2{,}495{,}529 = 2{,}018{,}456e^{k(6)}$$
$$\frac{2{,}495{,}529}{2{,}018{,}456} = e^{6k}$$
$$\ln\frac{2{,}495{,}529}{2{,}018{,}456} = \ln e^{6k}$$
$$\ln\frac{2{,}495{,}529}{2{,}018{,}456} = 6k$$
$$k = \frac{\ln\frac{2{,}495{,}529}{2{,}018{,}456}}{6} \approx 0.0354$$
The annual rate of growth was 3.5%.

74. Answers may vary

76.

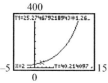

In 2002, spending was approximately $40.21 billion.

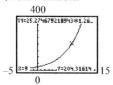

Spending is predicted to be $204.32 billion in 2009.

78.

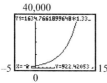

In 1998, revenue was approximately $922 million.

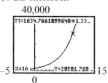

Revenue is predicted to be $28,582 in 2010.

80.

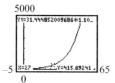

In 1987, health spending was approximately $415.7 billion.

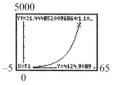

Health spending is predicted to be $4124.9 billion.

82. $Y_1 = 10^{0.5x}$, $Y_2 = 7$

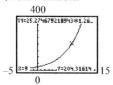

$x \approx 1.69$

84. $Y_1 = \ln(1.3x - 2.1) + 3.5x - 5$, $Y_2 = 0$

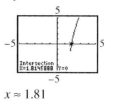

$x \approx 1.81$

The Bigger Picture

1. $\quad 8^x = 2^{x-3}$

$\quad 2^{3x} = 2^{x-3}$

$\quad 3x = x - 3$

$\quad 2x = -3$

$\quad x = -\dfrac{3}{2}$

2. $\quad 11^x = 5$

$\quad \log 11^x = \log 5$

$\quad x \log 11 = \log 5$

$\quad x = \dfrac{\log 5}{\log 11} \approx 0.6712$

3. $\quad -7x + 3 \le -5x + 13$

$\quad\quad -10 \le 2x$

$\quad\quad\quad -5 \le x$

The solution is $[-5, \infty)$.

4. $\quad -7 \le 3x + 6 \le 0$

$\quad -13 \le 3x \le -6$

$\quad -\dfrac{13}{3} \le x \le -2$

The solution is $\left[-\dfrac{13}{3}, -2 \right]$.

5. $\quad |5y + 3| < 3$

$\quad -3 < 5y + 3 < 3$

$\quad -6 < 5y < 0$

$\quad -\dfrac{6}{5} < y < 0$

The solution is $\left(-\dfrac{6}{5}, 0 \right)$.

6. $(x-6)(5x+1)=0$

$x-6=0$ or $5x+1=0$

$x=6$ 　　　 $5x=-1$

　　　　　　　　$x=-\dfrac{1}{5}$

The solutions are 6 and $-\dfrac{1}{5}$.

7. $\log_{13} 8 + \log_{13}(x-1)=1$

　　$\log_{13}(8x-8)=1$

　　　　$13^1 = 8x-8$

　　　　$21 = 8x$

　　　　$\dfrac{21}{8}=x$

8. $\left|\dfrac{3x-1}{4}\right|=2$

$\dfrac{3x-1}{4}=2$ or $\dfrac{3x-1}{4}=-2$

$3x-1=8$ 　　　 $3x-1=-8$

$3x=9$ 　　　　 $3x=-7$

$x=3$ 　　　　　 $x=-\dfrac{7}{3}$

The solutions are 3 and $-\dfrac{7}{3}$.

9. $|7x+1|>-2$ is a true statement for all x, so the solution is $(-\infty, \infty)$.

10. $x^2=4$

$x=\pm\sqrt{4}=\pm 2$

The solutions are 2 and -2.

11. $(x+5)^2=3$

$x+5=\pm\sqrt{3}$

$x=-5\pm\sqrt{3}$

The solutions are $-5+\sqrt{3}$ and $-5-\sqrt{3}$.

12. $\log_7(4x^2-27x)=1$

$7^1=4x^2-27x$

$0=4x^2-27x-7$

$0=(4x+1)(x-7)$

$4x+1=0$ or $x-7=0$

$4x=-1$ 　　　 $x=7$

$x=-\dfrac{1}{4}$

The solutions are $-\dfrac{1}{4}$ and 7.

Chapter 9 Vocabulary Check

1. For each one-to-one function, we can find its <u>inverse</u> function by switching the coordinates of the ordered pairs of the function.

2. The <u>composition</u> of functions f and g is $(f \circ g)(x) = f(g(x))$.

3. A function of the form $f(x)=b^x$ is called an <u>exponential</u> function if $b>0$, b is not 1, and x is a real number.

4. The graphs of f and f^{-1} are <u>symmetric</u> about the line $y=x$.

5. <u>Natural</u> logarithms are logarithms to base e.

6. <u>Common</u> logarithms are logarithms to base 10.

7. To see whether a graph is the graph of a one-to-one function, apply the <u>vertical</u> line test to see if it is a function, and then apply the <u>horizontal</u> line test to see if it is a one-to-one function.

8. A <u>logarithmic</u> function is a function that can be defined by $f(x)=\log_b x$ where x is a positive real number, b is a constant positive real number, and b is not 1.

Chapter 9 Review

1. $(f+g)(x)=f(x)+g(x)$

$=(x-5)+(2x+1)$

$=x-5+2x+1$

$=3x-4$

2. $(f-g)(x)=f(x)-g(x)$

$=(x-5)-(2x+1)$

$=x-5-2x-1$

$=-x-6$

3. $(f \cdot g)(x) = f(x) \cdot g(x)$
$= (x-5)(2x+1)$
$= 2x^2 + x - 10x - 5$
$= 2x^2 - 9x - 5$

4. $\left(\dfrac{g}{f}\right)(x) = \dfrac{g(x)}{f(x)} = \dfrac{2x+1}{x-5}, x \neq 5$

5. $(f \circ g)(x) = f(g(x))$
$= f(x+1)$
$= (x+1)^2 - 2$
$= x^2 + 2x - 1$

6. $(g \circ f)(x) = g(f(x))$
$= g(x^2 - 2)$
$= x^2 - 2 + 1$
$= x^2 - 1$

7. $(h \circ g)(2) = h(g(2)) = h(3) = 3^3 - 3^2 = 18$

8. $(f \circ f)(x) = f(f(x))$
$= f(x^2 - 2)$
$= (x^2 - 2)^2 - 2$
$= x^4 - 4x^2 + 4 - 2$
$= x^4 - 4x^2 + 2$

9. $(f \circ g)(-1) = f(g(-1)) = f(0) = 0^2 - 2 = -2$

10. $(h \circ h)(2) = h(h(2)) = h(4) = 4^3 - 4^2 = 48$

11. The function is one-to-one.
$h^{-1} = \{(14,-9),(8,6),(12,-11),(15,15)\}$

12. The function is not one-to-one.

13. The function is one-to-one.

Rank in Auto Thefts (Input)	2	4	1	3
U.S. Region (Output)	West	Midwest	South	Northeast

14. The function is not one-to-one.

15. $f(x) = \sqrt{x+2}$

 a. $f(7) = \sqrt{7+2} = \sqrt{9} = 3$

 b. $f^{-1}(3) = 7$

16. $f(x) = \sqrt{x+2}$

 a. $f(-1) = \sqrt{-1+2} = \sqrt{1} = 1$

 b. $f^{-1}(1) = -1$

17. The graph does not represent a one-to-one function.

18. The graph does not represent a one-to-one function.

19. The graph does not represent a one-to-one function.

20. The graph represents a one-to-one function.

21. $f(x) = x - 9$
$y = x - 9$
$x = y - 9$
$y = x + 9$
$f^{-1}(x) = x + 9$

22. $f(x) = x + 8$
$y = x + 8$
$x = y + 8$
$y = x - 8$
$f^{-1}(x) = x - 8$

23. $f(x) = 6x + 11$
$y = 6x + 11$
$x = 6y + 11$
$6y = x - 11$
$y = \dfrac{x-11}{6}$
$f^{-1}(x) = \dfrac{x-11}{6}$

24. $f(x) = 12x$

$y = 12x$

$x = 12y$

$y = \dfrac{x}{12}$

$f^{-1}(x) = \dfrac{x}{12}$

25. $f(x) = x^3 - 5$

$y = x^3 - 5$

$x = y^3 - 5$

$y^3 = x + 5$

$y = \sqrt[3]{x+5}$

$f^{-1}(x) = \sqrt[3]{x+5}$

26. $f(x) = \sqrt[3]{x+2}$

$y = \sqrt[3]{x+2}$

$x = \sqrt[3]{y+2}$

$x^3 = y + 2$

$y = x^3 - 2$

$f^{-1}(x) = x^3 - 2$

27. $g(x) = \dfrac{12x-7}{6}$

$y = \dfrac{12x-7}{6}$

$x = \dfrac{12y-7}{6}$

$6x = 12y - 7$

$12y = 6x + 7$

$y = \dfrac{6x+7}{12}$

$g^{-1}(x) = \dfrac{6x+7}{12}$

28. $r(x) = \dfrac{13}{2}x - 4$

$y = \dfrac{13}{2}x - 4$

$x = \dfrac{13}{2}y - 4$

$x + 4 = \dfrac{13}{2}y$

$y = \dfrac{2(x+4)}{13}$

$r^{-1}(x) = \dfrac{2(x+4)}{13}$

29. $y = g(x) = \sqrt{x}$

$x = \sqrt{y}$

$x^2 = y = g^{-1}(x),\ x \geq 0$

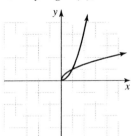

30. $h(x) = 5x - 5$

$y = 5x - 5$

$x = 5y - 5$

$5y = x + 5$

$y = \dfrac{x+5}{5}$

$h^{-1}(x) = \dfrac{x+5}{5}$

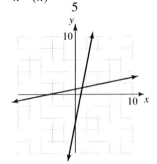

31. $f(x) = 2x - 3$

$y = 2x - 3$

$x = 2y - 3$

$y = \dfrac{x+3}{2}$

$f^{-1}(x) = \dfrac{x+3}{2}$

32. $4^x = 64$

$4^x = 4^3$

$x = 3$

33. $3^x = \dfrac{1}{9}$

$3^x = 3^{-2}$

$x = -2$

34. $2^{3x} = \dfrac{1}{16}$

$2^{3x} = 2^{-4}$

$3x = -4$

$x = -\dfrac{4}{3}$

35. $5^{2x} = 125$

$5^{2x} = 5^3$

$2x = 3$

$x = \dfrac{3}{2}$

36. $9^{x+1} = 243$

$(3^2)^{x+1} = 3^5$

$3^{2x+2} = 3^5$

$2x + 2 = 5$

$2x = 3$

$x = \dfrac{3}{2}$

37. $8^{3x-2} = 4$

$(2^3)^{3x-2} = 2^2$

$2^{9x-6} = 2^2$

$9x - 6 = 2$

$9x = 8$

$x = \dfrac{8}{9}$

38. $y = 3^x$

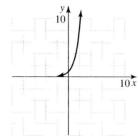

39. $y = \left(\dfrac{1}{3}\right)^x$

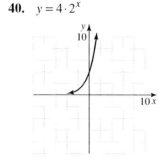

40. $y = 4 \cdot 2^x$

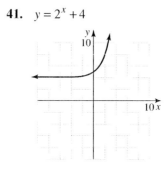

41. $y = 2^x + 4$

42. $A = P\left(1 + \dfrac{r}{n}\right)^{nt}$

$A = 1600\left(1 + \dfrac{0.09}{2}\right)^{(2)(7)}$

$A \approx 2963.11$

The amount accrued is \$2963.11.

43. $A = P\left(1 + \dfrac{r}{n}\right)^{nt}$

$A = 800\left(1 + \dfrac{0.07}{4}\right)^{(4)(5)}$

$A \approx 1131.82$

The certificate is worth \$1131.82 at the end of 5 years.

44. $y = 4 \cdot 2^x$

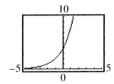

45. $\quad 49 = 7^2$
$\log_7 49 = 2$

46. $\quad 2^{-4} = \dfrac{1}{16}$
$\log_2 \dfrac{1}{16} = -4$

47. $\log_{1/2} 16 = -4$
$\left(\dfrac{1}{2}\right)^{-4} = 16$

48. $\log_{0.4} 0.064 = 3$
$\quad\quad 0.4^3 = 0.064$

49. $\log_4 x = -3$
$\quad x = 4^{-3} = \dfrac{1}{64}$

50. $\log_3 x = 2$
$\quad x = 3^2 = 9$

51. $\log_3 1 = x$
$\quad 3^x = 1$
$\quad 3^x = 3^0$
$\quad x = 0$

52. $\log_4 64 = x$
$\quad 4^x = 64$
$\quad 4^x = 4^3$
$\quad x = 3$

53. $\log_x 64 = 2$
$\quad x^2 = 64$
$\quad x = \pm\sqrt{64} = \pm 8$
$\quad x = 8$ since the base must be positive

54. $\log_x 81 = 4$
$\quad x^4 = 81$
$\quad x = \pm 3$
$\quad x = 3$ since the base must be positive

55. $\log_4 4^5 = x$
$\quad x = 5$

56. $\log_7 7^{-2} = x$
$\quad x = -2$

57. $5^{\log_5 4} = x$
$\quad x = 4$

58. $2^{\log_2 9} = x$
$\quad 9 = x$

59. $\log_2 (3x - 1) = 4$
$\quad 3x - 1 = 2^4$
$\quad 3x - 1 = 16$
$\quad 3x = 17$
$\quad x = \dfrac{17}{3}$

60. $\log_3 (2x + 5) = 2$
$\quad 2x + 5 = 3^2$
$\quad 2x + 5 = 9$
$\quad 2x = 4$
$\quad x = 2$

61. $\log_4 (x^2 - 3x) = 1$
$\quad x^2 - 3x = 4$
$\quad x^2 - 3x - 4 = 0$
$\quad (x+1)(x-4) = 0$
$\quad x = -1$ or $x = 4$

62. $\log_8 (x^2 + 7x) = 1$
$\quad x^2 + 7x = 8$
$\quad x^2 + 7x - 8 = 0$
$\quad (x+8)(x-1) = 0$
$\quad x = -8$ or $x = 1$

63. $y = 2^x$ and $y = \log_2 x$

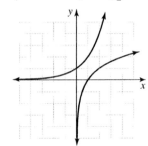

64. $y = \left(\dfrac{1}{2}\right)^x$ and $y = \log_{1/2} x$

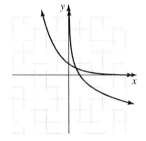

65. $\log_3 8 + \log_3 4 = \log_3(8 \cdot 4) = \log_3 32$

66. $\log_2 6 + \log_2 3 = \log_2(6 \cdot 3) = \log_2 18$

67. $\log_7 15 - \log_7 20 = \log_7 \dfrac{15}{20} = \log_7 \dfrac{3}{4}$

68. $\log 18 - \log 12 = \log \dfrac{18}{12} = \log \dfrac{3}{2}$

69. $\log_{11} 8 + \log_{11} 3 - \log_{11} 6 = \log_{11} \dfrac{(8)(3)}{6}$
$\qquad\qquad\qquad\qquad\qquad\qquad = \log_{11} 4$

70. $\log_5 14 + \log_5 3 - \log_5 21$
$\quad = \log_5(14 \cdot 3) - \log_5 21$
$\quad = \log_5 \dfrac{42}{21}$
$\quad = \log_5 2$

71. $2\log_5 x - 2\log_5(x+1) + \log_5 x$
$\quad = \log_5 x^2 - \log_5(x+1)^2 + \log_5 x$
$\quad = \log_5 \dfrac{(x^2)(x)}{(x+1)^2}$
$\quad = \log_5 \dfrac{x^3}{(x+1)^2}$

72. $4\log_3 x - \log_3 x + \log_3(x+2)$
$\quad = 3\log_3 x + \log_3(x+2)$
$\quad = \log_3 x^3 + \log_3(x+2)$
$\quad = \log_3 \left[x^3(x+2) \right]$
$\quad = \log_3(x^4 + 2x^3)$

73. $\log_3 \dfrac{x^3}{x+2} = \log_3 x^3 - \log_3(x+2)$
$\qquad\qquad = 3\log_3 x - \log_3(x+2)$

74. $\log_4 \dfrac{x+5}{x^2} = \log_4(x+5) - \log_4 x^2$
$\qquad\qquad = \log_4(x+5) - 2\log_4 x$

75. $\log_2 \dfrac{3x^2 y}{z} = \log_2(3x^2 y) - \log_2 z$
$\qquad\qquad = \log_2 3 + \log_2 x^2 + \log_2 y - \log_2 z$
$\qquad\qquad = \log_2 3 + 2\log_2 x + \log_2 y - \log_2 z$

76. $\log_7 \dfrac{yz^3}{x} = \log_7(yz^3) - \log_7 x$
$\qquad\qquad = \log_7 y + \log_7 z^3 - \log_7 x$
$\qquad\qquad = \log_7 y + 3\log_7 z - \log_7 x$

77. $\log_b 50 = \log_b (5)(5)(2)$
$\qquad\qquad = \log_b(5) + \log_b(5) + \log_b(2)$
$\qquad\qquad = 0.83 + 0.83 + 0.36$
$\qquad\qquad = 2.02$

78. $\log_b \dfrac{4}{5} = \log_b 4 - \log_b 5$
$\qquad\qquad = \log_b 2^2 - \log_b 5$
$\qquad\qquad = 2\log_b 2 - \log_b 5$
$\qquad\qquad = 2(0.36) - 0.83$
$\qquad\qquad = 0.72 - 0.83$
$\qquad\qquad = -0.11$

79. $\log 3.6 \approx 0.5563$

80. $\log 0.15 \approx -0.8239$

81. $\ln 1.25 \approx 0.2231$

82. $\ln 4.63 \approx 1.5326$

83. $\log 1000 = \log 10^3 = 3$

84. $\log \dfrac{1}{10} = \log 10^{-1} = -1$

85. $\ln \dfrac{1}{e} = \ln e^{-1} = -1$

86. $\ln e^4 = 4$

87. $\ln(2x) = 2$

$2x = e^2$

$x = \dfrac{e^2}{2}$

88. $\ln(3x) = 1.6$

$3x = e^{1.6}$

$x = \dfrac{e^{1.6}}{3}$

89. $\ln(2x - 3) = -1$

$2x - 3 = e^{-1}$

$x = \dfrac{e^{-1} + 3}{2}$

90. $\ln(3x + 1) = 2$

$3x + 1 = e^2$

$3x = e^2 - 1$

$x = \dfrac{e^2 - 1}{3}$

91. $\ln \dfrac{I}{I_0} = -kx$

$\ln \dfrac{0.03 I_0}{I_0} = -2.1x$

$\ln 0.03 = -2.1x$

$\dfrac{\ln 0.03}{-2.1} = x$

$x \approx 1.67$

The depth is 1.67 millimeters.

92. $\ln \dfrac{I}{I_0} = -kx$

$\ln \dfrac{0.02 I_0}{I_0} = -3.2x$

$\ln 0.02 = -3.2x$

$\dfrac{\ln 0.02}{-3.2} = x$

$x \approx 1.22$

2% of the original radioactivity will penetrate at a depth of approximately 1.22 millimeters.

93. $\log_5 1.6 = \dfrac{\log 1.6}{\log 5} \approx 0.2920$

94. $\log_3 4 = \dfrac{\log 4}{\log 3} \approx 1.2619$

95. $A = Pe^{rt}$

$A = 1450 e^{(0.06)(5)}$

$A \approx 1957.30$

The accrued amount is \$1957.30.

96. $A = Pe^{rt}$

$A = 940 e^{0.11(3)} = 940 e^{0.33} \approx 1307.51$

The investment grows to \$1307.51.

97. $3^{2x} = 7$

$\log 3^{2x} = \log 7$

$2x \log 3 = \log 7$

$x = \dfrac{\log 7}{2 \log 3} \approx 0.8856$

98. $6^{3x} = 5$

$\log 6^{3x} = \log 5$

$3x \log 6 = \log 5$

$x = \dfrac{\log 5}{3 \log 6} \approx 0.2994$

99. $3^{2x+1} = 6$

$\log 3^{2x+1} = \log 6$

$(2x + 1) \log 3 = \log 6$

$2x = \dfrac{\log 6}{\log 3} - 1$

$x = \dfrac{1}{2}\left(\dfrac{\log 6}{\log 3} - 1 \right) \approx 0.3155$

100. $4^{3x+2} = 9$

$\log 4^{3x+2} = \log 9$

$(3x + 2) \log 4 = \log 9$

$3x = \dfrac{\log 9}{\log 4} - 2$

$x = \dfrac{1}{3}\left(\dfrac{\log 9}{\log 4} - 2 \right) \approx -0.1383$

101. $5^{3x-5} = 4$

$\log 5^{3x-5} = \log 4$

$(3x - 5) \log 5 = \log 4$

$3x = \dfrac{\log 4}{\log 5} + 5$

$x = \dfrac{1}{3}\left(\dfrac{\log 4}{\log 5} + 5 \right) \approx 1.9538$

102.
$$8^{4x-2} = 3$$
$$\log 8^{4x-2} = \log 3$$
$$(4x-2)\log 8 = \log 3$$
$$4x = \frac{\log 3}{\log 8} + 2$$
$$x = \frac{1}{4}\left(\frac{\log 3}{\log 8} + 2\right) \approx 0.6321$$

103.
$$2 \cdot 5^{x-1} = 1$$
$$\log(2 \cdot 5^{x-1}) = \log 1$$
$$\log 2 + (x-1)\log 5 = 0$$
$$(x-1)\log 5 = -\log 2$$
$$x = -\frac{\log 2}{\log 5} + 1 \approx 0.5693$$

104.
$$3 \cdot 4^{x+5} = 2$$
$$4^{x+5} = \frac{2}{3}$$
$$\log 4^{x+5} = \log \frac{2}{3}$$
$$(x+5)\log 4 = \log \frac{2}{3}$$
$$x = \frac{\log\left(\frac{2}{3}\right)}{\log 4} - 5 \approx -5.2925$$

105.
$$\log_5 2 + \log_5 x = 2$$
$$\log_5 2x = 2$$
$$2x = 5^2$$
$$2x = 25$$
$$x = \frac{25}{2}$$

106.
$$\log_3 x + \log_3 10 = 2$$
$$\log_3(10x) = 2$$
$$10x = 3^2$$
$$10x = 9$$
$$x = \frac{9}{10}$$

107.
$$\log(5x) - \log(x+1) = 4$$
$$\log\frac{5x}{x+1} = 4$$
$$\frac{5x}{x+1} = 10^4$$
$$\frac{5x}{x+1} = 10,000$$
$$5x = 10,000x + 10,000$$
$$x = -1.0005$$

no solution, or $\varnothing$

108.
$$\ln(3x) - \ln(x-3) = 2$$
$$\ln\left(\frac{3x}{x-3}\right) = 2$$
$$\frac{3x}{x-3} = e^2$$
$$3x = e^2 x - 3e^2$$
$$3x - e^2 x = -3e^2$$
$$(3 - e^2)x = -3e^2$$
$$x = \frac{3e^2}{e^2 - 3}$$

109.
$$\log_2 x + \log_2 2x - 3 = 1$$
$$\log_2(x \cdot 2x) = 4$$
$$2x^2 = 2^4$$
$$2x^2 = 16$$
$$x^2 = 8$$
$$x = \pm 2\sqrt{2}$$

$-2\sqrt{2}$ is rejected since $\log_2\left(-2\sqrt{2}\right)$ is undefined. The solution is $2\sqrt{2}$.

110.
$$-\log_6(4x+7) + \log_6 x = 1$$
$$\log_6 \frac{x}{4x+7} = 1$$
$$\frac{x}{4x+7} = 6$$
$$x = 6(4x+7)$$
$$x = 24x + 42$$
$$x = -\frac{42}{23}$$

$-\frac{42}{23}$ is rejected since $\log_6\left(-\frac{42}{23}\right)$ is undefined.
There is no solution, or $\varnothing$.

111. $y = y_0 e^{kt}$

$\quad y = 155,000 e^{0.06(4)}$

$\quad\quad \approx 197,044$

There will be 197,044 ducks after 4 weeks.

112. $y = y_0 e^{kt}$

$\quad y = 2,971,650 e^{-0.00129(8)}$

$\quad\quad = 2,971,650 e^{-0.01032}$

$\quad\quad \approx 2,941,140$

The population of Armenia in the year 2015 will be approximately 2,941,140.

113. $y = y_0 e^{kt}$

$\quad 1,500,000,000 = 1,321,851,888 e^{0.00606t}$

$\quad \dfrac{1,500,000,000}{1,321,851,888} = e^{0.00606t}$

$\quad \ln \dfrac{1,500,000,000}{1,321,851,888} = \ln e^{0.00606t}$

$\quad \ln \dfrac{1,500,000,000}{1,321,851,888} = 0.00606t$

$\quad\quad t = \dfrac{1}{0.00606} \ln \dfrac{1,500,000,000}{1,321,851,888}$

$\quad\quad t \approx 20.9$

It will take approximately 20.9 years.

114. $y = y_0 e^{kt}$

$\quad 2(33,390,141) = 33,390,141 e^{0.009t}$

$\quad\quad 2 = e^{0.009t}$

$\quad\quad \ln 2 = \ln e^{0.009t}$

$\quad\quad \ln 2 = 0.009t$

$\quad\quad t = \dfrac{\ln 2}{0.009}$

$\quad\quad t \approx 77.0$

It will take approximately 77.0 years.

115. $y = y_0 e^{kt}$

$\quad 2(24,821,286) = 24,821,286 e^{0.018t}$

$\quad\quad 2 = e^{0.018t}$

$\quad\quad \ln 2 = \ln e^{0.018t}$

$\quad\quad \ln 2 = 0.018t$

$\quad\quad t = \dfrac{\ln 2}{0.018}$

$\quad\quad t \approx 38.5$

It will take approximately 38.5 years.

116. $A = P\left(1 + \dfrac{r}{n}\right)^{nt}$

$\quad 10,000 = 5000\left(1 + \dfrac{0.08}{4}\right)^{4t}$

$\quad\quad 2 = (1.02)^{4t}$

$\quad\quad \log 2 = \log 1.02^{4t}$

$\quad\quad \log 2 = 4t \log 1.02$

$\quad\quad t = \dfrac{\log 2}{4 \log 1.02} \approx 8.8$

It will take 8.8 years.

117. $A = P\left(1 + \dfrac{r}{n}\right)^{nt}$

$\quad 10,000 = 6000\left(1 + \dfrac{0.06}{12}\right)^{12t}$

$\quad\quad \dfrac{5}{3} = (1.005)^{12t}$

$\quad\quad \log \dfrac{5}{3} = \log 1.005^{12t}$

$\quad\quad \log \dfrac{5}{3} = 12t \log 1.005$

$\quad\quad t = \dfrac{1}{12}\left(\dfrac{\log\left(\frac{5}{3}\right)}{\log(1.005)}\right) \approx 8.5$

It was invested for approximately 8.5 years.

118. $Y_1 = e^x$, $Y_2 = 2$

$x \approx 0.69$

119. $Y_1 = 10^{0.3x}$, $Y_2 = 7$

$x \approx 2.82$

120.

The regression equation is $y = 0.219(1.078)^x$.

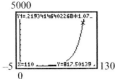

The cost is predicted to be $817 billion in 2010.

121. $7^{4x} = 49$

$7^{4x} = 7^2$

$4x = 2$

$x = \dfrac{1}{2}$

122. $3^x = \dfrac{1}{81}$

$3^x = 3^{-4}$

$x = -4$

123. $\log_4 4 = x$

$4^x = 4^1$

$x = 1$

124. $8^{3x-2} = 32$

$(2^3)^{(3x-2)} = 2^5$

$2^{9x-6} = 2^5$

$9x - 6 = 5$

$9x = 11$

$x = \dfrac{11}{9}$

125. $\log_5(x^2 - 4x) = 1$

$5^1 = x^2 - 4x$

$0 = x^2 - 4x - 5$

$0 = (x-5)(x+1)$

$x - 5 = 0$ or $x + 1 = 0$

$x = 5$ $\qquad$ $x = -1$

Both check, so the solutions are 5 and −1.

126. $\log_3 x = 4$

$3^4 = x$

$81 = x$

127. $\ln x = -3.2$

$e^{\ln x} = e^{-3.2}$

$x = e^{-3.2}$

128. $\log_4(3x - 1) = 2$

$4^2 = 3x - 1$

$16 + 1 = 3x$

$\dfrac{17}{3} = x$

129. $\ln x - \ln 2 = 1$

$\ln \dfrac{x}{2} = 1$

$e^{\ln \frac{x}{2}} = e^1$

$\dfrac{x}{2} = e$

$x = 2e$

130. $\log_5 x + \log_5 10 = 2$

$\log_5(10x) = 2$

$5^2 = 10x$

$\dfrac{25}{10} = x$

$\dfrac{5}{2} = x$

131. $\log_6 x - \log_6(4x + 7) = 1$

$\log_6 \dfrac{x}{4x+7} = 1$

$6^1 = \dfrac{x}{4x+7}$

$24x + 42 = x$

$23x = -42$

$x = -\dfrac{42}{23}$

$-\dfrac{42}{23}$ is rejected since $\log_6\left(-\dfrac{42}{23}\right)$ is undefined.

There is no solution, or $\varnothing$.

Chapter 9 Test

1. $f(x) = x$ and $g(x) = 2x - 3$

$(f \cdot g)(x) = f(x) \cdot g(x) = x(2x - 3) = 2x^2 - 3x$

2. $f(x) = x$ and $g(x) = 2x - 3$

$(f - g)(x) = f(x) - g(x)$

$= x - (2x - 3)$

$= -x + 3$

$= 3 - x$

3. $(f \circ h)(0) = f(h(0)) = f(5) = 5$

4. $(g \circ f)(x) = g(f(x)) = g(x) = x - 7$

5. $(g \circ h)(x) = g(h(x))$

$\qquad = g(x^2 - 6x + 5)$

$\qquad = x^2 - 6x + 5 - 7$

$\qquad = x^2 - 6x - 2$

6. $f(x) = 7x - 14,\ f^{-1}(x) = \dfrac{x+14}{7}$

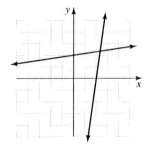

7. The graph represents a one-to-one function.

8. The graph does not represent a one-to-one function.

9. $y = 6 - 2x$ is one-to-one.

$\qquad x = 6 - 2y$

$\qquad 2y = -x + 6$

$\qquad y = \dfrac{-x+6}{2}$

$\qquad f^{-1}(x) = \dfrac{-x+6}{2}$

10. $f = \{(0,0),(2,3),(-1,5)\}$ is one-to-one.

$\qquad f^{-1} = \{(0,0),(3,2),(5,-1)\}$

11. The function is not one-to-one.

12. $\log_3 6 + \log_3 4 = \log_3 (6 \cdot 4) = \log_3 24$

13. $\log_5 x + 3\log_5 x - \log_5 (x+1)$

$\qquad = 4\log_5 x - \log_5 (x+1)$

$\qquad = \log_5 x^4 - \log_5 (x+1)$

$\qquad = \log_5 \dfrac{x^4}{x+1}$

14. $\log_6 \dfrac{2x}{y^3} = \log_6 2x - \log_6 y^3$

$\qquad\qquad = \log_6 2 + \log_6 x - 3\log_6 y$

15. $\log_b \left(\dfrac{3}{25}\right) = \log_b 3 - \log_b 25$

$\qquad\qquad = \log_b 3 - \log_b 5^2$

$\qquad\qquad = \log_b 3 - 2\log_b 5$

$\qquad\qquad = 0.79 - 2(1.16)$

$\qquad\qquad = -1.53$

16. $\log_7 8 = \dfrac{\ln 8}{\ln 7} \approx 1.0686$

17. $8^{x-1} = \dfrac{1}{64}$

$\qquad 8^{x-1} = 8^{-2}$

$\qquad x - 1 = -2$

$\qquad x = -1$

18. $\qquad 3^{2x+5} = 4$

$\qquad \log 3^{2x+5} = \log 4$

$\qquad (2x+5)\log 3 = \log 4$

$\qquad 2x = \dfrac{\log 4}{\log 3} - 5$

$\qquad x = \dfrac{1}{2}\left(\dfrac{\log 4}{\log 3} - 5\right)$

$\qquad x \approx -1.8691$

19. $\log_3 x = -2$

$\qquad x = 3^{-2}$

$\qquad x = \dfrac{1}{9}$

20. $\ln \sqrt{e} = x$

$\qquad \ln e^{1/2} = x$

$\qquad \dfrac{1}{2} = x$

21. $\log_8 (3x - 2) = 2$

$\qquad 3x - 2 = 8^2$

$\qquad 3x - 2 = 64$

$\qquad 3x = 66$

$\qquad x = \dfrac{66}{3} = 22$

22. $\log_5 x + \log_5 3 = 2$

$\qquad \log_5(3x) = 2$

$\qquad\qquad 3x = 5^2$

$\qquad\qquad 3x = 25$

$\qquad\qquad x = \dfrac{25}{3}$

23. $\log_4(x+1) - \log_4(x-2) = 3$

$\qquad \log_4 \dfrac{x+1}{x-2} = 3$

$\qquad\qquad \dfrac{x+1}{x-2} = 4^3$

$\qquad\qquad \dfrac{x+1}{x-2} = 64$

$\qquad\qquad x+1 = 64x - 128$

$\qquad\qquad 129 = 63x$

$\qquad\qquad \dfrac{129}{63} = x$

$\qquad\qquad \dfrac{43}{21} = x$

24. $\ln(3x+7) = 1.31$

$\qquad 3x+7 = e^{1.31}$

$\qquad\quad 3x = e^{1.31} - 7$

$\qquad\qquad x = \dfrac{e^{1.31} - 7}{3} \approx -1.0979$

25. $y = \left(\dfrac{1}{2}\right)^x + 1$

26. $y = 3^x$ and $y = \log_3 x$

27. $A = \left(1 + \dfrac{r}{n}\right)^{nt}, P = 4000, t = 3, r = 0.09,$

and $n = 12$

$A = 4000\left(1 + \dfrac{0.09}{12}\right)^{12(3)}$

$\quad = 4000(1.0075)^{36}$

$\quad \approx 5234.58$

$5234.58 will be in the account.

28. $A = \left(1 + \dfrac{r}{n}\right)^{nt}, P = 2000, A = 3000$

$r = 0.07, n = 2$

$3000 = 2000\left(1 + \dfrac{0.07}{2}\right)^{2t}$

$\quad 1.5 = (1.035)^{2t}$

$\log 1.5 = \log 1.035^{2t}$

$\log 1.5 = 2t \log 1.035$

$\qquad t = \dfrac{\log 1.5}{2\log 1.035} \approx 5.9$

It would take 6 years.

29. $y = y_0 e^{kt}$

$y = 57{,}000 e^{0.026(5)}$

$\quad = 57{,}000 e^{0.13}$

$\quad \approx 64{,}913$

There will be approximately 64,913 prairie dogs 5 years from now.

30. $\qquad y = y_0 e^{kt}$

$1000 = 400 e^{0.062(t)}$

$\quad 2.5 = e^{0.062t}$

$\ln 2.5 = \ln e^{0.062t}$

$0.062t = \ln 2.5$

$\qquad t = \dfrac{\ln 2.5}{0.062} \approx 14.8$

It will take the naturalists approximately 15 years to reach their goal.

31. $\log(1+k) = \dfrac{0.3}{D}, D = 56$

$\log(1+k) = \dfrac{0.3}{56}$

$\quad 1+k = 10^{0.3/56}$

$\qquad k = -1 + 10^{0.3/56}$

$\qquad k \approx 0.012$

The rate of population increase is approximately 1.2%.

32.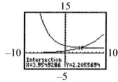

The solution is approximately 3.95.

Chapter 9 Cumulative Review

1. **a.** $(-8)(-1) = 8$

    b. $(-2)\dfrac{1}{6} = -\dfrac{1}{3}$

    c. $-1.2(0.3) = -0.36$

    d. $0(-11) = 0$

    e. $\left(\dfrac{1}{5}\right)\left(-\dfrac{10}{11}\right) = -\dfrac{2}{11}$

    f. $(7)(1)(-2)(-3) = 42$

    g. $8(-2)(0) = 0$

2. $\dfrac{1}{3}(x-2) = \dfrac{1}{4}(x+1)$

    $4(x-2) = 3(x+1)$

    $4x - 8 = 3x + 3$

    $x = 11$

3. $y = x^2$

    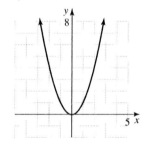

4. $y = f(x) = -3x + 4$, $m = -3$

    Perpendicular line: $m = \dfrac{1}{3}$, through $(-2, 6)$

    $y - y_1 = m(x - x_1)$

    $y - 6 = \dfrac{1}{3}[x - (-2)]$

    $y - 6 = \dfrac{1}{3}x + \dfrac{2}{3}$

    $y = \dfrac{1}{3}x + \dfrac{20}{3}$

    $f(x) = \dfrac{1}{3}x + \dfrac{20}{3}$

5. Equation 2 is twice the opposite of equation 1 and equation 3 is one-half of equation 1. Therefore, the system is dependent. The solution is $\{(x, y, z) | x - 5y - 2z = 6\}$.

6. The angles labeled $y°$ and $(x - 40)°$ are alternate interior angles, so $y = x - 40$. The angles labeled $x°$ and $y°$ are supplementary, so $x + y = 180$.

    $\begin{cases} y = x - 40 \\ x + y = 180 \end{cases}$

    Replace y with $x - 40$ in the second equation.
    $x + (x - 40) = 180$
    $\quad\quad\quad 2x = 220$
    $\quad\quad\quad\; x = 110$
    $y = x - 40 = 110 - 40 = 70$

7. **a.** $\dfrac{x^7}{x^4} = x^{7-4} = x^3$

    b. $\dfrac{5^8}{5^2} = 5^{8-2} = 5^6$

    c. $\dfrac{20x^6}{4x^5} = \dfrac{20}{4}x^{6-5} = 5x^1 = 5x$

    d. $\dfrac{12y^{10}z^7}{14y^8z^7} = \dfrac{12}{14}y^{10-8}z^{7-7} = \dfrac{6}{7}y^2z^0 = \dfrac{6y^2}{7}$

8. **a.** $(4a^3)^2 = 4^2(a^3)^2 = 16a^6$

    b. $\left(-\dfrac{2}{3}\right)^3 = \dfrac{(-2)^3}{3^3} = \dfrac{-8}{27} = -\dfrac{8}{27}$

c. $\left(\dfrac{4a^5}{b^3}\right)^3 = \dfrac{4^3(a^5)^3}{(b^3)^3} = \dfrac{64a^{15}}{b^9}$

d. $\left(\dfrac{3^{-2}}{x}\right)^{-3} = \dfrac{(3^{-2})^{-3}}{x^{-3}} = \dfrac{3^6}{x^{-3}} = 729x^3$

e. $(a^{-2}b^3c^{-4})^{-2} = (a^{-2})^{-2}(b^3)^{-2}(c^{-4})^{-2}$
$\qquad = a^4b^{-6}c^8$
$\qquad = \dfrac{a^4c^8}{b^6}$

9. a. $C(100) = \dfrac{2.6(100)+10,000}{100}$
$\qquad = 102.60$
The cost is \$102.60 per disc for 100 discs.

b. $C(1000) = \dfrac{2.6(1000)+10,000}{1000}$
$\qquad = 12.60$
The cost is \$12.60 per disc for 1000 discs.

10. a. $(3x-1)^2 = (3x)^2 - 2(3x)(1) + 1^2$
$\qquad = 9x^2 - 6x + 1$

b. $\left(\dfrac{1}{2}x+3\right)\left(\dfrac{1}{2}x-3\right) = \left(\dfrac{1}{2}x\right)^2 - 3^2$
$\qquad\qquad\qquad\qquad = \dfrac{1}{4}x^2 - 9$

c. $(2x-5)(6x+7) = 12x^2 + 14x - 30x - 35$
$\qquad\qquad\qquad = 12x^2 - 16x - 35$

11. a. $\dfrac{x}{4} + \dfrac{5x}{4} = \dfrac{6x}{4} = \dfrac{3x}{2}$

b. $\dfrac{5}{7z^2} + \dfrac{x}{7z^2} = \dfrac{5+x}{7z^2}$

c. $\dfrac{x^2}{x+7} - \dfrac{49}{x+7} = \dfrac{x^2-49}{x+7}$
$\qquad\qquad\qquad = \dfrac{(x+7)(x-7)}{x+7}$
$\qquad\qquad\qquad = x-7$

d. $\dfrac{x}{3y^2} - \dfrac{x+1}{3y^2} = \dfrac{x-x-1}{3y^2} = -\dfrac{1}{3y^2}$

12. $\dfrac{5}{x-2} + \dfrac{3}{x^2+4x+4} - \dfrac{6}{x+2}$

$= \dfrac{5}{x-2} + \dfrac{3}{(x+2)^2} - \dfrac{6}{x+2}$

$= \dfrac{5(x+2)^2 + 3(x-2) - 6(x-2)(x+2)}{(x-2)(x+2)(x+2)}$

$= \dfrac{-x^2 + 23x + 38}{(x-2)(x+2)^2}$

13. $\require{enclose}$
$$
\begin{array}{r}
3x^2 + 2x + 3 \\
x^2-1\enclose{longdiv}{3x^4 + 2x^3 \qquad -8x+6} \\
\underline{3x^4 \qquad -3x^2 \qquad\quad} \\
2x^3 + 3x^2 - 8x \\
\underline{2x^3 \qquad -2x\quad} \\
3x^2 - 6x + 6 \\
\underline{3x^2 \qquad -3} \\
-6x+9
\end{array}
$$

Solution: $3x^2 + 2x + 3 + \dfrac{-6x+9}{x^2-1}$

14. a. $\dfrac{\frac{a}{5}}{\frac{a-1}{10}} = \dfrac{a}{5} \cdot \dfrac{10}{a-1} = \dfrac{2a}{a-1}$

b. $\dfrac{\frac{3}{2+a} + \frac{6}{2-a}}{\frac{5}{a+2} - \frac{1}{a-2}} = \dfrac{\frac{3}{a+2} - \frac{6}{a-2}}{\frac{5}{a+2} - \frac{1}{a-2}}$

Multiply the numerator and the denominator by $(a+2)(a-2)$.

$\dfrac{3(a-2) - 6(a+2)}{5(a-2) - 1(a+2)} = \dfrac{3a-6-6a-12}{5a-10-a-2}$
$\qquad\qquad\qquad\qquad = \dfrac{-3a-18}{4a-12}$

c. $\dfrac{x^{-1} + y^{-1}}{xy} = \dfrac{\frac{1}{x} + \frac{1}{y}}{xy} = \dfrac{\left(\frac{1}{x} + \frac{1}{y}\right)xy}{(xy)(xy)} = \dfrac{y+x}{x^2y^2}$

15. $\dfrac{2x}{2x-1} + \dfrac{1}{x} = \dfrac{1}{2x-1}$

$(2x-1)x\left(\dfrac{2x}{2x-1} + \dfrac{1}{x}\right) = (2x-1)x\left(\dfrac{1}{2x-1}\right)$

$2x^2 + 2x - 1 = x$
$2x^2 + x - 1 = 0$
$(2x-1)(x+1) = 0$

$$2x-1=0 \quad \text{or} \quad x+1=0$$
$$2x=1 \qquad\qquad x=-1$$
$$x=\frac{1}{2}$$

$x=\dfrac{1}{2}$ makes the denominator $2x-1$ zero, so the only solution is $x=-1$.

16. $\dfrac{x^3-8}{x-2}=\dfrac{(x-2)(x^2+2x+4)}{(x-2)}$

$$=x^2+2x+4$$

17. Use distance = (rate)(time). Let c be the speed of the current.

	d	r	t
Upstream	72	$30-c$	$1.5t$
Downstream	72	$30+c$	t

Upstream: $72=1.5t(30-c)$ or $t=\dfrac{72}{1.5(30-c)}$

Downstream: $72=t(30+c)$ or $t=\dfrac{72}{30+c}$

$$\frac{72}{1.5(30-c)}=\frac{72}{30+c}$$
$$72(30+c)=72(1.5)(30-c)$$
$$2160+72c=3240-108c$$
$$180c=1080$$
$$c=6$$

The speed of the current is 6 miles per hour.

18. $\begin{array}{r|rrr} 2 & 8 & -12 & -7 \\ & & 16 & 8 \\ \hline & 8 & 4 & 1 \end{array}$

Solution: $8x+4+\dfrac{1}{x-2}$

19. a. $\sqrt[4]{81}=\sqrt[4]{3^4}=3$

b. $\sqrt[5]{-243}=\sqrt[5]{(-3)^5}=-3$

c. $-\sqrt{25}=-\sqrt{5^2}=-5$

d. $\sqrt[4]{-81}$ is not a real number.

e. $\sqrt[3]{64x^3}=\sqrt[3]{4^3 x^3}=4x$

20. $\dfrac{1}{a+5}=\dfrac{1}{3a+6}-\dfrac{a+2}{a^2+7a+10}$

$\dfrac{1}{a+5}=\dfrac{1}{3(a+2)}-\dfrac{a+2}{(a+2)(a+5)}$

$3(a+2)=a+5-3(a+2)$

$3a+6=a+5-3a-6$

$5a=-7$

$a=-\dfrac{7}{5}$

21. a. $\sqrt{x}\cdot\sqrt[4]{x}=x^{1/2}\cdot x^{1/4}=x^{3/4}=\sqrt[4]{x^3}$

b. $\dfrac{\sqrt{x}}{\sqrt[3]{x}}=\dfrac{x^{1/2}}{x^{1/3}}=x^{\frac{1}{2}-\frac{1}{3}}=x^{1/6}=\sqrt[6]{x}$

c. $\sqrt[3]{3}\cdot\sqrt{2}=3^{1/3}\cdot 2^{1/2}$
$$=3^{2/6}\cdot 2^{3/6}$$
$$=9^{1/6}\cdot 8^{1/6}$$
$$=72^{1/6}$$
$$=\sqrt[6]{72}$$

22. $y=kx$
$$\frac{1}{2}=12k$$
$$k=\frac{1}{24},\ y=\frac{1}{24}x$$

23. a. $\sqrt{3}\left(5+\sqrt{30}\right)=5\sqrt{3}+\sqrt{90}=5\sqrt{3}+3\sqrt{10}$

b. $\left(\sqrt{5}-\sqrt{6}\right)\left(\sqrt{7}+1\right)=\sqrt{35}+\sqrt{5}-\sqrt{42}-\sqrt{6}$

c. $\left(7\sqrt{x}+5\right)\left(3\sqrt{x}-\sqrt{5}\right)$
$$=21x-7\sqrt{5x}+15\sqrt{x}-5\sqrt{5}$$

d. $\left(4\sqrt{3}-1\right)^2$
$$=\left(4\sqrt{3}\right)^2-2\left(4\sqrt{3}\right)(1)+1^2$$
$$=16\cdot 3-8\sqrt{3}+1$$
$$=49-8\sqrt{3}$$

e. $\left(\sqrt{2x}-5\right)\left(\sqrt{2x}+5\right)=\left(\sqrt{2x}\right)^2-5^2$
$$=2x-25$$

f. $\left(\sqrt{x-3}+5\right)^2 = \left(\sqrt{x-3}\right)^2 + 2\sqrt{x-3}(5) + 5^2$

$\qquad\qquad = x - 3 + 10\sqrt{x-3} + 25$

$\qquad\qquad = x + 22 + 10\sqrt{x-3}$

24. a. $\sqrt[4]{81} = \sqrt[4]{3^4} = 3$

b. $\sqrt[3]{-27} = \sqrt[3]{(-3)^3} = -3$

c. $\sqrt{\dfrac{9}{64}} = \sqrt{\left(\dfrac{3}{8}\right)^2} = \dfrac{3}{8}$

d. $\sqrt[4]{x^{12}} = x^3$

e. $\sqrt[3]{-125y^6} = -5y^2$

25. $\dfrac{\sqrt[4]{x}}{\sqrt[4]{81y^5}} = \dfrac{\sqrt[4]{x}}{\sqrt[4]{81y^5}} \cdot \dfrac{\sqrt[4]{y^3}}{\sqrt[4]{y^3}} = \dfrac{\sqrt[4]{xy^3}}{3y^2}$

26. a. $a^{1/4}(a^{3/4} - a^{7/4}) = a^{4/4} - a^{8/4} = a - a^2$

b. $(x^{1/2} - 3)(x^{1/2} + 5)$

$\qquad = x^{2/2} + 5x^{1/2} - 3x^{1/2} - 15$

$\qquad = x + 2x^{1/2} - 15$

27. $\sqrt{4-x} = x - 2$

$\qquad \left(\sqrt{4-x}\right)^2 = (x-2)^2$

$\qquad\quad 4 - x = x^2 - 4x + 4$

$\qquad\qquad\quad 0 = x^2 - 3x$

$\qquad\qquad\quad 0 = x(x-3)$

$x = 0 \quad \text{or} \quad x - 3 = 0$

$\qquad\qquad\qquad\quad x = 3$

$x = 0$ does not check, so the only solution is $x = 3$.

28. a. $\sqrt{\dfrac{54}{6}} = \sqrt{9} = 3$

b. $\dfrac{\sqrt{108a^2}}{3\sqrt{3}} = \dfrac{1}{3}\sqrt{\dfrac{108a^2}{3}}$

$\qquad\qquad = \dfrac{1}{3}\sqrt{36a^2}$

$\qquad\qquad = \dfrac{1}{3}(6a)$

$\qquad\qquad = 2a$

c. $\dfrac{3\sqrt[3]{81a^5b^{10}}}{\sqrt[3]{3b^4}} = 3\sqrt[3]{\dfrac{81a^5b^{10}}{3b^4}}$

$\qquad\qquad = 3\sqrt[3]{27a^5b^6}$

$\qquad\qquad = 9ab^2\sqrt[3]{a^2}$

29. $\qquad 3x^2 - 9x + 8 = 0$

$\qquad\qquad x^2 - 3x + \dfrac{8}{3} = 0$

$\qquad\qquad\quad x^2 - 3x = -\dfrac{8}{3}$

$\qquad x^2 - 3x + \left(\dfrac{-3}{2}\right)^2 = -\dfrac{8}{3} + \left(\dfrac{-3}{2}\right)^2$

$\qquad\quad x^2 - 3x + \dfrac{9}{4} = -\dfrac{8}{3} + \dfrac{9}{4}$

$\qquad\qquad \left(x - \dfrac{3}{2}\right)^2 = -\dfrac{5}{12}$

$\qquad\qquad\quad x - \dfrac{3}{2} = \pm\sqrt{-\dfrac{5}{12}}$

$\qquad\qquad\quad x - \dfrac{3}{2} = \pm\dfrac{i\sqrt{5}}{2\sqrt{3}}$

$\qquad\qquad\quad x - \dfrac{3}{2} = \pm\dfrac{i\sqrt{15}}{6}$

$\qquad\qquad\qquad x = \dfrac{3}{2} \pm \dfrac{i\sqrt{15}}{6}$

$\qquad\qquad\qquad\quad = \dfrac{9}{6} \pm \dfrac{i\sqrt{15}}{6}$

$\qquad\qquad\qquad\quad = \dfrac{9 \pm i\sqrt{15}}{6}$

The solutions are $\dfrac{9 + i\sqrt{15}}{6}$ and $\dfrac{9 - i\sqrt{15}}{6}$.

30. a. $\dfrac{\sqrt{20}}{3} + \dfrac{\sqrt{5}}{4} = \dfrac{2\sqrt{5}}{3} + \dfrac{\sqrt{5}}{4}$

$\qquad\qquad = \dfrac{8\sqrt{5} + 3\sqrt{5}}{12}$

$\qquad\qquad = \dfrac{11\sqrt{5}}{12}$

b. $\sqrt[3]{\dfrac{24x}{27}} - \dfrac{\sqrt[3]{3x}}{2} = \dfrac{2\sqrt[3]{3x}}{3} - \dfrac{\sqrt[3]{3x}}{2}$

$\qquad\qquad\qquad = \dfrac{4\sqrt[3]{3x} - 3\sqrt[3]{3x}}{6}$

$\qquad\qquad\qquad = \dfrac{\sqrt[3]{3x}}{6}$

31.
$$\frac{3x}{x-2} - \frac{x+1}{x} = \frac{6}{x(x-2)}$$
$$3x(x) - (x+1)(x-2) = 6$$
$$3x^2 - x^2 + x + 2 = 6$$
$$2x^2 + x - 4 = 0$$
$$a = 2,\, b = 1,\, c = -4$$
$$x = \frac{-1 \pm \sqrt{1^2 - 4(2)(-4)}}{2(2)} = \frac{-1 \pm \sqrt{33}}{4}$$

32.
$$\sqrt[3]{\frac{27}{m^4 n^8}} = \frac{\sqrt[3]{27}}{\sqrt[3]{m^4 n^8}}$$
$$= \frac{3}{mn^2 \sqrt[3]{mn^2}}$$
$$= \frac{3 \cdot \sqrt[3]{m^2 n}}{mn^2 \sqrt[3]{mn^2} \cdot \sqrt[3]{m^2 n}}$$
$$= \frac{3\sqrt[3]{m^2 n}}{m^2 n^3}$$

33. $x^2 - 4x \le 0$
$$x(x - 4) = 0$$
$$x = 0,\, x = 4$$

Region	Test Point	$x(x-4) \le 0$	Result
$x < 0$	$x = -1$	$(-1)(-5) \le 0$	False
$0 < x < 4$	$x = 2$	$2(-2) \le 0$	True
$x > 4$	$x = 5$	$5(1) \le 0$	False

Solution: [0, 4]

34.
$$c^2 = a^2 + b^2$$
$$8^2 = 4^2 + b^2$$
$$64 = 16 + b^2$$
$$48 = b^2$$
$$\pm 4\sqrt{3} = b$$

$b > 0$ so the length is $4\sqrt{3}$ inches.

35. $F(x) = (x-3)^2 + 1$

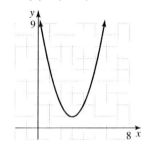

36. a. $i^8 = (i^2)^4 = (-1)^4 = 1$

b. $i^{21} = i(i^{20}) = i$

c. $i^{42} = i^2(i^{40}) = i^2 = -1$

d. $i^{-13} = \frac{1}{i^{13}} = \frac{1}{i(i^{12})} = \frac{1}{i} = \frac{i}{i^2} = -i$

37. $f(x) = x - 1$ and $g(x) = 2x - 3$

a.
$$(f + g)(x) = f(x) + g(x)$$
$$= x - 1 + 2x - 3$$
$$= 3x - 4$$

b.
$$(f - g)(x) = f(x) - g(x)$$
$$= x - 1 - (2x - 3)$$
$$= -x + 2$$

c.
$$(f \cdot g)(x) = f(x) \cdot g(x)$$
$$= (x - 1)(2x - 3)$$
$$= 2x^2 - 5x + 3$$

d. $\left(\dfrac{f}{g}\right)(x) = \dfrac{f(x)}{g(x)} = \dfrac{x - 1}{2x - 3}$, where $x \ne \dfrac{3}{2}$.

38. $4x^2 + 8x - 1 = 0$

$$x^2 + 2x - \frac{1}{4} = 0$$

$$x^2 + 2x = \frac{1}{4}$$

$$x^2 + 2x + \left(\frac{2}{2}\right)^2 = \frac{1}{4} + \left(\frac{2}{2}\right)^2$$

$$x^2 + 2x + 1 = \frac{1}{4} + 1$$

$$(x+1)^2 = \frac{5}{4}$$

$$x + 1 = \pm\sqrt{\frac{5}{4}}$$

$$x + 1 = \pm\frac{\sqrt{5}}{2}$$

$$x = -1 \pm \frac{\sqrt{5}}{2}$$

$$= \frac{-2 \pm \sqrt{5}}{2}$$

The solutions are $\dfrac{-2+\sqrt{5}}{2}$ and $\dfrac{-2-\sqrt{5}}{2}$.

39. $f(x) = x + 3$

$$y = x + 3$$
$$x = y + 3$$
$$y = x - 3$$
$$f^{-1}(x) = x - 3$$

40. $\left(x - \dfrac{1}{2}\right)^2 = \dfrac{x}{2}$

$$x^2 - x + \frac{1}{4} = \frac{1}{2}x$$

$$x^2 - \frac{3}{2}x + \frac{1}{4} = 0$$

$$4x^2 - 6x + 1 = 0$$

$$a = 4,\ b = -6,\ c = 1$$

$$x = \frac{-(-6) \pm \sqrt{(-6)^2 - 4(4)(1)}}{2(4)}$$

$$= \frac{6 \pm \sqrt{20}}{8}$$

$$= \frac{6 \pm 2\sqrt{5}}{8}$$

$$= \frac{3 \pm \sqrt{5}}{4}$$

The solutions are $\dfrac{3+\sqrt{5}}{4}$ and $\dfrac{3-\sqrt{5}}{4}$.

41. a. $\log_4 16 = \log_4 4^2 = 2$

b. $\log_{10} \dfrac{1}{10} = \log_{10} 10^{-1} = -1$

c. $\log_9 3 = \log_9 9^{1/2} = \dfrac{1}{2}$

42. $f(x) = -(x+1)^2 + 1$

Vertex: $(-1, 1)$

Axis of symmetry: $x = -1$

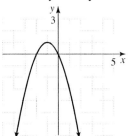

Chapter 10

Section 10.1

Practice Exercises

1. $x = \frac{1}{2}y^2$; $a = \frac{1}{2}$, $h = 0$, $k = 0$; vertex: (0, 0)

x	y
2	-2
$\frac{1}{2}$	-1
0	0
$\frac{1}{2}$	1
2	2

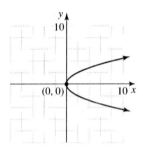

2. $x = -2(y+4)^2 - 1$; $a = -2$, $h = -1$, $k = -4$;
vertex: $(-1, -4)$

x	y
-9	-6
3	-5
-1	-4
-3	-3
-9	-2

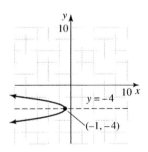

3.
$$y = -x^2 + 4x + 6$$
$$y - 6 = -x^2 + 4x$$
$$y - 6 = -(x^2 - 4x)$$
$$y - 6 - (+4) = -(x^2 - 4x + 4)$$
$$y - 10 = -(x - 2)^2$$
$$y = -(x - 2)^2 + 10$$

$a = -1$, $h = 2$, $k = 10$
vertex: (2, 10)

x	y
-1	1
0	6
1	9
2	10
3	9
4	6
5	1

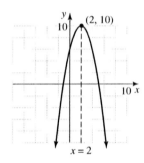

4. $x = 3y^2 + 6y + 4$

Find the vertex.

$$y = \frac{-b}{2a} = \frac{-6}{2(3)} = -1$$

$$x = 3(-1)^2 + 6(-1) + 4 = 3 - 6 + 4 = 1$$

vertex: $(1, -1)$
The axis of symmetry is the line $y = -1$.
Since $a > 0$, the parabola opens to the right.

$$x = 3(0)^2 + 6(0) + 4 = 4$$

The x-intercept is (4, 0).

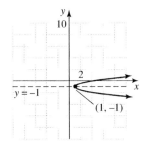

5. $x = y^2 + 4y - 1$

Solve the equation for y.

$y^2 + 4y + (-x - 1) = 0$

Here $a = 1$, $b = 4$, and $c = -x - 1$.

$y = \dfrac{-b \pm \sqrt{b^2 - 4ac}}{2a}$

$y = \dfrac{-4 \pm \sqrt{4^2 - 4(1)(-x - 1)}}{2(1)}$

$ = \dfrac{-4 \pm \sqrt{4^2 + 4(x + 1)}}{2}$

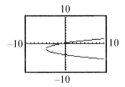

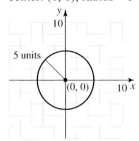

6. $\qquad x^2 + y^2 = 25$

$(x - 0)^2 + (y - 0)^2 = 5^2$

center: (0, 0); radius = 5

7. Algebraic Solution

$(x - 3)^2 + (y + 2)^2 = 4$

$h = 3$, $k = -2$, $r = \sqrt{4} = 2$

center: (3, −2)

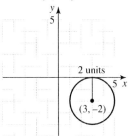

Graphical Solution

Solve the equation for y.

$(x - 3)^2 + (y + 2)^2 = 4$

$(y + 2)^2 = 4 - (x - 3)^2$

$y + 2 = \pm\sqrt{4 - (x - 3)^2}$

$y = -2 \pm \sqrt{4 - (x - 3)^2}$

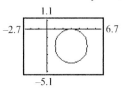

8. $x^2 + y^2 = 20$

$y^2 = 20 - x^2$

$y = \pm\sqrt{20 - x^2}$

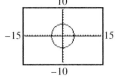

9. Center: (−2, −5); radius = 9

$(x - h)^2 + (y - k)^2 = r^2$

$h = -2$, $k = -5$, and $r = 9$.

The equation is $(x + 2)^2 + (y + 5)^2 = 81$.

10.
$$x^2 + y^2 + 6x - 2y = 6$$
$$(x^2 + 6x) + (y^2 - 2y) = 6$$
$$(x^2 + 6x + 9) + (y^2 - 2y + 1) = 6 + 9 + 1$$
$$(x+3)^2 + (y-1)^2 = 16$$
Center: $(-3, 1)$; radius $= \sqrt{16} = 4$

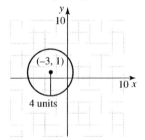

Vocabulary and Readiness Check

1. The circle, parabola, ellipse, and hyperbola are called the <u>conic sections</u>.

2. For a parabola that opens upward the lowest point is the <u>vertex</u>.

3. A <u>circle</u> is the set of all points in a plane that are the same distance from a fixed point. The fixed point is called the <u>center</u>.

4. The midpoint of a diameter of a circle is the <u>center</u>.

5. The distance from the center of a circle to any point of the circle is called the <u>radius</u>.

6. Twice a circle's radius is its <u>diameter</u>.

7. $y = x^2 - 7x + 5$; $a = 1$, upward

8. $y = -x^2 + 16$; $a = -1$, downward

9. $x = -y^2 - y + 2$; $a = -1$, to the left

10. $x = 3y^2 + 2y - 5$; $a = 3$, to the right

11. $y = -x^2 + 2x + 1$; $a = -1$, downward

12. $x = -y^2 + 2y - 6$; $a = -1$, to the left

Exercise Set 10.1

2. $x = -2y^2$
$$x = -2(y - 0)^2 + 0$$
Vertex: $(0, 0)$

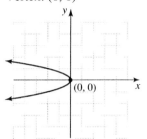

4. $x = (y - 4)^2 - 1$
Vertex: $(-1, 4)$

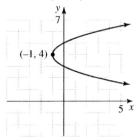

6. $x = -4(y - 2)^2 + 2$
Vertex: $(2, 2)$

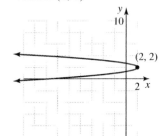

8.
$$x = y^2 - 6y + 6$$
$$x - 6 = y^2 - 6y$$
$$x - 6 + 9 = y^2 - 6y + 9$$
$$x + 3 = (y - 3)^2$$
$$x = (y - 3)^2 - 3$$
Vertex: $(-3, 3)$

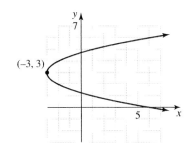

$(-3, 3)$

10.
$$y = x^2 + 4x - 5$$
$$y + 5 = x^2 + 4x$$
$$y + 5 + 4 = x^2 + 4x + 4$$
$$y + 9 = (x+2)^2$$
$$y = (x+2)^2 - 9$$
Vertex: $(-2, -9)$

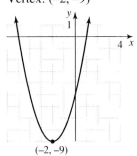

$(-2, -9)$

12.
$$x = 3y^2 + 6y + 7$$
$$x - 7 = 3(y^2 + 2y)$$
$$x - 7 + 3(1) = 3(y^2 + 2y + 1)$$
$$x - 4 = 3(y+1)^2$$
$$x = 3(y+1)^2 + 4$$
Vertex: $(4, -1)$

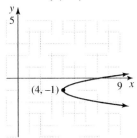

$(4, -1)$

14. $x^2 + y^2 = 100$
$$(x-0)^2 + (y-0)^2 = 10^2$$
Center: $(0, 0)$, radius $r = 10$.

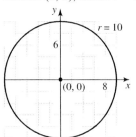

$r = 10$

$(0, 0)$

16. $(x-3)^2 + y^2 = 9$
$$(x-3)^2 + (y-0)^2 = 3^2$$
Center: $(3, 0)$, radius $r = 3$.

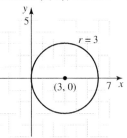

$r = 3$

$(3, 0)$

18. $(x+3)^2 + (y+3)^2 = 4$
$$(x+3)^2 + (y+3)^2 = 2^2$$
Center: $(-3, -3)$, radius $r = 2$.

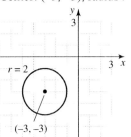

$r = 2$

$(-3, -3)$

20.
$$x^2 + 10x + y^2 = 0$$
$$(x^2 + 10x) + y^2 = 0$$
$$(x^2 + 10x + 25) + y^2 = 25$$
$$(x+5)^2 + (y-0)^2 = 5^2$$
Center: $(-5, 0)$, radius $r = 5$

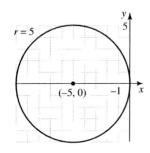

22.
$$x^2 + 6x - 4y + y^2 = 3$$
$$(x^2 + 6x) + (y^2 - 4y) = 3$$
$$(x^2 + 6x + 9) + (y^2 - 4y + 4) = 3 + 9 + 4$$
$$(x + 3)^2 + (y - 2)^2 = 16$$
Center: $(-3, 2)$, radius $r = \sqrt{16} = 4$.

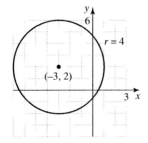

24.
$$x^2 + y^2 - 2x - 6y - 5 = 0$$
$$(x^2 - 2x) + (y^2 - 6y) = 5$$
$$(x^2 - 2x + 1) + (y^2 - 6y + 9) = 5 + 1 + 9$$
$$(x - 1)^2 + (y - 3)^2 = 15$$
Center: $(1, 3)$, radius $r = \sqrt{15}$.

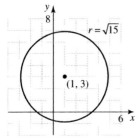

26. Center $(h, k) = (-7, 6)$, radius $r = 2$.
$$[x - (-7)]^2 + (y - 6)^2 = 2^2$$
$$(x + 7)^2 + (y - 6)^2 = 4$$

28. Center $(h, k) = (0, -6)$, radius $r = \sqrt{2}$.
$$(x - 0)^2 + [y - (-6)]^2 = \left(\sqrt{2}\right)^2$$
$$x^2 + (y + 6)^2 = 2$$

30. Center $(h, k) = (0, 0)$, radius $r = 4\sqrt{7}$.
$$(x - 0)^2 + (y - 0)^2 = \left(4\sqrt{7}\right)^2$$
$$x^2 + y^2 = 112$$

32. $x = y^2 + 2$
$$x = (y - 0)^2 + 2$$
Vertex: $(2, 0)$

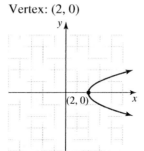

34. $y = (x + 3)^2 + 3$
Vertex: $(-3, 3)$

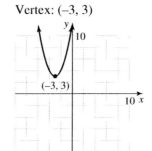

36. $x^2 + y^2 = 49$
Center: $(0, 0)$, radius $r = \sqrt{49} = 7$

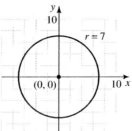

38. $x = (y-1)^2 + 4$

Vertex: (4, 1)

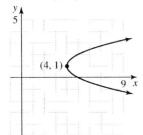

40. $(x+3)^2 + (y-1)^2 = 9$

Center: (–3, 1), radius $r = \sqrt{9} = 3$

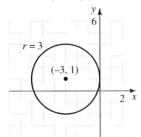

42. $x = -2(y+5)^2$

Vertex: (0, –5)

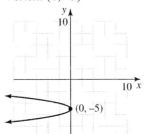

44. $x^2 + (y+5)^2 = 5$

Center: (0, –5), radius $r = \sqrt{5}$

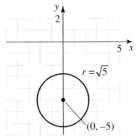

46. $y = 3(x-4)^2 + 2$

Vertex: (4, 2)

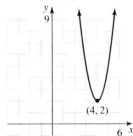

48. $2x^2 + 2y^2 = \dfrac{1}{2}$

$x^2 + y^2 = \dfrac{1}{4}$

Center: (0, 0), radius $r = \sqrt{\dfrac{1}{4}} = \dfrac{1}{2}$

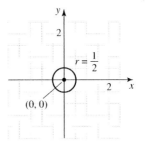

50. $\quad y = x^2 - 2x - 15$

$y + 15 + 1 = x^2 - 2x + 1$

$y + 16 = (x-1)^2$

$\quad\quad y = (x-1)^2 - 16$

Vertex: (1, –16)

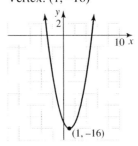

52.

$$x^2 + y^2 + 6x + 10y - 2 = 0$$
$$(x^2 + 6x) + (y^2 + 10y) = 2$$
$$(x^2 + 6x + 9) + (y^2 + 10y + 25) = 2 + 9 + 25$$
$$(x+3)^2 + (y+5)^2 = 36$$

Center: $(-3, -5)$, radius $r = \sqrt{36} = 6$

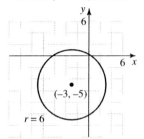

54.

$$x = y^2 + 6y + 2$$
$$x - 2 + 9 = y^2 + 6y + 9$$
$$x + 7 = (y+3)^2$$
$$x = (y+3)^2 - 7$$

Vertex: $(-7, -3)$

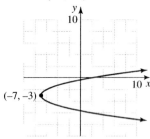

56.

$$x^2 + y^2 - 8y + 5 = 0$$
$$x^2 + (y^2 - 8y) = -5$$
$$x^2 + (y^2 - 8y + 16) = -5 + 16$$
$$x^2 + (y-4)^2 = 11$$

Center: $(0, 4)$, radius $r = \sqrt{11}$

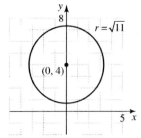

58.

$$x = -2y^2 - 4y$$
$$x + [-2(1)] = -2(y^2 + 2y + 1)$$
$$x - 2 = -2(y+1)^2$$
$$x = -2(y+1)^2 + 2$$

Vertex: $(2, -1)$

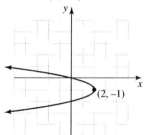

60.

$$\frac{x^2}{3} + \frac{y^2}{3} = 2$$
$$x^2 + y^2 = 6$$

Center: $(0, 0)$, radius $r = \sqrt{6}$

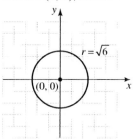

62.

$$y = 4x^2 - 40x + 105$$
$$y - 105 + 4(25) = 4(x^2 - 10x + 25)$$
$$y - 5 = 4(x-5)^2$$
$$y = 4(x-5)^2 + 5$$

Vertex: $(5, 5)$

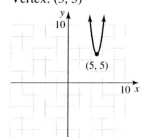

64. $y = 2x + 5$

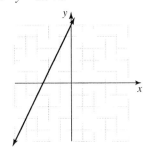

66. $y = 3$

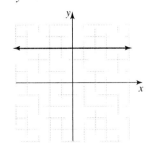

68. $\dfrac{1}{\sqrt{3}} = \dfrac{1 \cdot \sqrt{3}}{\sqrt{3} \cdot \sqrt{3}} = \dfrac{\sqrt{3}}{3}$

70. $\dfrac{4\sqrt{7}}{\sqrt{6}} = \dfrac{4\sqrt{7} \cdot \sqrt{6}}{\sqrt{6} \cdot \sqrt{6}} = \dfrac{4\sqrt{42}}{6} = \dfrac{2\sqrt{42}}{3}$

72. a. radius $= \dfrac{1}{2}$(diameter)

$= \dfrac{1}{2}$(33 meters)

$= 16.5$ meters

b. circumference $= \pi$(diameter)

$= \pi$(33 meters)

≈ 103.67 meters

c. $\dfrac{103.67}{30} \approx 3.5$ meters apart

d. center: $(0, 16.5)$

e. $(x - 0)^2 + (y - 16.5)^2 = 16.5^2$

$x^2 + (y - 16.5)^2 = 16.5^2$

74. a. radius $= \dfrac{1}{2}$(diameter)

$= \dfrac{1}{2}$(250 feet)

$= 125$ feet

b. Height $-$ diameter $= 264$ feet $- 250$ feet

$= 14$ feet

c. radius $+$ distance above ground

$= 125$ feet $+ 14$ feet

$= 139$ feet

d. center: $(0, 139)$

e. $(x - 0)^2 + (y - 139)^2 = 125^2$

$x^2 + (y - 139)^2 = 125^2$

76. Answers may vary

78. $y = a(x - h)^2 + k$

The parabola opens downward, so $a < 0$. The vertex is at $(0, 40)$, so $h = 0$ and $k = 40$. Thus, we have $y = ax^2 + 40$. To find a, let $(x, y) = (50, 0)$.

$0 = a(50)^2 + 40$

$-40 = 2500a$

$-\dfrac{2}{125} = a$

The equation is $y = -\dfrac{2}{125}x^2 + 40$.

80. $\dfrac{x^2}{3} + \dfrac{y^2}{3} = 2$

$x^2 + y^2 = 6$

$y^2 = 6 - x^2$

$y = \pm\sqrt{6 - x^2}$

82. $y = 4x^2 - 40x + 105$

Section 10.2

Practice Exercises

1. $\dfrac{x^2}{25} + \dfrac{y^2}{4} = 1$

   The equation is an ellipse with $a = 5$ and $b = 2$.
   The center is $(0, 0)$. The x-intercepts are $(5, 0)$
   and $(-5, 0)$. The y-intercepts are $(2, 0)$ and
   $(-2, 0)$.

   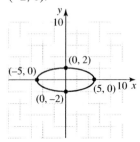

2. $9x^2 + 4y^2 = 36$

   $\dfrac{9x^2}{36} + \dfrac{4y^2}{36} = \dfrac{36}{36}$

   $\dfrac{x^2}{4} + \dfrac{y^2}{9} = 1$

   This is an equation of an ellipse with $a = 2$ and
   $b = 3$. The ellipse has center $(0, 0)$, x-intercepts
   $(2, 0)$ and $(-2, 0)$, and y-intercepts $(3, 0)$ and
   $(-3, 0)$.

   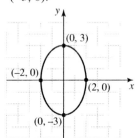

3. $\dfrac{(x-4)^2}{49} + \dfrac{(y+1)^2}{81} = 1$

   This ellipse has center $(4, -1)$.
   $a = 7$ and $b = 9$.
   Find four points on the ellipse.
   $(4 + 7, -1) = (11, -1)$
   $(4 - 7, -1) = (-3, -1)$
   $(4, -1 + 9) = (4, 8)$
   $(4, -1 - 9) = (4, -10)$

   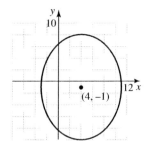

4. $\dfrac{x^2}{9} - \dfrac{y^2}{16} = 1$

   This is a hyperbola with $a = 3$ and $b = 4$. It has
   center $(0, 0)$ and x-intercepts $(3, 0)$ and $(-3, 0)$.
   The asymptotes pass through $(3, 4)$, $(3, -4)$,
   $(-3, 4)$, and $(-3, -4)$.

   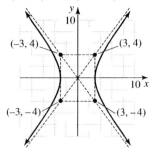

5. $9y^2 - 25x^2 = 225$

   $\dfrac{9y^2}{225} - \dfrac{25x^2}{225} = \dfrac{225}{225}$

   $\dfrac{y^2}{25} - \dfrac{x^2}{9} = 1$

   This is a hyperbola with $a = 3$ and $b = 5$. The
   center is at $(0, 0)$ with y-intercepts $(0, 5)$ and
   $(0, -5)$. The asymptotes pass through $(3, 5)$,
   $(3, -5)$, $(-3, 5)$, and $(-3, -5)$.

   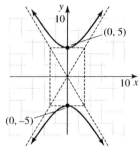

Vocabulary and Readiness Check

1. A <u>hyperbola</u> is the set of points in a plane such
   that the absolute value of the differences of their
   distances from two fixed points is constant.

2. An <u>ellipse</u> is the set of points in a plane such that the sum of their distances from two fixed points is constant.

3. The two fixed points are each called a <u>focus</u>.

4. The point midway between the foci is called the <u>center</u>.

5. The graph of $\dfrac{x^2}{a^2} - \dfrac{y^2}{b^2} = 1$ is a <u>hyperbola</u> with center <u>(0, 0)</u> and <u>x</u>-intercepts of <u>(a, 0) and (−a, 0)</u>.

6. The graph of $\dfrac{x^2}{b^2} + \dfrac{y^2}{a^2} = 1$ is an <u>ellipse</u> with center <u>(0, 0)</u> and x-intercepts of <u>(b, 0) and (−b, 0)</u>.

7. $\dfrac{x^2}{16} + \dfrac{y^2}{4} = 1$ is an ellipse.

8. $\dfrac{x^2}{16} - \dfrac{y^2}{4} = 1$ is a hyperbola.

9. $x^2 - 5y^2 = 3$ is a hyperbola.

10. $-x^2 + 5y^2 = 3$ or
$5y^2 - x^2 = 3$ is a hyperbola.

11. $-\dfrac{y^2}{25} + \dfrac{x^2}{36} = 1$ or
$\dfrac{x^2}{36} - \dfrac{y^2}{25} = 1$ is a hyperbola.

12. $\dfrac{y^2}{25} + \dfrac{x^2}{36} = 1$ is an ellipse.

Exercise Set 10.2

2. $\dfrac{x^2}{16} + \dfrac{y^2}{9} = 1$
$\dfrac{x^2}{4^2} + \dfrac{y^2}{3^2} = 1$
Center: (0, 0)
x-intercepts: (−4, 0), (4, 0)
y-intercepts: (0, −3), (0, 3)

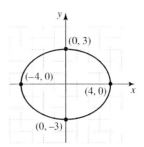

4. $x^2 + \dfrac{y^2}{4} = 1$
$\dfrac{x^2}{1^2} + \dfrac{y^2}{2^2} = 1$
Center: (0, 0)
x-intercepts: (−1, 0), (1, 0)
y-intercepts: (0, −2), (0, 2)

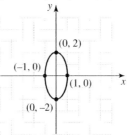

6. $x^2 + 4y^2 = 16$
$\dfrac{x^2}{16} + \dfrac{y^2}{4} = 1$
$\dfrac{x^2}{4^2} + \dfrac{y^2}{2^2} = 1$
Center: (0, 0)
x-intercepts: (−4, 0), (4, 0)
y-intercepts: (0, −2), (0, 2)

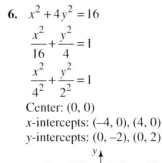

8. $36x^2 + y^2 = 36$
$x^2 + \dfrac{y^2}{36} = 1$
$\dfrac{x^2}{1^2} + \dfrac{y^2}{6^2} = 1$
Center: (0, 0)

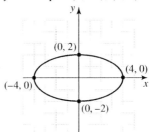

x-intercepts: $(-1, 0)$, $(1, 0)$
y-intercepts: $(0, -6)$, $(0, 6)$

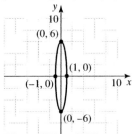

10. $\dfrac{(x-3)^2}{9} + \dfrac{(y+3)^2}{16} = 1$

$\dfrac{(x-3)^2}{3^2} + \dfrac{(y+3)^2}{4^2} = 1$

Center: $(3, -3)$
Other points:
$(3-3, -3) = (0, -3)$
$(3+3, -3) = (6, -3)$
$(3, -3-4) = (3, -7)$
$(3, -3+4) = (3, 1)$

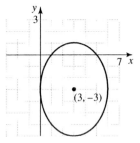

12. $\dfrac{(x+3)^2}{16} + \dfrac{(y+2)^2}{4} = 1$

$\dfrac{(x+3)^2}{4^2} + \dfrac{(y+2)^2}{2^2} = 1$

Center: $(-3, -2)$
Other points:
$(-3-4, -2) = (-7, -2)$
$(-3+4, -2) = (1, -2)$
$(-3, -2-2) = (-3, -4)$
$(-3, -2+2) = (-3, 0)$

14. $\dfrac{x^2}{36} - \dfrac{y^2}{36} = 1$

$\dfrac{x^2}{6^2} - \dfrac{y^2}{6^2} = 1$

$a = 6,\ b = 6$

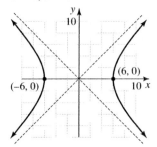

16. $\dfrac{y^2}{25} - \dfrac{x^2}{49} = 1$

$\dfrac{y^2}{5^2} - \dfrac{x^2}{7^2} = 1$

$a = 7,\ b = 5$

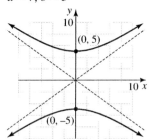

18. $4x^2 - y^2 = 36$

$\dfrac{x^2}{9} - \dfrac{y^2}{36} = 1$

$\dfrac{x^2}{3^2} - \dfrac{y^2}{6^2} = 1$

$a = 3,\ b = 6$

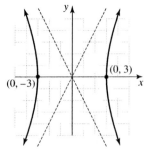

20. $4y^2 - 25x^2 = 100$

$$\frac{y^2}{25} - \frac{x^2}{4} = 1$$

$$\frac{y^2}{5^2} - \frac{x^2}{2^2} = 1$$

$a = 2,\ b = 5$

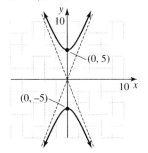

22. $(x-7)^2 + (y-2)^2 = 4$

Circle; center $(7, 2)$, radius $r = \sqrt{4} = 2$

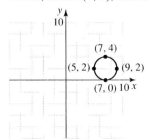

24. $y = x^2 + 12x + 36$

Parabola; $x = \dfrac{-b}{2a} = \dfrac{-12}{2(1)} = -6$

$y = (-6)^2 + 12(-6) + 36 = 0$

Vertex: $(-6, 0)$, opens upward

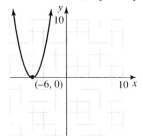

26. $\dfrac{y^2}{9} - \dfrac{x^2}{9} = 1$

$$\frac{y^2}{3^2} - \frac{x^2}{3^2} = 1$$

Hyperbola; center: $(0, 0)$

$a = 3,\ b = 3$

y-intercepts $(0, -3),\ (0, 3)$

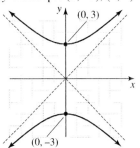

28. $\dfrac{x^2}{16} + \dfrac{y^2}{4} = 1$

$$\frac{x^2}{4^2} + \frac{y^2}{2^2} = 1$$

Ellipse; center: $(0, 0)$, $a = 4,\ b = 2$

x-intercepts $(-4, 0),\ (4, 0)$

y-intercepts $(0, -2),\ (0, 2)$

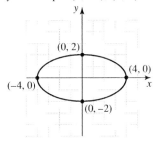

30. $x = y^2 + 4y - 1$

Parabola: $y = \dfrac{-b}{2a} = \dfrac{-4}{2(1)} = -2$

$x = (-2)^2 + 4(-2) - 1 = -5$

Vertex: $(-5, -2)$, opens to the right.

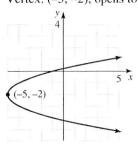

32. $9x^2 - 4y^2 = 36$

$$\frac{x^2}{4} - \frac{y^2}{9} = 1$$

$$\frac{x^2}{2^2} - \frac{y^2}{3^2} = 1$$

Hyperbola: center $= (0, 0)$

$a = 2,\ b = 3$

x-intercepts: (2, 0), (–2, 0)

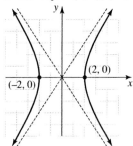

34. $\dfrac{(x-1)^2}{49}+\dfrac{(y+2)^2}{25}=1$

$\dfrac{(x-1)^2}{7^2}+\dfrac{(y+2)^2}{5^2}=1$

Ellipse; center: (1, –2)
$a=7, b=5$

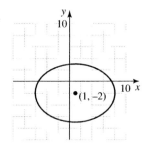

36. $\left(x+\dfrac{1}{2}\right)^2+\left(y-\dfrac{1}{2}\right)^2=1$

Circle; center: $\left(-\dfrac{1}{2},\dfrac{1}{2}\right)$, radius $r=1$

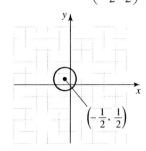

38. $x<5$ and $x<1$
$x<1$
$(-\infty, 1)$

40. $2x-1\ge 7$ or $-3x\le -6$
    $2x\ge 8$ or $x\ge 2$
      $x\ge 4$
$x\ge 2$
$[2, \infty)$

42. $(2x^3)(-4x^2)=-8x^5$

44. $-5x^2+x^2=-4x^2$

46. $\dfrac{x^2}{16}+\dfrac{y^2}{25}=1$

$\sqrt{16}=4$, so the distance between the
x-intercepts is $4+4=8$ units.
$\sqrt{25}=5$, so the distance between the
y-intercepts is $5+5=10$ units.
The distance between the *y*-intercepts is longer
by $10-8=2$ units.

48. $4x^2+y^2=16$

$\dfrac{x^2}{4}+\dfrac{y^2}{16}=1$

$\sqrt{4}=2$, so the distance between the *x*-intercepts
is $2+2=4$ units.
$\sqrt{16}=4$, so the distance between the
y-intercepts is $4+4=8$ units.
The distance between the *y*-intercepts is longer
by $8-4=4$ units.

50. $x^2+y^2=25$

$\dfrac{x^2}{25}+\dfrac{y^2}{25}=1$

This resembles the equation of an ellipse. An
ellipse is a circle when $a=b$.

52. A: $a^2=36,\ b^2=13$

B: $a^2=4,\ b^2=4$

C: $a^2=25,\ b^2=16$

D: $a^2=39,\ b^2=25$

E: $a^2=17,\ b^2=81$

F: $a^2=36,\ b^2=36$

G: $a^2=16,\ b^2=65$

H: $a^2=144,\ b^2=140$

54. A: $d=6$
B: $d=2$
C: $d=5$
D: $d=5$
E: $d=9$
F: $d=6$

G: $d = 4$

H: $d = 12$

56. They are greater than 0 and less than 1.

58. They are greater than 1.

60. Answers may vary

62. Center $= (1,782,000,000,\ 356,400,000)$

64. $x^2 + 4y^2 = 16$

$\qquad 4y^2 = 16 - x^2$

$\qquad y^2 = 4 - \dfrac{x^2}{4}; \quad y = \pm\sqrt{4 - 0.25x^2}$

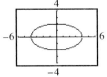

The answers are the same.

66. $\dfrac{(x+2)^2}{9} - \dfrac{(y-1)^2}{4} = 1$

Center: (–2, 1)

$a = 3,\ b = 2$

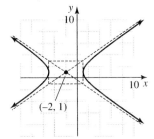

68. $\dfrac{(y+4)^2}{4} - \dfrac{x^2}{25} = 1$

Center: (0, –4)

$a = 5,\ b = 2$

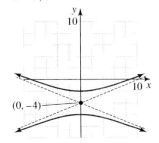

70. $\dfrac{(x-3)^2}{9} - \dfrac{(y-2)^2}{4} = 1$

Center: (3, 2)

$a = 3,\ b = 2$

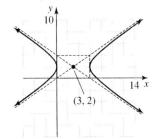

Integrated Review

1. $(x-7)^2 + (y-2)^2 = 4$

Circle; center: (7, 2),

radius: $r = \sqrt{4} = 2$

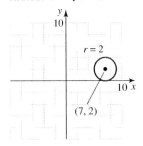

2. $y = x^2 + 4$

Parabola; vertex: (0, 4)

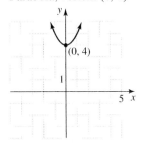

3. $y = x^2 + 12x + 36$

Parabola; $x = \dfrac{-b}{2a} = \dfrac{-12}{2(1)} = -6$

$y = (-6)^2 + 12(-6) + 36 = 0$

Vertex: (–6, 0)

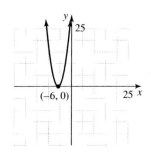

4. $\dfrac{x^2}{4} + \dfrac{y^2}{9} = 1$

Ellipse; center: $(0, 0)$
$a = 2, b = 3$

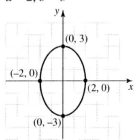

5. $\dfrac{y^2}{9} - \dfrac{x^2}{9} = 1$

Hyperbola; center: $(0, 0)$
$a = 3, b = 3$

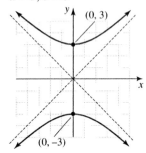

6. $\dfrac{x^2}{16} - \dfrac{y^2}{4} = 1$

Hyperbola; center: $(0, 0)$
$a = 4, b = 2$

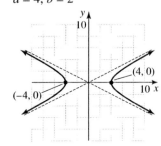

7. $\dfrac{x^2}{16} + \dfrac{y^2}{4} = 1$

Ellipse; center: $(0, 0)$
$a = 4, b = 2$

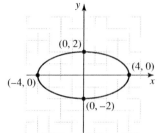

8. $x^2 + y^2 = 16$

Circle; center: $(0, 0)$
radius: $r = \sqrt{16} = 4$

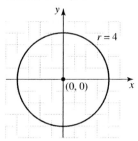

9. $x = y^2 + 4y - 1$

Parabola; $y = \dfrac{-b}{2a} = \dfrac{-4}{2(1)} = -2$

$x = (-2)^2 + 4(-2) - 1 = -5$
Vertex: $(-5, -2)$

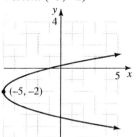

10. $x = -y^2 + 6y$

Parabola; $y = \dfrac{-b}{2a} = \dfrac{-6}{2(-1)} = 3$

$x = -(3)^2 + 6(3) = 9$
Vertex: $(9, 3)$

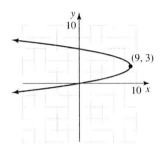

11. $9x^2 - 4y^2 = 36$

$$\frac{x^2}{4} - \frac{y^2}{9} = 1$$

Hyperbola; center: $(0, 0)$
$a = 2, b = 3$

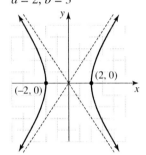

12. $9x^2 + 4y^2 = 36$

$$\frac{x^2}{4} + \frac{y^2}{9} = 1$$

Ellipse; center: $(0, 0)$
$a = 2, b = 3$

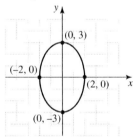

13. $\dfrac{(x-1)^2}{49} + \dfrac{(y+2)^2}{25} = 1$

Ellipse; center: $(1, -2)$,
$a = 7, b = 5$

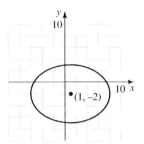

14. $\qquad y^2 = x^2 + 16$

$y^2 - x^2 = 16$

$$\frac{y^2}{16} - \frac{x^2}{16} = 1$$

Hyperbola; center: $(0, 0)$
$a = 4, b = 4$

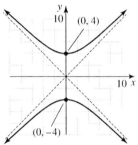

15. $\left(x + \dfrac{1}{2}\right)^2 + \left(y - \dfrac{1}{2}\right)^2 = 1$

Circle; center: $\left(-\dfrac{1}{2}, \dfrac{1}{2}\right)$, radius: $r = \sqrt{1} = 1$

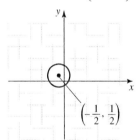

Section 10.3

Practice Exercises

1. $\begin{cases} y = -\sqrt{x} \\ x^2 + y^2 = 20 \end{cases}$

Substitute $-\sqrt{x}$ for y in the second equation.

$$x^2 + \left(-\sqrt{x}\right)^2 = 20$$
$$x^2 + x = 20$$
$$x^2 + x - 20 = 0$$
$$(x+5)(x-4) = 0$$
$$x = -5 \quad \text{or} \quad x = 4$$
Let $x = -5$.
$$y = -\sqrt{-5} \quad \text{Not a real number}$$
Let $x = 4$.
$$y = -\sqrt{4} = -2$$
The solution is $(4, -2)$.

2. $\begin{cases} x^2 - 4y = 4 \\ x + y = -1 \end{cases}$

Solve $x + y = -1$ for y.
$$y = -x - 1$$
Replace y with $-x - 1$ in the first equation and solve for x.
$$x^2 - 4(-x-1) = 4$$
$$x^2 + 4x + 4 = 4$$
$$x^2 + 4x = 0$$
$$x(x+4) = 0$$
$x = 0 \quad$ or $\quad x = -4$

Let $x = 0$,   Let $x = -4$,
$y = -0 - 1 = -1 \quad\quad y = -(-4) - 1 = 3$
The solutions are $(0, -1)$ and $(-4, 3)$.

3. $\begin{cases} x^2 + y^2 = 9 \\ x - y = 5 \end{cases}$

Solve the second equation for x.
$$x = y + 5$$
Let $x = y + 5$ in the first equation.
$$(y+5)^2 + y^2 = 9$$
$$y^2 + 10y + 25 + y^2 = 9$$
$$2y^2 + 10y + 16 = 0$$
$$y^2 + 5y + 8 = 0$$
By the quadratic formula,
$$y = \frac{-5 \pm \sqrt{5^2 - 4(1)(8)}}{2(1)} = \frac{-5 \pm \sqrt{-7}}{2}$$

$\sqrt{-7}$ is not a real number. There is no real solution, or $\varnothing$.

4. $\begin{cases} x^2 + 4y^2 = 16 \\ x^2 - y^2 = 1 \end{cases}$

Add the opposite of the second equation to the first.
$$x^2 + 4y^2 = 16$$
$$\underline{-x^2 + y^2 = -1}$$
$$0 + 5y^2 = 15$$
$$y^2 = 3$$
$$y = \pm\sqrt{3}$$

Let $y = \sqrt{3}$.   Let $y = -\sqrt{3}$.

$x^2 - \left(\sqrt{3}\right)^2 = 1 \quad\quad x^2 - \left(-\sqrt{3}\right)^2 = 1$

$\quad\quad x^2 - 3 = 1 \quad\quad\quad\quad\quad x^2 - 3 = 1$

$\quad\quad\quad x^2 = 4 \quad\quad\quad\quad\quad\quad\; x^2 = 4$

$\quad\quad\quad x = \pm 2 \quad\quad\quad\quad\quad\quad x = \pm 2$

The solutions are $\left(2, \sqrt{3}\right)$, $\left(2, -\sqrt{3}\right)$, $\left(-2, \sqrt{3}\right)$, and $\left(-2, -\sqrt{3}\right)$.

Exercise Set 10.3

2. $\begin{cases} x^2 + y^2 = 25 & (1) \\ 3x + 4y = 0 & (2) \end{cases}$

Solve E2 for y: $y = -\dfrac{3x}{4}$.

Substitute into E1.
$$x^2 + \left(-\frac{3x}{4}\right)^2 = 25$$
$$x^2 + \frac{9x^2}{16} = 25$$
$$16x^2 + 9x^2 = 400$$
$$25x^2 = 400$$
$$x^2 = 16$$
$$x = \pm 4$$
$x = 4 : y = -\dfrac{3(4)}{4} = -3$

$x = -4 : y = -\dfrac{3(-4)}{4} = 3$

The solutions are $(4, -3)$ and $(-4, 3)$.

4. $\begin{cases} 4x^2 + y^2 = 10 & (1) \\ y = x & (2) \end{cases}$

Substitute x for y in E1.

$$4x^2 + x^2 = 10$$
$$5x^2 = 10$$
$$x^2 = 2$$
$$x = \pm\sqrt{2}$$

Substitute these values into E2.

$$x = \sqrt{2}: y = x = \sqrt{2}$$
$$x = -\sqrt{2}: y = x = -\sqrt{2}$$

The solutions are $\left(\sqrt{2}, \sqrt{2}\right)$ and $\left(-\sqrt{2}, -\sqrt{2}\right)$.

6. $\begin{cases} x^2 + y^2 = 4 & (1) \\ x + y = -2 & (2) \end{cases}$

Solve E2 for y: $y = -x - 2$

Substitute into E1.

$$x^2 + (-x-2)^2 = 4$$
$$x^2 + x^2 + 4x + 4 = 4$$
$$2x^2 + 4x = 0$$
$$2x(x+2) = 0$$

$x = 0$ or $x = -2$

Substitute these values into the equation
$y = -x - 2$.

$$x = 0: y = -0 - 2 = -2$$
$$x = -2: y = -(-2) - 2 = 0$$

The solutions are $(0, -2)$ and $(-2, 0)$.

8. $\begin{cases} 4x^2 + 3y^2 = 35 & (1) \\ 5x^2 + 2y^2 = 42 & (2) \end{cases}$

Multiply E1 by 2 and E2 by –3 and add.

$$8x^2 + 6y^2 = 70$$
$$\underline{-15x^2 - 6y^2 = -126}$$
$$-7x^2 \qquad = -56$$
$$x^2 = 8$$
$$x = \pm 2\sqrt{2}$$

Substitute 8 for x^2 into E1.

$$4(8) + 3y^2 = 35$$
$$3y^2 = 3$$
$$y^2 = 1$$
$$y = \pm 1$$

The solutions are $\left(-2\sqrt{2}, -1\right)$, $\left(-2\sqrt{2}, 1\right)$,

$\left(2\sqrt{2}, -1\right)$, and $\left(2\sqrt{2}, 1\right)$.

10. $\begin{cases} x^2 + 2y^2 = 2 & (1) \\ x^2 - 2y^2 = 6 & (2) \end{cases}$

Add E1 and E2.

$$2x^2 = 8$$
$$x^2 = 4$$
$$x = \pm 2$$

Substitute 4 for x^2 in E1.

$$4 + 2y^2 = 2$$
$$2y^2 = -2$$
$$y^2 = -1$$

There are no real solutions. The solution is $\varnothing$.

12. $\begin{cases} y = x + 1 & (1) \\ x^2 - y^2 = 1 & (2) \end{cases}$

Substitute $x + 1$ for y in E2.

$$x^2 - (x+1)^2 = 1$$
$$x^2 - (x^2 + 2x + 1) = 1$$
$$-2x - 1 = 1$$
$$-2x = 2$$
$$x = -1$$

Substitute this value into E1.

$$y = -1 + 1 = 0$$

The solution is $(-1, 0)$.

14. $\begin{cases} 6x - y = 5 & (1) \\ xy = 1 & (2) \end{cases}$

Solve E1 for y: $y = 6x - 5$.

Substitute into E2.

$$x(6x - 5) = 1$$
$$6x^2 - 5x - 1 = 0$$
$$(6x + 1)(x - 1) = 0$$

$$x = -\frac{1}{6} \text{ or } x = 1$$

Substitute these values into the equation
$y = 6x - 5$.

$$x = -\frac{1}{6}: y = 6\left(-\frac{1}{6}\right) - 5 = -6$$
$$x = 1: y = 6(1) - 5 = 1$$

The solutions are $\left(-\frac{1}{6}, -6\right)$ and $(1, 1)$.

16. $\begin{cases} x^2 + y^2 = 9 & (1) \\ x + y = 5 & (2) \end{cases}$

Solve E2 for y: $y = 5 - x$.
Substitute into E1.
$$x^2 + (5-x)^2 = 9$$
$$x^2 + (25 - 10x + x^2) = 9$$
$$2x^2 - 10x + 16 = 0$$
$$x^2 - 5x + 8 = 0$$
$$x = \frac{5 \pm \sqrt{(-5)^2 - 4(1)(8)}}{2(1)} = \frac{5 \pm \sqrt{-7}}{2}$$

There are no real solutions. The solution is $\varnothing$.

18. $\begin{cases} x = y^2 - 3 & (1) \\ x = y^2 - 3y & (2) \end{cases}$

Substitute $y^2 - 3y$ for x in E1.
$$y^2 - 3y = y^2 - 3$$
$$-3y = -3$$
$$y = 1$$
Substitute this value into E2.
$$x = (1)^2 - 3(1) = -2$$
The solution is $(-2, 1)$.

20. $\begin{cases} 4x^2 - 2y^2 = 2 & (1) \\ -x^2 + y^2 = 2 & (2) \end{cases}$

Multiply E2 by 2 and add to E1.
$$\begin{array}{r} 4x^2 - 2y^2 = 2 \\ \underline{-2x^2 + 2y^2 = 4} \\ 2x^2 \qquad = 6 \\ x^2 = 3 \\ x = \pm\sqrt{3} \end{array}$$
Substitute 3 for x^2 into E2.
$$-3 + y^2 = 2$$
$$y^2 = 5$$
$$y = \pm\sqrt{5}$$
The solutions are $\left(-\sqrt{3}, -\sqrt{5}\right)$, $\left(-\sqrt{3}, \sqrt{5}\right)$, $\left(\sqrt{3}, -\sqrt{5}\right)$, and $\left(\sqrt{3}, \sqrt{5}\right)$.

22. $\begin{cases} x^2 + 2y^2 = 4 & (1) \\ x^2 - y^2 = 4 & (2) \end{cases}$

Multiply E2 by 2 and add to E1.
$$\begin{array}{r} x^2 + 2y^2 = 4 \\ \underline{2x^2 - 2y^2 = 8} \\ 3x^2 \qquad = 12 \\ x^2 = 4 \\ x = \pm 2 \end{array}$$
Replace x^2 with 4 in E1.
$$4 + 2y^2 = 4$$
$$2y^2 = 0$$
$$y^2 = 0$$
$$y = 0$$
The solutions are $(-2, 0)$ and $(2, 0)$.

24. $\begin{cases} x = -y^2 - 3 & (1) \\ x = y^2 - 5 & (2) \end{cases}$

Add E1 and E2.
$$\begin{array}{r} x = -y^2 - 3 \\ x = y^2 - 5 \\ 2x = -8 \\ x = -4 \end{array}$$
Substitute this value into E1.
$$-4 = -y^2 - 3$$
$$y^2 = 1$$
$$y = \pm 1$$
The solutions are $(-4, -1)$ and $(-4, 1)$.

26. $\begin{cases} x^2 + y^2 = 25 & (1) \\ x = y^2 - 5 & (2) \end{cases}$

Solve E2 for y^2: $y^2 = x + 5$.
Substitute into E1.
$$x^2 + (x + 5) = 25$$
$$x^2 + x - 20 = 0$$
$$(x + 5)(x - 4) = 0$$
$$x = -5 \text{ or } x = 4$$
Substitute these values into the equation
$y^2 = x + 5$.

$x = -5$: $y^2 = -5 + 5 = 0$ so $y = 0$
$x = 4$: $y^2 = 4 + 5 = 9$
$\qquad\qquad y = \pm 3$
The solutions are $(-5, 0)$, $(4, -3)$, and $(4, 3)$.

28. $\begin{cases} x^2 + y^2 = 1 & (1) \\ \qquad y = x^2 - 9 & (2) \end{cases}$

Solve E2 for x^2: $x^2 = y + 9$.

Substitute into E1.

$(y+9) + y^2 = 1$

$y^2 + y + 8 = 0$

$y = \dfrac{-1 \pm \sqrt{(1)^2 - 4(1)(8)}}{2(1)} = \dfrac{-1 \pm \sqrt{-31}}{2}$

There are no real solutions. The solution is $\varnothing$.

30. $\begin{cases} x^2 + y^2 = 16 & (1) \\ \qquad y = -\dfrac{1}{4}x^2 + 4 & (2) \end{cases}$

Solve E1 for x^2: $x^2 = 16 - y^2$.

Substitute into E2.

$y = -\dfrac{1}{4}(16 - y^2) + 4$

$y = -4 + \dfrac{1}{4}y^2 + 4$

$4y = y^2$

$0 = y^2 - 4y$

$0 = y(y-4)$

$y = 0$ or $y = 4$

Substitute these values into the equation

$x^2 = 16 - y^2$.

$y = 0 : x^2 = 16 - (0)^2$

$\qquad x^2 = 16$

$\qquad x = \pm 4$

$y = 4 : x^2 = 16 - (4)^2$

$\qquad x^2 = 0$

$\qquad x = 0$

The solutions are $(-4, 0)$, $(4, 0)$ and $(0, 4)$.

32. $y \le 1$

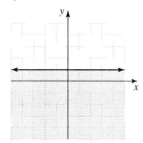

34. $3x - y \le 4$

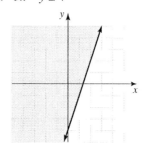

36. $P = 4(3x+2) = (12x+8)$ centimeters

38. $P = (4x) + (2x^2) + (3x^2 + 1) + (3x^2 + 7)$
$\qquad = (8x^2 + 4x + 8)$ feet

40. Answers may vary

42. There are 0, 1, or 2 possible real solutions.
Answers may vary

44. Let x and y represent the numbers.

$\begin{cases} x^2 + y^2 = 20 \\ xy = 8 \end{cases}$

Solve the second equation for y: $y = \dfrac{8}{x}$.

Substitute into the first equation.

$x^2 + \left(\dfrac{8}{x}\right)^2 = 20$

$x^2 + \dfrac{64}{x^2} = 20$

$x^4 - 20x^2 + 64 = 0$

$(x^2 - 16)(x^2 - 4) = 0$

$(x+4)(x-4)(x+2)(x-2) = 0$

$x = \pm 4$ or $x = \pm 2$

Substitute these values into the second equation.

$x = \pm 4 : \pm 4y = 8$

$\qquad\qquad y = \pm 2$

$x = \pm 2 : \pm 2y = 8$

$\qquad\qquad y = \pm 4$

The numbers are -2 and -4, and 2 and 4.

46. Let x and y be the length and width.

$\begin{cases} \qquad xy = 525 \\ 2x + 2y = 92 \end{cases}$

Solve the first equation for y: $y = \dfrac{525}{x}$.

Substitute into the second equation.

$$2x + 2\left(\frac{525}{x}\right) = 92$$

$$x + \frac{525}{x} = 46$$

$$x^2 - 46x + 525 = 0$$

$$(x - 25)(x - 21) = 0$$

$$x = 25 \quad \text{or} \quad x = 21$$

Using $x = 25$, $y = \dfrac{525}{x} = \dfrac{525}{25} = 21$.

Using $x = 21$, $y = \dfrac{525}{x} = \dfrac{525}{21} = 25$.

The dimensions are 25 feet by 21 feet.

48. $\begin{cases} p = -2x^2 + 90 \\ p = 9x + 34 \end{cases}$

Substitute.

$$9x + 34 = -2x^2 + 90$$

$$2x^2 + 9x - 56 = 0$$

$$(2x - 7)(x + 8) = 0$$

$$x = \frac{7}{2} = 3.5 \quad \text{or} \quad x = -8$$

Disregard the negative.

$$p = 9x + 34 = 9(3.5) + 34 = 65.5$$

The equilibrium quantity is 3.5 thousand (3500) frames, and the corresponding price is $65.50.

50. $\begin{cases} 4x^2 + y^2 = 10 \\ y = x \end{cases}$

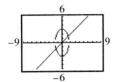

52. $\begin{cases} x = -y^2 - 3 \\ x = y^2 - 5 \end{cases}$

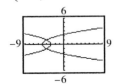

Section 10.4

Practice Exercises

1. $\dfrac{x^2}{36} + \dfrac{y^2}{16} \geq 1$

First graph the ellipse $\dfrac{x^2}{36} + \dfrac{y^2}{16} = 1$ as a solid curve. Choose (0, 0) as a test point.

$$\frac{x^2}{36} + \frac{y^2}{16} \geq 1$$

$$\frac{0^2}{36} + \frac{0^2}{16} \geq 1$$

$$0 \geq 1 \quad \text{False}$$

The solution set is the region that does not contain (0, 0).

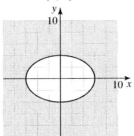

2. Graph the related equation $y = x^2 + 2$ and shade the region below the boundary curve since the inequality symbol is $\leq$.

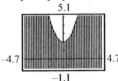

3. $16y^2 > 9x^2 + 144$

The related equation is $16y^2 = 9x^2 + 144$.

$$16y^2 - 9x^2 = 144$$

$$\frac{y^2}{9} - \frac{x^2}{16} = 1$$

Graph the hyperbola as a dashed curve.
Choose (0, 0), (0, 4), and (0, −4) as test points.

(0, 0): $16(0)^2 > 9(0)^2 + 144$

$$0 > 144 \quad \text{False}$$

(0, 4): $16(4)^2 > 9(0)^2 + 144$

$$256 > 144 \quad \text{True}$$

(0, −4): $16(-4)^2 > 9(0)^2 + 144$

$$256 > 144 \quad \text{True}$$

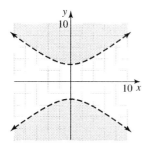

4. $\begin{cases} y \geq x^2 \\ y \leq -3x+2 \end{cases}$

Solve the related system $\begin{cases} y = x^2 \\ y = -3x+2 \end{cases}$.

Substitute $-3x + 2$ for y in the first equation.

$$x^2 = -3x + 2$$

$$x^2 + 3x - 2 = 0$$

$$x = \frac{-3 \pm \sqrt{3^2 - 4(1)(-2)}}{2(1)}$$

$$= \frac{-3 \pm \sqrt{17}}{2}$$

$$\approx 0.56 \text{ or } -3.56$$

$y = -3x + 2 \approx -3(0.56) + 2 = 0.32$

$y \approx -3(-3.56) + 2 = 12.68$

The points of intersection are approximately $(0.56, 0.32)$ and $(-3.56, 12.68)$.

Graph $y = x^2$ and $y = -3x + 2$ as solid curves.

The region of the solution set is above the parabola but below the line.

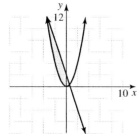

5. $\begin{cases} x^2 + y^2 < 16 \\ \dfrac{x^2}{4} - \dfrac{y^2}{9} < 1 \\ y < x+3 \end{cases}$

Graph $x^2 + y^2 = 16$, $\dfrac{x^2}{4} - \dfrac{y^2}{9} = 1$, and $y = x + 3$.

The test point $(0, 0)$ gives true statements for all three inequalities; thus, the innermost region is the solution set.

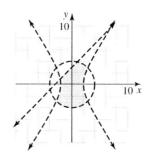

Exercise Set 10.4

2. $y < -x^2$

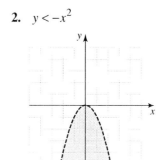

4. $x^2 + y^2 < 36$

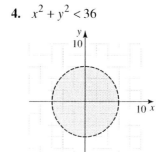

6. $x^2 - \dfrac{y^2}{9} \geq 1$

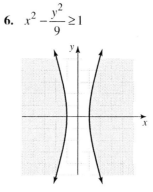

8. $y > (x+3)^2 + 2$

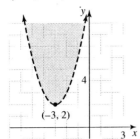

10. $x^2 + y^2 > 4$

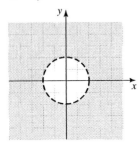

12. $y < -x^2 + 5$

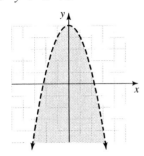

14. $\dfrac{x^2}{25} + \dfrac{y^2}{4} \geq 1$

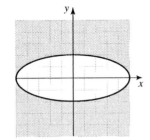

16. $\dfrac{y^2}{16} - \dfrac{x^2}{9} > 1$

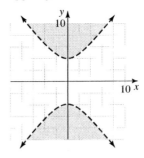

18. $y > (x-2)^2 + 1$

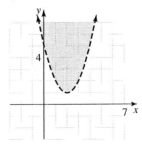

20. $y > x^2 + x - 2$

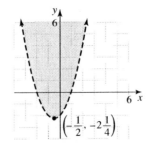

22. $\begin{cases} 3x - 4y \leq 12 \\ x^2 + y^2 < 16 \end{cases}$

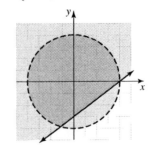

24. $\begin{cases} x^2 + y^2 \geq 9 \\ x^2 + y^2 \geq 16 \end{cases}$

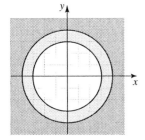

26. $\begin{cases} y \leq -x^2 + 3 \\ y \leq 2x - 1 \end{cases}$

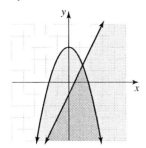

28. $\begin{cases} x^2 + y^2 \leq 9 \\ y < x^2 \end{cases}$

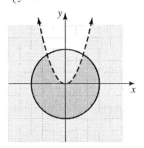

30. $\begin{cases} x^2 + (y-2)^2 \geq 9 \\ \dfrac{x^2}{4} + \dfrac{y^2}{25} < 1 \end{cases}$

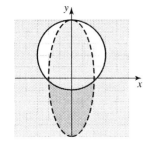

32. $\begin{cases} x^2 - y^2 \geq 1 \\ x \geq 0 \end{cases}$

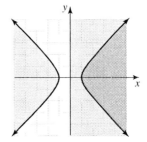

34. $\begin{cases} x - y < -1 \\ 4x - 3y > 0 \\ y > 0 \end{cases}$

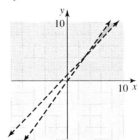

36. $\begin{cases} x^2 - y^2 \geq 1 \\ \dfrac{x^2}{16} + \dfrac{y^2}{4} \leq 1 \\ y \geq 1 \end{cases}$

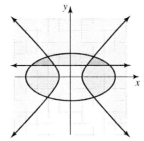

38. This is a function because a vertical line can cross the graph in no more than one place.

40. This is not a function because a vertical line can cross the graph in more than one place.

42. $f(x) = 3x^2 - 2$
$f(-3) = 3(-3)^2 - 2 = 3(9) - 2 = 25$

44. $f(x) = 3x^2 - 2$
$f(b) = 3(b)^2 - 2 = 3b^2 - 2$

46. Answers may vary

Chapter 10 Vocabulary Check

1. A <u>circle</u> is the set of all points in a plane that are the same distance from a fixed point, called the <u>center</u>.

2. A <u>nonlinear system of equations</u> is a system of equations at least one of which is not linear.

3. An <u>ellipse</u> is the set of points on a plane such that the sum of the distances of those points from two fixed points is a constant.

4. In a circle, the distance from the center to a point of the circle is called its <u>radius</u>.

5. A <u>hyperbola</u> is the set of points in a plane such that the absolute value of the difference of the distance from two fixed points is constant.

Chapter 10 Review

1. center (−4, 4), radius 3
$$[x-(-4)]^2 + (y-4)^2 = 3^2$$
$$(x+4)^2 + (y-4)^2 = 9$$

2. center (5, 0), radius 5
$$(x-5)^2 + (y-0)^2 = 5^2$$
$$(x-5)^2 + y^2 = 25$$

3. center (−7, −9), radius $\sqrt{11}$
$$[x-(-7)]^2 + [y-(-9)]^2 = \left(\sqrt{11}\right)^2$$
$$(x+7)^2 + (y+9)^2 = 11$$

4. center (0, 0), radius $\dfrac{7}{2}$
$$(x-0)^2 + (y-0)^2 = \left(\frac{7}{2}\right)^2$$
$$x^2 + y^2 = \frac{49}{4}$$

5. $x^2 + y^2 = 7$

Circle; center (0, 0), radius $r = \sqrt{7}$

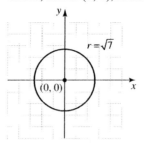

6. $x = 2(y-5)^2 + 4$

Parabola; vertex: (4, 5)

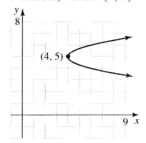

7. $x = -(y+2)^2 + 3$

Parabola; vertex: (3, −2)

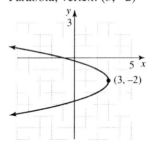

8. $(x-1)^2 + (y-2)^2 = 4$

Circle; center (1, 2), radius $r = \sqrt{4} = 2$

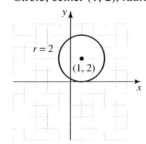

9. $y = -x^2 + 4x + 10$

Parabola; $x = \dfrac{-b}{2a} = \dfrac{-4}{2(-1)} = 2$

$y = -(2)^2 + 4(2) + 10 = 14$

Vertex: (2, 14)

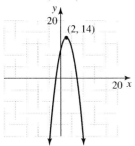

10. $x = -y^2 - 4y + 6$

Parabola; $y = \dfrac{-b}{2a} = \dfrac{-(-4)}{2(-1)} = -2$

$x = -(-2)^2 - 4(-2) + 6 = 10$

Vertex: (10, −2)

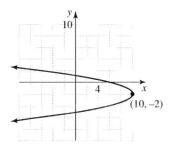

11. $x = \dfrac{1}{2}y^2 + 2y + 1$

Parabola; $y = \dfrac{-b}{2a} = \dfrac{-2}{2\left(\frac{1}{2}\right)} = -2$

$x = \dfrac{1}{2}(-2)^2 + 2(-2) + 1 = -1$

Vertex: (−1, −2)

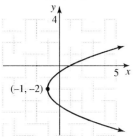

12. $y = -3x^2 + \dfrac{1}{2}x + 4$

Parabola; $x = \dfrac{-b}{2a} = \dfrac{-\frac{1}{2}}{2(-3)} = \dfrac{1}{12}$

$y = -3\left(\dfrac{1}{12}\right)^2 + \dfrac{1}{2}\left(\dfrac{1}{12}\right) + 4 = \dfrac{193}{48}$

Vertex: $\left(\dfrac{1}{12}, \dfrac{193}{48}\right)$

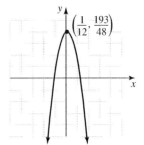

13.
$$x^2 + y^2 + 2x + y = \dfrac{3}{4}$$
$$(x^2 + 2x) + (y^2 + y) = \dfrac{3}{4}$$
$$(x^2 + 2x + 1) + \left(y^2 + y + \dfrac{1}{4}\right) = \dfrac{3}{4} + 1 + \dfrac{1}{4}$$
$$(x+1)^2 + \left(y + \dfrac{1}{2}\right)^2 = 2$$

Circle; center $\left(-1, -\dfrac{1}{2}\right)$, radius $r = \sqrt{2}$

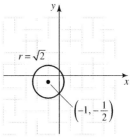

14.
$$x^2 + y^2 - 3y = \dfrac{7}{4}$$
$$x^2 + \left(y^2 - 3y + \dfrac{9}{4}\right) = \dfrac{7}{4} + \dfrac{9}{4}$$
$$x^2 + \left(y - \dfrac{3}{2}\right)^2 = 4$$

Circle; center $\left(0, \dfrac{3}{2}\right)$, radius $r = \sqrt{4} = 2$

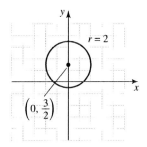

$\left(0, \dfrac{3}{2}\right)$

15. $4x^2 + 4y^2 + 16x + 8y = 1$

$(x^2 + 4x) + (y^2 + 2y) = \dfrac{1}{4}$

$(x^2 + 4x + 4) + (y^2 + 2y + 1) = \dfrac{1}{4} + 4 + 1$

$(x + 2)^2 + (y + 1)^2 = \dfrac{21}{4}$

Circle; center $(-2, -1)$, radius $r = \sqrt{\dfrac{21}{4}} = \dfrac{\sqrt{21}}{2}$

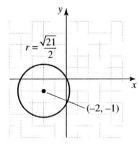

16. $x^2 + \dfrac{y^2}{4} = 1$

Center: $(0, 0)$; $a = 1$, $b = 2$

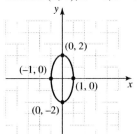

17. $x^2 - \dfrac{y^2}{4} = 1$

Center: $(0, 0)$; $a = 1$, $b = 2$

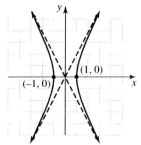

18. $\dfrac{x^2}{5} + \dfrac{y^2}{5} = 1$

$x^2 + y^2 = 5$

Center: $(0, 0)$; radius $r = \sqrt{5}$

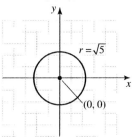

19. $\dfrac{x^2}{5} - \dfrac{y^2}{5} = 1$

Center: $(0, 0)$; $a = \sqrt{5}$, $b = \sqrt{5}$

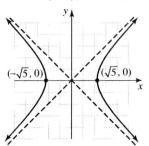

20. $-5x^2 + 25y^2 = 125$

$\dfrac{y^2}{5} - \dfrac{x^2}{25} = 1$

Center: $(0, 0)$; $a = 5$, $b = \sqrt{5}$

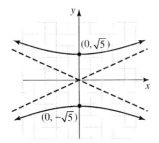

21. $4y^2 + 9x^2 = 36$

$$\frac{y^2}{9} + \frac{x^2}{4} = 1$$

Center: $(0, 0)$; $a = 2$, $b = 3$

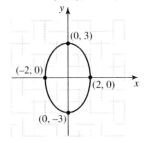

22. $x^2 - y^2 = 1$

Center: $(0, 0)$; $a = 1$, $b = 1$

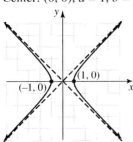

23. $\dfrac{(x+3)^2}{9} + \dfrac{(y-4)^2}{25} = 1$

Center: $(-3, 4)$; $a = 3$, $b = 5$

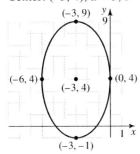

24. $$y^2 = x^2 + 9$$

$$y^2 - x^2 = 9$$

$$\frac{y^2}{9} - \frac{x^2}{9} = 1$$

Center: $(0, 0)$; $a = 3$, $b = 3$

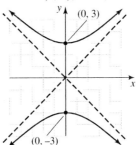

25. $x^2 = 4y^2 - 16$

$$16 = 4y^2 - x^2$$

$$1 = \frac{y^2}{4} - \frac{x^2}{16}$$

Center: $(0, 0)$; $a = 4$, $b = 2$

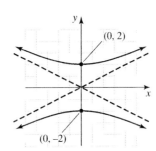

26. $100 - 25x^2 = 4y^2$

$$100 = 25x^2 + 4y^2$$

$$1 = \frac{x^2}{4} + \frac{y^2}{25}$$

Center: $(0, 0)$; $a = 2$, $b = 5$

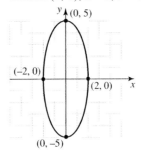

27. $\begin{cases} y = 2x - 4 & (1) \\ y^2 = 4x & (2) \end{cases}$

Substitute $2x - 4$ for y in E2.

$(2x-4)^2 = 4x$

$4x^2 - 16x + 16 = 4x$

$4x^2 - 20x + 16 = 0$

$x^2 - 5x + 4 = 0$

$(x-4)(x-1) = 0$

$x = 4 \ \text{or} \ x = 1$

Use these values in E1.

$x = 4 : y = 2(4) - 4 = 4$

$x = 1 : y = 2(1) - 4 = -2$

The solutions are $(4, 4)$ and $(1, -2)$.

28. $\begin{cases} x^2 + y^2 = 4 & (1) \\ x - y = 4 & (2) \end{cases}$

Solve E2 for x: $x = y + 4$.
Substitute into E1.

$(y+4)^2 + y^2 = 4$

$(y^2 + 8y + 16) + y^2 = 4$

$2y^2 + 8y + 12 = 0$

$y^2 + 4y + 6 = 0$

$y = \dfrac{-4 \pm \sqrt{(4)^2 - 4(1)(6)}}{2(1)} = \dfrac{-4 \pm \sqrt{-8}}{2}$

There are no real solutions. The solution is $\varnothing$.

29. $\begin{cases} y = x + 2 & (1) \\ y = x^2 & (2) \end{cases}$

Substitute $x + 2$ for y in E2.

$x + 2 = x^2$

$0 = x^2 - x - 2$

$0 = (x-2)(x+1)$

$x = 2 \ \text{or} \ x = -1$

Use these values in E1.

$x = 2 : y = 2 + 2 = 4$

$x = -1 : y = -1 + 2 = 1$

The solutions are $(2, 4)$ and $(-1, 1)$.

30. $\begin{cases} x^2 + 4y^2 = 16 & (1) \\ x^2 + y^2 = 4 & (2) \end{cases}$

Multiply E2 by -1 and add to E1.

$\begin{array}{r} x^2 + 4y^2 = 16 \\ -x^2 - y^2 = -4 \\ \hline 3y^2 = 12 \\ y^2 = 4 \\ y = \pm 2 \end{array}$

Replace y^2 with 4 in E2.

$x^2 + 4 = 4$

$x^2 = 0$

$x = 0$

The solutions are $(0, 2)$ and $(0, -2)$.

31. $\begin{cases} 4x - y^2 = 0 & (1) \\ 2x^2 + y^2 = 16 & (2) \end{cases}$

Solve E1 for y^2: $y^2 = 4x$.
Substitute into E2.

$2x^2 + 4x = 16$

$2x^2 + 4x - 16 = 0$

$x^2 + 2x - 8 = 0$

$(x+4)(x-2) = 0$

$x = -4 \ \text{or} \ x = 2$

Use these values in the equation $y^2 = 4x$.

$x = -4 : y^2 = 4(-4)$

$\qquad y^2 = -16 \ (\text{no real solutions})$

$x = 2 : y^2 = 4(2)$

$\qquad y^2 = 8$

$\qquad y = \pm\sqrt{8} = \pm 2\sqrt{2}$

The solutions are $\left(2, -2\sqrt{2}\right)$ and $\left(2, 2\sqrt{2}\right)$.

32. $\begin{cases} x^2 + 2y = 9 & (1) \\ 5x - 2y = 5 & (2) \end{cases}$

Add E1 and E2.

$\begin{array}{r} x^2 + 2y = 9 \\ 5x - 2y = 5 \\ \hline x^2 + 5x = 14 \end{array}$

$x^2 + 5x - 14 = 0$

$(x+7)(x-2) = 0$

$x = -7 \ \text{or} \ x = 2$

Use these values in E1.

$x = -7 : (-7)^2 + 2y = 9$

$\qquad 49 + 2y = 9$

$\qquad 2y = -40$

$\qquad y = -20$

$x = 2 : (2)^2 + 2y = 9$

$\qquad 4 + 2y = 9$

$\qquad 2y = 5$

$\qquad y = \dfrac{5}{2}$

The solutions are $(-7, -20)$ and $\left(2, \dfrac{5}{2}\right)$.

33. $\begin{cases} y = 3x^2 + 5x - 4 & (1) \\ y = 3x^2 - x + 2 & (2) \end{cases}$

Substitute.

$3x^2 + 5x - 4 = 3x^2 - x + 2$

$\qquad 6x = 6$

$\qquad x = 1$

Use this value in E1.

$y = 3(1)^2 + 5(1) - 4 = 4$

The solution is $(1, 4)$.

34. $\begin{cases} x^2 - 3y^2 = 1 & (1) \\ 4x^2 + 5y^2 = 21 & (2) \end{cases}$

Multiply E1 by -4 and add to E2.

$-4x^2 + 12y^2 = -4$

$\underline{4x^2 + 5y^2 = 21}$

$\qquad 17y^2 = 17$

$\qquad y^2 = 1$

$\qquad y = \pm 1$

Replace y^2 with 1 in E1.

$x^2 - 3(1) = 1$

$\qquad x^2 = 4$

$\qquad x = \pm 2$

The solutions are $(-2, -1)$, $(-2, 1)$, $(2, -1)$ and $(2, 1)$.

35. Let x and y be the length and width.

$\begin{cases} xy = 150 \\ 2x + 2y = 50 \end{cases}$

Solve the first equation for y: $y = \dfrac{150}{x}$.

Substitute into E2.

$2x + 2\left(\dfrac{150}{x}\right) = 50$

$x + \dfrac{150}{x} = 25$

$x^2 + 150 = 25x$

$x^2 - 25x + 150 = 0$

$(x - 15)(x - 10) = 0$

$x = 15$ or $x = 10$

Substitute these values into E1.

$15y = 150 \qquad\qquad 10y = 150$

$y = 10 \qquad\qquad y = 15$

The room is 15 feet by 10 feet.

36. Four real solutions are possible.

37. $y \le -x^2 + 3$

Graph $y = -x^2 + 3$ as a solid curve.

Test Point	$y \le -x^2 + 3$; Result
$(0, 0)$	$0 \le -(0)^2 + 3$; True

Shade the region containing $(0, 0)$.

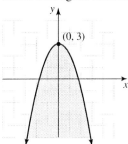

38. $x^2 + y^2 < 9$

First graph the circle as a dashed curve.

Test Point	$x^2 + y^2 < 9$; Result
$(0, 0)$	$0^2 + 0^2 < 9$; True

Shade the region containing $(0, 0)$.

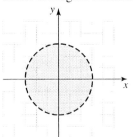

39. $\begin{cases} 2x \le 4 \\ x+y \ge 1 \end{cases}$

First graph $2x = 4$, or $x = 2$, as a solid line, and shade to the left of the line. Next, graph $x + y = 1$ as a solid line.

Test Point	$x+y \ge 1$; Result
$(0, 0)$	$0 + 0 \ge 1$; False

Shade the region which does not contain $(0, 0)$. The solution to the system is the intersection.

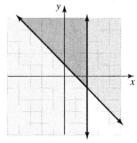

40. $\dfrac{x^2}{4} + \dfrac{y^2}{9} \ge 1$

First graph the ellipse as a solid curve.

Test Point	$\dfrac{x^2}{4}+\dfrac{y^2}{9} \ge 1$; Result
$(0, 0)$	$\dfrac{(0)^2}{4}+\dfrac{(0)^2}{9} \ge 1$; False

Shade the region that does not contain $(0, 0)$.

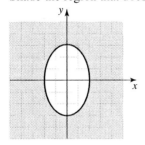

41. $\begin{cases} x^2 + y^2 < 4 \\ x^2 - y^2 \le 1 \end{cases}$

First graph the first circle as a dashed curve.

Test Point	$x^2 + y^2 < 4$; Result
$(0, 0)$	$0^2 + 0^2 < 4$; True

Shade the region containing $(0, 0)$. Next, graph the hyperbola as a solid curve.

Test Point	$x^2 - y^2 \le 1$; Result
$(-2, 0)$	$(-2)^2 - 0^2 \le 1$; False
$(0, 0)$	$0^2 - 0^2 \le 1$; True
$(2, 0)$	$2^2 - 0^2 \le 1$; False

Shade the region containing $(0, 0)$. The solution to the system is the intersection.

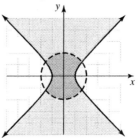

42. $\begin{cases} x^2 + y^2 \le 16 \\ x^2 + y^2 \ge 4 \end{cases}$

First graph the first circle as a solid curve.

Test Point	$x^2 + y^2 \le 16$; Result
$(0, 0)$	$0^2 + 0^2 \le 16$; True

Shade the region containing $(0, 0)$. Next, graph the second circle as a solid curve.

Test Point	$x^2 + y^2 \ge 4$; Result
$(0, 0)$	$0^2 + 0^2 \ge 4$; False

Shade the region which does not contain $(0, 0)$. The solution to the system is the intersection.

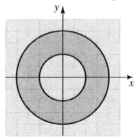

43. center: (−7, 8); radius = 5
$$(x-h)^2 + (y-k)^2 = r^2$$
$$(x+7)^2 + (y-8)^2 = 25$$

44. $3x^2 + 6x + 3y^2 = 9$
$$x^2 + 2x + y^2 = 3$$
$$x^2 + 2x + 1 + y^2 = 3 + 1$$
$$(x+1)^2 + y^2 = 4$$
This is a circle with center (−1, 0) and radius 2.

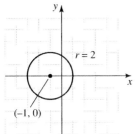

45. $y = x^2 + 6x + 9$
$$y = (x+3)^2$$
This is a parabola that opens upward with vertex (−3, 0).

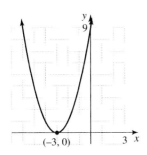

46. $x = y^2 + 6y + 9$
$$x = (y+3)^2$$
This is a parabola that opens to the right with vertex (0, −3).

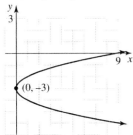

47. $\dfrac{y^2}{4} - \dfrac{x^2}{16} = 1$
This is a hyperbola with center (0, 0), $a = 4$ and $b = 2$.

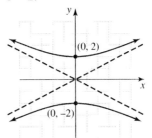

48. $\dfrac{y^2}{4} + \dfrac{x^2}{16} = 1$
This is an ellipse with center (0, 0), $a = 4$ and $b = 2$. The intercepts are (4, 0), (−4, 0), (0, 2), and (0, −2).

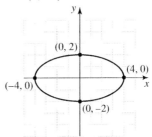

49. $\dfrac{(x-2)^2}{4} + (y-1)^2 = 1$
This is an ellipse with center (2, 1), $a = 2$ and $b = 1$.

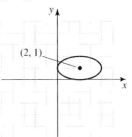

50. $y^2 = x^2 + 6$
$$y^2 - x^2 = 6$$
$$\dfrac{y^2}{6} - \dfrac{x^2}{6} = 1$$
This is a hyperbola with center (0, 0), $a = \sqrt{6}$ and $b = \sqrt{6}$.

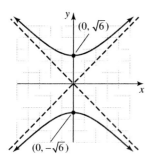

51.
$$y^2 + x^2 = 4x + 6$$
$$y^2 + (x^2 - 4x) = 6$$
$$y^2 + (x^2 - 4x + 4) = 6 + 4$$
$$y^2 + (x - 2)^2 = 10$$

This is a circle with center (2, 0) and radius $\sqrt{10}$.

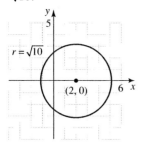

52.
$$x^2 + y^2 - 8y = 0$$
$$x^2 + y^2 - 8y + 16 = 16$$
$$x^2 + (y - 4)^2 = 16$$

This is a circle with center (0, 4) and radius $\sqrt{16} = 4$.

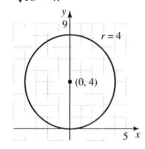

53. $6(x - 2)^2 + 9(y + 5)^2 = 36$
$$\frac{(x - 2)^2}{6} + \frac{(y + 5)^2}{4} = 1$$

This is an ellipse with center (2, –5), $a = \sqrt{6}$, and $b = 2$.

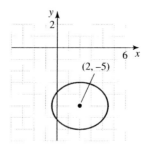

54. $\dfrac{x^2}{16} - \dfrac{y^2}{25} = 1$

This is a hyperbola with center (0, 0), $a = 4$, $b = 5$, and x-intercepts (4, 0) and (–4, 0).

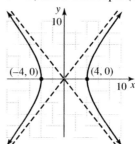

55. $\begin{cases} y = x^2 - 5x + 1 & (1) \\ y = -x + 6 & (2) \end{cases}$

Substitute $-x + 6$ for y in E2.
$$-x + 6 = x^2 - 5x + 1$$
$$0 = x^2 - 4x - 5$$
$$0 = (x - 5)(x + 1)$$
$$x = 5 \text{ or } x = -1$$

Use these values in E2.
$$x = 5 : y = -(5) + 6 = 1$$
$$x = -1 : y = -(-1) + 6 = 7$$

The solutions are (5, 1) and (–1, 7).

56. $\begin{cases} x^2 + y^2 = 10 & (1) \\ 9x^2 + y^2 = 18 & (2) \end{cases}$

Multiply E1 by –1 and add to E2.
$$-x^2 - y^2 = -10$$
$$\underline{9x^2 + y^2 = 18}$$
$$8x^2 = 8$$
$$x^2 = 1$$
$$x = \pm 1$$

Replace x^2 with 1 in E1.

$1 + y^2 = 10$

$y^2 = 9$

$y = \pm 3$

The solutions are $(-1, -3)$, $(-1, 3)$, $(1, -3)$ and $(1, 3)$.

57. $x^2 - y^2 < 1$

First graph the hyperbola as dashed curves.

Test Point	$x^2 - y^2 < 1$; Result
$(-2, 0)$	$(-2)^2 - 0^2 < 1$; False
$(0, 0)$	$0^2 - 0^2 < 1$; True
$(2, 0)$	$2^2 - 0^2 < 1$; False

Shade the region containing $(0, 0)$.

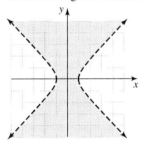

58. $\begin{cases} y > x^2 \\ x + y \geq 3 \end{cases}$

First graph the parabola as a dashed curve.

Test Point	$y > x^2$; Result
$(0, 1)$	$1 > 0^2$; True

Shade the region containing $(0, 1)$. Next, graph $x + y = 3$ as a solid line.

Test Point	$x + y \geq 3$; Result
$(0, 0)$	$0 + 0 \geq 3$; False

Shade the region which does not contain $(0, 0)$. The solution to the system is the overlapping region.

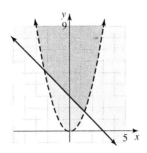

Chapter 10 Test

1. $x^2 + y^2 = 36$

Circle; center: $(0, 0)$, radius $r = \sqrt{36} = 6$

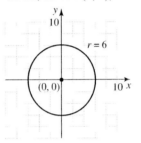

2. $x^2 - y^2 = 36$

$\dfrac{x^2}{36} - \dfrac{y^2}{36} = 1$

Hyperbola; center: $(0, 0)$, $a = 6$, $b = 6$

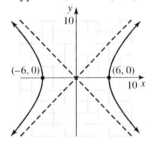

3. $16x^2 + 9y^2 = 144$

$\dfrac{x^2}{9} + \dfrac{y^2}{16} = 1$

Ellipse; center: $(0, 0)$, $a = 3$, $b = 4$

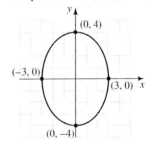

4. $y = x^2 - 8x + 16$

$y = (x - 4)^2$

Parabola; vertex: (4, 0)

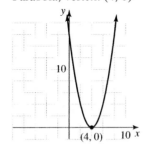

5. $x^2 + y^2 + 6x = 16$

$(x^2 + 6x) + y^2 = 16$

$(x^2 + 6x + 9) + y^2 = 16 + 9$

$(x + 3)^2 + y^2 = 25$

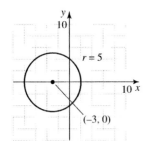

6. $x = y^2 + 8y - 3$

$x + 16 = (y^2 + 8y + 16) - 3$

$x = (y + 4)^2 - 19$

Parabola; vertex: (−4, −19)

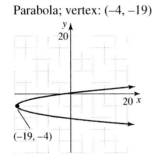

7. $\dfrac{(x-4)^2}{16} + \dfrac{(y-3)^2}{9} = 1$

Ellipse: center: (4, 3), $a = 4$, $b = 3$

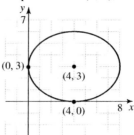

8. $y^2 - x^2 = 1$

Hyperbola: center: (0, 0), $a = 1$, $b = 1$

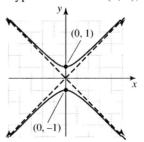

9. $\begin{cases} x^2 + y^2 = 26 \quad (1) \\ x^2 - 2y^2 = 23 \quad (2) \end{cases}$

Solve E1 for x^2: $x^2 = 26 - y^2$.

Substitute into E2.

$(26 - y^2) - 2y^2 = 23$

$-3y^2 = -3$

$y^2 = 1$

$y = \pm 1$

Replace y^2 with 1 in E1.

$x^2 + 1 = 26$

$x^2 = 25$

$x = \pm 5$

The solutions are (−5, −1), (−5, 1), (5, −1), and (5, 1).

10. $\begin{cases} y = x^2 - 5x + 6 \quad (1) \\ y = 2x \quad\quad\quad\;\;\; (2) \end{cases}$

Substitute $2x$ for y in E1.

$2x = x^2 - 5x + 6$

$0 = x^2 - 7x + 6$

$0 = (x - 6)(x - 1)$

$x = 6$ or $x = 1$

Use these values in E2.

$x = 6: y = 2(6) = 12$
$x = 1: y = 2(1) = 2$
The solutions are (1, 2) and (6, 12).

11. $\begin{cases} 2x + 5y \geq 10 \\ \quad\quad y \geq x^2 + 1 \end{cases}$

First graph $2x + 5y = 10$ as a solid line.

Test Point	$2x + 5y \geq 10$; Result
(0, 0)	$2(0) + 5(0) \geq 10$; False

Shade the region which does not contain (0, 0).
Next, graph $y = x^2 + 1$ as a solid curve.

Test Point	$y \geq x^2 + 1$; Result
(0, 0)	$0 \geq 0^2 + 1$; False

Shade the region which does not contain (0, 0).
The solution to the system is the intersection.

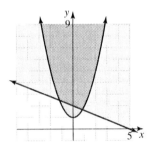

12. $\begin{cases} \dfrac{x^2}{4} + y^2 \leq 1 \\ \quad x + y > 1 \end{cases}$

First graph the ellipse as a solid curve.

Test Point	$\dfrac{x^2}{4} + y^2 \leq 1$; Result
(0, 0)	$\dfrac{0^2}{4} + 0^2 \leq 1$; True

Shade the region containing (0, 0). Next, graph
$x + y = 1$ as a dashed line.

Test Point	$x + y > 1$; Result
(0, 0)	$0 + 0 > 1$; False

Shade the region which does not contain (0, 0).

The solution to the system is the intersection.

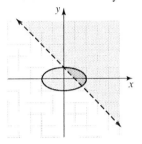

13. $\begin{cases} x^2 + y^2 \geq 4 \\ x^2 + y^2 < 16 \\ \quad\quad y \geq 0 \end{cases}$

First graph the circle $x^2 + y^2 = 4$ as a solid curve.

Test Point	$x^2 + y^2 \geq 4$; Result
(0, 0)	$0^2 + 0^2 \geq 4$; False

Shade the region which does not contain (0, 0).
Next graph the circle $x^2 + y^2 = 16$ as a dashed curve.

Test Point	$x^2 + y^2 < 16$; Result
(0, 0)	$0^2 + 0^2 < 16$; True

Shade the region containing (0, 0). Now graph
the inequality $y \geq 0$ by shading the region above
the x-axis. The solution to the system is the
intersection.

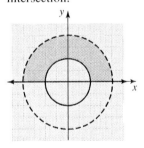

14. $100x^2 + 225y^2 = 22,500$

$\dfrac{x^2}{225} + \dfrac{y^2}{100} = 1$

$a = \sqrt{225} = 15$
$b = \sqrt{100} = 10$
Width = 15 + 15 = 30 feet
Height = 10 feet

Chapter 10 Cumulative Review

1. $4 \cdot (9y) = (4 \cdot 9)y = 36y$

2. $3x + 4 > 1 \quad$ and $\quad 2x - 5 \le 9$
    $\quad 3x > -3 \quad$ and $\quad\quad 2x \le 14$
    $\quad\quad x > -1 \quad$ and $\quad\quad x \le 7$
    $-1 < x \le 7$
    $(-1, 7]$

3. $x = -2y$
    $y = -\dfrac{1}{2}x$

x	$y = -\frac{1}{2}x$
-2	1
0	0
4	-2

    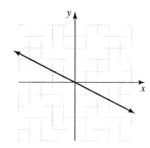

4. $(3, 2), (1, -4)$
    $m = \dfrac{-4 - 2}{1 - 3} = \dfrac{-6}{-2} = 3$

5. $\begin{cases} 3x + \dfrac{y}{2} = 2 \ (1) \\ 6x + y = 5 \ (2) \end{cases}$

    Multiply E1 by -2 and add to E2.
    $-6x - y = -4$
    $\underline{6x + y = 5}$
    $0 = 1$
    This is a false statement. Therefore, the solution is $\varnothing$.

6. Let $x =$ speed of one plane. Then
    $x + 25 =$ speed of the other plane.
    $d_{\text{plane 1}} + d_{\text{plane 2}} = 650$ miles
    $\quad 2x + 2(x + 25) = 650$
    $\quad\quad 2x + 2x + 50 = 650$
    $\quad\quad\quad\quad\quad 4x = 600$
    $\quad\quad\quad\quad\quad\quad x = 150$
    $x + 25 = 150 + 25 = 175$
    The planes are traveling at 150 mph and 175 mph.

7. **a.** $(5x^2)^3 = 5^3 (x^2)^3 = 125x^6$

    b. $\left(\dfrac{2}{3}\right)^3 = \dfrac{2^3}{3^3} = \dfrac{8}{27}$

    c. $\left(\dfrac{3p^4}{q^5}\right)^2 = \dfrac{3^2 (p^4)^2}{(q^5)^2} = \dfrac{9p^8}{q^{10}}$

    d. $\left(\dfrac{2^{-3}}{y}\right)^{-2} = \dfrac{(2^{-3})^{-2}}{y^{-2}}$
    $\phantom{\left(\dfrac{2^{-3}}{y}\right)^{-2}} = 2^6 y^2$
    $\phantom{\left(\dfrac{2^{-3}}{y}\right)^{-2}} = 64y^2$

    e. $(x^{-5}y^2 z^{-1})^7 = (x^{-5})^7 (y^2)^7 (z^{-1})^7$
    $\phantom{(x^{-5}y^2 z^{-1})^7} = x^{-35} y^{14} z^{-7}$
    $\phantom{(x^{-5}y^2 z^{-1})^7} = \dfrac{y^{14}}{x^{35} z^7}$

8. **a.** $\dfrac{4^8}{4^3} = 4^{8-3} = 4^5$

    b. $\dfrac{y^{11}}{y^5} = y^{11-5} = y^6$

    c. $\dfrac{32x^7}{4x^6} = \dfrac{32}{4}x^{7-6} = 8x$

    d. $\dfrac{18a^{12}b^6}{12a^8 b^6} = \dfrac{18}{12}a^{12-8}b^{6-6} = \dfrac{3}{2}a^4 b^0 = \dfrac{3a^4}{2}$

9.
$$2x^2 = \frac{17}{3}x + 1$$
$$3(2x^2) = 3\left(\frac{17}{3}x + 1\right)$$
$$6x^2 = 17x + 3$$
$$6x^2 - 17x - 3 = 0$$
$$(6x + 1)(x - 3) = 0$$
$$6x + 1 = 0 \quad \text{or} \quad x - 3 = 0$$
$$6x = -1 \quad \text{or} \quad x = 3$$
$$x = -\frac{1}{6}$$

The solutions are $-\dfrac{1}{6}$ and 3.

10. a. $\quad 3y^2 + 14y + 15 = (3y + 5)(y + 3)$

b.
$$20a^5 + 54a^4 + 10a^3$$
$$= 2a^3(10a^2 + 27a + 5)$$
$$= 2a^3(2a + 5)(5a + 1)$$

c. $\quad (y - 3)^2 - 2(y - 3) - 8$

Let $u = y - 3$. Then $u^2 = (y - 3)^2$ and

$$u^2 - 2u - 8 = (u - 4)(u + 2)$$
$$= [(y - 3) - 4][(y - 3) + 2]$$
$$= (y - 7)(y - 1)$$

11.
$$\frac{7}{x - 1} + \frac{10x}{x^2 - 1} - \frac{5}{x + 1}$$
$$= \frac{7}{x - 1} + \frac{10x}{(x + 1)(x - 1)} - \frac{5}{x + 1}$$
$$= \frac{7(x + 1) + 10x - 5(x - 1)}{(x + 1)(x - 1)}$$
$$= \frac{7x + 7 + 10x - 5x + 5}{(x + 1)(x - 1)}$$
$$= \frac{12x + 12}{(x + 1)(x - 1)}$$
$$= \frac{12(x + 1)}{(x + 1)(x - 1)}$$
$$= \frac{12}{x - 1}$$

12.
$$\frac{2}{3a - 15} - \frac{a}{25 - a^2}$$
$$= \frac{2}{3(a - 5)} + \frac{a}{a^2 - 25}$$
$$= \frac{2}{3(a - 5)} + \frac{a}{(a + 5)(a - 5)}$$
$$= \frac{2(a + 5) + 3a}{3(a + 5)(a - 5)}$$
$$= \frac{2a + 10 + 3a}{3(a + 5)(a - 5)}$$
$$= \frac{5a + 10}{3(a + 5)(a - 5)}$$

13. a.
$$\frac{\frac{2x}{27y^2}}{\frac{6x^2}{9}} = \frac{2x}{27y^2} \cdot \frac{9}{6x^2} = \frac{1}{3y^2} \cdot \frac{1}{3x} = \frac{1}{9xy^2}$$

b.
$$\frac{\frac{5x}{x + 2}}{\frac{10}{x - 2}} = \frac{5x}{x + 2} \cdot \frac{x - 2}{10} = \frac{x(x - 2)}{2(x + 2)}$$

c.
$$\frac{\frac{x}{y^2} + \frac{1}{y}}{\frac{y}{x^2} + \frac{1}{x}} = \frac{\left(\frac{x}{y^2} + \frac{1}{y}\right)x^2 y^2}{\left(\frac{y}{x^2} + \frac{1}{x}\right)x^2 y^2}$$
$$= \frac{x^3 + x^2 y}{y^3 + xy^2}$$
$$= \frac{x^2(x + y)}{y^2(y + x)}$$
$$= \frac{x^2}{y^2}$$

14. a.
$$(a^{-1} - b^{-1})^{-1} = \left(\frac{1}{a} - \frac{1}{b}\right)^{-1}$$
$$= \left(\frac{b - a}{ab}\right)^{-1}$$
$$= \frac{ab}{b - a}$$

b. $\dfrac{2 - \frac{1}{x}}{4x - \frac{1}{x}} = \dfrac{\left(2 - \frac{1}{x}\right)x}{\left(4x - \frac{1}{x}\right)x}$

$\qquad = \dfrac{2x - 1}{4x^2 - 1}$

$\qquad = \dfrac{2x - 1}{(2x + 1)(2x - 1)}$

$\qquad = \dfrac{1}{2x + 1}$

15.

$$\begin{array}{r} 2x - 5 \\ x+2\overline{)2x^2 - x - 10} \\ \underline{2x^2 + 4x} \\ -5x - 10 \\ \underline{-5x - 10} \\ 0 \end{array}$$

Answer: $2x - 5$

16. $\dfrac{2}{x+3} = \dfrac{1}{x^2 - 9} - \dfrac{1}{x - 3}$

$\dfrac{2}{x+3} = \dfrac{1}{(x+3)(x-3)} - \dfrac{1}{x-3}$

$2(x - 3) = 1 - 1(x + 3)$

$2x - 6 = 1 - x - 3$

$2x - 6 = -x - 2$

$3x = 4$

$x = \dfrac{4}{3}$

17.

$$\begin{array}{r|rrrrrr} 4 & 4 & -25 & 35 & 0 & 17 & 0 & 0 \\ & & 16 & -36 & -4 & -16 & 4 & 16 \\ \hline & 4 & -9 & -1 & -4 & 1 & 4 & 16 \end{array}$$

Thus, $P(4) = 16$.

18. $y = \dfrac{k}{x}$

$3 = \dfrac{k}{\frac{2}{3}}$

$k = 3\left(\dfrac{2}{3}\right) = 2$

Thus, the equation is $y = \dfrac{2}{x}$.

19. $\dfrac{2x}{x-3} + \dfrac{6 - 2x}{x^2 - 9} = \dfrac{x}{x+3}$

$\dfrac{2x}{x-3} + \dfrac{-2(x-3)}{(x+3)(x-3)} = \dfrac{x}{x+3}$

$\dfrac{2x}{x-3} - \dfrac{2}{x+3} = \dfrac{x}{x+3}$

$\dfrac{2x}{x-3} = \dfrac{x}{x+3} + \dfrac{2}{x+3}$

$\dfrac{2x}{x-3} = \dfrac{x+2}{x+3}$

$2x(x + 3) = (x + 2)(x - 3)$

$2x^2 + 6x = x^2 - x - 6$

$x^2 + 7x + 6 = 0$

$(x + 6)(x + 1) = 0$

$x + 6 = 0 \quad \text{or} \quad x + 1 = 0$

$x = -6 \quad \text{or} \qquad x = -1$

The solutions are -6 and -1.

20. a. $\sqrt[5]{-32} = -2$ because $(-2)^5 = -32$.

b. $\sqrt[4]{625} = 5$ because $5^4 = 625$.

c. $-\sqrt{36} = -6$ because $6^2 = 36$.

d. $-\sqrt[3]{-27x^3} = -(-3x) = 3x$

e. $\sqrt{144y^2} = 12y$

21. Let $t =$ time it will take together.

$\dfrac{1}{4} + \dfrac{1}{5} = \dfrac{1}{t}$

$20t\left(\dfrac{1}{4} + \dfrac{1}{5}\right) = 20t\left(\dfrac{1}{t}\right)$

$5t + 4t = 20$

$9t = 20$

$t = \dfrac{20}{9} = 2\dfrac{2}{9}$

It will take them $2\dfrac{2}{9}$ hours. No, they can not finish before the movie starts.

22. a. $\dfrac{\sqrt{32}}{\sqrt{4}} = \sqrt{\dfrac{32}{4}} = \sqrt{8} = \sqrt{4 \cdot 2} = 2\sqrt{2}$

b. $\dfrac{\sqrt[3]{240y^2}}{5\sqrt[3]{3y^{-4}}} = \dfrac{1}{5}\sqrt[3]{\dfrac{240y^2}{3y^{-4}}}$

$= \dfrac{1}{5}\sqrt[3]{80y^6}$

$= \dfrac{1}{5}\sqrt[3]{8y^6 \cdot 10}$

$= \dfrac{2y^3\sqrt[3]{10}}{5}$

c. $\dfrac{\sqrt[5]{64x^9y^2}}{\sqrt[5]{2x^2y^{-8}}} = \sqrt[5]{\dfrac{64x^9y^2}{2x^2y^{-8}}}$

$= \sqrt[5]{32x^7y^{10}}$

$= \sqrt[5]{32x^5y^{10} \cdot x^2}$

$= 2xy^2\sqrt[5]{x^2}$

23. a. $\sqrt[3]{1} = 1$

b. $\sqrt[3]{-64} = -4$

c. $\sqrt[3]{\dfrac{8}{125}} = \dfrac{\sqrt[3]{8}}{\sqrt[3]{125}} = \dfrac{2}{5}$

d. $\sqrt[3]{x^6} = x^2$

e. $\sqrt[3]{-27x^9} = -3x^3$

24. a. $\sqrt{5}\left(2 + \sqrt{15}\right) = 2\sqrt{5} + \sqrt{5} \cdot \sqrt{15}$

$= 2\sqrt{5} + \sqrt{75}$

$= 2\sqrt{5} + 5\sqrt{3}$

b. $\left(\sqrt{3} - \sqrt{5}\right)\left(\sqrt{7} - 1\right)$

$= \sqrt{3} \cdot \sqrt{7} - \sqrt{3} \cdot 1 - \sqrt{5} \cdot \sqrt{7} + \sqrt{5} \cdot 1$

$= \sqrt{21} - \sqrt{3} - \sqrt{35} + \sqrt{5}$

c. $\left(2\sqrt{5} - 1\right)^2 = \left(2\sqrt{5}\right)^2 - 2 \cdot 2\sqrt{5} \cdot 1 + 1^2$

$= 4(5) - 4\sqrt{5} + 1$

$= 21 - 4\sqrt{5}$

d. $\left(3\sqrt{2} + 5\right)\left(3\sqrt{2} - 5\right) = \left(3\sqrt{2}\right)^2 - 5^2$

$= 9(2) - 25$

$= 18 - 25$

$= -7$

25. a. $z^{2/3}\left(z^{1/3} - z^5\right) = z^{2/3 + 1/3} - z^{2/3 + 5}$

$= z^{3/3} - z^{2/3 + 15/3}$

$= z - z^{17/3}$

b. $\left(x^{1/3} - 5\right)\left(x^{1/3} + 2\right)$

$= x^{1/3} \cdot x^{1/3} + 2x^{1/3} - 5x^{1/3} - 5(2)$

$= x^{2/3} - 3x^{1/3} - 10$

26. $\dfrac{-2}{\sqrt{3} + 3} = \dfrac{-2\left(\sqrt{3} - 3\right)}{\left(\sqrt{3} + 3\right)\left(\sqrt{3} - 3\right)}$

$= \dfrac{-2\left(\sqrt{3} - 3\right)}{\left(\sqrt{3}\right)^2 - 3^2}$

$= \dfrac{-2\left(\sqrt{3} - 3\right)}{3 - 9}$

$= \dfrac{-2\left(\sqrt{3} - 3\right)}{-6}$

$= \dfrac{\sqrt{3} - 3}{3}$

27. a. $\dfrac{\sqrt{20}}{\sqrt{5}} = \sqrt{\dfrac{20}{5}} = \sqrt{4} = 2$

b. $\dfrac{\sqrt{50x}}{2\sqrt{2}} = \dfrac{1}{2}\sqrt{\dfrac{50x}{2}} = \dfrac{1}{2}\sqrt{25x} = \dfrac{5\sqrt{x}}{2}$

c. $\dfrac{7\sqrt[3]{48x^4y^8}}{\sqrt[3]{6y^2}} = 7\sqrt[3]{\dfrac{48x^4y^8}{6y^2}}$

$= 7\sqrt[3]{8x^4y^6}$

$= 7\sqrt[3]{8x^3y^6 \cdot x}$

$= 7 \cdot 2xy^2\sqrt[3]{x}$

$= 14xy^2\sqrt[3]{x}$

d. $\dfrac{2\sqrt[4]{32a^8b^6}}{\sqrt[4]{a^{-1}b^2}} = 2\sqrt[4]{\dfrac{32a^8b^6}{a^{-1}b^2}}$

$= 2\sqrt[4]{32a^9b^4}$

$= 2\sqrt[4]{16a^8b^4 \cdot 2a}$

$= 2 \cdot 2a^2b\sqrt[4]{2a}$

$= 4a^2b\sqrt[4]{2a}$

28.
$$\sqrt{2x-3} = x-3$$
$$\left(\sqrt{2x-3}\right)^2 = (x-3)^2$$
$$2x-3 = x^2 - 6x + 9$$
$$0 = x^2 - 8x + 12$$
$$0 = (x-6)(x-2)$$
$$x-6 = 0 \text{ or } x-2 = 0$$
$$x = 6 \text{ or } \quad x = 2$$
Discard 2 as an extraneous solution. The solution is 6.

29. a.
$$\frac{\sqrt{45}}{4} - \frac{\sqrt{5}}{3} = \frac{3\sqrt{5}}{4} - \frac{\sqrt{5}}{3}$$
$$= \frac{9\sqrt{5} - 4\sqrt{5}}{12}$$
$$= \frac{5\sqrt{5}}{12}$$

b.
$$\sqrt[3]{\frac{7x}{8}} + 2\sqrt[3]{7x} = \frac{\sqrt[3]{7x}}{2} + 2\sqrt[3]{7x}$$
$$= \frac{\sqrt[3]{7x}}{2} + \frac{4\sqrt[3]{7x}}{2}$$
$$= \frac{5\sqrt[3]{7x}}{2}$$

30.
$$9x^2 - 6x = -4$$
$$9x^2 - 6x + 4 = 0$$
$$a = 9, b = -6, c = 4$$
$$b^2 - 4ac = (-6)^2 - 4(9)(4)$$
$$= 36 - 144$$
$$= -108$$
Two complex but not real solutions

31.
$$\sqrt{\frac{7x}{3y}} = \frac{\sqrt{7x}}{\sqrt{3y}} = \frac{\sqrt{7x} \cdot \sqrt{3y}}{\sqrt{3y} \cdot \sqrt{3y}} = \frac{\sqrt{21xy}}{3y}$$

32.
$$\frac{4}{x-2} - \frac{x}{x+2} = \frac{16}{x^2-4}$$
$$\frac{4}{x-2} - \frac{x}{x+2} = \frac{16}{(x+2)(x-2)}$$
$$4(x+2) - x(x-2) = 16$$
$$4x + 8 - x^2 + 2x = 16$$
$$0 = x^2 - 6x + 8$$
$$0 = (x-4)(x-2)$$
$$x-4 = 0 \text{ or } x-2 = 0$$
$$x = 4 \text{ or } \quad x = 2$$
Discard the solution 2 as extraneous. The solution is 4.

33.
$$\sqrt{2x-3} = 9$$
$$\left(\sqrt{2x-3}\right)^2 = 9^2$$
$$2x-3 = 81$$
$$2x = 84$$
$$x = 42$$
The solution is 42.

34.
$$x^3 + 2x^2 - 4x \geq 8$$
$$x^3 + 2x^2 - 4x - 8 \geq 0$$
$$x^2(x+2) - 4(x+2) \geq 0$$
$$(x+2)(x^2-4) \geq 0$$
$$(x+2)(x+2)(x-2) \geq 0$$
$$(x+2)^2(x-2) \geq 0$$
$$(x+2)^2 = 0 \text{ or } x-2 = 0$$
$$x+2 = 0 \text{ or } \quad x = 2$$
$$x = -2$$

Region	Test Point	$(x+2)^2(x-2) \geq 0$ Result
A: $(-\infty, -2)$	-3	$(-1)^2(-5) \geq 0$ False
B: $(-2, 2)$	0	$(2)^2(-2) \geq 0$ False
C: $(2, \infty)$	3	$(5)^2(1) \geq 0$ True

Solution: $[2, \infty)$

35. a. $i^7 = i^4 \cdot i^3 = 1 \cdot (-i) = -i$

b. $i^{20} = (i^4)^5 = 1^5 = 1$

c. $i^{46} = i^{44} \cdot i^2 = (i^4)^{11} \cdot (-1) = 1^{11}(-1) = -1$

d. $i^{-12} = \frac{1}{i^{12}} = \frac{1}{(i^4)^3} = \frac{1}{1^3} = 1$

36. $f(x) = (x+2)^2 - 1$

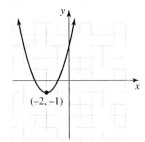

37.
$$p^2 + 2p = 4$$
$$p^2 + 2p + \left(\frac{2}{2}\right)^2 = 4 + 1$$
$$p^2 + 2p + 1 = 5$$
$$(p+1)^2 = 5$$
$$p + 1 = \pm\sqrt{5}$$
$$p = -1 \pm \sqrt{5}$$

The solutions are $-1+\sqrt{5}$ and $-1-\sqrt{5}$.

38. $f(x) = -x^2 - 6x + 4$

The maximum will occur at the vertex.
$$x = \frac{-b}{2a} = \frac{-(-6)}{2(-1)} = -3$$
$$f(-3) = -(-3)^2 - 6(-3) + 4 = 13$$

The maximum value is 13.

39.
$$\frac{1}{4}m^2 - m + \frac{1}{2} = 0$$
$$4\left(\frac{1}{4}m^2 - m + \frac{1}{2}\right) = 4(0)$$
$$m^2 - 4m + 2 = 0$$
$$a = 1, b = -4, c = 2$$
$$m = \frac{-(-4) \pm \sqrt{(-4)^2 - 4(1)(2)}}{2(1)}$$
$$= \frac{4 \pm \sqrt{16 - 8}}{2}$$
$$= \frac{4 \pm \sqrt{8}}{2}$$
$$= \frac{4 \pm 2\sqrt{2}}{2}$$
$$= 2 \pm \sqrt{2}$$

The solutions are $2+\sqrt{2}$ and $2-\sqrt{2}$.

40.
$$f(x) = \frac{x+1}{2}$$
$$y = \frac{x+1}{2}$$
$$x = \frac{y+1}{2}$$
$$2x = y + 1$$
$$2x - 1 = y$$
$$f^{-1}(x) = 2x - 1$$

41.
$$p^4 - 3p^2 - 4 = 0$$
$$(p^2 - 4)(p^2 + 1) = 0$$
$$(p+2)(p-2)(p^2 + 1) = 0$$
$$p + 2 = 0 \quad \text{or} \quad p - 2 = 0 \quad \text{or} \quad p^2 + 1 = 0$$
$$p = -2 \quad \text{or} \quad p = 2 \quad \text{or} \quad p^2 = -1$$
$$p = \pm i$$

The solutions are -2, 2, $-i$, and i.

42. $f(x) = x^2 - 3x + 2$
$g(x) = -3x + 5$

a.
$$(f \circ g)(x) = f[g(x)]$$
$$= f(-3x + 5)$$
$$= (-3x + 5)^2 - 3(-3x + 5) + 2$$
$$= 9x^2 - 30x + 25 + 9x - 15 + 2$$
$$= 9x^2 - 21x + 12$$

b.
$$(f \circ g)(-2) = f[g(-2)]$$
$$= f[-3(-2) + 5]$$
$$= f(11)$$
$$= (11)^2 - 3(11) + 2$$
$$= 121 - 33 + 2$$
$$= 90$$

c.
$$(g \circ f)(x) = g[f(x)]$$
$$= g(x^2 - 3x + 2)$$
$$= -3(x^2 - 3x + 2) + 5$$
$$= -3x^2 + 9x - 6 + 5$$
$$= -3x^2 + 9x - 1$$

d.
$$(g \circ f)(5) = g[f(5)]$$
$$= g[(5)^2 - 3(5) + 2]$$
$$= g(12)$$
$$= -3(12) + 5$$
$$= -36 + 5$$
$$= -31$$

43. $\dfrac{x+2}{x-3} \le 0$

$x + 2 = 0$ or $x - 3 = 0$
$\qquad x = -2$ or $\qquad x = 3$

Region	Test Point	$\dfrac{x+2}{x-3} \le 0$ Result
A: $(-\infty, -2)$	-3	$\dfrac{-1}{-6} \le 0$; False
B: $(-2, 3)$	0	$\dfrac{2}{-3} \le 0$; True
C: $(3, \infty)$	4	$\dfrac{6}{1} \le 0$; False

Solution: $[-2, 3)$

44. $4x^2 + 9y^2 = 36$

$\dfrac{x^2}{9} + \dfrac{y^2}{4} = 1$

Ellipse: center $(0, 0)$, $a = 3$, $b = 2$

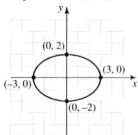

45. $g(x) = \dfrac{1}{2}(x+2)^2 + 5$

Vertex: $(-2, 5)$, axis: $x = -2$

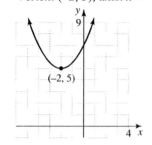

46. a. $64^x = 4$

$(4^2)^x = 4$

$4^{2x} = 4$

$2x = 1$

$x = \dfrac{1}{2}$

b. $125^{x-3} = 25$

$(5^3)^{x-3} = 5^2$

$5^{3x-9} = 5^2$

$3x - 9 = 2$

$3x = 11$

$x = \dfrac{11}{3}$

c. $\dfrac{1}{81} = 3^{2x}$

$3^{-4} = 3^{2x}$

$-4 = 2x$

$-\dfrac{4}{2} = x$

$-2 = x$

47. $f(x) = x^2 - 4x - 12$

$x = \dfrac{-b}{2a} = \dfrac{-(-4)}{2(1)} = 2$

$f(2) = (2)^2 - 4(2) - 12 = -16$

Vertex: $(2, -16)$

48. $\begin{cases} x + 2y < 8 \\ \quad y \ge x^2 \end{cases}$

First, graph $x + 2y = 8$ as a dashed line.

Test Point	$x + 2y < 8$; Result
$(0, 0)$	$0 + 2(0) < 8$; True

Shade the region containing $(0, 0)$. Next, graph the parabola $y = x^2$ as a solid curve.

Test Point	$y \ge x^2$; Result
$(0, 1)$	$1 \ge 0^2$; True

Shade the region containing (0, 1). The solution to the system is the intersection.

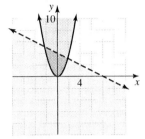

49. $(2, -5), (1, -4)$

$$d = \sqrt{[-4-(-5)]^2 + (1-2)^2}$$
$$= \sqrt{1^2 + (-1)^2}$$
$$= \sqrt{2} \approx 1.414$$

50. $\begin{cases} x^2 + y^2 = 36 & (1) \\ \quad\quad y = x+6 & (2) \end{cases}$

Substitute $x+6$ for y in E1.

$$x^2 + (x+6)^2 = 36$$
$$x^2 + (x^2 + 12x + 36) = 36$$
$$2x^2 + 12x = 0$$
$$2x(x+6) = 0$$

$2x = 0$ or $x+6 = 0$

$x = 0$ or $\quad\quad x = -6$

Use these values in E2 to find y.

$x = 0: y = 0+6 = 6$

$x = -6: y = -6+6 = 0$

The solutions are $(0, 6)$ and $(-6, 0)$.

Chapter 11

Section 11.1

Practice Problems

1. $a_n = 5 + n^2$

    $a_1 = 5 + 1^2 = 5 + 1 = 6$

    $a_2 = 5 + 2^2 = 5 + 4 = 9$

    $a_3 = 5 + 3^2 = 5 + 9 = 14$

    $a_4 = 5 + 4^2 = 5 + 16 = 21$

    $a_5 = 5 + 5^2 = 5 + 25 = 30$

    Thus, the first five terms of the sequence are 6, 9, 14, 21, and 30.

2. $a_n = \dfrac{(-1)^n}{5n}$

    a. $a_1 = \dfrac{(-1)^1}{5(1)} = -\dfrac{1}{5}$

    b. $a_4 = \dfrac{(-1)^4}{5(4)} = \dfrac{1}{20}$

    c. $a_{30} = \dfrac{(-1)^{30}}{5(30)} = \dfrac{1}{150}$

    d. $a_{19} = \dfrac{(-1)^{19}}{5(19)} = -\dfrac{1}{95}$

3. a. $1, 3, 5, 7, \ldots$

    These numbers are the first four odd natural numbers, so a general term might be $a_n = (2n - 1)$.

    b. $3, 9, 27, 81, \ldots$

    These numbers are all powers of 3 ($3 = 3^1$, $9 = 3^2$, $27 = 3^3$, and $81 = 3^4$), so a general term might be $a_n = 3^n$.

    c. $\dfrac{1}{2}, \dfrac{2}{3}, \dfrac{3}{4}, \dfrac{4}{5}, \ldots$

    The numerators are the first four natural numbers and each denominator is one greater than the numerator, so a general term might be $a_n = \dfrac{n}{n+1}$.

    d. $-\dfrac{1}{2}, -\dfrac{1}{3}, -\dfrac{1}{4}, -\dfrac{1}{5}, \ldots$

    The denominators are consecutive natural numbers beginning with 2 and each term is negative, so a general term might be $a_n = -\dfrac{1}{n+1}$.

4. $v_n = 3950(0.8)^n$

    $v_3 = 3950(0.8)^3$

    $\quad = 3950(0.512)$

    $\quad = 2022.4$

    The value of the copier after three years is $2022.40.

Vocabulary and Readiness Check

1. The nth term of the sequence a_n is called the general term.

2. A finite sequence is a function whose domain is $\{1, 2, 3, 4, \ldots, n\}$ where n is some natural number.

3. An infinite sequence is a function whose domain is $\{1, 2, 3, 4, \ldots\}$.

4. $a_n = 7^n$

    $a_1 = 7^1 = 7$

5. $a_n = \dfrac{(-1)^n}{n}$

    $a_1 = \dfrac{(-1)^1}{1} = -1$

6. $a_n = (-1)^n \cdot n^4$

    $a_1 = (-1)^1 \cdot 1^4 = -1$

Exercise Set 11.1

2. $a_n = 5 - n$

    $a_1 = 5 - 1 = 4$

    $a_2 = 5 - 2 = 3$

    $a_3 = 5 - 3 = 2$

    $a_4 = 5 - 4 = 1$

    $a_5 = 5 - 5 = 0$

    Thus, the first five terms of the sequence are 4, 3, 2, 1, 0.

4. $a_n = (-2)^n$

$a_1 = (-2)^1 = -2$

$a_2 = (-2)^2 = 4$

$a_3 = (-2)^3 = -8$

$a_4 = (-2)^4 = 16$

$a_5 = (-2)^5 = -32$

Thus, the first five terms of the sequence are
$-2, 4, -8, 16, -32$.

6. $a_n = \dfrac{1}{7-n}$

$a_1 = \dfrac{1}{7-1} = \dfrac{1}{6}$

$a_2 = \dfrac{1}{7-2} = \dfrac{1}{5}$

$a_3 = \dfrac{1}{7-3} = \dfrac{1}{4}$

$a_4 = \dfrac{1}{7-4} = \dfrac{1}{3}$

$a_5 = \dfrac{1}{7-5} = \dfrac{1}{2}$

Thus, the first five terms of the sequence are
$\dfrac{1}{6}, \dfrac{1}{5}, \dfrac{1}{4}, \dfrac{1}{3}, \dfrac{1}{2}.$

8. $a_n = -6n$

$a_1 = -6(1) = -6$

$a_2 = -6(2) = -12$

$a_3 = -6(3) = -18$

$a_4 = -6(4) = -24$

$a_5 = -6(5) = -30$

Thus, the first five terms of the sequence are
$-6, -12, -18, -24, -30$.

10. $a_n = n^2 + 2$

$a_1 = 1^2 + 2 = 3$

$a_2 = 2^2 + 2 = 6$

$a_3 = 3^2 + 2 = 11$

$a_4 = 4^2 + 2 = 18$

$a_5 = 5^2 + 2 = 27$

Thus, the first five terms of the sequence are 3, 6,
11, 18, 27.

12. $a_n = 3^{n-2}$

$a_1 = 3^{1-2} = 3^{-1} = \dfrac{1}{3}$

$a_2 = 3^{2-2} = 3^0 = 1$

$a_3 = 3^{3-2} = 3^1 = 3$

$a_4 = 3^{4-2} = 3^2 = 9$

$a_5 = 3^{5-2} = 3^3 = 27$

Thus, the first five terms of the sequence are

$\dfrac{1}{3}, 1, 3, 9, 27.$

14. $a_n = 1 - 3n$

$a_1 = 1 - 3(1) = -2$

$a_2 = 1 - 3(2) = -5$

$a_3 = 1 - 3(3) = -8$

$a_4 = 1 - 3(4) = -11$

$a_5 = 1 - 3(5) = -14$

Thus, the first five terms of the sequence are
$-2, -5, -8, -11, -14$.

16. $a_n = (-1)^{n+1}(n-1)$

$a_1 = (-1)^{1+1}(1-1) = 1(0) = 0$

$a_2 = (-1)^{2+1}(2-1) = -1(1) = -1$

$a_3 = (-1)^{3+1}(3-1) = 1(2) = 2$

$a_4 = (-1)^{4+1}(4-1) = -1(3) = -3$

$a_5 = (-1)^{5+1}(5-1) = 1(4) = 4$

Thus, the first five terms of the sequence are 0, -1,
2, -3, 4.

18. $a_n = -n^2$

$a_{15} = -(15)^2 = -225$

20. $a_n = 100 - 7n$

$a_{50} = 100 - 7(50) = -250$

22. $a_n = \dfrac{n}{n+4}$

$a_{24} = \dfrac{24}{24+4} = \dfrac{24}{28} = \dfrac{6}{7}$

24. $a_n = 5^{n+1}$

$a_3 = 5^{3+1} = 5^4 = 625$

26. $a_n = \dfrac{n+3}{n+4}$

$a_8 = \dfrac{8+3}{8+4} = \dfrac{11}{12}$

28. $a_n = \dfrac{(-1)^n}{2n}$

$a_{100} = \dfrac{(-1)^{100}}{2(100)} = \dfrac{1}{200}$

30. $a_n = 8 - n^2$

$a_{20} = 8 - (20)^2 = 8 - 400 = -392$

32. $a_n = \dfrac{n-4}{(-2)^n}$

$a_6 = \dfrac{6-4}{(-2)^6} = \dfrac{2}{64} = \dfrac{1}{32}$

34. $a_n = 2 + 5(n-1)$ or $a_n = 5n - 3$

36. $a_n = -4(-4)^{n-1}$ or $a_n = (-4)^n$

38. $a_n = \dfrac{2}{5}\left(\dfrac{1}{5}\right)^{n-1}$ or $a_n = \dfrac{2}{5^n}$

40. $a_4 = 50(3)^{4-1} = 50(27) = 1350$ bacteria

$a_1 = 50(3)^{1-1} = 50(1) = 50$ bacteria

42. $a_n = 12 + 3(n-1)$

$a_8 = 12 + 3(8-1) = 12 + 21 = 33$ seats

44. $a_n = 2700 + 150(n-1)$

In 2000, $n = 1$ and
$a_1 = 2700 + 150(1-1) = 2700$ students
In 2001, $n = 2$ and
$a_2 = 2700 + 150(2-1) = 2850$ students
In 2002, $n = 3$ and
$a_3 = 2700 + 150(3-1) = 3000$ students
In 2003, $n = 4$ and
$a_4 = 2700 + 150(4-1) = 3150$ students
In 2004, $n = 5$ and
$a_5 = 2700 + 150(5-1) = 3300$ students

46. Answers may vary

48. $f(x) = (x-2)^2 + 1$

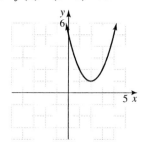

50. $f(x) = 3(x-3)^2 + 4$

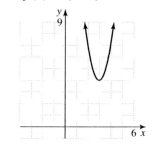

52. $(-2, -1)$ and $(-1, 5)$

$d = \sqrt{[5-(-1)]^2 + [-1-(-2)]^2}$

$= \sqrt{36+1}$

$= \sqrt{37}$ units

54. $(10, -14)$ and $(5, -11)$

$d = \sqrt{(5-10)^2 + [-11-(-14)]^2}$

$= \sqrt{25+9}$

$= \sqrt{34}$ units

56. $a_n = \dfrac{\sqrt{n}}{\sqrt{n}+1}$

n	$u(n)$
1	.5
2	.58579
3	.63397
4	.66667
5	.69098
6	.7101
7	.72571
u(n)◻f(n)/(f(n)…	

The first five terms of the sequence $a_n = \dfrac{\sqrt{n}}{\sqrt{n}+1}$

are 0.5, 0.5858, 0.6340, 0.6667, 0.6910.

58. $a_n = \left(1 + \dfrac{0.05}{n}\right)^n$

The first five terms of the sequence

$a_n = \left(1 + \dfrac{0.05}{n}\right)^n$ are 1.05, 1.0506, 1.0508,

1.0509, 1.0510.

Section 11.2

Practice Problems

1. $a_1 = 4$

$a_2 = 4 + 5 = 9$

$a_3 = 9 + 5 = 14$

$a_4 = 14 + 5 = 19$

$a_5 = 19 + 5 = 24$

The first five terms are 4, 9, 14, 19, 24.

2. a. $a_n = a_1 + (n-1)d$

Here, $a_1 = 2$ and $d = -3$.

$a_n = 2 + (n-1)(-3) = 2 - 3n + 3 = 5 - 3n$

b. $a_n = 5 - 3n$

$a_{12} = 5 - 3 \cdot 12 = 5 - 36 = -31$

3. Since the sequence is arithmetic, the ninth term is

$a_9 = a_1 + (9-1)d = a_1 + 8d$.

a_1 is the first term of the sequence, so $a_1 = 3$. d is the constant difference, so $d = a_2 - a_1 = 9 - 3 = 6$.

Thus,

$a_9 = a_1 + 8d = 3 + 8 \cdot 6 = 51$.

4. We need to find a_1 and d. The given facts, $a_3 = 23$ and $a_8 = 63$, lead to a system of linear equations.

$\begin{cases} a_3 = a_1 + (3-1)d \\ a_8 = a_1 + (8-1)d \end{cases}$ or $\begin{cases} 23 = a_1 + 2d \\ 63 = a_1 + 7d \end{cases}$

We solve the system by elimination. Multiply both sides of the second equation by -1.

$\begin{cases} 23 = a_1 + 2d \\ -1(63) = -1(a_1 + 7d) \end{cases}$ or $\begin{cases} 23 = a_1 + 2d \\ -63 = -a_1 - 7d \end{cases}$

$\quad\quad\quad -40 = \quad\quad -5d$

$\quad\quad\quad\quad\quad 8 = d$

To find a_1, let $d = 8$ in $23 = a_1 + 2d$.

$23 = a_1 + 2(8)$

$23 = a_1 + 16$

$7 = a_1$

Thus, $a_1 = 7$ and $d = 8$, so

$a_n = 7 + (n-1)(8) = 7 + 8n - 8 = -1 + 8n$ and

$a_6 = -1 + 8 \cdot 6 = 47$.

5. The first term, a_1, is 57,000, and d is 2200.

$a_n = 57{,}000 + (n-1)(2200)$

$ = 54{,}800 + 2200n$

$a_3 = 54{,}800 + 2200 \cdot 3 = 61{,}400$

The salary for the third year is \$61,400.

6. $a_1 = 8$

$a_2 = 8(-3) = -24$

$a_3 = -24(-3) = 72$

$a_4 = 72(-3) = -216$

The first four terms are 8, -24, 72, and -216.

7. $a_n = a_1 r^{n-1}$

Here, $a_1 = 64$ and $r = \dfrac{1}{4}$.

Evaluate a_n for $n = 7$.

$a_7 = 64 \left(\dfrac{1}{4}\right)^{7-1}$

$ = 64 \left(\dfrac{1}{4}\right)^6$

$ = 64 \left(\dfrac{1}{4096}\right)$

$ = \dfrac{1}{64}$

8. Since the sequence is geometric and $a_1 = -3$, the seventh term must be $a_1 r^{7-1}$, or $-3r^6$. r is the common ratio of terms, so r must be $\dfrac{6}{-3}$, or -2.

$a_7 = -3r^6$

$a_7 = -3(-2)^6 = -192$

9. Notice that $\dfrac{27}{4} \div \dfrac{9}{2} = \dfrac{3}{2}$, so $r = \dfrac{3}{2}$.

$$a_2 = a_1 \left(\dfrac{3}{2}\right)^{2-1}$$

$$\dfrac{9}{2} = a_1 \left(\dfrac{3}{2}\right)^1, \quad \text{or} \quad a_1 = 3$$

The first term is 3, and the common ration is $\dfrac{3}{2}$.

10. Since the culture is reduced by one-half each day, the population sizes are modeled by a geometric sequence. Here, $a_1 = 4800$ and $r = \dfrac{1}{2}$.

$$a_n = a_1 r^{n-1} = 4800 \left(\dfrac{1}{2}\right)^{n-1}$$

$$a_7 = 4800 \left(\dfrac{1}{2}\right)^{7-1} = 75$$

The bacterial culture should measure 75 units at the beginning of day 7.

Vocabulary and Readiness Check

1. A <u>geometric</u> sequence is one in which each term (after the first) is obtained by multiplying the preceding term by a constant r. The constant r is called the common <u>ratio</u>.

2. An <u>arithmetic</u> sequence is one in which each term (after the first) differs from the preceding term by a constant amount d. The constant d is called the common <u>difference</u>.

3. The general term of an arithmetic sequence is $a_n = a_1 + (n-1)d$ where a_1 is the <u>first</u> term and d is the common <u>difference</u>.

4. The general term of a geometric sequence is $a_n = a_1 r^{n-1}$ where a_1 is the <u>first</u> term and r is the common <u>ratio</u>.

Exercise Set 11.2

2. $a_n = a_1 + (n-1)d$
$a_1 = 3; \ d = 10$
$a_1 = 3$
$a_2 = 3 + (2-1)10 = 13$
$a_3 = 3 + (3-1)10 = 23$
$a_4 = 3 + (4-1)10 = 33$
$a_5 = 3 + (5-1)10 = 43$

4. $a_n = a_1 + (n-1)d$
$a_1 = -20, \ d = 3$
$a_1 = -20$
$a_2 = -20 + (2-1)3 = -17$
$a_3 = -20 + (3-1)3 = -14$
$a_4 = -20 + (4-1)3 = -11$
$a_5 = -20 + (5-1)3 = -8$

6. $a_n = a_1 r^{n-1}$
$a_1 = -2, \ r = 2$
$a_1 = -2(2)^{1-1} = -2$
$a_2 = -2(2)^{2-1} = -4$
$a_3 = -2(2)^{3-1} = -8$
$a_4 = -2(2)^{4-1} = -16$
$a_5 = -2(2)^{5-1} = -32$

8. $a_n = a_1 r^{n-1}$
$a_1 = 1, \ r = \dfrac{1}{3}$
$a_1 = 1\left(\dfrac{1}{3}\right)^{1-1} = 1$
$a_2 = 1\left(\dfrac{1}{3}\right)^{2-1} = \dfrac{1}{3}$
$a_3 = 1\left(\dfrac{1}{3}\right)^{3-1} = \dfrac{1}{9}$
$a_4 = 1\left(\dfrac{1}{3}\right)^{4-1} = \dfrac{1}{27}$
$a_5 = 1\left(\dfrac{1}{3}\right)^{5-1} = \dfrac{1}{81}$

10. $a_n = a_1 + (n-1)d$
$a_1 = 32, \ d = -4$
$a_{12} = 32 + (12-1)(-4) = -12$

12. $a_n = a_1 r^{n-1}$
$a_1 = 3, \ r = 3$
$a_5 = 3(3)^{5-1} = 3(3)^4 = 243$

14. $a_n = a_1 r^{n-1}$
$a_1 = 5, \ r = -4$
$a_6 = 5(-4)^{6-1} = 5(-4)^5 = -5120$

16. $a_n = a_1 + (n-1)d$
$a_1 = -3$ and $d = 0 - (-3) = 3$
$a_{13} = -3 + (13-1)3 = 33$

18. $a_n = a_1 r^{n-1}$

$a_1 = 5$ and $r = \dfrac{10}{5} = 2$

$a_9 = 5(2)^{9-1} = 5(2)^8 = 1280$

20. $a_n = a_1 r^{n-1}$

$a_1 = \dfrac{1}{2}$ and $r = \dfrac{3/2}{1/2} = 3$

$a_6 = \dfrac{1}{2}(3)^{6-1} = \dfrac{1}{2}(3)^5 = \dfrac{243}{2}$

22. $\begin{cases} a_2 = a_1 + (2-1)d \\ a_{10} = a_1 + (10-1)d \end{cases}$

$\begin{cases} 6 = a_1 + d \\ 30 = a_1 + 9d \end{cases}$

$\begin{cases} -6 = -a_1 - d \\ 30 = a_1 + 9d \end{cases}$

Adding yields $24 = 8d$ or $d = 3$.
Then $a_1 = 6 - 3 = 3$
$a_{25} = 3 + (25-1)3 = 3 + 72 = 75$

24. $a_2 = 15, \ a_3 = 3$

$r = \dfrac{3}{15} = \dfrac{1}{5}$

$a_2 = a_1 r^{2-1}$

$15 = a_1\left(\dfrac{1}{5}\right)$

$75 = a_1$

26. $a_3 = 4, \ a_4 = -12$

$r = \dfrac{-12}{4} = -3$

$a_3 = a_1 r^{3-1}$

$4 = a_1(-3)^2$

$\dfrac{4}{9} = a_1$

28. Answers may vary

30. Arithmetic; $a_1 = 8, \ d = 8$

32. Geometric; $a_1 = 2, \ r = 3$

34. Arithmetic; $a_1 = \dfrac{2}{3}, \ d = \dfrac{2}{3}$

36. Geometric; $a_1 = y, \ r = -3$

38. Arithmetic; $a_1 = t, \ d = -1$

40. $a_1 = 8, \ r = -3$

$a_5 = 8(-3)^{5-1} = 8(-3)^4 = 648$

42. $a_1 = 9, \ d = 5$

$a_4 = 9 + (4-1)5 = 9 + 15 = 24$

44. $a_1 = 2, \ d = \dfrac{4}{3} - \dfrac{5}{3} = -\dfrac{1}{3}$

$a_{11} = 2 + (11-1)\left(-\dfrac{1}{3}\right) = 2 - \dfrac{10}{3} = -\dfrac{4}{3}$

46. $a_1 = 5, \ d = 2 - 5 = -3$

$a_{18} = 5 + (18-1)(-3) = 5 - 51 = -46$

48. $a_3 = -28, \ a_4 = -56$

$r = \dfrac{-56}{-28} = 2$

$a_3 = a_1 r^{3-1}$

$-28 = a_1(2)^2$

$-7 = a_1$

50. $a_1 = 20, \ d = 17 - 20 = -3$

$a_n = 20 + (n-1)(-3)$ or $a_n = 23 - 3n$

$a_5 = 23 - 3(5) = 8$

There are 8 cans in the fifth row. Solving $a_n \geq 0$

yields $n \leq 7\dfrac{2}{3}$ so $n = 7$ and thus there are 7 rows.

$a_7 = 23 - 3(7) = 2$

There are two cans in the top row.

52. $a_n = a_1 r^{n-1}$

$a_1 = 500,000(1.15)^0 = 500,000$

$a_2 = 500,000(1.15)^1 = 575,000$

$a_3 = 500,000(1.15)^2 = 661,250$

$a_4 = 500,000(1.15)^3 = 760,437.50$

The predicted value at the end of the third year is
$760,437.60.

54. Geometric

$a_n = a_1 r^{n-1}, \ a_1 = 50, \ r = 0.80$

$a_4 = 50(0.80)^3 = 25.6$

The length of the fourth swing is 25.6 inches.

56. $a_n = 15 + (n-1)5$ or $a_n = 10 + 5n$

$a_7 = 10 + 5(7) = 45$

$60 = 10 + 5n$

$50 = 5n$

$n = 10$

After 7 weeks, her riding time is 45 minutes. It takes her 10 weeks to reach 1 hour of riding time.

58. $5(1) + 5(2) + 5(3) + 5(4) = 5 + 10 + 15 + 20$
$$= 50$$

60. $2(2-4) + 3(3-4) + 4(4-4)$

$= 2(-2) + 3(-1) + 4(0)$

$= -4 - 3 + 0$

$= -7$

62. $\dfrac{1}{4(1)} + \dfrac{1}{4(2)} + \dfrac{1}{4(3)} = \dfrac{1}{4} + \dfrac{1}{8} + \dfrac{1}{12}$

$$= \dfrac{6}{24} + \dfrac{3}{24} + \dfrac{2}{24}$$

$$= \dfrac{11}{24}$$

64. $a_1 = \$3720,\ d = -\$268.50$

The first four terms of the sequence are \$3720, \$3451.50, \$3183, \$2914.50.

66. $a_1 = 26.8,\ r = 2.5$

The first four terms of the sequence are 26.8, 67, 167.5, 418.75.

68. Answers may vary

Section 11.3

Practice Problems

1. a. $\displaystyle\sum_{i=0}^{4} \dfrac{i-3}{4} = \dfrac{0-3}{4} + \dfrac{1-3}{4} + \dfrac{2-3}{4} + \dfrac{3-3}{4} + \dfrac{4-3}{4}$

$= \left(-\dfrac{3}{4}\right) + \left(-\dfrac{2}{4}\right) + \left(-\dfrac{1}{4}\right) + 0 + \dfrac{1}{4}$

$= -\dfrac{5}{4},\ \text{or } -1\dfrac{1}{4}$

b. $\displaystyle\sum_{i=2}^{5} 3^i = 3^2 + 3^3 + 3^4 + 3^5$

$= 9 + 27 + 81 + 243$

$= 360$

2. a. Since the difference of each term and the preceding term is 5, the terms correspond to the first six terms of the arithmetic sequence $a_n = 5 + (n-1)5 = 5n$. Thus, in summation notation,

$$5 + 10 + 15 + 20 + 25 + 30 = \sum_{i=1}^{6} 5i.$$

b. Since each term is the product of the preceding term and $\dfrac{1}{5}$, these terms correspond to the first four terms of the geometric sequence $a_n = \dfrac{1}{5}\left(\dfrac{1}{5}\right)^{n-1} = \left(\dfrac{1}{5}\right)^n$.

In summation notation,

$$\dfrac{1}{5} + \dfrac{1}{25} + \dfrac{1}{125} + \dfrac{1}{625} = \sum_{i=1}^{4} \left(\dfrac{1}{5}\right)^i.$$

3. $S_4 = \displaystyle\sum_{i=1}^{4} \dfrac{2+3i}{i^2}$

$= \dfrac{2+3\cdot1}{1^2} + \dfrac{2+3\cdot2}{2^2} + \dfrac{2+3\cdot3}{3^2} + \dfrac{2+3\cdot4}{4^2}$

$= \dfrac{5}{1} + \dfrac{8}{4} + \dfrac{11}{9} + \dfrac{14}{16}$

$= 5 + 2 + \dfrac{11}{9} + \dfrac{7}{8}$

$= \dfrac{655}{72},\ \text{or } 9\dfrac{7}{72}$

4. $S_5 = \displaystyle\sum_{i=1}^{5} i(2i-1)$

$= 1(2\cdot1-1) + 2(2\cdot2-1) + 3(2\cdot3-1)$

$\qquad + 4(2\cdot4-1) + 5(2\cdot5-1)$

$= 1 + 6 + 15 + 28 + 45$

$= 95$

There are 95 plants after 5 years.

Vocabulary and Readiness Check

1. A series is an __infinite__ series if it is the sum of all the terms of the sequence.

2. A series is a __finite__ series if it is the sum of a finite number of terms.

3. A shorthand notation for denoting a series when the general term of the sequence is known is called <u>summation</u> notation.

4. In the notation $\sum\limits_{i=1}^{7}(5i-2)$, the Σ is the Greek uppercase letter <u>sigma</u> and the i is called the <u>index of summation</u>.

5. The sum of the first n terms of a sequence is a finite series known as a <u>partial sum</u>.

6. For the notation in Exercise 4 above, the beginning value of i is $\underline{1}$ and the ending value of i is $\underline{7}$.

Exercise Set 11.3

2. $\sum\limits_{i=1}^{5}(i+6) = 7+8+9+10+11 = 45$

4. $\sum\limits_{i=2}^{3}(5i-1) = (5(2)-1)+(5(3)-1)$
$= 9+14$
$= 23$

6. $\sum\limits_{i=3}^{5}i^3 = 3^3+4^3+5^3 = 27+64+125 = 216$

8. $\sum\limits_{i=2}^{4}\left(\dfrac{2}{i+3}\right) = \dfrac{2}{2+3}+\dfrac{2}{3+3}+\dfrac{2}{4+3}$
$= \dfrac{2}{5}+\dfrac{2}{6}+\dfrac{2}{7}$
$= \dfrac{107}{105}$

10. $\sum\limits_{i=1}^{3}\dfrac{1}{3i} = \dfrac{1}{3(1)}+\dfrac{1}{3(2)}+\dfrac{1}{3(3)}$
$= \dfrac{1}{3}+\dfrac{1}{6}+\dfrac{1}{9}$
$= \dfrac{11}{18}$

12. $\sum\limits_{i=3}^{6}-4i = -4(3)-4(4)-4(5)-4(6)$
$= -12-16-20-24$
$= -72$

14. $\sum\limits_{i=2}^{4}i(i-3) = 2(2-3)+3(3-3)+4(4-3)$
$= 2(-1)+3(0)+4(1)$
$= 2$

16. $\sum\limits_{i=1}^{4}3^{i-1} = 3^0+3^1+3^2+3^3$
$= 1+3+9+27$
$= 40$

18. $\sum\limits_{i=2}^{5}\dfrac{6-i}{6+i} = \dfrac{6-2}{6+2}+\dfrac{6-3}{6+3}+\dfrac{6-4}{6+4}+\dfrac{6-5}{6+5}$
$= \dfrac{4}{8}+\dfrac{3}{9}+\dfrac{2}{10}+\dfrac{1}{11}$
$= \dfrac{371}{330}$

20. $a_1 = 4,\, d = 3$
$a_n = 4+(n-1)3 = 3n+1$
$\sum\limits_{i=1}^{4}(3i+1)$

22. $a_1 = 5,\, r = 2$
$a_n = 5(2)^{n-1}$
$\sum\limits_{i=1}^{6}5(2)^{i-1}$

24. $a_1 = 5,\, d = -4$
$a_n = 5+(n-1)(-4) = -4n+9$
$\sum\limits_{i=1}^{4}(-4i+9)$

26. $a_1 = 80,\, r = \dfrac{1}{4}$
$a_n = 80\left(\dfrac{1}{4}\right)^{n-1} = \dfrac{80}{4^{n-1}} = \dfrac{4^2\cdot 5}{4^{n-1}} = \dfrac{5}{4^{n-3}}$
$\sum\limits_{i=1}^{5}\dfrac{5}{4^{i-3}}$

28. $1+(-4)+9+(-16) = \sum\limits_{i=1}^{4}(-1)^{i-1}i^2$

30. $S_2 = \sum\limits_{i=1}^{2} i(i-6)$

$= 1(1-6) + 2(2-6)$

$= -5 - 8$

$= -13$

32. $S_7 = \sum\limits_{i=1}^{7} (-1)^{i-1} = 1-1+1-1+1-1+1 = 1$

34. $S_5 = \sum\limits_{i=1}^{5} \dfrac{(-1)^i}{2i} = -\dfrac{1}{2} + \dfrac{1}{4} - \dfrac{1}{6} + \dfrac{1}{8} - \dfrac{1}{10} = -\dfrac{47}{120}$

36. $S_5 = \sum\limits_{i=1}^{5} (i-1)^2 = 0^2 + 1^2 + 2^2 + 3^2 + 4^2 = 30$

38. $S_3 = \sum\limits_{i=1}^{3} (i+4)^2 = 5^2 + 6^2 + 7^2 = 110$

40. 2, 3, 4, 5, 6, 7

$a_n = 1 + n$

$S_6 = \sum\limits_{i=1}^{6} (1+i) = 2+3+4+5+6+7 = 27$

The total number of surfers is 27.

42. $a_n = 100(2)^n$, where n represents the number of 6-hour periods.

$a_4 = 100(2)^4 = 100(16) = 1600$ bacteria

The number of bacteria present after 24 hours is 1600.

44. $a_3 = (3-1)(3+3) = 2(6) = 12$

There were 12 otters born in the third year.

$S_3 = \sum\limits_{i=1}^{3} [(i-1)(i+3)] = 0(4) + 1(5) + 2(6) = 17$

There were 17 otters born in the first three years.

46. $a_n = 200 - 6n$

2007: $a_1 = 200 - 6(1) = 194$

2008: $a_2 = 200 - 6(2) = 188$

2009: $a_3 = 200 - 6(3) = 182$

2010: $a_4 = 200 - 6(4) = 176$

The decrease in 2010 is 176 pairs.
The total decrease for the four-year period is
194 + 188 + 182 + 176 = 740 pairs of birds.

48. Job A: $S_5 = \sum\limits_{i=1}^{5} (20{,}000 + (i-1)1200) = 112{,}000$

Job B: $S_5 = \sum\limits_{i=1}^{5} (18{,}000 + (i-1)2500) = 115{,}000$

Job B pays \$3000 more over the next five years.

50. Answers may vary

52. $\dfrac{-3}{1 - \frac{1}{7}} = \dfrac{-3 \cdot 7}{\left(1 - \frac{1}{7}\right) \cdot 7} = \dfrac{-21}{7 - 1} = \dfrac{-21}{6} = -\dfrac{7}{2}$

54. $\dfrac{\frac{6}{11}}{1 - \frac{1}{10}} = \dfrac{\left(\frac{6}{11}\right) \cdot 110}{\left(1 - \frac{1}{10}\right) \cdot 110} = \dfrac{60}{110 - 11} = \dfrac{60}{99} = \dfrac{20}{33}$

56. $\dfrac{2(1-5^3)}{1-5} = \dfrac{2(-124)}{-4} = 62$

58. $\dfrac{12}{2}(2+19) = 6(21) = 126$

60. a. $\sum\limits_{i=1}^{6} 5i^3 = 5(1)^3 + 5(2)^3 + 5(3)^3 + 5(4)^3$

$+ 5(5)^3 + 5(6)^3$

$= 5 + 40 + 135 + 320 + 625 + 1080$

b. $5 \cdot \sum\limits_{i=1}^{6} i^3 = 5(1^3 + 2^3 + 3^3 + 4^3 + 5^3 + 6^3)$

$= 5(1 + 8 + 27 + 64 + 125 + 216)$

c. Answers may vary

d. True; answers may vary

Integrated Review

1. $a_n = n - 3$

$a_1 = 1 - 3 = -2$

$a_2 = 2 - 3 = -1$

$a_3 = 3 - 3 = 0$

$a_4 = 4 - 3 = 1$

$a_5 = 5 - 3 = 2$

Therefore, the first five terms are $-2, -1, 0, 1, 2$.

2. $a_n = \dfrac{7}{1+n}$

$a_1 = \dfrac{7}{1+1} = \dfrac{7}{2}$

$a_2 = \dfrac{7}{1+2} = \dfrac{7}{3}$

$a_3 = \dfrac{7}{1+3} = \dfrac{7}{4}$

$a_4 = \dfrac{7}{1+4} = \dfrac{7}{5}$

$a_5 = \dfrac{7}{1+5} = \dfrac{7}{6}$

The first five terms are $\dfrac{7}{2}, \dfrac{7}{3}, \dfrac{7}{4}, \dfrac{7}{5},$ and $\dfrac{7}{6}$.

3. $a_n = 3^{n-1}$

$a_1 = 3^{1-1} = 3^0 = 1$

$a_2 = 3^{2-1} = 3^1 = 3$

$a_3 = 3^{3-1} = 3^2 = 9$

$a_4 = 3^{4-1} = 3^3 = 27$

$a_5 = 3^{5-1} = 3^4 = 81$

The first five terms are 1, 3, 9, 27, and 81.

4. $a_n = n^2 - 5$

$a_1 = 1^2 - 5 = 1 - 5 = -4$

$a_2 = 2^2 - 5 = 4 - 5 = -1$

$a_3 = 3^2 - 5 = 9 - 5 = 4$

$a_4 = 4^2 - 5 = 16 - 5 = 11$

$a_5 = 5^2 - 5 = 25 - 5 = 20$

The first five terms are $-4, -1, 4, 11,$ and 20.

5. $(-2)^n; a_6$

$a_6 = (-2)^6 = 64$

6. $-n^2 + 2; a_4$

$a_4 = -(4)^2 + 2 = -16 + 2 = -14$

7. $\dfrac{(-1)^n}{n}; a_{40}$

$a_{40} = \dfrac{(-1)^{40}}{40} = \dfrac{1}{40}$

8. $\dfrac{(-1)^n}{2n}; a_{41}$

$a_{41} = \dfrac{(-1)^{41}}{2(41)} = \dfrac{-1}{82} = -\dfrac{1}{82}$

9. $a_1 = 7; d = -3$

$a_1 = 7$

$a_2 = 7 - 3 = 4$

$a_3 = 4 - 3 = 1$

$a_4 = 1 - 3 = -2$

$a_5 = -2 - 3 = -5$

The first five terms are 7, 4, 1, $-2, -5$.

10. $a_1 = -3; r = 5$

$a_1 = -3$

$a_2 = -3(5) = -15$

$a_3 = -15(5) = -75$

$a_4 = -75(5) = -375$

$a_5 = -375(5) = -1875$

The first five terms are $-3, -15, -75, -375, -1875$.

11. $a_1 = 45; r = \dfrac{1}{3}$

$a_1 = 45$

$a_2 = 45\left(\dfrac{1}{3}\right) = 15$

$a_3 = 15\left(\dfrac{1}{3}\right) = 5$

$a_4 = 5\left(\dfrac{1}{3}\right) = \dfrac{5}{3}$

$a_5 = \dfrac{5}{3}\left(\dfrac{1}{3}\right) = \dfrac{5}{9}$

The first five terms are $45, 15, 5, \dfrac{5}{3}, \dfrac{5}{9}$.

12. $a_1 = -12; d = 10$

$a_1 = -12$

$a_2 = -12 + 10 = -2$

$a_3 = -2 + 10 = 8$

$a_4 = 8 + 10 = 18$

$a_5 = 18 + 10 = 28$

The first five terms are $-12, -2, 8, 18, 28$.

13. $a_1 = 20; \ d = 9$

$a_n = a_1 + (n-1)d$

$a_{10} = 20 + (10-1)9$

$\quad = 20 + 81$

$\quad = 101$

14. $a_1 = 64; \ r = \dfrac{3}{4}$

$a_n = a_1 r^{n-1}$

$a_6 = 64\left(\dfrac{3}{4}\right)^{6-1}$

$\quad = 64\left(\dfrac{3}{4}\right)^5$

$\quad = 64\left(\dfrac{243}{1024}\right)$

$\quad = \dfrac{243}{16}$

15. $a_1 = 6; \ r = \dfrac{-12}{6} = -2$

$a_n = a_1 r^{n-1}$

$a_7 = 6(-2)^{7-1} = 6(-2)^6 = 6(64) = 384$

16. $a_1 = -100; \ d = -85 - (-100) = 15$

$a_n = a_1 + (n-1)d$

$a_{20} = -100 + (20-1)(15)$

$\quad = -100 + (19)(15)$

$\quad = -100 + 285$

$\quad = 185$

17. $a_4 = -5, \ a_{10} = -35$

$a_n = a_1 + (n-1)d$

$\begin{cases} a_4 = a_1 + (4-1)d \\ a_{10} = a_1 + (10-1)d \end{cases}$

$\begin{cases} -5 = a_1 + 3d \\ -35 = a_1 + 9d \end{cases}$

Multiply eq. 2 by -1, then add the equations.

$\begin{cases} \qquad -5 = a_1 + 3d \\ (-1)(-35) = -1(a_1 + 9d) \end{cases}$

$\begin{cases} -5 = a_1 + 3d \\ 35 = -a_1 - 9d \end{cases}$

$30 = -6d$

$-5 = d$

To find a_1, let $d = -5$ in

$-5 = a_1 + 3d$

$-5 = a_1 + 3(-5)$

$10 = a_1$

Thus, $a_1 = 10$ and $d = -5$, so

$a_n = 10 + (n-1)(-5) = -5n + 15$

$a_5 = -5(5) + 15 = -10$

18. $a_4 = 1; \ a_7 = \dfrac{1}{125}$

$a_n = a_1 r^{n-1}$

$a_4 = a_1 r^{4-1} \ \text{ so } \ 1 = a_1 r^3$

$a_7 = a_1 r^{71} \ \text{ so } \ \dfrac{1}{125} = a_1 r^6$

Since $a_1 r^6 = (a_1 r^3)r^3, \ \dfrac{1}{125} = 1 \cdot r^3$ and $r = \dfrac{1}{5}$.

$a_5 = a_4 \cdot r \ \text{ so } \ a_5 = 1 \cdot \dfrac{1}{5} = \dfrac{1}{5}$

19. $\displaystyle\sum_{i=1}^{4} 5i = 5(1) + 5(2) + 5(3) + 5(4)$

$\qquad\qquad = 5 + 10 + 15 + 20$

$\qquad\qquad = 50$

20. $\displaystyle\sum_{i=1}^{7} (3i + 2)$

$= (3(1) + 2) + (3(2) + 2) + (3(3) + 2)$

$\quad + (3(4) + 2) + (3(5) + 2) + (3(6) + 2)$

$\quad + (3(7) + 2)$

$= 5 + 8 + 11 + 14 + 17 + 20 + 23$

$= 98$

21. $\displaystyle\sum_{i=3}^{7} 2^{i-4}$

$= 2^{3-4} + 2^{4-4} + 2^{5-4} + 2^{6-4} + 2^{7-4}$

$= 2^{-1} + 2^0 + 2^1 + 2^2 + 2^3$

$= \dfrac{1}{2} + 1 + 2 + 4 + 8$

$= 15\dfrac{1}{2}$

$= \dfrac{31}{2}$

22. $\displaystyle\sum_{i=2}^{5}\frac{i}{i+1} = \frac{2}{2+1}+\frac{3}{3+1}+\frac{4}{4+1}+\frac{5}{5+1}$

$\qquad = \frac{2}{3}+\frac{3}{4}+\frac{4}{5}+\frac{5}{6}$

$\qquad = \frac{61}{20}$

23. $S_3 = \displaystyle\sum_{i=1}^{3} i(i-4)$

$\qquad = 1(1-4)+2(2-4)+3(3-4)$

$\qquad = -3-4-3$

$\qquad = -10$

24. $S_{10} = \displaystyle\sum_{i=1}^{10}(-1)^i(i+1)$

$\qquad = (-1)^1(1+1)+(-1)^2(2+1)$

$\qquad\quad +(-1)^3(3+1)+(-1)^4(4+1)$

$\qquad\quad +(-1)^5(5+1)+(-1)^6(6+1)$

$\qquad\quad +(-1)^7(7+1)+(-1)^8(8+1)$

$\qquad\quad +(-1)^9(9+1)+(-1)^{10}(10+1)$

$\qquad = -2+3-4+5-6+7-8+9-10+11$

$\qquad = 5$

Section 11.4

Practice Problems

1. $2, 9, 16, 23, 30$
Use the formula for S_n of an arithmetic sequence, replacing n with 5, a_1 with 2, and a_n with 30.

$S_n = \dfrac{n}{2}(a_1+a_n)$

$S_5 = \dfrac{5}{2}(2+30) = \dfrac{5}{2}(32) = 80$

2. Because 1, 2, 3, …, 50 is an arithmetic sequence, use the formula for S_n with $n = 50$, $a_1 = 1$, and $a_n = 50$.

$S_n = \dfrac{n}{2}(a_1+a_n)$

$S_5 = \dfrac{50}{2}(1+50) = 25(51) = 1275$

3. The list 6, 7, …, 15 is the first 10 terms of an arithmetic sequence. Use the formula for S_n with $n = 10$, $a_1 = 6$, and $a_n = 15$.

$S_{10} = \dfrac{10}{2}(6+15) = 5(21) = 105$

There are a total of 105 blocks of ice.

4. $32, 8, 2, \dfrac{1}{2}, \dfrac{1}{8}$

Use the formula for the partial sum S_n of the terms of a geometric sequence. Here, $n = 5$, the first term $a_1 = 32$, and the common ratio $r = \dfrac{1}{4}$.

$S_n = \dfrac{a_1(1-r^n)}{1-r}$

$S_5 = \dfrac{32\left[1-\left(\frac{1}{4}\right)^5\right]}{1-\frac{1}{4}}$

$\quad = \dfrac{32\left(1-\frac{1}{1024}\right)}{\frac{3}{4}}$

$\quad = \dfrac{32-\frac{1}{32}}{\frac{3}{4}}$

$\quad = \dfrac{\frac{1023}{32}}{\frac{3}{4}}$

$\quad = \dfrac{1023}{32}\cdot\dfrac{4}{3}$

$\quad = \dfrac{341}{8}$

$\quad = 42\dfrac{5}{8}$

5. The donations are modeled by the first seven terms of a geometric sequence. Evaluate S_n when $n = 7$, $a_1 = 250{,}000$, and $r = 0.8$.

$S_7 = \dfrac{250{,}000[1-(0.8)^7]}{1-0.8} = 987{,}856$

The total amount donated during the seven years is \$987,856.

6. $7, \dfrac{7}{4}, \dfrac{7}{16}, \dfrac{7}{64}, \ldots$

For this geometric sequence $r = \dfrac{1}{4}$. Since $|r| < 1$, use the formula for S_∞ of a geometric sequence with $a_1 = 7$ and $r = \dfrac{1}{4}$.

$S_\infty = \dfrac{a_1}{1-r} = \dfrac{7}{1-\frac{1}{4}} = \dfrac{7}{\frac{3}{4}} = \dfrac{28}{3} = 9\dfrac{1}{3}$

7. We must find the sum of the terms of an infinite geometric sequence whose first term, a_1, is 36 and whose common ratio, r, is 0.96. Since $|r| < 1$, we may use the formula for S_∞.

$$S_\infty = \frac{a_1}{1-r} = \frac{36}{1-0.96} = \frac{36}{0.04} = 900$$

The ball travels a total distance of 900 inches before it comes to a rest.

Vocabulary and Readiness Check

1. Each term after the first is 5 more than the preceding term; the sequence is <u>arithmetic</u>.

2. Each term after the first is 2 times the preceding term; the sequence is <u>geometric</u>.

3. Each term after the first is −3 times the preceding term; the sequence is <u>geometric</u>.

4. Each term after the first is 2 more than the preceding term; the sequence is <u>arithmetic</u>.

5. Each term after the first is 7 more than the preceding term; the sequence is <u>arithmetic</u>.

6. Each term after the first is −1 times the preceding term; the sequence is <u>geometric</u>.

Exercise Set 11.4

2. $d = -4$ and $a_7 = -7 + (7-1)(-4) = -31$

$$S_7 = \frac{7}{2}[-7 + (-31)] = \frac{7}{2}(-38) = -133$$

4. $n = 8, a_1 = -1, r = -2$

$$S_8 = \frac{-1\left[1 - (-2)^8\right]}{1 - (-2)} = \frac{-1(-255)}{3} = 85$$

6. $n = 4, a_1 = -4, a_4 = -16$

$$S_4 = \frac{4}{2}[-4 + (-16)] = 2(-20) = -40$$

8. $n = 5, a_1 = \frac{1}{3}, r = -2$

$$S_5 = \frac{\frac{1}{3}[1 - (-2)^5]}{1 - (-2)} = \frac{\frac{1}{3}(33)}{3} = \frac{11}{3}$$

10. $n = 8, a_1 = -1, a_8 = -8$

$$S_8 = \frac{8}{2}[-1 + (-8)] = 4(-9) = -36$$

12. $n = 5, a_1 = -1, a_5 = -9$

$$S_5 = \frac{5}{2}[-1 + (-9)] = \frac{5}{2}(-10) = -25$$

14. $a_1 = 45, r = \frac{1}{3}$

$$S_\infty = \frac{45}{1 - \frac{1}{3}} = \frac{45}{\frac{2}{3}} = 45 \cdot \frac{3}{2} = 67.5$$

16. $a_1 = \frac{3}{5}, r = \frac{1}{4}$

$$S_\infty = \frac{\frac{3}{5}}{1 - \frac{1}{4}} = \frac{\frac{3}{5}}{\frac{3}{4}} = \frac{3}{5} \cdot \frac{4}{3} = \frac{4}{5}$$

18. $a_1 = -16, r = \frac{1}{4}$

$$S_\infty = \frac{-16}{1 - \frac{1}{4}} = \frac{-16}{\frac{3}{4}} = -16 \cdot \frac{4}{3} = -\frac{64}{3}$$

20. $a_1 = -3, r = -\frac{1}{5}$

$$S_\infty = \frac{-3}{1 - \left(-\frac{1}{5}\right)} = \frac{-3}{\frac{6}{5}} = -3 \cdot \frac{5}{6} = -\frac{5}{2}$$

22. $a_1 = 6, r = -\frac{2}{3}$

$$S_\infty = \frac{6}{1 - \left(-\frac{2}{3}\right)} = \frac{6}{\frac{5}{3}} = 6 \cdot \frac{3}{5} = \frac{18}{5}$$

24. $S_{12} = \frac{12}{2}(a_1 + a_{12})$
$$= 6[-3 + (-113)]$$
$$= 6(-116)$$
$$= -696$$

26. $a_1 = -2, \ r = 3$

$$S_5 = \frac{a_1(1 - r^5)}{1 - r}$$
$$= \frac{-2(1 - 3^5)}{1 - 3}$$
$$= \frac{-2(-242)}{-2}$$
$$= -242$$

28. $a_1 = -\dfrac{1}{4}, r = 3$

$$S_4 = \dfrac{a_1(1-r^4)}{1-r}$$
$$= \dfrac{-\frac{1}{4}(1-3^4)}{1-3}$$
$$= \dfrac{-\frac{1}{4}(-80)}{-2}$$
$$= \dfrac{20}{-2}$$
$$= -10$$

30. $S_{15} = \dfrac{15}{2}(a_1 + a_{15})$
$$= \dfrac{15}{2}[-5 + (-61)]$$
$$= \dfrac{15}{2}(-66)$$
$$= -495$$

32. $S_{18} = \dfrac{18}{2}(a_1 + a_{18})$
$$= \dfrac{18}{2}\left(10 + \dfrac{3}{2}\right)$$
$$= 9\left(\dfrac{23}{2}\right)$$
$$= \dfrac{207}{2}$$

34. $3, $2.90, $2.80, $2.70, $2.60
$d = -0.10$ and $a_9 = 3 + 8(-0.10) = 2.20$
$$S_9 = \dfrac{9}{2}(3 + 2.20) = 4.5(5.20) = 23.40$$

The total cost of sending a nine-page document is $23.40.

36. $a_1 = 1, a_{15} = 15$
$$S_{15} = \dfrac{15}{2}(1 + 15) = \dfrac{15}{2}(16) = 120 \text{ points}$$

38. $a_1 = 16, d = 32$
$$a_8 = 16 + (8-1)(32) = 240$$
$$S_8 = \dfrac{8}{2}(16 + 240) = 4(256) = 1024$$

The parachutist drops 240 feet during the eighth second, and a total of 1024 feet during the first 8 seconds.

40. $a_1 = 5, r = 2$
$$a_6 = 5(2)^{6-1} = 5(2)^5 = 160$$
$$S_6 = \dfrac{5(1-2^6)}{1-2} = \dfrac{5(-63)}{-1} = 315$$

She lost $160 on the sixth bet and a total of $315 on these six bets.

42. $a_1 = 300, r = \dfrac{2}{5}$
$$S_\infty = \dfrac{a_1}{1-r} = \dfrac{300}{1-\frac{2}{5}} = \dfrac{300}{\frac{3}{5}} = 500$$

It makes 500 revolutions before coming to rest.

44. $a_1 = 250, d = 50$
$$a_{22} = 250 + 21(50) = 1300$$
$$S_{22} = \dfrac{22}{2}(250 + 1300)$$
$$= 11(1550)$$
$$= 17,050$$

He deposited $1300 on the twenty-first birthday. The total deposited over the 21 years was $17,050.

46. $a_1 = 6400, r = \dfrac{1}{4}$
$$S_5 = \dfrac{a_1(1-r^5)}{1-r}$$
$$= \dfrac{6400\left(1-\left(\frac{1}{4}\right)^5\right)}{1-\frac{1}{4}}$$
$$= \dfrac{6400\left(1-\frac{1}{1024}\right)}{\frac{3}{4}}$$
$$= 8525$$

8525 weevils were killed over the five days.

48. $a_1 = 80, d = 40;\ a_5 = 80 + 4(40) = 240$
$$S_5 = \dfrac{5}{2}(80 + 240) = \dfrac{5}{2}(320) = 800$$

They attracted 800 new customers during the first five days.

50. $8 \cdot 7 \cdot 6 \cdot 5 \cdot 4 \cdot 3 \cdot 2 \cdot 1 = 40,320$

52. $\dfrac{5 \cdot 4 \cdot 3 \cdot 2 \cdot 1}{3 \cdot 2 \cdot 1} = 5 \cdot 4 = 20$

54. $(x-2)^2 = x^2 - 2 \cdot x \cdot 2 + 2^2$
$$= x^2 - 4x + 4$$

56. $(3x+2)^3 = (3x+2)(3x+2)^2$

$\qquad = (3x+2)(9x^2+12x+4)$

$\qquad = 27x^3 +36x^2 +12x+18x^2 +24x+8$

$\qquad = 27x^3 +54x^2 +36x+8$

58. $0.5\overline{454} = \dfrac{54}{100} + \dfrac{54}{10,000} + \dfrac{54}{1,000,000} + \cdots$

$\qquad a_1 = \dfrac{54}{100}, r = \dfrac{1}{100}$

$\qquad S_\infty = \dfrac{\frac{54}{100}}{1-\frac{1}{100}} = \dfrac{\frac{54}{100}}{\frac{99}{100}} = \dfrac{54}{99} = \dfrac{6}{11}$

60. Answers may vary

Section 11.5

Practice Problems

1. $(p+r)^7$

The $n = 7$ row of Pascal's triangle is

1   7   21   35   35   21   7   1

Using the $n = 7$ row of Pascal's triangle as the coefficients, $(p + r)^7$ can be expanded as

$p^7 +7p^6r+21p^5r^2 +35p^4r^3 +35p^3r^4 +21p^2r^5 +7pr^6 +r^7$

2. a. $\dfrac{6!}{7!} = \dfrac{6\cdot 5\cdot 4\cdot 3\cdot 2\cdot 1}{7\cdot 6\cdot 5\cdot 4\cdot 3\cdot 2\cdot 1} = \dfrac{1}{7}$

b. $\dfrac{8!}{4!2!} = \dfrac{8\cdot 7\cdot 6\cdot 5\cdot 4!}{4!\,\cdot 2\cdot 1}$

$\qquad\quad = \dfrac{8\cdot 7\cdot 6\cdot 5}{2\cdot 1}$

$\qquad\quad = 4\cdot 7\cdot 6\cdot 5$

$\qquad\quad = 840$

c. $\dfrac{5!}{4!1!} = \dfrac{5\cdot 4\cdot 3\cdot 2\cdot 1}{4\cdot 3\cdot 2\cdot 1\cdot 1} = 5$

d. $\dfrac{9!}{9!0!} = \dfrac{9!}{9!\cdot 1} = 1$

3. $(a+b)^9$

Let $n = 9$ in the binomial formula.

$(a+b)^9 = a^9 + \dfrac{9}{1!}a^8b+ \dfrac{9\cdot 8}{2!}a^7b^2 + \dfrac{9\cdot 8\cdot 7}{3!}a^6b^3 + \dfrac{9\cdot 8\cdot 7\cdot 6}{4!}a^5b^4 + \dfrac{9\cdot 8\cdot 7\cdot 6\cdot 5}{5!}a^4b^5 + \dfrac{9\cdot 8\cdot 7\cdot 6\cdot 5\cdot 4}{6!}a^3b^6$

$\qquad\qquad + \dfrac{9\cdot 8\cdot 7\cdot 6\cdot 5\cdot 4\cdot 3}{7!}a^2b^7 + \dfrac{9\cdot 8\cdot 7\cdot 6\cdot 5\cdot 4\cdot 3\cdot 2}{8!}ab^8 + b^9$

$\qquad = a^9 +9a^8b+36a^7b^2 +84a^6b^3 +126a^5b^4 +126a^4b^5 +84a^3b^6 +36a^2b^7 +9ab^8 +b^9$

4. $(a+5)^3$

Replace b with 5 in the binomial formula.

$$(a+5)^3 = a^3 + \frac{3}{1!}a^2(5) + \frac{3\cdot 2}{2!}a(5)^2 + (5)^3$$
$$= a^3 + 3a^2(5) + 3a(25) + 125$$
$$= a^3 + 15a^2 + 75a + 125$$

5. $(3x-2y)^3$

Let $a = 3x$ and $b = -2y$ in the binomial formula.

$$(3x-2y)^3 = (3x)^3 + \frac{3}{1!}(3x)^2(-2y) + \frac{3\cdot 2}{2!}(3x)(-2y)^2 + (-2y)^3$$
$$= 27x^3 + 3(9x^2)(-2y) + 3(3x)(4y^2) - 8y^3$$
$$= 27x^3 - 54x^2y + 36xy^2 - 8y^3$$

6. $(x-4y)^{11}$

Use the formula with $n = 11$, $a = x$, $b = -4y$, and $r + 1 = 7$. Notice that, since $r + 1 = 7$, $r = 6$.

$$\frac{n!}{r!(n-r)!}a^{n-r}b^r = \frac{11!}{6!5!}x^5(-4y)^6 = 462x^5(4096y^6) = 1{,}892{,}352x^5y^6$$

Vocabulary and Readiness Check

1. $0! = \underline{1}$

2. $1! = \underline{1}$

3. $4! = 4 \cdot 3 \cdot 2 \cdot 1 = \underline{24}$

4. $2! = 2 \cdot 1 = \underline{2}$

5. $3!0! = 3 \cdot 2 \cdot 1 \cdot 1 = \underline{6}$

6. $0!2! = 1 \cdot 2 \cdot 1 = \underline{2}$

Exercise Set 11.5

2. $(x+y)^4 = x^4 + 4x^3y + 6x^2y^2 + 4xy^3 + y^4$

4. $(a+b)^6 = a^6 + 6a^5b + 15a^4b^2 + 20a^3b^3 + 15a^2b^4 + 6ab^5 + b^6$

6. $(q-r)^7 = q^7 - 7q^6r + 21q^5r^2 - 35q^4r^3 + 35q^3r^4 - 21q^2r^5 + 7qr^6 - r^7$

8. 1 8 28 56 70 56 28 8 1

10. $\dfrac{6!}{0!} = \dfrac{6\cdot 5\cdot 4\cdot 3\cdot 2\cdot 1}{1} = 720$

12. $\dfrac{8!}{5!} = \dfrac{8\cdot 7\cdot 6\cdot 5!}{5!} = 8\cdot 7\cdot 6 = 336$

14. $\dfrac{9!}{5!3!} = \dfrac{9 \cdot 8 \cdot 7 \cdot 6 \cdot 5!}{5!3!} = \dfrac{9 \cdot 8 \cdot 7 \cdot 6}{3 \cdot 2 \cdot 1} = 9 \cdot 8 \cdot 7 = 504$

16. $\dfrac{10!}{4!6!} = \dfrac{10 \cdot 9 \cdot 8 \cdot 7 \cdot 6!}{4!6!} = \dfrac{10 \cdot 9 \cdot 8 \cdot 7}{4 \cdot 3 \cdot 2 \cdot 1} = 10 \cdot 3 \cdot 7 = 210$

18. Let $a = x, b = y,$ and $n = 8$ in the binomial theorem.

$$(x+y)^8 = x^8 + \frac{8}{1!}x^7 y + \frac{8 \cdot 7}{2!}x^6 y^2 + \frac{8 \cdot 7 \cdot 6}{3!}x^5 y^3 + \frac{8 \cdot 7 \cdot 6 \cdot 5}{4!}x^4 y^4 + \frac{8 \cdot 7 \cdot 6 \cdot 5 \cdot 4}{5!}x^3 y^5 + \frac{8 \cdot 7 \cdot 6 \cdot 5 \cdot 4 \cdot 3}{6!}x^2 y^6$$
$$+ \frac{8 \cdot 7 \cdot 6 \cdot 5 \cdot 4 \cdot 3 \cdot 2}{7!}xy^7 + y^8$$
$$= x^8 + 8x^7 y + 28x^6 y^2 + 56x^5 y^3 + 70x^4 y^4 + 56x^3 y^5 + 28x^2 y^6 + 8xy^7 + y^8$$

20. Let $a = x, b = 3y,$ and $n = 6$ in the binomial theorem.

$$(x+3y)^6 = x^6 + \frac{6}{1!}x^5(3y) + \frac{6 \cdot 5}{2!}x^4(3y)^2 + \frac{6 \cdot 5 \cdot 4}{3!}x^3(3y)^3 + \frac{6 \cdot 5 \cdot 4 \cdot 3}{4!}x^2(3y)^4 + \frac{6 \cdot 5 \cdot 4 \cdot 3 \cdot 2}{5!}x(3y)^5 + (3y)^6$$
$$= x^6 + 18x^5 y + 135x^4 y^2 + 540x^3 y^3 + 1215x^2 y^4 + 1458xy^5 + 729y^6$$

22. Let $a = b, b = c,$ and $n = 6$ in the binomial theorem.

$$(b+c)^6 = b^6 + \frac{6}{1!}b^5 c + \frac{6 \cdot 5}{2!}b^4 c^2 + \frac{6 \cdot 5 \cdot 4}{3!}b^3 c^3 + \frac{6 \cdot 5 \cdot 4 \cdot 3}{4!}b^2 c^4 + \frac{6 \cdot 5 \cdot 4 \cdot 3 \cdot 2}{5!}bc^5 + c^6$$
$$= b^6 + 6b^5 c + 15b^4 c^2 + 20b^3 c^3 + 15b^2 c^4 + 6bc^5 + c^6$$

24. Let $a = 3m, b = n,$ and $n = 4$ in the binomial theorem.

$$(3m+n)^4 = (3m)^4 + \frac{4}{1!}(3m)^3 n + \frac{4 \cdot 3}{2!}(3m)^2 n^2 + \frac{4 \cdot 3 \cdot 2}{3!}(3m)n^3 + n^4$$
$$= 81m^4 + 108m^3 n + 54m^2 n^2 + 12mn^3 + n^4$$

26. Let $a = m, b = -4,$ and $n = 6$ in the binomial theorem.

$$(m-4)^6 = m^6 + \frac{6}{1!}m^5(-4) + \frac{6 \cdot 5}{2!}m^4(-4)^2 + \frac{6 \cdot 5 \cdot 4}{3!}m^3(-4)^3 + \frac{6 \cdot 5 \cdot 4 \cdot 3}{4!}m^2(-4)^4$$
$$+ \frac{6 \cdot 5 \cdot 4 \cdot 3 \cdot 2}{5!}m(-4)^5 + (-4)^6$$
$$= m^6 - 24m^5 + 240m^4 - 1280m^3 + 3840m^2 - 6144m + 4096$$

28. Let $a = 4, b = -3x,$ and $n = 5$ in the binomial theorem.

$$(4-3x)^5 = 4^5 + \frac{5}{1!}(4)^4(-3x) + \frac{5 \cdot 4}{2!}(4)^3(-3x)^2 + \frac{5 \cdot 4 \cdot 3}{3!}(4)^2(-3x)^3 + \frac{5 \cdot 4 \cdot 3 \cdot 2}{4!}(4)(-3x)^4 + (-3x)^5$$
$$= 1024 - 3840x + 5760x^2 - 4320x^3 + 1620x^4 - 243x^5$$

30. Let $a = 3, b = 2a,$ and $n = 4$ in the binomial theorem.

$$(3+2a)^4 = 3^4 + \frac{4}{1!}(3)^3(2a) + \frac{4 \cdot 3}{2!}(3)^2(2a)^2 + \frac{4 \cdot 3 \cdot 2}{3!}(3)(2a)^3 + (2a)^4$$
$$= 81 + 216a + 216a^2 + 96a^3 + 16a^4$$

32. Let $a = x, b = -y, r = 3,$ and $n = 6$ in the formula given.

$$\frac{6!}{3!3!}x^{6-3}(-y)^3 = -20x^3y^3$$

34. Let $a = 5x, b = -y, r = 9,$ and $n = 9$ in the formula given.

$$\frac{9!}{9!0!}x^{9-9}(-y)^9 = -y^9$$

36. Let $a = 3q, b = -7r, r = 0,$ and $n = 6$ in the formula given.

$$\frac{6!}{0!6!}(3q)^{6-0}(-7r)^0 = 729q^6$$

38. Let $a = a, b = b, r = 3,$ and $n = 8$ in the formula given.

$$\frac{8!}{3!5!}a^{8-3}b^3 = 56a^5b^3$$

40. Let $a = m, b = 5n, r = 2,$ and $n = 7$ in the formula given.

$$\frac{7!}{2!5!}m^{7-2}(5n)^2 = 525m^5n^2$$

42. $g(x) = 3(x-1)^2$

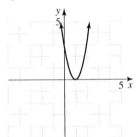

Not one-to-one

44. $F(x) = -2$

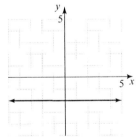

Not one-to-one

46. $h(x) = -(x+1)^2 - 4$

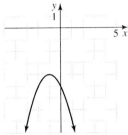

Not one-to-one

48. Let $a = \sqrt{x}, b = -\sqrt{5}, r = 2, n = 6.$

$$\frac{6!}{2!4!}\left(\sqrt{x}\right)^4\left(-\sqrt{5}\right)^2 = 75x^2$$

50. $\begin{pmatrix} 4 \\ 3 \end{pmatrix} = \frac{4!}{3!1!} = \frac{4 \cdot 3 \cdot 2 \cdot 1}{(3 \cdot 2 \cdot 1) \cdot 1} = \frac{4}{1} = 4$

52. $\begin{pmatrix} 12 \\ 11 \end{pmatrix} = \frac{12!}{11!1!} = \frac{12 \cdot 11!}{11! \cdot 1} = \frac{12}{1} = 12$

Chapter 11 Vocabulary Check

1. A <u>finite sequence</u> is a function whose domain is the set of natural numbers $\{1, 2, 3, ..., n\}$, where n is some natural number.

2. The <u>factorial of n</u>, written $n!$, is the product of the first n consecutive natural numbers.

3. An <u>infinite sequence</u> is a function whose domain is the set of natural numbers.

4. A <u>geometric sequence</u> is a sequence in which each term (after the first) is obtained by multiplying the preceding term by a constant amount r. The constant r is called the <u>common ratio</u> of the sequence.

5. A sum of the terms of a sequence is called a <u>series</u>.

6. The nth term of the sequence a_n is called the <u>general term</u>.

7. An <u>arithmetic sequence</u> is a sequence in which each term (after the first) differs from the preceding term by a constant amount d. The constant d is called the <u>common difference</u> of the sequence.

8. A triangle array of the coefficients of the terms of the expansions of $(a+b)^n$ is called <u>Pascal's triangle</u>.

Chapter 11 Review

1. $a_n = -3n^2$

   $a_1 = -3(1)^2 = -3$
   $a_2 = -3(2)^2 = -12$
   $a_3 = -3(3)^2 = -27$
   $a_4 = -3(4)^2 = -48$
   $a_5 = -3(5)^2 = -75$

2. $a_n = n^2 + 2n$

   $a_1 = 1^2 + 2(1) = 3$
   $a_2 = 2^2 + 2(2) = 8$
   $a_3 = 3^2 + 2(3) = 15$
   $a_4 = 4^2 + 2(4) = 24$
   $a_5 = 5^2 + 2(5) = 35$

3. $a_n = \dfrac{(-1)^n}{100}$

   $a_{100} = \dfrac{(-1)^{100}}{100} = \dfrac{1}{100}$

4. $a_n = \dfrac{2n}{(-1)^2}$

   $a_{50} = \dfrac{2(50)}{(-1)^2} = 100$

5. $\dfrac{1}{6\cdot 1}, \dfrac{1}{6\cdot 2}, \dfrac{1}{6\cdot 3}, \dots$

   In general, $a_n = \dfrac{1}{6n}$.

6. $-1, 4, -9, 16, \dots$

   $a_n = (-1)^n n^2$

7. $a_n = 32n - 16$

   $a_5 = 32(5) - 16 = 144$ feet
   $a_6 = 32(6) - 16 = 176$ feet
   $a_7 = 32(7) - 16 = 208$ feet

8. $a_n = 100(2)^{n-1}$

   $10,000 = 100(2)^{n-1}$
   $100 = 2^{n-1}$
   $\log 100 = (n-1)\log 2$
   $n = \dfrac{\log 100}{\log 2} + 1 \approx 7.6$

   Eighth day culture will be at least 10,000. Since $n = 1$ corresponds to the end of the first day, the original amount corresponds to $n = 0$.

   $a_0 = 100(2)^{-1} = 100\left(\dfrac{1}{2}\right) = 50$

   The original measure of the culture was 50.

9. 2006: $a_1 = 660,000$

   2007: $a_2 = 660,000(2) = 1,320,000$
   2008: $a_3 = 1,320,000(2) = 2,640,000$
   2009: $a_4 = 2,640,000(2) = 5,280,000$
   2010: $a_5 = 5,280,000(2) = 10,560,000$

   There will be 10,560,000 acres of infested trees in 2010.

10. $a_n = 50 + (n-1)8$

    $a_1 = 50$
    $a_2 = 50 + 8 = 58$
    $a_3 = 50 + 2(8) = 66$
    $a_4 = 50 + 3(8) = 74$
    $a_5 = 50 + 4(8) = 82$
    $a_6 = 50 + 5(8) = 90$
    $a_7 = 50 + 6(8) = 98$
    $a_8 = 50 + 7(8) = 106$
    $a_9 = 50 + 8(8) = 114$
    $a_{10} = 50 + 9(8) = 122$

    There are 122 seats in the tenth row.

11. $a_1 = -2, \; r = \dfrac{2}{3}$

    $a_1 = -2$

    $a_2 = -2\left(\dfrac{2}{3}\right) = -\dfrac{4}{3}$

    $a_3 = \left(-\dfrac{4}{3}\right)\left(\dfrac{2}{3}\right) = -\dfrac{8}{9}$

    $a_4 = \left(-\dfrac{8}{9}\right)\left(\dfrac{2}{3}\right) = -\dfrac{16}{27}$

    $a_5 = \left(-\dfrac{16}{27}\right)\left(\dfrac{2}{3}\right) = -\dfrac{32}{81}$

12. $a_n = 12 + (n-1)(-1.5)$

$a_1 = 12$

$a_2 = 12 + (1)(-1.5) = 10.5$

$a_3 = 12 + 2(-1.5) = 9$

$a_4 = 12 + 3(-1.5) = 7.5$

$a_5 = 12 + 4(-1.5) = 6$

13. $a_n = -5 + (n-1)^4$

$a_{30} = 5 + (30-1)4 = 111$

14. $a_n = 2 + (n-1)\dfrac{3}{4}$

$a_{11} = 2 + 10\left(\dfrac{3}{4}\right) = \dfrac{19}{2}$

15. 12, 7, 2,...

$a_1 = 12,\ d = -5,\ n = 20$

$a_{20} = 12 + (20-1)(-5) = -83$

16. $a_n = a_1 r^{n-1},\ a_1 = 4,\ r = \dfrac{3}{2}$

$a_6 = 4\left(\dfrac{3}{2}\right)^{6-1} = \dfrac{243}{8}$

17. $a_4 = 18,\ a_{20} = 98$

$\begin{cases} a_4 = a_1 + (4-1)d \\ a_{20} = a_1 + (20-1)d \end{cases}$

$\begin{cases} 18 = a_1 + 3d \\ 98 = a_1 + 19d \end{cases}$

$\begin{cases} -18 = -a_1 - 3d \\ \ \ 98 = a_1 + 19d \end{cases}$

Adding yields $80 = 16d$ or $d = 5$.

Then $a_1 = 18 - 3(5) = 3$.

18. $a_3 = -48,\ a_4 = 192$

$r = \dfrac{a_4}{a_3} = \dfrac{192}{-48} = -4$

$a_3 = a_1 r^{3-1}$

$-48 = a_1(-4)^2$

$-48 = 16a_1$

$-3 = a_1$

$r = -4,\ a_1 = -3$

19. $\dfrac{3}{10},\ \dfrac{3}{10^2},\ \dfrac{3}{10^3}, \dots$

In general, $a_n = \dfrac{3}{10^n}$

20. 50, 58, 66, ...

$a_n = 50 + (n-1)8$ or $a_n = 42 + 8n$

21. $\dfrac{8}{3}$, 4, 6, ...

Geometric; $a_1 = \dfrac{8}{3}$,

$r = \dfrac{4}{\frac{8}{3}} = 4 \cdot \dfrac{3}{8} = \dfrac{12}{8} = \dfrac{3}{2}$

22. $-10.5,\ -6.1,\ -1.7$

Arithmetic; $a_1 = -10.5$,

$d = -6.1 - (-10.5) = 4.4$

23. $7x,\ -14x,\ 28x$

Geometric; $a_1 = 7x,\ r = -2$

24. neither

25. $a_1 = 8,\ r = 0.75$

$a_1 = 8$

$a_2 = 8(0.75) = 6$

$a_3 = 8(0.75)^2 = 4.5$

$a_4 = 8(0.75)^3 \approx 3.4$

$a_5 = 8(0.75)^4 \approx 2.5$

$a_6 = 8(0.75)^5 \approx 1.9$

Yes, a ball that rebounds to a height of 2.5 feet after the fifth bounce is good, since $2.5 \geq 1.9$.

26. $a_1 = 25,\ d = -4$

$a_n = a_1 + (n-1)d$

$a_n = 25 + (n-1)(-4) = 29 - 4n$

$a_7 = 25 + 6(-4) = 1$

Continuing the progression as far as possible leaves 1 can in the top row.

27. $a_1 = 1,\ r = 2$

$a_n = 2^{n-1}$

$a_{10} = 2^9 = 512$

$a_{30} = 2^{29} = 536{,}870{,}912$

You save \$512 on the tenth day and \$536,870,912 on the thirtieth day.

28. $a_n = a_1 r^{n-1}$, $a_1 = 30$, $r = 0.7$

$a_5 = 30(0.7)^4 = 7.203$

The length is 7.203 inches on the fifth swing.

29. $a_1 = 900$, $d = 150$

$a_n = 900 + (n-1)150 = 150_n + 750$

$a_6 = 900 + (6-1)150 = 1650$

Her salary is \$1650 per month at the end of training.

30. $\dfrac{1}{512}, \dfrac{1}{256}, \dfrac{1}{128}, \ldots$

first fold: $a_1 = \dfrac{1}{256}$, $r = 2$

$a_{15} = \dfrac{1}{256}(2)^{15-1} = 64$

After 15 folds, the thickness is 64 inches.

31. $\displaystyle\sum_{i=1}^{5}(2i-1) = [2(1)-1] + [2(2)-1] + [2(3)-1]$

$\qquad\qquad\qquad + [2(4)-1] + [2(5)-1]$

$\qquad\qquad = 1 + 3 + 5 + 7 + 9$

$\qquad\qquad = 25$

32. $\displaystyle\sum_{i=1}^{5} i(i+2) = 1(1+2) + 2(2+2) + 3(3+2)$

$\qquad\qquad\qquad + 4(4+2) + 5(5+2)$

$\qquad\qquad = 3 + 8 + 15 + 24 + 35$

$\qquad\qquad = 85$

33. $\displaystyle\sum_{i=2}^{4} \dfrac{(-1)^i}{2i} = \dfrac{(-1)^2}{2(2)} + \dfrac{(-1)^3}{2(3)} + \dfrac{(-1)^4}{2(4)}$

$\qquad\qquad = \dfrac{1}{4} - \dfrac{1}{6} + \dfrac{1}{8}$

$\qquad\qquad = \dfrac{5}{24}$

34. $\displaystyle\sum_{i=3}^{5} 5(-1)^{i-1} = 5(-1)^{3-1} + 5(-1)^{4-1} + 5(-1)^{5-1}$

$\qquad\qquad\qquad = 5(1) + 5(-1) + 5(1)$

$\qquad\qquad\qquad = 5 - 5 + 5$

$\qquad\qquad\qquad = 5$

35. $a_n = (n-3)(n+2)$

$S_4 = \displaystyle\sum_{i=1}^{4}(i-3)(i+2)$

$\quad = (1-3)(1+2) + (2-3)(2+2)$

$\qquad\quad + (3-3)(3+2) + (4-3)(4+2)$

$\quad = -6 - 4 + 0 + 6$

$\quad = -4$

36. $a_n = n^2$

$S_6 = \displaystyle\sum_{i=1}^{6} i^2$

$\quad = (1)^2 + (2)^2 + (3)^2 + (4)^2 + (5)^2 + (6)^2$

$\quad = 91$

37. $a_n = -8 + (n-1)3 = 3n - 11$

$S_5 = \displaystyle\sum_{i=1}^{5}(3i - 11)$

$\quad = [3(1)-11] + [3(2)-11] + [3(3)-11]$

$\qquad\quad + [3(4)-11] + [3(5)-11]$

$\quad = -8 - 5 - 2 + 1 + 4$

$\quad = -10$

38. $a_n = 5(4)^{n-1}$

$S_3 = \displaystyle\sum_{i=1}^{3} 5(4)^{i-1} = 5(4)^0 + 5(4)^1 + 5(4)^2 = 105$

39. $1 + 3 + 9 + 27 + 81 + 243$

$= 3^0 + 3^1 + 3^2 + 3^3 + 3^4 + 3^5$

$= \displaystyle\sum_{i=1}^{6} 3^{i-1}$

40. $6 + 2 + (-2) + (-6) + (-10) + (-14) + (-18)$

$a_1 = 6$, $d = -4$

$a_n = 6 + (n-1)(-4)$

$\displaystyle\sum_{i=1}^{7}[6 + (i-1)(-4)]$

41. $\dfrac{1}{4} + \dfrac{1}{16} + \dfrac{1}{64} + \dfrac{1}{256} = \dfrac{1}{4^1} + \dfrac{1}{4^2} + \dfrac{1}{4^3} + \dfrac{1}{4^4}$

$\qquad\qquad\qquad = \displaystyle\sum_{i=1}^{4} \dfrac{1}{4^i}$

42. $1 + \left(-\dfrac{3}{2}\right) + \dfrac{9}{4} = \left(-\dfrac{3}{2}\right)^0 + \left(-\dfrac{3}{2}\right)^1 + \left(-\dfrac{3}{2}\right)^2$

$\qquad = \displaystyle\sum_{i=1}^{3} \left(-\dfrac{3}{2}\right)^{i-1}$

43. $a_1 = 20, \; r = 2$

$a_n = 20(2)^n$ represents the number of yeast, where n represents the number of 8-hour periods. Since $48 = 6(8)$ here, $n = 6$.

$a_6 = 20(2)^6 = 1280$

There are 1280 yeast after 48 hours.

44. $a_n = n^2 + 2n - 1$

$a_4 = (4)^2 + 2(4) - 1 = 23$

$S_4 = \displaystyle\sum_{i=1}^{4} (i^2 + 2i - 1)$

$\qquad = (1 + 2 - 1) + (4 + 4 - 1) + (9 + 6 - 1)$
$\qquad\quad + (16 + 8 - 1)$
$\qquad = 46$

23 cranes are born in the fourth year and 46 cranes are born in the first four years.

45. For Job A: $a_1 = 39,500, \; d = 2200$;

$a_5 = 39,500 + (5 - 1)2200 = \$48,330$
For Job B: $a_1 = 41,000, \; d = 1400$
$a_5 = 41,000 + (5 - 1)1400 = \$46,600$

For the fifth year, Job A has a higher salary.

46. $a_n = 200(0.5)^n$

$a_3 = 200(0.5)^3 = 25$

$S_3 = \displaystyle\sum_{i=1}^{3} 200(0.5)^i$

$\qquad = 200(0.5) + 200(0.5)^2 + 200(0.5)^3$
$\qquad = 175$

25 kilograms decay in the third year and 175 kilograms decay in the first three years.

47. 15, 19, 23, ...

$a_1 = 15, \; d = 4, \; a_6 = 15 + (6 - 1)4 = 35$

$S_6 = \dfrac{6}{2}[15 + 35] = 150$

48. 5, −10, 20, ...

$a_1 = 5, \; r = -2$

$S_n = \dfrac{a_1(1 - r^n)}{1 - r}$

$S_9 = \dfrac{5(1 - (-2)^9)}{1 - (-2)} = 855$

49. $a_1 = 1, \; d = 2, \; n = 30, \; a_{30} = 1 + (30 - 1)2 = 59$

$S_{30} = \dfrac{30}{2}[1 + 59] = 900$

50. 7, 14, 21, 28, ...

$a_n = 7 + (n - 1)7$
$a_{20} = 7 + (20 - 1)7 = 140$
$S_{20} = \dfrac{20}{2}(7 + 140) = 1470$

51. 8, 5, 2, ...

$a_1 = 8, \; d = -3, \; n = 20$
$a_{20} = 8 + (20 - 1)(-3) = -49$

$S_{20} = \dfrac{20}{2}[8 + (-49)]$
$\qquad = -410$

52. $\dfrac{3}{4}, \dfrac{9}{4}, \dfrac{27}{4}, ...$

$a_1 = \dfrac{3}{4}, \; r = 3$

$S_8 = \dfrac{\dfrac{3}{4}(1 - 3^8)}{1 - 3} = 2460$

53. $a_1 = 6, \; r = 5$

$S_4 = \dfrac{6(1 - 5^4)}{1 - 5} = 936$

54. $a_1 = -3, \; d = -6$

$a_n = -3 + (n - 1)(-6)$
$a_{100} = -3 + (100 - 1)(-6) = -597$

$S_{100} = \dfrac{100}{2}(-3 + (-597)) = -30,000$

55. $5, \dfrac{5}{2}, \dfrac{5}{4}, \ldots$

$a_1 = 5, \ r = \dfrac{1}{2}$

$S_\infty = \dfrac{5}{1 - \frac{1}{2}} = 10$

56. $18, -2, \dfrac{2}{9}, \ldots$

$a_1 = 18, \ r = -\dfrac{1}{9}$

$S_\infty = \dfrac{18}{1 + \frac{1}{9}} = \dfrac{81}{5}$

57. $-20, -4, -\dfrac{4}{5}, \ldots$

$a_1 = -20, \ r = \dfrac{1}{5}$

$S_\infty = \dfrac{-20}{1 - \frac{1}{5}} = -25$

58. $0.2, 0.02, 0.002, \ldots$

$a_1 = 0.2 = \dfrac{1}{5}, \ r = \dfrac{1}{10}$

$S_\infty = \dfrac{\frac{1}{5}}{1 - \frac{1}{10}} = \dfrac{2}{9}$

59. $a_1 = 20,000, \ r = 1.15, \ n = 4$

$a_4 = 20,000(1.15)^{4-1} = 30,418$

$S_4 = \dfrac{20,000(1 - 1.15^4)}{1 - 1.15} = 99,868$

He earned \$30,418 during the fourth year and \$99,868 over the four years.

60. $a_n = 40(0.8)^{n-1}$

$a_4 = 40(0.8)^{4-1} = 20.48$

$S_4 = \dfrac{40(1 - 0.8^4)}{1 - 0.8} = 118.08$

He takes 20 minutes to assemble the fourth television and 118 minutes to assemble the first four televisions.

61. $a_1 = 100, d = -7, n = 7$

$a_7 = 100 + (7-1)(-7) = 58$

$S_7 = \dfrac{7}{2}(100 + 58) = 553$

The rent for the seventh day is \$58 and the rent for 7 days is \$553.

62. $a_1 = 15, \ r = 0.8$

$S_\infty = \dfrac{15}{1 - 0.8} = 75$ feet downward

$a_1 = 15(0.8) = 12, \ r = 0.8$

$S_\infty = \dfrac{12}{1 - 0.8} = 60$ feet upward

The total distance is 135 feet.

63. $1800, 600, 200, \ldots$

$a_1 = 1800, \ r = \dfrac{1}{3}, \ n = 6$

$S_6 = 1800\dfrac{\left(1 - \left(\frac{1}{3}\right)^6\right)}{1 - \frac{1}{3}} \approx 2696$

Approximately 2696 mosquitoes were killed during the first six days after the spraying.

64. $1800, 600, 200, \ldots$

For which n is $a_n < 1$?

$a_n = 1800\left(\dfrac{1}{3}\right)^{n-1} < 1$

$\left(\dfrac{1}{3}\right)^{n-1} < \dfrac{1}{1800}$

$(n-1)\log\dfrac{1}{3} < \log\dfrac{1}{1800}$

$(n-1)\log 3^{-1} < \log 1800^{-1}$

$(n-1)(-\log 3) < -\log 1800$

$n - 1 > \dfrac{-\log 1800}{-\log 3}$

$n > 1 + \dfrac{\log 1800}{\log 3}$

$n > 7.8$

No longer effective on the 8th day

$S_8 = \dfrac{1800\left(1 - \left(\frac{1}{3}\right)^8\right)}{1 - \frac{1}{3}} \approx 2700$

About 2700 mosquitoes were killed.

65. $0.5\overline{55} = 0.5 + 0.05 + 0.005 + \cdots$

$a_1 = 0.5, \ r = 0.1$

$S_\infty = \dfrac{0.5}{1 - 0.1} = \dfrac{0.5}{0.9} = \dfrac{5}{9}$

66. 27, 30, 33, …

$$a_n = 27 + (n-1)(3)$$
$$a_{20} = 27 + (20-1)(3) = 84$$
$$S_{20} = \frac{20}{2}(27 + 84) = 1110$$

There are 1110 seats in the theater.

67. $(x+z)^5 = x^5 + 5x^4z + 10x^3z^2 + 10x^2z^3 + 5xz^4 + z^5$

68. $(y-r)^6 = y^6 + 6y^5(-r) + 15y^4(-r)^2 + 20y^3(-r)^3 + 15y^2(-r)^4 + 6y(-r)^5 + (-r)^6$
$$= y^6 - 6y^5r + 15y^4r^2 - 20y^3r^3 + 15y^2r^4 - 6yr^5 + r^6$$

69. $(2x+y)^4 = (2x)^4 + 4(2x)^3y + 6(2x)^2y^2 + 4(2x)y^3 + y^4$
$$= 16x^4 + 32x^3y + 24x^2y^2 + 8xy^3 + y^4$$

70. $(3y-z)^4 = (3y)^4 + 4(3y)^3(-z) + 6(3y)^2(-z)^2 + 4(3y)(-z)^3 + (-z)^4$
$$= 81y^4 - 108y^3z + 54y^2z^2 - 12yz^3 + z^4$$

71. $(b+c)^8 = b^8 + \frac{8}{1!}b^7c + \frac{8\cdot7}{2!}b^6c^2 + \frac{8\cdot7\cdot6}{3!}b^5c^3 + \frac{8\cdot7\cdot6\cdot5}{4!}b^4c^4 + \frac{8\cdot7\cdot6\cdot5\cdot4}{5!}b^3c^5$
$$+ \frac{8\cdot7\cdot6\cdot5\cdot4\cdot3}{6!}b^2c^6 + \frac{8\cdot7\cdot6\cdot5\cdot4\cdot3\cdot2}{7!}bc^7 + c^8$$
$$= b^8 + 8b^7c + 28b^6c^2 + 56b^5c^3 + 70b^4c^4 + 56b^3c^5 + 28b^2c^6 + 8bc^7 + c^8$$

72. $(x-w)^7 = x^7 + \frac{7}{1!}x^6(-w) + \frac{7\cdot6}{2!}x^5(-w)^2 + \frac{7\cdot6\cdot5}{3!}x^4(-w)^3 + \frac{7\cdot6\cdot5\cdot4}{4!}x^3(-w)^4 + \frac{7\cdot6\cdot5\cdot4\cdot3}{5!}x^2(-w)^5$
$$+ \frac{7\cdot6\cdot5\cdot4\cdot3\cdot2}{6!}x(-w)^6 + (-w)^7$$
$$= x^7 - 7x^6w + 21x^5w^2 - 35x^4w^3 + 35x^3w^4 - 21x^2w^5 + 7xw^6 - w^7$$

73. $(4m-n)^4 = (4m)^4 + \frac{4}{1!}(4m)^3(-n) + \frac{4\cdot3}{2!}(4m)^2(-n)^2 + \frac{4\cdot3\cdot2}{3!}(4m)(-n)^3 + (-n)^4$
$$= 256m^4 - 256m^3n + 96m^2n^2 - 16mn^3 + n^4$$

74. $(p-2r)^5 = p^5 + \frac{5}{1!}p^4(-2r) + \frac{5\cdot4}{2!}p^3(-2r)^2 + \frac{5\cdot4\cdot3}{3!}p^2(-2r)^3 + \frac{5\cdot4\cdot3\cdot2}{4!}p(-2r)^4 + (-2r)^5$
$$= p^5 - 10p^4r + 40p^3r^2 - 80p^2r^3 + 80pr^4 - 32r^5$$

75. The 4th term corresponds to $r = 3$.
$$\frac{7!}{3!(7-3)!}a^{7-3}b^3 = 35a^4b^3$$

76. The 11th term corresponds to $r = 10$.
$$\frac{10!}{10!0!}y^{10-10}(2z)^{10} = 1024z^{10}$$

Chapter 11 Test

1. $a_n = \dfrac{(-1)^n}{n+4}$

   $a_1 = \dfrac{(-1)^1}{1+4} = -\dfrac{1}{5}$

   $a_2 = \dfrac{(-1)^2}{2+4} = \dfrac{1}{6}$

   $a_3 = \dfrac{(-1)^3}{3+4} = -\dfrac{1}{7}$

   $a_4 = \dfrac{(-1)^4}{4+4} = \dfrac{1}{8}$

   $a_5 = \dfrac{(-1)^5}{5+4} = -\dfrac{1}{9}$

2. $a_n = 10 + 3(n-1)$

   $a_{80} = 10 + 3(80-1) = 247$

3. $\dfrac{2}{5}, \dfrac{2}{25}, \dfrac{2}{125}, \dots$

   In general, $a_n = \dfrac{2}{5}\left(\dfrac{1}{5}\right)^{n-1}$ or $a_n = \dfrac{2}{5^n}$.

4. $(-1)^1 9 \cdot 1, (-1)^2 9 \cdot 2, \dots, a_n = (-1)^n 9n$

5. $a_n = 5(2)^{n-1}, S_5 = \dfrac{5(1-2^5)}{1-2} = 155$

6. $a_n = 18 + (n-1)(-2)$

   $a_1 = 18, a_{30} = 18 + (30-1)(-2) = -40$

   $S_{30} = \dfrac{30}{2}[18-40] = -330$

7. $a_1 = 24, \; r = \dfrac{1}{6}$

   $S_\infty = \dfrac{24}{1-\frac{1}{6}} = \dfrac{144}{5}$

8. $\dfrac{3}{2}, -\dfrac{3}{4}, \dfrac{3}{8}, \dots$

   $a_1 = \dfrac{3}{2}, \; r = -\dfrac{1}{2}$

   $S_\infty = \dfrac{\frac{3}{2}}{1-\left(-\frac{1}{2}\right)} = 1$

9. $\displaystyle\sum_{i=1}^{4} i(i-2) = 1(1-2)+2(2-2)+3(3-2)+4(4-2)$
$$= -1+0+3+8-20+40-80$$
$$= 10$$

10. $\displaystyle\sum_{i=2}^{4} 5(2)^i(-1)^{i-1} = 5(2)^2(-1)^{2-1}+5(2)^3(-1)^{3-1}+5(2)^4(-1)^{4-1} = -20+40-80 = -60$

11. $(a-b)^6 = a^6-6a^5b+15a^4b^2-20a^3b^3+15a^2b^4-6ab^5+b^6$

12. $(2x+y)^5 = (2x)^5+\dfrac{5}{1!}(2x)^4y+\dfrac{5\cdot4}{2!}(2x)^3y^2+\dfrac{5\cdot4\cdot3}{3!}(2x)^2y^3+\dfrac{5\cdot4\cdot3\cdot2}{4!}(2x)y^4+y^5$
$$= 32x^5+80x^4y+80x^3y^2+40x^2y^3+10xy^4+y^5$$

13. $a_n = 250+75(n-1)$
$a_{10} = 250+75(10-1) = 925$
There were 925 people in the town at the beginning of the tenth year.
$a_1 = 250+75(1-1) = 250$
There were 250 people in the town at the beginning of the first year.

14. $1, 3, 5, \ldots$
$a_1 = 1, d = 2, n = 8$
$a_8 = 1+(8-1)2 = 15$
$1+3+5+7+9+11+13+15$
$S_8 = \dfrac{8}{2}[1+15] = 64$
There were 64 shrubs planted in the 8 rows.

15. $a_1 = 80, r = \dfrac{3}{4}, n = 4$
$$a_4 = 80\left(\dfrac{3}{4}\right)^{4-1} = 33.75$$
The arc length is 33.75 cm on the 4th swing.
$$S_4 = \dfrac{80\left(1-\left(\frac{3}{4}\right)^4\right)}{1-\frac{3}{4}} = 218.75$$
The total of the arc lengths is 218.75 cm for the first 4 swings.

16. $a_1 = 80, r = \dfrac{3}{4}$
$$S_\infty = \dfrac{80}{1-\frac{3}{4}} = 320$$
The total of the arc lengths is 320 cm before the pendulum comes to rest.

17. 16, 48, 80,...

$$a_{10} = 16 + (10-1)32 = 304$$

He falls 304 feet during the 10th second.

$$S_{10} = \frac{10}{2}[16 + 304] = 1600$$

He falls 1600 feet during the first 10 seconds.

18. $0.42\overline{42} = 0.42 + 0.0042 + 0.000042$

$$a_1 = 0.42 = \frac{42}{100}, \; r = 0.01 = \frac{1}{100}$$

$$S_\infty = \frac{\frac{42}{100}}{1 - \frac{1}{100}} = \frac{42}{100} \cdot \frac{100}{99} = \frac{14}{33}$$

Thus, $0.42\overline{42} = \frac{14}{33}$.

Chapter 11 Cumulative Review

1. a. $\dfrac{20}{-4} = -5$

b. $\dfrac{-9}{-3} = 3$

c. $-\dfrac{3}{8} \div 3 = -\dfrac{3}{8} \cdot \dfrac{1}{3} = -\dfrac{1}{8}$

d. $\dfrac{-40}{10} = -4$

e. $\dfrac{-1}{10} \div \dfrac{-2}{5} = \dfrac{1}{10} \cdot \dfrac{5}{2} = \dfrac{1}{4}$

f. $\dfrac{8}{0}$ is undefined.

2. a. $3a - (4a + 3) = 3a - 4a - 3 = -a - 3$

b. $(5x - 3) + (2x + 6) = 7x + 3$

c. $4(2x - 5) - 3(5x + 1) = 8x - 20 - 15x - 3$
$$= -7x - 23$$

3. Let x = the original price, then
$$x - 0.08x = 2162$$
$$0.92x = 2162$$
$$x = 2350$$
The original price is $2350.

4. Let x = the price before taxes, then
$$x + 0.06x = 344.50$$
$$1.06x = 344.50$$
$$x = 325$$
The price before taxes was $325.

5. $3y - 2x = 7$
$$3y = 2x + 7$$
$$y = \frac{1}{3}(2x + 7)$$
$$y = \frac{2x}{3} + \frac{7}{3}$$

6. If the line is to be parallel, then the slope has to be the same as the slope of the given line.

Therefore, $m = \dfrac{3}{2}$.

$$(y - (-2)) = \frac{3}{2}(x - 3)$$
$$y + 2 = \frac{3}{2}(x - 3)$$
$$y = \frac{3}{2}x - \frac{13}{2}$$
$$f(x) = \frac{3}{2}x - \frac{13}{2}$$

7. a. $(3x^6)(5x) = 3 \cdot 5 x^{6+1} = 15x^7$

b. $(-2.4x^3 p^2)(4xp^{10}) = -2.4 \cdot 4 x^{3+1} p^{2+10}$
$$= -9.6x^4 p^{12}$$

8. $y^3 + 5y^2 - y = 5$
$$y^3 + 5y^2 - y - 5 = 0$$
$$(y^3 + 5y^2) + (-y - 5) = 0$$
$$y^2(y + 5) - 1(y + 5) = 0$$
$$(y^2 - 1)(y + 5) = 0$$
$$(y + 1)(y - 1)(y + 5) = 0$$
$$y = -5, \, -1, \, 1$$

9.
$$\begin{array}{r|rrrrr} -2 & 1 & -2 & -11 & 5 & 34 \\ & & -2 & 8 & 6 & -22 \\ \hline & 1 & -4 & -3 & 11 & 12 \end{array}$$

Answer: $x^3 - 4x^2 - 3x + 11 + \dfrac{12}{x + 2}$

10. $\dfrac{5}{3a-6} - \dfrac{a}{a-2} + \dfrac{3+2a}{5a-10}$

$= \dfrac{5}{3(a-2)} - \dfrac{a}{a-2} + \dfrac{3+2a}{5(a-2)}$

$= \dfrac{5\cdot 5 - 3\cdot 5a + 3(3+2a)}{3\cdot 5(a-2)}$

$= \dfrac{25 - 15a + 9 + 6a}{15(a-2)}$

$= \dfrac{34 - 9a}{15(a-2)}$

11. a. $\sqrt{50} = \sqrt{2}\sqrt{25} = 5\sqrt{2}$

b. $\sqrt[3]{24} = \sqrt[3]{8}\sqrt[3]{3} = 2\sqrt[3]{3}$

c. $\sqrt{26} = \sqrt{26}$

d. $\sqrt[4]{32} = \sqrt[4]{16}\sqrt[4]{2} = 2\sqrt[4]{2}$

12. $\sqrt{3x+6} - \sqrt{7x-6} = 0$

$\sqrt{3x+6} = \sqrt{7x-6}$

$\left(\sqrt{3x+6}\right)^2 = \left(\sqrt{7x-6}\right)^2$

$3x+6 = 7x-6$

$-4x = -12$

$x = 3$

13. $2420 = 2000(1+r)^2$

$\dfrac{2420}{2000} = (1+r)^2$

$\dfrac{121}{100} = (1+r)^2$

$\pm\sqrt{\dfrac{121}{100}} = 1+r$

$\pm\dfrac{11}{10} = 1+r$

$-1 \pm \dfrac{11}{10} = r$

Discard the negative value.

$r = -1 + \dfrac{11}{10} = \dfrac{1}{10} = 0.10$

The interest rate is 10%.

14. a. $\sqrt[3]{\dfrac{4}{3x}} = \dfrac{\sqrt[3]{4}}{\sqrt[3]{3x}} = \left(\dfrac{\sqrt[3]{9x^2}}{\sqrt[3]{9x^2}}\right) = \dfrac{\sqrt[3]{36x^2}}{3x}$

b. $\dfrac{\sqrt{2}+1}{\sqrt{2}-1} = \dfrac{\sqrt{2}+1}{\sqrt{2}-1}\cdot\left(\dfrac{\sqrt{2}+1}{\sqrt{2}+1}\right)$

$= \dfrac{2 + 2\sqrt{2} + 1}{2-1}$

$= 3 + 2\sqrt{2}$

15. $(x-3)^2 - 3(x-3) - 4 = 0$

$x^2 - 6x + 9 - 3x + 9 - 4 = 0$

$x^2 - 9x + 14 = 0$

$(x-2)(x-7) = 0$

$x = 2, 7$

16. $\dfrac{10}{(2x+4)^2} - \dfrac{1}{2x+4} = 3$

$10 - (2x+4) = 3(2x+4)^2$

$10 - 2x - 4 = 3(4x^2 + 16x + 16)$

$-2x + 6 = 12x^2 + 48x + 48$

$12x^2 + 50x + 42 = 0$

$6x^2 + 25x + 21 = 0$

$(6x+7)(x+3) = 0$

$x = -\dfrac{7}{6}, -3$

17. $\dfrac{5}{x+1} < -2$

$x + 1 = 0$

$x = -1$

Solve $\dfrac{5}{x+1} = -2.$

$(x+1)\dfrac{5}{x+1} = (x+1)(-2)$

$5 = -2x - 2$

$7 = -2x$

$-\dfrac{7}{2} = x$

Region	Test Point	$\dfrac{5}{x+1} < -2$; Result
$\left(-\infty, -\dfrac{7}{2}\right)$	$x = -6$	$\dfrac{5}{-5} < -2$; False
$\left(-\dfrac{7}{2}, -1\right)$	$x = -2$	$\dfrac{5}{-1} < -2$; True
$(-1, \infty)$	$x = 4$	$\dfrac{5}{5} < -2$; False

The solution set is $\left(-\dfrac{7}{2}, -1\right)$.

18. $f(x) = (x+2)^2 - 6$

Axis of symmetry: $x = -2$

vertex: $(-2, -6)$

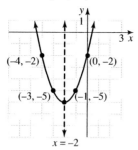

19. $f(t) = -16t^2 + 20t$

The maximum height occurs at the vertex.

$t = \dfrac{-20}{2(-16)} = \dfrac{5}{8}$

$f\left(\dfrac{5}{8}\right) = -16\left(\dfrac{5}{8}\right)^2 + 20\left(\dfrac{5}{8}\right) = \dfrac{25}{4}$

The maximum height of $\dfrac{25}{4}$ feet occurs at $\dfrac{5}{8}$ second.

20. $f(x) = x^2 + 3x - 18$

$a = 1, b = 3, c = -18$

$x = \dfrac{-3}{2(1)} = -\dfrac{3}{2}$

$f\left(-\dfrac{3}{2}\right) = \left(-\dfrac{3}{2}\right)^2 + 3\left(\dfrac{3}{2}\right) - 18 = -\dfrac{81}{4}$

The vertex is $\left(-\dfrac{3}{2}, -\dfrac{81}{4}\right)$.

21. a. $(f \circ g)(2) = f(g(2)) = f(5) = 5^2 = 25$

$(g \circ f)(2) = g(f(2)) = g(4) = 4 + 3 = 7$

b. $(f \circ g)(x) = f(x+3)$

$= (x+3)^2$

$= x^2 + 6x + 9$

$(g \circ f)(x) = g(x^2) = x^2 + 3$

22. $f(x) = -2x + 3$

$y = -2x + 3$

$x = -2y + 3$

$x - 3 = -2y$

$\dfrac{x-3}{-2} = y$

$f^{-1}(x) = -\dfrac{x-3}{2}$ or $f^{-1}(x) = \dfrac{3-x}{2}$

23. $f^{-1} = \{(1,0), (7,-2), (-6,3), (4,4)\}$

24. a. $(f \circ g)(2) = f(g(2)) = f(3) = 3^2 - 2 = 7$

$(g \circ f)(2) = g(f(2)) = g(2) = 2 + 1 = 3$

b. $(f \circ g)(x) = f(x+1)$

$= (x+1)^2 - 2$

$= x^2 + 2x - 1$

$(g \circ f)(x) = g(x^2 - 2) = x^2 - 2 + 1 = x^2 - 1$

25. a. $2^x = 16$

$2^x = 2^4$

$x = 4$

b. $9^x = 27$

$(3^2)^x = 3^3$

$2x = 3$

$x = \dfrac{3}{2}$

c. $4^{x+3} = 8^x$

$(2^2)^{x+3} = (2^3)^x$

$2^{2x+6} = 2^{3x}$

$2x + 6 = 3x$

$x = 6$

26. a. $\log_2 32 = x$
$$2^x = 32$$
$$2^x = 2^5$$
$$x = 5$$

b. $\log_4 \dfrac{1}{64} = x$
$$4^x = \dfrac{1}{64}$$
$$4^x = 4^{-3}$$
$$x = -3$$

c. $\log_{\frac{1}{2}} x = 5$
$$\left(\dfrac{1}{2}\right)^5 = x$$
$$x = \dfrac{1}{32}$$

27. a. $\log_3 3^2 = 2$

b. $\log_7 7^{-1} = -1$

c. $5^{\log_5 3} = 3$

d. $2^{\log_2 6} = 6$

28. a. $4^x = 64$
$$\left(2^2\right)^x = 2^6$$
$$2x = 6$$
$$x = 3$$

b. $8^x = 32$
$$\left(2^3\right)^x = 2^5$$
$$3x = 5$$
$$x = \dfrac{5}{3}$$

c. $9^{x+4} = 243^x$
$$(3^2)^{x+4} = (3^5)^x$$
$$3^{2x+8} = 3^{5x}$$
$$2x + 8 = 5x$$
$$8 = 3x$$
$$x = \dfrac{8}{3}$$

29. a. $\log_{11} 10 + \log_{11} 3 = \log_{11}(10 \cdot 3) = \log_{11} 30$

b. $\log_3 \dfrac{1}{2} + \log_3 12 = \log_3 \left(\dfrac{1}{2} \cdot 12\right) = \log_3 6$

c. $\log_2(x+2) + \log_2 x = \log_2[(x+2)x]$
$$= \log_2(x^2 + 2x)$$

30. a. $\log 100,000 = \log_{10} 10^5 = 5$

b. $\log 10^{-3} = \log_{10} 10^{-3} = -3$

c. $\ln \sqrt[5]{e} = \ln e^{1/5} = \dfrac{1}{5}$

d. $\ln e^4 = 4$

31. $A = Pe^{rt}$
$$A = 1600e^{0.09(5)} \approx 2509.30$$
2509.30 is owed after 5 years.

32. a. $\log_6 5 + \log_6 4 = \log_6(5 \cdot 4) = \log_6 20$

b. $\log_8 12 - \log_8 4 = \log_8 \dfrac{12}{4} = \log_8 3$

c. $2\log_2 x + 3\log_2 x - 2\log_2(x-1)$
$$= 5\log_2 x - \log_2(x-1)^2$$
$$= \log_2 x^5 - \log_2(x-1)^2$$
$$= \log_2 \dfrac{x^5}{(x-1)^2}$$

33. $3^x = 7$
$$\log 3^x = \log 7$$
$$x\log 3 = \log 7$$
$$x = \dfrac{\log 7}{\log 3} \approx 1.7712$$

34. $10,000 = 5000\left(1 + \dfrac{0.02}{4}\right)^{4t}$
$$2 = (1.005)^{4t}$$
$$\ln 2 = \ln 1.005^{4t}$$
$$\ln 2 = 4t\ln(1.005)$$
$$t = \dfrac{\ln 2}{4\ln 1.005} \approx 34.7$$
It takes 34.7 years.

35. $\log_4(x-2) = 2$

$$4^2 = x - 2$$
$$x - 2 = 16$$
$$x = 18$$

36. $\log_4 10 - \log_4 x = 2$

$$\log_4 \frac{10}{x} = 2$$
$$4^2 = \frac{10}{x}$$
$$16 = \frac{10}{x}$$
$$16x = 10$$
$$x = \frac{5}{8}$$

37. $\dfrac{x^2}{16} - \dfrac{y^2}{25} = 1$

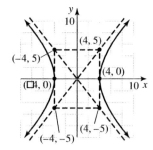

38. $(8, 5), (-2, 4)$

$$d = \sqrt{(-2-8)^2 + (4-5)^2} = \sqrt{101} \text{ units}$$

39. $\begin{cases} y = \sqrt{x} \\ x^2 + y^2 = 6 \end{cases}$

Replace y with $\sqrt{x}$ in the first equation.

$$(x)^2 + \left(\sqrt{x}\right)^2 = 6$$
$$x^2 + x - 6 = 0$$
$$(x+3)(x-2) = 0$$
$$x = -3 (\text{discard}) \text{ or } x = 2$$
$$x = 2: \ y = \sqrt{x} = \sqrt{2}$$
$$\left(2, \sqrt{2}\right)$$

40. $\begin{cases} x^2 + y^2 = 36 \\ x - y = 6 \Rightarrow x = y + 6 \end{cases}$

Replace x with $y + 6$ in the first equation.

$$(y+6)^2 + y^2 = 36$$
$$2y^2 + 12y = 0$$
$$2y(y+6) = 0$$
$$y = 0 \qquad \text{or} \qquad y = -6$$
$$x = 0 + 6 = 6 \qquad x = -6 + 6 = 0$$
$$(0, -6); (6, 0)$$

41. $\dfrac{x^2}{9} + \dfrac{y^2}{16} \le 1$

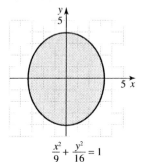

$$\frac{x^2}{9} + \frac{y^2}{16} = 1$$

42.

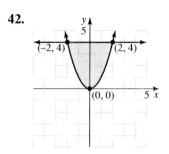

43. $a_n = n^2 - 1$

$$a_1 = 1^2 - 1 = 0$$
$$a_2 = 2^2 - 1 = 3$$
$$a_3 = 3^2 - 1 = 8$$
$$a_4 = 4^2 - 1 = 15$$
$$a_5 = 5^2 - 1 = 24$$

44. $a_n = \dfrac{n}{n+4}$

$$a_8 = \frac{8}{8+4} = \frac{8}{12} = \frac{2}{3}$$

45. $a_1 = 2, \ d = 9 - 2 = 7$

$$a_{11} = 2 + (11-1)(7) = 72$$

46. $a_1 = 2, \ r = \dfrac{10}{2} = 5$

$$a_6 = 2(5)^{6-1} = 2(5)^5 = 6250$$

47. **a.** $\displaystyle\sum_{i=0}^{6}\frac{i-2}{2}=\frac{0-2}{2}+\frac{1-2}{2}+\frac{2-2}{2}+\frac{3-2}{2}+\frac{4-2}{2}+\frac{5-2}{2}+\frac{6-2}{2}$

$$=-1-\frac{1}{2}+0+\frac{1}{2}+1+\frac{3}{2}+2$$

$$=\frac{7}{2}$$

b. $\displaystyle\sum_{i=3}^{5}2^i=2^3+2^4+2^5=8+16+32=56$

48. **a.** $\displaystyle\sum_{i=0}^{4}i(i+1)=0(0+1)+1(1+1)+2(2+1)+3(3+1)+4(4+1)$

$$=0+2+6+12+20$$

$$=40$$

b. $\displaystyle\sum_{i=0}^{3}2^i=2^0+2^1+2^2+2^3=1+2+4+8=15$

49. $a_1=1,\ a_{30}=30$

$$S_n=\frac{n}{2}(a_1+a_n)=\frac{30}{2}(1+30)=465$$

50. $(x-y)^6$ where $a=x,\ b=-y,\ n=6,$ and $r=2.$

$$\frac{6!}{2!(6-2)!}x^{6-2}y^2=15x^4y^2$$

The third term in the expansion of $(x-y)^6$ is $15x^4y^2$.

Appendices

A.2 Practice Final Exam

1. $\sqrt{216} = \sqrt{36 \cdot 6} = \sqrt{36} \cdot \sqrt{6} = 6\sqrt{6}$

2. $\dfrac{\left(4 - \sqrt{16}\right) - (-7 - 20)}{-2(1 - 4)^2} = \dfrac{(4 - 4) - (-27)}{-2(-3)^2}$

$$= \dfrac{0 + 27}{-2(9)}$$

$$= \dfrac{27}{-18}$$

$$= -\dfrac{3}{2}$$

3. $\left(\dfrac{1}{125}\right)^{-1/3} = 125^{1/3} = \sqrt[3]{125} = \sqrt[3]{5^3} = 5$

4. $(-9x)^{-2} = \dfrac{1}{(-9x)^2} = \dfrac{1}{(-9)^2 x^2} = \dfrac{1}{81x^2}$

5. $\dfrac{\dfrac{5}{x} - \dfrac{7}{3x}}{\dfrac{9}{8x} - \dfrac{1}{x}} = \dfrac{24x\left(\dfrac{5}{x} - \dfrac{7}{3x}\right)}{24x\left(\dfrac{9}{8x} - \dfrac{1}{x}\right)}$

$$= \dfrac{24x\left(\dfrac{5}{x}\right) - 24x\left(\dfrac{7}{3x}\right)}{24x\left(\dfrac{9}{8x}\right) - 24x\left(\dfrac{1}{x}\right)}$$

$$= \dfrac{24 \cdot 5 - 8 \cdot 7}{3 \cdot 9 - 24}$$

$$= \dfrac{120 - 56}{27 - 24}$$

$$= \dfrac{64}{3}$$

6. $\left(\dfrac{64c^{4/3}}{a^{-2/3}b^{5/6}}\right)^{1/2} = \dfrac{64^{1/2} c^{\frac{4}{3} \cdot \frac{1}{2}}}{a^{-\frac{2}{3} \cdot \frac{1}{2}} b^{\frac{5}{6} \cdot \frac{1}{2}}}$

$$= \dfrac{8c^{2/3}}{a^{-1/3} b^{5/12}}$$

$$= \dfrac{8a^{1/3} c^{2/3}}{b^{5/12}}$$

7. a.

Sales (Dollars)	8000	9000	10,000	11,000	12,000
Gross Monthly Pay (Dollars)	1900	1950	2000	2050	2100

    b. $12(2050) = 24,600$

           If her sales are \$11,000 per month, her gross annual pay is \$24,600.

    c.   For a gross monthly pay of \$2200, she must sell \$14,000 each month.

8. $\begin{aligned} 3x^2y - 27y^3 &= 3y(x^2 - 9y^2) \\ &= 3y[x^2 - (3y)^2] \\ &= 3y(x + 3y)(x - 3y) \end{aligned}$

9. $\begin{aligned} 16y^3 - 2 &= 2(8y^3 - 1) \\ &= 2[(2y)^3 - 1^3] \\ &= 2(2y - 1)[(2y)^2 + 2y \cdot 1 + 1^2] \\ &= 2(2y - 1)(4y^2 + 2y + 1) \end{aligned}$

10. $\begin{aligned} x^2y - 9y - 3x^2 + 27 &= y(x^2 - 9) - 3(x^2 - 9) \\ &= (x^2 - 9)(y - 3) \\ &= (x + 3)(x - 3)(y - 3) \end{aligned}$

11. $(4x^3y - 3x - 4) - (9x^3y + 8x + 5)$

$= 4x^3y - 3x - 4 - 9x^3y - 8x - 5$

$= 4x^3y - 9x^3y - 3x - 8x - 4 - 5$

$= -5x^3y - 11x - 9$

12. $\begin{aligned} (6m + n)^2 &= (6m)^2 + 2(6m)(n) + n^2 \\ &= 36m^2 + 12mn + n^2 \end{aligned}$

13. $(2x - 1)(x^2 - 6x + 4)$

$= 2x(x^2 - 6x + 4) - 1(x^2 - 6x + 4)$

$= 2x^3 - 12x^2 + 8x - x^2 + 6x - 4$

$= 2x^3 - 13x^2 + 14x - 4$

14. $\begin{aligned} \frac{3x^2 - 12}{x^2 + 2x - 8} \div \frac{6x + 18}{x + 4} &= \frac{3x^2 - 12}{x^2 + 2x - 8} \cdot \frac{x + 4}{6x + 18} \\ &= \frac{3(x^2 - 4)}{(x + 4)(x - 2)} \cdot \frac{x + 4}{6(x + 3)} \\ &= \frac{3(x + 2)(x - 2)(x + 4)}{(x + 4)(x - 2) \cdot 6(x + 3)} \\ &= \frac{x + 2}{2(x + 3)} \end{aligned}$

15. $\dfrac{2x^2+7}{2x^4-18x^2}-\dfrac{6x+7}{2x^4-18x^2}=\dfrac{(2x^2+7)-(6x+7)}{2x^4-18x^2}$

$=\dfrac{2x^2+7-6x-7}{2x^4-18x^2}$

$=\dfrac{2x^2-6x}{2x^2(x^2-9)}$

$=\dfrac{2x(x-3)}{2x^2(x+3)(x-3)}$

$=\dfrac{1}{x(x+3)}$

16. $\dfrac{3}{x^2-x-6}+\dfrac{2}{x^2-5x+6}$

$=\dfrac{3}{(x-3)(x+2)}+\dfrac{2}{(x-2)(x-3)}$

$=\dfrac{3(x-2)}{(x-3)(x+2)(x-2)}+\dfrac{2(x+2)}{(x-2)(x-3)(x+2)}$

$=\dfrac{3(x-2)+2(x+2)}{(x-3)(x+2)(x-2)}$

$=\dfrac{3x-6+2x+4}{(x-3)(x+2)(x-2)}$

$=\dfrac{5x-2}{(x-3)(x+2)(x-2)}$

17. $\sqrt{125x^3}-3\sqrt{20x^3}=\sqrt{25x^2\cdot5x}-3\sqrt{4x^2\cdot5x}$

$=5x\sqrt{5x}-3\cdot2x\sqrt{5x}$

$=5x\sqrt{5x}-6x\sqrt{5x}$

$=(5x-6x)\sqrt{5x}$

$=-x\sqrt{5x}$

18. $\left(\sqrt{5}+5\right)\left(\sqrt{5}-5\right)=\left(\sqrt{5}\right)^2-5^2=5-25=-20$

19.

$$\begin{array}{r}
2x^2-x-2 \\
2x+1{\overline{\smash{\big)}\,4x^3+0x^2-5x+0}} \\
\underline{4x^3+2x^2} \\
-2x^2-5x \\
\underline{-2x^2-x} \\
-4x+0 \\
\underline{-4x-2} \\
2
\end{array}$$

$(4x^3-5x)\div(2x+1)=2x^2-x-2+\dfrac{2}{2x+1}$

20. <u>Algebraic Solution:</u>

$15x+26=-2(x+1)-1$

$15x+26=-2x-2-1$

$15x+26=-2x-3$

$17x+26=-3$

$17x=-29$

$x=-\dfrac{29}{17}\approx-1.70588$

<u>Graphical Solution:</u>

Graph $y_1=15x+26$ and $y_2=-2(x+1)-1$.

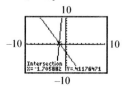

The solution is $-\dfrac{29}{17}$.

21. $|6x-5|-3=-2$

$|6x-5|=1$

$6x-5=-1$ or $6x-5=1$

$6x=4$ or $6x=6$

$x=\dfrac{4}{6}$ or $x=1$

$x=\dfrac{2}{3}$

Both solutions check.

22. $3n(7n-20)=96$

$21n^2-60n=96$

$21n^2-60n-96=0$

$3(7n^2-20n-32)=0$

$3(7n+8)(n-4)=0$

$7n+8=0$ or $n-4=0$

$n=-\dfrac{8}{7}$ or $n=4$

Both solutions check.

23.
$$-3 < 2(x-3) \le 4$$
$$-3 < 2x - 6 \le 4$$
$$-3 + 6 < 2x - 6 + 6 \le 4 + 6$$
$$3 < 2x \le 10$$
$$\frac{3}{2} < \frac{2x}{2} \le \frac{10}{2}$$
$$\frac{3}{2} < x \le 5$$
$$\left(\frac{3}{2}, 5\right]$$

24.
$$|3x + 1| > 5$$
$$3x + 1 < -5 \quad \text{or} \quad 3x + 1 > 5$$
$$3x < -6 \qquad\qquad 3x > 4$$
$$x < -2 \qquad\qquad x > \frac{4}{3}$$
$$(-\infty, -2) \cup \left(\frac{4}{3}, \infty\right)$$

25.
$$\frac{x^2 + 8}{x} - 1 = \frac{2(x+4)}{x}$$
$$x\left(\frac{x^2 + 8}{x} - 1\right) = x\left(\frac{2(x+4)}{x}\right)$$
$$x^2 + 8 - x = 2(x+4)$$
$$x^2 - x + 8 = 2x + 8$$
$$x^2 - 3x = 0$$
$$x(x - 3) = 0$$
$$x = 0 \quad \text{or} \quad x - 3 = 0$$
$$x = 3$$
The only solution is 3.

26.
$$y^2 - 3y = 5$$
$$y^2 - 3y - 5 = 0$$
$$y = \frac{-(-3) \pm \sqrt{(-3)^2 - 4(1)(-5)}}{2(1)}$$
$$y = \frac{3 \pm \sqrt{9 + 20}}{2}$$
$$y = \frac{3 \pm \sqrt{29}}{2}$$

27.
$$x = \sqrt{x - 2} + 2$$
$$x - 2 = \sqrt{x - 2}$$
$$(x - 2)^2 = \left(\sqrt{x - 2}\right)^2$$
$$x^2 - 4x + 4 = x - 2$$
$$x^2 - 5x + 6 = 0$$
$$(x - 2)(x - 3) = 0$$
$$x - 2 = 0 \quad \text{or} \quad x - 3 = 0$$
$$x = 2 \quad \text{or} \qquad x = 3$$

28.
$$2x^2 - 7x > 15$$
$$2x^2 - 7x - 15 > 0$$
$$(2x + 3)(x - 5) > 0$$
$$2x + 3 = 0 \quad \text{or} \quad x - 5 = 0$$
$$x = -\frac{3}{2} \quad \text{or} \qquad x = 5$$

Region	Test Point	$2x^2 - 7x > 15$ Result
$\left(-\infty, -\frac{3}{2}\right)$	-3	$39 > 15$ True
$\left(-\frac{3}{2}, 5\right)$	0	$0 > 15$ False
$(5, \infty)$	6	$30 > 15$ True

$$\left(-\infty, -\frac{3}{2}\right) \cup (5, \infty)$$

29.
$$\begin{cases} \dfrac{x}{2} + \dfrac{y}{4} = -\dfrac{3}{4} \\ x + \dfrac{3}{4}y = -4 \end{cases}$$

$$\begin{cases} -8\left(\dfrac{x}{2} + \dfrac{y}{4}\right) = -8\left(-\dfrac{3}{4}\right) \\ 4\left(x + \dfrac{3}{4}y\right) = 4(-4) \end{cases}$$

$$-4x - 2y = 6$$
$$\underline{4x + 3y = -16}$$
$$y = -10$$

Let $y = -10$ in the second equation.

$$x + \frac{3}{4}y = -4$$

$$x + \frac{3}{4}(-10) = -4$$

$$x - \frac{15}{2} = -\frac{8}{2}$$

$$x = \frac{7}{2}$$

The solution is $\left(\frac{7}{2}, -10\right)$.

30. $4x + 6y = 7$

$$6y = -4x + 7$$

$$y = -\frac{2}{3}x + \frac{7}{6}$$

slope $= -\frac{2}{3}$, y-intercept $\left(0, \frac{7}{6}\right)$

Plot points: $\left(0, \frac{7}{6}\right), \left(\frac{7}{4}, 0\right), \left(-3, \frac{19}{6}\right)$

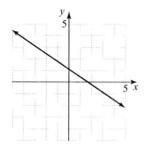

31. $2x - y > 5$

Graph $2x - y = 5$ with a dashed line because the inequality is $>$.

x	$2x - y = 5$	y
0	$2(0) - y = 5$	-5
1	$2(1) - y = 5$	-3
3	$2(3) - y = 5$	1

Test point $(0, 0)$: $2(0) - 0 \overset{?}{>} 5$
$$0 > 5 \quad \text{False}$$

Shade the region that does not include $(0, 0)$.

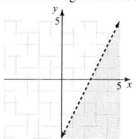

32. $y = -3$

The graph of $y = -3$ is a horizontal line with a y-intercept of $(0, -3)$.

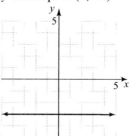

33. $g(x) = -|x + 2| - 1$

x	$g(x) = -|x + 2| - 1$	$g(x)$
-5	$-|-5 + 2| - 1 = -4$	-4
-4	$-|-4 + 2| - 1 = -3$	-3
-3	$-|-3 + 2| - 1 = -2$	-2
-2	$-|-2 + 2| - 1 = -1$	-1
-1	$-|-1 + 2| - 1 = -2$	-2
0	$-|0 + 2| - 1 = -3$	-3
1	$-|1 + 2| - 1 = -4$	-4

Domain: All real numbers, $(-\infty, \infty)$
Range: $(-\infty, -1]$

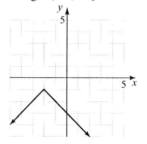

34. $h(x) = x^2 - 4x + 4$

x-intercept: Let $h(x) = 0$ and solve for x.

$0 = x^2 - 4x + 4$

$0 = (x-2)^2$

$x - 2 = 0$

$x = 2$

x-intercept: (2, 0)

y-intercept: Let $x = 0$.

$h(0) = 0^2 - 4(0) + 4 = 4$

y-intercept: (0, 4)

x-coordinate of vertex:

$-\dfrac{b}{2a} = -\dfrac{-4}{2(1)} = 2$

vertex: (2, 0)

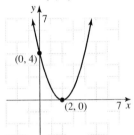

35. $f(x) = \begin{cases} -\dfrac{1}{2}x & \text{if} \quad x \le 0 \\ 2x - 3 & \text{if} \quad x > 0 \end{cases}$

If $x \le 0$

x	$-\frac{1}{2}x$	$f(x)$
0	$-\frac{1}{2}(0)$	0
-2	$-\frac{1}{2}(-2)$	1
-4	$-\frac{1}{2}(-4)$	2

If $x > 0$

x	$2x - 3$	$f(x)$
1	$2(1) - 3$	-1
2	$2(2) - 3$	1
3	$2(3) - 3$	3

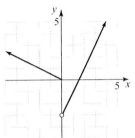

Domain: $(-\infty, \infty)$

Range: $(-3, \infty)$

36. through (4, −2) and (6, −3)

$\text{slope} = m = \dfrac{y_2 - y_1}{x_2 - x_1} = \dfrac{-3 - (-2)}{6 - 4} = \dfrac{-1}{2}$

$y - y_1 = m(x - x_1)$

$y - (-2) = -\dfrac{1}{2}(x - 4)$

$y + 2 = -\dfrac{1}{2}x + 2$

$y = -\dfrac{1}{2}x$

$f(x) = -\dfrac{1}{2}x$

37. through (−1, 2) and perpendicular to $3x - y = 4$

Find the slope of $3x - y = 4$ by writing the equation in slope-intercept form.

$3x - y = 4$

$-y = -3x + 4$

$y = 3x - 4$

The slope is 3. The slope of a line perpendicular

to this line is $-\dfrac{1}{3}$.

Substitute $m = -\dfrac{1}{3}$ and $(x_1, y_1) = (-1, 2)$ in the

equation:

$y - y_1 = m(x - x_1)$

$y - 2 = -\dfrac{1}{3}[x - (-1)]$

$y - 2 = -\dfrac{1}{3}(x + 1)$

$y - 2 = -\dfrac{1}{3}x - \dfrac{1}{3}$

$y = -\dfrac{1}{3}x + \dfrac{5}{3}$

$f(x) = -\dfrac{1}{3}x + \dfrac{5}{3}$

38. $(x_1, y_1) = (-6, 3);\ (x_2, y_2) = (-8, -7)$

$$d = \sqrt{(x_2 - x_1)^2 + (y_2 - y_1)^2}$$
$$= \sqrt{[-8 - (-6)]^2 + (-7 - 3)^2}$$
$$= \sqrt{(-2)^2 + (-10)^2}$$
$$= \sqrt{4 + 100}$$
$$= \sqrt{104}$$
$$= 2\sqrt{26}\ \text{units}$$

39. $(x_1, y_1) = (-2, -5);\ (x_2, y_2) = (-6, 12)$

$$\text{midpoint} = \left(\frac{x_1 + x_2}{2}, \frac{y_1 + y_2}{2}\right)$$
$$= \left(\frac{-2 + (-6)}{2}, \frac{-5 + 12}{2}\right)$$
$$= \left(\frac{-8}{2}, \frac{7}{2}\right)$$
$$= \left(-4, \frac{7}{2}\right)$$

40. $\sqrt{\dfrac{9}{y}} = \dfrac{\sqrt{9}}{\sqrt{y}} = \dfrac{\sqrt{9}}{\sqrt{y}} \cdot \dfrac{\sqrt{y}}{\sqrt{y}} = \dfrac{\sqrt{9} \cdot \sqrt{y}}{\sqrt{y} \cdot \sqrt{y}} = \dfrac{3\sqrt{y}}{y}$

41. $\dfrac{4 - \sqrt{x}}{4 + 2\sqrt{x}} = \dfrac{4 - \sqrt{x}}{4 + 2\sqrt{x}} \cdot \dfrac{4 - 2\sqrt{x}}{4 - 2\sqrt{x}}$

$$= \frac{\left(4 - \sqrt{x}\right)\left(4 - 2\sqrt{x}\right)}{\left(4 + 2\sqrt{x}\right)\left(4 - 2\sqrt{x}\right)}$$
$$= \frac{16 - 12\sqrt{x} + 2x}{16 - 4x}$$
$$= \frac{2\left(8 - 6\sqrt{x} + x\right)}{2(8 - 2x)}$$
$$= \frac{8 - 6\sqrt{x} + x}{8 - 2x}$$

42. The graph of y_1 is below the graph of y_2 for x-values less than -3. The solution set for $y_1 < y_2$ is $(-\infty, -3)$.

43. Let $x =$ population of New York, then $x + 1.3 =$ Seoul's population, and $2x - 10.2 =$ Tokyo's population.

$$x + (x + 1.3) + (2x - 10.2) = 78.3$$
$$4x - 8.9 = 78.3$$
$$4x = 87.2$$
$$x = 21.8$$

$x + 1.3 = 23.1$
$2x - 10.2 = 33.4$
The populations are as follows:
New York: 21.8 million; Seoul: 23.1 million; Tokyo: 33.4 million

44. Let $x =$ the number.

$$(x + 1) \cdot \left(2 \cdot \frac{1}{x}\right) = \frac{12}{5}$$
$$\frac{2}{x}(x + 1) = \frac{12}{5}$$
$$5x\left[\frac{2}{x}(x + 1)\right] = 5x\left(\frac{12}{5}\right)$$
$$10(x + 1) = x \cdot 12$$
$$10x + 10 = 12x$$
$$10 = 2x$$
$$5 = x$$

The number is 5.

45. a. Let $x =$ the number of years after 1990.

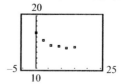

The data appear to be quadratic.

b.

The quadratic regression equation is

$$y = 0.019x^2 - 0.465x + 16.65.$$

The birth rate in 2012 is predicted to be 15.83 births per 1000 people.

46. Use the Pythagorean Theorem.

$$c^2 = a^2 + b^2$$
$$20^2 = x^2 + (x + 8)^2$$
$$400 = x^2 + x^2 + 16x + 64$$
$$0 = 2x^2 + 16x - 336$$
$$0 = 2(x^2 + 8x - 168)$$

$x = \dfrac{-8 \pm \sqrt{8^2 - 4(1)(-168)}}{2(1)}$

$x = \dfrac{-8 \pm \sqrt{736}}{2}$

$x \approx -17.6 \quad \text{or} \quad x \approx 9.6$

Discard a negative distance.

$x + 8 + x = 9.6 + 8 + 9.6 = 27.2$

$27.2 - 20 = 7.2$ or about 7

A person saves about 7 feet.

47. a. Find the vertex.

$s(t) = -16t^2 + 32t + 256$

t-value: $\dfrac{-b}{2a} = \dfrac{-32}{2(-16)} = 1$

$s(t)$-value:

$s(1) = -16(1)^2 + 32(1) + 256 = 272$

The maximum height is 272 feet.

b. Let $s(t) = 0$ and solve for t.

$0 = -16t^2 + 32t + 256$

$0 = -16(t^2 - 2t - 16)$

$t = \dfrac{-(-2) \pm \sqrt{(-2)^2 - 4(1)(-16)}}{2(1)}$

$t = \dfrac{2 \pm \sqrt{68}}{2}$

$t = \dfrac{2 \pm 2\sqrt{17}}{2}$

$t = 1 \pm \sqrt{17}$

$t \approx -3.12 \quad \text{or} \quad t \approx 5.12$

Discard a negative time.

The stone will hit the water in approximately 5.12 seconds.

48. Let $x = $ amount of 10% solution to add to mixture.

solution	amount of solution	amount of fructose
10%	x	$0.10x$
20%	$20 - x$	$0.20(20 - x)$
17.5%	20	$0.175(20)$

$0.10x + 0.20(20 - x) = 0.175(20)$

$0.10x + 4 - 0.20x = 3.5$

$-0.10x = -0.5$

$x = 5$

$20 - x = 15$

Therefore, mix 5 gallons of 10% solution with 15 gallons of 20% solution.

49. $-\sqrt{-8} = -\sqrt{4 \cdot (-1) \cdot 2} = -\sqrt{4} \cdot \sqrt{-1} \cdot \sqrt{2} = -2i\sqrt{2}$

50. $(12 - 6i) - (12 - 3i) = 12 - 6i - 12 + 3i$

$= 12 - 12 - 6i + 3i$

$= 0 - 3i$

$= -3i$

51. $(4 + 3i)^2 = (4 + 3i)(4 + 3i)$

$= 16 + 12i + 12i + 9i^2$

$= 16 + 24i - 9$

$= 7 + 24i$

52. $\dfrac{1 + 4i}{1 - i} = \dfrac{1 + 4i}{1 - i} \cdot \dfrac{1 + i}{1 + i}$

$= \dfrac{(1 + 4i)(1 + i)}{(1 - i)(1 + i)}$

$= \dfrac{1 + 5i + 4i^2}{1 - i^2}$

$= \dfrac{1 + 5i - 4}{1 - (-1)}$

$= \dfrac{-3 + 5i}{2}$

$= -\dfrac{3}{2} + \dfrac{5}{2}i$

53. $g(x) = x - 7$ and $h(x) = x^2 - 6x + 5$

$(g \circ h)(x) = (x^2 - 6x + 5) - 7 = x^2 - 6x - 2$

54. $f(x) = 6 - 2x$ is a one-to-one function since there is only one $f(x)$ value for each x-value.

Inverse:

$y = 6 - 2x \qquad \Rightarrow \qquad x = 6 - 2y$

$x + 2y = 6$

$2y = -x + 6$

$y = \dfrac{-x + 6}{2}$

$f^{-1}(x) = \dfrac{-x + 6}{2}$

55. $\log_5 x + 3\log_5 x - \log_5(x + 1)$

$= \log_5 x + \log_5 x^3 - \log_5(x + 1)$

$= \log_5 x \cdot x^3 - \log_5(x + 1)$

$= \log_5 x^4 - \log_5(x + 1)$

$= \log_5 \dfrac{x^4}{x + 1}$

56. $8^{x-1} = \dfrac{1}{64}$

$(2^3)^{x-1} = \dfrac{1}{2^6}$

$2^{3(x-1)} = 2^{-6}$

$3(x-1) = -6$

$3x - 3 = -6$

$3x = -3$

$x = -1$

57. $3^{2x+5} = 4$

$\log 3^{2x+5} = \log 4$

$(2x+5)\log 3 = \log 4$

$2x + 5 = \dfrac{\log 4}{\log 3}$

$2x = \dfrac{\log 4}{\log 3} - 5$

$x = \dfrac{1}{2}\left(\dfrac{\log 4}{\log 3} - 5 \right)$

$x \approx -1.8691$

58. $\log_8(3x-2) = 2$

$8^2 = 3x - 2$

$64 = 3x - 2$

$66 = 3x$

$22 = x$

59. $\log_4(x+1) - \log_4(x-2) = 3$

$\log_4 \dfrac{x+1}{x-2} = 3$

$4^3 = \dfrac{x+1}{x-2}$

$64 = \dfrac{x+1}{x-2}$

$64(x-2) = x+1$

$64x - 128 = x+1$

$63x = 129$

$x = \dfrac{129}{63} = \dfrac{43}{21}$

60. Graph $y_1 = e^{0.2x}$ and $y_2 = e^{-0.4x} + 2$.

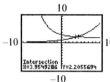

The solution is approximately 3.95.

61. $y = \left(\dfrac{1}{2} \right)^x + 1$

x	$\left(\frac{1}{2}\right)^x + 1$	y
-3	$\left(\frac{1}{2}\right)^{-3} + 1 = 9$	9
-2	$\left(\frac{1}{2}\right)^{-2} + 1 = 5$	5
-1	$\left(\frac{1}{2}\right)^{-1} + 1 = 3$	3
0	$\left(\frac{1}{2}\right)^{0} + 1 = 2$	2
1	$\left(\frac{1}{2}\right)^{1} + 1 = 1\frac{1}{2}$	$1\frac{1}{2}$
2	$\left(\frac{1}{2}\right)^{2} + 1 = 1\frac{1}{4}$	$1\frac{1}{4}$
3	$\left(\frac{1}{2}\right)^{3} + 1 = 1\frac{1}{8}$	$1\frac{1}{8}$

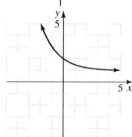

62. Let $y_0 = 57{,}000$, $k = 0.026$, $t = 5$.

$y = y_0 e^{kt}$

$y = 57{,}000 e^{0.026(5)}$

$y \approx 64{,}913$

In 5 years, there will be 64,913 prairie dogs.

63. $x^2 - y^2 = 36$

$x^2 - y^2 = 6^2$

hyperbola, with x-intercepts $(-6, 0)$, $(6, 0)$

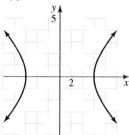

64. $16x^2 + 9y^2 = 144$

$$\frac{16x^2}{144} + \frac{9y^2}{144} = \frac{144}{144}$$

$$\frac{x^2}{9} + \frac{y^2}{16} = 1$$

Ellipse, x-intercepts $(-3, 0)$, $(3, 0)$

          y-intercepts $(0, -4)$, $(0, 4)$

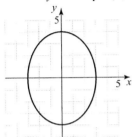

65. $\quad\quad x^2 + y^2 + 6x = 16$

$$(x^2 + 6x + 9) + y^2 = 16 + 9$$

$$(x + 3)^2 + y^2 = 25$$

$$[x - (-3)]^2 + (y - 0)^2 = 5^2$$

circle with center $(-3, 0)$ and radius 5

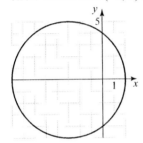

66. $\begin{cases} x^2 + y^2 = 26 \\ x^2 - 2y^2 = 23 \end{cases}$

Multiply equation (2) by -1 and add the equations.

$$x^2 + y^2 = 26$$
$$\underline{-x^2 + 2y^2 = -23}$$
$$3y^2 = 3$$
$$y^2 = 1$$
$$y = \pm 1$$

Substitute $y = -1$ and $y = 1$ into equation (1).

$$x^2 + (-1)^2 = 26$$
$$x^2 = 25$$
$$x = \pm 5$$

$$x^2 + 1^2 = 26$$
$$x^2 = 25$$
$$x = \pm 5$$

The solutions are $(-5, -1)$, $(-5, 1)$, $(5, -1)$, $(5, 1)$.

67. $a_n = \dfrac{(-1)^n}{n + 4}$

$$a_1 = \frac{(-1)^1}{1 + 4} = -\frac{1}{5}$$

$$a_2 = \frac{(-1)^2}{2 + 4} = \frac{1}{6}$$

$$a_3 = \frac{(-1)^3}{3 + 4} = -\frac{1}{7}$$

$$a_4 = \frac{(-1)^4}{4 + 4} = \frac{1}{8}$$

$$a_5 = \frac{(-1)^5}{5 + 4} = -\frac{1}{9}$$

The first five terms are $-\dfrac{1}{5}, \dfrac{1}{6}, -\dfrac{1}{7}, \dfrac{1}{8}, -\dfrac{1}{9}$.

68. $a_n = 5(2)^{n-1}$

$$a_1 = 5(2)^{1-1} = 5(2)^0 = 5$$
$$r = 2$$
$$n = 5$$

$$S_n = \frac{a_1(1 - r^n)}{1 - r}$$

$$S_5 = \frac{5(1 - 2^5)}{1 - 2} = \frac{5(1 - 32)}{-1} = 155$$

69. Sequence $\dfrac{3}{2}, -\dfrac{3}{4}, \dfrac{3}{8}, \ldots$

$$a_1 = \frac{3}{2}, \, r = -\frac{1}{2}$$

$$S_\infty = \frac{a_1}{1 - r} = \frac{\frac{3}{2}}{1 - \left(-\frac{1}{2}\right)} = \frac{\frac{3}{2}}{\frac{3}{2}} = 1$$

70. $\displaystyle\sum_{i=1}^{4} i(i - 2) = 1(1 - 2) + 2(2 - 2) + 3(3 - 2) + 4(4 - 2)$

$$= 1(-1) + 2(0) + 3(1) + 4(2)$$
$$= -1 + 0 + 3 + 8$$
$$= 10$$

71. $(2x+y)^5 = \binom{5}{0}(2x)^5 + \binom{5}{1}(2x)^4(y) + \binom{5}{2}(2x)^3(y)^2 + \binom{5}{3}(2x)^2(y)^3 + \binom{5}{4}(2x)^1(y)^4 + \binom{5}{5}y^5$

$= 2^5 x^5 + 5 \cdot 2^4 x^4 y + 10 \cdot 2^3 x^3 y^2 + 10 \cdot 2^2 x^2 y^3 + 5 \cdot 2xy^4 + y^5$

$= 32x^5 + 80x^4 y + 80x^3 y^2 + 40x^2 y^3 + 10xy^4 + y^5$

Appendix B.3 Exercise Set

2. $V = \dfrac{4}{3}\pi r^3$

$= \dfrac{4}{3}\pi (3 \text{ mi})^3$

$= 36\pi \text{ cu mi}$

$\approx 36\left(\dfrac{22}{7}\right) \text{ cu mi}$

$= 113\dfrac{1}{7} \text{ cu mi}$

$SA = 4\pi r^2$

$= 4\pi (3 \text{ mi})^2$

$= 36\pi \text{ sq mi}$

$\approx 36\left(\dfrac{22}{7}\right) \text{ sq mi}$

$= 113\dfrac{1}{7} \text{ sq mi}$

4. $V = lwh$

$= (8 \text{ cm})(4 \text{ cm})(4 \text{ cm})$

$= 128 \text{ cu cm}$

$SA = 2lh + 2wh + 2lw$

$= 2(8 \text{ cm})(4 \text{ cm}) + 2(8 \text{ cm})(4 \text{ cm}) + 2(4 \text{ cm})(4 \text{ cm})$

$= 64 \text{ sq cm} + 64 \text{ sq cm} + 32 \text{ sq cm}$

$= 160 \text{ sq cm}$

6. $V = \pi r^2 h$

$= \pi (5 \text{ ft})^2 (6 \text{ ft})$

$= 150\pi \text{ cu ft}$

$\approx 150\left(\dfrac{22}{7}\right) \text{ cu ft}$

$= 471\dfrac{3}{7} \text{ cu ft}$

$SA = 2\pi rh + 2\pi r^2$

$= 2\pi (5 \text{ ft})(6 \text{ ft}) + 2\pi (5 \text{ ft})^2$

$= 60\pi \text{ sq ft} + 50\pi \text{ sq ft}$

$= 110\pi \text{ sq ft}$

$\approx 110\left(\dfrac{22}{7}\right) \text{ sq ft}$

$= 345\dfrac{5}{7} \text{ sq ft}$

8. $V = \frac{1}{3}\pi r^2 h$

$\quad = \frac{1}{3}\pi \left(1\frac{3}{4} \text{ in.}\right)^2 (9 \text{ in.})$

$\quad = \frac{147}{16}\pi \text{ cu in.}$

$\quad \approx \frac{147}{16}\left(\frac{22}{7}\right) \text{ cu in.}$

$\quad = 28\frac{7}{8} \text{ cu in.}$

10. $V = lwh$

$\quad = (3 \text{ ft})(2 \text{ ft})(3 \text{ ft})$

$\quad = 18 \text{ cu ft}$

$SA = 2lh + 2wh + 2lw$

$\quad = 2(3 \text{ ft})(3 \text{ ft}) + 2(2 \text{ ft})(3 \text{ ft}) + 2(3 \text{ ft})(2 \text{ ft})$

$\quad = 18 \text{ sq ft} + 12 \text{ sq ft} + 12 \text{ sq ft}$

$\quad = 42 \text{ sq ft}$

12. $V = \frac{1}{3}\pi r^2 h$

$\quad \approx \frac{1}{3}\left(\frac{22}{7}\right)(14 \text{ ft})^2 (15 \text{ ft})$

$\quad = 3080 \text{ cu ft}$

14. $SA = 6s^2 = 6(5 \text{ ft})^2 = 150 \text{ sq ft}$

16. $V = \frac{4}{3}\pi r^3$

$\quad \approx \frac{4}{3}(3.14)(2 \text{ cm})^3$

$\quad \approx 33.49 \text{ cu cm}$

18. $V = \frac{1}{2}\left(\frac{4}{3}\pi r^3\right)$

$\quad \approx \frac{1}{2}\left(\frac{4}{3}\cdot\frac{22}{7}\right)(10 \text{ in.})^3$

$\quad = 2095\frac{5}{21} \text{ cu in.}$

20. $SA = 2\pi r h + 2\pi r^2$

$\quad = 2\pi(3 \text{ ft})(8 \text{ ft}) + 2\pi(3 \text{ ft})^2$

$\quad = 48\pi \text{ sq ft} + 18\pi \text{ sq ft}$

$\quad = 66\pi \text{ sq ft}$

22. $V = lwh$

$\quad = (3 \text{ ft})\left(1\frac{1}{2} \text{ ft}\right)\left(1\frac{3}{4} \text{ ft}\right)$

$\quad = 7\frac{7}{8} \text{ cu ft}$

24. $V = \frac{1}{3}s^2 h$

$\quad = \frac{1}{3}(7 \text{ in.})^2 (10 \text{ in.})$

$\quad = 163\frac{1}{3} \text{ cu in.}$

Appendix C Exercise Set

2. $f(x) = 5|x|$

Find and plot ordered-pair solutions.

x	$f(x) = 5|x|$
-1	$5|-1| = 5$
0	$5|0| = 0$
1	$5|1| = 5$

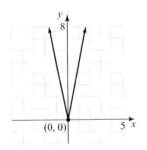

4. $f(x) = \frac{1}{3}|x|$

Find and plot ordered-pair solutions.

x	$f(x) = \frac{1}{3}|x|$
-3	1
0	0
3	1

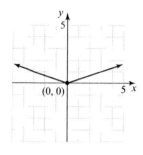

6. $g(x) = 3|x| + 2$
Write in the form $g(x) = a|x - h| + k$.
$g(x) = 3|x - 0| + 2$

• vertex is $(h, k) = (0, 2)$

• since $a > 0$, V-shape opens up

• since $|a| = |3| = 3 > 1$, the graph is narrower than $y = |x|$

x	$g(x) = 3|x| + 2$
-1	$3|-1| + 2 = 5$
0	$3|0| + 2 = 2$
1	$3|1| + 2 = 5$

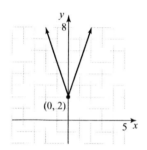

8. $h(x) = -\dfrac{1}{3}|x|$

• vertex is $(0, 0)$

• since $a < 0$, V-shape opens down

• since $|a| = \left|-\dfrac{1}{3}\right| = \dfrac{1}{3} < 1$, the graph is wider than $y = |x|$

x	$h(x) = -\dfrac{1}{3}|x|$
-3	$-\dfrac{1}{3}|-3| = -1$
0	$-\dfrac{1}{3}|0| = 0$
3	$-\dfrac{1}{3}|3| = -1$

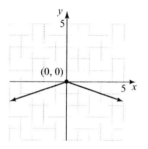

10. $f(x) = 3|x - 2|$
Write in the form $f(x) = a|x - h| + k$.
$f(x) = 3|x - 2| + 0$

• vertex is $(h, k) = (2, 0)$

• since $a > 0$, V-shape opens up

• since $|a| = |3| = 3 > 1$, the graph is narrower than $y = |x|$

x	$f(x) = 3|x - 2|$
-1	$3|-1 - 2| = 9$
0	$3|0 - 2| = 6$
3	$3|3 - 2| = 3$

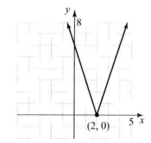

12. $g(x) = -\dfrac{1}{2}|x| - 3$

Write in the form $g(x) = a|x - h| + k$.

$g(x) = -\dfrac{1}{2}|x - 0| + (-3)$

- vertex is $(h, k) = (0, -3)$

- since $a < 0$, V-shape opens down

- since $|a| = \left|-\dfrac{1}{2}\right| = \dfrac{1}{2} < 1$, the graph is wider than $y = |x|$

x	$g(x) = -\frac{1}{2}|x| - 3$
-2	$-\frac{1}{2}|-2| - 3 = -4$
0	$-\frac{1}{2}|0| - 3 = -3$
2	$-\frac{1}{2}|2| - 3 = -4$

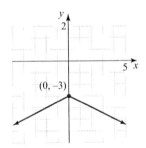

14. $f(x) = -3|x - 1| + 5$

This function is already written in the form $f(x) = a|x - h| + k$.

- vertex is $(h, k) = (1, 5)$

- since $a < 0$, V-shape opens down

- since $|a| = |-3| = 3 > 1$, the graph is narrower than $y = |x|$

x	$f(x) = -3|x - 1| + 5$
-1	$-3|-1 - 1| + 5 = -1$
0	$-3|0 - 1| + 5 = 2$
2	$-3|2 - 1| + 5 = 2$

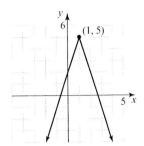

16. $f(x) = \dfrac{3}{4}|x + 1| - 4$

Write in the form $f(x) = a|x - h| + k$.

$f(x) = \dfrac{3}{4}|x - (-1)| + (-4)$

- vertex is $(h, k) = (-1, -4)$

- since $a > 0$, V-shape opens up

- since $|a| = \left|\dfrac{3}{4}\right| = \dfrac{3}{4} < 1$, the graph is wider than $y = |x|$

x	$f(x) = \frac{3}{4}|x + 1| - 4$
-5	$\frac{3}{4}|-5 + 1| - 4 = -1$
-1	$\frac{3}{4}|-1 + 1| - 4 = -4$
3	$\frac{3}{4}|3 + 1| - 4 = -1$

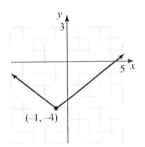

Appendix D

Vocabulary and Readiness Check

1. $\begin{vmatrix} 7 & 2 \\ 0 & 8 \end{vmatrix} = 56$

2. $\begin{vmatrix} 6 & 0 \\ 1 & 2 \end{vmatrix} = 12$

3. $\begin{vmatrix} -4 & 2 \\ 0 & 8 \end{vmatrix} = -32$

4. $\begin{vmatrix} 5 & 0 \\ 3 & -5 \end{vmatrix} = -25$

5. $\begin{vmatrix} -2 & 0 \\ 3 & -10 \end{vmatrix} = 20$

6. $\begin{vmatrix} -1 & 4 \\ 0 & -18 \end{vmatrix} = 18$

Appendix D Exercise Set

2. $\begin{vmatrix} -5 & 1 \\ 1 & -4 \end{vmatrix} = ad - bc = -5(-4) - 1(1) = 20 - 1 = 19$

4. $\begin{vmatrix} 4 & -1 \\ 9 & 8 \end{vmatrix} = ad - bc = 4(8) - (-1)(9) = 32 + 9 = 41$

6. $\begin{vmatrix} -40 & 8 \\ 70 & -14 \end{vmatrix} = -40(-14) - 8(70) = 560 - 560 = 0$

8. $\begin{vmatrix} \frac{5}{7} & \frac{1}{3} \\ \frac{6}{7} & \frac{2}{3} \end{vmatrix} = \frac{5}{7}\left(\frac{2}{3}\right) - \left(\frac{1}{3}\right)\left(\frac{6}{7}\right) = \frac{10}{21} - \frac{6}{21} = \frac{4}{21}$

10. $\begin{cases} 4x - y = 5 \\ 3x - 3 = 0 \end{cases}$ or $\begin{cases} 4x - 1y = 5 \\ 3x + 0y = 3 \end{cases}$

$D = \begin{vmatrix} 4 & -1 \\ 3 & 0 \end{vmatrix} = 0 - (-3) = 3$

$D_x = \begin{vmatrix} 5 & -1 \\ 3 & 0 \end{vmatrix} = 0 - (-3) = 3$

$D_y = \begin{vmatrix} 4 & 5 \\ 3 & 3 \end{vmatrix} = 12 - 15 = -3$

$x = \dfrac{D_x}{D} = \dfrac{3}{3} = 1$

$y = \dfrac{D_y}{D} = \dfrac{-3}{3} = -1$

The solution is $(1, -1)$.

12. $\begin{cases} y = 2x - 5 \\ 8x - 4y = 20 \end{cases}$ or $\begin{cases} -2x + y = -5 \\ 8x - 4y = 20 \end{cases}$

$D = \begin{vmatrix} -2 & 1 \\ 8 & -4 \end{vmatrix} = 8 - 8 = 0$

Since $D = 0$, Cramer's Rule cannot be used.
Notice equation (2) is equation (1) multiplied by
-4. The solution is $\{(x, y)| y = 2x - 5\}$.

14. $\begin{cases} 4x - y = 9 \\ 2x + 3y = -27 \end{cases}$

$D = \begin{vmatrix} 4 & -1 \\ 2 & 3 \end{vmatrix} = 12 + 2 = 14$

$D_x = \begin{vmatrix} 9 & -1 \\ -27 & 3 \end{vmatrix} = 27 - 27 = 0$

$D_y = \begin{vmatrix} 4 & 9 \\ 2 & -27 \end{vmatrix} = -108 - 18 = -126$

$x = \dfrac{D_x}{D} = \dfrac{0}{14} = 0$ and $y = \dfrac{D_y}{D} = \dfrac{-126}{14} = -9$

The solution is $(0, -9)$.

16. $\begin{cases} 3x - y = 2 \\ -5x + 2y = 0 \end{cases}$

$D = \begin{vmatrix} 3 & -1 \\ -5 & 2 \end{vmatrix} = 6 - 5 = 1$

$D_x = \begin{vmatrix} 2 & -1 \\ 0 & 2 \end{vmatrix} = 4 - 0 = 4$

$D_y = \begin{vmatrix} 3 & 2 \\ -5 & 0 \end{vmatrix} = 0 + 10 = 10$

$x = \dfrac{D_x}{D} = \dfrac{4}{1} = 4$ and $y = \dfrac{D_y}{D} = \dfrac{10}{1} = 10$

The solution is $(4, 10)$.

18. $\begin{cases} \dfrac{1}{2}x - \dfrac{1}{3}y = -3 \\ \dfrac{1}{8}x + \dfrac{1}{6}y = 0 \end{cases}$

$D = \begin{vmatrix} \frac{1}{2} & -\frac{1}{3} \\ \frac{1}{8} & \frac{1}{6} \end{vmatrix} = \frac{1}{12} + \frac{1}{24} = \frac{1}{8}$

$D_x = \begin{vmatrix} -3 & -\frac{1}{3} \\ 0 & \frac{1}{6} \end{vmatrix} = -\frac{1}{2} - 0 = -\frac{1}{2}$

$D_y = \begin{vmatrix} \frac{1}{2} & -3 \\ \frac{1}{8} & 0 \end{vmatrix} = 0 + \frac{3}{8} = \frac{3}{8}$

$x = \dfrac{D_x}{D} = \dfrac{-\frac{1}{2}}{\frac{1}{8}} = -4$ and $y = \dfrac{D_y}{D} = \dfrac{\frac{3}{8}}{\frac{1}{8}} = 3$

The solution is $(-4, 3)$.

20. Expand by column 1.

$$\begin{vmatrix} -6 & 4 & 2 \\ 1 & 0 & 5 \\ 0 & 3 & 1 \end{vmatrix} = -6 \begin{vmatrix} 0 & 5 \\ 3 & 1 \end{vmatrix} - 1 \begin{vmatrix} 4 & 2 \\ 3 & 1 \end{vmatrix} + 0 \begin{vmatrix} 4 & 2 \\ 0 & 5 \end{vmatrix}$$
$$= -6(0-15) - 1(4-6) + 0$$
$$= 90 + 2$$
$$= 92$$

22. Expand by column 3.

$$\begin{vmatrix} 5 & 2 & 1 \\ 3 & -6 & 0 \\ -2 & 8 & 0 \end{vmatrix} = 1 \begin{vmatrix} 3 & -6 \\ -2 & 8 \end{vmatrix} - 0 \begin{vmatrix} 5 & 2 \\ -2 & 8 \end{vmatrix} + 0 \begin{vmatrix} 5 & 2 \\ 3 & -6 \end{vmatrix}$$
$$= 1(24-12) - 0 + 0$$
$$= 12$$

24. Expand by row 1.

$$\begin{vmatrix} 0 & 1 & 2 \\ 3 & -1 & 2 \\ 3 & 2 & -2 \end{vmatrix} = 0 \begin{vmatrix} -1 & 2 \\ 2 & -2 \end{vmatrix} - 1 \begin{vmatrix} 3 & 2 \\ 3 & -2 \end{vmatrix} + 2 \begin{vmatrix} 3 & -1 \\ 3 & 2 \end{vmatrix}$$
$$= 0 - 1(-6-6) + 2(6+3)$$
$$= 12 + 18$$
$$= 30$$

26. Expand by row 1.

$$\begin{vmatrix} 2 & -2 & 1 \\ 4 & 1 & 3 \\ 3 & 1 & 2 \end{vmatrix} = 2 \begin{vmatrix} 1 & 3 \\ 1 & 2 \end{vmatrix} + 2 \begin{vmatrix} 4 & 3 \\ 3 & 2 \end{vmatrix} + 1 \begin{vmatrix} 4 & 1 \\ 3 & 1 \end{vmatrix}$$
$$= 2(2-3) + 2(8-9) + 1(4-3)$$
$$= -2 - 2 + 1$$
$$= -3$$

28. $\begin{cases} 4y - 3z = -2 \\ 8x - 4y = 4 \\ -8x + 4y + z = -2 \end{cases}$

$$D = \begin{vmatrix} 0 & 4 & -3 \\ 8 & -4 & 0 \\ -8 & 4 & 1 \end{vmatrix} = 0 - 4 \begin{vmatrix} 8 & 0 \\ -8 & 1 \end{vmatrix} - 3 \begin{vmatrix} 8 & -4 \\ -8 & 4 \end{vmatrix}$$
$$= 0 - 4(8-0) - 3(32-32)$$
$$= -32$$

$$D_x = \begin{vmatrix} -2 & 4 & -3 \\ 4 & -4 & 0 \\ -2 & 4 & 1 \end{vmatrix} = -3 \begin{vmatrix} 4 & -4 \\ -2 & 4 \end{vmatrix} - 0 + 1 \begin{vmatrix} -2 & 4 \\ 4 & -4 \end{vmatrix}$$
$$= -3(16-8) + 1(8-16)$$
$$= -32$$

$$D_y = \begin{vmatrix} 0 & -2 & -3 \\ 8 & 4 & 0 \\ -8 & -2 & 1 \end{vmatrix} = 0 + 2 \begin{vmatrix} 8 & 0 \\ -8 & 1 \end{vmatrix} - 3 \begin{vmatrix} 8 & 4 \\ -8 & -2 \end{vmatrix}$$
$$= 2(8-0) - 3(-16+32)$$
$$= -32$$

$$D_z = \begin{vmatrix} 0 & 4 & -2 \\ 8 & -4 & 4 \\ -8 & 4 & -2 \end{vmatrix} = 0 - 4 \begin{vmatrix} 8 & 4 \\ -8 & -2 \end{vmatrix} - 2 \begin{vmatrix} 8 & -4 \\ -8 & 4 \end{vmatrix}$$
$$= -4(-16+32) - 2(32-32)$$
$$= -64$$

$$x = \frac{D_x}{D} = \frac{-32}{-32} = 1, \quad y = \frac{D_y}{D} = \frac{-32}{-32} = 1,$$

$$z = \frac{D_z}{D} = \frac{-64}{-32} = 2$$

The solution is $(1, 1, 2)$.

30. $\begin{cases} 5x + y + 3z = 1 \\ x - y - 3z = -7 \\ -x + y = 1 \end{cases}$

$$D = \begin{vmatrix} 5 & 1 & 3 \\ 1 & -1 & -3 \\ -1 & 1 & 0 \end{vmatrix}$$
$$= 5 \begin{vmatrix} -1 & -3 \\ 1 & 0 \end{vmatrix} - 1 \begin{vmatrix} 1 & -3 \\ -1 & 0 \end{vmatrix} + 3 \begin{vmatrix} 1 & -1 \\ -1 & 1 \end{vmatrix}$$
$$= 5(0+3) - 1(0-3) + 3(1-1)$$
$$= 15 + 3 + 0$$
$$= 18$$

$$D_x = \begin{vmatrix} 1 & 1 & 3 \\ -7 & -1 & -3 \\ 1 & 1 & 0 \end{vmatrix}$$
$$= 1 \begin{vmatrix} -1 & -3 \\ 1 & 0 \end{vmatrix} - 1 \begin{vmatrix} -7 & -3 \\ 1 & 0 \end{vmatrix} + 3 \begin{vmatrix} -7 & -1 \\ 1 & 1 \end{vmatrix}$$
$$= 1(0+3) - 1(0+3) + 3(-7+1)$$
$$= 3 - 3 + (-18)$$
$$= -18$$

$$D_y = \begin{vmatrix} 5 & 1 & 3 \\ 1 & -7 & -3 \\ -1 & 1 & 0 \end{vmatrix}$$
$$= 5 \begin{vmatrix} -7 & -3 \\ 1 & 0 \end{vmatrix} - 1 \begin{vmatrix} 1 & -3 \\ -1 & 0 \end{vmatrix} + 3 \begin{vmatrix} 1 & -7 \\ -1 & 1 \end{vmatrix}$$
$$= 5(0+3) - 1(0-3) + 3(1-7)$$
$$= 15 + 3 - 18$$
$$= 0$$

$$D_z = \begin{vmatrix} 5 & 1 & 1 \\ 1 & -1 & -7 \\ -1 & 1 & 1 \end{vmatrix}$$
$$= 5 \begin{vmatrix} -1 & -7 \\ 1 & 1 \end{vmatrix} - 1 \begin{vmatrix} 1 & -7 \\ -1 & 1 \end{vmatrix} + 1 \begin{vmatrix} 1 & -1 \\ -1 & 1 \end{vmatrix}$$
$$= 5(-1+7) - 1(1-7) + 1(1-1)$$
$$= 30 + 6 + 0$$
$$= 36$$

$x = \dfrac{D_x}{D} = \dfrac{-18}{18} = -1, \quad y = \dfrac{D_y}{D} = \dfrac{0}{18} = 0,$

$z = \dfrac{D_z}{D} = \dfrac{36}{18} = 2$

The solution is $(-1, 0, 2)$.

32. $\begin{cases} 2x - 3y + z = 5 \\ x + y + z = 0 \\ 4x + 2y + 4z = 4 \end{cases}$

$D = \begin{vmatrix} 2 & -3 & 1 \\ 1 & 1 & 1 \\ 4 & 2 & 4 \end{vmatrix} = 2\begin{vmatrix} 1 & 1 \\ 2 & 4 \end{vmatrix} + 3\begin{vmatrix} 1 & 1 \\ 4 & 4 \end{vmatrix} + 1\begin{vmatrix} 1 & 1 \\ 4 & 2 \end{vmatrix}$

$\qquad = 2(4-2) + 3(4-4) + 1(2-4)$
$\qquad = 4 + 0 + (-2)$
$\qquad = 2$

$D_x = \begin{vmatrix} 5 & -3 & 1 \\ 0 & 1 & 1 \\ 4 & 2 & 4 \end{vmatrix} = 5\begin{vmatrix} 1 & 1 \\ 2 & 4 \end{vmatrix} + 3\begin{vmatrix} 0 & 1 \\ 4 & 4 \end{vmatrix} + 1\begin{vmatrix} 0 & 1 \\ 4 & 2 \end{vmatrix}$

$\qquad = 5(4-2) + 3(0-4) + 1(0-4)$
$\qquad = 10 - 12 - 4$
$\qquad = -6$

$D_y = \begin{vmatrix} 2 & 5 & 1 \\ 1 & 0 & 1 \\ 4 & 4 & 4 \end{vmatrix} = 2\begin{vmatrix} 0 & 1 \\ 4 & 4 \end{vmatrix} + 5\begin{vmatrix} 1 & 1 \\ 4 & 4 \end{vmatrix} + 1\begin{vmatrix} 1 & 0 \\ 4 & 4 \end{vmatrix}$

$\qquad = 2(0-4) + 5(4-4) + 1(4-0)$
$\qquad = -8 + 0 + 4$
$\qquad = -4$

$D_z = \begin{vmatrix} 2 & -3 & 5 \\ 1 & 1 & 0 \\ 4 & 2 & 4 \end{vmatrix} = 2\begin{vmatrix} 1 & 0 \\ 2 & 4 \end{vmatrix} + 3\begin{vmatrix} 1 & 0 \\ 4 & 4 \end{vmatrix} + 5\begin{vmatrix} 1 & 1 \\ 4 & 2 \end{vmatrix}$

$\qquad = 2(4-0) + 3(4-0) + 5(2-4)$
$\qquad = 8 + 12 + (-10)$
$\qquad = 10$

$x = \dfrac{D_x}{D} = \dfrac{-6}{2} = -3, \quad y = \dfrac{D_y}{D} = \dfrac{-4}{2} = -2,$

$z = \dfrac{D_z}{D} = \dfrac{10}{2} = 5$

The solution is $(-3, -2, 5)$.

34. $\begin{cases} 4x + 5y = 10 \\ 3y + 2z = -6 \\ x + y + z = 3 \end{cases}$

$D = \begin{vmatrix} 4 & 5 & 0 \\ 0 & 3 & 2 \\ 1 & 1 & 1 \end{vmatrix} = 4\begin{vmatrix} 3 & 2 \\ 1 & 1 \end{vmatrix} - 5\begin{vmatrix} 0 & 2 \\ 1 & 1 \end{vmatrix} + 0$

$\qquad = 4(3-2) - 5(0-2)$
$\qquad = 4 + 10$
$\qquad = 14$

$D_x = \begin{vmatrix} 10 & 5 & 0 \\ -6 & 3 & 2 \\ 3 & 1 & 1 \end{vmatrix} = 10\begin{vmatrix} 3 & 2 \\ 1 & 1 \end{vmatrix} - 5\begin{vmatrix} -6 & 2 \\ 3 & 1 \end{vmatrix} + 0$

$\qquad = 10(3-2) - 5(-6-6)$
$\qquad = 10 + 60$
$\qquad = 70$

$D_y = \begin{vmatrix} 4 & 10 & 0 \\ 0 & -6 & 2 \\ 1 & 3 & 1 \end{vmatrix} = 4\begin{vmatrix} -6 & 2 \\ 3 & 1 \end{vmatrix} - 10\begin{vmatrix} 0 & 2 \\ 1 & 1 \end{vmatrix} + 0$

$\qquad = 4(-6-6) - 10(0-2)$
$\qquad = -48 + 20$
$\qquad = -28$

$D_z = \begin{vmatrix} 4 & 5 & 10 \\ 0 & 3 & -6 \\ 1 & 1 & 3 \end{vmatrix} = 4\begin{vmatrix} 3 & -6 \\ 1 & 3 \end{vmatrix} - 5\begin{vmatrix} 0 & -6 \\ 1 & 3 \end{vmatrix} + 10\begin{vmatrix} 0 & 3 \\ 1 & 1 \end{vmatrix}$

$\qquad = 4(9+6) - 5(0+6) + 10(0-3)$
$\qquad = 60 - 30 + (-30)$
$\qquad = 0$

$x = \dfrac{D_x}{D} = \dfrac{70}{14} = 5, \quad y = \dfrac{D_y}{D} = \dfrac{-28}{14} = -2,$

$z = \dfrac{D_z}{D} = \dfrac{0}{14} = 0$

The solution is $(5, -2, 0)$.

36. $\begin{vmatrix} 6 & 1 \\ -2 & x \end{vmatrix} = 26$

$6 \cdot x - 1 \cdot (-2) = 26$
$6x + 2 = 26$
$6x = 24$
$x = 4$

38. 0; answers may vary

Appendix E

Viewing Window and Interpreting Window Settings Exercise Set

2. Yes, since every coordinate is between -10 and 10.

4. No, since 15 is greater than 10.

6. Answers may vary; any values such that Xmin < -18, Ymin < 20, Xmax > 20, and Ymax > 90.

8. Answers may vary; any values such that Xmin < -3, Ymin < -5, Xmax > 15, and Ymax > 5.

10. Answers may vary; any values such that Xmin < -30, Ymin < 0, Xmax > 40, and Ymax > 800.

12.   Xmin $= -20$ Ymin $= -20$
       Xmax $= 20$ Ymax $= 20$
        Xscl $= 5$ Yscl $= 5$

14.   Xmin $= -27$ Ymin $= -6$
       Xmax $= 27$ Ymax $= 6$
        Xscl $= 3$ Yscl $= 1$

16.   Xmin $= -50$ Ymin $= -20$
       Xmax $= 50$ Ymax $= 20$
        Xscl $= 10$ Yscl $= 4$

18.   Xmin $= -100$ Ymin $= -20$
       Xmax $= 100$ Ymax $= 20$
        Xscl $= 10$ Yscl $= 2$

20.   Xmin $= -500$ Ymin $= -800$
       Xmax $= 700$ Ymax $= 400$
        Xscl $= 100$ Yscl $= 200$

Graphing Equations and Square Viewing Window Exercise Set

2. Setting A:

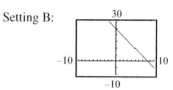

Setting B:

Setting B shows all intercepts.

4. Setting A:

Setting B:

Setting A shows all intercepts.

6. Setting A:

Setting B:

Setting B shows all intercepts.

8. $7y = -3x$, or $y = -\dfrac{3}{7}x$

10. $4x + 6y = 20$, or $y = -\dfrac{2}{3}x + \dfrac{10}{3}$

12. $y = 2$

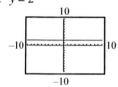

14. $x - 5y = 9$, or $y = \dfrac{1}{5}x - \dfrac{9}{5}$

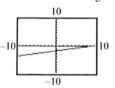

16. $y = \sqrt{2x}$

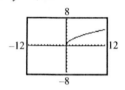

18. $y = x^2 - 5$

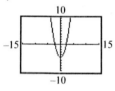

20. $y = |x - 2|$

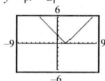

22. $1.5x - 3.7y = 40.3$

$$-3.7y = -1.5x + 40.3$$

$$y = \frac{1.5x - 40.3}{3.7}$$

Standard window:

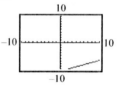

Adjusted window:

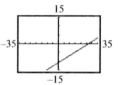